Financial Aid
for Hispanic Americans
2014-2016

RSP FINANCIAL AID DIRECTORIES
OF INTEREST TO MINORITIES

College Student's Guide to Merit and Other No-Need Funding
Selected as one of the "Outstanding Titles of the Year" by *Choice,* this directory describes 1,300 no-need funding opportunities for college students. 490 pages. ISBN 1588412350. $32.50, plus $7 shipping.

Directory of Financial Aids for Women
There are nearly 1,500 funding programs set aside for women described in this biennial directory, which has been called "the cream of the crop" by *School Library Journal* and the "best available reference source" by *Guide to Reference.* 504 pages. ISBN 1588412504. $45, plus $7 shipping.

Financial Aid for African Americans
More than 1,300 funding opportunities open to African American college students, professionals, and postdoctorates are described in this award-winning directory. 502 pages. ISBN 1588412423. $45, plus $7 shipping.

Financial Aid for Asian Americans
This is the source to use if you are looking for funding for Asian Americans, including college-bound high school seniors, undergraduates, graduate students, professionals, and postdoctorates; nearly 950 sources of free money are described here. 356 pages. ISBN 1588412431. $40, plus $7 shipping.

Financial Aid for Hispanic Americans
The 1,175 biggest and best sources of free money available to undergraduates, graduates students, professionals, and postdoctorates of Mexican, Puerto Rican, Central American, or other Latin American heritage are described here. 458 pages. ISBN 158841244X. $42.50, plus $7 shipping.

Financial Aid for Native Americans
Detailed information is provided on nearly 1,400 funding opportunities open to American Indians, Native Alaskans, and Native Pacific Islanders for college, graduate school, or professional activities. 504 pages. ISBN 1588412458. $45, plus $7 shipping.

Financial Aid for Research and Creative Activities Abroad
Described here are more than 1,000 scholarships, fellowships, grants, etc. available to support research, professional, or creative activities abroad. 413 pages. ISBN 1588412512. $45, plus $7 shipping.

Financial Aid for Study and Training Abroad
This directory, which the reviewers call "invaluable," describes nearly 1,000 financial aid opportunities available to support study abroad. 353 pages. ISBN 1588412520. $40, plus $7 shipping.

Financial Aid for Veterans, Military Personnel, & Their Families
According to *Reference Book Review,* this directory (with its 1,100 entries) is "the most comprehensive guide available on the subject." 429 pages. ISBN 1588412482. $40, plus $7 shipping.

High School Senior's Guide to Merit and Other No-Need Funding
Here's your guide to 1,100 funding programs that *never* look at income level when making awards to college-bound high school seniors. 411 pages. ISBN 1588412369. $29.95, plus $7 shipping.

Money for Graduate Students in the Arts & Humanities
Use this directory to identify 1,000 funding opportunities available to support graduate study and research in the arts/humanities. 287 pages. ISBN 1588412296. $42.50, plus $7 shipping.

Money for Graduate Students in the Biological Sciences
This unique directory focuses solely on funding for graduate study/research in the biological sciences (800+ funding opportunities). 241 pages. ISBN 158841230X. $37.50, plus $7 shipping.

Money for Graduate Students in the Health Sciences
Described here are 1,000+ funding opportunities just for students interested in a graduate degree in dentistry, medicine, nursing, nutrition, pharmacology, etc. 313 pages. ISBN 1588412318. $42.50, plus $7 shipping.

Money for Graduate Students in the Physical & Earth Sciences
Nearly 900 funding opportunities for graduate students in the physical and earth sciences are described in detail here. 280 pages. ISBN 1588412326. $40, plus $7 shipping.

Money for Graduate Students in the Social & Behavioral Sciences
Looking for money for a graduate degree in the social/behavioral sciences? Here are 1,100 funding programs for you. 319 pages. ISBN 1588412334. $42.50, plus $7 shipping.

Financial Aid for Hispanic Americans 2014-2016

Gail Ann Schlachter
R. David Weber

A Listing of Scholarships, Fellowships, Grants, Awards, and Other Sources of Free Money Available Primarily or Exclusively to Hispanic Americans, Plus a Set of Six Indexes (Program Title, Sponsoring Organization, Residency, Tenability, Subject, and Deadline Date)

Reference Service Press
El Dorado Hills, California

ISBN 10: 158841244X
ISBN 13: 9781588412447

10 9 8 7 6 5 4 3 2 1

Reference Service Press (RSP) began in 1977 with a single financial aid publication *(The Directory of Financial Aids for Women)* and now specializes in the development of financial aid resources in multiple formats, including books, large print books, print-on-demand reports, eBooks, and online sources. Long recognized as a leader in the field, RSP has been called by the *Simba Report on Directory Publishing* "a true success in the world of independent directory publishers." Both Kaplan Educational Centers and Military.com have hailed RSP as "the leading authority on scholarships."

Reference Service Press
El Dorado Hills Business Park
5000 Windplay Drive, Suite 4
El Dorado Hills, CA 95762-9319
(916) 939-9620
Fax: (916) 939-9626
E-mail: info@rspfunding.com
Visit our web site: www.rspfunding.com

Manufactured in the United States of America
Price: $42.50, plus $7 shipping.

ACADEMIC INSTITUTIONS, LIBRARIES, ORGANIZATIONS AND OTHER QUANTITY BUYERS:
Discounts on this book are available for bulk purchases. E-mail or call for information on our discount programs.

Contents

Introduction

WHY THIS DIRECTORY IS NEEDED

Despite our country's ongoing economic problems and increased college costs, the financial aid picture for minorities has never looked brighter. Currently, billions of dollars are set aside each year specifically for Hispanic Americans, African Americans, Asian Americans, and Native Americans. This funding is open to minorities at any level (high school through postdoctoral and professional) for a variety of activities, including study, research, travel, training, career development, and creative projects.

While numerous print and online listings have been prepared to identify and describe general financial aid opportunities (those open to all segments of society), those resources have never covered more than a small portion of the programs designed primarily or exclusively for minorities. As a result, many advisors, librarians, scholars, researchers, and students often have been unaware of the extensive funding available to Hispanic Americans and other minorities. But, with the ongoing publication of *Financial Aid for Hispanic Americans* that has all changed. Here, in just one place, Hispanic American students, professionals, and postdoctorates now have current and detailed information about the special resources set aside specifically for them.

Financial Aid for Hispanic Americans is prepared biennially as part of Reference Service Press' four-volume *Minority Funding Set* (the other volumes in the set cover funding for African Americans, Asian Americans, and Native Americans). Each of the volumes in this set is sold separately, or the complete set can be purchased at a discounted price. For more information, e-mail Reference Service Press's marketing department (info@rspfunding.com) or visit www.rspfunding.com/prod_prodalpha.html.

No other source, in print or online, offers the extensive coverage of funding for minorities provided by these titles. That's why the Grantsmanship Center labeled the set "a must for every organization serving minorities," *Reference Sources for Small and Medium-Sized Libraries* called the titles "the absolute best guides for finding funding," and *Reference Books Bulletin* selected each of the volumes in the *Minority Funding Set* as their "Editor's Choice." *Financial Aid for Hispanic Americans,* itself, has also received rave reviews. The National Chicano Council on Higher Education called it "a most necessary publication," it was chosen as a "Recommended Resource" by the Ventures Scholars Program, and *Vista: The Hispanic Magazine* pronounced it a "very comprehensive work." Perhaps *Reference Books Bulletin* sums up best the critical reaction to *Financial Aid for Hispanic Americans:* "accurate, comprehensive financial aid information in an easy to use, well arranged format."

WHAT'S UPDATED?

The preparation of each new edition of *Financial Aid for Hispanic Americans* involves extensive updating and revision. To make sure that the information included here is both reliable and current, the editors at Reference Service Press 1) reviewed and updated all relevant programs covered in the previous edition of the directory, 2) collected information on all programs open to Hispanic Americans that were added to Reference Service Press' funding database since the last edition of the directory, and then 3) searched extensively for new program leads in a variety of sources, including printed directories, news reports, journals, newsletters, house organs, annual reports, and sites on the Internet. We only include program descriptions that are written directly from information supplied by the sponsoring organization in print or online (no information is ever taken from secondary sources). When that information could not be found, we sent up to four data collection letters (followed by up to three telephone or e-mail inquiries, if necessary) to those sponsors. Despite our best efforts, however, some sponsoring organizations still failed to respond and, as a result, their programs are not included in this edition of the directory.

The 2014-2016 edition of *Financial Aid for Hispanic Americans* completely revises and updates the previous (seventh) edition. Programs that have ceased operations have been dropped from the listing. Similarly, programs that have broadened their scope and no longer focus on Hispanic Americans have also been removed from the directory. Profiles of continuing programs have been rewritten to reflect current requirements; nearly 85 percent of the continuing programs reported substantive changes in their locations, requirements (particularly application deadline), benefits, or eligibility requirements since the 2012-2014 edition. In addition, hundreds of new entries have been added to the program section of the directory. The resulting listing describes the nearly 1,175 biggest and best sources of free money available to Hispanic Americans, including scholarships, fellowships, grants, awards, and other funding opportunities.

WHAT MAKES THIS DIRECTORY UNIQUE?

The 2014-2016 edition of *Financial Aid for Hispanic Americans* will help Hispanic Americans (persons whose origins are from Mexico, Central America, Puerto Rico, Cuba, or other Latin American countries) tap into the billions of dollars available to them, as minorities, for study, research, creative activities, past accomplishments, future projects, professional development, and many other activities. The listings cover every major subject area, are sponsored by more than 900 different private and public agencies and organizations, and are open to Hispanic Americans at any level, from college-bound high school students through professionals and postdoctorates.

Not only does *Financial Aid for Hispanic Americans* provide the most comprehensive coverage of available funding (1,173 entries), but it also displays the most informative program descriptions (on the average, more than twice the detail found in any other listing). In addition to this extensive and focused coverage, *Financial Aid for Hispanic Americans* also offers several other unique features. First of all, hundreds of funding opportunities listed here have never been covered in any other source. So, even if you have checked elsewhere, you will want to look at *Financial Aid for Hispanic Americans* for additional leads. And, here's another plus: all of the funding programs in this edition of the directory offer "free" money; not one of the programs will ever require you to pay anything back (provided, of course, that you meet the program requirements).

Further, unlike other funding directories, which generally follow a straight alphabetical arrangement, *Financial Aid for Hispanic Americans* groups entries by intended recipients (undergraduates, graduate students, or professionals/postdoctorates), to make it easy for you to search for appropriate programs. This same convenience is offered in the indexes, where program title, sponsoring organization, geographic, subject, and deadline date entries are each subdivided by recipient group.

Finally, we have tried to anticipate all the ways you might wish to search for funding. The volume is organized so you can identify programs not only by intended recipient, but also by subject focus, sponsoring organization, program title, residency requirements, where the money can be spent, and even deadline date. Plus, we've included all the information you'll need to decide if a program is right for you: purpose, eligibility requirements, financial data, duration, special features, limitations, number awarded, and application date. You even get fax numbers, toll-free numbers, e-mail address, and web site (when available), along with complete contact information.

WHAT'S EXCLUDED?

While this book is intended to be the most comprehensive source of information on funding available to Hispanic Americans, there are some programs we've specifically excluded from the directory:

- *Programs that do not accept applications from U.S. citizens or residents.* If a program is open only to foreign nationals or excludes Americans from applying, it is not covered.

SAMPLE ENTRY

(1) **[804]**

(2) **NATIONAL SOCIETY OF HISPANIC MBAS FOUNDATION SCHOLARSHIP PROGRAM**

(3) National Society of Hispanic MBAs
Attn: NSHMBA Foundation
450 East John Carpenter Freeway, Suite 200
Irving, TX 75062
(214) 596-9338
Fax: (214) 596-9325
E-mail: scholarships@nshmba.org
Web: www.nshmba.org/scholarship

(4) **Summary** To provide financial assistance to members of the National Society of Hispanic MBAs (NSHMBA) who are interested in working on a master's degree in business administration.

(5) **Eligibility** This program is open to NSHMBA members who are interested in working full or part time on a master's degree in management or business at an AACSB-accredited college or university in the United States or Puerto Rico. Applicants must be U.S. citizens or permanent residents and of Hispanic background (1 parent must be fully Hispanic or both parents must be half Hispanic). They must have a GPA of 3.0 or higher. Selection is based on academic achievement, a personal statement of goals and aspirations, community service, and NSHMBA ambassadorship; financial need is considered for applicants who wish to be considered for the top awards.

(6) **Financial data** Stipends range from $10,000 to $2,500. All awards include a travel voucher for $250 to attend an NSHMBA conference.

(7) **Duration** 1 year; may be renewed until completion of a master's degree, provided the recipient maintains a GPA of 3.0 or higher and participates in NSHMBA activities during the year.

(8) **Additional information** This program is administered by Scholarship Management Services, a division of Scholarship America.

(9) **Number awarded** Varies each year; recently, more than 100 of these scholarships were awarded, including 5 top awards at $10,000 each.

(10) **Deadline** April of each year.

DEFINITION

(1) **Entry number:** The consecutive number that is given to each entry and used to identify the entry in the index.

(2) **Program title:** Title of scholarship, fellowship, grant, award, or other source of free money described in the directory.

(3) **Sponsoring organization:** Name, address, and telephone number, toll-free number, fax number, e-mail address, and/or web site (when information was available) for organization sponsoring the program.

(4) **Summary:** Identifies the major program requirements; read the rest of the entry for additional detail.

(5) **Eligibility:** Qualifications required of applicants, plus information on application procedure and selection process.

(6) **Financial data:** Financial details of the program, including fixed sum, average amount, or range of funds offered, expenses for which funds may and may not be applied, and cash-related benefits supplied (e.g., room and board).

(7) **Duration:** Period for which support is provided; renewal prospects.

(8) **Additional information:** Any unusual (generally nonmonetary) benefits, features, restrictions, or limitations associated with the program.

(9) **Number awarded:** Total number of recipients each year or other specified period.

(10) **Deadline:** The month by which applications must be submitted.

- *Programs that are open equally to all segments of the population.* Only funding opportunities set aside primarily or exclusively for Hispanic Americans are included here.

- *Money for study or research outside the United States.* Since there are comprehensive and up-to-date directories that describe the available funding for study and research abroad (see the list of Reference Service Press publications opposite the directory's title page), only programs that fund activities in the United States are covered here.

- *Very restrictive programs.* In general, programs are excluded if they are open only to a limited geographic area (less than a state) or offer limited financial support (less than $1,000). Note, however, that the vast majority of programs included here go way beyond that, paying up to full tuition or stipends that exceed $25,000 a year!

- *Programs administered by individual academic institutions solely for their own students.* The directory identifies "portable" programs—ones that can be used at any number of schools. Financial aid administered by individual schools specifically for their own students is not covered. Check directly with the schools you are considering to get information on their offerings.

- *Money that must be repaid.* Only "free money" is identified here. If a program requires repayment or charges interest, it's not listed. Now you can find out about billions of dollars in aid and know (if you meet the program requirements) that not one dollar of that will ever need to be repaid.

HOW THE DIRECTORY IS ORGANIZED

Financial Aid for Hispanic Americans is divided into two sections: 1) a detailed list of funding opportunities open to Hispanic Americans and 2) a set of six indexes to help you pinpoint appropriate funding programs.

Financial Aid Programs Open to Hispanic Americans. The first section of the directory describes 1,173 sources of free money available to Hispanic Americans. The focus is on financial aid aimed at American citizens or residents to support study, research, or other activities in the United States. The programs listed here are sponsored by more than 900 different government agencies, professional organizations, corporations, sororities and fraternities, foundations, religious groups, educational associations, and military/veterans organizations. All areas of the sciences, social sciences, and humanities are covered.

To help you focus your search, the entries in this section are grouped into the following three chapters:

- **Undergraduates:** Included here are 500 scholarships, grants, awards, and other sources of free money that support undergraduate study, training, research, or creative activities. These programs are open to high school seniors, high school graduates, currently-enrolled college students, and students returning to college after an absence. Money is available to support these students in any type of public or private postsecondary institution, ranging from technical schools and community colleges to major universities in the United States.

- **Graduate Students:** Described here are 420 fellowships, grants, awards, and other sources of free money that support post-baccalaureate study, training, research, and creative activities. These programs are open to students applying to, currently enrolled in, or returning to a master's, doctoral, professional, or specialist program in public or private graduate schools in the United States.

- **Professionals/Postdoctorates:** Included here are more than 250 funding programs for U.S. citizens or residents who 1) are in professional positions (e.g., artists, writers), whether or not they have an advanced degree; 2) are master's or professional degree recipients; 3) have earned a doctoral degree or its equivalent (e.g., Ph.D., Ed.D., M.D.); or 4) have recognized stature as established scientists, scholars, academicians, or researchers.

Within each of these three chapters, entries appear alphabetically by program title. Since some of the programs supply assistance to more than one specific group, those are listed in all relevant chapters. For example, the Congressional Hispanic Caucus Institute Scholarship Awards support students working on either a bachelor's or master's degree, so the program is described in both the Undergraduates *and* Graduate Students chapters.

Each program entry has been designed to give you a concise profile that, as the sample on page 7 illustrates, includes Information (when available) on organization address and telephone numbers (including toll-free and fax numbers), e-mail address and web site, purpose, eligibility, money awarded, duration, special features, limitations, number of awards, and application deadline.

The information reported for each of the programs in this section was gathered from research conducted through the beginning of 2014. While the listing is intended to cover as comprehensively as possible the biggest and best sources of free money available to Hispanic Americans, some sponsoring organizations did not post information online or respond to our research inquiries and, consequently, are not included in this edition of the directory.

Indexes. To help you find the aid you need, we have constructed six indexes; these will let you access the listings by program title, sponsoring organization, residency, tenability, subject focus, and deadline date. These indexes use a word-by-word alphabetical arrangement. Note: numbers in the index refer to entry numbers, not to page numbers in the book.

Program Title Index. If you know the name of a particular funding program and want to find out where it is covered in the directory, use the Program Title Index. To assist you in your search, every program is listed by all its known names, former names, and abbreviations. Since one program can be included in more than one place (e.g., a program providing assistance to both undergraduate and graduate students is described in both the first and second chapters), each entry number in the index has been coded to indicate the intended recipient group ("U" = Undergraduates; "G" = Graduate Students; "P = Professionals/Postdoctorates). By using this coding system, you can avoid duplicate entries and turn directly to the programs that match your eligibility characteristics.

Sponsoring Organization Index. This index makes it easy to identify agencies that offer funding primarily or exclusively to Hispanic Americans. More than 900 organizations are indexed here. As in the Program Title Index, we've used a code to help you determine which organizations sponsor programs that match your educational level.

Residency Index. Some programs listed in this book are restricted to Hispanic Americans in a particular state or region. Others are open to Hispanic Americans wherever they live. This index helps you identify programs available only to residents in your area as well as programs that have no residency requirements. Further, to assist you in your search, we've also indicated the recipient level for the funding offered to residents in each of the areas listed in the index.

Tenability Index. This index identifies the geographic locations where the funding described in *Financial Aid for Hispanic Americans* may be used. Index entries (city, county, state, region) are arranged alphabetically (word by word) and subdivided by recipient group. Use this index when you are looking for money to support your activities in a particular geographic area.

Subject Index. This index allows you to identify the subject focus of each of the financial aid opportunities described in *Financial Aid for Hispanic Americans.* More than 250 different subject terms are listed. Extensive "see" and "see also" references, as well as recipient group subdivisions, will help you locate appropriate funding opportunities.

Calendar Index. Since most financial aid programs have specific deadline dates, some may have closed by the time you begin to look for funding. You can use the Calendar Index to determine which programs are still open. This index is arranged by recipient group (Undergraduates, Graduate Students, and Professionals/Postdoctorates) and subdivided by the month during which the deadline falls. Filing dates can and quite often do vary from year to year; consequently, this index should be used only as a guide for deadlines beyond 2016.

HOW TO USE THE DIRECTORY

Here are some tips to help you get the most out of the funding opportunities listed in *Financial Aid for Hispanic Americans*.

To Locate Funding by Recipient Group.   To bring together programs with a similar educational focus, this directory is divided into three chapters: Undergraduates, Graduate Students, and Professionals/Postdoctorates. If you want to get an overall picture of the sources of free money available to Hispanic Americans in any of these categories, turn to the appropriate chapter and then review the entries there. Since each of these chapters functions as a self-contained entity, you can browse through any of them without having to first consulting an index.

To Find Information on a Particular Financial Aid Program.   If you know the name of a particular financial aid program, and the group eligible for that award, then go directly to the appropriate chapter in the directory (e.g., Undergraduates, Graduate Students), where you will find the program profiles arranged alphabetically by title. To save time, though, you should always check the Program Title Index first if you know the name of a specific award but are not sure in which chapter it has been listed. Plus, since we index each program by all its known names and abbreviations, you'll also be able to track down a program there when you may not know its exact official title.

To Locate Programs Sponsored by a Particular Organization.   The Sponsoring Organization Index makes it easy to identify agencies that provide financial assistance to Hispanic Americans or to identify specific financial aid programs offered by a particular organization. Each entry number in the index is coded to identify recipient group (Undergraduates, Graduate Students, Professionals/Postdoctorates), so that you can easily target appropriate entries.

To Browse Quickly Through the Listings.   Look at the listings in the chapter that relates to you (Undergraduates, Graduate Students, or Professionals/Postdoctorates) and read the "Summary" paragraph in each entry. In seconds, you'll know if this is an opportunity that you might want to pursue. If it is, be sure to read the rest of the information in the entry, to make sure you meet all of the program requirements before writing or going online for an application form. Please save your time and energy. Don't apply if you don't qualify!

To Locate Funding Available to Hispanic Americans from or Tenable in a Particular City, County, or State.   The Residency Index identifies financial aid programs open to Hispanic Americans in a specific state, region, etc. The Tenability Index shows where the money can be spent. In both indexes, "see" and "see also" references are used liberally, and index entries for a particular geographic area are subdivided by recipient group (Undergraduates, Graduate Students, and Professionals/Postdoctorates) to help you identify the funding that's right for you. When using these indexes, always check the listings under the term "United States," since the programs indexed there have no geographic restrictions and can be used in any area.

To Locate Financial Aid Programs Open to Hispanic Americans in a Particular Subject Area.   Turn to the Subject Index first if you are interested in identifying funding programs for Hispanic Americans that are focused on a particular subject area. To make your search easier, the intended recipient groups (Undergraduates, Graduate Students, Professionals/Postdoctorates) are clearly labeled in the more than 250 subject listings. Extensive cross-references are also provided. Since a large number of programs are not restricted by subject, be sure to check the references listed under the "General programs" heading in the index, in addition to the specific terms that directly relate to your interest areas. The listings under "General programs" can be used to fund activities in any subject area (although the programs may be restricted in other ways).

To Locate Financial Aid Programs for Hispanic Americans by Deadline Date.   If you are working with specific time constraints and want to weed out the financial aid programs whose filing dates you won't be able to meet, turn first to the Calendar Index and check the program references listed under the appropriate recipient group and month. Note: not all sponsoring organizations supplied deadline information; those programs are listed under the "Deadline not specified" entries in the index. To identify every relevant financial aid program, regardless of filing date, go the appropriate chapter and read through all the entries there that match your educational level.

To Locate Financial Aid Programs Open to All Segments of the Population. Only programs available to Hispanic Americans are listed in this publication. However, there are thousands of other programs that are open equally to all segments of the population. To identify these programs, talk to your local librarian, check with your financial aid office on campus, look at the list of RSP print resources on the page opposite the title page in this directory, or see if your library subscribes to Reference Service Press' interactive online funding database: *RSP FundingFinder.* For more information on that award-winning resource, go online to: www.rspfunding.com/esubscriptions.html.

PLANS TO UPDATE THE DIRECTORY

This volume, covering 2014-2016, is the eighth edition of *Financial Aid for Hispanic Americans.* The next biennial edition will cover the years 2016-2018 and will be issued by the beginning of 2016.

OTHER RELATED PUBLICATIONS

In addition to *Financial Aid for Hispanic Americans,* Reference Service Press publishes several other titles dealing with fundseeking, including the award-winning *Directory of Financial Aids for Women; Financial Aid for Persons with Disabilities and Their Families;* and *Financial Aid for Veterans, Military Personnel, and Their Families.* Since each of these titles focuses on a separate population group, there is very little duplication in the listings. For more information on Reference Service Press' award-winning publications, write to the company at 5000 Windplay Drive, Suite 4, El Dorado Hills, CA 95762, give us a call at (916) 939-9620, fax us at (916) 939-9626, send us an e-mail at info@rspfunding.com, or visit our expanded web site: www.rspfunding.com.

ACKNOWLEDGEMENTS

A debt of gratitude is owed all the organizations that contributed information to the 2014-2016 edition of *Financial Aid for Hispanic Americans.* Their generous cooperation has helped to make this publication a current and comprehensive survey of awards.

ABOUT THE AUTHORS

Dr. Gail Ann Schlachter has worked for more than three decades as a library manager, a library educator, and an administrator of library-related publishing companies. Among the reference books to her credit are the biennially-issued *Directory of Financial Aids for Women* and two award-winning bibliographic guides: *Minorities and Women: A Guide to Reference Literature in the Social Sciences* (which was chosen as an "outstanding reference book of the year" by *Choice)* and *Reference Sources in Library and Information Services* (which won the first Knowledge Industry Publications "Award for Library Literature"). She was the reference book review editor for *RQ* (now *Reference and User Services Quarterly)* for 10 years, is a past president of the American Library Association's Reference and User Services Association, is the former editor-in-chief of the *Reference and User Services Association Quarterly,* and is currently serving her sixth term on the American Library Association's governing council. In recognition of her outstanding contributions to reference service, Dr. Schlachter has been named the University of Wisconsin School of Library and Information Studies "Alumna of the Year" and has been awarded both the Isadore Gilbert Mudge Citation and the Louis Shores/Oryx Press Award.

Dr. R. David Weber taught history and economics at Los Angeles Harbor College (in Wilmington, California) for many years and continues to teach history there as an emeritus professor. During his years at Harbor College, and earlier at East Los College, he directed the Honors Program and was frequently chosen the "Teacher of the Year." He has written a number of critically-acclaimed reference works, including *Dissertations in Urban History* and the three-volume *Energy Information Guide.* With Gail Schlachter, he is the author of Reference Service Press' *Financial Aid for Persons with Disabilities and Their Families,* which was selected by *Library Journal* as one of the "best reference books of the year," and a number of other financial aid titles, including the *College Student's Guide to Merit and Other No-Need Funding,* which was chosen as one of the "outstanding reference books of the year" by *Choice.*

Financial Aid Programs Open to Hispanic Americans

Undergraduates ●

Graduate Students ●

Professionals/Postdoctorates ●

Undergraduates

Listed alphabetically by program title and described in detail here are 500 scholarships, forgivable loans, grants, awards, and other sources of "free money" set aside for Hispanic Americans who are college-bound high school seniors or continuing and returning undergraduate students. This funding is available to support study, training, research, and/or creative activities in the United States.

[1]
ABC LATINO MINISTRIES SCHOLARSHIP

American Baptist Churches USA
Attn: American Baptist Home Mission Societies
National Coordinator for Intercultural Ministries
P.O. Box 851
Valley Forge, PA 19482-0851
(610) 768-2421   Toll Free: (800) ABC-3USA, ext. 2421
Fax: (610) 768-2453
E-mail: Salvador.Orellana@abc-usa.org
Web: www.abhms.org

Summary   To provide financial assistance to Latinos who are interested in preparing for or furthering a church career in the American Baptist Church (ABC).

Eligibility   This program is open to Latino members of the ABC or its recognized institutions who demonstrate financial need. They must be enrolled full time at an accredited institution, working on an undergraduate degree or first professional degree in a seminary. Applicants must be currently serving or planning to serve in a vocation with the church or with its recognized institutions. They must be U.S. citizens who have been a member of an American Baptist Church for at least 1 year.

Financial Data   The stipends range from $500 to $3,000 per year.

Duration   1 year; may be renewed.

Number awarded   Varies each year.

Deadline   May of each year.

[2]
ABERCROMBIE & FITCH FUTURE LEADERS SCHOLARSHIP

¡Adelante! U.S. Education Leadership Fund
8415 Datapoint Drive, Suite 400
San Antonio, TX 78229
(210) 692-1971   Toll Free: (877) 692-1971
Fax: (210) 692-1951   E-mail: info@adelantefund.org
Web: www.adelantefund.org/#!abercrombie—fitch/c1qa

Summary   To provide financial assistance to Hispanic students majoring in business at colleges in any state.

Eligibility   This program is open to Hispanic students entering their sophomore, junior, or senior year at colleges and universities in any state. Applicants must be working on a degree in business. They must have a GPA of 3.0 or higher, provide a resume of their community service activities, be U.S. citizens or permanent residents, agree to attend the Adelante Leadership Institute, and provide a letter of recommendation.

Financial Data   The stipend is $1,000.

Duration   1 year.

Additional data   This fund was established by the Hispanic Association of Colleges and Universities in 1997 and became a separate organization in 1999. This program is sponsored by Abercrombie & Fitch.

Number awarded   Varies each year.

Deadline   May of each year.

[3]
ACA/MARTIN LUTHER KING JR. SCHOLARSHIP AWARDS

American Correctional Association
Attn: Scholarship Award Committee
206 North Washington Street, Suite 200
Alexandria, VA 22314
(703) 224-0000   Toll Free: (800) ACA-JOIN
Fax: (703) 224-0179   E-mail: jenniferb@aca.org
Web: www.aca.org/pastpresentfuture/awards.asp

Summary   To provide financial assistance for undergraduate or graduate study to Hispanic Americans and other minorities interested in a career in the criminal justice field.

Eligibility   Members of the American Correctional Association (ACA) may nominate a minority person for these awards. Nominees do not need to be ACA members, but they must have been accepted to or be enrolled in an undergraduate or graduate program in criminal justice at a 4-year college or university. Along with the nomination package, they must submit a 250-word essay describing their reflections on the ideals and philosophies of Dr. Martin Luther King and how they have attempted to emulate those qualities in their lives. They must provide documentation of financial need, academic achievement, and commitment to the principles of Dr. King.

Financial Data   A stipend is awarded (amount not specified). Funds are paid directly to the recipient's college or university.

Number awarded   1 each year.

Deadline   May of each year.

[4]
ACT SIX SCHOLARSHIPS

Act Six
c/o Degrees of Change
1109 A Street, Suite 101
P.O. Box 1573
Tacoma, WA 98401
(253) 642-6712   E-mail: tim.herron@actsix.org
Web: www.actsix.org

Summary   To provide financial assistance to Hispanic Americans and other residents of Washington and Oregon who come from diverse backgrounds and are interested in attending designated private faith-based universities in those states.

Eligibility   This program is open to high school seniors or recent graduates and planning to enter college as freshmen who come from diverse, multicultural backgrounds. Applicants must be residents of the following regions and interested in attending designated colleges for that region: Portland: George Fox University or Warner Pacific College; Spokane: Gonzaga University or Whitworth University; Tacoma-Seattle: Gonzaga University, Northwest University, Pacific Lutheran University, Trinity Lutheran College, or Whitworth University; or Yakima Valley: Heritage University. Students are not required to make a faith commitment, but they must be willing to explore Christian spirituality as it relates to service and leadership. Ethnicity and family income are considered as factors in selecting an intentionally diverse group of scholars, but there are no income restrictions and students from all ethnic backgrounds are encouraged to apply.

Financial Data The program makes up the difference between any other assistance the student receives and full tuition. For recipients who demonstrate financial need in excess of tuition, awards cover some or all of the cost of room and board, books, travel, and personal expenses.

Duration 1 year; may be renewed.

Number awarded Varies each year; recently, 65 of these scholarships were awarded.

Deadline October of each year.

[5]
ACTUARIAL DIVERSITY SCHOLARSHIPS

Actuarial Foundation
Attn: Actuarial Education and Research Fund Committee
475 North Martingale Road, Suite 600
Schaumburg, IL 60173-2226
(847) 706-3535   Fax: (847) 706-3599
E-mail: scholarships@actfnd.org
Web: www.actuarialfoundation.org

Summary To provide financial assistance to Hispanic American and other minority undergraduate students who are preparing for a career in actuarial science.

Eligibility This program is open to members of minority groups, defined as having at least 1 birth parent who is Black/African American, Hispanic, Native North American, or Pacific Islander. Applicants must be graduating high school seniors or current full-time undergraduate students working on or planning to work on a degree at an accredited 2- or 4-year college or university that may lead to a career in the actuarial profession. They must have a GPA of 3.0 or higher; high school seniors must also have a minimum score of 28 on the ACT mathematics examination or 600 on the SAT mathematics examination. Along with their application, they must submit a 1- or 2-page personal statement that covers why they are interested in becoming an actuary, the steps they are taking to enter the actuarial profession, participation in actuarial internships, and participation in extracurricular activities. Financial need is not considered in the selection process.

Financial Data Annual stipends are $1,000 for high school seniors applying for freshman year, $2,000 for college freshmen applying for sophomore year and for college sophomores applying for junior year, $3,000 for college juniors applying for senior year, or $3,000 for college seniors applying for graduate school or continuing graduate students.

Duration 1 year; may be renewed, provided the recipient remains enrolled full time, in good academic standing, in a course of study that may lead to a career in the actuarial profession, and (for college juniors and higher) passes actuarial examinations.

Additional data This program began in 1977 by the Casualty Actuarial Society and the Society of Actuaries. In 2008, it was transferred to the Actuarial Foundation.

Number awarded Varies each year; recently, 32 of these scholarships were awarded.

Deadline May of each year.

[6]
A.D. OSHERMAN SCHOLARSHIP FUND

Greater Houston Community Foundation
Attn: Scholarship Coordinator
5120 Woodway Drive, Suite 6000
Houston, TX 77056
(713) 333-2205   Fax: (713) 333-2220
E-mail: lgardner@ghcf.org
Web: www.ghcf.org/Recieve/Scholarships

Summary To provide financial assistance to Hispanic Americans and members of other designated groups who are residents of Texas and attending or planning to attend college in any state.

Eligibility This program is open to Texas residents who are graduating high school seniors or full-time freshmen, sophomores, or juniors at an accredited public 2- or 4-year college or university in any state. Applicants must qualify as a member of a recognized minority group, the first in their family to attend college, or a veteran with active service, particularly service in Iraq or Afghanistan. They must have a GPA of 2.75 or higher and a history of community service. Financial need is considered in the selection process.

Financial Data The stipend is $2,500 per year for students at 4-year universities or $1,500 per year for students at 2-year colleges.

Duration 1 year; recipients may reapply.

Number awarded 2 each year.

Deadline March of each year.

[7]
ADDIE B. MORRIS SCHOLARSHIP

American Association of Railroad Superintendents
P.O. Box 200
La Fox, IL 60147
(630) 762-0754   E-mail: aars@supt.org
Web: www.railroadsuperintendents.org/Scholarships

Summary To provide financial assistance to undergraduate and graduate students, with preference given to Hispanic Americans and other minorities working on a degree in transportation.

Eligibility This program is open to full-time undergraduate and graduate students enrolled at accredited colleges and universities in Canada or the United States. Applicants must have completed enough credits to have standing as a sophomore and must have a GPA of 2.75 or higher. Preference is given to minority students enrolled in the transportation field who can demonstrate financial need.

Financial Data The stipend is $1,000. Funds are sent directly to the recipient's institution.

Duration 1 year.

Number awarded 1 or more each year.

Deadline May of each year.

[8]
ADELANTE'S SCORING FOR EDUCATION SCHOLARSHIP

¡Adelante! U.S. Education Leadership Fund
8415 Datapoint Drive, Suite 400
San Antonio, TX 78229
(210) 692-1971   Toll Free: (877) 692-1971
Fax: (210) 692-1951   E-mail: info@adelantefund.org
Web: www.adelantefund.org/#!scholarships/crij

Summary To provide financial assistance to Hispanic students majoring in any field at colleges in Texas or Oklahoma.

Eligibility This program is open to Hispanic students entering their freshman year or currently enrolled as full-time freshmen or sophomores at colleges, universities, and community colleges in Texas or Oklahoma. Applicants may be majoring in any field, but they must have a GPA of 3.0 or higher. They must agree to attend the Adelante Leadership Institute.

Financial Data The stipend is $1,500.

Duration 1 year.

Additional data This fund was established by the Hispanic Association of Colleges and Universities in 1997 and became a separate organization in 1999.

Number awarded Varies each year.

Deadline May of each year.

[9]
ADVANCING HISPANIC EXCELLENCE IN TECHNOLOGY, ENGINEERING, MATH AND SCIENCE (AHETEMS) GENERAL SCHOLARSHIPS

Society of Hispanic Professional Engineers Foundation, Inc.
Attn: Advancing Hispanic Excellence in Technology, Engineering, Math and Science
13181 Crossroads Parkway North, Suite 450
P.O. Box 93577
City of Industry, CA 91715
(323) 725-3970, ext. 118   Fax: (323) 622-1046
E-mail: shpefoundation@shpe.org
Web: www.shpefoundation.org

Summary To provide financial assistance to undergraduate and graduate students of Hispanic descent who are preparing for a career in science, technology, engineering, mathematics (STEM), or a related field.

Eligibility This program is open to students of Hispanic descent who are accepted into or attending an accredited 2- or 4-year college or university in the United States or Puerto Rico and are members of the Society of Hispanic Professional Engineers (SHPE). Applicants must be working or planning to work full time on a degree in a STEM or related field. High school seniors and undergraduates must have a GPA of 2.75 or higher; graduate students must have a GPA of 3.0 or higher. Along with their application, they must submit a 500-word personal statement covering their community involvement, leadership, academic achievements, research internship and co-op experiences, and short-term and long-term goals and aspirations. Both merit-based and need-based scholarships are available. U.S. citizenship or permanent resident status is not required.

Financial Data Stipends range from $1,000 to $3,000.

Duration 1 year.

Additional data Advancing Hispanic Excellence in Technology, Engineering, Math and Science (AHETEMS) was established in 2004 by the Society of Hispanic Professional Engineers (SHPE) as an independent nonprofit foundation.

Number awarded 1 or more each year.

Deadline April of each year.

[10]
AFPD MINORITY SCHOLARSHIPS

Associated Food and Petroleum Dealers
Attn: AFPD Foundation
5779 West Maple Road
West Bloomfield, MI 48322
(248) 671-9600   Toll Free: (800) 666-6233
Fax: (866) 601-9610   E-mail: info@afpdonline.org
Web: www.afpdonline.org/michigan-scholarship.php

Summary To provide financial assistance to Hispanic American and other minority high school seniors and current college students from Michigan who are enrolled or planning to enroll at a college in any state.

Eligibility This program is open to Michigan residents who are high school seniors or college freshmen, sophomores, or juniors. Applicants must be members of 1 of the following minority groups: African American, Hispanic, Asian, Native American, or Arab/Chaldean. They must be enrolled or planning to enroll full time at a college or university in any state. Preferential consideration is given to applicants with a membership affiliation in the Associated Food and Petroleum Dealers (AFPD), although membership is not required. Selection is based on academic performance, leadership, and participation in school and community activities; college grades are considered if the applicant is already enrolled in college.

Financial Data The stipend is $1,500.

Duration 1 year; nonrenewable.

Additional data This program is administered by International Scholarship and Tuition Services, Inc. The AFPD was formed in 2006 by a merger of the Associated Food Dealers of Michigan and the Great Lakes Petroleum Retailers and Allied Trades Association.

Number awarded At least 10 each year, of which at least 3 must be awarded to member customers.

Deadline March of each year.

[11]
AGA INVESTING IN THE FUTURE STUDENT RESEARCH FELLOWSHIPS

American Gastroenterological Association
Attn: AGA Research Foundation
Research Awards Manager
4930 Del Ray Avenue
Bethesda, MD 20814-2512
(301) 222-4012   Fax: (301) 654-5920
E-mail: awards@gastro.org
Web: www.gastro.org/aga-foundation/grants

Summary To provide funding for research on digestive diseases or nutrition to undergraduate and medical students who are Hispanic Americans or from other underrepresented minority groups.

Eligibility This program is open to undergraduate and medical students at accredited U.S. institutions who are African Americans, Hispanic/Latino Americans, Alaska Natives, American Indians, or Natives of the U.S. Pacific Islands. Applicants must be interested in conducting research on digestive diseases or nutrition. They may not hold similar salary support awards from other agencies (e.g., American Liver Foundation, Crohn's and Colitis Foundation). Research must be conducted under the supervision of a preceptor who is a full-time faculty member at an institution in a state other than the student's, directing a research project in a gastroenterology-related area, and a member of the American Gastroenterological Association (AGA).

Financial Data Fellowships provide payment of housing, travel, and a stipend of $5,000.

Duration 8 to 10 weeks. The work may take place at any time during the year.

Number awarded 10 each year.

Deadline February of each year.

[12]
AHETEMS NORTHROP GRUMMAN SCHOLARSHIPS

Society of Hispanic Professional Engineers Foundation, Inc.
Attn: Advancing Hispanic Excellence in Technology, Engineering, Math and Science
13181 Crossroads Parkway North, Suite 450
P.O. Box 93577
City of Industry, CA 91715
(323) 725-3970, ext. 118   Fax: (323) 622-1046
E-mail: shpefoundation@shpe.org
Web: www.shpefoundation.org

Summary To provide financial assistance to undergraduate student members of the Society of Hispanic Professional Engineers (SHPE) who are working on a degree in engineering or a related field at an Historically Black College or University (HBCU), an Hispanic Service Institution (HSI), or other specified universities.

Eligibility This program is open to entering full-time sophomores, juniors, or seniors at an accredited university in the United States or Puerto Rico that is an HBCU, an HIS, or another designated institution. Applicants must be majoring in computer science, engineering (aerospace, computer, electrical, industrial, mechanical, or systems), mathematics, naval architecture, or physics. They must have a GPA of 3.0 or higher. Along with their application, they must submit a 500-word personal statement covering their community involvement, leadership, academic achievements, research internship and co-op experiences, and short-term and long-term goals and aspirations. Selection is based on merit. U.S. citizenship is required.

Financial Data The stipend is $5,000.

Duration 1 year.

Additional data Advancing Hispanic Excellence in Technology, Engineering, Math and Science (AHETEMS) was established in 2004 by the Society of Hispanic Professional Engineers (SHPE) as an independent nonprofit foundation. This program is sponsored by Northrop Grumman. The other designated institutions are California Polytechnic State University at San Luis Obispo, California Institute of Technology, Georgia Institute of Technology, Massachusetts Institute of Technology, North Carolina State University, Ohio State University, Pennsylvania State University, Purdue University, Uni-

versity of California at Los Angeles, University of Illinois at Urbana-Champaign, University of Maryland, University of Michigan, University of Southern California, University of Virginia, and Virginia Polytechnic Institute and State University.

Number awarded 1 or more each year.

Deadline April of each year.

[13]
AHLEF/HYATT HOTELS FUND FOR MINORITY LODGING MANAGEMENT STUDENTS

American Hotel & Lodging Educational Foundation
Attn: Manager of Foundation Programs
1201 New York Avenue, N.W., Suite 600
Washington, DC 20005-3931
(202) 289-3100   Fax: (202) 289-3199
E-mail: scholarships@ahlef.org
Web: www.ahlef.org/content.aspx?id=19468

Summary To provide financial assistance to Hispanic American and other minority college students working on a degree in hotel management.

Eligibility This program is open to students majoring in hospitality management at a 4-year college or university as at least a junior. Applicants must be members of a minority group (African American, Hispanic, American Indian, Alaskan Native, Asian, or Pacific Islander). They must be enrolled full time. Along with their application, they must submit a 500-word essay on their personal background, including when they became interested in the hospitality field, the traits they possess or will need to succeed in the industry, and their plans as related to their educational and career objectives and future goals. Selection is based on industry-related work experience; financial need; academic record and educational qualifications; professional, community, and extracurricular activities; personal attributes, including career goals; the essay; and neatness and completeness of the application. U.S. citizenship or permanent resident status is required.

Financial Data The stipend is $2,000.

Duration 1 year.

Additional data Funding for this program, established in 1988, is provided by Hyatt Hotels & Resorts.

Number awarded Varies each year; recently, 18 of these scholarships were awarded. Since this program was established, it has awarded scholarships worth $588,000 to 294 minority students.

Deadline April of each year.

[14]
AHORA (APPLIED HISPANIC OPPORTUNITY AND RECOGNITION AWARD) SCHOLARSHIPS

Hispanic Scholarship Consortium
Attn: Scholarship Selection Committee
1107 South Eighth Street
Austin, TX 78704
(512) 368-2956   Fax: (512) 692-1831
E-mail: scholarships@hispanicscholar.org
Web: www.hispanicscholar.org

Summary To provide financial assistance to Hispanic American and other members of the American Health Information Management Association (AHIMA) who are interested in working on an undergraduate or graduate degree in health information management (HIM) or health information technology (HIT) and will contribute to diversity in the profession.

Eligibility This program is open to seniors graduating from high schools in Texas who are of Hispanic heritage and have a GPA of 3.0 or higher. They must be planning to enroll full time at an accredited 2- or 4-year college or university in the state and major in a field of STEM. Selection is based on academic record, community service, financial need, and a personal interview. U.S. citizenship or permanent resident status is required.

Financial Data The stipend is $2,000 per year.

Duration 1 year; may be renewed, provided the recipient remains enrolled full time, maintains a GPA of 3.0 or higher, and participates in at least 25 hours of community service per semester.

Additional data This program is sponsored by Hispanics in Partnership at Applied Materials.

Number awarded 1 or more each year.

Deadline August of each year.

[15]
ALAN COMPTON AND BOB STANLEY MINORITY AND INTERNATIONAL SCHOLARSHIP

Baptist Communicators Association
Attn: Scholarship Committee
1519 Menlo Drive
Kennesaw, GA 30152
(770) 425-3728   E-mail: mmdempsey@bellsouth.net
Web: www.baptistcommunicators.org/about/scholarship.cfm

Summary To provide financial assistance to Hispanic American, other minority, and international students who are working on an undergraduate degree to prepare for a career in Baptist communications.

Eligibility This program is open to undergraduate students of minority or international origin. Applicants must be majoring in communications, English, journalism, or public relations and have a GPA of 2.5 or higher. Their vocational objective must be in Baptist communications. Along with their application, they must submit a statement explaining why they want to receive this scholarship.

Financial Data The stipend is $1,000.

Duration 1 year; recipients may reapply.

Additional data This program began in 1996.

Number awarded 1 each year.

Deadline March of each year.

[16]
ALBUQUERQUE HISPANO CHAMBER OF COMMERCE OPPORTUNITY SCHOLARSHIP

Albuquerque Hispano Chamber of Commerce
Attn: Scholarship Coordinator
1309 Fourth Street, S.W.
Albuquerque, NM 87102
(505) 842-9003   Fax: (505) 764-9664
Web: www.ahcnm.org/Scholarship_Applications.aspx

Summary To provide financial assistance to Hispanic residents of New Mexico who have been out of high school for at least 1 year and are interested in attending college in the state.

Eligibility This program is open to Hispanic residents of New Mexico who are at least 19 years of age. Applicants must have earned their high school diploma or GED at least 1 year previously and be interested in continuing their postsecondary education at a New Mexico institution. Along with their application, they must submit an essay of 300 to 500 words on their financial need, educational and career goals, how those goals relate to their ethnic background, and their philosophy toward their Hispanic heritage.

Financial Data A stipend is awarded (amount not specified).

Duration 1 year.

Number awarded 1 or more each year.

Deadline March of each year.

[17]
ALMA EXLEY SCHOLARSHIP

Community Foundation of Greater New Britain
Attn: Scholarship Manager
74A Vine Street
New Britain, CT 06052-1431
(860) 229-6018, ext. 305   Fax: (860) 225-2666
E-mail: cfarmer@cfgnb.org
Web: www.cfgnb.org

Summary To provide financial assistance to Hispanic American and other minority college students in Connecticut who are interested in preparing for a teaching career.

Eligibility This program is open to students of color (African Americans, Asian Americans, Hispanic Americans, and Native Americans) enrolled in a teacher preparation program in Connecticut. Applicant must 1) have been admitted to a traditional teacher preparation program at an accredited 4-year college or university in the state; or 2) be participating in the Alternate Route to Certification (ARC) program sponsored by the Connecticut Department of Higher Education.

Financial Data The stipend is $1,500 per year for students at a 4-year college or university or $500 for a student in the ARC program.

Duration 2 years for students at 4-year colleges or universities; 1 year for students in the ARC program.

Number awarded 2 each year: 1 to a 4-year student and 1 to an ARC student.

Deadline October of each year.

[18]
ALTRIA SCHOLARS

Virginia Foundation for Independent Colleges
Attn: Director of Development
8010 Ridge Road, Suite B
Richmond, VA 23229-7288
(804) 288-6609   Toll Free: (800) 230-6757
Fax: (804) 282-4635   E-mail: info@vfic.org
Web: www.vfic.org/scholarships/scholarships_vfic.html

Summary To provide financial assistance to students (especially Hispanic Americans and other underrepresented minorities) who are majoring in designated fields at a college or university that is a member of the Virginia Foundation for Independent Colleges (VFIC).

Eligibility This program is open to sophomores who are enrolled as full-time second-semester sophomores at 1 of the 15 VFIC member institutions. Applicants must be nominated by their institution. They must have a GPA of 3.0 or higher and a declared major in accounting, biology, business management, business, chemistry, computer science, economics, engineering, finance, marketing, or physics. Selection is based on merit and financial need. Special consideration is given to underserved populations. U.S. citizenship is required.

Financial Data The stipend is $5,000 per year.

Duration 1 year (the junior year). May be renewed for the senior year, provided the recipient maintains a GPA of 3.0 or higher and a record of good citizenship and conduct.

Additional data Funding for this program, established in 2001, is provided by Altria Group (parent company of Philip Morris USA). Recipients also have an opportunity to apply for paid internships with Altria. The 15 member institutions are Bridgewater College, Emory and Henry College, Hampden-Sydney College, Hollins University, Lynchburg College, Mary Baldwin College, Marymount University, Randolph College, Randolph-Macon College, Roanoke College, Shenandoah University, Sweet Briar College, University of Richmond, Virginia Wesleyan College, and Washington and Lee University.

Number awarded 10 each year.

Deadline October of each year.

[19]
ALVAN T.–VIOLA D. FULLER JUNIOR RESEARCH FELLOWSHIP

American Cancer Society-New England Division
30 Speen Street
Framingham, MA 01701
(508) 270-3109   Toll Free: (800) 952-7664, ext. 3109
Fax: (508) 270-4607   E-mail: koconnor@cancer.org
Web: www.cancer.org

Summary To provide funding for cancer research during the summer to undergraduate students (particularly Hispanic American and other minority students) in New England.

Eligibility This program is open to residents of New England currently enrolled as juniors or seniors at a college or university in any state. Applicants must be interested in working on a summer research project at a teaching hospital, university, or medical school in New England. They must be interested in working under the supervision of an accomplished cancer investigator. Preference is given to student with advanced science course work, laboratory skills, and an interest in research. Minority students and those with American Cancer Society volunteer experience are especially encouraged to apply.

Financial Data The grant is $4,500.

Duration 10 weeks during the summer.

Number awarded 1 or more each year.

Deadline January of each year.

[20]
AMAC AVIATION AND PROFESSIONAL DEVELOPMENT SCHOLARSHIPS

Airport Minority Advisory Council
Attn: AMAC Educational and Scholarship Program, Inc.
2001 Jefferson Davis Highway, Suite 500
Arlington, VA 22202
(703) 414-2622, ext. 4   Fax: (703) 414-2686
E-mail: aaron.pope@amac-org.com
Web: www.amac-org.com/scholarships.html

Summary To provide financial assistance to Hispanic American and other minority high school seniors and undergraduates who are preparing for a career in the aviation industry and are interested in participating in the Airport Minority Advisory Council (AMAC).

Eligibility This program is open to high school seniors and current undergraduates who have a GPA of 2.5 or higher and a record of involvement in community and extracurricular activities. Applicants must be working on a bachelor's degree in accounting, architecture, aviation, business administration, engineering, or finance as preparation for a career in the aviation or airport industry. They must be interested in participating in the AMAC program, including having an endorsement from a current AMAC member, becoming a member if they are awarded a scholarship, and communicating with AMAC once each semester during the term of the scholarship. Along with their application, they must submit a 1-page essay on their career goals and why they have chosen their particular field of study. Financial need is not considered in the selection process. U.S. citizenship is required.

Financial Data The stipend is $2,000 per year.

Duration 1 year; recipients may reapply.

Number awarded 4 each semester.

Deadline August of each year for spring semester; April of each year for spring semester.

[21]
AMELIA KEMP MEMORIAL SCHOLARSHIP

Women of the Evangelical Lutheran Church in America
Attn: Scholarships
8765 West Higgins Road
Chicago, IL 60631-4101
(773) 380-2741   Toll Free: (800) 638-3522, ext. 2741
Fax: (773) 380-2419   E-mail: valora.starr@elca.org
Web: www.womenoftheelca.org

Summary To provide financial assistance to Hispanic American and other lay women of color who are members of Evangelical Lutheran Church of America (ELCA) congregations and who wish to study on the undergraduate, graduate, professional, or vocational school level.

Eligibility This program is open to ELCA lay women of color who are at least 21 years of age and have experienced an interruption of at least 2 years in their education since high school. Applicants must have been admitted to an educational institution to prepare for a career in other than ordained ministry. U.S. citizenship is required.

Financial Data The maximum stipend is $1,000.

Duration Up to 2 years.

Number awarded 1 or more each year.

Deadline February of each year.

[22]
AMERICAN ASSOCIATION OF BLACKS IN ENERGY NATIONAL SCHOLARSHIPS

American Association of Blacks in Energy
Attn: Scholarship Committee
1625 K Street, N.W., Suite 405
Washington, DC 20006
(202) 371-9530 Fax: (202) 371-9218
E-mail: info@aabe.org
Web: www.aabe.org/index.php?component=pages&id=4

Summary To provide financial assistance to Hispanic American and other underrepresented minority high school seniors who are interested in preparing for a career in a field related to energy in college.

Eligibility This program is open to members of minority groups underrepresented in energy-related fields (African Americans, Hispanics, and Native Americans) who are graduating high school seniors. Applicants must have a GPA of 3.0 or higher overall and in mathematics and science courses. They must be planning to attend an accredited college or university to major in business, engineering, mathematics, technology, or the physical sciences. Along with their application, they must submit a 350-word essay that includes why they should receive this scholarship and how their professional career objectives relate to the energy field. Financial need is considered in the selection process. All applications must be submitted to the local office of the sponsoring organization in the student's state. For a list of local offices, contact the scholarship committee at the national office. The highest-ranked applicant receives the Premier Award.

Financial Data The stipends are $3,000. The Premier Award is $5,000. All funds are paid directly to the students upon proof of enrollment at an accredited college or university.

Duration 1 year; nonrenewable.

Number awarded 6 each year (1 in each of the organization's regions); of those 6 winners, 1 is chosen to receive the Premier Award.

Deadline February of each year.

[23]
AMERICAN ASSOCIATION OF UNIVERSITY WOMEN CAREER DEVELOPMENT GRANTS

American Association of University Women
Attn: AAUW Educational Foundation
301 ACT Drive, Department 60
P.O. Box 4030
Iowa City, IA 52243-4030
(319) 337-1716, ext. 60 Fax: (319) 337-1204
E-mail: aauw@act.org
Web: www.aauw.org

Summary To provide financial assistance to Hispanic American and other women who are seeking career advancement, career change, or reentry into the workforce.

Eligibility This program is open to women who are U.S. citizens or permanent residents, have earned a bachelor's degree, received their most recent degree more than 4 years ago, and are making career changes, seeking to advance in current careers, or reentering the workforce. Applicants must be interested in working toward a master's degree, second bachelor's or associate degree, professional degree (e.g., M.D., J.D.), certification program, or technical school certifi-

cate. They must be planning to undertake course work at an accredited 2- or 4-year college or university (or a technical school that is licensed, accredited, or approved by the U.S. Department of Education). Primary consideration is given to women of color and women pursuing their first advanced degree or credentials in nontraditional fields. Support is not provided for prerequisite course work or for Ph.D. course work or dissertations. Selection is based on demonstrated commitment to education and equity for women and girls, reason for seeking higher education or technical training, degree to which study plan is consistent with career objectives, potential for success in chosen field, documentation of opportunities in chosen field, feasibility of study plans and proposed time schedule, validity of proposed budget and budget narrative (including sufficient outside support), and quality of written proposal.

Financial Data Grants range from $2,000 to $12,000. Funds may be used for tuition, fees, books, supplies, local transportation, dependent child care, or purchase of a computer required for the study program.

Duration 1 year, beginning in July; nonrenewable.

Additional data The filing fee is $35.

Number awarded Varies each year; recently, 63 of these grants, with a value of $670,000, were awarded.

Deadline December of each year.

[24]
AMERICAN CHEMICAL SOCIETY SCHOLARS PROGRAM

American Chemical Society
Attn: Scholars Program
1155 16th Street, N.W.
Washington, DC 20036
(202) 872-6250 Toll Free: (800) 227-5558, ext. 6250
Fax: (202) 872-4361 E-mail: scholars@acs.org
Web: portal.acs.org

Summary To provide financial assistance to Hispanic American and other underrepresented minority students who have a strong interest in chemistry and a desire to prepare for a career in a chemically-related science.

Eligibility This program is open to 1) college-bound high school seniors; 2) freshmen, sophomores, and juniors enrolled full time at an accredited college or university; 3) community college students planning to transfer to a 4-year school; and 4) community college students working on a 2-year degree. Applicants must be African American, Hispanic/Latino, or Native American. They must be majoring or planning to major in chemistry, biochemistry, chemical engineering, or other chemically-related fields, such as environmental science, materials science, or toxicology, in preparation for a career in the chemical sciences or chemical technology. Students planning careers in medicine or pharmacy are not eligible. U.S. citizenship or permanent resident status is required. Selection is based on academic record (GPA of 3.0 or higher), career objective, leadership ability, participation in school activities, community service, and financial need.

Financial Data Annual stipends are $2,500 for freshmen, $3,000 for sophomores, or $5,000 for seniors. Funds are sent directly to the recipient's college or university.

Duration 1 year; may be renewed.

Additional data This program began in 1994.

Number awarded Approximately 135 new awards are granted each year.

Deadline February of each year.

[25]
AMERICAN GI FORUM WOMEN'S RE-ENTRY SCHOLARSHIPS

American GI Forum of the United States
2870 North Speer Boulevard, Suite 103
Denver, CO 80211
(303) 458-1700   Toll Free: (866) 244-3628
Fax: (303) 458-1634   E-mail: agifnat@gmail.com
Web: www.agifusa.org/women

Summary To provide financial assistance to mature women who are members of the American GI Forum (an Hispanic veterans organization) and interested in returning to college.

Eligibility This program is open to women who have been members of a women's chapter of the American GI Forum for at least 2 years. Applicants must be at least 25 years of age and enrolled or planning to enroll at a college or university as a full- or part-time student. Along with their application, they must submit transcripts, 3 letters of recommendation, proof of income, and a biographical essay.

Financial Data A stipend is awarded (amount not specified).

Duration 1 year; recipients may reapply.

Additional data The American GI Forum is the largest federally-charter Hispanic veterans organization in the United States.

Number awarded 1 or more each year.

Deadline Deadline not specified.

[26]
AMERICAN HEALTH INFORMATION MANAGEMENT ASSOCIATION FOUNDATION DIVERSITY SCHOLARSHIPS

American Health Information Management Association
Attn: AHIMA Foundation
233 North Michigan Avenue, 21st Floor
Chicago, IL 60601-5809
(312) 233-1175   Fax: (312) 233-1475
E-mail: info@ahimafoundation.org
Web: www.ahimafoundation.org

Summary To provide financial assistance to members of the American Health Information Management Association (AHIMA) who are interested in working on an undergraduate or graduate degree in health information management (HIM) or health information technology (HIT) and who will contribute to diversity in the profession.

Eligibility This program is open to AHIMA members who are enrolled at least half time in a program accredited by the Commission on Accreditation for Health Informatics and Information Management Education (CAHIM). Applicants must be working on a degree in HIM or HIT at the associate, bachelor's, post-baccalaureate, master's, or doctoral level. They must have a GPA of 3.5 or higher and at least 1 full semester remaining after the date of the award. To qualify for this support, applicants must demonstrate how they will contribute to diversity in the health information management profession; diversity is defined as differences in race, ethnicity, nationality, gender, sexual orientation, socioeconomic status, age, physical capabilities, and religious beliefs. Selection is based on GPA and academic achievement, volunteer and work experience, commitment to the HIM profession, quality and relevance of references, and completeness and clarity of thought.

Financial Data Stipends are $1,000 for associate degree students, $1,500 for bachelor's degree or post-baccalaureate certificate students, $2,000 for master's degree students, or $2,500 for doctoral degree students.

Duration 1 year.

Number awarded Varies each year; recently, 9 of these scholarships were awarded: 6 to undergraduates and 3 to graduate students.

Deadline September of each year.

[27]
AMERICAN INSTITUTE OF ARCHITECTS MINORITY/DISADVANTAGED SCHOLARSHIP PROGRAM

American Institute of Architects
Attn: American Architectural Foundation
1799 New York Avenue, N.W.
Washington, DC 20006-5292
(202) 626-7511   Fax: (202) 626-7420
E-mail: scholarships@aia.org
Web: www.aia.org/education/aiab081881

Summary To provide financial assistance to Hispanic American and other high school and college students from minority and/or disadvantaged backgrounds who are interested in studying architecture in college.

Eligibility This program is open to students from minority and/or disadvantaged backgrounds who are high school seniors, students in a community college or technical school transferring to an accredited architectural program, or college freshmen entering a professional degree program at an accredited program of architecture. Students who have completed 1 or more years of a 4-year college curriculum are not eligible. Initially, candidates must be nominated by 1 of the following organizations or persons: an individual architect or firm, a chapter of the American Institute of Architects (AIA), a community design center, a guidance counselor or teacher, the dean or professor at an accredited school of architecture, or the director of a community or civic organization. Nominees are reviewed and eligible candidates are invited to complete an application form in which they write an essay describing the reasons they are interested in becoming an architect and provide documentation of academic excellence and financial need. Selection is based primarily on financial need.

Financial Data Stipends range from $3,000 to $4,000 per year, depending upon individual need. Students must apply for supplementary funds from other sources.

Duration 9 months; may be renewed for up to 2 additional years.

Additional data This program, established in 1970, is offered jointly by the American Architectural Foundation (AAF) and the AIA.

Number awarded Up to 5 each year.

Deadline April of each year.

[28]
AMERICAN METEOROLOGICAL SOCIETY INDUSTRY MINORITY SCHOLARSHIPS

American Meteorological Society
Attn: Development and Student Program Manager
45 Beacon Street
Boston, MA 02108-3693
(617) 227-2426, ext. 3907   Fax: (617) 742-8718
E-mail: dFernandez@ametsoc.org
Web: www.ametsoc.org

Summary To provide financial assistance to Hispanic Americans and other underrepresented minority students entering college and planning to major in meteorology or an aspect of atmospheric sciences.

Eligibility This program is open to members of minority groups traditionally underrepresented in the sciences (especially Hispanics, Native Americans, and Blacks/African Americans) who are entering their freshman year at a college or university and planning to work on a degree in the atmospheric or related oceanic and hydrologic sciences. Applicants must submit an official high school transcript showing grades from the past 3 years, a letter of recommendation from a high school teacher or guidance counselor, a copy of scores from an SAT or similar national entrance exam, and a 500-word essay on a topic that changes annually; recently, applicants were invited to write on global change and how they would use their college education in atmospheric science (or a closely-related field) to make their community a better place in which to live. Selection is based on the essay and academic performance in high school.

Financial Data The stipend is $3,000 per year.

Duration 1 year; may be renewed for the second year of college study.

Additional data This program is funded by grants from industry and by donations to the American Meteorological Society (AMS) 21st Century Campaign. Requests for an application must be accompanied by a self-addressed stamped envelope.

Number awarded Varies each year; recently, 5 of these scholarships were awarded.

Deadline February of each year.

[29]
AMERICAN METEOROLOGICAL SOCIETY NAMED SCHOLARSHIPS

American Meteorological Society
Attn: Development and Student Program Manager
45 Beacon Street
Boston, MA 02108-3693
(617) 227-2426, ext. 3907   Fax: (617) 742-8718
E-mail: dFernandez@ametsoc.org
Web: www.ametsoc.org

Summary To provide financial assistance to undergraduates (particularly Hispanic Americans, other minorities, women, and students with disabilities) who are majoring in meteorology or an aspect of atmospheric sciences.

Eligibility This program is open to full-time students entering their final year of undergraduate study and majoring in meteorology or an aspect of the atmospheric or related oceanic and hydrologic sciences. Applicants must intend to make atmospheric or related sciences their career. They must be U.S. citizens or permanent residents enrolled at a U.S. institution and have a cumulative GPA of 3.25 or higher. Along with their application, they must submit 200-word essays on 1) their most important attributes and achievements that qualify them for this scholarship; and 2) their career goals in the atmospheric or related sciences. Financial need is considered in the selection process. The sponsor specifically encourages applications from women, minorities, and students with disabilities who are traditionally underrepresented in the atmospheric and related sciences.

Financial Data Stipend amounts vary each year.

Duration 1 year.

Additional data All scholarships awarded through this program are named after individuals who have assisted the sponsor in various ways.

Number awarded Varies each year; recently, 20 of these scholarships were awarded.

Deadline February of each year.

[30]
AMERICAN PLANNING ASSOCIATION/JUDITH MCMANUS PRICE SCHOLARSHIPS

American Planning Association
Attn: Leadership Affairs Associate
205 North Michigan Avenue, Suite 1200
Chicago, IL 60601
(312) 431-9100   Fax: (312) 786-6700
E-mail: fellowship@planning.org
Web: www.planning.org/scholarships/apa

Summary To provide financial assistance to Hispanic Americans, other underrepresented minority students, and women enrolled in undergraduate or graduate degree programs at recognized planning schools.

Eligibility This program is open to undergraduate and graduate students in urban and regional planning who are women or members of the following minority groups: African American, Hispanic American, or Native American. Applicants must be citizens of the United States and able to document financial need. They must intend to work as practicing planners in the public sector. Along with their application, they must submit a 2-page personal and background statement describing how their education will be applied to career goals and why they chose planning as a career path. Selection is based (in order of importance), on: 1) commitment to planning as reflected in their personal statement and on their resume; 2) academic achievement and/or improvement during the past 2 years; 3) letters of recommendation; 4) financial need; and 5) professional presentation.

Financial Data Stipends range from $2,000 to $4,000 per year. The money may be applied to tuition and living expenses only. Payment is made to the recipient's university and divided by terms in the school year.

Duration 1 year; recipients may reapply.

Additional data This program began in 2002.

Number awarded Varies each year; recently, 3 of these scholarships were awarded.

Deadline April of each year.

[31]
AMS FRESHMAN UNDERGRADUATE SCHOLARSHIPS

American Meteorological Society
Attn: Development and Student Program Manager
45 Beacon Street
Boston, MA 02108-3693
(617) 227-2426, ext. 3907   Fax: (617) 742-8718
E-mail: dFernandez@ametsoc.org
Web: www.ametsoc.org

Summary   To provide financial assistance to high school seniors (particularly Hispanic Americans, other minorities, women, and individuals with disabilities) who are planning to attend college to prepare for a career in the atmospheric or related oceanic or hydrologic sciences.

Eligibility   This program is open to high school seniors entering their freshman year of college to work on a bachelor's degree in the atmospheric or related oceanic or hydrologic sciences. Applicants must be U.S. citizens or permanent residents planning to enroll full time. Along with their application, they must submit a 500-word essay on how they believe their college education, and what they learn in the atmospheric and related sciences, will help them to serve society during their professional career. Selection is based on performance in high school, including academic records, recommendations, scores from a national examination, and the essay. Financial need is not considered. The sponsor specifically encourages applications from women, minorities, and students with disabilities who are traditionally underrepresented in the atmospheric and related oceanic sciences.

Financial Data   The stipend is $2,500 per academic year.

Duration   1 year; may be renewed for the second year of college study.

Number awarded   Varies each year; recently, 14 of these scholarships were awarded.

Deadline   February of each year.

[32]
ANA MULTICULTURAL EXCELLENCE SCHOLARSHIP

American Association of Advertising Agencies
Attn: AAAA Foundation
1065 Avenue of the Americas, 16th Floor
New York, NY 10018
(212) 262-2500   E-mail: ameadows@aaaa.org
Web: www.aaaa.org

Summary   To provide financial assistance to Hispanic American and other multicultural students who are working on an undergraduate degree in advertising.

Eligibility   This program is open to undergraduate students who are U.S. citizens of proven multicultural heritage and have at least 1 grandparent of multicultural heritage. Applicants must be participating in the Multicultural Advertising Intern Program (MAIP). They must be entering their senior year at an accredited college or university in the United States and have a GPA of 3.0 or higher. Selection is based on academic ability.

Financial Data   The stipend is $2,500.

Duration   1 year.

Additional data   This program was established by the Association of National Advertisers (ANA) in 2001. The American Association of Advertising Agencies (AAAA) assumed administration in 2003.

Number awarded   2 each year.

Deadline   Deadline not specified.

[33]
ANTHONY LAMANNA SCHOLARSHIP

Hispanic Scholarship Consortium
Attn: Scholarship Selection Committee
1107 South Eighth Street
Austin, TX 78704
(512) 368-2956   Fax: (512) 692-1831
E-mail: scholarships@hispanicscholar.org
Web: www.hispanicscholar.org

Summary   To provide financial assistance and work experience to female high school seniors of Hispanic heritage from Texas who have been involved with *Latinitas* Magazine or its programs and plan to attend college in any state.

Eligibility   This program is open to female seniors graduating from high schools in Texas who are of Hispanic heritage and have a GPA of 3.0 or higher. Applicants must have been involved with *Latinitas* Magazine or a Latinitas program. They must be planning to enroll full time at an accredited 2- or 4-year college or university in any state and be available to participate in an internship with the magazine. Selection is based on academic record, community service, financial need, and a personal interview. U.S. citizenship or permanent resident status is required.

Financial Data   The stipend is $2,000 per year.

Duration   1 year; may be renewed, provided the recipient remains enrolled full time, maintains a GPA of 3.0 or higher, and participates in at least 25 hours of community service per semester.

Additional data   This program is sponsored by *Latinitas* Magazine. Scholarship winners must also participate in a year-long internship with the magazine.

Number awarded   1 or more each year.

Deadline   August of each year.

[34]
AP-GOOGLE JOURNALISM AND TECHNOLOGY SCHOLARSHIP PROGRAM

Online News Association
Attn: Scholarship Manager
P.O. Box 65741
Washington, DC 20035
(646) 290-7900   E-mail: irving@journalists.org
Web: journalists.org/next-gen/ap-google-scholarship

Summary   To recognize and reward undergraduate and graduate students (especially Hispanic Americans and those from other diverse backgrounds) who propose outstanding projects "at the intersection of journalism and technology."

Eligibility   This program is open to full-time undergraduates (at least sophomores) and graduate students at U.S. institutions who have at least 1 year of study remaining and a GPA of 3.0 or higher. Students from diverse backgrounds (defined as ethnic and racial minorities, members of the lesbian, gay, bisexual, and transgender (LGBT) community, and students with disabilities) and those attending rural area institutions are strongly encouraged to apply. Some scholarships are reserved for students who can demonstrate financial need. Applicants must develop original journalistic content with computer science elements; they should explain how their strategy moves digital journalism forward or provides valuable lessons or outcomes. Examples include data visualization, data mining, mobile devices and applications, 3-D storytelling, digital ethics, or microcomputers. In the selection process, emphasis is placed on innovation and creativity. U.S. citizenship is required.

Financial Data The award is a $20,000 scholarship, of which half is paid to the winner's institution at the beginning of the first semester and half at the beginning of the second semester, provided the recipient earns a GPA of 3.0 or higher for the first semester.

Duration The competition is held annually.

Additional data This competition is supported by Google.

Number awarded 6 each year.

Deadline February of each year.

[35]
APPLE PROGRAM

American Psychological Association
Attn: Division 41 (American Psychology-Law Society)
c/o Jennifer Hunt, Minority Affairs Committee Chair
Buffalo State University of New York, Psychology
  Department
Classroom Building C308
1300 Elmwood Avenue
Buffalo, NY 14222
(716) 878-3421   E-mail: huntjs@buffalostate.edu
Web: www.ap-ls.org/grantsfunding/APPLEprogram.php?t=4

Summary To provide an opportunity for undergraduate students (particularly Hispanic Americans and members of other underrepresented groups) to gain research and other experience to prepare them for graduate work in psychology and law.

Eligibility This program is open to undergraduate students who are members of underrepresented groups, including, but are not limited to, racial and ethnic minorities; first-generation college students; lesbian, gay, bisexual, and transgender students; and physically disabled students. Applicants must be interested in participating in a program in which they work on research for approximately 10 hours per week; participate in GRE classes and/or other development opportunities; attend a conference of the American Psychology-Law Society (AP-LS); submit a proposal to present their research at an AP-LS conference or in the Division 41 program of an American Psychological Association (APA) conference; submit a summary of their research experience to the AP-LS Minority Affairs Committee chair within 1 month of its completion; and correspond with a secondary mentor from the Minority Affairs Committee to participate in the ongoing assessment of this program. Selection is based on the quality of the proposed research and mentoring experience and the potential for the student to become a successful graduate student.

Financial Data Grants range up to $3,000, including a stipend of $1,200 per semester or $800 per quarter or summer, $100 for research expenses, and up to $500 to attend the AP-LS conference.

Duration Up to 1 year.

Additional data The abbreviation APPLE in the program title stands for Access Path to Psychology and Law Experience.<NA>5 each year.

Deadline November of each year.

[36]
APPRAISAL INSTITUTE MINORITIES AND WOMEN EDUCATIONAL SCHOLARSHIP PROGRAM

Appraisal Institute
Attn: Appraisal Institute Education Trust
200 West Madison Street, Suite 1500
Chicago, IL 60606
(312) 335-4133   Fax: (312) 335-4134
E-mail: educationtrust@appraisalinstitute.org
Web: www.appraisalinstitute.org

Summary To provide financial assistance to Hispanic American, other minority, and women undergraduate students majoring in real estate or allied fields.

Eligibility This program is open to members of groups underrepresented in the real estate appraisal profession. Those groups include women, American Indians, Alaska Natives, Asians and Pacific Islanders, Blacks or African Americans, and Hispanics. Applicants must be full- or part-time students enrolled in real estate courses within a degree-granting college, university, or junior college. They must have a GPA of 2.5 or higher and be able to demonstrate financial need. U.S. citizenship is required.

Financial Data The stipend is $1,000. Funds are paid directly to the recipient's institution to be used for tuition and fees.

Duration 1 year.

Number awarded At least 1 each year.

Deadline April of each year.

[37]
APS SCHOLARSHIPS FOR MINORITY UNDERGRADUATE PHYSICS MAJORS

American Physical Society
Attn: Committee on Minorities
One Physics Ellipse
College Park, MD 20740-3844
(301) 209-3232   Fax: (301) 209-0865
Web: www.aps.org

Summary To provide financial assistance to Hispanic American and other underrepresented minority students interested in studying physics on the undergraduate level.

Eligibility Any African American, Hispanic American, or Native American who plans to major in physics and who is a high school senior or college freshman or sophomore may apply. U.S. citizenship or permanent resident status is required. The selection committee especially encourages applications from students who are attending or planning to attend institutions with historically or predominantly Black, Hispanic, or Native American enrollment. Selection is based on commitment to the study of physics and plans to work on a physics baccalaureate degree.

Financial Data Stipends are $2,000 per year in the first year or $3,000 in the second year; funds must be used for tuition, room, and board. In addition, $500 is awarded to the host department.

Duration 1 year; renewable for 1 additional year with the approval of the APS selection committee.

Additional data APS conducts this program, which began in 1980 as the Corporate-Sponsored Scholarships for Minority Undergraduate Students Who Major in Physics, in conjunction with the Corporate Associates of the American Institute of Physics. Each scholarship is sponsored by a corporation, which is normally designated as the sponsor. A corporation generally sponsors from 1 to 10 scholarships, depending upon its size and utilization of physics in the business.

Number awarded Varies each year; recently, 39 of these scholarships were awarded.

Deadline January of each year.

[38]
ARIZONA HISPANIC CHAMBER OF COMMERCE SCHOLARSHIP

Arizona Community Foundation
Attn: Education and Scholarships Manager
2201 East Camelback Road, Suite 405B
Phoenix, AZ 85016
(602) 682-2040   Toll Free: (800) 222-8221
Fax: (602) 381-1575   E-mail: jmedina@azfoundation.org
Web: azfoundation.academicworks.com

Summary To provide financial assistance to upper-division students of Hispanic heritage who are working on a bachelor's degree in business at a college in Arizona.

Eligibility This program is open to students entering their junior or senior year in a business degree program at an accredited college or university in Arizona. Applicants must have at least 1 parent of Hispanic heritage. They must be enrolled full time and have a GPA of 3.0 or higher. Preference is given to applicants who have a recognized physical disability or are dependents of or employees of a company that is a member of the Arizona Hispanic Chamber of Commerce.

Financial Data The stipend is $5,000 per year.

Duration 1 year; may be renewed 1 additional year.

Additional data This program is sponsored by the Arizona Hispanic Chamber of Commerce. Recipients are paired with a mentor from the chamber.

Number awarded Varies each year.

Deadline March of each year.

[39]
ARKANSAS SPACE GRANT CONSORTIUM STEM MAJORS UNDERREPRESENTED MINORITY STUDENT SCHOLARSHIPS

Arkansas Space Grant Consortium
c/o University of Arkansas at Little Rock
Graduate Institute of Technology
2801 South University Avenue
Little Rock, AR 72204
(501) 569-8212   Fax: (501) 569-8039
E-mail: asgc@ualr.edu
Web: asgc.ualr.edu/documents

Summary To provide funding to Hispanic American and other underrepresented minority students at designated universities in Arkansas who are interested in working on a space-related project in fields of science, technology, engineering, and mathematics (STEM).

Eligibility This program is open to African American, Hispanic, and Native American undergraduate students at colleges and universities that participate in the Arkansas Space Grant Consortium (ASGC). Applicants must be interested in developing a project in fields of STEM that have relevance to the work of the U.S. National Aeronautics and Space Administration (NASA). Students must be U.S. citizens and have a GPA of 2.0 or higher.

Financial Data The grant is $2,000. An additional $500 is available to support travel for each project.

Additional data ASGC member institutions are Arkansas State University, Arkansas Tech University, Harding University, Henderson State University, Hendrix College, Lyon College, Ouachita Baptist University, Southern Arkansas University, University of Arkansas at Fayetteville, University of Arkansas at Fort Smith, University of Arkansas at Little Rock, University of Arkansas at Montecito, University of Arkansas at Pine Bluff, University of Arkansas for Medical Sciences, University of Central Arkansas, and University of the Ozarks. This program is funded by NASA.

Number awarded Varies each year.

Deadline Applications may be submitted at any time. Grants are awarded until funds are exhausted.

[40]
ARKANSAS SPACE GRANT CONSORTIUM STEM TEACHING MAJORS UNDERREPRESENTED MINORITY STUDENT SCHOLARSHIPS

Arkansas Space Grant Consortium
c/o University of Arkansas at Little Rock
Graduate Institute of Technology
2801 South University Avenue
Little Rock, AR 72204
(501) 569-8212   Fax: (501) 569-8039
E-mail: asgc@ualr.edu
Web: asgc.ualr.edu/documents

Summary To provide funding to Hispanic American and other underrepresented minority students at designated universities in Arkansas who are interested in working on a space-related educational project in fields of science, technology, engineering, and mathematics (STEM).

Eligibility This program is open to African American, Hispanic, and Native American undergraduate students at colleges and universities that participate in the Arkansas Space Grant Consortium (ASGC). Applicants must be planning a career in STEM related disciplines at either the K-12 or college level. They must be interested in developing an educational project and/or curricula in fields of STEM that have relevance to the work of the U.S. National Aeronautics and Space Administration (NASA). Students must be U.S. citizens and have a GPA of 2.0 or higher.

Financial Data The grant is $2,000. An additional $500 is available to support travel for each project.

Additional data ASGC member institutions are Arkansas State University, Arkansas Tech University, Harding University, Henderson State University, Hendrix College, Lyon College, Ouachita Baptist University, Southern Arkansas University, University of Arkansas at Fayetteville, University of Arkansas at Fort Smith, University of Arkansas at Little Rock, University of Arkansas at Montecito, University of Arkansas at Pine Bluff, University of Arkansas for Medical Sciences, University of Central Arkansas, and University of the Ozarks. This program is funded by NASA.

Number awarded Varies each year.

Deadline Applications may be submitted at any time. Grants are awarded until funds are exhausted.

[41]
ARTHUR H. GOODMAN MEMORIAL SCHOLARSHIPS

CDC Small Business Finance
Attn: Scholarship Program
2448 Historic Decatur Road, Suite 200
San Diego, CA 92106
(619) 291-3594   Toll Free: (800) 611-5170
Fax: (619) 291-6954
Web: cdcloans.com

Summary To provide financial assistance to Hispanic Americans, other minorities, and women who are transitioning from a community college in California or Arizona to a 4-year university in those states and interested in preparing for a career related to community development.

Eligibility This program is open to women and minorities who are residents of or attending school in California. Applicants must have completed 2 years of community college study with a GPA of 3.0 or higher and be ready to transfer to a 4-year college or university. They must be interested in preparing for a career in business, government, nonprofit, public service, or other profession that will improve their community. Along with their application, they must submit a 3-page personal statement on their community involvement and volunteerism, why they volunteer, how it has influenced them personally and their career goals, how their volunteerism has impacted individuals or the community, an individual or event that has influenced their decision to attend college and/or select their desired career, their future goals and how they include community involvement, and why they feel they are a strong candidate for this scholarship. Financial need is considered in the selection process.

Financial Data Stipends range from $1,500 to $3,000.

Duration 1 year.

Additional data This program began in 1998 with a fund administered through the San Diego Foundation.

Number awarded Approximately 4 each year.

Deadline May of each year.

[42]
ARTS AWARD

TELACU Education Foundation
Attn: College Success Program
5400 East Olympic Boulevard, Suite 300
Los Angeles, CA 90022
(323) 721-1655   Fax: (323) 721-3560
E-mail: collegesuccess@telacu.com
Web: www.telacu.com

Summary To provide financial assistance to Latino students from eligible communities in California, Texas, Illinois, and New York who are interested in studying the arts at a college or university in any state.

Eligibility This program is open to Latino residents of selected communities in southern California, selected cities in Texas, the Greater Chicagoland area of Illinois, or the state

of New York. Applicants must 1) be a first-generation college student; 2) be from a low-income family; and 3) have a GPA of 2.5 or higher. They must be enrolled or planning to enroll full time at a college or university in any state and major in fine arts, music, dance, drama, or theater. Selection is based on leadership potential, professional and extracurricular achievement, commitment to the development and economic empowerment of communities, and financial need. Priority is given to students attending institutions that provide matching funds (for a list, contact the sponsor).

Financial Data Stipends range from $500 to $5,000 per year.

Duration 1 year; may be renewed up to 3 additional years, provided the recipient remains enrolled full time, maintains a GPA of 2.75 or higher, and volunteers for at least 20 hours of community service.

Additional data The eligible areas in California include underserved communities in Los Angeles, Orange, and San Bernardino counties such as unincorporated areas of east Los Angeles and the cities of Baldwin Park, Bell Gardens, Commerce, Huntington Park, Los Angeles, Montebello, Ontario, Pico Rivera, Pomona, San Bernardino, Santa Ana, and South Gate. The cities in Texas are Austin, Edinburg, Laredo, Rio Grande City, San Antonio.

Number awarded 1 or more each year.

Deadline March of each year.

[43]
ASCPA EDUCATIONAL FOUNDATION DIVERSITY SCHOLARSHIPS

Alabama Society of Certified Public Accountants
Attn: ASCPA Educational Foundation
1103 South Perry Street
P.O. Box 5000
Montgomery, AL 36103
(334) 834-7650   Toll Free: (800) 227-1711
Web: www.ascpa.org

Summary To provide financial assistance to Hispanic American and other minority accounting students at colleges and universities in Alabama.

Eligibility This program is open to minority (Black or African American, Hispanic or Latino, Native American, or Asian) residents of any state enrolled at least half time at colleges and universities in Alabama with at least 1 full year of school remaining. Applicants must have declared a major in accounting and have completed intermediate accounting courses. They must have a GPA of 3.0 or higher overall and in all accounting classes. Along with their application, they must submit a 25-word essay on why the scholarship is important to them. Financial need is not considered in the selection process. Preference is given to students who have a strong interest in a career as a C.P.A. in Alabama. U.S. citizenship or permanent resident status is required.

Financial Data The stipend is $2,500.

Duration 1 year.

Additional data This program began in 2012.

Number awarded 4 each year.

Deadline March of each year.

[44]
ASLA COUNCIL OF FELLOWS SCHOLARSHIPS

Landscape Architecture Foundation
Attn: Leadership in Landscape Scholarship Program
818 18th Street, N.W., Suite 810
Washington, DC 20006-3520
(202) 331-7070　　　　　　　　　Fax: (202) 331-7079
E-mail: scholarships@lafoundation.org
Web: www.lafoundation.org

Summary　To provide financial assistance to upper-division students, especially Hispanic Americans and those from other disadvantaged and underrepresented groups, who are working on a degree in landscape architecture.

Eligibility　This program is open to landscape architecture students in the third, fourth, or fifth year of undergraduate work. Preference is given to, and 1 scholarship is reserved for, members of underrepresented ethnic or cultural groups. Applicants must submit a 500-word essay on how they envision themselves contributing to the profession of landscape architecture, 2 letters of recommendation, documentation of financial need, and (for students applying for the scholarship reserved for underrepresented groups) a statement identifying their association with a specific ethnic or cultural group. U.S. citizenship or permanent resident status is required.

Financial Data　The stipend is $4,000. Students also receive a 1-year membership in the American Society of Landscape Architects (ASLA), general registration fees for the ASLA annual meeting, and a travel stipend to attend the meeting.

Duration　1 year.

Additional data　This program is sponsored by ASLA and administered by the Landscape Architecture Foundation.

Number awarded　2 each year, of which 1 is reserved for a member of an underrepresented group.

Deadline　February of each year.

[45]
ASSE UPS DIVERSITY SCHOLARSHIPS

American Society of Safety Engineers
Attn: ASSE Foundation
Scholarship Award Program
1800 East Oakton Street
Des Plaines, IL 60018
(847) 699-2929　　　　　　　　　Fax: (847) 768-3434
E-mail: bzylstra@asse.org
Web: www.asse.org

Summary　To provide financial assistance to Hispanic American and other minority upper-division students working on a degree related to occupational safety.

Eligibility　This program is open to students who are U.S. citizens and members of minority ethnic or racial groups. Applicants must be majoring in occupational safety, health, environment, industrial hygiene, occupational health nursing, or a closely-related field (e.g., industrial or environmental engineering). They must be full-time students who have completed at least 60 semester hours with a GPA of 3.0 or higher. Membership in the American Society of Safety Engineers (ASSE) is not required, but preference is given to members.

Financial Data　The stipend is $5,250 per year.

Duration　1 year; recipients may reapply.

Additional data　Funding for this program is provided by the UPS Foundation. Recipients may also be provided with the opportunity to attend a professional development conference related to safety.

Number awarded　3 each year.

Deadline　November of each year.

[46]
ASSOCIATION FOR COMPENSATORY EDUCATORS OF TEXAS STUDENT SCHOLARSHIPS

Association for Compensatory Educators of Texas
Attn: Scholarship Chair
P.O. Box 3516
Humble, TX 77347
(832) 644-5020　　　　　　　　　Fax: (832) 644-8520
E-mail: mcguirej@cfbisd.edu
Web: www.acetx.org

Summary　To provide financial assistance to high school seniors in Texas who have participated in a compensatory education program (e.g., bilingual/ESL, migrant) and plan to attend college in any state.

Eligibility　This program is open to seniors graduating from high schools in Texas and planning to attend a college, university, or other postsecondary institution in any state. Applicants must have participated for at least 2 years, at some time in their school career, in a federal- or state-funded compensatory education program (e.g., bilingual/ESL, homeless, migrant, pregnant or parenting). Along with their application, they must submit a brief essay on the problems they have faced in grades preK-12 and how the school programs helped them to be successful. The highest-scoring applicant receives the Wade and Sandy Burroughs Scholarship.

Financial Data　The stipend is $1,000. The winner of the Wade and Sandy Burroughs Scholarship receives an additional $500.

Duration　1 year.

Number awarded　20 each year.

Deadline　March of each year.

[47]
ASSOCIATION FOR WOMEN GEOSCIENTISTS MINORITY SCHOLARSHIP

Association for Women Geoscientists
Attn: AWG Foundation
12000 North Washington Street, Suite 285
Thornton, CO 80241
(303) 412-6219　　　　　　　　　Fax: (303) 253-9220
E-mail: minorityscholarship@awg.org
Web: www.awg.org/EAS/scholarships.html

Summary　To provide financial assistance to Hispanic American and other underrepresented minority women who are interested in working on an undergraduate degree in the geosciences.

Eligibility　This program is open to women who are African American, Hispanic, or Native American (including Eskimo, Hawaiian, Samoan, or American Indian). Applicants must be full-time students working on, or planning to work on, an undergraduate degree in the geosciences (including geology, geophysics, geochemistry, hydrology, meteorology, physical oceanography, planetary geology, or earth science education). They must submit a 500-word essay on their academic and career goals, 2 letters of recommendation, high school and/or college transcripts, and SAT or ACT scores. Financial need is not considered in the selection process. U.S. citizenship is required.

Financial Data A total of $6,000 is available for this program each year.

Duration 1 year; may be renewed.

Additional data This program, first offered in 2004, is supported by ExxonMobil Foundation.

Number awarded 1 or more each year.

Deadline June of each year.

[48]
ASSOCIATION OF CUBAN ENGINEERS SCHOLARSHIPS

Association of Cuban Engineers
c/o Dr. Helena Solo-Gabriele
University of Miami, College of Engineering
1251 Memorial Drive, EB252
Coral Gables, FL 33146
(305) 284-2908   Fax: (305) 284-3492
E-mail: hmsolo@miami.edu
Web: aic-ace.com

Summary To provide financial assistance to undergraduate and graduate students of Cuban American heritage who are interested in preparing for a career in engineering.

Eligibility This program is open to U.S. citizens and legal residents who have completed at least 30 units of college work in the United States and are working on an undergraduate or graduate degree in engineering. Applicants must be attending an ABET-accredited college or university within the United States or Puerto Rico as a full-time student and have a GPA of 3.0 or higher. They must be of Cuban or other Hispanic heritage (at least 1 grandparent Cuban or other Hispanic nationality). Along with their application, they must submit brief essays on their family history, professional goals, extracurricular activities, work experience, and how they will help other Cuban and Hispanic engineering students in the future. Financial need is not considered in the selection process.

Financial Data Stipends range from $500 to $2,000.

Duration 1 year; may be renewed.

Additional data This program also includes the Pedro O. Martinez Scholarship and the Luciano de Goicochea Award (for students at the University of Miami), the Antonio Choy Award (for a student at the University of Florida), and the Noel Betancourt Award (for a student at Florida International University).

Number awarded Varies each year; recently, 10 of these scholarships were awarded.

Deadline November of each year.

[49]
ATKINS NORTH AMERICA ACHIEVEMENT SCHOLARSHIP

Conference of Minority Transportation Officials
Attn: National Scholarship Program
1875 I Street, N.W., Suite 500
Washington, DC 20006
(703) 234-4072   Fax: (202) 318-0364
Web: www.comto.org/?page=Scholarships

Summary To provide financial assistance to Hispanic American and other minority high school seniors and undergraduates interested in working on a degree in transportation or a related field.

Eligibility This program is open to seniors graduating from high school with a GPA of 3.0 or higher and students currently enrolled as full-time undergraduates. Applicants must be studying or planning to study transportation, engineering, planning, management, or a related discipline They must be able to demonstrate leadership and active commitment to community service. Along with their application, they must submit a cover letter with a 500-word statement of career goals. Financial need is not considered in the selection process. U.S. citizenship or legal resident status is required.

Financial Data The stipend is $2,000. Funds are paid directly to the recipient's college or university.

Duration 1 year.

Additional data The Conference of Minority Transportation Officials (COMTO) was established in 1971 to promote, strengthen, and expand the roles of minorities in all aspects of transportation. This program is sponsored by Atkins North America. Recipients are expected to attend the COMTO National Scholarship Luncheon.

Number awarded 1 each year.

Deadline May of each year.

[50]
ATKINS TRANSPORTATION YOU HIGH SCHOOL SCHOLARSHIP

Women's Transportation Seminar
Attn: WTS Foundation
1701 K Street, N.W., Suite 800
Washington, DC 20006
(202) 955-5085   Fax: (202) 955-5088
E-mail: wts@wtsinternational.org
Web: www.wtsinternational.org/education/scholarships

Summary To provide financial assistance to female high school seniors (particularly Hispanic American and other minority women) who are studying fields of science, technology, engineering, or mathematics (STEM) and planning to attend college to prepare for a career in transportation.

Eligibility This program is open to women who are high school seniors with a GPA of 3.0 or higher. Applicants must be studying STEM fields in high school and be planning to attend college to prepare for a career in transportation (e.g., civil engineering, city planning, logistics, automotive engineering, truck repair). Along with their application, they must submit a 500-word statement about their career goals after graduation and why they think they should receive the scholarship. Applications must be submitted first to a local chapter; the chapters forward selected applications for consideration on the national level. Minority women are especially encouraged to apply. Selection is based on transportation involvement and goals, job skills, academic record, and leadership potential; financial need is not considered.

Financial Data   The stipend is $1,000.

Duration   1 year.

Additional data   Local chapters may also award additional funding to winners for their area.

Number awarded   1 each year.

Deadline   Applications must be submitted by November to a local WTS chapter.

[51]
ATLANTA RETAILERS ASSOCIATION AND COCA-COLA LIVE POSITIVELY SCHOLARSHIP PROGRAM

Hispanic Scholarship Fund
Attn: Selection Committee
1411 West 190th Street, Suite 325
Gardena, CA 90248
Toll Free: (877) HSF-INFO   E-mail: scholar1@hsf.net
Web: www.hsf.net

Summary   To provide financial assistance to Hispanic high school seniors in Georgia who plan to attend college in the United States or designated territories.

Eligibility   This program is open to seniors of Hispanic heritage who are graduating from high schools in Georgia and have a GPA of 3.0 or higher. Applicants must be U.S. citizens or permanent residents (must have a permanent resident card or a passport stamped I-551). They must be planning to enroll full time at an accredited 2- or 4-year college or university in the United States, Puerto Rico, the U.S. Virgin Islands, or Guam. Their proposed major may be in any field. Selection is based on academic achievement, personal strengths, leadership, and financial need.

Financial Data   The stipend is $5,000 or $2,000.

Duration   1 year.

Additional data   This program is jointly sponsored by the Atlanta Retailers Association, Coca-Cola, and the Hispanic Scholarship Fund (HSF).

Number awarded   7 each year: 2 at $5,000 and 5 at $2,000.

Deadline   December of each year.

[52]
AURELIO "LARRY" JAZO MIGRANT SCHOLARSHIP

Geneseo Migrant Center
Attn: Scholarship Funds
3 Mt. Morris-Leicester Road
Leicester, NY 14481
(585) 658-7960   Toll Free: (800) 245-5681
Fax: (585) 658-7969   E-mail: dkatter@gvboces.org
Web: www.migrant.net/migrant/scholarships/index.htm

Summary   To provide financial assistance for college to high school seniors from Illinois who come from migrant farmworker families.

Eligibility   This program is open to migrant farmworker students with a history of migration to and/or within Illinois. Applicants must have senior status in high school and plans to attend a postsecondary institution or other advanced training. Along with their application, they must submit a statement of at least 250 words on their background and interest in higher education, at least 1 letter of recommendation, and a copy of their current Migrant Certificate of Eligibility (COE). Selection is based on demonstrated commitment to educational goals, participation in school and Migrant Education Outreach Program (MEOP) activities, participation in community and/or non-school activities, citizenship, evidence of high mobility (interstate or intrastate), record of overcoming unusual obstacles, and financial need.

Financial Data   The stipend is $1,000.

Duration   1 year.

Number awarded   1 or more each year.

Deadline   May of each year.

[53]
BACCALAUREATE (DIDACTIC OR COORDINATED PROGRAM) SCHOLARSHIPS

Academy of Nutrition and Dietetics
Attn: Foundation
120 South Riverside Plaza, Suite 2000
Chicago, IL 60606-6995
(312) 899-0040   Toll Free: (800) 877-1600, ext. 1133
Fax: (312) 899-4817   E-mail: scholarships@eatright.org
Web: www.eatright.org/Foundation/scholarships

Summary   To provide financial assistance to underrepresented minorities and other undergraduate student members of the Academy of Nutrition and Dietetics.

Eligibility   This program is open to ADA members enrolled at a CADE-accredited/approved college or university program for at least junior status in the dietetics program. Applicants must be U.S. citizens or permanent residents and show promise of being a valuable, contributing member of the profession. Some scholarships require membership in a specific dietetic practice group, residency in a specific state, or underrepresented minority group status. The same application form can be used for all categories.

Financial Data   Stipends normally range from $500 to $3,000; recently, they averaged approximately $1,870.

Duration   1 year.

Additional data   The Academy of Nutrition and Dietetics was formerly the American Dietetic Association.

Number awarded   Between 30 and 35 each year.

Deadline   February of each year.

[54]
BARBARA JORDAN MEMORIAL SCHOLARSHIPS

Association of Texas Professional Educators
Attn: ATPE Foundation
305 East Huntland Drive, Suite 300
Austin, TX 78752-3792
Toll Free: (800) 777-ATPE   Fax: (512) 302-5884
E-mail: admin@atpefoundation.org
Web: www.atpefoundation.org/scholarships.asp

Summary   To provide financial assistance to upper-division and graduate students from any state who are enrolled in educator preparation programs at predominantly ethnic minority institutions in Texas.

Eligibility   This program is open to juniors, seniors, and graduate students from any state who are enrolled in educator preparation programs at predominantly ethnic minority institutions in Texas. Applicants must submit a 2-page essay on their personal educational philosophy, why they want to become an educator, who influenced them the most in making their career decision, and why they are applying for the scholarship. Financial need is not considered in the selection process.

Financial Data The stipend is $1,500.

Duration 1 year.

Additional data The qualifying institutions are Huston-Tillotson College, Jarvis Christian College, Our Lady of the Lake University, Paul Quinn College, Prairie View A&M University, St. Mary's University of San Antonio, Sul Ross State University, Sul Ross State University Rio Grande College, Texas A&M International University, Texas A&M University at Kingsville, Texas Southern University, University of Houston, University of Houston-Downtown, University of Texas at Brownsville and Texas Southmost College, University of Texas at El Paso, University of Texas at San Antonio, University of Texas-Pan American, University of the Incarnate Word, and Wiley College.

Number awarded Up to 6 each year.

Deadline May of each year.

[55]
BECHTEL UNDERGRADUATE FELLOWSHIP AWARD

National Action Council for Minorities in Engineering
Attn: University Programs
440 Hamilton Avenue, Suite 302
White Plains, NY 10601-1813
(914) 539-4010 Fax: (914) 539-4032
E-mail: scholarships@nacme.org
Web: www.nacme.org/NACME_D.aspx?pageid=105

Summary To provide financial assistance to Hispanic American and other underrepresented minority college juniors majoring in construction engineering.

Eligibility This program is open to African American, Latino, and American Indian college juniors who have a GPA of 3.0 or higher and have demonstrated academic excellence, leadership skills, and a commitment to science and engineering as a career. Applicants must be enrolled full time at an ABET-accredited engineering program and preparing for a career in a construction-related engineering discipline.

Financial Data The stipend is $2,500 per year. Funds are sent directly to the recipient's university.

Duration Up to 2 years.

Additional data This program was established by the Bechtel Group Foundation.

Number awarded 2 each year.

Deadline April of each year.

[56]
BEHAVIORAL SCIENCES STUDENT FELLOWSHIPS IN EPILEPSY

Epilepsy Foundation
Attn: Research Department
8301 Professional Place
Landover, MD 20785-2353
(301) 459-3700 Toll Free: (800) EFA-1000
Fax: (301) 577-2684 TDD: (800) 332-2070
E-mail: grants@efa.org
Web: www.epilepsyfoundation.org

Summary To provide funding to undergraduate and graduate students (particularly Hispanic Americans, other minorities, women, and students with disabilities) who are interested in working on a summer research project in a behavioral science field relevant to epilepsy.

Eligibility This program is open to undergraduate and graduate students in a behavioral science program relevant to epilepsy research or clinical care, including, but not limited to, sociology, social work, psychology, anthropology, nursing, economics, vocational rehabilitation, counseling, or political science. Applicants must be interested in working on an epilepsy research project under the supervision of a qualified mentor. Because the program is designed as a training opportunity, the quality of the training plans and environment are considered in the selection process. Other selection criteria include the quality of the proposed project, the relevance of the proposed work to epilepsy, the applicant's interest in the field of epilepsy, the applicant's qualifications, and the mentor's qualifications (including his or her commitment to the student and the project), and the quality of the training environment for research related to epilepsy. U.S. citizenship is not required, but the project must be conducted in the United States. Applications from women, members of minority groups, and people with disabilities are especially encouraged. The program is not intended for students working on a dissertation research project.

Financial Data The grant is $3,000.

Duration 3 months during the summer.

Additional data This program is supported by the American Epilepsy Society, Abbott Laboratories, Ortho-McNeil Pharmaceutical Corporation, and Pfizer Inc.

Number awarded Varies each year.

Deadline March of each year.

[57]
BERRIEN FRAGOS THORN ARTS SCHOLARSHIPS FOR MIGRANT FARMWORKERS

Geneseo Migrant Center
Attn: Scholarship Funds
3 Mt. Morris-Leicester Road
Leicester, NY 14481
(585) 658-7960 Toll Free: (800) 245-5681
Fax: (585) 658-7969 E-mail: dkatter@gvboces.org
Web: www.migrant.net/migrant/scholarships/index.htm

Summary To provide financial assistance to migrant farmworkers who are interested in developing their talents in the arts.

Eligibility This program is open to students with a "history of migration to obtain work in agriculture." Applicants must be at least 16 years of age, but they do not need to be enrolled in school. They must be interested in pursuing further development of their talents in 1 of the following disciplines: visual arts (e.g., painting, sculpture, photography); performing arts (e.g., dance, theater, music); media (e.g., film, video, animation, computer graphics); literature (e.g., poetry, short stories); or crafts (e.g., traditional folk arts, furniture, weaving, pottery). Students may submit either a complete application that includes a budget and portfolio or samples of work, or only a partial form providing basic personal information and letters of recommendation. U.S. citizenship is not required.

Financial Data The maximum grant is $2,500 for students who submit the complete application or $500 for those who submit only partial forms.

Duration These are 1-time grants.

Number awarded Varies each year.

Deadline Complete applications must be submitted by May or October of each year. Partial forms may be submitted at any time.

[58]
BILL BERNBACH DIVERSITY SCHOLARSHIPS

American Association of Advertising Agencies
Attn: AAAA Foundation
1065 Avenue of the Americas, 16th Floor
New York, NY 10018
(212) 262-2500   E-mail: bbscholarship@ddb.com
Web: www.aaaa.org

Summary To provide financial assistance to Hispanic American and other multicultural students who are interested in working on an undergraduate or graduate degree in advertising at designated schools.

Eligibility This program is open to African Americans, Asian Americans, Hispanic Americans, and Native Americans (including American Indians, Alaska Natives, Native Hawaiians, and other Pacific Islanders) who are interested in studying the advertising creative arts at designated institutions as a full-time student. Applicants must be working on or have already received an undergraduate degree and be able to demonstrate creative talent and promise. They must be U.S. citizens, nationals, or permanent residents. Along with their application, they must submit 10 samples of creative work in their respective field of expertise.

Financial Data The stipend is $5,000.

Duration 1 year.

Additional data This program, which began in 1998, is currently sponsored by DDB Worldwide. The participating schools are the Art Center College of Design (Pasadena, California), Creative Circus (Atlanta, Georgia), Miami Ad School (Miami Beach, Florida), University of Texas at Austin, VCU Brandcenter (Richmond, Virginia), Savannah College of Art and Design (Savannah, Georgia), University of Oregon (Eugene), City College of New York, School of Visual Arts (New York, New York), Fashion Institute of Technology (New York, New York), and Brigham Young University (Provo, Utah).

Number awarded 3 each year.

Deadline October of each year.

[59]
BILL DICKEY GOLF SCHOLARSHIPS

Bill Dickey Scholarship Association
Attn: Scholarship Committee
1140 East Washington Street, Suite 103
Phoenix, AZ 85034
(602) 258-7851   Fax: (602) 258-3412
E-mail: assistant@bdscholar.org
Web: www.nmjgsa.org/scholarships.php

Summary To provide financial assistance to Hispanic American and other minority high school seniors and undergraduate students who excel at golf.

Eligibility This program is open to graduating high school seniors and current undergraduate students who are members of minority groups (African American, Asian/Pacific Islander, Hispanic, or American Indian/Alaskan Native). Applicants must submit a 500-word essay on a topic that changes annually but relates to minorities and golf. Selection is based on academic achievement; personal recommendations; participation in golf, school, and community activities; and financial need.

Financial Data Stipends range from 1-time awards of $1,000 to 4-year awards of $3,500 per year. Funds are paid directly to the recipient's college.

Duration 1 year or longer.

Additional data This sponsor was established in 1984 as the National Minority Junior Golf Association and given its current name in 2006. Support is provided by the Jackie Robinson Foundation, PGA of America, Anheuser-Busch, the Tiger Woods Foundation, and other cooperating organizations.

Number awarded Varies; generally 80 or more each year.

Deadline April of each year.

[60]
BIRMINGHAM CHAPTER AABE SCHOLARSHIPS

American Association of Blacks in Energy-Birmingham
   Chapter
Attn: Scholarship Committee
P.O. Box 3035
Birmingham, AL 35202
(205) 325-3578   E-mail: larringt@southernco.com
Web: www.aabe.org/index.php?component=pages&id=161

Summary To provide financial assistance to Hispanic Americans and members of other underrepresented minority groups who are high school seniors in Alabama and planning to major in an energy-related field at a college in any state.

Eligibility This program is open to seniors graduating from high schools in Alabama and planning to attend a college or university in any state. Applicants must be African Americans, Hispanics, or Native Americans who have a GPA of 3.0 or higher and who can demonstrate financial need. Their intended major must be business, engineering, technology, mathematics, the physical sciences, or other energy-related field. Along with their application, they must submit a 350-word statement on why they should receive this scholarship, how their professional career objectives relate to energy, and any other relevant information.

Financial Data The stipend is $5,000.

Duration 1 year.

Additional data The winner is eligible to compete for regional and national scholarships.

Number awarded 1 each year.

Deadline February of each year.

[61]
BLANDY EXPERIMENTAL FARM RESEARCH EXPERIENCES FOR UNDERGRADUATES PROGRAM

University of Virginia
Attn: Blandy Experimental Farm
400 Blandy Farm Lane
Boyce, VA 22620
(540) 837-1758, ext. 292   Fax: (540) 837-1523
E-mail: blandy@virginia.edu
Web: blandy.virginia.edu/research/undergraduate-research

Summary To provide an opportunity for undergraduates (particularly Hispanic Americans, other underrepresented minorities, women, and students with disabilities) to conduct ecological and evolutionary research during the summer at the Blandy Experimental Farm in Clarke County, Virginia.

Eligibility This program is open to undergraduate students interested in ecological and evolutionary biology. Applicants must submit a proposal for a research project at the farm under the mentorship of a professional staff member. Current research interests of the staff include plant reproductive ecology, aquatic community ecology, biological invasions, plant population biology, conservation biology, pollination, and plant succession. Interested students should submit, along with their application, a current transcript, 2 letters of recommendation, a statement describing how this program would contribute to their education and career goals, and the names of the mentors whose research areas interest them. They must be U.S. citizens, nationals, or permanent residents. Applications are especially encouraged from underrepresented minorities, persons with disabilities, and women.

Financial Data Students receive a $5,500 stipend, an additional meal budget, free housing, and a modest budget for supplies and travel.

Duration 11 weeks, from late May through mid-August.

Additional data This program, established in 1993, receives funding support from the Research Experiences for Undergraduates (REU) program of the National Science Foundation.

Number awarded 10 each year.

Deadline February of each year.

[62]
BOOKER T. WASHINGTON SCHOLARSHIPS

National FFA Organization
Attn: Scholarship Office
6060 FFA Drive
P.O. Box 68960
Indianapolis, IN 46268-0960
(317) 802-4419   Fax: (317) 802-5419
E-mail: scholarships@ffa.org
Web: www.ffa.org

Summary To provide financial assistance to Hispanic American and other minority FFA members who are interested in studying agriculture in college.

Eligibility This program is open to members who are graduating high school seniors planning to enroll full time in college. Applicants must be members of a minority ethnic group (African American, Asian American, Pacific Islander, Hispanic, Alaska Native, or American Indian) planning to work on a 4-year degree in agriculture. Selection is based on aca-demic achievement (10 points for GPA, 10 points for SAT or ACT score, 10 points for class rank), leadership in FFA activities (30 points), leadership in community activities (10 points), and participation in the Supervised Agricultural Experience (SAE) program (30 points). U.S. citizenship is required.

Financial Data The stipend is $1,000. Funds are paid directly to the recipient.

Duration 1 year; nonrenewable.

Number awarded 5 each year.

Deadline February of each year.

[63]
BROWN AND CALDWELL MINORITY SCHOLARSHIP

Brown and Caldwell
Attn: Scholarship Program
201 North Civic Drive, Suite 115
P.O. Box 8045
Walnut Creek, CA 94596
(925) 937-9010   Fax: (925) 937-9026
E-mail: scholarships@brwncald.com
Web: www.brownandcaldwell.com/scholarships.asp

Summary To provide financial assistance to Hispanic American and other minority students working on an undergraduate or graduate degree in an environmental or engineering field.

Eligibility This program is open to members of minority groups (African Americans, Hispanics, Asians, Pacific Islanders, Native Americans, or Alaska Natives) who are full-time juniors, seniors, or graduate students at an accredited 4-year college or university. Applicants must have a GPA of 3.0 or higher and a declared major in civil, chemical, or environmental engineering or an environmental science (e.g., biology, ecology, geology, hydrogeology). They must be U.S. citizens or permanent residents. Along with their application, they must submit an essay (up to 250 words) on their future career goals in environmental science. Financial need is not considered in the selection process.

Financial Data The stipend is $5,000.

Duration 1 year.

Number awarded 4 each year.

Deadline April of each year.

[64]
BUICK ACHIEVERS SCHOLARSHIP PROGRAM

Scholarship America
Attn: Scholarship Management Services
One Scholarship Way
P.O. Box 297
St. Peter, MN 56082
(507) 931-1682   Toll Free: (866) 243-4644
Fax: (507) 931-9168
E-mail: buickachievers@scholarshipamerica.org
Web: www.buickachievers.com

Summary To provide financial assistance to students (particularly Hispanic Americans, other minorities, women, and those with ties to the military) who are entering college for the first time and planning to major in specified fields related to engineering, design, or business.

Eligibility This program is open to high school seniors and graduates who are planning to enroll full time at an accredited 4-year college or university as first-time freshmen. Applicants must be planning to major in fields of engineering (chemical, computer, controls, electrical, energy, environmental, industrial, manufacturing, materials, mechanical, plastic/polymers, or software); technology (automotive technology, computer science, engineering technology, information technology); design (graphic, industrial, product, transportation); or business (accounting, business administration, ergonomics, finance, industrial hygiene, international business, labor and industrial relations, management information systems, marketing, mathematics, occupational health and safety, production management, statistics, or supply chain/logistics). U.S. citizenship or permanent resident status is required. Selection is based on academic achievement, financial need, participation and leadership in community and school activities, work experience, educational and career goals, and other unusual circumstances. Special consideration is given to first-generation college students, women, minorities, military veterans, and dependents of military personnel.

Financial Data Stipends are $25,000 or $2,000 per year.

Duration 1 year. The $25,000 awards may be renewed up to 3 additional years (or 4 years for students entering a 5-year engineering program), provided the recipient remains enrolled full time, continues to major in an eligible field, and maintains a GPA of 3.0 or higher. The $2,000 awards are non-renewable.

Additional data This program, which began in 2011, is funded by the General Motors Foundation.

Number awarded 1,100 each year: 100 at $25,000 and 1,000 at $2,000.

Deadline February of each year.

[65]
BUSINESS AWARD

TELACU Education Foundation
Attn: College Success Program
5400 East Olympic Boulevard, Suite 300
Los Angeles, CA 90022
(323) 721-1655   Fax: (323) 721-3560
E-mail: collegesuccess@telacu.com
Web: www.telacu.com

Summary To provide financial assistance to Latino students from eligible communities in California, Texas, Illinois, and New York who are interested in studying business at a college or university in any state.

Eligibility This program is open to Latino residents of selected communities in southern California, selected cities in Texas, the Greater Chicagoland area of Illinois, or the state of New York. Applicants must 1) be a first-generation college student; 2) be from a low-income family; and 3) have a GPA of 2.5 or higher. They must be enrolled or planning to enroll full time at a college or university in any state and major in business. Selection is based on leadership potential, professional and extracurricular achievement, commitment to the development and economic empowerment of communities, and financial need. Priority is given to students attending institutions that provide matching funds (for a list, contact the sponsor).

Financial Data Stipends range from $500 to $5,000 per year.

Duration 1 year; may be renewed up to 3 additional years, provided the recipient remains enrolled full time, maintains a GPA of 2.75 or higher, and volunteers for at least 20 hours of community service.

Additional data The eligible areas in California include underserved communities in Los Angeles, Orange, and San Bernardino counties such as unincorporated areas of east Los Angeles and the cities of Baldwin Park, Bell Gardens, Commerce, Huntington Park, Los Angeles, Montebello, Ontario, Pico Rivera, Pomona, San Bernardino, Santa Ana, and South Gate. The cities in Texas are Austin, Edinburg, Laredo, Rio Grande City, San Antonio.

Number awarded 1 or more each year.

Deadline March of each year.

[66]
CALDER SUMMER UNDERGRADUATE RESEARCH PROGRAM

Fordham University
Attn: Louis Calder Center Biological Field Station
53 Whippoorwill Road
P.O. Box 887
Armonk, NY 10504
(914) 273-3078, ext. 10   Fax: (914) 273-2167
E-mail: REUatCalder@fordham.edu
Web: www.fordham.edu

Summary To provide an opportunity for undergraduates (particularly Hispanic Americans, other underrepresented minorities, women, and individuals with disabilities) to pursue research activities in biology at Fordham University's Louis Calder Center Biological Field Station during the summer.

Eligibility This program is open to undergraduates interested in conducting a summer research project of their own design at the center. Applicants must be U.S. citizens, nationals, or permanent residents. Fields of interest must relate to the activities of staff who will serve as mentors on the projects; those include forest ecology, limnology, wildlife ecology, microbial ecology, Lyme disease, insect-plant interactions, evolutionary ecology, and the effects of urbanization on ecosystem processes. Applications from underrepresented minorities (African Americans, Hispanics, American Indians, Native Hawaiians, Pacific Islanders, and Alaska Natives), persons with disabilities, and women are especially encouraged.

Financial Data The program provides a stipend of $5,000, housing on the site, and support for research supplies and local travel.

Duration 10 weeks during the summer.

Additional data This program has operated since 1967 with support from the Research Experiences for Undergraduates (REU) program of the National Science Foundation.

Number awarded Up to 10 each year.

Deadline February of each year.

[67]
CALIFORNIA ASSOCIATION OF LATINO SUPERINTENDENTS AND ADMINISTRATORS SCHOLARSHIPS

California Association of Latino Superintendents and
Administrators
1029 J Street, Suite 500
Sacramento, CA 95814
(916) 329-3847
Web: www.calsa.org/scholarships

Summary To provide financial assistance to Latino/a high school seniors in California who plan to attend college in any state.

Eligibility This program is open to Latino/a seniors graduating from public high schools in California in a district of a member of the Association of Latino Superintendents and Administrators (CALSA). Applicants must be planning to enroll at a 4-year university in any state and be sponsored by the CALSA member. Along with their application, they must submit a 250-word essay on where they plan to attend college, their proposed major, why they have chosen that area of study, why a college education is important to them, how a college degree will assist them in making a contribution to themselves and their community, and why they should be granted a CALSA scholarship.

Financial Data The stipend is $1,000.

Duration 1 year.

Additional data This program, which began in 2006, is currently supported by De La Rosa & Co.

Number awarded 20 each year.

Deadline April of each year.

[68]
CALIFORNIA DIETETIC ASSOCIATION FOUNDATION SCHOLARSHIP HONORING BERNICE AARONS

California Dietetic Association
Attn: CDA Foundation
7740 Manchester Avenue, Suite 102
Playa del Rey, CA 90293-8499
(310) 822-0177   Fax: (310) 823-0264
E-mail: patsmith@dietitian.org
Web: www.dietitian.org/d_cdaf/cdaf_outreach.html

Summary To provide financial assistance to residents of California (particularly Hispanic Americans, other minorities, men, and persons with disabilities) who are members of the Academy of Nutrition and Dietetics (AND) and interested in participating in specified types of programs in any state.

Eligibility This program is open to California residents who are AND members and 1) entering the first or second year of an approved Dietetic Technician Program in any state; 2) entering at least the second year of an accredited Coordinated Program (CP) or Didactic Program in Dietetics (DPD) in any state; or 3) accepted to an accredited Supervised Practice Program in any state to begin within 6 months. Along with their application, they must submit a letter of application that includes a discussion of their career goals. Selection is based on that letter (15%), academic ability (25%), work or volunteer experience (15%), letters of recommendation (15%), extracurricular activities (5%), and financial need (25%).

Applications are especially encouraged from ethnic minorities, men, and people with physical disabilities.

Financial Data The stipend is normally $1,000.

Duration 1 year.

Additional data The California Dietetic Association is the California affiliate of the AND.

Number awarded 1 each year.

Deadline April of each year.

[69]
CALIFORNIA TABLE GRAPE FIELD WORKER SCHOLARSHIPS

California Table Grape Commission
Attn: Scholarship Committee
392 West Fallbrook, Suite 101
Fresno, CA 93711-6150
(559) 447-8350   Toll Free: (800) 813-8478
Fax: (559) 447-9184
E-mail: info@grapesfromcalifornia.com
Web: www.freshcaliforniagrapes.com/scholarships.php

Summary To provide financial assistance to the children of California table grape field workers who are interested in attending a college in the state.

Eligibility This program is open to high school graduates or seniors graduating in June. They, or their parents, must have worked in either of the 2 previous California table grape harvests. Farmers and their families, raisin and wine grape workers, students currently enrolled in college, permanent staff and members of the California Table Grape Commission and their families, and commission suppliers are not eligible. Applicants must intend to attend a 2- or 4-year college or university in California as a full-time student. Selection is based on academic performance, financial need, obstacles overcome, leadership ability and/or community service, and ability to succeed.

Financial Data The stipend is $20,000 for students at 4-year universities or $3,500 for students at 2-year colleges.

Duration 1 year; may be renewed, provided the recipient remains enrolled full time with a GPA of 2.0 or higher.

Additional data This program began in 1984.

Number awarded 6 each year: 3 to students at 4-year universities and 3 to students at 2-year colleges.

Deadline March of each year.

[70]
CAMMER-HILL GRANT

Wisconsin Women of Color Network, Inc.
Attn: Scholarship Committee
P.O. Box 2337
Madison, WI 53701-2337
E-mail: contact@womenofcolornetwork-wis.org
Web: www.womenofcolornetwork-wis.org/scholarship.html

Summary To provide financial assistance for vocational/technical school or community college to Hispanic American and other adult women of color from Wisconsin.

Eligibility This program is open to residents of Wisconsin who are adult women of color planning to continue their education at a vocational/technical school or community college in any state. Applicants must be a member of 1 of the following groups: African American, Asian, American Indian, or Hispanic. They must be able to demonstrate financial need.

Along with their application, they must submit a 1-page essay on how this scholarship will help them accomplish their educational goal. U.S. citizenship is required.
Financial Data A stipend is awarded (amount not specified).
Duration 1 year.
Additional data This program began in 1994.
Number awarded 1 each year.
Deadline May of each year.

[71]
CAMP SCHOLARSHIPS
Migrant Students Foundation
305 Prospect Avenue, Suite 4
Lewiston, ID 83501
(509) 368-7132   E-mail: support@migrantstudents.org
Web: www.migrantstudents.org
Summary To provide financial assistance for college to high school seniors from migrant or seasonal farmworker families.
Eligibility This program is open to migrant and seasonal farmworkers and their families working in agricultural activities directly related to the production of crops, dairy products, poultry, or livestock; the cultivation or harvesting of trees; or fish farms. Applicants may verify eligibility in 1 of 3 ways: 1) participation during high school or eligibility to participate in a Title 1 Migrant Education Program; 2) participation or eligibility to participate in the Workforce Investment Act (WIA); or 3) verification that they or their parents have spent at least 75 days during the past 24 months as a migrant and/or seasonal (not year-round) farmworker as their primary employment. They must also plan to enroll as a freshman at a 4-year college or university that participates in the College Assistance Migrant Program (CAMP) of the U.S. Department of Education to complete a bachelor's degree, be a U.S. citizen or permanent resident, and be able to document financial need.
Financial Data The stipends range from $750 to $4,000, depending on the need of the recipients and the school they attend.
Duration 1 year.
Additional data Currently, nearly 40 colleges and universities participate in the CAMP program, including schools in Arizona, California, Colorado, Florida, Georgia, Idaho, Kansas, Kentucky, Maine, Maryland, Michigan, Mississippi, Missouri, New Mexico, New York, North Carolina, Oregon, Pennsylvania, Puerto Rico, Texas, Washington, and Wisconsin.
Number awarded Approximately 2,000 each year.
Deadline February of each year.

[72]
CANFIT PROGRAM CULINARY ARTS SCHOLARSHIPS
Communities-Adolescents-Nutrition-Fitness
Attn: Scholarship Program
2140 Shattuck Avenue, Suite 610
Berkeley, CA 94704
(510) 644-1533   Toll Free: (800) 200-3131
Fax: (510) 644-1535   E-mail: info@canfit.org
Web: www.canfit.org/scholarships

Summary To provide financial assistance to Hispanic American and other minority culinary arts students in California.
Eligibility This program is open to American Indians, Alaska Natives, African Americans, Asian Americans, Pacific Islanders, and Latinos/Hispanics from California who are enrolled at a culinary arts college in the state. Applicants are not required to have completed any college units. Along with their application, they must submit 1) documentation of financial need; 2) letters of recommendation from 2 individuals; 3) a 1-to 2-page letter describing their academic goals and involvement in community nutrition and/or physical education activities; and 4) an essay of 500 to 1,000 words on a topic related to healthy foods for youth from low-income communities of color.
Financial Data A stipend is awarded (amount not specified).
Number awarded 1 or more each year.
Deadline March of each year.

[73]
CANFIT PROGRAM UNDERGRADUATE SCHOLARSHIPS
Communities-Adolescents-Nutrition-Fitness
Attn: Scholarship Program
2140 Shattuck Avenue, Suite 610
Berkeley, CA 94704
(510) 644-1533   Toll Free: (800) 200-3131
Fax: (510) 644-1535   E-mail: info@canfit.org
Web: www.canfit.org/scholarships
Summary To provide financial assistance to Hispanic American and other minority undergraduate students who are working on a degree in nutrition or physical education in California.
Eligibility This program is open to American Indians, Alaska Natives, African Americans, Asian Americans, Pacific Islanders, and Latinos/Hispanics from California who are enrolled in an approved bachelor's degree program in nutrition or physical education in the state. Applicants must have completed at least 50 semester units and have a GPA of 2.5 or higher. Along with their application, they must submit 1) documentation of financial need; 2) letters of recommendation from 2 individuals; 3) a 1-to 2-page letter describing their academic goals and involvement in community nutrition and/or physical education activities; and 4) an essay of 500 to 1,000 words on a topic related to healthy foods for youth from low-income communities of color.
Financial Data A stipend is awarded (amount not specified).
Number awarded 1 or more each year.
Deadline March of each year.

[74]
CAPSTONE CORPORATION SCHOLARSHIP AWARD

National Naval Officers Association-Washington, D.C.
  Chapter
c/o LCDR Stephen Williams
P.O. Box 30784
Alexandria, VA 22310
(703) 566-3840   Fax: (703) 566-3813
E-mail: Stephen.Williams@navy.mil
Web: dcnnoa.memberlodge.com

Summary To provide financial assistance to Hispanic American and other minority high school seniors from the Washington, D.C. area who plan to attend college in any state.

Eligibility This program is open to minority seniors graduating from high schools in the Washington, D.C. metropolitan area who plan to enroll full time at an accredited 2- or 4-year college or university in any state. Applicants must have a GPA of 3.0 or higher and be U.S. citizens or permanent residents. Selection is based on academic achievement, community involvement, and financial need.

Financial Data The stipend is $1,000.

Duration 1 year; nonrenewable.

Additional data Recipients are not required to join or affiliate with the military in any way. This program is supported by Capstone Corporation, a minority-owned business incorporated in 1986 by former active-duty Navy officers.

Number awarded 1 each year.

Deadline March of each year.

[75]
CAREFIRST BLUECROSS BLUESHIELD SCHOLARSHIP PROGRAM

Hispanic College Fund
Attn: Scholarship Processing
1300 L Street, N.W., Suite 975
Washington, DC 20005
(202) 296-5400   Toll Free: (800) 644-4223
Fax: (202) 296-3774   E-mail: hcf-info@hispanicfund.org
Web: scholarships.hispanicfund.org/applications

Summary To provide financial assistance to Hispanic American students working on an undergraduate or graduate degree in a field related to health care, science, or business.

Eligibility This program is open to undergraduate and graduate students of Hispanic background (at least 1 grandparent must be 100% Hispanic) who are enrolled or planning to enroll full time at an accredited college or university in any state or Puerto Rico. Applicants must have a GPA of 3.0 or higher; be interested in working on a degree in a field related to health care, science, or business; and be able to demonstrate financial need. They must either 1) be U.S. citizens or permanent residents; or 2) have graduated from a high school in the United States after having attended for at least 3 years. Preference is given to applicants who reside or attend college in Maryland, the District of Columbia, or northern Virginia.

Financial Data Stipends range from $500 to $5,000, depending on need and academic achievement. Funds are paid directly to the recipient's college or university to help cover tuition and fees.

Duration 1 year; recipients may reapply.

Additional data This program is sponsored by CareFirst BlueCross BlueShield, which provides health insurance in Maryland, the District of Columbia, and portions of northern Virginia. All applications must be submitted online; no paper applications are available.

Number awarded Varies each year.

Deadline February of each year.

[76]
CARMEN E. TURNER SCHOLARSHIPS

Conference of Minority Transportation Officials
Attn: National Scholarship Program
1875 I Street, N.W., Suite 500
Washington, DC 20006
(703) 234-4072   Fax: (202) 318-0364
Web: www.comto.org/?page=Scholarships

Summary To provide financial assistance for college or graduate school to Hispanic American and other members of the Conference of Minority Transportation Officials (COMTO).

Eligibility This program is open to undergraduate and graduate students who have been members of COMTO for at least 1 year. Applicants must be working on a degree in a field related to transportation and have a GPA of 2.5 or higher. They must be enrolled at least half time. Along with their application, they must submit a cover letter with a 500-word statement of career goals. Financial need is not considered in the selection process. U.S. citizenship or legal resident status is required.

Financial Data The stipend is $3,500. Funds are paid directly to the recipient's college or university.

Duration 1 year.

Additional data COMTO was established in 1971 to promote, strengthen, and expand the roles of minorities in all aspects of transportation. Recipients are expected to attend the COMTO National Scholarship Luncheon.

Number awarded 1 each year.

Deadline May of each year.

[77]
CAROL HAYES TORIO MEMORIAL UNDERGRADUATE SCHOLARSHIP

California Dietetic Association
Attn: CDA Foundation
7740 Manchester Avenue, Suite 102
Playa del Rey, CA 90293-8499
(310) 822-0177   Fax: (310) 823-0264
E-mail: patsmith@dietitian.org
Web: www.dietitian.org/d_cdaf/cdaf_outreach.html

Summary To provide financial assistance to residents of California (particularly Hispanic Americans, other minorities, men, and individuals with physical disabilities) who are members of the Academy of Nutrition and Dietetics (AND) and interested in working on an undergraduate degree at a school in any state.

Eligibility This program is open to California residents who are AND members and 1) entering at least the second year of an accredited Coordinated Program (CP) or Didactic Program in Dietetics (DPD) in any state; or 2) accepted to an accredited Supervised Practice Program in any state to begin within 6 months. Along with their application, they must submit a letter of application that includes a discussion of their career goals. Selection is based on that letter (15%), academic ability (25%), work or volunteer experience (15%), letters of recommendation (15%), extracurricular activities (5%), and financial need (25%). Applications are especially encouraged from ethnic minorities, men, and people with physical disabilities.

Financial Data   The stipend is normally $1,000.

Duration   1 year.

Additional data   The California Dietetic Association is the California affiliate of the AND.

Number awarded   1 each year.

Deadline   April of each year.

[78]
CARY INSTITUTE OF ECOSYSTEM STUDIES RESEARCH EXPERIENCES FOR UNDERGRADUATES PROGRAM

Cary Institute of Ecosystem Studies
Attn: Undergraduate Research Program
2801 Sharon Turnpike
P.O. Box AB
Millbrook, NY 12545
(845) 677-7600, ext. 326   Fax: (845) 677-5976
E-mail: smithp@caryinstitute.org
Web: www.caryinstitute.org/students/reu-program

Summary   To provide undergraduate students (particularly Hispanic Americans and other students with diverse backgrounds) with an opportunity to conduct research during the summer at the Cary Institute of Ecosystem Studies (IES) at Millbrook, New York.

Eligibility   This program is open to undergraduate freshmen, sophomores, juniors, and first semester seniors. Applicants must be interested in conducting an independent research project of their own design under the guidance of a mentor scientist. They must identify their interest in ecological research, their current career plans, and how participating in this program could help them in their degree program and their future pursuits. Recently, research topics focused on translational ecology. The program welcomes applications from students of diverse backgrounds at schools in all parts of the country. U.S. citizenship or permanent resident status is required.

Financial Data   The stipend is $6,000. Housing and a $600 allowance for food are also provided.

Duration   12 weeks during the summer.

Additional data   This program is supported by the National Science Foundation as part of its Research Experiences for Undergraduates (REU) program.

Number awarded   8 to 12 each year.

Deadline   February of each year.

[79]
CCNMA SCHOLARSHIPS

CCNMA: Latino Journalists of California
c/o ASU Cronkite School of Journalism
725 Arizona Avenue, Suite 206
Santa Monica, CA 90401-1734
(424) 229-9482   E-mail: ccnmainfo@ccnma.org
Web: www.ccnma.org

Summary   To provide financial assistance to Latino students from California who are interested in preparing for a career in journalism.

Eligibility   This program is open to high school seniors and college students of Latino descent who are California residents attending a college or university in any state or students from other states attending a college or university in California. Applicants may major in any field, but they must enroll full time and be able to prove a sincere interest in preparing for a career in journalism. They must submit 1) an autobiographical essay of 300 to 500 words, including their family background, any hardships they have experienced, why they want to be a journalist, and what they believe is the role of Latino journalists in the news media; 2) samples of their journalism-related work (e.g., newspaper articles, photographs, or TV or radio audition tapes); 3) transcripts; and 4) letters of reference. Finalists are interviewed. Selection is based on academic achievement, commitment to the journalism field, awareness of Latino issues, and financial need.

Financial Data   Stipends range from $500 to $1,000.

Duration   1 year.

Additional data   This program includes the Joel Garcia Memorial Scholarship, the George Ramos Memorial Scholarship, and the Frank del Olmo Memorial Scholarship. The sponsor was formerly named the California Chicano News Media Association.

Number awarded   Varies each year; recently, 7 of these scholarships were awarded.

Deadline   March of each year.

[80]
CEA MINORITY STUDENT SCHOLARSHIPS

Colorado Education Association
Attn: Ethnic Minority Advisory Council
1500 Grant Street
Denver, CO 80203
(303) 837-1500   Toll Free: (800) 332-5939
Web: www.coloradoea.org

Summary   To provide financial assistance to Hispanic American and other minority high school seniors in Colorado who are children of members of the Colorado Education Association (CEA) and planning to attend college in any state.

Eligibility   This program is open to seniors graduating from high schools in Colorado who are members of a minority ethnic group, defined to include American Indians/Alaska Natives, Asians, Blacks, Hispanics, Native Hawaiians/Pacific Islanders, and multi-ethnic. Applicants must be the dependent child of an active, retired, or deceased CEA member. They must be planning to attend an accredited institution of higher education in any state. Along with their application, they must submit brief statements on 1) their need for this scholarship; and 2) why they plan to pursue a college education.

Financial Data   The stipend is $1,000.

Duration   1 year; nonrenewable.

Number awarded   4 each year.

Deadline   March of each year.

[81]
CENTRAL FLORIDA CHAPTER NBMBAA SCHOLARSHIPS

National Black MBA Association-Central Florida Chapter
Attn: Scholarship Committee Chair
P.O. Box 692696
Orlando, FL 32869-2696
(321) 578-8305   E-mail: scholarships@cflblackmba.org
Web: www.cflblackmba.org

Summary To provide financial assistance to Hispanic Americans or members of another minority group who are residents of any state working on a degree in business at a university in Florida.

Eligibility This program is open to members of the following groups from any state: African American/Black, American Indian/Alaska Native, Asian American/Pacific Islander, or Hispanic/Latino. Applicants must be enrolled in a business program at an AACSB-accredited college or university in Florida. They must have a GPA of 3.0 or higher. Along with their application, they must submit a 2-page essay on a topic that changes annually but relates to minorities and business. Selection is based on that essay, transcripts, a resume, and extracurricular activities. The highest-ranked applicant receives a named scholarship sponsored by Darden Restaurants.

Financial Data The Darden Named Scholarship is $5,000; a total of $10,000 in scholarships is awarded each year.

Duration 1 year.

Number awarded Varies each year.

Deadline October of each year.

[82]
CENTRAL INTELLIGENCE AGENCY UNDERGRADUATE SCHOLARSHIP PROGRAM

Central Intelligence Agency
Attn: Human Resource Management
Recruitment and Retention Center, 4B14-034 DD1
Washington, DC 20505
(703) 371-2107
Web: https:

Summary To provide college funding and work experience to high school seniors and college sophomores (particularly Hispanic Americans, other minorities, and students with disabilities) who would be interested in working for the Central Intelligence Agency (CIA) after graduation from college.

Eligibility This program is open to U.S. citizens who are either high school seniors or college freshmen or sophomores. Seniors must be at least 18 years of age by April of the year they apply and have minimum scores of 1500 on the SAT (1000 on critical reading and mathematics and 500 on writing) or 21 on the ACT. All applicants must have a GPA of 3.0 or higher and be able to demonstrate financial need (household income of $70,000 or less for a family of 4 or $80,000 or less for a family of 5 or more) and be able to meet the same employment standards as permanent employees of the CIA. This program was developed, in part, to assist minority and disabled students, but it is open to all students who meet the requirements.

Financial Data Scholars are provided a salary, an optional benefits package (health, dental, and vision insurance, life insurance, and retirement), and up to $18,000 per year for tuition, fees, books, and supplies. They must agree to continue employment with the CIA after college graduation for a period 1.5 times the length of their college support.

Duration 1 year; may be renewed if the student maintains a GPA of 3.0 or higher and full-time enrollment in a 4- or 5-year college program.

Additional data Scholars work each summer at a CIA facility. In addition to a salary, they receive the cost of transportation between school and the Washington, D.C. area and a housing allowance.

Number awarded Varies each year.

Deadline October of each year.

[83]
CHATEAU STE. MICHELLE SCHOLARSHIP FUND

College Success Foundation
1605 N.W. Sammamish Road, Suite 200
Issaquah, WA 98027-5388
(425) 416-2000   Toll Free: (877) 655-4097
Fax: (425) 416-2001
E-mail: info@collegesuccessfoundation.org
Web: www.collegesuccessfoundation.org

Summary To provide financial assistance to Hispanic American and other underrepresented minority residents of Washington (especially those whose families work in agriculture) who are attending or planning to attend college in the state.

Eligibility This program is open to residents of Washington who are high school seniors or college freshmen or sophomores. Applicants must be enrolled or planning to enroll full time at a 4-year college or university in the state. They must have a GPA of 2.75 or higher and be able to demonstrate financial need (family income of $39,000 or less for a family of 1, rising to $94,000 or less for a family of 7). Preference is given to members of underrepresented groups whose parents work in the agricultural sector.

Financial Data The stipend is $5,000 per year.

Duration 1 year; may be renewed up to 3 additional years.

Additional data This program began in 2001.

Number awarded Varies each year; since the program was established, it has awarded more than $2.9 million in scholarships.

Deadline March of each year.

[84]
CHCI-TELEMUNDO SCHOLAR INTERN PROGRAM

Congressional Hispanic Caucus Institute, Inc.
911 Second Street, N.E.
Washington, DC 20002
(202) 543-1771   Toll Free: (800) EXCEL-DC
Fax: (202) 546-2143   E-mail: chci@chci.org
Web: www.chci.org/scholarships

Summary To provide an educational stipend and work experience at news facilities of Telemundo in Miami to undergraduate students of Hispanic descent.

Eligibility This program is open to U.S. citizens and permanent residents who are of Hispanic descent and currently enrolled full time as sophomores or juniors at an accredited 4-year university. Applicants must be interested in a paid summer internship of at least 80 hours at Telemundo's news station in Miami. Available placements include consumer marketing, digital media, news, research, sourcing, or sports. Financial need is considered in the selection process.

Financial Data Participants receive a salary from Telemundo; upon verification of completion of 80 hours of paid summer employment, they also receive an educational stipend of $1,000 from the Congressional Hispanic Caucus Institute (CHCI).

Duration The stipend supports 1 year of study.

Number awarded Varies each year; recently, 2 of these scholarship/internships were awarded.

Deadline January of each year.

[85]
CHCI-UNITED HEALTH FOUNDATION SCHOLAR INTERN PROGRAM

Congressional Hispanic Caucus Institute, Inc.
911 Second Street, N.E.
Washington, DC 20002
(202) 543-1771   Toll Free: (800) EXCEL-DC
Fax: (202) 546-2143   E-mail: chci@chci.org
Web: www.chci.org/scholarships

Summary To provide an educational stipend and work experience at community health organizations to undergraduate and graduate students of Hispanic descent.

Eligibility This program is open to U.S. citizens and permanent residents who are of Hispanic descent and currently enrolled full time at an accredited community college, 4-year university, or graduate/professional program. Applicants must be working on a health-related degree, including (but not limited to) nursing, pre-medicine or medicine, dentistry, public health, nutrition, or other health care field. They must obtain a paid internship at a community-based health organization that will require a total of at least 80 hours of service. Financial need is considered in the selection process.

Financial Data Participants receive a salary from the health organization where they work; upon verification of completion of 80 hours of paid employment, they also receive an educational stipend of $1,000 from the Congressional Hispanic Caucus Institute (CHCI).

Duration The stipend supports 1 year of study.

Additional data Funding for this program is provided by United Health Foundation.

Number awarded Varies each year; recently, 18 of these scholarship/internships were awarded: 14 to undergraduates, and 4 to graduate students.

Deadline April of each year.

[86]
CHICANO/LATINO COMMUNITY COLLEGE SCHOLARSHIP

Scholarship Administrative Services, Inc.
Attn: MEFUSA Program
457 Ives Terrace
Sunnyvale, CA 94087

Summary To provide financial assistance to Chicano/Latino high school seniors who are interested in attending a community college.

Eligibility This program is open to Chicano/Latino seniors graduating from high schools anywhere in the United States. Applicants must be planning to attend a community college

on a full-time basis. Along with their application, they must submit a 1,000-word essay on their educational and career goals, how a community college education will help them to achieve those goals, and how they plan to serve the Chicano/Latino community after completing their education. Selection is based on the essay, high school GPA (2.5 or higher), SAT or ACT scores, involvement in the Chicano/Latino community, and financial need.

Financial Data The stipend is $5,000 per year.

Duration 1 year; may be renewed 1 additional year if the recipient maintains full-time enrollment and a GPA of 2.5 or higher.

Additional data This program is sponsored by the Minority Educational Foundation of the United States of America (MEFUSA) and administered by Scholarship Administrative Services, Inc. MEFUSA was established in 2001 to meet the needs of minority students who "show a determination to get a college degree," but who, for financial or other personal reasons, are not able to attend a 4-year college or university. Requests for applications should be accompanied by a self-addressed stamped envelope, the student's e-mail address, and the name of the source where they found the scholarship information.

Number awarded Up to 100 each year.

Deadline April of each year.

[87]
CHILDREN'S MERCY HOSPITALS PEDIATRIC NURSING SCHOLARSHIP

National Association of Hispanic Nurses
Attn: National Awards and Scholarship Committee Chair
1455 Pennsylvania Avenue, N.W., Suite 400
Washington, DC 20004
(202) 387-2477   Fax: (202) 483-7183
E-mail: info@thehispanicnurses.org
Web: www.nahnnet.org/NAHNScholarships.html

Summary To provide financial assistance to members of the National Association of Hispanic Nurses (NAHN) who are interested in preparing for a career in pediatric nursing.

Eligibility Eligible are members of the association enrolled in associate, diploma, baccalaureate, graduate, or practical/vocational nursing programs in pediatric nursing. Applicants must have a GPA of 3.0 or higher. Along with their application, they must submit a letter of recommendation; a 300-word essay that reflects their qualifications and potential for leadership in nursing in the Hispanic community; a resume that includes earned certificates, awards, and special honors; information on their financial status; and an official transcript. U.S. citizenship or permanent resident status is required.

Financial Data The stipend is $2,500.

Duration 1 year.

Additional data Support for this program, which began in 2013, is provided by Children's Mercy Hospitals of Kansas City, Missouri.

Number awarded 1 or more each year.

Deadline June of each year.

[88]
CHRISTIAN COLLEGE LEADERS SCHOLARSHIPS

Foundation for College Christian Leaders
2658 Del Mar Heights Road
PMB 266
Del Mar, CA 92014
(858) 481-0848   E-mail: LMHays@aol.com
Web: www.collegechristianleader.com

Summary   To provide financial assistance for college to Christian students (particularly Hispanic Americans and other minorities) who are from California, Oregon, or Washington.

Eligibility   This program is open to entering or continuing undergraduate students who reside or attend college in California, Oregon, or Washington. Applicants must have a GPA of 3.0 or higher, be able to document financial need (parents must have a combined income of less than $75,000), and be able to demonstrate Christian testimony and Christian leadership. Selection is based on identified leadership history, academic achievement, financial need, and demonstrated academic, vocational, and ministry training to further the Kingdom of Jesus Christ. Special consideration is given to minority students.

Financial Data   A stipend is awarded (amount not specified).

Duration   1 year; may be renewed.

Additional data   The foundation, formerly known as the Eckmann Foundation, was founded in 1988.

Number awarded   Varies each year.

Deadline   May of each year.

[89]
CIENCIA NATIONAL SCHOLARSHIPS

National Alliance for Hispanic Health
Alliance/Merck *Ciencia* Hispanic Scholars Program
1501 16th Street, N.W.
Washington, DC 20036
(202) 387-5000   Toll Free: (866) 783-2645
Web: www.alliancescholars.org/applications

Summary   To provide financial assistance to Hispanic college students who are majoring in a field of science, technology, engineering, or mathematics (STEM).

Eligibility   This program is open to students of Hispanic heritage from any state, Puerto Rico, or other U.S. territories who are enrolled full time at an accredited college or university. Applicants must have a declared major in a STEM discipline and a GPA of 2.75 or higher. They must be working on a bachelor's degree, including a degree offered by a partnership between a community college and a 4-year institution.

Financial Data   The stipend is $2,000.

Duration   1 year; nonrenewable.

Additional data   This program, which began in 2009, operates as a partnership of the National Alliance for Hispanic Health, the Health Foundation for the Americas, the Merck Institute for Science Education, and the Merck Company Foundation.

Number awarded   25 each year.

Deadline   February of each year.

[90]
CINTHYA FELIX SCHOLARSHIP

Latino Medical Student Association
c/o Amaranta Craig, Scholarship Vice President
1355 Willard, Apartment B
San Francisco, CA 94117
E-mail: VP_Scholarship@lmsa.net
Web: www.lmsa.net/default.asp?contentID=9

Summary   To provide financial assistance to undergraduate and graduate student members of the Latino Medical Student Association (LMSA) in selected western states who are preparing for a career in medicine.

Eligibility   This program is open to LMSA members who are 1) residents of or attending school in its western region (Arizona, California, Oregon, Utah, and Washington); 2) enrolled at least as sophomores at a 4-year university or in a graduate program; 3) able to demonstrate a desire to advance the state of health care and education in Latino communities through extracurricular activities and/or membership in civic organizations; and 4) committed to preparing for a professional career in medicine and dedicated to serving the Latino and underserved communities. Applicants are eligible regardless of their immigrant or citizenship status, as long as the university they attend allows them to enroll and register for classes. Along with their application, they must submit a 1-page personal statement describing their family and personal background, educational objectives, community involvement, financial need, and how they would assist LMSA in its mission to provide health care to the Latino and/or other underserved communities.

Financial Data   A stipend is awarded (amount not specified).

Duration   1 year.

Additional data   Until 2002, this organization was known as the Chicano/Latino Medical Student Association of California. This program was established in 2011.

Number awarded   Varies each year.

Deadline   November of each year.

[91]
CISCO DIVERSITY SCHOLARSHIPS

Society of Hispanic Professional Engineers Foundation, Inc.
Attn: Advancing Hispanic Excellence in Technology, Engineering, Math and Science
13181 Crossroads Parkway North, Suite 450
P.O. Box 93577
City of Industry, CA 91715
(323) 725-3970, ext. 118   Fax: (323) 622-1046
E-mail: shpefoundation@shpe.org
Web: www.shpefoundation.org

Summary   To provide financial assistance to undergraduate and graduate student members of the Society of Hispanic Professional Engineers (SHPE) who are working on a degree in designated fields of science, technology, engineering or mathematics (STEM).

Eligibility   This program is open to full-time students who are either 1) rising sophomores or juniors; or 2) entering first-year graduate students. Applicants must be working on a degree in computer information systems, computer science, engineering (computer, electrical, or systems), management information systems, mathematics, physics, or technology management. They must have a GPA of 3.0 or higher. Along with their application, they must submit a 500-word personal statement on the event or experience that has had the greatest influence in shaping their character. Selection is based on that statement, potential for an commitment to a career in technology, leadership and community involvement, participation in their SHPE chapter activities, and interest in an internship with Cisco Systems. U.S. citizenship or permanent resident status is required.

Financial Data The stipend is $5,000.

Duration 1 year.

Additional data Advancing Hispanic Excellence in Technology, Engineering, Math and Science (AHETEMS) was established in 2004 by SHPE as an independent nonprofit foundation. This program is sponsored by Cisco Systems.

Number awarded 5 each year.

Deadline April of each year.

[92]
CISCO'S FUTURE SCHOLARSHIPS

Society of Women Engineers
Attn: Scholarship Selection Committee
203 North LaSalle Street, Suite 1675
Chicago, IL 60601-1269
(312) 596-5223 Toll Free: (877) SWE-INFO
Fax: (312) 644-8557 E-mail: scholarships@swe.org
Web: societyofwomenengineers.swe.org

Summary To provide financial assistance to Hispanic American and other undergraduate women, who are members of the Society of Women Engineers (SWE) and majoring in designated engineering specialties.

Eligibility This program is open to SWE members who are entering their sophomore or junior year at a 4-year ABET-accredited college or university. Preference is given to members of underrepresented ethnic or racial groups, candidates with disabilities, and veterans. Applicants must be working full time on a degree in computer science or computer or electrical engineering and have a GPA of 3.0 or higher. They must be U.S. citizens or permanent residents. Financial need is considered in the selection process.

Financial Data The stipend is $5,000.

Duration 1 year.

Additional data This program is sponsored by Cisco Systems.

Number awarded 5 each year.

Deadline February of each year.

[93]
CLARKE WATSON SCHOLARSHIPS

American Association of Blacks in Energy-Denver Area Chapter
Attn: Scholarship Committee
14405 West Colfax Avenue, Suite 264
Lakewood, CO 80401-3206
E-mail: Janice.Brown@nrel.gov
Web: www.aabe.org/index.php?component=pages&id=270

Summary To provide financial assistance to Hispanic Americans and members of other underrepresented minority groups who are high school seniors in Colorado and planning to major in an energy-related field at a college in any state.

Eligibility This program is open to seniors graduating from high schools in Colorado who are planning to work on a bachelor's degree at a college or university in any state. Applicants must be African Americans, Hispanics, or Native Americans who have a GPA of 3.0 or higher and who can demonstrate financial need. They must be planning to major in a field of business, engineering, technology, physical science, or mathematics related to energy. Along with their application, they must submit a 350-word statement on why they should receive this scholarship, how their professional career objectives relate to energy, and any other relevant information. U.S. citizenship is required.

Financial Data The stipend is $1,000. Funds are disbursed directly to the recipient's college or university.

Duration 1 year; may be renewed.

Additional data Winners are eligible to compete for regional and national scholarships.

Number awarded 2 each year.

Deadline February of each year.

[94]
COCA-COLA FAMILY DOLLAR SCHOLARSHIP PROGRAM

Hispanic Scholarship Fund
Attn: Selection Committee
1411 West 190th Street, Suite 325
Gardena, CA 90248
Toll Free: (877) HSF-INFO E-mail: scholar1@hsf.net
Web: www.hsf.net

Summary To provide financial assistance to Hispanic American high school seniors in most states who plan to attend college in the United States or designated territories.

Eligibility This program is open to seniors of Hispanic heritage who are graduating from high schools in all states except Alaska, Hawaii, Montana, Oregon, and Washington and have a GPA of 3.0 or higher. Applicants must be U.S. citizens or permanent residents (must have a permanent resident card or a passport stamped I-551). They must be planning to enroll full time at an accredited 2- or 4-year college or university in the United States, Puerto Rico, the U.S. Virgin Islands, or Guam. Their proposed major may be in any field. Selection is based on academic achievement, personal strengths, leadership, and financial need.

Financial Data The stipend is $10,000 or $5,000.

Duration 1 year.

Additional data This program is jointly sponsored by Family Dollar Stores, Coca-Cola, and the Hispanic Scholarship Fund (HSF).

Number awarded 4 each year: 1 at $10,000 and 3 at $5,000.

Deadline December of each year.

[95]
COCA-COLA GIANT FOOD STORES SCHOLARSHIP PROGRAM

Hispanic Scholarship Fund
Attn: Selection Committee
1411 West 190th Street, Suite 325
Gardena, CA 90248
Toll Free: (877) HSF-INFO E-mail: scholar1@hsf.net
Web: www.hsf.net

Summary To provide financial assistance to Hispanic American high school seniors in designated states who plan to attend college in the United States or designated territories.

Eligibility This program is open to seniors of Hispanic heritage who are graduating from high schools in Maryland, Pennsylvania, Virginia, or West Virginia and have a GPA of 3.0 or higher. Applicants must be U.S. citizens or permanent residents (must have a permanent resident card or a passport stamped I-551). They must be planning to enroll full time at an accredited 2- or 4-year college or university in the United States, Puerto Rico, the U.S. Virgin Islands, or Guam. Their proposed major may be in any field. Selection is based on academic achievement, personal strengths, leadership, and financial need.

Financial Data The stipend is $5,000.

Duration 1 year.

Additional data This program is jointly sponsored by Giant Food Stores, Coca-Cola, and the Hispanic Scholarship Fund (HSF).

Number awarded 2 each year.

Deadline December of each year.

[96]
COCA-COLA HISPANIC HERITAGE MONTH CONTEST AND SWEEPSTAKES SCHOLARSHIP PROGRAM

Hispanic Scholarship Fund
Attn: Selection Committee
1411 West 190th Street, Suite 325
Gardena, CA 90248
Toll Free: (877) HSF-INFO   E-mail: scholar1@hsf.net
Web: www.hsf.net

Summary To recognize and reward, with college scholarships, Hispanic American high school seniors in any state who post photographs of themselves online and plan to attend college in the United States or designated territories.

Eligibility This program is open to seniors of Hispanic heritage who are graduating from high schools in any state and have a GPA of 3.0 or higher. Applicants must be U.S. citizens or permanent residents (must have a permanent resident card or a passport stamped I-551). They must be planning to enroll full time at an accredited 4-year college or university in the United States, Puerto Rico, the U.S. Virgin Islands, or Guam. Their proposed major may be in any field. Along with their application, they must submit a photograph of themselves holding their favorite Coca-Cola beverage which they post on the Internet. Parents, friends, teachers, and others then engage in online voting for their favorite applicant.

Financial Data Prizes, in the form of college scholarships, include $20,000 as the grand prize, $10,000 as first prizes, and $2,500 as second prizes.

Duration 1 year.

Additional data This program is jointly sponsored by Coca-Cola and the Hispanic Scholarship Fund (HSF).

Number awarded 21 each year: 1 grand prize, 4 first prizes, and 16 second prizes.

Deadline December of each year.

[97]
COCA-COLA LA MICHOACANA SCHOLARSHIP PROGRAM

Hispanic Scholarship Fund
Attn: Selection Committee
1411 West 190th Street, Suite 325
Gardena, CA 90248
Toll Free: (877) HSF-INFO   E-mail: scholar1@hsf.net
Web: www.hsf.net

Summary To provide financial assistance to Hispanic American high school seniors in Oklahoma and Texas who plan to attend college in the United States or designated territories.

Eligibility This program is open to seniors of Hispanic heritage who are graduating from high schools in Oklahoma or Texas and have a GPA of 3.0 or higher. Applicants must be U.S. citizens or permanent residents (must have a permanent resident card or a passport stamped I-551). They must be planning to enroll full time at an accredited 2- or 4-year college or university in the United States, Puerto Rico, the U.S. Virgin Islands, or Guam. Their proposed major may be in any field. Selection is based on academic achievement, personal strengths, leadership, and financial need.

Financial Data The stipend is $1,000.

Duration 1 year.

Additional data This program is jointly sponsored by La Michoacana Meat Market, Coca-Cola, and the Hispanic Scholarship Fund (HSF).

Number awarded 18 each year.

Deadline December of each year.

[98]
COCA-COLA MEIJER SCHOLARSHIP PROGRAM

Hispanic Scholarship Fund
Attn: Selection Committee
1411 West 190th Street, Suite 325
Gardena, CA 90248
Toll Free: (877) HSF-INFO   E-mail: scholar1@hsf.net
Web: www.hsf.net

Summary To provide financial assistance to Hispanic American high school seniors in Illinois who plan to attend college in the United States or designated territories.

Eligibility This program is open to seniors of Hispanic heritage who are graduating from high schools in Illinois and have a GPA of 3.0 or higher. Applicants must be U.S. citizens or permanent residents (must have a permanent resident card or a passport stamped I-551). They must be planning to enroll full time at an accredited 2- or 4-year college or university in the United States, Puerto Rico, the U.S. Virgin Islands, or Guam. Their proposed major may be in any field. Selection is based on academic achievement, personal strengths, leadership, and financial need.

Financial Data The stipend is $10,000 or $2,000.

Duration 1 year.

Additional data This program is jointly sponsored by Meijer supercenters, Coca-Cola, and the Hispanic Scholarship Fund (HSF).

Number awarded 4 each year: 2 at $10,000 and 2 at $2,000.

Deadline December of each year.

[99]
COCHRAN/GREENE SCHOLARSHIP

National Naval Officers Association-Washington, D.C.
  Chapter
Attn: Scholarship Program
2701 Park Center Drive, A1108
Alexandria, VA 22302
(703) 566-3840   Fax: (703) 566-3813
E-mail: Stephen.Williams@Navy.mil
Web: dcnnoa.memberlodge.com

Summary To provide financial assistance to Hispanic American and other minority female high school seniors from the Washington, D.C. area who are interested in attending college in any state.

Eligibility This program is open to female minority seniors graduating from high schools in the Washington, D.C. metropolitan area who plan to enroll full time at an accredited 2- or 4-year college or university in any state. Applicants must have a GPA of 2.5 or higher and be U.S. citizens or permanent residents. Selection is based on academic achievement, community involvement, and financial need.

Financial Data The stipend is $1,500.

Duration 1 year; nonrenewable.

Additional data Recipients are not required to join or affiliate with the military in any way.

Number awarded 1 each year.

Deadline March of each year.

[100]
COLGATE "BRIGHT SMILES, BRIGHT FUTURES" MINORITY SCHOLARSHIPS

American Dental Hygienists' Association
Attn: Institute for Oral Health
444 North Michigan Avenue, Suite 3400
Chicago, IL 60611-3980
(312) 440-8900, ext. 204   Fax: (312) 440-6726
E-mail: institute@adha.net
Web: www.adha.org/ioh/programs/scholarships.htm

Summary To provide financial assistance to 1) Hispanic American and other minority students (females or males) and 2) males of any race who are members of the Student American Dental Hygienists' Association (SADHA) or the American Dental Hygienists' Association (ADHA) and enrolled in certificate programs in dental hygiene.

Eligibility This program is open to members of groups currently underrepresented in the dental hygiene profession (Native Americans, African Americans, Hispanics, Asians, and males) who are active members of the SADHA or the ADHA. Applicants must have a GPA of 3.0 or higher, be able to document financial need of at least $1,500, and have completed at least 1 year of full-time enrollment in an accredited dental hygiene certificate program in the United States. Along with their application, they must submit a statement that covers their long-term career goals, their intended contribution to the dental hygiene profession, their professional interests, and how their extracurricular activities and their degree enhance the attainment of their goals.

Financial Data The stipend ranges from $1,000 to $2,000.

Duration 1 year; nonrenewable.

Additional data These scholarships are sponsored by the Colgate-Palmolive Company.

Number awarded 2 each year.

Deadline January of each year.

[101]
COLLABORATIVE RESEARCH EXPERIENCE FOR UNDERGRADUATES IN COMPUTER SCIENCE AND ENGINEERING

Computing Research Association
1828 L Street, N.W., Suite 800
Washington, DC 20036-5104
(202) 234-2111   Fax: (202) 667-1066
E-mail: creu@cra.org
Web: cra-w.org/undergraduate

Summary To provide funding to Hispanic American, other underrepresented minority, and female undergraduate students who are interested in conducting a research project in computer science or engineering.

Eligibility This program is open to teams of 2 or 4 undergraduates who have completed 2 years of study, including at least 4 courses in computer science or computer engineering, at a college or university in the United States. Applicants must be interested in conducting a research project directly related to computer science or computer engineering. They must apply jointly with 1 or 2 sponsoring faculty members. Teams consisting of all women or all underrepresented minorities are especially encouraged to apply; teams may also include students from non-underrepresented groups, but financial support is available only to underrepresented students. U.S. citizenship or permanent resident status is required.

Financial Data The program provides a stipend of $3,000 for the academic year. Students who wish to participate in an optional summer extension receive an additional stipend of $4,000. Additional funding up to $1,500 per team may be available for purchase of supporting materials and/or travel to conferences to present the work.

Duration 1 academic year plus an optional summer extension.

Additional data This program is sponsored by the Computing Research Association's Committee on the Status of Women in Computing Research (CRA-W) and the Coalition to Diversify Computing (CDC) in cooperation with the National Science Foundation.

Number awarded Varies each year; recently, 21 teams of students received support from this program.

Deadline May of each year.

[102]
COLLEGE STUDENT PRE-COMMISSIONING INITIATIVE

U.S. Coast Guard
Attn: Recruiting Command
2300 Wilson Boulevard, Suite 500
Arlington, VA 22201
(703) 235-1775   Toll Free: (877) NOW-USCG
Fax: (703) 235-1881
E-mail: Margaret.A.Jackson@uscg.mil
Web: www.gocoastguard.com

Summary To provide financial assistance to college students at Hispanic Serving Institutions or other minority institutions who are willing to serve in the Coast Guard following graduation.

Eligibility This program is open to students entering their junior or senior year at a college or university designated as an Historically Black College or University (HBCU), Hispanic Serving Institution (HSI), Tribal College or University (TCU), or the University of Hawaii (at Manoa, Hilo, or West Oahu), Argosy University (Hawaii), or the Institute of American Indian and Alaska Native Culture (Santa Fe, New Mexico). Applicants must be U.S. citizens; have a GPA of 2.5 or higher; have scores of 1100 or higher on the critical reading and mathematics SAT, 23 or higher on the ACT, 4AQR/4PFAR on the ASTB, or 109 or higher on the SVAB GT; be between 19 and 27 years of age; and meet all physical requirements for a Coast Guard commission. They must agree to attend the Coast Guard Officer Candidate School following graduation and serve on active duty as an officer for at least 3 years.

Financial Data Those selected to participate receive full payment of tuition, books, and fees; monthly housing and food allowances; medical and life insurance; special training in leadership, management, law enforcement, navigation, and marine science; 30 days of paid vacation per year; and a monthly salary of up to $2,200.

Duration Up to 2 years.

Number awarded Varies each year.

Deadline January of each year.

[103]
COLORADO EDUCATIONAL SERVICES AND DEVELOPMENT ASSOCIATION DIVERSITY SCHOLARSHIPS

Colorado Educational Services and Development Association
P.O. Box 40214
Denver, CO 80204
(303) 256-9785   E-mail: kim.medina@jwu.edu
Web: www.cesda.org/664.html

Summary To provide financial assistance to high school seniors in Colorado who are planning to attend college in the state and are either first-generation college students or members of underrepresented ethnic or racial minorities.

Eligibility This program is open to seniors graduating from high schools in Colorado who are 1) the first member of their family to attend college; 2) a member of an underrepresented ethnic or racial minority (African American, Asian/Pacific Islander, American Indian, Hispanic/Chicano/Latino); and/or 3) able to demonstrate financial need. Applicants must have a GPA of 2.8 or higher and be planning to enroll at a 2- or 4-year college or university in Colorado. U.S. citizenship or permanent resident status is required. Selection is based on leadership and community service (particularly within minority communities), past academic performance, personal and professional accomplishments, personal attributes, special abilities, academic goals, and financial need.

Financial Data The stipend is $1,000.

Duration 1 year; nonrenewable.

Number awarded Varies each year.

Deadline March of each year.

[104]
COMMUNITY COUNCIL OF IDAHO HISPANIC STUDENT SCHOLARSHIP PROGRAM

Community Council of Idaho, Inc.
Attn: Hispanic Student Scholarship Program
317 Happy Day Boulevard, Suite 250
Caldwell, ID 83607
(208) 454-1652   Fax: (208) 459-0448
E-mail: info@ccimail.org
Web: www.communitycouncilofidaho.org

Summary To provide financial assistance to Hispanic high school seniors in Idaho who plan to attend college in the state.

Eligibility This program is open to residents of Idaho who are of Latino origin. Applicants must be planning to enter college in Idaho as freshmen in the following fall. They must have a GPA of 2.5 or higher. Selection is based on a 1-page statement on educational goals, high school transcripts, 3 letters of recommendation, and financial need.

Financial Data The stipend is $1,000.

Duration 1 year; nonrenewable.

Additional data This organization was formerly known as the Idaho Migrant Council, Inc. and designated its scholarship program the Idaho Migrant Council Latino Scholarship Fund. Recipients are expected to attend the sponsor's annual meeting in September to accept their award.

Number awarded Varies each year; recently, 11 of these scholarships were awarded.

Deadline April of each year.

[105]
COMMUNITY LEADERSHIP AWARD

TELACU Education Foundation
Attn: College Success Program
5400 East Olympic Boulevard, Suite 300
Los Angeles, CA 90022
(323) 721-1655   Fax: (323) 721-3560
E-mail: collegesuccess@telacu.com
Web: www.telacu.com

Summary To provide financial assistance to Latino students from eligible communities in California, Texas, Illinois, and New York who can demonstrate outstanding leadership abilities and are interested in attending college in any state.

Eligibility This program is open to Latino residents of selected communities in southern California, selected cities in Texas, the Greater Chicagoland area of Illinois, or the state of New York. Applicants must 1) be a first-generation college student; 2) be from a low-income family; 3) have a GPA of 2.5 or higher; and 4) be able to demonstrate outstanding leadership abilities. They must be enrolled or planning to enroll full time at a college or university in any state. Selection is based on leadership potential, professional and extracurricular achievement, commitment to the development and economic empowerment of communities, and financial need. Priority is given to students attending institutions that provide matching funds (for a list, contact the sponsor).

Financial Data The stipend is $2,500.

Duration 1 year.

Additional data The eligible areas in California include underserved communities in Los Angeles, Orange, and San Bernardino counties such as unincorporated areas of east

Los Angeles and the cities of Baldwin Park, Bell Gardens, Commerce, Huntington Park, Los Angeles, Montebello, Ontario, Pico Rivera, Pomona, San Bernardino, Santa Ana, and South Gate. The cities in Texas are Austin, Edinburg, Laredo, Rio Grande City, and San Antonio.

Number awarded 1 each year.

Deadline March of each year.

[106]
CONGRESSIONAL HISPANIC CAUCUS INSTITUTE SCHOLARSHIP AWARDS

Congressional Hispanic Caucus Institute, Inc.
911 Second Street, N.E.
Washington, DC 20002
(202) 543-1771   Toll Free: (800) EXCEL-DC
Fax: (202) 546-2143   E-mail: chci@chci.org
Web: www.chci.org/scholarships

Summary To provide financial assistance for college or graduate school to students of Hispanic descent.

Eligibility This program is open to U.S. citizens and permanent residents who are Hispanic as defined by the U.S. Census Bureau (individuals of Mexican, Puerto Rican, Cuban, Central and South American, and other Spanish and Latin American descent). Applicants must be attending or planning to attend an accredited community college, 4-year university, or professional or graduate program as a full-time student. Along with their application, they must submit a 1-page essay on the field of study they plan to pursue and how the Latino community will benefit. Selection is based on demonstrated financial need, consistent active participation in public and/or community service activities, and good writing skills. There are no GPA or academic major requirements.

Financial Data The stipend is $5,000 for graduate students, $2,500 for students at 4-year institutions, or $1,000 for students at 2-year community colleges. Funds are intended to cover tuition, room and board, textbooks, and other educational expenses associated with college enrollment. The stipend may be divided over the number of years required to complete a degree (e.g., a freshman entering a 4-year institution may receive $625 per year for 4 years).

Duration 1 year.

Number awarded Varies each year; recently, 130 of these scholarships were awarded: 10 to community college students, 114 to undergraduates, and 6 to graduate students.

Deadline April of each year.

[107]
CONNECTICUT ASSOCIATION OF LATINOS IN HIGHER EDUCATION SCHOLARSHIPS

Connecticut Association of Latinos in Higher Education, Inc.
950 Main Street, Suite 1104
Hartford, CT 06103-1207
(860) 906-5234   E-mail: ca-CALAHE@ccc.commnet.edu
Web: www.calahe.org/scholarships

Summary To provide financial assistance to Latino residents of Connecticut who are interested in attending college in any state.

Eligibility This program is open to graduating high school seniors, GED recipients, and current college students who have been residents of Connecticut during the preceding 12 months. Applicants must come from a Latino background and have a GPA of 3.0 or higher. They must be attending or planning to attend an accredited institution of higher education in any state. U.S. citizenship or permanent resident status is required. Selection is based on academic achievement, financial need, community service, and an essay on "How do you feel education is going to impact your ability to continue assisting others to pursue an education?"

Financial Data The stipend is $1,000.

Duration 1 year.

Additional data This program includes the John Soto Scholarship, the Marta Vallin Memorial Scholarship (limited to students attending Gateway Community College), and the Thomas M. Blake Memorial Scholarship (limited to students from the Hartford Public Schools).

Number awarded Varies each year; recently, 21 of these scholarships were awarded.

Deadline April of each year.

[108]
CONNECTICUT CHAPTER AABE SCHOLARSHIPS

American Association of Blacks in Energy-Connecticut Chapter
Attn: Scholarship Committee
P.O. Box 1898
Hartford, CT 06144
(203) 499-2418   E-mail: presctchapter@gmail.com
Web: www.aabe.org/index.php?component=pages&id=827

Summary To provide financial assistance to Hispanic Americans and members of other underrepresented minority groups who are high school seniors in Connecticut and western Massachusetts and planning to major in an energy-related field at a college in any state.

Eligibility This program is open to seniors graduating from high schools in Connecticut or western Massachusetts and planning to work on a bachelor's degree at a college or university in any state. Applicants must be African Americans, Hispanics, or Native Americans who have a GPA of 3.0 or higher and who can demonstrate financial need. Their intended major must be a field of business, engineering, mathematics, or science (e.g., chemistry, geology, meteorology, physics) related to energy. Along with their application, they must submit a 350-word statement on why they should receive this scholarship, their professional career objectives, and any other relevant information.

Financial Data The stipend is $2,500. Funds are disbursed directly to the students.

Duration 1 year; nonrenewable.

Additional data Winners are eligible to compete for regional and national scholarships. This program began in 2003.

Number awarded 4 or 5 each year. Since this program began, it has awarded 45 scholarships with a total value of $109,000.

Deadline April of each year.

[109]
CONNECTICUT MINORITY TEACHER INCENTIVE PROGRAM

Connecticut Office of Financial and Academic Affairs for Higher Education
Attn: Student Financial Aid
61 Woodland Street
Hartford, CT 06105-2326
(860) 947-1853   Toll Free: (800) 842-0229 (within CT)
Fax: (860) 947-1314   E-mail: mtip@ctdhe.org
Web: www.ctohe.org/SFA/default.htm

Summary To provide financial assistance to Hispanic Americans and other minority upper-division college students in Connecticut who are interested in teaching at public schools in the state.

Eligibility This program is open to juniors and seniors enrolled full time in Connecticut college and university teacher preparation programs. Applicants must be members of a minority group, defined as African American, Hispanic/Latino, Asian American, or Native American. They must be nominated by the education dean at their institution.

Financial Data The maximum stipend is $5,000 per year. In addition, if recipients complete a credential and begin teaching at a public school in Connecticut within 16 months of graduation, they may receive up to $2,500 per year, for up to 4 years, to help pay off college loans.

Duration Up to 2 years.

Number awarded Varies each year.

Deadline October of each year.

[110]
CONNTESOL SCHOLARSHIPS

Connecticut Teachers of English to Speakers of Other Languages
P.O. Box 304
Norwich, CT 06360-0304
E-mail: ConnTESOL@gmail.com
Web: www.conntesol.net

Summary To provide financial assistance to Connecticut residents whose native language is not English and who are attending or planning to attend college in any state.

Eligibility This program is open to residents of Connecticut whose first language is not English. Awards are presented in 4 categories: 1) high school seniors entering a 2-year college; 2) high school seniors entering a 4-year college or university; 3) high school seniors who are presently or were previously enrolled in English Language Learning (ELL) or bilingual education classes and entering a 2- or 4-year college or university (designated the CAPELL Scholarship for its sponsor, the Connecticut Administrators of Programs for English Language Learners); and 4) adult education students entering a college or university. Applicants must submit an essay of 250 to 500 words on how the education they are receiving in the United States is influencing their life.

Financial Data The stipend is $1,000.

Duration 1 year.

Number awarded At least 4 each year (1 in each category).

Deadline April of each year.

[111]
CONVENCION BAUTISTA HISPANA DE TEXAS SCHOLARSHIP

Baptist General Convention of Texas
Attn: Hispanic Education Initiative
333 North Washington
Dallas, TX 75246-1798
(214) 828-5279   Fax: (214) 828-5284
E-mail: lou.merryman@texasbaptists.org
Web: texasbaptists.org

Summary To provide financial assistance to Hispanic members of Baptist churches in Texas who are interested in attending college in any state.

Eligibility This program is open to members of congregations affiliated with the Baptist General Convention of Texas who are currently participating in an Hispanic-related ministry. Applicants must be enrolled or planning to enroll at a college or university in any state. They may be of any age and be participating in their youth, singles, and/or adults group at church. Along with their application, they must submit essays of 5 to 7 sentences on any 2 of the following: 1) why they are pursuing higher education; 2) in what way their education will help them serve Christ in their church; or 3) what their challenges are in working toward higher education.

Financial Data The stipend is $1,000 per year.

Duration 1 year; may be renewed up to 2 additional years.

Number awarded 1 or more each year.

Deadline May of each year.

[112]
CORNELL UNIVERSITY SUMMER PROGRAM IN ASTRONOMY AND ASTROPHYSICS

Cornell University
Department of Astronomy
Attn: REU Astronomy Coordinator
510 Space Sciences Building
Ithaca, NY 14853-6801
(607) 255-0288   Fax: (607) 255-1767
E-mail: pf46@cornell.edu
Web: www.astro.cornell.edu/specialprograms/reu/reu.html

Summary To provide an opportunity for undergraduate students (particularly Hispanic Americans, other underrepresented minorities, women, and individuals with disabilities) to work on astronomy research projects at Cornell University during the summer.

Eligibility This program is open to undergraduate students who have completed at least 1 year of academic training. Applicants must be interested in working with Cornell University faculty and research staff on projects covering a wide range of disciplines in radio, infrared, and radar astronomy and related theoretical topics. They must be U.S. citizens, nationals, or permanent residents. Applications are especially encouraged from underrepresented minorities, persons with disabilities, and women.

Financial Data The stipend is $6,200. Other support includes $1,000 for relocation and housing and up to $1,000 round-trip transportation to Ithaca, New York.

Duration 8 weeks during the summer.

Additional data This program is funded by the National Science Foundation as part of its Research Experiences for Undergraduates (REU) Program.

Number awarded 8 each year.

Deadline February of each year.

[113]
CORPORATE SCHOLARSHIP TEXAS INSTRUMENTS

Society of Hispanic Professional Engineers Foundation, Inc.
Attn: Advancing Hispanic Excellence in Technology, Engineering, Math and Science
13181 Crossroads Parkway North, Suite 450
P.O. Box 93577
City of Industry, CA 91715
(323) 725-3970, ext. 118   Fax: (323) 622-1046
E-mail: shpefoundation@shpe.org
Web: www.shpefoundation.org

Summary To provide financial assistance to undergraduate and graduate student members of the Society of Hispanic Professional Engineers (SHPE) who are working on a degree in specified fields of science, technology, engineering, or mathematics (STEM), especially at designated universities.

Eligibility This program is open to full-time undergraduate and graduate student members of SHPE. Preference is given to members working on a degree in computer or electrical engineering; alternate eligible fields include chemical engineering, computer science, electrical engineering technology, electronic technology, management information systems, materials science, mechanical engineering, microelectronics, or physics. Applicants must have a GPA of 3.0 or higher. They must be eligible to work in the United States. Along with their application, they must submit a 500-word personal statement covering their community involvement, leadership, academic achievements, research internship and co-op experiences, and short-term and long-term goals and aspirations. Selection is based on motivation and aptitude for a career in STEM. Preferred universities include Arizona State University, Georgia Tech University, Stanford University, Texas A&M University, Texas Tech University, University of Florida, University of Illinois, University of Maryland, University of Michigan, University of Texas at Austin, and University of Texas at Dallas. First priority is given to bachelor's degree students, although master's and doctoral candidates are also eligible.

Financial Data The stipend is $2,700.

Duration 1 year.

Additional data Advancing Hispanic Excellence in Technology, Engineering, Math and Science (AHETEMS) was established in 2004 by SHPE as an independent nonprofit foundation. This program is sponsored by Texas Instruments.

Number awarded 1 or more each year.

Deadline April of each year.

[114]
CORRINE WILLIAMS SCHOLARSHIP

California Dietetic Association
Attn: CDA Foundation
7740 Manchester Avenue, Suite 102
Playa del Rey, CA 90293-8499
(310) 822-0177   Fax: (310) 823-0264
E-mail: patsmith@dietitian.org
Web: www.dietitian.org/d_cdaf/cdaf_outreach.html

Summary To provide financial assistance to residents of California (particularly Hispanic Americans, other minorities, men, and individuals with disabilities) who are members of the Academy of Nutrition and Dietetics (AND) and interested in participating in specified types of programs in any state.

Eligibility This program is open to California residents who are AND members and 1) entering the first or second year of an approved Dietetic Technician Program in any state; 2) entering at least the second year of an accredited Coordinated Program (CP) or Didactic Program in Dietetics (DPD) in any state; or 3) accepted to an accredited Supervised Practice Program in any state to begin within 6 months. Along with their application, they must submit a letter of application that includes a discussion of their career goals. Selection is based on that letter (15%), academic ability (25%), work or volunteer experience (15%), letters of recommendation (15%), extracurricular activities (5%), and financial need (25%). Applications are especially encouraged from ethnic minorities, men, and people with physical disabilities.

Financial Data The stipend is normally $1,000.

Duration 1 year.

Additional data This program began in 2010. The California Dietetic Association is the California affiliate of the AND.

Number awarded 1 each year.

Deadline April of each year.

[115]
CRACKER BARREL-MINORITY TEACHER EDUCATION SCHOLARSHIPS

Florida Fund for Minority Teachers, Inc.
Attn: Executive Director
G415 Norman Hall
P.O. Box 117045
Gainesville, FL 32611-7045
(352) 392-9196, ext. 21   Fax: (352) 846-3011
E-mail: info@ffmt.org
Web: www.ffmt.org

Summary To provide funding to Hispanic American and other minority Florida residents who are preparing for a career as a teacher.

Eligibility This program is open to Florida residents who are African American/Black, Hispanic/Latino, Asian American/Pacific Islander, or American Indian/Alaskan Native. Applicants must be entering their junior year in a teacher education program at a participating college or university in Florida. Special consideration is given to community college graduates. Selection is based on writing ability, communication skills, overall academic performance, and evidence of commitment to the youth of America (preferably demonstrated through volunteer activities).

Financial Data The stipend is $2,000 per year. Recipients are required to teach 1 year in a Florida public school for each year they receive the scholarship. If they fail to teach in a public school, they are required to repay the total amount of support received at an annual interest rate of 8%.

Duration Up to 2 consecutive years, provided the recipient remains enrolled full time with a GPA of 2.5 or higher.

Additional data For a list of the 16 participating public institutions and the 18 participating private institutions, contact the Florida Fund for Minority Teachers (FFMT). Recipients are also required to attend the annual FFMT recruitment and retention conference.

Number awarded Varies each year.

Deadline July of each year for fall semester; November of each year for spring semester.

[116]
CRCNA RACE RELATIONS MULTIRACIAL STUDENT SCHOLARSHIP

Christian Reformed Church
Attn: Office of Race Relations
2850 Kalamazoo Avenue, S.E.
Grand Rapids, MI 49560-0200
(616) 224-5883　　　　Toll Free: (877) 279-9994
Fax: (616) 224-0834　　　E-mail: elugo@crcna.org
Web: www.crcna.org/race/scholarships

Summary To provide financial assistance to Hispanic American and other minority undergraduate and graduate students who are interested in attending colleges related to the Christian Reformed Church in North America (CRCNA).

Eligibility This program is open to students of color in the United States and Canada. Normally, applicants are expected to be members of CRCNA congregations who plan to pursue their educational goals at Calvin Theological Seminary or any of the colleges affiliated with the CRCNA. They must be interested in training for the ministry of racial reconciliation in church and/or in society. Students who have no prior history with the CRCNA must attend a CRCNA-related college or seminary for a full academic year before they are eligible to apply for this program. Students entering their sophomore year must have earned a GPA of 2.0 or higher as freshmen; students entering their junior year must have earned a GPA of 2.3 or higher as sophomores; students entering their senior year must have earned a GPA of 2.6 or higher as juniors.

Financial Data First-year students receive $500 per semester. Other levels of students may receive up to $2,000 per academic year.

Duration 1 year.

Additional data This program was first established in 1971 and revised in 1991. Recipients are expected to train to engage actively in the ministry of racial reconciliation in church and in society. They must be able to work in the United States or Canada upon graduating and must consider working for 1 of the agencies of the CRCNA.

Number awarded Varies each year; recently, 31 students received a total of $21,000 in support.

Deadline March of each year.

[117]
CTA/MARTIN LUTHER KING, JR. MEMORIAL SCHOLARSHIP FUND

California Teachers Association
Attn: CTA Foundation for Teaching and Learning
1705 Murchison Drive
P.O. Box 921
Burlingame, CA 94011-0921
(650) 697-1400　　　　E-mail: scholarships@cta.org
Web: www.cta.org

Summary To provide financial assistance for college or graduate school to Hispanic Americans and other racial and ethnic minorities who are members of the California Teachers Association (CTA), children of members, or members of the Student CTA.

Eligibility This program is open to members of racial or ethnic minority groups (African Americans, American Indians/ Alaska Natives, Asians/Pacific Islanders, and Hispanics) who are 1) active CTA members; 2) dependent children of active, retired, or deceased CTA members; or 3) members of Student CTA. Applicants must be interested in preparing for a teaching career in public education or already engaged in such a career.

Financial Data Stipends vary each year; recently, they ranged from $1,000 to $4,000.

Duration 1 year.

Number awarded Varies each year; recently, 25 of these scholarships were awarded: 5 to CTA members, 10 to children of CTA members, and 10 to Student CTA members.

Deadline February of each year.

[118]
CUMMINS/HENAAC SCHOLARS PROGRAM

Great Minds in STEM
Attn: HENAAC Scholars Program
602 Monterey Pass Road
Monterey Park, CA 91754
(323) 262-0997　　　　Fax: (323) 262-0946
E-mail: gcruz@greatmindsinstem.org
Web: www.greatmindsinstem.org

Summary To provide financial assistance to Hispanic undergraduate and graduate students working on a degree in a field of science, technology, engineering, or mathematics (STEM).

Eligibility This program is open to Hispanic students who are working on an undergraduate or graduate degree in a field of STEM. Applicants must be of Hispanic origin and/or must significantly participate in and promote organizations and activities in the Hispanic community. They must have a GPA of 3.0 or higher. Along with their application, they must submit a 700-word essay on a topic that changes annually. Selection is based on leadership, academic achievements, and campus and community activities; financial need is not considered. U.S. citizenship or permanent resident status is required.

Financial Data Stipends range from $500 to $10,000.

Duration 1 year; recipients may reapply.

Additional data The Hispanic Engineer National Achievement Awards Conference (HENAAC) was established in 1989 and initiated a scholarship program in 2000. In 2010, the sponsoring organization officially adopted its current name, but it continues to hold the annual HENAAC conference, at which the scholarships are presented. This program is sponsored by Cummins, Inc. Recipients must attend the conference to accept their scholarship.

Number awarded Varies each year; recently, 8 of these scholarships were awarded.

Deadline April of each year.

[119]
CUMMINS SCHOLARSHIPS

Society of Women Engineers
Attn: Scholarship Selection Committee
203 North LaSalle Street, Suite 1675
Chicago, IL 60601-1269
(312) 596-5223   Toll Free: (877) SWE-INFO
Fax: (312) 644-8557   E-mail: scholarships@swe.org
Web: societyofwomenengineers.swe.org

Summary To provide financial assistance to minority and other women working on an undergraduate or graduate degree in computer science or designated engineering specialties.

Eligibility This program is open to women who are sophomores, juniors, seniors, or graduate students at 4-year ABET-accredited colleges and universities. Applicants must be working full time on a degree in computer science or automotive, chemical, computer, electrical, industrial, manufacturing, materials, or mechanical engineering and have a GPA of 3.5 or higher. Preference is given to members of groups underrepresented in engineering or computer science. Selection is based on merit. U.S. citizenship or permanent resident status is required.

Financial Data The stipend is $1,000.

Duration 1 year.

Additional data This program is sponsored by Cummins, Inc.

Number awarded 2 each year.

Deadline February of each year.

[120]
CWGGF SCHOLARSHIPS

California Association of Winegrape Growers
Attn: California Wine Grape Growers Foundation
1325 J Street, Suite 1560
Sacramento, CA 95814
(916) 379-8995   Toll Free: (800) 241-1800
Fax: (916) 379-8999   E-mail: info@cawg.org
Web: cwggf.org/scholarship-info_293.html

Summary To provide financial assistance for college to high school seniors in California whose parent(s) work in the grape wine vineyards.

Eligibility This program is open to high school seniors in California who plan to attend a branch of the University of California, a branch of the California State University system, or a community college in the state. Applicants must have a parent or legal guardian who was employed as a vineyard worker by a winegrape grower during either or both of the 2 preceding seasons. Along with their application, they must submit a high school transcript, a copy of their SAT or ACT scores (if they are planning to attend a 4-year university), a letter of recommendation from a school official, and a 2-page essay on themselves and their career goals. Applications are available in both English and Spanish. Selection is based on financial need, demonstrated academic ability, community involvement and leadership, work history, and determination to succeed.

Financial Data The stipend is $2,000 per year at a 4-year university or $1,000 per year at a community college.

Duration 4 years at branches of the University of California or California State University system; 2 years at community colleges.

Additional data Recipients must enroll in 12 college units each semester while receiving scholarship money.

Number awarded 6 each year: 2 at 4-year universities and 4 at community colleges.

Deadline March of each year.

[121]
DAISY PABON SCHOLARSHIP

Puerto Rican Civic Club, Inc.
Attn: Scholarship Committee
P.O. Box 765
San Jose, CA 95106
(408) 475-7722   E-mail: puertorros@hotmail.com
Web: www.puertoricancivicclub.org

Summary To provide financial assistance to residents of California who are of Puerto Rican ancestry and interested in working on an undergraduate or graduate degree in any field at a school in any state.

Eligibility This program is open to students of Puerto Rican descent who are residents of California enrolled or planning to enroll at a college or university in any state. Applicants must be high school seniors, high school graduates, GED recipients, undergraduates, or graduate students. They must have a GPA of 2.5 or higher. Selection is based on academic record, extracurricular activities, work experience, community service, an essay, and financial need.

Financial Data Stipends range from $500 to $1,000.

Duration 1 year.

Number awarded Varies each year; recently, 4 of these scholarships were awarded.

Deadline May of each year.

[122]
DAMON P. MOORE SCHOLARSHIP

Indiana State Teachers Association
Attn: Scholarships
150 West Market Street, Suite 900
Indianapolis, IN 46204-2875
(317) 263-3369   Toll Free: (800) 382-4037
Fax: (800) 777-6128   E-mail: mshoup@ista-in.org
Web: www.ista-in.org/dynamic.aspx?id=1212

Summary To provide financial assistance to Hispanic and other minority high school seniors in Indiana who are interested in studying education in college.

Eligibility This program is open to ethnic minority public high school seniors in Indiana who are interested in studying education in college. Selection is based on academic achievement, leadership ability as expressed through co-curricular activities and community involvement, recommendations, and a 300-word essay on their educational goals and how they plan to use this scholarship.

Financial Data The stipend is $1,000.

Duration 1 year; may be renewed for 2 additional years if the recipient maintains at least a "C+" average.

Additional data This program began in 1987.

Number awarded 1 each year.

Deadline February of each year.

[123]
DAVID EVANS AND ASSOCIATES SCHOLARSHIPS

David Evans and Associates, Inc.
2100 S.W. River Parkway
Portland, OR 97201
(503) 223-2701   Toll Free: (800) 721-1916
Fax: (503) 223-6663
Web: www.deainc.com/scholarships.aspx

Summary To provide financial assistance to Hispanic Americans, other minorities, and women who are working on an undergraduate degree in civil engineering or geomatics at colleges in designated states.

Eligibility This program is open to women and minority undergraduates majoring in civil engineering (including transportation, structural, land development, or environmental) or geomatics. Applicants must be enrolled at a college or university in Arizona, California, Colorado, Idaho, New York, Oregon, or Washington. They must have a GPA of 3.0 or higher.

Financial Data The stipend is $3,000.

Duration 1 year; nonrenewable.

Number awarded 2 each year.

Deadline April of each year.

[124]
DEFENSE INTELLIGENCE AGENCY UNDERGRADUATE TRAINING ASSISTANCE PROGRAM

Defense Intelligence Agency
Attn: Human Resources, HCH-4
200 MacDill Boulevard, Building 6000
Bolling AFB, DC 20340-5100
(202) 231-2736   Fax: (202) 231-4889
TDD: (202) 231-5002   E-mail: staffing@dia.mil
Web: www.dia.mil/careers/students

Summary To provide financial aid and work experience to high school seniors and lower-division students (particularly Hispanic Americans, other minorities, women, and students with disabilities) who are interested in majoring in specified fields and working for the U.S. Defense Intelligence Agency (DIA).

Eligibility This program is open to graduating high school seniors and college freshmen and sophomores interested in working full time on a baccalaureate degree in 1 of the following fields in college: biology, chemistry, computer science, engineering, foreign area studies, intelligence analysis, international relations, microbiology, pharmacology, physics, political science, or toxicology. High school seniors must have a GPA of 2.75 or higher and either 1) an SAT combined critical reading and mathematics score of 1000 or higher plus 500 or higher on the writing portion or 2) an ACT score of 21 or higher. College freshmen and sophomores must have a GPA of 3.0 or higher. All applicants must be able to demonstrate financial need (household income ceiling of $70,000 for a family of 4 or $80,000 for a family of 5 or more) and leadership abilities through extracurricular activities, civic involvement, volunteer work, or part-time employment. Students and all members of their immediate family must be U.S. citizens. Minorities, women, and persons with disabilities are strongly encouraged to apply.

Financial Data Students accepted into this program receive tuition (up to $18,000 per year) at an accredited college or university selected by the student and endorsed by the sponsor; reimbursement for books and needed supplies; an annual salary to cover college room and board expenses and for summer employment; and a position at the sponsoring agency after graduation. Recipients must work for DIA after college graduation for at least 1 and a half times the length of study. For participants who leave DIA earlier than scheduled, the agency arranges for payments to reimburse DIA for the total cost of education (including the employee's pay and allowances).

Duration 4 years, provided the recipient maintains a GPA of 2.75 during the freshman year and 3.0 or higher in subsequent semesters.

Additional data Recipients are provided a challenging summer internship and guaranteed a job at the agency in their field of study upon graduation.

Number awarded Only a few are awarded each year.

Deadline October of each year.

[125]
DENNY'S HUNGRY FOR EDUCATION SCHOLARSHIPS

Hispanic Association of Colleges and Universities
Attn: National Scholarship Program
8415 Datapoint Drive, Suite 400
San Antonio, TX 78229
(210) 692-3805   Fax: (210) 692-0823
TDD: (800) 855-2880   E-mail: scholarship@hacu.net
Web: www.hacu.net/hacu/Scholarships.asp

Summary To provide financial assistance to undergraduate and graduate students majoring in business or hospitality at member institutions of the Hispanic Association of Colleges and Universities (HACU) in designated states.

Eligibility This program is open to full- and part-time undergraduate and graduate students at 2- and 4-year HACU member institutions in Arizona, California, Colorado, Florida, Georgia, Illinois, Nevada, New Mexico, New York, South Carolina, Texas, or Washington, D.C. Applicants must be working on a degree in business or hospitality and have a GPA of 3.0 or higher. Along with their application, they must submit a 500-word essay on how Denny's can help in the fight against childhood hunger in the United States.

Financial Data The stipend is $1,000.

Duration 1 year.

Additional data This program is sponsored by Denny's and administered by HACU.

Number awarded 1 or more each year.

Deadline June of each year.

[126]
DEPARTMENT OF HOMELAND SECURITY SUMMER FACULTY AND STUDENT RESEARCH TEAM PROGRAM

Oak Ridge Institute for Science and Education
Attn: Science and Engineering Education
P.O. Box 117
Oak Ridge, TN 37831-0117
(865) 574-1447   Fax: (865) 241-5219
E-mail: Patti.Obenour@orau.gov
Web: see.orau.org

Summary To provide an opportunity for teams of students and faculty from minority-serving educational institutions to conduct research during the summer in areas of interest to the Department of Homeland Security (DHS).

Eligibility This program is open to teams of up to 2 students (undergraduate and/or graduate) and 1 faculty from Historically Black Colleges and Universities (HBCUs), Hispanic Serving Institutions (HSIs), Tribal Colleges and Universities (TCUs), Alaska Native Serving Institutions (ANSIs), and Native Hawaiian Serving Institutions (NHSIs). Applicants must be interested in conducting research at designated DHS Centers of Excellence in science, technology, engineering, or mathematics related to homeland security (HS-STEM), including explosives detection, mitigation, and response; social and behavioral sciences; risk, economics, and decision sciences; human factors; chemical threats and countermeasures; biological threats and countermeasures; community, commerce, and infrastructure resilience; food and agricultural security; transportation security; border security; immigration studies; maritime and port security; infrastructure protection; natural disasters and related geophysical studies; emergency preparedness and response; communications and interoperability; or advanced data analysis and visualization. Faculty must have a full-time appointment at an eligible institution and have received a Ph.D. in an HS-STEM discipline no more than 7 years previously; at least 2 years of full-time research and/or teaching experience is preferred. Students must have a GPA of 3.0 or higher and be enrolled full time. Undergraduates must be entering their junior or senior year. U.S. citizenship is required. Selection is based on relevance and intrinsic merit of the research (40%), faculty applicant qualifications (30%), academic benefit to the faculty applicant and his/her institution (10%), and student applicant qualifications (20%).

Financial Data Stipends are $1,200 per week for faculty, $600 per week for graduate students, and $500 per week for undergraduates. Faculty members who live more than 50 miles from their assigned site may receive a housing allowance of $1,500 and travel expenses up to an additional $500. Limited travel expenses for 1 round trip are reimbursed for undergraduate and graduate students living more than 50 miles from their assigned site.

Duration 12 weeks during the summer.

Additional data This program is funded by DHS and administered by Oak Ridge Institute for Science and Education (ORISE). Recently, the available DHS Centers of Excellence were the Center for Advancing Microbial Risk Assessment (led by Michigan State University and Drexel University); the National Center for Risk and Economic Analysis of Terrorism Events (led by University of Southern California); the National Center for Food Protection and Defense (led by University of Minnesota); the Center of Excellence for Zoo-

notic and Animal Disease Defense (led by Texas A&M University and Kansas State University); the National Consortium for the Study of Terrorism and Responses to Terrorism (led by University of Maryland); the Center of Excellence for Awareness and Localization of Explosives-Related Threats (led by Northeastern University and University of Rhode Island); the National Center for Border Security and Immigration (led by the University of Arizona and the University of Texas at El Paso); the Center for Maritime, Island and Remote and Extreme Environment Security (led by the University of Hawaii and Stevens Institute of Technology); the Coastal Hazards Center of Excellence (led by the University of North Carolina at Chapel Hill and Jackson State University); the National Transportation Security Center of Excellence (consisting of 7 institutions); and the Center of Excellence in Command, Control, and Interoperability (led by Purdue University and Rutgers University).

Number awarded Approximately 12 teams are selected each year.

Deadline January of each year.

[127]
DEPARTMENT OF TRANSPORTATION/ EISENHOWER GRANTS FOR RESEARCH AND INTERN FELLOWSHIPS

Department of Transportation
Federal Highway Administration
Attn: Universities and Grants Programs
4600 North Fairfax Drive, Suite 800
Arlington, VA 22203-1553
(703) 235-0538   Toll Free: (877) 558-6873
Fax: (703) 235-0593   E-mail: transportationedu@dot.gov
Web: www.fhwa.dot.gov/tpp/ddetfp.htm

Summary To enable students (particularly those at Minority Serving Institutions) to participate in transportation-related research activities either at facilities of the U.S. Department of Transportation (DOT) Federal Highway Administration in the Washington, D.C. area or as interns for private or public organizations.

Eligibility This program is open to 1) students in their junior year of a baccalaureate program who will complete their junior year before being awarded a fellowship; 2) students in their senior year of a baccalaureate program; and 3) students who have completed their baccalaureate degree and are enrolled in a program leading to a master's, Ph.D., or equivalent degree. Applicants must be enrolled full time at an accredited U.S institution of higher education and planning to enter the transportation profession after completing their higher education. They must be U.S. citizens or have an I-20 (foreign student) or I-551 (permanent resident) identification card. For research fellowships, they select 1 or more projects from a current list of research activities underway at various DOT facilities; the research is conducted with academic supervision provided by a faculty adviser from their home university (which grants academic credit for the research project) and with technical direction provided by the DOT staff. Intern fellowships provide students with opportunities to perform transportation-related research, development, technology transfer, and other activities at public and private sector organizations. Specific requirements for the target projects vary; most require engineering backgrounds, but others involve transportation planning, information management, public administration, physics, materials science, statistical analysis, operations research, chemistry, economics, technology transfer, urban studies, geography, and urban and regional planning. The DOT encourages students at Historically Black Colleges and Universities (HBCUs), Hispanic Serving Institutions (HSIs), and Tribal Colleges and Universities (TCUs) to apply for these grants. Selection is based on match of the student's qualifications with the proposed research project (including the student's ability to accomplish the project in the available time), recommendation letters regarding the nominee's qualifications to conduct the research, academic records (including class standing, GPA, and transcripts), and transportation work experience (if any), including the employer's endorsement.

Financial Data Fellows receive full tuition and fees that relate to the academic credits for the approved research project (to a maximum of $10,000) and a monthly stipend of $1,450 for undergraduates, $1,700 for master's students, or $2,000 for doctoral students. An allowance for travel to and from the DOT facility where the research is conducted is also provided, but selectees are responsible for their own housing accommodations. Recipients are also provided with a 1-time allowance of up to $1,500 to attend the annual Transportation Research Board (TRB) meeting.

Duration Projects normally range from 3 to 12 months.

Number awarded Varies each year; recently, 9 students participated in this program.

Deadline Applications remain open until each project is filled.

[128]
DIETETIC TECHNICIAN PROGRAM SCHOLARSHIPS

Academy of Nutrition and Dietetics
Attn: Foundation
120 South Riverside Plaza, Suite 2000
Chicago, IL 60606-6995
(312) 899-0040   Toll Free: (800) 877-1600, ext. 1133
Fax: (312) 899-4817   E-mail: scholarships@eatright.org
Web: www.eatright.org/Foundation/scholarships

Summary To provide financial assistance to underrepresented minorities and other student members of the Academy of Nutrition and Dietetics who are in the second year of a dietetic technician program.

Eligibility This program is open to ADA student members in the second year of study in an accredited dietetic technician program. Applicants must be U.S. citizens or permanent residents and show promise of being a valuable, contributing member of the profession. Some scholarships require membership in a specific dietetic practice group, residency in a specific state, or underrepresented minority group status. The same application form can be used for all categories.

Financial Data Stipends normally range from $500 to $3,000; recently, they averaged approximately $1,870.

Duration 1 year.

Additional data The Academy of Nutrition and Dietetics was formerly the American Dietetic Association.

Number awarded Varies each year; recently, 2 of these scholarships were awarded.

Deadline February of each year.

[129]
DISTRIBUTED RESEARCH EXPERIENCES FOR UNDERGRADUATES (DREU)

Computing Research Association
1828 L Street, N.W., Suite 800
Washington, DC 20036-5104
(202) 234-2111   Fax: (202) 667-1066
E-mail: dreu@cra.org
Web: cra-w.org/undergraduate

Summary To provide an opportunity for Hispanic American and other underrepresented undergraduate students to work on a research project in computer science or engineering during the summer.

Eligibility This program is open to members of underrepresented groups (women, Hispanics, African Americans, and American Indians) who are entering their junior or senior year of college. Applicants must be interested in conducting a summer research project directly related to computer science or computer engineering under the mentorship of a faculty member at the mentor's home university. They must be U.S. citizens or permanent residents. Selection is based on the student's potential for success in graduate school, the match between the student's experience and skills and the needs of a participating professor's research project, the student's potential gain from the experience, and the possibility that the student's participation will advance the goals of the program.

Financial Data Students receive a stipend of $600 per week plus relocation travel assistance up to $500.

Duration 10 weeks during the summer.

Additional data This program began in 1994 as the Distributed Mentor Project (DMP) by the Computing Research Association's Committee on the Status of Women in Computing Research (CRA-W). In 2007, the Coalition to Diversify Computing (CDC) became a cosponsor of the program and in 2009 it was given its current name. From the beginning, funding has been provided by the National Science Foundation. Other sponsors have included the Henry Luce Foundation (current), USENIX, and AAAI.

Number awarded Varies each year; recently, 53 students were selected to participate in this program.

Deadline February of each year.

[130]
DIVERSITY COMMITTEE SCHOLARSHIP

American Society of Safety Engineers
Attn: ASSE Foundation
Scholarship Award Program
1800 East Oakton Street
Des Plaines, IL 60018
(847) 699-2929   Fax: (847) 768-3434
E-mail: bzylstra@asse.org
Web: www.asse.org

Summary To provide financial assistance to Hispanic American and other diverse upper-division or graduate students who are working on a degree related to occupational safety.

Eligibility This program is open to students who are working on an undergraduate or graduate degree in occupational safety, health, environment, industrial hygiene, occupational health nursing, or a closely-related field (e.g., industrial or environmental engineering). Applicants must be full-time students who have completed at least 60 semester hours with a GPA of 3.0 or higher as undergraduates or at least 9 semester hours as graduate students. A goal of this program is to support individuals regardless of race, ethnicity, gender, religion, personal beliefs, age, sexual orientation, physical challenges, geographic location, university, or specific area of study. U.S. citizenship is not required. Membership in the American Society of Safety Engineers (ASSE) is not required, but preference is given to members.

Financial Data The stipend is $1,000 per year.

Duration 1 year; recipients may reapply.

Number awarded 1 each year.

Deadline November of each year.

[131]
DIVERSITY IN PLANNING AWARD

American Planning Association-California Chapter
Attn: California Planning Foundation
c/o Paul Wack
California Polytechnic State University at San Luis Obispo
City and Regional Planning Department
San Luis Obispo, CA 93407-0283
(805) 756-6331   Fax: (805) 756-1340
E-mail: pwack@calpoly.edu
Web: www.californiaplanningfoundation.org

Summary To provide financial assistance to Hispanic American and other undergraduate and graduate students in accredited planning programs at California universities who will increase diversity in the profession.

Eligibility This program is open to students entering their final year for an undergraduate or master's degree in an accredited planning program at a university in California. Applicants must be students who will increase diversity in the planning profession. Selection is based on academic performance, professional promise, and financial need.

Financial Data The stipend is $3,000. The award includes a 1-year student membership in the American Planning Association (APA) and payment of registration for the APA California Conference.

Duration 1 year.

Additional data The accredited planning programs are at 3 campuses of the California State University system (California State Polytechnic University at Pomona, California Polytechnic State University at San Luis Obispo, and San Jose State University), 3 campuses of the University of California (Berkeley, Irvine, and Los Angeles), and the University of Southern California.

Number awarded 1 each year.

Deadline March of each year.

[132]
DIVERSITY IN PSYCHOLOGY AND LAW RESEARCH AWARD

American Psychological Association
Attn: Division 41 (American Psychology-Law Society)
c/o Diane Sivasubramaniam, Minority Affairs Committee Chair
Swinburne University of Technology
Faculty of Life and Social Sciences
Mail H31
P.O. Box 218
Hawthorn, VIC 3122
Australia
61 3 9214 5858 E-mail: dsivasubramaniam@swin.edu.au
Web: www.ap-ls.org

Summary To provide funding to Hispanic American and other student members of the American Psychology-Law Society (AP-LS) who are interested in conducting a research project related to diversity.

Eligibility This program is open to undergraduate and graduate student members of AP-LS who are interested in conducting research on issues related to psychology, law, multiculturalism, and/or diversity (e.g., research pertaining to psycholegal issues on race, gender, culture, sexual orientation). Students from underrepresented groups are strongly encouraged to apply; underrepresented groups include, but are not limited to: racial and ethnic minorities; first-generation college students; lesbian, gay, bisexual, and transgender students; and physically disabled students. Applicants must submit a project description that includes a statement of the research problem, the project's likely impact on the field of psychology and law broadly, methodology, budget, and an overview of relevant literature. Selection is based on the impact of the project on diversity and multiculturalism and the expected completion within the allocated time.

Financial Data The grant is $1,000.

Duration The project must be completed within 1 year.

Number awarded Up to 4 each year.

Deadline November of each year.

[133]
DOLLARS FOR SCHOLARS PROGRAM

United Methodist Higher Education Foundation
Attn: Scholarships Administrator
60 Music Square East, Suite 350
P.O. Box 340005
Nashville, TN 37203-0005
(615) 649-3990   Toll Free: (800) 811-8110
Fax: (615) 649-3980
E-mail: umhefscholarships@umhef.org
Web: www.umhef.org/UMDFSapp.php

Summary To provide financial assistance to Hispanic American and other students at Methodist colleges, universities, and seminaries whose home churches agree to contribute to their support.

Eligibility The Double Your Dollars for Scholars program is open to students attending or planning to attend a United Methodist-related college, university, or seminary as a full-time student. Applicants must have been an active, full member of a United Methodist Church for at least 1 year prior to applying. Their home church must nominate them and agree to contribute to their support. Many of the United Methodist colleges and universities have also agreed to contribute matching funds for a Triple Your Dollars for Scholars Program, and a few United Methodist conference foundations have agreed to contribute additional matching funds for a Quadruple Your Dollars for Scholars Program. Awards are granted on a first-come, first-served basis. Some of the awards are designated for Hispanic, Asian, and Native American (HANA) students funded by the General Board of Higher Education and Ministry.

Financial Data The sponsoring church contributes $1,000 and the United Methodist Higher Education Foundation (UMHEF) contributes a matching $1,000. Students who attend a participating United Methodist college or university receive an additional $1,000 for the Triple Your Dollars for Scholars Program, and those from a participating conference receive a fourth $1,000 increment for the Quadruple Your Dollars for Scholars Program.

Duration 1 year; may be renewed as long as the recipients maintain satisfactory academic progress as defined by their institution.

Additional data Currently, participants in the Double Your Dollars for Scholars program include 1 United Methodist seminary and theological school, 1 professional school, 19 senior colleges and universities, and 1 2-year college. The Triple Your Dollars for Scholars program includes an additional 12 United Methodist seminaries and theological schools, 72 senior colleges and universities, and 4 2-year colleges (for a complete list, consult the UMHEF). The conference foundations participating in the Quadruple Your Dollars for Scholars Program are limited to the Alabama-West Florida United Methodist Foundation, the East Ohio United Methodist Foundation, the Kentucky United Methodist Foundation, the Missouri United Methodist Foundation (for students at Saint Paul School of Theology or Central Methodist University), the Nashville Area United Methodist Foundation, the North Carolina United Methodist Foundation (for students at Louisburg College, Methodist University, or North Carolina Wesleyan College), the Georgia United Methodist Foundation, the Oklahoma United Methodist Foundation (for students at Oklahoma City University), the United Methodist Foundation of Arkansas, and the United Methodist Foundation of Western North Carolina.

Number awarded 350 each year, including 25 designated for HANA students.

Deadline Local churches must submit applications in February of each year for senior colleges, universities, and seminaries or May of each year for 2-year colleges.

[134]
DON SAHLI–KATHY WOODALL MINORITY STUDENT SCHOLARSHIP

Tennessee Education Association
801 Second Avenue North
Nashville, TN 37201-1099
(615) 242-8392   Toll Free: (800) 342-8367
Fax: (615) 259-4581   E-mail: mjohnson@tea.nea.org
Web: www.teateachers.org

Summary To provide financial assistance to Hispanic American and other minority high school seniors in Tennessee who are interested in majoring in education at a college or university in the state.

Eligibility This program is open to minority high school seniors in Tennessee who are planning to attend a college or university in the state and major in education. Application must be made either by a Future Teachers of America chapter affiliated with the Tennessee Education Association (TEA) or by the student with the recommendation of an active TEA member. Selection is based on academic record, leadership ability, financial need, and demonstrated interest in becoming a teacher.

Financial Data The stipend is $1,000.

Duration 1 year.

Number awarded 1 each year.

Deadline February of each year.

[135]
DONALD AND ITASKER THORNTON MEMORIAL SCHOLARSHIP

Thornton Sisters Foundation
P.O. Box 21
Atlantic Highlands, NJ 07716-0021
(732) 872-1353   E-mail: tsfoundation2001@yahoo.com
Web: www.thornton-sisters.com/ttsf.htm

Summary To provide financial assistance for college to Hispanic American and other women of color in New Jersey.

Eligibility This program is open to women of color (defined as African Americans, Latino Americans, Caribbean Americans, and Native Americans) who are graduating from high schools in New Jersey. Applicants must have a grade average of "C+" or higher and be able to document financial need. They must be planning to attend an accredited 4-year college or university. Along with their application, they must submit a 500-word essay describing their family background, personal and financial hardships, honors or academic distinctions, and community involvement and activities.

Financial Data A stipend is awarded (amount not specified). Funds are to be used for tuition and/or books.

Duration 1 year; nonrenewable.

Number awarded 1 or more each year.

Deadline May of each year.

[136]
DR. AMANDA PEREZ SCHOLARSHIP

Latino Medical Student Association
c/o Amaranta Craig, Scholarship Vice President
1355 Willard, Apartment B
San Francisco, CA 94117
E-mail: VP_Scholarship@lmsa.net
Web: www.lmsa.net/default.asp?contentID=9

Summary To provide financial assistance to college freshmen who are pre-medical student members of the Latino Medical Student Association (LMSA) in its western region and planning to attend medical school.

Eligibility This program is open to college freshmen who are LMSA members, residents of its western region (Arizona, California, Oregon, Utah, and Washington), and enrolled in a pre-medical program at a 4-year university in any state. Applicants should be able to demonstrate a desire to advance the state of health care and education in Latino communities through extracurricular activities and/or membership in civic organizations. They must be committed to preparing for a professional career in medicine and dedicated to serving the

Latino and underserved communities. Along with their application, they must submit a 1-page personal statement describing their family and personal background, educational objectives, community involvement, financial need, and how they would assist LMSA in its mission to provide health care to the Latino and underserved communities.

Financial Data A stipend is awarded (amount not specified).

Duration 1 year.

Additional data Until 2002, this organization was known as the Chicano/Latino Medical Student Association of California. This program was established in 2008.

Number awarded Varies each year.

Deadline February of each year.

[137]
DR. JUAN ANDRADE, JR. SCHOLARSHIP FOR YOUNG HISPANIC LEADERS

United States Hispanic Leadership Institute
Attn: Scholarship Committee
431 South Dearborn Street, Suite 1203
Chicago, IL 60605
(312) 427-8683   Toll Free: (800) 959-5151
Fax: (312) 427-5183   E-mail: jtorrez@ushli.org
Web: www.ushli.org/student/scholarship.php

Summary To provide financial assistance for college to Hispanic students in the United States.

Eligibility This program is open to U.S. citizens and permanent residents who are enrolled or accepted for enrollment as full-time students at a 2- or 4-year college or university in the United States. Applicants must have at least 1 parent of Hispanic ancestry. They must be able to demonstrate financial need. Along with their application, they must submit 1) a 250- to 500-word essay on their family history, life and/or work experiences that have influenced them, pertinent extracurricular and community involvement activities, and a self-description; 2) a 500- to 750-word essay on the future of Hispanics in America, the kind of leadership needed, and any role they hope to play in providing such leadership; 3) a transcript; and 4) 3 letters of reference.

Financial Data The stipend is $1,000 for students at 4-year institutions or $500 for students at 2-year institutions.

Duration 1 year.

Additional data This program began in 1994. Recipients are expected to pay for their own travel expenses to Chicago to attend a luncheon of the sponsor where they are introduced. Expenses for lodging and meals are covered by the sponsor.

Number awarded 1 or more each year. Since this program was established, it has awarded $310,500 in scholarships to 305 students.

Deadline October of each year.

[138]
DR. JUAN D. VILLARREAL–HDA FOUNDATION SCHOLARSHIPS

Hispanic Dental Association
Attn: HDA Foundation
1111 14th Street, N.W., Suite 1100
Washington, DC 20005
(202) 629-3628   Fax: (202) 629-3802
E-mail: scholarships@hdassoc.org
Web: www.hdassoc.org

Summary To provide financial assistance to members of the Hispanic Dental Association (HDA) at institutions in Texas.

Eligibility This program is open to HDA members who have been accepted or are currently enrolled at an accredited dental school or dental hygiene program in Texas as a full-time student. Applicants must have permanent resident status in the United States. Along with their application, they must submit a 250-word essay on why they want to be a dentist or dental hygienist and how they will help improve their community when they have reached their goal. Selection is based on commitment and dedication to improving the oral health of the Hispanic community, leadership skills, scholastic achievement, and community service.

Financial Data Stipends are $1,000 or $500.

Duration 1 year.

Additional data This program began in 1995.

Number awarded Varies each year; recently, 2 dental students and 1 dental hygiene student received these scholarships.

Deadline June of each year.

[139]
DR. MARTIN LUTHER KING, JR. SCHOLARSHIP

North Carolina Association of Educators, Inc.
Attn: Minority Affairs Commission
700 South Salisbury Street
P.O. Box 27347
Raleigh, NC 27611-7347
(919) 832-3000, ext. 205
Toll Free: (800) 662-7924, ext. 205
Fax: (919) 839-8229   E-mail: joy.bradford@ncae.org
Web: www.ncae.org/get-involved/awards

Summary To provide financial assistance to minority and other high school seniors in North Carolina who plan to attend college in any state.

Eligibility This program is open to seniors graduating from high schools in North Carolina who plan to attend a college or university in any state. They must have a GPA of 2.5 or higher. Along with their application, they must submit an essay on how the philosophies and ideals of Dr. Martin Luther King influenced their life. Applications are considered and judged by members of the association's Minority Affairs Commission. Selection is based on the essay, academic record, extracurricular activities and affiliations, accomplishments (honors and awards, leadership, and work experience), and financial need.

Financial Data A stipend is awarded (amount not specified).

Duration 1 year.

Number awarded 1 or more each year.

Deadline March of each year.

[140]
DREAM ACT STUDENT ACTIVIST SCHOLARSHIP PROGRAM

Mexican American Legal Defense and Educational Fund
634 South Spring Street, 11th Floor
Los Angeles, CA 90014-1974
(213) 629-2512   Fax: (213) 629-0266
Web: www.maldef.org/leadership/scholarships/index.html

Summary To provide financial assistance for college or graduate school to Dream Act student activists.

Eligibility This program is open to undergraduate and graduate students who have been advocates for the Dream Act and all immigrant rights. Eligibility extends to students seeking to enroll in college for the first time or to re-enroll following a leave of absence. Applicants must submit 500-word essays on their 1) background and financial need; 2) activism in support of the Dream Act and immigrant rights; and 3) future plans.

Financial Data Stipends range up to $5,000.

Duration 1 year.

Number awarded 1 or more each year.

Deadline June of each year.

[141]
DWIGHT DAVID EISENHOWER TRANSPORTATION FELLOWSHIP PROGRAM FOR HISPANIC-SERVING INSTITUTIONS

Department of Transportation
Federal Highway Administration
Attn: Universities and Grants Programs
4600 North Fairfax Drive, Suite 800
Arlington, VA 22203-1553
(703) 235-0538   Toll Free: (877) 558-6873
Fax: (703) 235-0593   E-mail: transportationedu@dot.gov
Web: www.fhwa.dot.gov/tpp/ddetfp.htm

Summary To provide financial assistance to undergraduate and graduate students working on a degree in a transportation-related field at an Hispanic Serving Institution (HSI).

Eligibility This program is open to students working on a bachelor's, master's, or doctoral degree at a federally-designated 4-year HSI. Applicants must be working on a degree in a transportation-related field (e.g., engineering, business, aviation, architecture, public policy and analysis, urban and regional planning). They must be U.S. citizens or have an I-20 (foreign student) or I-551 (permanent resident) identification card. Undergraduates must be entering at least their junior year and have a GPA of 3.0 or higher. Graduate students must have a GPA of at least 3.25. Selection is based on their proposed plan of study, academic achievement (based on class standing, GPA, and transcripts), transportation work experience, and letters of recommendation.

Financial Data Fellows receive payment of full tuition and fees (to a maximum of $10,000) and a monthly stipend of $1,450 for undergraduates, $1,700 for master's students, or $2,000 for doctoral students. They are also provided with a 1-time allowance of up to $1,500 to attend the annual Transportation Research Board (TRB) meeting.

Duration 1 year.

Additional data This program is administered by the participating HSIs: California State University at Fullerton, California State University at Los Angeles, Polytechnic University of Puerto Rico, Texas A&M University at Kingsville, the University of Puerto Rico at Mayaguez, the University of Texas at El Paso, or the University of Texas at San Antonio.

Number awarded Varies each year.

Deadline January of each year.

[142]
DWIGHT MOSLEY SCHOLARSHIPS

United States Tennis Association
Attn: USTA Serves
70 West Red Oak Lane
White Plains, NY 10604
(914) 696-7223   E-mail: foundation@usta.com
Web: www.usta.com

Summary To provide financial assistance to female and male high school seniors who are Hispanic American or from other diverse ethnic backgrounds, have participated in an organized community tennis program, and plan to attend college in any state.

Eligibility This program is open to high school seniors from diverse ethnic backgrounds who have excelled academically, demonstrated achievements in leadership, and participated extensively in an organized community tennis program. Applicants must be planning to enroll as a full-time undergraduate student at a 4-year college or university. They must have a GPA of 3.0 or higher and be able to demonstrate financial need and sportsmanship. Along with their application, they must submit an essay of 1 to 2 pages about how their participation in a tennis and education program has influenced their life, including examples of special mentors, volunteer service, and future goals. Females and males are considered separately.

Financial Data The stipend is $2,500 per year. Funds are paid directly to the recipient's college or university.

Duration 4 years.

Number awarded 2 each year: 1 female and 1 male.

Deadline February of each year.

[143]
ED BRADLEY SCHOLARSHIP

Radio Television Digital News Foundation
Attn: Programs, Awards, and Membership Manager
529 14th Street, N.W., Suite 425
Washington, DC 20045
(202) 725-8318   Fax: (202) 223-4007
E-mail: katies@rtdna.org
Web: www.rtdna.org/pages/education/scholarship-info.php

Summary To provide financial assistance to Hispanic American and other minority undergraduate students who are preparing for a career in electronic journalism.

Eligibility This program is open to sophomore or more advanced minority undergraduate students enrolled in an electronic journalism sequence at an accredited or nationally-recognized college or university. Applicants must submit 1 to 3 examples of their journalistic skills on audio CD or DVD (no more than 15 minutes total, accompanied by scripts); a description of their role on each story and a list of who worked on each story and what they did; a 1-page statement explaining why they are preparing for a career in electronic journalism with reference to their specific career preference (radio, television, online, reporting, producing, or newsroom management); a resume; and a letter of reference from their dean or faculty sponsor explaining why they are a good candidate for the award and certifying that they have at least 1 year of school remaining.

Financial Data The stipend is $10,000, paid in semiannual installments of $5,000 each.

Duration 1 year.

Additional data The Radio Television Digital News Foundation (RTDNF) also provides an all-expense paid trip to the Radio Television Digital News Association (RTDNA) annual international conference. The RTDNF was formerly the Radio and Television News Directors Foundation (RTNDF). Previous winners of any RTDNF scholarship or internship are not eligible.

Number awarded 1 each year.

Deadline May of each year.

[144]
EDSA MINORITY SCHOLARSHIP

Landscape Architecture Foundation
Attn: Leadership in Landscape Scholarship Program
818 18th Street, N.W., Suite 810
Washington, DC 20006-3520
(202) 331-7070   Fax: (202) 331-7079
E-mail: scholarships@lafoundation.org
Web: www.lafoundation.org

Summary To provide financial assistance to Hispanic American and other minority college students who are interested in studying landscape architecture.

Eligibility This program is open to African American, Hispanic, Native American, and minority college students of other cultural and ethnic backgrounds. Applicants must be entering their final 2 years of undergraduate study in landscape architecture. Along with their application, they must submit a 500-word essay on a design or research effort they plan to pursue (explaining how it will contribute to the advancement of the profession and to their ethnic heritage), 3 work samples, and 2 letters of recommendation. Selection is based on professional experience, community involvement, extracurricular activities, and financial need.

Financial Data The stipend is $5,000.

Additional data This scholarship was formerly designated the Edward D. Stone, Jr. and Associates Minority Scholarship.

Number awarded 1 each year.

Deadline February of each year.

[145]
EDUCATION ASSISTANCE PROGRAM

Accountancy Board of Ohio
77 South High Street, 18th Floor
Columbus, OH 43215-6128
(614) 466-4135   Fax: (614) 466-2628
Web: acc.ohio.gov/CPAExam/Education-Assistance.aspx

Summary To provide financial assistance to Hispanic American or other minority/financially disadvantaged students enrolled in an accounting education program at Ohio academic institutions approved by the Accountancy Board of Ohio.

Eligibility This program is open to minority and financially disadvantaged Ohio residents who apply as full-time juniors or seniors in an accounting program at an accredited college or university in the state. Students who remain in good standing at their institutions and who enter a qualified fifth-year program are then eligible to receive these funds. Minority is defined as people with significant ancestry from Africa (excluding the Middle East), Asia (excluding the Middle East), Central America and the Caribbean islands, South America, and the islands of the Pacific Ocean; in addition, persons with significant ancestry from the original peoples of North America who are of non-European descent. Financial disadvantage is defined according to information provided on the Free Application for Federal Student Aid (FAFSA). U.S. citizenship or permanent resident status is required.

Financial Data The amount of the stipend is determined annually but does not exceed the in-state tuition at Ohio public universities (currently, $13,067).

Duration 1 year (the fifth year of an accounting program). Funds committed to students who apply as juniors must be used within 4 years and funds committed to students who apply as seniors must be used within 3 years. The award is nonrenewable and may only be used when the student enrolls in the fifth year of a program.

Number awarded Several each year.

Deadline Applications may be submitted at any time.

[146]
EDUCATION AWARD

TELACU Education Foundation
Attn: College Success Program
5400 East Olympic Boulevard, Suite 300
Los Angeles, CA 90022
(323) 721-1655   Fax: (323) 721-3560
E-mail: collegesuccess@telacu.com
Web: www.telacu.com

Summary To provide financial assistance to Latino students from eligible communities in California, Texas, Illinois, and New York who are interested in attending college in any state to prepare for a career as a teacher.

Eligibility This program is open to Latino residents of selected communities in southern California, selected cities in Texas, the Greater Chicagoland area of Illinois, or the state of New York. Applicants must 1) be a first-generation college student; 2) be from a low-income family; and 3) have a GPA of 2.5 or higher. They must be enrolled or planning to enroll full time at a college or university in any state and preparing for a career as a teacher. Selection is based on leadership potential, professional and extracurricular achievement, commitment to the development and economic empowerment of communities, and financial need. Priority is given to students attending institutions that provide matching funds (for a list, contact the sponsor).

Financial Data Stipends range from $500 to $5,000 per year.

Duration 1 year; may be renewed up to 3 additional years, provided the recipient remains enrolled full time, maintains a GPA of 2.75 or higher, and volunteers for at least 20 hours of community service.

Additional data The eligible areas in California include underserved communities in Los Angeles, Orange, and San Bernardino counties such as unincorporated areas of east Los Angeles and the cities of Baldwin Park, Bell Gardens, Commerce, Huntington Park, Los Angeles, Montebello, Ontario, Pico Rivera, Pomona, San Bernardino, Santa Ana, and South Gate. The cities in Texas are Austin, Edinburg, Laredo, Rio Grande City, San Antonio.

Number awarded 1 or more each year.

Deadline March of each year.

[147]
EDWARD S. ROTH MANUFACTURING ENGINEERING SCHOLARSHIP

Society of Manufacturing Engineers
Attn: SME Education Foundation
One SME Drive
P.O. Box 930
Dearborn, MI 48121-0930
(313) 425-3300   Toll Free: (800) 733-4763, ext. 3300
Fax: (313) 425-3411   E-mail: foundation@sme.org
Web: www.smeef.org/scholarships

Summary To provide financial assistance to Hispanic Americans and other students enrolled or planning to work on a bachelor's or master's degree in manufacturing engineering at selected universities.

Eligibility This program is open to U.S. citizens who are graduating high school seniors or currently-enrolled undergraduate or graduate students. Applicants must be enrolled or planning to enroll as a full-time student at 1 of 13 selected 4-year universities to work on a bachelor's or master's degree in manufacturing engineering. They must have a GPA of 3.0 or higher. Preference is given to 1) students demonstrating financial need; 2) minority students; and 3) students participating in a co-op program. Some preference may also be given to graduating high school seniors and graduate students. Along with their application, they must submit a 300-word essay that covers their career and educational objectives, how this scholarship will help them attain those objectives, and why they want to enter this field.

Financial Data Stipend amounts vary; recently, the value of all scholarships provided by this foundation averaged approximately $2,330.

Duration 1 year; may be renewed.

Additional data The eligible institutions are California Polytechnic State University at San Luis Obispo, California State Polytechnic State University at Pomona, University of Miami (Florida), Bradley University (Illinois), Central State University (Ohio), Miami University (Ohio), Boston University, Worcester Polytechnic Institute (Massachusetts), University of Massachusetts, St. Cloud State University (Minnesota), University of Texas-Pan American, Brigham Young University (Utah), and Utah State University.

Number awarded 2 each year.

Deadline January of each year.

[148]
ELI LILLY AND COMPANY/BLACK DATA PROCESSING ASSOCIATES SCHOLARSHIP

Black Data Processing Associates
Attn: BDPA Education Technology Foundation
4423 Lehigh Road, Number 277
College Park, MD 20740
(513) 284-4968   Fax: (202) 318-2194
E-mail: scholarships@betf.org
Web: www.betf.org/scholarships/eli-lilly.shtml

Summary To provide financial assistance to Hispanic American and other minority high school seniors or current college students who are interested in studying information technology at a college in any state.

Eligibility This program is open to graduating high school seniors and current college undergraduates who are members of minority groups (African American, Hispanic, Asian, or Native American). Applicants must be enrolled or planning to enroll at an accredited 4-year college or university and work on a degree in information technology. They must have a GPA of 3.0 or higher. Along with their application, they must submit a 500-word essay on why information technology is important. Selection is based on that essay, academic achievement, leadership ability through academic or civic involvement, and participation in community service activities. U.S. citizenship or permanent resident status is required.

Financial Data The stipend is $2,500. Funds may be used to pay for tuition, fees, books, room and board, or other college-related expenses.

Duration 1 year; nonrenewable.

Additional data The BDPA established its Education and Technology Foundation (BETF) in 1992 to advance the skill sets needed by African American and other minority adults and young people to compete in the information technology industry. This program is sponsored by Eli Lilly and Company.

Number awarded 1 or more each year.

Deadline July of each year.

[149]
EMPIRE STATE DIVERSITY HONORS SCHOLARSHIP PROGRAM

State University of New York
Attn: Office of Diversity, Equity and Inclusion
State University Plaza
353 Broadway
Albany, NY 12246
(518) 320-1189
Web: www.suny.edu/provost/odee/programs.cfm

Summary To provide financial assistance to residents of New York (particularly Hispanic Americans and other underrepresented minorities) who are attending campuses of the State University of New York (SUNY) and will contribute to the diversity of the student body.

Eligibility This program is open to U.S. citizens and permanent residents who are New York residents and enrolled as undergraduate students at any of the participating SUNY colleges. Applicants must be able to demonstrate 1) how they will contribute to the diversity of the student body, primarily by having overcome a disadvantage or other impediment to success in higher education; and 2) high academic achievement. Economic disadvantage, although not a requirement, may be the basis for eligibility. Membership in a racial or ethnic group that is underrepresented at the applicant's school or program may serve as a plus factor in making awards, but may not form the sole basis of selection.

Financial Data The maximum stipend provided by the SUNY system is half the student's cost of attendance or $3,000, whichever is less. The individual campus must match the SUNY award in an equal amount.

Duration 1 year; renewable.

Number awarded Varies each year; recently, nearly 1,000 students at 46 SUNY institutions received support from this program.

Deadline Deadline not specified.

[150]
ENCOURAGE MINORITY PARTICIPATION IN OCCUPATIONS WITH EMPHASIS ON REHABILITATION

Courage Center
Attn: EMPOWER Scholarship Program
3915 Golden Valley Road
Minneapolis, MN 55422
(763) 520-0214   Toll Free: (888) 8-INTAKE
Fax: (763) 520-0562   TDD: (763) 520-0245
E-mail: empower@couragecenter.org
Web: www.couragecenter.org

Summary To provide financial assistance to Hispanic Americans and other students of color from Minnesota and western Wisconsin interested in attending college in any state to prepare for a career in the medical rehabilitation field.

Eligibility This program is open to ethnically diverse students accepted at or enrolled in an institution of higher learning in any state. Applicants must be residents of Minnesota or western Wisconsin (Burnett, Pierce, Polk, and St. Croix counties). They must be able to demonstrate a career interest in the medical rehabilitation field by a record of volunteer involvement related to health care and must have a GPA of 2.0 or higher. Along with their application, they must submit a 1-page essay that covers their experiences and interactions to date with the area of volunteering, what they have accomplished and gained from those experiences, how those experiences will assist them in their future endeavors, why education is important to them, how this scholarship will help them with their financial need and their future career goals.

Financial Data The stipend is $1,500.

Duration 1 year.

Additional data This program, established in 1995, is also identified by its acronym as the EMPOWER Scholarship Award.

Number awarded 2 each year.

Deadline May of each year.

[151]
ENDOCRINE SOCIETY SUMMER RESEARCH FELLOWSHIPS

Endocrine Society
Attn: Summer Research Fellowships
8401 Connecticut Avenue, Suite 900
Chevy Chase, MD 20815
(301) 951-2616   Toll Free: (888) 363-6274
Fax: (301) 576-7787   E-mail: awards@endo-society.org
Web: www.endo-society.org

Summary To provide funding to undergraduate, medical, and graduate students (particularly Hispanic Americans and other underrepresented minorities) who are interested in conducting a research project during the summer in endocrinology.

Eligibility This program is open to full-time students who are undergraduates in the third year of study or higher, medical students beyond their first year of study, and first-year graduate students. Applicants must be interested in participating in a research project under the supervision of a mentor. The mentor must be an active member of the Endocrine Society. Each member may sponsor only 1 student. Projects must be relevant to an aspect of endocrinology and are expected to have clearly defined research goals; students should not function as aides or general research assistants. Applications on behalf of underrepresented minority students are especially encouraged.

Financial Data The grant of $4,000 provides funding for a stipend, fringe benefits, and indirect costs.

Duration 10 to 12 weeks during the summer.

Additional data At the conclusion of the fellowship period, students must submit a 1-page summary of their research project explaining how the fellowship affected their consideration of a career in endocrinology.

Number awarded 20 each year.

Deadline January of each year.

[152]
ENTERPRISE RENT-A-CAR INTERN/ SCHOLARSHIP PROGRAM

Statewide Hispanic Chamber of Commerce of New Jersey
Attn: Scholarship Selection Committee
One Gateway Center, Suite 2409
Newark, NJ 07102
(973) 900-5886   Fax: (866) 226-1828
E-mail: chamber@shccnj.org
Web: www.shccnj.org/scholarship

Summary To provide financial assistance to Hispanic Americans, other minorities, and women who are interested in attending college to prepare for a career in computer and video game arts.

Eligibility This program is open to residents of New Jersey who are Hispanic (at least 1 parent must be fully Hispanic) and currently enrolled as juniors at a 4-year accredited college or university in the state. Applicants must have a GPA of 2.5 or higher and a major in accounting, business administration, communications, marketing, or a related field. They must have a record of prior work experience in service or retail sales or related college activities (e.g., athletics, community service, academic organizations, social clubs). The program offers an internship at Enterprise Rent-A-Car offices in the New York-New Jersey-Connecticut tri-state area, and applicants must be eligible and available to work there. They must have a driver's license and a satisfactory motor vehicle record. Financial need is not considered in the selection process.

Financial Data The program provides a paid internship during the summer between the junior and senior year and a stipend of $2,000 for the senior year.

Duration 8 weeks during the summer for the internship; 1 academic year (the senior year) for the scholarship.

Additional data This program is sponsored by Enterprise Rent-A-Car.

Number awarded 1 or more each year.

Deadline April of each year.

[153]
ENTERTAINMENT SOFTWARE ASSOCIATION FOUNDATION SCHOLARSHIPS

Entertainment Software Association
Attn: ESA Foundation
317 Madison Avenue, 22nd Floor
New York, NY 10017
(917) 522-3250
Web: www.esafoundation.org/scholarship.asp

Summary To provide financial assistance to Hispanic Americans, other minorities, and women who are interested in attending college to prepare for a career in computer and video game arts.

Eligibility This program is open to women and members of minority groups who are high school seniors or undergraduates currently enrolled full time at an accredited 4-year college or university. Applicants must be interested in working on a degree leading to a career in computer and video game arts. They must be U.S. citizens and have a GPA of 2.75 or higher.

Financial Data The stipend is $3,000.

Duration 1 year; nonrenewable.

Additional data This program began in 2007.

Number awarded Up to 30 each year: 15 to graduating high school seniors and 15 to current undergraduates.

Deadline May of each year.

[154]
EPA GREATER RESEARCH OPPORTUNITIES (GRO) FELLOWSHIPS FOR UNDERGRADUATE ENVIRONMENTAL STUDY

Environmental Protection Agency
Attn: National Center for Environmental Research
Ariel Rios Building
1200 Pennsylvania Avenue, N.W.
Washington, DC 20460
(202) 347-8049   Toll Free: (800) 490-9194
E-mail: boddie.georgette@epa.gov
Web: www.epa.gov/careers/fellowships

Summary To provide financial aid and summer internships to undergraduates who are enrolled fields related to the environment at colleges and universities (particularly Minority Serving Institutions) that receive limited federal funding.

Eligibility This program is open to U.S. citizens or permanent residents who are enrolled full time at a college or university in this country that receives less than $35 million in federal research and development expenditures. Students attending eligible institutions with significant minority enrollment (defined as Minority-Serving Institutions) are particularly encouraged to apply. Applicants must have at least 2 years remaining for completion of a bachelor's degree in an environmentally-related field, such as biology, health, the social sciences, or engineering. They must be available to work as interns at an EPA facility during the summer between their junior and senior years. A goal of the program is to meet the need for scientists from underrepresented backgrounds, so the sponsor strongly encourages women, minorities, and persons with disabilities to apply. A minimum average of "B" overall is required.

Financial Data The fellowship provides up to $20,700 per year for academic support and $8,600 for internship support.

Duration The final 2 years of baccalaureate study, including 12 weeks during the summer between those years.

Additional data This program began in 1982. It was formerly known as Culturally Diverse Academic Institutions Undergraduate Student Fellowships program and subsequently as Minority Academic Institutions Undergraduate Student Fellowships.

Number awarded Approximately 40 each year.

Deadline December of each year.

[155]
ESPERANZA SCHOLARSHIP

New York Women in Communications, Inc.
Attn: NYWICI Foundation
355 Lexington Avenue, 15th Floor
New York, NY 10017-6603
(212) 297-2133   Fax: (212) 370-9047
E-mail: nywicipr@nywici.org
Web: www.nywici.org/foundation/scholarships

Summary To provide financial assistance to Hispanic women who are residents of designated eastern states and interested in preparing for a career in communications at a college or graduate school in any state.

Eligibility This program is open to Hispanic women who are seniors graduating from high schools in New York, New Jersey, Connecticut, or Pennsylvania or undergraduate or graduate students who are permanent residents of those states; they must be attending or planning to attend a college or university in any state. Graduate students must be members of New York Women in Communications, Inc. (NYWICI). Also eligible are Hispanic women who reside outside the 4 states but are currently enrolled at a college or university within 1 of the 5 boroughs of New York City. All applicants must be working on a degree in a communications-related field (e.g., advertising, broadcasting, communications, English, film, journalism, marketing, digital media, public relations) and have a GPA of 3.2 or higher. Along with their application, they must submit a 2-page resume; a personal essay of 300 words on an assigned topic that changes annually; 2 letters of recommendation; and an official transcript. Selection is based on academic record, need, demonstrated leadership, participation in school and community activities, honors and other awards or recognition, work experience, goals and aspirations, and unusual personal and/or family circumstances. U.S. citizenship is required.

Financial Data The stipend ranges up to $10,000.

Duration 1 year.

Additional data This program is funded by Macy's and Bloomingdale's.

Number awarded 1 each year.

Deadline January of each year.

[156]
EXCELLENCE IN DIVERSITY SCHOLARSHIPS

New Jersey Utilities Association
50 West State Street, Suite 1117
Trenton, NJ 08608
(609) 392-1000   Fax: (609) 396-4231
E-mail: info@njua.com
Web: www.njua.com/html/njua_eeo_scholarship.cfm

Summary To provide financial assistance to high school seniors in New Jersey who are Hispanic Americans, members of other minority groups, females, or individuals with disabilities and interested in attending college in any state.

Eligibility This program is open to seniors graduating from high schools in New Jersey who are women, minorities (Black or African American, Hispanic or Latino, American Indian or Alaska Native, Asian, Native Hawaiian or Pacific Islander, or 2 or more races), and persons with disabilities. Applicants must be planning to work on a bachelor's degree at a college or university in any state. Along with their application, they must submit a 500-word essay explaining their career ambition and why they have chosen that career. Children of employees of any New Jersey Utilities Association-member company are ineligible. Selection is based on overall academic excellence and demonstrated financial need. U.S. citizenship or permanent resident status is required.

Financial Data The stipend is $1,500 per year. Funds are paid to the recipient's college or university.

Duration 4 years.

Number awarded 2 each year.

Deadline March of each year.

[157]
EXXONMOBIL BERNARD HARRIS MATH AND SCIENCE SCHOLARSHIPS

Council of the Great City Schools
1301 Pennsylvania Avenue, N.W., Suite 702
Washington, DC 20004
(202) 393-2427   Fax: (202) 393-2400
Web: www.cgcs.org/Page/47

Summary To provide financial assistance to Hispanic and African American high school seniors interested in studying science, technology, engineering, or mathematics (STEM) in college.

Eligibility This program is open to African American and Hispanic seniors graduating from high schools in a district that is a member of the Council of the Great City Schools, a coalition of 65 of the nation's largest urban public school systems. Applicants must be planning to enroll full time at a 4-year college or university and major in a STEM field of study. They must have a GPA of 3.0 or higher. Along with their application, they must submit 1-page essays on 1) how mathematics and science education has impacted their lives so far; and

2) why they have chosen to prepare for a career in a STEM field. Selection is based on those essays; academic achievement; extracurricular activities, community service, or other experiences that demonstrate commitment to a career in a STEM field; and 3 letters of recommendation. Financial need is not considered. Males and females are judged separately.

Financial Data The stipend is $5,000.

Duration 1 year; nonrenewable.

Additional data This program, which began in 2010, is sponsored by the ExxonMobil Corporation and The Harris Foundation.

Number awarded 4 each year: an African American male and female and an Hispanic male and female.

Deadline May of each year.

[158]
EXXONMOBIL LOFT FELLOWSHIPS

Hispanic Heritage Foundation
1444 Duke Street
Alexandria, VA 22314
(202) 861-9797   Toll Free: (866) 665-2112
Fax: (202) 861-9799 E-mail: LOFT@hispanicheritage.org
Web: www.hispanicheritage.org/loft_int.php?sec=200

Summary To provide financial assistance to Hispanic undergraduate and graduate students who participate in the Latinos on Fast Track (LOFT) program.

Eligibility This program is open to Hispanic sophomores, juniors, seniors, and graduate students at 4-year colleges and universities who are U.S. citizens or permanent residents and fluent in English. Applicants must be working on a degree and preparing for a career in chemistry, engineering (chemical, civil, computer, electrical, environmental, industrial, materials, mechanical, or petroleum), geology, material sciences, mathematics, or physics. Their GPA must be at least 3.5. They must be participating in the LOFT program with an ExxonMobil engineer or scientist as mentor. Along with their application, they must submit an essay of 500 to 700 words that covers why they chose their major, how they intend to prepare for an active career related to their major, and why they should be considered for this program.

Financial Data Selected LOFT participants receive $1,000 scholarships.

Duration The scholarships are presented annually and are nonrenewable.

Additional data The LOFT program involves 5 meetings of 1 hour each with the mentor (virtually or in person), participation in an online ExxonMobil mentee program that introduces them to career opportunities with the company, the possibility to interview for ExxonMobil internships or full-time positions upon successful completion of the program, and the possibility of these scholarships.

Number awarded 20 each year.

Deadline Deadline not specified.

[159]
FARM CREDIT EAST SCHOLARSHIPS

Farm Credit East
Attn: Scholarship Program
240 South Road
Enfield, CT 06082
(860) 741-4380   Toll Free: (800) 562-2235
Fax: (860) 741-4389
E-mail: specialoffers@famcrediteast.com
Web: www.farmcrediteast.com

Summary To provide financial assistance to Hispanic American and other residents of designated northeastern states who plan to attend school in any state to work on an undergraduate or graduate degree in a field related to agriculture, forestry, or fishing.

Eligibility This program is open to residents of Massachusetts, Connecticut, Rhode Island, New Jersey, and portions of New York and New Hampshire. Applicants must be working on or planning to work on an associate, bachelor's, or graduate degree in production agriculture, agribusiness, the forest products industry, or commercial fishing at a college or university in any state. They must submit a 200-word essay on why they wish to prepare for a career in agriculture, forestry, or fishing. Selection is based on the essay, extracurricular activities (especially farm work experience and activities indicative of an interest in preparing for a career in agriculture or agribusiness), and interest in agriculture. The program includes diversity scholarships reserved for members of minority groups (Black or African American, American Indian or Alaska Native, Asian, Native Hawaiian or other Pacific Islander, or Hispanic or Latino).

Financial Data The stipend is $1,500. Funds are paid directly to the student to be used for tuition, room and board, books, and other academic charges.

Duration 1 year; nonrenewable.

Additional data Recipients are given priority for an internship with the sponsor in the summer following their junior year. Farm Credit East was formerly named First Pioneer Farm Credit.

Number awarded Up to 28 each year, including several diversity scholarships.

Deadline April of each year.

[160]
FIESTA DE INDEPENDENCIA FOUNDATION SCHOLARSHIPS

Hispanic Scholarship Consortium
Attn: Scholarship Selection Committee
1107 South Eighth Street
Austin, TX 78704
(512) 368-2956   Fax: (512) 692-1831
E-mail: scholarships@hispanicscholar.org
Web: www.hispanicscholar.org

Summary To provide financial assistance to high school seniors of Hispanic heritage from Texas who plan to attend college in any state.

Eligibility This program is open to seniors graduating from high schools in Texas who are of Hispanic heritage and have a GPA of 3.0 or higher. Applicants must be planning to enroll full time at an accredited 2- or 4-year college or university in the United States. Selection is based on academic record, community service, financial need, and a personal interview. U.S. citizenship or permanent resident status is required.

Financial Data The stipend is $2,000 per year.

Duration 1 year; may be renewed, provided the recipient remains enrolled full time, maintains a GPA of 3.0 or higher, and participates in at least 25 hours of community service per semester.

Additional data This program is sponsored by the Fiesta de Independencia Foundation.

Number awarded 1 or more each year.

Deadline August of each year.

[161]
FLEMING/BLASZCAK SCHOLARSHIP

Society of Plastics Engineers
Attn: SPE Foundation
13 Church Hill Road
Newtown, CT 06740
(203) 740-5447   Fax: (203) 775-1157
E-mail: foundation@4spe.org
Web: www.4spe.org/spe-foundation

Summary To provide financial assistance to Mexican American undergraduate and graduate students who have a career interest in the plastics industry.

Eligibility This program is open to full-time undergraduate and graduate students of Mexican descent who are enrolled at a 4-year college or university. Applicants must be U.S. citizens or legal residents. They must be majoring in or taking courses that would be beneficial to a career in the plastics or polymer industry (e.g., plastics engineering, packaging, polymer sciences, chemistry, physics, chemical engineering, mechanical engineering, industrial engineering). Along with their application, they must submit 3 letters of recommendation; a high school and/or college transcript; a 1- to 2-page statement telling why they are applying for the scholarship, their qualifications, and their educational and career goals in the plastics industry; their employment history; a list of current and past school activities and community activities and honors; information on their financial need; and documentation of their Mexican heritage.

Financial Data The stipend is $2,000. Funds are paid directly to the recipient's school.

Duration 1 year.

Number awarded 1 each year.

Deadline February of each year.

[162]
FLORIDA BOARD OF ACCOUNTANCY MINORITY SCHOLARSHIPS

Florida Department of Business and Professional Regulation
Attn: Division of Certified Public Accounting
240 N.W. 76th Drive, Suite A
Gainesville, FL 32607-6656
(850) 487-1395   Fax: (352) 333-2508
Web: www.myfloridalicense.com/dbpr/cpa

Summary To provide financial assistance to minority and female residents of Florida who are entering the fifth year of an accounting program.

Eligibility This program is open to Florida residents who have completed at least 120 credit hours at a college or university in the state and have a GPA of 2.5 or higher. Applicants must be planning to remain in school as a full-time student for the fifth year required to sit for the C.P.A. examination. They must be members of a minority group, defined to include African Americans, Hispanic Americans, Asian Americans, Native Americans, or women. Selection is based on scholastic ability and performance and financial need.

Financial Data The stipend is $3,000 per semester.

Duration 1 semester; may be renewed 1 additional semester.

Number awarded Varies each year; a total of $100,000 is available for this program annually.

Deadline May of each year.

[163]
FLORIDA CHAPTER AABE SCHOLARSHIPS

American Association of Blacks in Energy-Florida
  Chapter
c/o Atanya Lewis, Scholarship Committee
700 Universe Boulevard, JNE/JB
Juno Beach, FL 33408
E-mail: Atanya.Lewis@fpl.com
Web: www.aabe.org/index.php?component=pages&id=811

Summary To provide financial assistance to Hispanic Americans and members of other underrepresented minority groups who are high school seniors in any state and planning to major in an energy-related field at a college in Florida.

Eligibility This program is open to seniors graduating from high schools in any state and planning to attend an accredited college or university in Florida. Applicants must be African Americans, Hispanics, or Native Americans who have a GPA of 3.0 or higher and who can demonstrate financial need. Their intended major must be business, engineering, technology, mathematics, the physical sciences, or other energy-related field. Along with their application, they must submit a 350-word statement on why they should receive this scholarship, how their professional career objectives relate to energy, and any other relevant information.

Financial Data A stipend is awarded (amount not specified).

Duration 1 year.

Additional data The winner is eligible to compete for regional and national scholarships.

Number awarded Varies each year; a total of $5,000 is available for this program annually.

Deadline February of each year.

[164]
FLORIDA MINORITY TEACHER EDUCATION SCHOLARSHIPS

Florida Fund for Minority Teachers, Inc.
Attn: Executive Director
G415 Norman Hall
P.O. Box 117045
Gainesville, FL 32611-7045
(352) 392-9196, ext. 21   Fax: (352) 846-3011
E-mail: info@ffmt.org
Web: www.ffmt.org

Summary To provide funding to Hispanic Americans and members of other minority groups in Florida who are preparing for a career as a teacher.

Eligibility This program is open to Florida residents who are African American/Black, Hispanic/Latino, Asian American/Pacific Islander, or American Indian/Alaskan Native. Applicants must be entering their junior year in a teacher education program at a participating college or university in Florida. Special consideration is given to community college graduates. Selection is based on writing ability, communication skills, overall academic performance, and evidence of commitment to the youth of America (preferably demonstrated through volunteer activities).

Financial Data The stipend is $4,000 per year. Recipients are required to teach 1 year in a Florida public school for each year they receive the scholarship. If they fail to teach in a public school, they are required to repay the total amount of support received at an annual interest rate of 8%.

Duration Up to 2 consecutive years, provided the recipient remains enrolled full time with a GPA of 2.5 or higher.

Additional data For a list of the 16 participating public institutions and the 18 participating private institutions, contact the Florida Fund for Minority Teachers (FFMT). Recipients are also required to attend the annual FFMT recruitment and retention conference.

Number awarded Varies each year.

Deadline July of each year for fall semester; November of each year for spring semester.

[165]
FORD BLUE OVAL NATION-WIDE UNDERGRADUATE SCHOLARSHIPS

Hispanic College Fund
Attn: Scholarship Processing
1300 L Street, N.W., Suite 975
Washington, DC 20005
(202) 296-5400   Toll Free: (800) 644-4223
Fax: (202) 296-3774   E-mail: hcf-info@hispanicfund.org
Web: scholarships.hispanicfund.org/applications

Summary To provide financial assistance to Hispanic American students working on an undergraduate degree in any field.

Eligibility This program is open to U.S. citizens and permanent residents of Hispanic background (at least 1 grandparent must be 100% Hispanic) who are enrolled or planning to enroll full time at an accredited college or university in any state. Applicants must have a GPA of 3.0 or higher and be able to demonstrate financial need. They may be working on an undergraduate degree in any field.

Financial Data Stipends range from $500 to $5,000, depending on need and academic achievement. Funds are paid directly to the recipient's college or university to help cover tuition and fees.

Duration 1 year; recipients may reapply.

Additional data This program is sponsored by Ford Motor Company. All applications must be submitted online; no paper applications are available.

Number awarded Varies each year.

Deadline February of each year.

[166]
FORD BLUE OVAL PUERTO RICO SCHOLARSHIPS

Hispanic College Fund
Attn: Scholarship Processing
1300 L Street, N.W., Suite 975
Washington, DC 20005
(202) 296-5400   Toll Free: (800) 644-4223
Fax: (202) 296-3774   E-mail: hcf-info@hispanicfund.org
Web: scholarships.hispanicfund.org/applications

Summary To provide financial assistance to undergraduate students in Puerto Rico majoring in any field.

Eligibility This program is open to U.S. citizens and permanent residents who live in Puerto Rico and are enrolled or planning to enroll full time at an accredited college or university in the Commonwealth. Applicants must have a GPA of 3.0 or higher and be able to demonstrate financial need. They may be studying any academic discipline.

Financial Data Stipends range from $500 to $5,000, depending on need and academic achievement. Funds are paid directly to the recipient's college or university to help cover tuition and fees.

Duration 1 year; recipients may reapply.

Additional data This program is sponsored by Ford Motor Company. All applications must be submitted online; no paper applications are available.

Number awarded Varies each year.

Deadline February of each year.

[167]
FORT WORTH HOPE SCHOLARSHIP

Hispanic Organization of Postal Employees Fort Worth Chapter
Attn: Scholarship Committee
P.O. Box 162422
Fort Worth, TX 76161-2422
E-mail: ftwhope@gmail.com
Web: www.hope-inc.com/IIfortworthchapter.html

Summary To provide financial assistance to Hispanic and other students who are related to a postal employee in Texas and are interested in attending college in any state.

Eligibility This program is open to seniors in public or private high schools, high school graduates, and GED recipients who are enrolled or planning to enroll full time at a college, university, or trade/vocational school in any state. Applicants must be the relative of a postal employee in Texas. They must have a GPA of 2.5 or higher. Along with their application, they must submit a 500-word essay on how their family background has affected the way they see the world.

Financial Data A stipend is awarded (amount not specified).

Duration 1 year.

Additional data A goal of the sponsor is to enable more Hispanics to attend college.

Number awarded Varies each year; recently, 8 of these scholarships were awarded.

Deadline April of each year.

[168]
FORUM FOR CONCERNS OF MINORITIES SCHOLARSHIPS

American Society for Clinical Laboratory Science
Attn: Forum for Concerns of Minorities
1861 International Drive, Suite 200
McLean, VA 22102
(571) 748-3770   E-mail: ascls@ascls.org
Web: www.ascls.org

Summary To provide financial assistance to Hispanic Americans and other minority students in clinical laboratory scientist and clinical laboratory technician programs.

Eligibility This program is open to minority students who are enrolled in a program in clinical laboratory science, including clinical laboratory science/medical technology (CLS/MT) and clinical laboratory technician/medical laboratory technician (CLT/MLT). Applicants must be able to demonstrate financial need. Membership in the American Society for Clinical Laboratory Science is encouraged but not required.

Financial Data Stipends depend on the need of the recipients and the availability of funds.

Duration 1 year.

Number awarded 2 each year: 1 to a CLS/MT student and 1 to a CLT/MLT student.

Deadline March of each year.

[169]
FOURTH DISTRICT MOSAIC SCHOLARSHIP

American Advertising Federation-District 4
c/o Maria Lucas, Governor
Farah & Farah
10 West Adams Street
Jacksonville, FL 32202
(904) 807-3113   Toll Free: (800) 533-5555
Fax: (904) 355-5599   E-mail: mlucas@farahandfarah.com
Web: 4aaf.com/education/scholarships

Summary To provide financial assistance to Hispanic American and other minority undergraduate and graduate students from any state who are enrolled at colleges and universities in Florida and interested in entering the field of advertising.

Eligibility This program is open to undergraduate and graduate students from any state enrolled at accredited colleges and universities in Florida who are U.S. citizens or permanent residents of African, African American, Hispanic, Hispanic American, Indian, Native American, Asian, Asian American, or Pacific Islander descent. Applicants must be working on a bachelor's or master's degree in advertising, marketing, communications, public relations, art, graphic arts, or a related field. They must have an overall GPA of 3.0 or higher. Along with their application, they must submit a 250-word essay on why multiculturalism, diversity, and inclusion are important in the advertising, marketing, and communications industry today. Preference is given to members of the American Advertising Federation.

Financial Data The stipend is $1,000.

Duration 1 year.

Number awarded 1 or more each year.

Deadline February of each year.

[170]
FRAMELINE COMPLETION FUND

Frameline
Attn: Completion Fund
145 Ninth Street, Suite 300
San Francisco, CA 94103
(415) 703-8650   Fax: (415) 861-1404
E-mail: info@frameline.org
Web: www.frameline.org/filmmaker-support

Summary   To provide funding to lesbian, gay, bisexual, and transgender (LGBT) film/video artists (particularly Hispanic Americans, other film/video artists of color, and women).

Eligibility   This program is open to LGBT artists who are in the last stages of the production of documentary, educational, narrative, animated, or experimental projects about or of interest to LGBT people and their communities. Applicants may be independent artists, students, producers, or nonprofit corporations. They must be interested in completion work and must have 90% of the production completed; projects in development, script-development, pre-production, or production are not eligible. Student projects are eligible only if the student maintains artistic and financial control of the project. Women and people of color are especially encouraged to apply. Selection is based on financial need, the contribution the grant will make to completing the project, assurances that the project will be completed, and the statement the project makes about LGBT people and/or issues of concern to them and their communities.

Financial Data   Grants range from $1,000 to $5,000.

Duration   These are 1-time grants.

Additional data   This program began in 1990.

Number awarded   Varies each year; recently, 5 of these grants were awarded. Since this program was established, it has provided $389,200 in support to 118 films.

Deadline   October of each year.

[171]
FRANCIS M. KEVILLE MEMORIAL SCHOLARSHIP

Construction Management Association of America
Attn: CMAA Foundation
7926 Jones Branch Drive, Suite 800
McLean, VA 22101-3303
(703) 356-2622   Fax: (703) 356-6388
E-mail: foundation@cmaanet.org
Web: www.cmaafoundation.org

Summary   To provide financial assistance to minority and female undergraduate and graduate students working on a degree in construction management.

Eligibility   This program is open to women and members of minority groups who are enrolled as full-time undergraduate or graduate students. Applicants must have completed at least 1 year of study and have at least 1 full year remaining for a bachelor's or master's degree in construction management or a related field. Along with their application, they must submit essays on why they are interested in a career in construction management and why they should be awarded this scholarship. Selection is based on that essay (20%), academic performance (40%), recommendation of the faculty adviser (15%), and extracurricular activities (25%); a bonus of

5% is given to student members of the Construction Management Association of America (CMAA).

Financial Data   The stipend is $3,000. Funds are disbursed directly to the student's university.

Duration   1 year.

Number awarded   1 each year.

Deadline   June of each year.

[172]
FRANK KAZMIERCZAK MEMORIAL MIGRANT SCHOLARSHIP

Geneseo Migrant Center
Attn: Scholarship Funds
3 Mt. Morris-Leicester Road
Leicester, NY 14481
(585) 658-7960   Toll Free: (800) 245-5681
Fax: (585) 658-7969   E-mail: dkatter@gvboces.org
Web: www.migrant.net/migrant/scholarships/index.htm

Summary   To provide financial assistance for college to students from migrant farmworker families who are interested in preparing for a career in teaching.

Eligibility   This program is open to migrant farmworkers and their children who are interested in preparing for a career as a teacher. Priority is given to applicants who have experienced mobility within the past 3 years. They must submit a personal essay of 300 to 500 words on their reasons for wanting to become a teacher, 2 letters of recommendation, and an official school transcript. Selection is based on financial need, academic achievement, and history of migration for agricultural employment. U.S. citizenship is not required.

Financial Data   The stipend is $1,000.

Duration   1 year.

Number awarded   1 each year.

Deadline   January of each year.

[173]
FRANK T. MARTIN LEADERSHIP SCHOLARSHIP

Conference of Minority Transportation Officials
Attn: National Scholarship Program
1875 I Street, N.W., Suite 500
Washington, DC 20006
(703) 234-4072   Fax: (202) 318-0364
Web: www.comto.org/?page=Scholarships

Summary   To provide financial assistance to Hispanic American and other minority undergraduate and graduate students working on a degree in transportation or a related field.

Eligibility   This program is open to full-time undergraduate and graduate students who are working on a degree in transportation, engineering, planning, or a related discipline. They must be able to demonstrate leadership and active commitment to community service. Along with their application, they must submit a cover letter with a 500-word statement of career goals. Financial need is not considered in the selection process. U.S. citizenship or legal resident status is required.

Financial Data   The stipend is $3,000. Funds are paid directly to the recipient's college or university.

Duration   1 year.

Additional data The Conference of Minority Transportation Officials (COMTO) was established in 1971 to promote, strengthen, and expand the roles of minorities in all aspects of transportation. This program is sponsored by Atkins North America. Recipients are expected to attend the COMTO National Scholarship Luncheon.

Number awarded 1 each year.

Deadline May of each year.

[174]
FRIENDS OF SENATOR JACK PERRY MIGRANT SCHOLARSHIP

Geneseo Migrant Center
Attn: Scholarship Funds
3 Mt. Morris-Leicester Road
Leicester, NY 14481
(585) 658-7960   Toll Free: (800) 245-5681
Fax: (585) 658-7969   E-mail: dkatter@gvboces.org
Web: www.migrant.net/migrant/scholarships/index.htm

Summary To provide financial assistance for college to migrant farmworker high school seniors with a history of involvement in New York.

Eligibility This program is open to students from migrant farmworker families who have a history of migration to and/or within New York. Applicants must have senior status in high school and plans to attend a postsecondary institution or other advanced training, preferably in New York. Seniors at high schools outside New York are eligible if they have a history of movement to the state. If no eligible high school seniors apply, current college students may be considered. Along with their application, they must submit a statement of at least 250 words on their background and interest in higher education, at least 1 letter of recommendation, and a copy of their current Migrant Certificate of Eligibility (COE). Selection is based on demonstrated commitment to educational goals, participation in school and Migrant Education Outreach Program (MEOP) activities, participation in community and/or non-school activities, citizenship, evidence of high mobility (interstate or intrastate), record of overcoming unusual obstacles, and financial need.

Financial Data A stipend is awarded (amount not specified).

Duration 1 year.

Number awarded 1 or more each year.

Deadline April of each year.

[175]
GATES MILLENNIUM SCHOLARS PROGRAM

Bill and Melinda Gates Foundation
P.O. Box 10500
Fairfax, VA 22031-8044
Toll Free: (877) 690-GMSP   Fax: (703) 205-2079
Web: www.gmsp.org

Summary To provide financial assistance to Hispanic American and other outstanding low-income minority students, particularly those interested in majoring in specific fields in college.

Eligibility This program is open to African Americans, Alaska Natives, American Indians, Hispanic Americans, and Asian Pacific Islander Americans who are graduating high school seniors with a GPA of 3.3 or higher. Principals, teach-ers, guidance counselors, tribal higher education representatives, and other professional educators are invited to nominate students with outstanding academic qualifications, particularly those likely to succeed in the fields of computer science, education, engineering, library science, mathematics, public health, or science. Nominees should have significant financial need and have demonstrated leadership abilities through participation in community service, extracurricular, or other activities. U.S. citizenship, nationality, or permanent resident status is required. Nominees must be planning to enter an accredited college or university as a full-time, degree-seeking freshman in the following fall.

Financial Data The program covers the cost of tuition, fees, books, and living expenses not paid for by grants and scholarships already committed as part of the recipient's financial aid package.

Duration 4 years or the completion of the undergraduate degree, if the recipient maintains at least a 3.0 GPA.

Additional data This program, established in 1999, is funded by the Bill and Melinda Gates Foundation and administered by the United Negro College Fund with support from the American Indian Graduate Center, the Hispanic Scholarship Fund, and the Asian & Pacific Islander American Scholarship Fund.

Number awarded 1,000 new scholarships are awarded each year.

Deadline January of each year.

[176]
GATEWAYS TO THE LABORATORY PROGRAM

Cornell University
Attn: Weill Cornell/Rockefeller/Sloan-Kettering Tri-
 Institutional MD-PhD Program
Gateways to the Laboratory Program
1300 York Avenue, Room C-103
New York, NY 10065-4805
(212) 746-6023   Fax: (212) 746-8678
E-mail: mdphd@mcd.cornell.edu
Web: www.med.cornell.edu/mdphd/summerprogram

Summary To provide Hispanic American and other underrepresented minority or disadvantaged college freshmen and sophomores with an opportunity to participate in a summer research project in New York City through the Tri-Institutional MD-PhD Program of Weill Cornell Medical College, Rockefeller University, and Sloan-Kettering Institute.

Eligibility This program is open to college freshmen and sophomores who are defined by the National Institutes of Health (NIH) as in need of special recruitment and retention, i.e., members of racial and ethnic groups underrepresented in health-related sciences (American Indians or Alaska Natives, Blacks or African Americans, Hispanics or Latinos, and Native Hawaiians or Other Pacific Islanders), persons with disabilities, and individuals from disadvantaged backgrounds (low-income or from a rural or inner-city environment). Applicants must be interested in continuing on to a combined M.D./Ph.D. program following completion of their undergraduate degree. They should have a GPA of 3.0 or higher and have completed a college level calculus class. Along with their application, they must submit an essay summarizing their laboratory experience, research interests, and goals. U.S. citizenship or permanent resident status is required.

Financial Data Students receive a research stipend of $4,300 and reimbursement of travel expenses. At the end of the summer, 1 family member receives airfare and hotel accommodations to come to New York for the final presentations.

Duration 10 weeks, during the summer.

Additional data Interns work independently on a research project at Weill Cornell Medical College, Rockefeller University, or Memorial Sloan-Kettering Cancer Center, all located across the street from each other on the Upper East Side of New York City.

Number awarded 15 each year.

Deadline January of each year.

[177]
GE HISPANIC FORUM SCHOLARSHIP PROGRAM

Hispanic Scholarship Fund
Attn: Selection Committee
1411 West 190th Street, Suite 325
Gardena, CA 90248
Toll Free: (877) HSF-INFO   E-mail: scholar1@hsf.net
Web: www.hsf.net/Scholarship-Programs.aspx

Summary To provide financial assistance to Hispanic undergraduate and graduate students from designated states and communities who are working on a degree in specified fields.

Eligibility This program is open to U.S. citizens and permanent residents (must have a permanent resident card or a passport stamped I-551) who are of Hispanic heritage. Applicants must be enrolled as full-time sophomores, juniors, seniors, fifth-year undergraduates, or master's degree students at a 4-year college or university and have a GPA of 3.0 or higher. They must be working on a degree in accounting, aeronautics/aviation, aerospace engineering, biochemistry, bioengineering/biotechnology, biology, business administration, chemical engineering, chemistry, civil engineering, computational biology/bioinformatics, computer engineering, computer sciences, cybernetics/robotics, economics, electrical engineering, engineering, finance, industrial engineering/technology, information technology/management information systems, international business, management, manufacturing engineering, marketing, materials science/engineering, mathematics/statistics, mechanical engineering, neuroscience, nuclear engineering, petroleum engineering, physics, science, supply chain management, telecommunications. The program is limited to students who reside in and attend school in 1) the states of Arizona or New Hampshire; 2) Puerto Rico; or 3) the metropolitan areas of Atlanta, Austin, Boston, Chicago, Cincinnati, Dallas, Denver, Detroit, Erie (Pennsylvania), Fairfield County (Connecticut), Greenville, Hartford, Houston, Jacksonville, Kansas City (Missouri), Los Angeles, Louisville, Miami, Milwaukee, New York, Philadelphia (including southern New Jersey), Salt Lake City, San Antonio, San Francisco, Seattle, Schenectady, Twin Cities (Minnesota), Tampa Bay, or Wilmington (North Carolina). Selection is based on academic achievement, personal strengths, leadership, and financial need.

Financial Data The stipend is $2,500.

Duration 1 year.

Additional data This program is funded by the GE Hispanic Forum, which provides mentors to recipients.

Number awarded 1 or more each year.

Deadline January of each year.

[178]
GENERAL ELECTRIC FUND/LEAGUE OF UNITED LATIN AMERICAN CITIZENS SCHOLARSHIPS

League of United Latin American Citizens
Attn: LULAC National Education Service Centers
1133 19th Street, N.W., Suite 1000
Washington, DC 20036
(202) 835-9646   Fax: (202) 835-9685
E-mail: scholarships@lnesc.org
Web: www.lnesc.org/site/296/Scholarships

Summary To provide financial assistance to Hispanic and other minority students who are studying engineering or business in college.

Eligibility This program is open to minority students who will be enrolled as college sophomores and working full time on a baccalaureate degree in engineering or business at colleges or universities in the United States approved by the League of United Latin American Citizens (LULAC) and General Electric. Applicants must have a GPA of 3.25 or higher and be U.S. citizens or legal residents. Selection is based on academic performance, likelihood of preparing for a career in business or engineering, performance in business or engineering subjects, writing ability, extracurricular activities, and community involvement.

Financial Data The stipend is $5,000 per year. Funds are to be used to pay for tuition, required fees, room and board, and required educational materials and books; they are sent directly to the college or university and deposited in the scholarship recipient's name.

Duration 1 year; may be renewed if the recipient maintains a GPA of 3.0 or higher.

Additional data Funding for this program is provided by the GE Foundation. LULAC was established in 1929 to support the educational activities of Hispanics, but this scholarship is open to all minority students.

Number awarded Varies each year; recently, 9 of these scholarships were awarded.

Deadline August of each year.

[179]
GENERATION GOOGLE SCHOLARSHIPS

Google Inc.
Attn: Scholarships
1600 Amphitheatre Parkway
Mountain View, CA 94043-8303
(650) 253-0000   Fax: (650) 253-0001
E-mail: generationgoogle@google.com
Web: www.google.com

Summary To provide financial assistance to Hispanic Americans and members of other underrepresented groups planning to work on a bachelor's degree in a computer-related field.

Eligibility This program is open to high school seniors planning to enroll full time at a college or university in the United States or Canada. Applicants must be members of a group underrepresented in computer science: African Americans, Hispanics, American Indians, women, or people with a disability. They must be interested in working on a bachelor's degree in computer science, computer engineering, software engineering, or a related field. Selection is based on academic achievement (GPA of 3.2 or higher), leadership, commitment to and passion for computer science and technology through involvement in their community, and financial need.

Financial Data The stipend is $10,000 per year for U.S. students or $C5,000 for Canadian students.

Duration 1 year; may be renewed for up to 3 additional years or until graduation, whichever comes first.

Additional data Recipients are also invited to attend Google's Computer Science Summer Institute at either Mountain View, California or Cambridge, Massachusetts in the summer.

Number awarded Varies each year.

Deadline February of each year.

[180]
GEORGE CAMPBELL, JR. FELLOWSHIP IN ENGINEERING

National Action Council for Minorities in Engineering
Attn: University Programs
440 Hamilton Avenue, Suite 302
White Plains, NY 10601-1813
(914) 539-4010   Fax: (914) 539-4032
E-mail: scholarships@nacme.org
Web: www.nacme.org/NACME_D.aspx?pageid=105

Summary To provide financial assistance to Hispanic American and other underrepresented minority college sophomores majoring in engineering or related fields.

Eligibility This program is open to African American, Latino, and American Indian college sophomores who have a GPA of 3.0 or higher and have demonstrated academic excellence, leadership skills, and a commitment to science and engineering as a career. Applicants must be enrolled full time at an ABET-accredited engineering program. Fields of study include all areas of engineering as well as computer science, materials science, mathematics, operations research, or physics.

Financial Data The stipend is $5,000 per year. Funds are sent directly to the recipient's university.

Duration Up to 3 years.

Number awarded 1 each year.

Deadline April of each year.

[181]
GEORGE GENG ON LEE MINORITIES IN LEADERSHIP SCHOLARSHIP

Capture the Dream, Inc.
Attn: Scholarship Program
484 Lake Park Avenue, Suite 15
Oakland, CA 94610
(510) 343-3635   E-mail: info@capturethedream.org
Web: www.capturethedream.org/programs/scholarship.php

Summary To provide financial assistance to Hispanic Americans and other minorities in California who can demonstrate leadership and are interested in attending college in any state.

Eligibility This program is open to residents of California who are members of minority groups and either graduating high school seniors or current full-time undergraduates at 4-year colleges and universities in any state. Applicants must

submit a 1,000-word essay on why they should be selected to receive this scholarship, using their experiences within school, work, and home to display the challenges they have faced as a minority and how they overcame adversity to assume a leadership role. They should also explain how their career goals and future aspirations will build them as a future minority leader. Selection is based on academic performance, community service, leadership history, professional recommendations, and financial need. U.S. citizenship or permanent resident status is required.

Financial Data The stipend is $1,000.

Duration 1 year.

Number awarded 1 or more each year.

Deadline July of each year.

[182]
GERALDO RIVERA SCHOLARSHIP

National Association of Hispanic Journalists
Attn: Scholarship Committee
1050 Connecticut Avenue, N.W., Tenth Floor
Washington, DC 20036
(202) 662-7145   Toll Free: (888) 346-NAHJ
Fax: (202) 662-7144   E-mail: nahj@nahj.org
Web: www.nahj12.com/scholarships

Summary To provide financial assistance to college senior and graduate student members of the National Association of Hispanic Journalists (NAHJ) who are interested in preparing for a career in television broadcast journalism.

Eligibility This program is open to Hispanic American college seniors and graduate students who are interested in preparing for a career in English- or Spanish-language television broadcast journalism. Applicants must be enrolled full time at a college or university in the United States or Puerto Rico. They must be NAHJ members. Along with their application, they must submit transcripts, a 1-page resume, 2 letters of recommendation, work samples, and a 1,000-word autobiographical essay that includes why they are interested in a career in journalism, what inspired them to prepare for a career in the field, what hardships or obstacles they have experienced while trying to realize their goal of becoming a journalist, and the role Latino journalists play in the news industry. Selection is based on commitment to the field of journalism, academic achievement, awareness of the Latino community, and financial need.

Financial Data The stipend ranges up to $5,000.

Duration 1 year.

Number awarded 1 each year.

Deadline January of each year.

[183]
GERRY VANDAVEER SCHOLARSHIP

Kansas Association of Migrant Directors
c/o Cynthia Adcock
USD 305
P.O. Box 797
Salina, KS 67402
(785) 309-4718   E-mail: Cynthia.Adcock@usd305.com

Summary To provide financial assistance for college to current or former migrants graduating from high schools in Kansas.

Eligibility This program is open to seniors graduating from high schools in Kansas and GED recipients who are current or former migrants. Applicants must be planning to attend a college or university in Kansas as a full-time student. Along with their application, they must submit a paragraph about their educational goals, explaining why they want to go to college and describing their plans after graduation. Selection is based on the essay, GPA, school performance, and financial need.

Financial Data A stipend is awarded (amount not specified).

Duration 4 semesters (2 years).

Number awarded Varies each year; recently, 2 of these scholarships were awarded.

Deadline March of each year.

[184]
GILBERT G. POMPA MEMORIAL ENDOWED SCHOLARSHIP

¡Adelante! U.S. Education Leadership Fund
8415 Datapoint Drive, Suite 400
San Antonio, TX 78229
(210) 692-1971   Toll Free: (877) 692-1971
Fax: (210) 692-1951   E-mail: info@adelantefund.org
Web: www.adelantefund.org/#!scholarships/crij

Summary To provide financial assistance to undergraduates at colleges in Texas (especially Hispanic women) who are enrolled in a pre-law program.

Eligibility This program is open to full-time students who have completed at least 90 credit hours at an accredited college or university in Texas. Preference is given to women of Hispanic descent. Applicants may be majoring in any field, but preference is given to those enrolled in a pre-law program and/or planning to attend law school. They must be U.S. citizens or permanent residents and have a GPA of 2.75 or higher.

Financial Data The stipend is $1,000.

Duration 1 year.

Additional data This fund was established by the Hispanic Association of Colleges and Universities in 1997 and became a separate organization in 1999.

Number awarded Varies each year.

Deadline May of each year.

[185]
GO RED MULTICULTURAL SCHOLARSHIP FUND

American Heart Association
Attn: Go Red for Women
7272 Greenville Avenue
Dallas, TX 75231-4596
Toll Free: (800) AHA-USA1
E-mail: GoRedScholarship@heart.org
Web: www.goredforwomen.org/goredscholarship.aspx

Summary To provide financial assistance to women from multicultural backgrounds who are preparing for a career in a field of health care.

Eligibility This program is open to women who are currently enrolled at an accredited college, university, health care institution, or program and have a GPA of 3.0 or higher. Applicants must be undergraduates of Hispanic, African American, or other minority origin. They must be preparing for

a career as a nurse, physician, or allied health care worker. Selection is based on community involvement, a personal letter, transcripts, and 2 letters of recommendation.

Financial Data The stipend is $2,500.

Duration 1 year.

Additional data This program, which began in 2012, is supported by Macy's.

Number awarded Varies each year; recently, 16 of these scholarships were awarded.

Deadline November of each year.

[186]
GOLDEN APPLE SCHOLARS OF ILLINOIS

Golden Apple Foundation
Attn: Scholars Program
8 South Michigan Avenue, Suite 700
Chicago, IL 60603-3463
(312) 407-0006   Fax: (312) 407-0344
E-mail: info@goldenapple.org
Web: www.goldenapple.org/golden-apple-scholars

Summary To provide funding to high school seniors in Illinois (particularly minority and bilingual students) who wish to study education at an Illinois college and teach in the state.

Eligibility This program is open to high school seniors at schools in Illinois. Students must be nominated by a teacher, principal, guidance counselor, or other non-family adult; self-nominations are also accepted. Nominees must be committed to teaching as a profession and must be interested in attending 1 of 53 designated colleges and universities in Illinois. A limited number of openings are also available to sophomores at those designated Illinois institutions. The program strongly encourages nomination of prospective teachers for which there is currently a shortage, especially minority and bilingual teachers. Selection is based on 7 essays included on the application, ACT scores and transcripts, letters of reference, and an interview.

Financial Data Scholars receive a scholarship/loan of $2,500 per year for their freshman and sophomore year and $5,000 per year for their junior and senior year. They also receive a stipend of $2,000 per year for participating in a summer teaching internship. If they complete a bachelor's degree and teach for 5 years in an Illinois school of need, the loan is forgiven. Schools of need are defined as those either having Chapter I status by the U.S. Department of Education or having mediocre to poor PSAE or ISAT scores.

Duration 4 years, provided the recipient maintains a GPA of 2.0 or higher during the freshman year and 2.5 or higher in subsequent years. Students who enter the program as sophomores receive 2 years of support.

Additional data During the annual summer institutes, scholars participate in teaching internships and seminars on the art and craft of teaching. This program was established in 1988.

Number awarded Varies each year; recently, 110 of these scholarships were awarded.

Deadline Nominations must be submitted by November of each year.

[187]
GOLDEN DOOR SCHOLARS PROGRAM

Golden Door Scholars
c/o Red Ventures
1101 521 Corporate Center Drive
Fort Mill, SC 29707
E-mail: info@goldendoorscholars.org
Web: www.goldendoorscholars.org/apply-now.html

Summary To provide financial assistance for college to undocumented students, especially those from North Carolina and South Carolina.

Eligibility This program is open to undocumented students who are high school seniors or high school graduates who have not yet entered a 4-year college (including students currently attending a community college). Applicants must be planning to work on a 4-year degree. They must be eligible for Deferred Action for Childhood Arrivals (DACA). Along with their application, they must submit brief statements on their intended field of concentration, why they are choosing it, and why they should be selected as a recipient of this scholarship. Strong preference is given to applicants from North Carolina and South Carolina.

Financial Data The program provides funding to cover tuition (less other scholarships), room, and board. The program cooperates with participating colleges and universities in North Carolina and South Carolina that have agreed to provide recipients with substantial scholarship support or reduced tuition.

Duration Until completion of a 4-year degree.

Additional data This program began in 2012.

Number awarded Varies each year, depending on the availability of funding and support from participating institutions.

Deadline October of each year.

[188]
GOLDMAN SACHS SCHOLARSHIP FOR EXCELLENCE

Goldman Sachs
Attn: Human Capital Management
200 West Street, 25th Floor
New York, NY 10282
E-mail: Iris.Birungi@gs.com
Web: www.goldmansachs.com

Summary To provide financial aid and work experience to Hispanic American and other underrepresented minority students preparing for a career in the financial services industry.

Eligibility This program is open to undergraduate students of Black, Latino, or Native American heritage. Applicants must be entering their sophomore or junior year and have a GPA of 3.4 or higher. Students with all majors and disciplines are encouraged to apply, but they must be able to demonstrate an interest in the financial services industry. Along with their application, they must submit 2 essays of 500 words or fewer on the following topics: 1) why they are interested in the financial services industry; and 2) how they have demonstrated team-oriented leadership through their involvement with a campus-based or community-based organization. Selection is based on academic achievement, interest in the financial services industry, community involvement, and demonstrated leadership and teamwork capabilities.

Financial Data Sophomores receive a stipend of $5,000, a summer internship at Goldman Sachs, an opportunity to receive a second award upon successful completion of the internship, and an offer to return for a second summer internship. Juniors receive a stipend of $10,000 and a summer internship at Goldman Sachs.

Duration Up to 2 years.

Additional data This program was initiated in 1994 when it served only students at 4 designated Historically Black Colleges and Universities: Florida A&M University, Howard University, Morehouse College, and Spelman College. It has since been expanded to serve underrepresented minority students in all states.

Number awarded 1 or more each year.

Deadline January of each year.

[189]
GOOGLE SCHOLARSHIP PROGRAM

Hispanic College Fund
Attn: Scholarship Processing
1300 L Street, N.W., Suite 975
Washington, DC 20005
(202) 296-5400   Toll Free: (800) 644-4223
Fax: (202) 296-3774   E-mail: hcf-info@hispanicfund.org
Web: scholarships.hispanicfund.org/applications

Summary To provide financial assistance to Hispanic American upper-division and graduate students who are interested in preparing for a career in computer science or computer engineering.

Eligibility This program is open to U.S. citizens and permanent residents of Hispanic background (at least 1 grandparent must be 100% Hispanic) who are entering their junior or senior year of college or who are enrolled in graduate school. Applicants must be working on a bachelor's, master's, or Ph.D. degree in computer science or computer engineering and have a cumulative GPA of 3.0 or higher. They must be enrolled at an accredited college or university in the 50 states or Puerto Rico as a full-time student. Financial need is considered in the selection process.

Financial Data This stipend is $10,000. Funds are paid directly to the recipient's college or university to help cover tuition and fees.

Duration 1 year; recipients may reapply.

Additional data This program is sponsored by Google. All applications must be submitted online; no paper applications are available.

Number awarded Varies each year.

Deadline February of each year.

[190]
GORDON STAFFORD SCHOLARSHIP IN ARCHITECTURE

Gordon Stafford Scholarship
Attn: Scholarship Selection Committee
622 20th Street
Sacramento, CA 95814
(916) 930-5900   Fax: (916) 930-5800
E-mail: scholarship@gsscholarship.com
Web: www.skwarchitects.com/about/scholarship

Summary To provide financial assistance to Hispanic Americans and members of other minority groups from California who are interested in studying architecture at a college in any state.

Eligibility This program is open to California residents accepted by an accredited school of architecture in any state as first-year or transfer students. Applicants must be U.S. citizens or permanent residents who are persons of color (defined as Black, Hispanic, Native American, Pacific-Asian, or Asian-Indian). They must submit a 500-word statement expressing their desire to study architecture. Finalists are interviewed and must travel to Sacramento, California at their own expense for the interview.

Financial Data The stipend is $2,000 per year. That includes $1,000 deposited in the recipient's school account and $1,000 paid to the recipient directly.

Duration 1 year; may be renewed up to 4 additional years.

Additional data This program began in 1995 to celebrate the 50th anniversary of the architectural firm that sponsors it, Stafford King Wiese Architects.

Number awarded Up to 5 of these scholarships may be active at a time.

Deadline June of each year.

[191]
GOYA FOODS CULINARY ARTS AND FOOD SCIENCES SCHOLARSHIPS

Hispanic Scholarship Fund
Attn: Selection Committee
1411 West 190th Street, Suite 325
Gardena, CA 90248
Toll Free: (877) HSF-INFO   E-mail: scholar1@hsf.net
Web: www.hsf.net

Summary To provide financial assistance to Hispanic high school seniors from selected states who plan to attend college in any state and major in culinary arts or food science.

Eligibility This program is open to U.S. citizens and permanent residents (must have a permanent resident card or a passport stamped I-551) who are of Hispanic heritage and residents of California (Imperial, Kern, Kings, Los Angeles, Madera, Merced, Orange, Riverside, San Bernardino, San Diego, Santa Barbara, Tulare, or Ventura counties only), Connecticut, Delaware, Florida, Georgia, Illinois, Indiana, Kentucky, Louisiana, Maine, Maryland, Massachusetts, Michigan, Nevada, New Hampshire, New Jersey, New Mexico, New York, North Carolina, Ohio, Oklahoma, Pennsylvania, Rhode Island, South Carolina, Texas, Vermont, Virginia, or Wisconsin. Applicants must be graduating high school seniors planning to enroll full time at a 4-year college or university in any state and major in culinary arts or food science. They must have a GPA of 3.0 or higher. Selection is based on academic achievement, personal strengths, leadership, and financial need.

Financial Data The stipend is $5,000 per year.

Duration 1 year; may be renewed up to 3 additional years, provided the recipient completes at least 10 hours per month of community service.

Additional data This program began in 2012 with support from GOYA Foods.

Number awarded 4 each year.

Deadline January of each year.

[192]
GREATER HOUSTON RETAILERS ASSOCIATION AND COCA-COLA LIVE POSITIVELY SCHOLARSHIP PROGRAM

Hispanic Scholarship Fund
Attn: Selection Committee
1411 West 190th Street, Suite 325
Gardena, CA 90248
Toll Free: (877) HSF-INFO   E-mail: scholar1@hsf.net
Web: www.hsf.net

Summary To provide financial assistance to Hispanic high school seniors in Texas who plan to attend college in the United States or designated territories.

Eligibility This program is open to seniors of Hispanic heritage who are graduating from high schools in Texas and have a GPA of 3.0 or higher. Applicants must be U.S. citizens or permanent residents (must have a permanent resident card or a passport stamped I-551). They must be planning to enroll full time at an accredited 2- or 4-year college or university in the United States, Puerto Rico, the U.S. Virgin Islands, or Guam. Their proposed major may be in any field. Selection is based on academic achievement, personal strengths, leadership, and financial need.

Financial Data The stipend is $5,000 or $1,000.

Duration 1 year.

Additional data This program is jointly sponsored by the Greater Houston Retailers Association, Coca-Cola, and the Hispanic Scholarship Fund (HSF).

Number awarded 37 each year: 2 at $5,000 and 35 at $1,000.

Deadline December of each year.

[193]
GULF COAST CHAPTER AABE SCHOLARSHIPS

American Association of Blacks in Energy-Gulf Coast Chapter
Attn: Scholarship Committee
P.O. Box 1115
Gulfport, MS 39502
(850) 505-2294   E-mail: TELocket@southernco.com
Web: www.aabe.org/index.php?component=pages&id=322

Summary To provide financial assistance to Hispanic Americans and members of other underrepresented minority groups who are high school seniors in southern Alabama, Florida, or Mississippi and planning to major in an energy-related field at a college in any state.

Eligibility This program is open to seniors graduating from high schools in southern Alabama, Florida, or Mississippi and planning to attend a college or university in any state. Applicants must be African Americans, Hispanics, or Native Americans who have a GPA of 3.0 or higher and who can demonstrate financial need. Their intended major must be business, engineering, technology, mathematics, the physical sciences, or other energy-related field. Along with their application, they must submit a 350-word statement on why they should receive this scholarship, how their professional career objectives relate to energy, and any other relevant information.

Financial Data The stipend is $1,500.

Duration 1 year.

Additional data The winner is eligible to compete for regional and national scholarships.

Number awarded 6 each year.

Deadline February of each year.

[194]
HACEMOS SCHOLARSHIP PROGRAM OF THE HISPANIC COLLEGE FUND

Hispanic College Fund
Attn: Scholarship Processing
1300 L Street, N.W., Suite 975
Washington, DC 20005
(202) 296-5400   Toll Free: (800) 644-4223
Fax: (202) 296-3774   E-mail: hcf-info@hispanicfund.org
Web: scholarships.hispanicfund.org/applications

Summary To provide financial assistance to Hispanic American students from designated areas who are working on an undergraduate degree in any field.

Eligibility This program is open to U.S. citizens and permanent residents who are either of Hispanic background (at least 1 grandparent must be 100% Hispanic) or are the dependent of a member of HACEMOS (the Hispanic/Latino Employee Association of AT&T) in 1 of its chapters. Applicants must be enrolled or planning to enroll full time at an accredited college or university in the United States or Puerto Rico and have a GPA of 3.0 or higher. They may be working on an undergraduate degree in any field. Preference is given to applicants who can demonstrate financial need.

Financial Data Stipends range from $500 to $2,000, depending on need and academic achievement. Funds are paid directly to the recipient's college or university to help cover tuition and fees.

Duration 1 year; recipients may reapply.

Additional data This program is sponsored by HACEMOS. Its chapters are located in Arizona, Atlanta, Austin, central Florida, Chicago, Connecticut, Dallas, Detroit Metro, Fresno, Fort Worth, Houston, Joplin, Kansas City, Lubbock, Michigan, Nashville, New York, North Carolina, Oklahoma, Orange County, Puerto Rico, San Antonio, San Diego, San Ramon, south Florida, St. Louis, and Washington, D.C. All applications must be submitted online; no paper applications are available.

Number awarded Varies each year.

Deadline March of each year.

[195]
HANA SCHOLARSHIPS

United Methodist Church
Attn: General Board of Higher Education and Ministry
Office of Loans and Scholarships
1001 19th Avenue South
P.O. Box 340007
Nashville, TN 37203-0007
(615) 340-7344   Fax: (615) 340-7367
E-mail: umscholar@gbhem.org
Web: www.gbhem.org

Summary To provide financial assistance to upper-division and graduate Methodist students who are of Hispanic, Asian, Native American, or Pacific Islander ancestry.

Eligibility This program is open to full-time juniors, seniors, and graduate students at accredited colleges and universities in the United States who have been active, full members of a United Methodist Church (UMC) for at least 1 year prior to

applying. Applicants must have at least 1 parent who is Hispanic, Asian, Native American, or Pacific Islander. They must be able to demonstrate involvement in their Hispanic, Asian, or Native American (HANA) community in the UMC. Selection is based on that involvement, academic ability (GPA of at least 2.85), and financial need. U.S. citizenship or permanent resident status is required.

Financial Data The maximum stipend is $3,000 for undergraduates or $5,000 for graduate students.

Duration 1 year; recipients may reapply.

Number awarded 50 each year.

Deadline February of each year.

[196]
HARVARD SCHOOL OF PUBLIC HEALTH SUMMER PROGRAM IN BIOLOGICAL SCIENCES IN PUBLIC HEALTH

Harvard School of Public Health
Attn: Division of Biological Sciences
655 Huntington Avenue, Building 2, Room 111
Boston, MA 02115
(617) 432-4397   Fax: (617) 432-0433
E-mail: BPH@hsph.harvard.edu
Web: www.hsph.harvard.edu

Summary To enable Hispanic American and other minority or disadvantaged college science students to participate in a summer research project in biological sciences at Harvard School of Public Health.

Eligibility This program is open to U.S. citizens, nationals, and permanent residents who are 1) members of ethnic groups underrepresented in graduate education (African Americans, Hispanics/Latinos, American Indians, Alaskan Natives, Pacific Islanders, and Native Hawaiians); 2) first-generation college students; and 3) students from an economically disadvantaged background. Applicants must be entering their junior or senior year with a GPA of 3.0 or higher and be interested in preparing for a research career in the biological sciences. They must be interested in participating in a summer research project related to biological science questions that are important to the prevention of disease, especially such public health questions as cancer, infections (malaria, tuberculosis, parasites), lung diseases, common diseases of aging, diabetes, and obesity.

Financial Data The program provides a stipend of at least $3,600, a travel allowance of up to $500, and free dormitory housing.

Duration 9 weeks, beginning in mid-June.

Additional data Recipients conduct research under the mentorship of Harvard faculty members who are specialists in cancer cell biology, immunology and infectious diseases, molecular and cellular toxicology, environmental health sciences, nutrition, and cardiovascular research. Funding for this program is provided by the National Institutes of Health.

Number awarded Up to 10 each year.

Deadline January of each year.

[197]
HARVARD-SMITHSONIAN CENTER FOR ASTROPHYSICS SOLAR SUMMER INTERN PROGRAM

Harvard-Smithsonian Center for Astrophysics
Attn: Solar REU Program
60 Garden Street, Mail Stop 70
Cambridge, MA 02138
(617) 496-7703   E-mail: dnickerson-at-cfa@harvard.edu
Web: www.cfa.harvard.edu/opportunities/solar_reu

Summary To provide an opportunity for undergraduates (particularly Hispanic Americans, other underrepresented minorities, women, and students with disabilities) to participate in a summer research program at the Harvard-Smithsonian Center for Astrophysics (CfA).

Eligibility This program is open to U.S. citizens, nationals, and permanent residents who are full-time undergraduates, preferably those entering their junior or senior year. Applicants must be interested in working during the summer on a project in either of 2 CfA divisions: high energy astrophysics (which focuses on X-ray astronomy) or solar, stellar, and planetary sciences (which focuses on understanding star and planet formation and the physical processes in the Sun, stars, and stellar systems). Applications from underrepresented minorities, persons with disabilities, and women are encouraged.

Financial Data The stipend is $5,000. Housing and travel expenses are also covered.

Duration 10 weeks during the summer.

Number awarded 8 each year.

Deadline February of each year.

[198]
HATTIE J. HILLIARD SCHOLARSHIP

Wisconsin Women of Color Network, Inc.
Attn: Scholarship Committee
P.O. Box 2337
Madison, WI 53701-2337
E-mail: contact@womenofcolornetwork-wis.org
Web: www.womenofcolornetwork-wis.org/scholarship.html

Summary To provide financial assistance to Hispanic Americans and other women of color from Wisconsin who are interested in studying art at a school in any state.

Eligibility This program is open to residents of Wisconsin who are women of color enrolled or planning to enroll at a college, university, or vocational/technical school in any state. Applicants must be a member of 1 of the following groups: African American, Asian, American Indian, or Hispanic. Their field of study must be art, graphic art, commercial art, or a related area. They must be able to demonstrate financial need. Along with their application, they must submit a 1-page essay on how this scholarship will help them accomplish their educational goal. U.S. citizenship is required.

Financial Data A stipend is awarded (amount not specified).

Duration 1 year.

Additional data This program began in 1995.

Number awarded 1 each year.

Deadline May of each year.

[199]
HAZ LA U SCHOLARSHIP PROGRAM OF THE HISPANIC SCHOLARSHIP FUND

Hispanic Scholarship Fund
Attn: Selection Committee
1411 West 190th Street, Suite 325
Gardena, CA 90248
Toll Free: (877) HSF-INFO   E-mail: scholar1@hsf.net
Web: www.hsf.net

Summary To provide financial assistance to Hispanic American high school seniors who are interested in working on their first undergraduate degree.

Eligibility This program is open to U.S. citizens and permanent residents (must have a permanent resident card or a passport stamped I-551) of Hispanic heritage. Applicants must be high school seniors planning to enroll full time at an accredited institution in the United States, Puerto Rico, Guam, or the U.S. Virgin Islands as a freshman at a 4-year college or university or a first-year student at a 2-year college. They must have a GPA of 3.0 or higher. Selection is based on academic achievement, personal strengths, leadership, and financial need.

Financial Data The stipend is $15,000 or $2,500.

Duration 1 year; nonrenewable.

Additional data This program is sponsored by Colgate-Palmolive as part of its "Haz La U" ("Make the U") program.

Number awarded 21 each year: 1 at $15,000 and 20 at $2,500.

Deadline December of each year.

[200]
HEALTH RESEARCH AND EDUCATIONAL TRUST SCHOLARSHIPS

New Jersey Hospital Association
Attn: Health Research and Educational Trust
760 Alexander Road
P.O. Box 1
Princeton, NJ 08543-0001
(609) 275-4224   Fax: (609) 452-8097
Web: www.njha.com/education/scholarships

Summary To provide financial assistance to New Jersey residents (particularly Hispanic Americans, other minorities, and women) who are working on an undergraduate or graduate degree in a field related to health care administration at a school in any state.

Eligibility This program is open to residents of New Jersey enrolled in an upper-division or graduate program in hospital or health care administration, public administration, nursing, or other allied health profession at a school in any state. Graduate students working on an advanced degree to prepare to teach nursing are also eligible. Applicants must have a GPA of 3.0 or higher and be able to demonstrate financial need. Along with their application, they must submit a 2-page essay (on which 50% of the selection is based) describing their academic plans for the future. Minorities and women are especially encouraged to apply.

Financial Data The stipend is $2,000.

Duration 1 year.

Additional data This program began in 1983.

Number awarded Varies each year; recently, 3 of these scholarships were awarded.

Deadline July of each year.

[201]
HEARTLAND LATINO LEADERSHIP CONFERENCE ACADEMIC SCHOLARSHIPS

Heartland Latino Leadership Conference
Attn: Academic Scholarship Committee
P.O. Box 7570
Omaha, NE 68107
(402) 554-2830 E-mail: Scholarship@heartlandlatino.org
Web: www.heartlandlatino.org

Summary To provide financial assistance to Latino residents of Nebraska who are interested in attending college in the state.

Eligibility This program is open to Nebraska residents of Latino/Hispanic heritage who are graduating high school seniors, current college students, or adults interested in attending college to work on their first undergraduate degree. Applicants must be attending or planning to attend a college or university in Nebraska. Along with their application, they must submit a 2-page essay that includes how they feel a college education will help them make a difference in the Latino community, their concept of leadership and a person in their life who demonstrates those qualities, the impact of their leadership within extracurricular activities in which they have participated during the past 2 years, and a significant challenge facing Latinos and strategies to address the challenges.

Financial Data The stipend is $1,000. Funds are paid directly to the student's postsecondary institution.

Duration 1 year.

Number awarded 15 each year.

Deadline September of each year.

[202]
H-E-B/ADELANTE FUTURE LEADERS SCHOLARSHIP

¡Adelante! U.S. Education Leadership Fund
8415 Datapoint Drive, Suite 400
San Antonio, TX 78229
(210) 692-1971   Toll Free: (877) 692-1971
Fax: (210) 692-1951   E-mail: info@adelantefund.org
Web: www.adelantefund.org/#!scholarships/crij

Summary To provide financial assistance to Hispanic students entering their freshman or sophomore year at a college in selected areas of Texas.

Eligibility This program is open to Hispanic students entering their freshman or sophomore year at community colleges and universities in selected areas of Texas. Applicants must enroll full time but they may be majoring in any field. They must have a GPA of 3.0 or higher, provide a resume of their community service activities, be U.S. citizens or permanent residents, agree to attend the Adelante Leadership Institute, and provide a letter of recommendation.

Financial Data The stipend is $1,000.

Duration 1 year.

Additional data This fund was established by the Hispanic Association of Colleges and Universities in 1997 and became a separate organization in 1999. This program is sponsored by H.E. Butt Grocery Company (H-E-B). The eligible areas of Texas are Austin, Beeville, Brownsville, Corpus Christi, Del Rio, Eagle Pass, Edinburg, Houston, Kerrville, Kingsville, Laredo, McAllen, Midland, San Angelo, San Antonio, San Marcos, Seguin, Uvalde, and Victoria.

Number awarded Varies each year.

Deadline May of each year.

[203]
HECUA SCHOLARSHIPS FOR SOCIAL JUSTICE

Higher Education Consortium for Urban Affairs
Attn: Student Services
2233 University Avenue West, Suite 210
St. Paul, MN 55114-1698
(651) 287-3300   Toll Free: (800) 554-1089
Fax: (651) 659-9421   E-mail: hecua@hecua.org
Web: www.hecua.org/programs/scholarships

Summary To provide financial assistance to Hispanic Americans and other students from targeted groups who are enrolled in programs of the Higher Education Consortium for Urban Affairs (HECUA) at participating colleges and universities.

Eligibility This program is open to students at member colleges and universities who are participating in HECUA programs. Applicants must be a first-generation college student, from a low-income family, and/or a student of color. Along with their application, they must submit a reflective essay, drawing on their life experiences and their personal and academic goals, on what they believe they can contribute to the mission of HECUA to equip students with the knowledge, experiences, tools, and passion to address issues of social justice and social change. The essay should also explain how the HECUA program will benefit them and the people, issues, and communities they care about.

Financial Data The stipend is $1,500. Funds are applied as a credit to the student's HECUA program fees for the semester.

Duration 1 semester.

Additional data This program began in 2006. Consortium members include Augsburg College (Minneapolis, Minnesota), Augustana College (Sioux Falls, South Dakota), Carleton College (Northfield, Minnesota), College of Saint Scholastica (Duluth, Minnesota), Colorado College (Colorado Springs, Colorado), Denison University (Granville, Ohio), Gustavus Adolphus College (St. Peter, Minnesota), Hamline University (St. Paul, Minnesota), Macalester College (St. Paul, Minnesota), Saint Mary's University (Winona, Minnesota), Saint Catherine University (St. Paul, Minnesota), Saint Olaf College (Northfield, Minnesota), Swarthmore College (Swarthmore, Pennsylvania), University of Minnesota (Twin Cities, Duluth, Morris, Crookston, Rochester), University of Saint Thomas (St. Paul, Minnesota), and Viterbo University (La Crosse, Wisconsin).

Number awarded Several each year.

Deadline April of each year for summer and fall programs; November of each year for January and spring programs.

[204]
HENAAC HIGH SCHOOL SENIOR/COLLEGE FRESHMAN AWARDS

Great Minds in STEM
Attn: HENAAC Scholars Program
602 Monterey Pass Road
Monterey Park, CA 91754
(323) 262-0997   Fax: (323) 262-0946
E-mail: gcruz@greatmindsinstem.org
Web: www.greatmindsinstem.org

Summary To provide financial assistance to Hispanic high school seniors and college freshmen planning to major in fields of science, technology, engineering, or mathematics (STEM).

Eligibility This program is open to Hispanic high school seniors and college freshmen who are enrolled or planning to enroll at a college or university and major in a STEM field. Applicants must be of Hispanic origin and/or must significantly participate in and promote organizations and activities in the Hispanic community. They must have a GPA of 3.0 or higher. Along with their application, they must submit a 700-word essay on a topic that changes annually. Selection is based on leadership, academic achievements, and campus and community activities; financial need is not considered.

Financial Data Stipends range from $500 to $10,000.

Duration 1 year; recipients may reapply.

Additional data The Hispanic Engineer National Achievement Awards Conference (HENAAC) was established in 1989 and initiated a scholarship program in 2000. In 2010, the sponsoring organization officially adopted its current name, but it continues to hold the annual HENAAC conference, at which the scholarships are presented. Recipients must attend the conference to accept their scholarship.

Number awarded Varies each year; recently, 5 of these scholarships were awarded.

Deadline April of each year.

[205]
HENAAC STUDENT LEADERSHIP AWARDS

Great Minds in STEM
Attn: HENAAC Scholars Program
602 Monterey Pass Road
Monterey Park, CA 91754
(323) 262-0997   Fax: (323) 262-0946
E-mail: gcruz@greatmindsinstem.org
Web: www.greatmindsinstem.org

Summary To provide financial assistance to Hispanic undergraduate and graduate students working on a degree in fields of science, technology, engineering, or mathematics (STEM).

Eligibility This program is open to Hispanic undergraduate and graduate students who are enrolled at a college or university and working on a degree in a STEM field. Applicants must be of Hispanic origin and/or must significantly participate in and promote organizations and activities in the Hispanic community. They must have a GPA of 3.0 or higher. Along with their application, they must submit a 700-word essay on a topic that changes annually; recently, students were asked to write on how they see their academic major contributing to global efforts and technology and how they, in their field of study, will contribute to global progress as well as actively contribute to their local communities. Selection is

based on leadership, academic achievements, and campus and community activities; financial need is not considered.

Financial Data The stipend is $10,000.

Duration 1 year.

Additional data The Hispanic Engineer National Achievement Awards Conference (HENAAC) was established in 1989 and initiated a scholarship program in 2000. In 2010, the sponsoring organization officially adopted its current name, but it continues to hold the annual HENAAC conference, at which the scholarships are presented. Recipients must attend the conference to accept their scholarship.

Number awarded 2 each year: 1 undergraduate and 1 graduate student.

Deadline April of each year.

[206]
HILDA SANCHEZ-HENKE MEMORIAL SCHOLARSHIP

Minnesota Association of Administrators of State and
   Federal Education Programs
c/o Matthew Mohs, Treasurer
2140 Timmy Street
St. Paul, MN 55120
(651) 632-3787   E-mail: matthew.mohs@spps.org
Web: www.maasfep.org/scholarships.shtml

Summary To provide financial assistance to Hispanic high school seniors in Minnesota who have participated in a Title I or Migrant Education Program and plan to attend college in any state.

Eligibility This program is open to seniors graduating from high schools in Minnesota who have participated in a Title I or Migrant Education Program while in high school. Applicants must be planning to attend a 2- or 4-year college, university, or vocational/technical school in any state. They must have a GPA of 2.5 or higher. Along with their application, they must submit 1) a 100-word essay on how the Title I or Migrant Education Program helped them with their education; 2) a 100-word essay on their plans for the future; and 3) a 250-word essay on a challenging experience they have had in their life and how they overcame it. Selection is based on those essays, desire for education beyond high school, study habits, positive attitude, and interest in school, community, and/or work-related activities.

Financial Data The stipend is $2,000.

Duration 1 year.

Number awarded 1 each year.

Deadline January of each year.

[207]
HISPANIC AMERICAN COMMITMENT TO EDUCATIONAL RESOURCES (HACER) SCHOLARSHIP PROGRAM

Ronald McDonald House Charities
Attn: U.S. Scholarship Program
One Kroc Drive
Oak Brook, IL 60523
(630) 623-7048   Fax: (630) 623-7488
E-mail: info@rmhc.org
Web: rmhc.org/what-we-do/rmhc-u-s-scholarships

Summary To provide financial assistance for college to Hispanic high school seniors in specified geographic areas.

Eligibility This program is open to high school seniors in designated McDonald's market areas who are legal residents of the United States and have at least 1 parent of Hispanic heritage. Applicants must be planning to enroll full time at an accredited 2- or 4-year college, university, or vocational/technical school. They must have a GPA of 2.7 or higher. Along with their application, they must submit a personal statement, up to 2 pages in length, on their Hispanic background, career goals, and desire to contribute to their community; information about unique, personal, or financial circumstances may be added. Selection is based on that statement, high school transcripts, a letter of recommendation, and financial need.

Financial Data Most awards are $1,000 per year. Funds are paid directly to the recipient's school.

Duration 1 year; nonrenewable.

Additional data This program is a component of the Ronald McDonald House Charities U.S. Scholarship Program, which began in 1985. It is administered by International Scholarship and Tuition Services, Inc., 200 Crutchfield Avenue, Nashville, TN 37210, (615) 320-3149, Fax: (615) 320-3151, E-mail: info@applyists.com. For a list of participating McDonald's market areas, contact Ronald McDonald House Charities (RMHC).

Number awarded Varies each year; since RMHC began this program, it has awarded more than $44 million in scholarships.

Deadline January of each year.

[208]
HISPANIC AMERICAN POLICE COMMAND OFFICERS ASSOCIATION SCHOLARSHIP AWARD

Boy Scouts of America
Attn: Learning for Life
1329 West Walnut Hill Lane
P.O. Box 152225
Irving, TX 75015-2225
(972) 580-2428   Toll Free: (855) 806-9992
Fax: (972) 580-2137   E-mail: exploring@lflmail.org
Web: exploring.learningforlife.org

Summary To provide financial assistance for college to Explorer Scouts of Hispanic or Latino heritage who plan a career in law enforcement.

Eligibility This program is open to Explorer Scouts who are of Hispanic or Latino ancestry and seniors in high school or current undergraduate students. Applicants must be active members of a Law Enforcement Explorer post registered with Boy Scouts of America and working on or planning to work on a college degree in law enforcement or criminal justice. They must have a GPA of 3.0 or higher and a record of demonstrated leadership and volunteer service experience. Along with their application, they must submit a 750-word essay on why they want to prepare for a career in the law enforcement or criminal justice profession. Selection is based on that essay, academic record, ability to make a meaningful contribution to society in present and future, character and ethics, and leadership abilities in Law Enforcement Exploring and their community.

Financial Data The stipend is $1,000. Funds are disbursed directly to the recipient's college or university.

Duration 1 year; nonrenewable.

Additional data This program is sponsored by the Hispanic American Police Command Officers Association,.

Number awarded 1 each year.

Deadline April of each year.

[209]
HISPANIC ANNUAL SALUTE SCHOLARSHIPS

Hispanic Annual Salute
Attn: Ray Hurtado
P.O. Box 40720
Denver, CO 80204
(303) 996-3965   Fax: (303) 577-8111
E-mail: rhurtado@denver.bbb.org
Web: www.hispanicannualsalute.org/scholarshipinfo.html

Summary To provide financial assistance to Hispanic high school seniors in Colorado who have been active in community service and plan to attend college in any state.

Eligibility This program is open to seniors graduating from high schools in Colorado and planning to enroll at a college or university in any state. Applicants must have made notable volunteer contributions to the Hispanic community, especially in unpaid volunteer activities not related to fulfilling a requirement for a school activity. They must have a cumulative GPA of 2.5 or higher. Along with their application, they must submit a 300-word essay on what motivates them to volunteer, how they encourage others to volunteer, and the volunteer activity that has impacted their life the most and why. Selection is based on that essay, letters of recommendation, and academic achievement.

Financial Data The stipend is $2,000.

Duration 1 year.

Additional data Recipients are required to attend the Annual Salute gala in February.

Number awarded Varies each year; recently, 10 of these scholarships were awarded.

Deadline November of each year.

[210]
HISPANIC BUSINESS COUNCIL SCHOLARSHIPS

Hispanic Business Council Scholarship Foundation of
 New Jersey, Inc.
492-C Cedar Lane, Suite 313
Teaneck, NJ 07666
E-mail: info@hbcsf.org
Web: www.hbcsf.org

Summary To provide financial assistance to Hispanic high school seniors in New Jersey who plan to attend college in any state.

Eligibility This program is open to seniors graduating from high schools in New Jersey who are of Hispanic heritage. Applicants must be planning to enroll full time at an accredited college, university, community college, or technical school in any state. They must have a GPA of 3.0 or higher and be able to demonstrate financial need. Along with their application, they must submit a 250-word essay on 1 of the following topics: 1) how their academic studies will impact their future; or 2) a significant experience, achievement, or ethical dilemma they faced and its impact on them.

Financial Data A stipend is awarded (amount not specified). Funds are paid directly to the recipient's college.

Duration 1 year; may be renewed, provided the recipient maintains a GPA of 3.0 or higher and completes at least 80 hours of community service.

Number awarded Varies each year.

Deadline February of each year.

[211]
HISPANIC HERITAGE YOUTH AWARDS

Hispanic Heritage Foundation
1444 Duke Street
Alexandria, VA 22314
(202) 861-9797   Toll Free: (866) 665-2112
Fax: (202) 861-9799   E-mail: info@hispanicheritage.org
Web: www.hispanicheritage.org/hispanic.php

Summary To recognize and reward, with college scholarships or grants for community service projects, Hispanic high school juniors from selected metropolitan areas throughout the country who have excelled in various areas of activity.

Eligibility This program is open to high school juniors who are U.S. citizens or permanent residents and of Hispanic heritage (at least 1 parent must be able to trace family origins to Spain, Portugal, Brazil, Latin America, or the Spanish-speaking Caribbean). Recently, awards were available to students in 10 metropolitan regions: Atlanta, Chicago, Dallas, Houston, Los Angeles, Miami, New York, Phoenix, San Jose/San Francisco Bay area, and Washington, D.C. Applicants competed in the following 5 categories: business (for students interested in the field of business, management, business development, entrepreneurship, etc.); education (for students interested in education, teaching, coaching, or academic administration); engineering and mathematics (for students who have an interest and skill in technology, mathematics, or engineering or wish to prepare for a career in those fields); health care science (for students who express an interest in a branch of medicine, including those who are preparing for a career as a doctor, nurse, pharmacist, health care administrator, or public health specialist); and community service (for students who demonstrate a passion for helping the community and others, have a strong commitment to community service projects, and have spent countless hours volunteering). They must have a GPA of 3.0 or higher. Along with their application, they must submit an essay that describes their personal qualities and strengths, dedication to community service and the impact it has had on their life, future career goals, areas of interest, and significance of heritage and/or family in their life. Selection criteria include, but are not limited to, the following: academic achievement, compelling essay responses, meritorious achievements in the applicant's chosen category, contribution to the community, overall character as a role model, and letters of recommendation.

Financial Data In each category and each city, regional winners receive $1,000. Awards are in the form of educational grants that recipients may use for their college education or to fund a community service project that they will plan, oversee, and sustain. The regional winners then advance to a national competition. National winners receive a state-of-the-art laptop computer and an all-expense paid trip to the national awards ceremony.

Duration The awards are presented annually and are nonrenewable.

Additional data This program began in 1998 with sponsorship by the Fannie Mae Foundation for 5 cities and 1 category. As the program has gained additional sponsors, it has expanded to additional categories and cities. Recent sponsors have included BBVA for business, Target for education, ExxonMobil for engineering and mathematics, CVS Caremark for health care science, and Southwest Airlines for community service. Awardees must attend, at their own expense, a local awards ceremony for the region they have selected.

Number awarded Recently, 50 regional winners were selected: 1 in each of the 5 categories from each of the 10 cities. From those, 5 national winners were chosen: 1 in each of the categories.

Deadline June of each year.

[212]
HISPANIC LEADERSHIP DEVELOPMENT FUND

United Methodist Church
General Board of Global Ministries
Attn: United Methodist Committee on Relief
Health and Welfare Ministries
475 Riverside Drive, Room 330
New York, NY 10115
(212) 870-3871   Toll Free: (800) UMC-GBGM
E-mail: jyoung@gbgm-umc.org
Web: new.gbgm-umc.org/umcor/work/health/scholarships

Summary To provide financial assistance to Methodists and other Christians of Hispanic descent who are preparing for a career in a health-related field.

Eligibility This program is open to undergraduate and graduate students who are U.S. citizens or permanent residents of Hispanic descent. Applicants must be professed Christians, preferably United Methodists. They must be working on an undergraduate or graduate degree to enter or continue in a health-related field. Financial need is considered in the selection process.

Financial Data The stipend is $2,000.

Duration 1 year.

Additional data This program began in 1986.

Number awarded Varies each year.

Deadline June of each year.

[213]
HISPANIC METROPOLITAN CHAMBER SCHOLARSHIPS

Hispanic Metropolitan Chamber
Attn: Scholarship Committee
333 S.W. Fifth Avenue, Suite 100
P.O. Box 1837
Portland, OR 97207
(503) 222-0280   Fax: (503) 243-5597
E-mail: hmcc@qwest.net
Web: www.hmccoregon.com/scholarships

Summary To provide financial assistance to Hispanic residents of Oregon and Clark County, Washington who are interested in attending college or graduate school in any state.

Eligibility This program is open to residents of Oregon and Clark County, Washington who are of Hispanic ancestry. Applicants must have a GPA of 3.0 or higher and be enrolled or planning to enroll in an accredited community college, 4-year university, or graduate school in any state. Along with their application, they must submit 250-word essays on how their heritage has influenced their life and long-term goals, and either why they should be selected to receive another scholarship (for renewal applicants) or a community activity in which they have participated and how it has benefited the Latino community in the past year (for first-time applicants). If they wish to be considered for a scholarship for low-income families, they may also submit documentation of financial need. U.S. citizenship or permanent resident status is required.

Financial Data Stipends range from $2,000 to $5,500.

Duration 1 year; may be renewed.

Additional data Matching funds are provided to students who choose to attend George Fox University, Lewis and Clark College, Linfield College, Oregon State University, Portland State University, University of Oregon, University of Portland, Western Oregon University, Whitman College, or Willamette University.

Number awarded Varies each year; recently, 50 of these scholarships were awarded: 1 at $5,500, 1 at $5,000, 2 at $4,500, 2 at $3,250, 3 at $3,000, 10 at $2,500, and 31 at $2,000.

Deadline January of each year.

[214]
HISPANIC PUBLIC RELATIONS ASSOCIATION SCHOLARSHIP PROGRAM

Hispanic Public Relations Association-Los Angeles
  Chapter
Attn: Scholarship Program Director
P.O. Box 86760
Los Angeles, CA 90086-0760
(323) 359-8869   E-mail: hpra.scholarships@yahoo.com
Web: www.hpra-usa.org/la/scholarship-program

Summary To provide financial assistance to Hispanic undergraduate students from California who are attending college in the state and preparing for a career in public relations.

Eligibility This program is open to residents of California who are of at least 25% Hispanic descent and entering the junior or senior year at a 4-year college or university in the state. Applicants must have a GPA of 2.7 or higher cumulatively and 3.0 or higher in their major subject. They must be majoring in public relations, communications, journalism, advertising, and/or marketing. Students majoring in other disciplines but planning to work in the public relations industry are also eligible. Along with their application, they must submit a letter of recommendation, official university transcripts, a 1- to 2-page personal statement explaining their career and educational aspirations as well as their involvement in the Hispanic community, a 1-page resume, documentation of financial need, and writing samples. Any materials submitted in Spanish must include an English translation. The applicant whose contributions to the community are judged most outstanding receives the Esther Renteria Community Service Scholarship.

Financial Data The stipend is $2,000. The student selected as the winner of the Esther Renteria Community Service Scholarship receives an additional $1,000.

Duration 1 year.

Additional data Recipients are expected to attend the sponsor's Premio Awards dinner in October.

Number awarded Varies each year; recently, 5 of these scholarships were awarded (of whom 1 received the Esther Renteria Community Service Scholarship).

Deadline April of each year.

[215]
HISPANIC SCHOLARSHIP FUND/3S SCHOLARSHIP

Hispanic Scholarship Fund
Attn: Selection Committee
1411 West 190th Street, Suite 325
Gardena, CA 90248
Toll Free: (877) HSF-INFO   E-mail: scholar1@hsf.net
Web: www.hsf.net

Summary To provide financial assistance for undergraduate study to Hispanic American residents of designated areas.

Eligibility This program is open to U.S. citizens and permanent residents (must have a permanent resident card or a passport stamped I-551) of Hispanic heritage who are 25 years of age or younger. Applicants must be enrolled or planning to enroll full time at a 2- or 4-year accredited institution in the United States, Puerto Rico, the U.S. Virgin Islands, or Guam and have a GPA of 3.0 or higher. They must be residents of 1) designated cities in California, Missouri, or Texas; 2) specified cities (Atlanta, Chicago, Hartford, Nashville, New Haven, New York City; 3) the states of Arizona, Florida, Michigan, New Jersey, North Carolina, Oklahoma, or Pennsylvania; 4) the commonwealth of Puerto Rico; or 5) Washington, D.C. Selection is based on academic achievement, personal strengths, leadership, and financial need.

Financial Data The stipend ranges from $1,000 to $2,500, depending on the student's location.

Duration 1 year.

Additional data This program is sponsored by HACEMOS (the Hispanic/Latino Employee Association of AT&T) as a benefit for dependents of its members, but all qualified Hispanic students are eligible to apply. For a list of eligible cities, contact the Hispanic Scholarship Fund.

Number awarded Varies each year.

Deadline February of each year.

[216]
HISPANIC SCHOLARSHIP FUND GENERAL COLLEGE SCHOLARSHIPS

Hispanic Scholarship Fund
Attn: Selection Committee
1411 West 190th Street, Suite 325
Gardena, CA 90248
Toll Free: (877) HSF-INFO   E-mail: scholar1@hsf.net
Web: www.hsf.net

Summary To provide financial assistance for college or graduate school to Hispanic American students.

Eligibility This program is open to U.S. citizens and permanent residents (must have a permanent resident card or a passport stamped I-551). Applicants must be of Hispanic heritage and enrolled or planning to enroll full time in a degree program at an accredited community college, 4-year university, or graduate school in the United States, Puerto Rico, Guam, or the U.S. Virgin Islands. They must have a GPA of 3.0 or higher and have applied for federal financial aid. Selection is based on academic achievement, personal strengths, leadership, and financial need.

Financial Data Stipends normally range from $1,000 to $5,000 per year.

Duration 1 year; recipients may reapply.

Additional data Since this program began in 1975, more than $334 million has been awarded to nearly 100,000 Hispanic students.

Number awarded Varies each year; recently, this program awarded more than $29 million in scholarships to more than 4,300 students.

Deadline December of each year.

[217]
HOLY FAMILY MEMORIAL SCHOLARSHIP PROGRAM

Holy Family Memorial
Attn: Human Resources
2300 Western Avenue
P.O. Box 1450
Manitowoc, WI 54221-1450
(920) 320-4031   Toll Free: (800) 994-3662, ext. 4031
Fax: (920) 320-8522   E-mail: recruiter@hfmhealth.org
Web: www.hfmhealth.org/scholarships

Summary To provide funding to students (particularly Hispanic Americans and other minorities) who are working on a degree in a health-related area and willing to work at a designated hospital in Wisconsin following completion of their degree.

Eligibility This program is open to students working on a degree in health-related areas that include, but are not limited to, nursing, pharmacy, sonography, occupational therapy, physical therapy, speech/language pathology, respiratory therapy, or radiology. Applicants must have a GPA of 3.0 or higher. Selection is based on a personal interview, likelihood for professional success, customer service orientation, work ethic, enthusiasm, and professionalism. Minorities are especially encouraged to apply.

Financial Data Stipends are $800 per semester ($1,600 per year) for students at technical colleges, $2,000 per semester ($4,000 per year) for students at public universities, or $2,500 per semester ($5,000 per year) for students at private universities. Recipients must commit to working 6 months for each semester of support received at Holy Family Memorial in Manitowoc, Wisconsin following completion of their degree.

Duration 1 semester; renewable.

Number awarded Varies each year.

Deadline Deadline not specified.

[218]
HONEYWELL INTERNATIONAL SCHOLARSHIPS

Society of Women Engineers
Attn: Scholarship Selection Committee
203 North LaSalle Street, Suite 1675
Chicago, IL 60601-1269
(312) 596-5223   Toll Free: (877) SWE-INFO
Fax: (312) 644-8557   E-mail: scholarships@swe.org
Web: societyofwomenengineers.swe.org

Summary To provide financial assistance to women (particularly minority women) who are interested in studying specified fields of engineering in college.

Eligibility This program is open to women who are graduating high school seniors or rising college sophomores, juniors, or seniors. Applicants must be enrolled or planning to enroll full time at an ABET-accredited 4-year college or university and major in computer science or aerospace, chemical, computer, electrical, industrial, manufacturing, materials, or mechanical engineering. They must have a GPA of 3.5 or higher. Preference is given to members of groups underrepresented in computer science and engineering. U.S. citizenship or permanent resident status is required. Financial need is considered in the selection process.

Financial Data The stipend is $5,000.

Duration 1 year.

Additional data This program is sponsored by Honeywell International Inc.

Number awarded 3 each year.

Deadline February of each year for current college students; May of each year for high school seniors.

[219]
HPRA-NY SCHOLARSHIP PROGRAM

Hispanic Public Relations Association-New York Chapter
c/o Andy Checo, President
MundoFox New York
28 East 28th Street, 12th Floor
New York, NY 10016
(212) 378-0400   Fax: (212) 378-0470
E-mail: info@ny.npra-usa.org
Web: www.hpra-usa.org/ny/scholarships

Summary To provide financial assistance to Hispanic undergraduate students from Connecticut, New Jersey, and New York who are attending college in those states and preparing for a career in public relations.

Eligibility This program is open to residents of Connecticut, New Jersey, and New York who are of Hispanic descent and entering the junior or senior year at a 4-year college or university in those states. Applicants must have a GPA of 2.7 or higher cumulatively and 3.0 or higher in their major subject. They must be majoring in public relations, communications, journalism, advertising, and/or marketing. Along with their application, they must submit a letter of recommendation, official university transcripts, a 1-page personal statement explaining their career and educational aspirations as well as their involvement in the Hispanic community, and a 1-page resume.

Financial Data The stipend is $2,000.

Duration 1 year.

Additional data This program began in 2013. Recipients are invited to attend the sponsor's Premio Awards dinner in Los Angeles in October.

Number awarded 1 each year.

Deadline August of each year.

[220]
IBM CORPORATION SWE SCHOLARSHIPS

Society of Women Engineers
Attn: Scholarship Selection Committee
203 North LaSalle Street, Suite 1675
Chicago, IL 60601-1269
(312) 596-5223   Toll Free: (877) SWE-INFO
Fax: (312) 644-8557   E-mail: scholarships@swe.org
Web: societyofwomenengineers.swe.org

Summary To provide financial assistance to undergraduate women (particularly Hispanic American women and those from other underrepresented minority groups) who are majoring in designated engineering specialties.

Eligibility This program is open to women who are entering their sophomore or junior year at a 4-year ABET-accredited college or university. Applicants must be working full time on a degree in computer science or electrical or computer engineering and have a GPA of 3.4 or higher. Preference is given to members of groups underrepresented in engineering or computer science. Selection is based on merit. U.S. citizenship or permanent resident status is required.

Financial Data The stipend is $1,000.

Duration 1 year.

Additional data This program is sponsored by the IBM Corporation.

Number awarded 5 each year.

Deadline February of each year.

[221]
IDAHO LATINO SCHOLARSHIP FUND

Idaho Hispanic Chamber of Commerce
Attn: Idaho Latino Scholarship Foundation
c/o Trudy McGavin, Education Committee Chair
1605 South Phillippi Street
Boise, ID 83705
(208) 891-9883   E-mail: info@idaholsf.org
Web: www.idahosaberfoundation.org

Summary To provide financial assistance to Latino residents of Idaho who are attending or planning to attend a college or university in the state.

Eligibility This program is open to residents of Idaho who are of Hispanic/Latino descent. Applicants must be graduating high school seniors planning to attend or college students already attending a college, university, or vocational/technical school in Idaho. They must have a GPA of 2.5 or higher and a record of leadership in school, community, and/or other service organizations that promote, enhance, or strengthen diversity. Along with their application, they must submit an essay on an assigned topic; their essay should include information on their personal family background and history; academic, leadership, and community service experience; plan of study and future goals; and the financial obstacles that they feel are impacting their ability to engage in postsecondary education.

Financial Data The stipend provides full payment of tuition and fees, to a maximum of $5,000 per year.

Duration 1 year.

Additional data This program began in 2007 when the sponsor was named the Idaho Saber Foundation.

Number awarded 1 or more each year. Since the program was established, it has awarded 7 scholarships.

Deadline April of each year.

[222]
ILLINOIS DREAM FUND SCHOLARSHIPS

Illinois Dream Fund
191 North Wacker Drive, Suite 3700
Chicago, IL 60606-1698
E-mail: info@illinoisdreamfund.org
Web: www.illinoisdreamfund.org

Summary To provide financial assistance to undocumented residents of Illinois who are interested in attending college in any state.

Eligibility This program is open to undocumented immigrants who are incoming freshmen, current undergraduates, or transfer students. Applicants must have resided with their parents or guardians while attending high school in Illinois and have graduated (or be graduating) from a high school or received a GED in Illinois after attending an Illinois high school for at least 3 years. They must have a GPA of 2.5 or higher and be attending or planning to attend a college or university in any state. Financial need is considered in the selection process.

Financial Data The stipend is $6,000 for students at 4-year institutions or $2,000 for students at 2-year colleges. Funds are paid directly to the recipient's school.

Duration 1 year.

Number awarded Varies each year.

Deadline February of each year.

[223]
ILLINOIS LEGISLATIVE LATINO CAUCUS FOUNDATION SCHOLARSHIPS

Illinois Legislative Latino Caucus Foundation
c/o Jesse H. Ruiz
Drinker Biddle
191 North Wacker Drive, Suite 3700
Chicago, IL 60606-1698
(312) 569-1135   E-mail: jesse.ruiz@dbr.com
Web: www.illcf.org

Summary To provide financial assistance to Latinos and other residents of Illinois who are attending college in the state.

Eligibility This program is open to residents of Illinois currently enrolled as an undergraduate at a 2- or 4-year college or university in the state. Applicants must submit a 250-word statement explaining why receipt of this scholarship will help them achieve their educational and career goals. Financial need is considered in the selection process.

Financial Data A stipend is awarded (amount not specified).

Duration 1 year.

Number awarded Varies each year.

Deadline October of each year.

[224]
ILLINOIS MIGRANT COUNCIL ADULT EDUCATION SCHOLARSHIPS

Illinois Migrant Council
Attn: Director of Migrant Education Services
118 South Clinton Street, Suite 500
Chicago, IL 60661
(312) 663-1522   Fax: (312) 663-1994
E-mail: bpessin@illinoismigrant.org
Web: www.illinoismigrant.org

Summary To provide financial assistance for college to Hispanic and other minority migrant and seasonal farmworkers and their families in Illinois.

Eligibility This program is open to Illinois residents who are Hispanic or other minority migrant or seasonal farmworkers and their families. Applicants must have been accepted by an Illinois vocational institute or 2- or 4-year college or university. They must have a high school diploma or GED and be able to meet low income guidelines.

Financial Data A stipend is awarded (amount not specified).

Duration 1 year.

Number awarded Varies each year.

Deadline Applications may be submitted at any time.

[225]
ILLINOIS NURSES FOUNDATION CENTENNIAL SCHOLARSHIP

Illinois Nurses Association
Attn: Illinois Nurses Foundation
105 West Adams Street, Suite 1420
Chicago, IL 60603
(312) 419-2900   Fax: (312) 419-2920
E-mail: inf@illinoisnurses.com
Web: www.illinoisnurses.com

Summary To provide financial assistance to nursing undergraduate and graduate students who are Hispanic American or members of other underrepresented groups.

Eligibility This program is open to students working on an associate, bachelor's, or master's degree at an accredited NLNAC or CCNE school of nursing. Applicants must be members of a group underrepresented in nursing (African Americans, Hispanics, American Indians, Asians, and males). Undergraduates must have earned a passing grade in all nursing courses taken to date and have a GPA of 2.85 or higher. Graduate students must have completed at least 12 semester hours of graduate work and have a GPA of 3.0 or higher. All applicants must be willing to 1) act as a spokesperson to other student groups on the value of the scholarship to continuing their nursing education; and 2) be profiled in any media or marketing materials developed by the Illinois Nurses Foundation. Along with their application, they must submit a narrative of 250 to 500 words on how they, as nurses, plan to affect policy at either the state or national level that impacts on nursing or health care generally, or how they believe they will impact the nursing profession in general.

Financial Data A stipend is awarded (amount not specified).

Duration 1 year.

Number awarded 1 or more each year.

Deadline March of each year.

[226]
ILUMINA SCHOLARSHIP PROGRAM

The Pro Bolivia Committee USA
P.O. Box 41267
Arlington, VA 22204
(571) 234-7354   E-mail: iluminascholarship@gmail.com
Web: www.proboliviausa.org/educacion/beca_ilumina

Summary To provide financial assistance to residents of California, Maryland, Virginia, and Washington D.C. who are of Bolivian descent and interested in attending college in any state.

Eligibility This program is open to residents of California, Maryland, Virginia, and Washington, D.C. who are graduating high school seniors or undergraduates currently enrolled at an accredited postsecondary institution in any state. Applicants must be Bolivian or of Bolivian descent (either parent born in Bolivia). They must have a GPA of 2.8 or higher. Along with their application, they must submit a 300-word essay on how they have contributed to their Bolivian community. Selection is based that essay, academic achievement, extracurricular activities, leadership positions in the community, and financial need.

Financial Data The stipend is $1,000.

Duration 1 year; nonrenewable.

Number awarded 6 each year.

Deadline June of each year.

[227]
INDIANA CHAPTER AABE SCHOLARSHIPS

American Association of Blacks in Energy-Indiana Chapter
Attn: Scholarship Committee
P.O. Box 44531
Indianapolis, IN 46244
(317) 684-4934   E-mail: aabram@nisource.com
Web: www.aabe.org/index.php?component=pages&id=348

Summary To provide financial assistance to Hispanic Americans and members of other underrepresented minority groups who are high school seniors in Indiana and planning to major in an energy-related field at a college in any state.

Eligibility This program is open to seniors graduating from high schools in Indiana and planning to work on a bachelor's degree at a college or university in any state. Applicants must be African Americans, Hispanics, or Native Americans who have a GPA of 3.0 or higher and are able to demonstrate financial need. Their intended major must be a field of business, engineering, physical science, mathematics, or technology related to energy. Along with their application, they must submit a 350-word statement on why they should receive this scholarship, their professional career objectives, and any other relevant information.

Financial Data The stipend is $1,000 or $500.

Duration 1 year; nonrenewable.

Additional data Winners are eligible to compete for regional and national scholarships.

Number awarded 3 each year: 1 at $1,000 and 2 at $500.

Deadline February of each year.

[228]
INDIANA INDUSTRY LIAISON GROUP SCHOLARSHIP

Indiana Industry Liaison Group
c/o Tony Pickell, Vice Chair
AAP Precision Planning, LLC
6215 Meridian Street West Drive
Indianapolis, IN 46260
(317) 590-4797 E-mail: vchair@indianailg.org
Web: www.indianailg.org/scholardetails.html

Summary To provide financial assistance to Hispanic American and other students from any state who are enrolled at colleges and universities in Indiana and have been involved in activities to promote diversity.

Eligibility This program is open to residents of any state currently enrolled at an accredited college or university in Indiana. Applicants must either 1) be enrolled in programs or classes related to diversity/Affirmative Action (AA)/Equal Employment Opportunity (EEO); or 2) have work or volunteer experience with diversity/AA/EEO organizations. Along with their application, they must submit an essay of 400 to 500 words on 1 of the following topics: 1) their personal commitment to diversity/AA/EEO within their community or business; 2) a time or situation in which they were able to establish and/or sustain a commitment to diversity; 3) a time when they have taken a position in favor of affirmative action and/or diversity; or 4) activities in which they have participated within their community that demonstrate their personal commitment to moving the community's diversity agenda forward. Financial need is not considered in the selection process.

Financial Data The stipend is $1,000.

Duration 1 year.

Number awarded 1 each year.

Deadline January of each year.

[229]
INDIANA MINORITY TEACHER/SPECIAL EDUCATION SERVICES SCHOLARSHIP

State Student Assistance Commission of Indiana
Attn: Grants and Scholarships
W462 Indiana Government Center South
402 West Washington Street
Indianapolis, IN 46204
(317) 232-2355 Toll Free: (888) 528-4719 (within IN)
Fax: (317) 232-3260 E-mail: grants@ssaci.in.gov
Web: www.in.gov/ssaci/2342.htm

Summary To provide funding to Hispanic and Black undergraduate students in Indiana interested in preparing for a teaching career and to other residents of the state preparing for a career in special education, occupational therapy, or physical therapy.

Eligibility This program is open to 1) Black and Hispanic students seeking teacher certification; 2) students seeking special education teaching certification; or 3) students seeking occupational or physical therapy certification. Applicants must be Indiana residents and U.S. citizens who are enrolled or accepted for enrollment as full-time students at an academic institution in Indiana. Students who are already enrolled in college must have a GPA of 2.0 or higher. Applicants must be preparing to teach in an accredited elementary or secondary school in Indiana or to work as an occupational or physical therapist at a school or rehabilitation facility. Financial need may be considered, but it is not a requirement. In the selection process, awards are presented in the following priority order: 1) minority students seeking a renewal scholarship; 2) newly-enrolling minority students; 3) non-minority students seeking a renewal scholarship; and 4) newly-enrolling non-minority students.

Financial Data Minority students demonstrating financial need may receive up to $4,000 per year. For non-minority students, the maximum award is $1,000. For 3 out of the 5 years following graduation, recipients must teach full time in an elementary or secondary school in Indiana or practice as an occupational or physical therapist at a school or rehabilitation facility in the state. If they fail to meet that service requirement, they are required to reimburse the state of Indiana for all funds received.

Duration 1 year; may be renewed up to 3 additional years if recipients maintain a 2.0 GPA. They may, however, take up to 6 years to complete the program from the start of receiving the first scholarship.

Additional data This program began in 1988 to address the critical shortage of Black and Hispanic teachers in Indiana. An amendment in 1990 added the field of special education, and in 1991 the fields of occupational and physical therapy were added. Participating colleges in Indiana select the recipients. Students must submit their application to the financial aid office of the college they plan to attend (not to the State Student Assistance Commission of Indiana).

Number awarded Varies each year.

Deadline Each participating college or university establishes its own filing deadline for this program.

[230]
INTERMOUNTAIN SECTION AWWA DIVERSITY SCHOLARSHIP

American Water Works Association-Intermountain
Section
Attn: Member Services Coordinator
3430 East Danish Road
Sandy, UT 94093
(801) 712-1619, ext. 2 Fax: (801) 487-6699
E-mail: nicoleb@ims-awwa.org
Web: ims-awwa.site-ym.com/group/StudentPO

Summary To provide financial assistance to Hispanic Americans, other minorities, and women who are interested in working on an undergraduate or graduate degree in the field of water quality, supply, and treatment at a university in Idaho or Utah.

Eligibility This program is open to 1) women; and 2) students who identify as Hispanic or Latino, Black or African American, Native Hawaiian or other Pacific Islander, Asian, or American Indian or Alaska Native. Applicants must be entering or enrolled in an undergraduate or graduate program at a college or university in Idaho or Utah that relates to water quality, supply, or treatment. Along with their application, they must submit a 2-page essay on their academic interests and career goals and how those relate to water quality, supply, or treatment. Selection is based on that essay, letters of recommendation, and potential to contribute to the field of water quality, supply, and treatment in the Intermountain West.

Financial Data The stipend is $1,000. The winner also receives a 1-year student membership in the Intermountain

Section of the American Water Works Association (AWWA) and a 1-year subscription to *Journal AWWA*.

Duration   1 year; nonrenewable.

Number awarded   1 each year.

Deadline   October of each year.

[231]
INTERPUBLIC GROUP SCHOLARSHIP AND INTERNSHIP

New York Women in Communications, Inc.
Attn: NYWICI Foundation
355 Lexington Avenue, 15th Floor
New York, NY 10017-6603
(212) 297-2133   Fax: (212) 370-9047
E-mail: nywicipr@nywici.org
Web: www.nywici.org/foundation/scholarships

Summary   To provide financial aid and work experience to Hispanic American and other minority women who are residents of designated eastern states and enrolled as juniors at a college in any state to prepare for a career in advertising or public relations.

Eligibility   This program is open to female residents of New York, New Jersey, Connecticut, or Pennsylvania who are from ethnically diverse groups and currently enrolled as juniors at a college or university in any state. Also eligible are women who reside outside the 4 states but are currently enrolled at a college or university within 1 of the 5 boroughs of New York City. Applicants must be preparing for a career in advertising or public relations and have a GPA of 3.2 or higher. They must be available for a summer internship with Interpublic Group (IPG) in New York City. Along with their application, they must submit a 2-page resume; a personal essay of 300 words on an assigned topic that changes annually; 2 letters of recommendation; and an official transcript. Selection is based on academic record, need, demonstrated leadership, participation in school and community activities, honors and other awards or recognition, work experience, goals and aspirations, and unusual personal and/or family circumstances. U.S. citizenship is required.

Financial Data   The scholarship stipend ranges up to $10,000; the internship is salaried (amount not specified).

Duration   1 year.

Additional data   This program is sponsored by IPG, a holding company for a large number of firms in the advertising industry.

Number awarded   2 each year.

Deadline   January of each year.

[232]
ISBA SCHOLARSHIPS

Idaho State Broadcasters Association
1674 West Hill Road, Suite 3
Boise, ID 83702
(208) 345-3072   Fax: (208) 343-8946
E-mail: isba@qwestoffice.net
Web: bestinbroadcasting.com

Summary   To provide financial assistance to students (particularly minority and other diverse students) at Idaho colleges and universities who are preparing for a career in the broadcasting field.

Eligibility   This program is open to full-time students at Idaho schools who are preparing for a career in broadcasting, including business administration, sales, journalism, or engineering. Applicants must have a GPA of at least 2.0 for the first 2 years of school or 2.5 for the last 2 years. Along with their application, they must submit a letter of recommendation from the general manager of a broadcasting station that is a member of the Idaho State Broadcasters Association and a 1-page essay describing their career plans and why they want the scholarship. Applications are encouraged from a broad and diverse student population. Financial need is not considered in the selection process.

Financial Data   The stipend is $1,000.

Duration   1 year.

Number awarded   At least 2 each year.

Deadline   March of each year.

[233]
ITW SCHOLARSHIPS

Society of Women Engineers
Attn: Scholarship Selection Committee
203 North LaSalle Street, Suite 1675
Chicago, IL 60601-1269
(312) 596-5223   Toll Free: (877) SWE-INFO
Fax: (312) 644-8557   E-mail: scholarships@swe.org
Web: societyofwomenengineers.swe.org

Summary   To provide financial assistance to Hispanic Americans and other undergraduate women majoring in designated engineering specialties.

Eligibility   This program is open to women who are entering their junior year at a 4-year ABET-accredited college or university. Applicants must be working full time on a degree in computer science, electrical or mechanical engineering, or polymer science. They must have a GPA of 3.0 or higher. Preference is given to members of groups underrepresented in engineering or computer science. Selection is based on merit. U.S. citizenship or permanent resident status is required.

Financial Data   The stipend is $2,500 per year.

Duration   1 year; may be renewed 1 additional year.

Additional data   This program is sponsored by Illinois Tool Works, Inc.

Number awarded   2 each year.

Deadline   February of each year.

[234]
J. PARIS MOSLEY SCHOLARSHIP

Cleveland Foundation
Attn: Scholarship Processing
1422 Euclid Avenue, Suite 1300
Cleveland, OH 44115-2001
(216) 861-3810   Fax: (216) 861-1729
E-mail: Hello@clevefdn.org
Web: www.clevelandfoundation.org

Summary   To provide financial assistance for college to high school seniors in any state who are deaf (preference given to Hispanic Americans and other underrepresented minority applicants) or whose primary caregivers are deaf.

Eligibility   This program is open to high school seniors in any state who are deaf or hard of hearing or the children or grandchildren of deaf or hard of hearing parents or grandparents. Applicants must be planning to attend a college, university, vocational school, or other postsecondary program in any state. They must use some form of sign language, have a GPA of 2.5 or higher, and be able to demonstrate financial need. Preference is given to students of African American, Latino American, or Native American descent.

Financial Data A stipend is awarded (amount not specified).

Duration 1 year.

Number awarded 1 or more each year.

Deadline April of each year.

[235]
JACKIE ROBINSON SCHOLARSHIPS

Jackie Robinson Foundation
Attn: Education and Leadership Development Program
75 Varick Street, Second Floor
New York, NY 10013-1917
(212) 290-8600   Fax: (212) 290-8081
E-mail: general@jackierobinson.org
Web: www.jackierobinson.org

Summary To provide financial assistance for college to Hispanic American and other minority high school seniors.

Eligibility This program is open to members of an ethnic minority group who are high school seniors accepted at a 4-year college or university. Applicants must have a mathematics and critical reading SAT score of 1000 or higher or ACT score of 21 or higher. Selection is based on academic achievement, financial need, dedication towards community service, and leadership potential. U.S. citizenship is required.

Financial Data The maximum stipend is $7,500 per year.

Duration 4 years.

Additional data The program also offers personal and career counseling on a year-round basis, a week of interaction with other scholarship students from around the country, and assistance in obtaining summer jobs and permanent employment after graduation. It was established in 1973 by a grant from Chesebrough-Pond.

Number awarded Varies each year; recently, 181 of these scholarships were awarded.

Deadline March of each year.

[236]
JAMES B. MORRIS SCHOLARSHIPS

James B. Morris Scholarship Fund
Attn: Scholarship Selection Committee
P.O. Box 12145
Des Moines, IA 50312
(515) 864-0922
Web: www.morrisscholarship.org

Summary To provide financial assistance to Hispanic American and other minority undergraduate, graduate, and law students from Iowa.

Eligibility This program is open to minority students (African Americans, Asian/Pacific Islanders, Hispanics, or Native Americans) who are interested in working on an undergraduate or graduate degree. Applicants must be either Iowa residents attending a college or university anywhere in the United States or non-Iowa residents who are attending a college or university in Iowa. Along with their application, they must submit an essay of 250 to 500 words on why they are applying for

this scholarship, activities or organizations in which they are involved, and their future plans. Selection is based on the essay, academic achievement (GPA of 2.5 or higher), community service, and financial need. U.S. citizenship is required.

Financial Data The stipend ranges from $1,000 to $2,500 per year.

Duration 1 year; may be renewed.

Additional data This fund was established in 1978 in honor of the J.B. Morris family, who founded the Iowa branch of the National Association for the Advancement of Colored People and published the *Iowa Bystander* newspaper. The program includes the Ann Chapman Scholarships, the Vincent Chapman, Sr. Scholarships, and the Brittany Hall Memorial Scholarships.

Number awarded Varies each year; recently, 19 of these scholarships were awarded.

Deadline March of each year.

[237]
JAMES CARLSON MEMORIAL SCHOLARSHIP

Oregon Student Access Commission
Attn: Grants and Scholarships Division
1500 Valley River Drive, Suite 100
Eugene, OR 97401-2146
(541) 687-7395   Toll Free: (800) 452-8807, ext. 7395
Fax: (541) 687-7414   TDD: (800) 735-2900
E-mail: awardinfo@osac.state.or.us
Web: www.oregonstudentaid.gov/scholarships.aspx

Summary To provide financial assistance to Oregon residents from diverse environments (including Hispanic Americans) who are majoring in education on the undergraduate or graduate school level at a school in any state.

Eligibility This program is open to residents of Oregon who are U.S. citizens or permanent residents and enrolled at a college or university in any state. Applicants must be either 1) college seniors or fifth-year students majoring in elementary or secondary education; or 2) graduate students working on an elementary or secondary certificate. Full-time enrollment and financial need are required. Priority is given to 1) students who come from diverse environments and submit an essay of 250 to 350 words on their experience living or working in diverse environments; 2) dependents of members of the Oregon Education Association; and 3) applicants committed to teaching autistic children.

Financial Data Stipends for scholarships offered by the Oregon Student Access Commission (OSAC) range from $200 to $10,000 but recently averaged $2,300.

Duration 1 year.

Additional data This program is administered by the OSAC with funds provided by the Oregon Community Foundation.

Number awarded Varies each year; recently, 3 of these scholarships were awarded.

Deadline February of each year.

[238]
JAMES J. WYCHOR SCHOLARSHIPS

Minnesota Broadcasters Association
Attn: Scholarship Program
3033 Excelsior Boulevard, Suite 440
Minneapolis, MN 55416
(612) 926-8123   Toll Free: (800) 245-5838
Fax: (612) 926-9761
E-mail: llasere@minnesotabroadcasters.com
Web: www.minnesotabroadcasters.com/membership

Summary To provide financial assistance to minority or other Minnesota residents interested in studying broadcasting at a college in any state.

Eligibility This program is open to residents of Minnesota who are accepted or enrolled at an accredited postsecondary institution in any state offering a broadcast-related curriculum. Applicants must have a high school or college GPA of 3.0 or higher and must submit a 500-word essay on why they wish to prepare for a career in broadcasting or electronic media. Employment in the broadcasting industry is not required, but students who are employed must include a letter from their general manager describing the duties they have performed as a radio or television station employee and evaluating their potential for success in the industry. Financial need is not considered in the selection process. Some of the scholarships are awarded only to minority or women candidates.

Financial Data The stipend is $1,500.

Duration 1 year; recipients who are college seniors may reapply for an additional 1-year renewal as a graduate student.

Number awarded 10 each year, distributed as follows: 3 within the 7-county metro area, 5 allocated geographically throughout the state (northeast, northwest, central, southeast, southwest), and 2 reserved specifically for women and minority applicants.

Deadline June of each year.

[239]
JIMMY A. YOUNG MEMORIAL EDUCATION RECOGNITION AWARD

American Association for Respiratory Care
Attn: American Respiratory Care Foundation
9425 North MacArthur Boulevard, Suite 100
Irving, TX 75063-4706
(972) 243-2272   Fax: (972) 484-2720
E-mail: info@arcfoundation.org
Web: www.arcfoundation.org

Summary To provide financial assistance to college students, especially Hispanic Americans and other minorities, interested in becoming respiratory therapists.

Eligibility Candidates must be enrolled in an accredited respiratory therapy program, have completed at least 1 semester/quarter of the program, and have a GPA of 3.0 or higher. Preference is given to nominees of minority origin. Applications must include 6 copies of an original referenced paper on some aspect of respiratory care and letters of recommendation. The foundation prefers that the candidates be nominated by a school or program, but any student may initiate a request for sponsorship by a school (in order that a deserving candidate is not denied the opportunity to compete simply because the school does not initiate the application).

Financial Data The stipend is $1,000. The award also provides airfare, 1 night's lodging, and registration for the association's international congress.

Duration 1 year.

Number awarded 1 each year.

Deadline June of each year.

[240]
JOHN AND MURIEL LANDIS SCHOLARSHIPS

American Nuclear Society
Attn: Scholarship Coordinator
555 North Kensington Avenue
La Grange Park, IL 60526-5535
(708) 352-6611   Toll Free: (800) 323-3044
Fax: (708) 352-0499   E-mail: outreach@ans.org
Web: www.new.ans.org/honors/scholarships

Summary To provide financial assistance to undergraduate or graduate students (particularly Hispanic Americans, other minorities, and women) who are interested in preparing for a career in nuclear-related fields and can demonstrate financial need.

Eligibility This program is open to undergraduate and graduate students at colleges or universities located in the United States who are preparing for, or planning to prepare for, a career in nuclear science, nuclear engineering, or a nuclear-related field. Qualified high school seniors are also eligible. Applicants must have greater than average financial need and have experienced circumstances that render them disadvantaged. Along with their application, they must submit an essay on their academic and professional goals, experiences that have affected those goals, etc. Selection is based on that essay, academic achievement, letters of recommendation, and financial need. Women and members of minority groups are especially urged to apply. U.S. citizenship is not required.

Financial Data The stipend is $5,000, to be used to cover tuition, books, fees, room, and board.

Duration 1 year; nonrenewable.

Number awarded Up to 9 each year.

Deadline January of each year.

[241]
JOHN S. MARTINEZ LEADERSHIP SCHOLARSHIP

National Hispanic Caucus of State Legislators
444 North Capitol Street, N.W., Suite 404
Washington, DC 20001
(202) 434-8070   Fax: (202) 434-8072
E-mail: rhina@nhcsl.org
Web: www.nhcsl.org/scholarship.php

Summary To provide financial assistance for college to Hispanic high school students in states that have an Hispanic member of the state legislature.

Eligibility This program is open to juniors and seniors at public high schools in any of the 36 states that have an Hispanic member of the state legislature. Candidates must be nominated by a school official or an Hispanic legislator. Nominees must be of Hispanic descent, have a GPA of 3.0 or higher, be U.S. citizens, and be planning to enroll full time at a college or university in any state. Financial need is considered in the selection process.

Financial Data The stipend is $3,000.

Duration 1 year; nonrenewable.

Additional data This program began in 2012 with support from Comcast.

Number awarded Varies each year; recently, 11 of these scholarships were awarded.

Deadline September of each year.

[242]
JOHN T. SMITH SCHOLARSHIPS

Kentucky Community and Technical College System
Attn: Financial Aid
300 North Main Street
Versailles, KY 40383
(859) 256-3100   Toll Free: (877) 528-2748 (within KY)
Web: www.kctcs.edu

Summary To provide financial assistance to Hispanic American and other minority students attending or planning to attend participating institutions within the Kentucky Community and Technical College System (KCTCS).

Eligibility This program is open to minority residents of Kentucky who are attending or planning to attend a participating KCTCS institution. Applicants must be enrolled or planning to enroll in a transfer program to a 4-year institution. They must be able to demonstrate unmet financial need and a GPA of 2.5 or higher. Most colleges require full-time enrollment.

Financial Data Stipends vary at each participating college, but they are intended to provide full payment of tuition and required fees.

Duration 1 year; may be renewed 1 additional year.

Number awarded Varies each year.

Deadline Each college sets its own deadline.

[243]
JOSE A. VILA-ESPINOSA SCHOLARSHIP

Cuban-American Association of Civil Engineers
Attn: Delfin A. Molins, Academic Scholarship Committee
P.O. Box 227966
Miami, FL 33222
(305) 525-3915   E-mail: delfin@miamidade.gov
Web: www.c-aace.org/?page_id=1004

Summary To provide financial assistance to Cuban American undergraduates from any state who are studying civil engineering at a college in Florida.

Eligibility This program is open to students from any state who have completed at least 80 credits in a civil engineering program at a college or university in Florida. Applicants must be Cuban, of Cuban descent, or of Hispanic heritage and able to speak, read, and write Spanish fluently. The must have a GPA of 3.0 or higher and be able to demonstrate financial need. Along with their application, they must submit a 500-word essay on why they think they deserve this scholarship.

Financial Data The stipend is $1,000.

Duration 1 year.

Number awarded 3 each year.

Deadline November of each year.

[244]
JOSE F. SILVA MEMORIAL SCHOLARSHIPS

Great Minds in STEM
Attn: HENAAC Scholars Program
602 Monterey Pass Road
Monterey Park, CA 91754
(323) 262-0997   Fax: (323) 262-0946
E-mail: gcruz@greatmindsinstem.org
Web: www.greatmindsinstem.org

Summary To provide financial assistance to Hispanic undergraduate students from any state who are enrolled at universities in Texas or California and majoring in electrical engineering.

Eligibility This program is open to Hispanic undergraduate students from any state who are majoring in electrical engineering at a college or university in California or Texas. Applicants must be of Hispanic origin and/or must significantly participate in and promote organizations and activities in the Hispanic community. They must have a GPA of 3.0 or higher. Along with their application, they must submit a 700-word essay on a topic that changes annually. Selection is based on leadership, academic achievements, and campus and community activities; financial need is not considered. U.S. citizenship is required.

Financial Data Stipends range from $500 to $10,000.

Duration 1 year; recipients may reapply.

Additional data The Hispanic Engineer National Achievement Awards Conference (HENAAC) was established in 1989 and initiated a scholarship program in 2000. In 2010, the sponsoring organization officially adopted its current name, but it continues to hold the annual HENAAC conference, at which the scholarships are presented. This program is sponsored by Raytheon. Recipients must attend the conference to accept their scholarship.

Number awarded Varies each year; recently, 2 of these scholarships were awarded.

Deadline April of each year.

[245]
JOSE MARTI SCHOLARSHIP CHALLENGE GRANT FUND

Florida Department of Education
Attn: Office of Student Financial Assistance
325 West Gaines Street
Tallahassee, FL 32399-0400
(850) 410-5160   Toll Free: (888) 827-2004
Fax: (850) 487-1809   E-mail: osfa@fldoe.org
Web: www.floridastudentfinancialaid.org

Summary To provide financial assistance to Hispanic American high school seniors and graduate students in Florida.

Eligibility This program is open to Florida residents of Spanish culture who were born in, or whose natural parent was born in, Mexico or a Hispanic country of the Caribbean, Central America, or South America. Applicants must be citizens or eligible noncitizens of the United States, be enrolled or planning to enroll as full-time undergraduate or graduate students at an eligible postsecondary school in Florida, be able to demonstrate financial need as determined by a nationally-recognized needs analysis service, and have earned a cumulative GPA of 3.0 or higher in high school or, if a graduate school applicant, in undergraduate course work.

Financial Data The maximum grant is $2,000 per academic year. Available funds are contingent upon matching contributions from private sources.

Duration 1 year; may be renewed if the student maintains full-time enrollment and a GPA of 3.0 or higher and continues to demonstrate financial need.

Number awarded Varies each year; recently, this program awarded 11 new and 27 renewal grants.

Deadline March of each year.

[246]
JOSEPHINE AND BENJAMIN WEBBER TRUST SCHOLARSHIPS

Arizona Association of Family and Consumer Sciences
Attn: Webber Trusts Committee
Kathryn L. Hatch
4843 North Via Sonrisa
Tucson, AZ 85718-5724
(502) 577-6109   E-mail: klhatch@u.arizona.edu
Web: ag.arizona.edu/webbertrusts

Summary To provide financial assistance to Hispanic women from mining towns in Arizona who are interested in working on an undergraduate or graduate degree in a field related to family and consumer sciences at a school in the state.

Eligibility This program is open to Hispanic women who reside in the following Arizona mining towns: Ajo, Arizona City, Bisbee, Clifton, Douglas, Duncan, Globe, Green Valley, Hayden, Kingman, Kearny, Mammoth, Morenci, Prescott, Safford, Sahuarita, San Manuel, Seligman, Superior, or Winkelman. If too few female Hispanic residents of those towns apply, the program may be open to 1) non-Hispanic women who live in those towns; and/or 2) Hispanic women who currently live elsewhere in Arizona and whose parents or grandparents had lived or continue to live in those communities. Applicants must be enrolled or planning to enroll at a college or university in Arizona to work on an undergraduate or graduate degree. Eligible fields of study include those in the following categories: foods, nutrition, and/or dietetics; restaurant and food service management; culinary arts; family studies; interior design; family and consumer science education; dietetic education; early childhood education; or apparel and clothing. Financial need is considered in the selection process.

Financial Data Funding at public colleges and universities provides for payment of tuition and fees, books, educational supplies, housing, food, and transportation to and from campus. At private institutions, stipend amounts are equivalent to those at public schools.

Duration 1 year; may be renewed for a total of 8 semesters and 2 summers of undergraduate study or 4 semesters and 2 summers of graduate study.

Additional data This program began in 1980.

Number awarded Varies each year; recently, 5 of these scholarships were awarded.

Deadline March of each year.

[247]
JUSTINE E. GRANNER MEMORIAL SCHOLARSHIP

Iowa United Methodist Foundation
2301 Rittenhouse Street
Des Moines, IA 50321
(515) 974-8927
Web: www.iumf.org/generalscholarships.html

Summary To provide financial assistance to Hispanic Americans and other ethnic minorities in Iowa interested in majoring in a health-related field.

Eligibility This program is open to ethnic minority students preparing for a career in nursing, public health, or a related field at a college or school of nursing in Iowa. Applicants must have a GPA of 3.0 or higher. They must submit transcripts, 3 letters of recommendation, ACT and/or SAT scores, and documentation of financial need. Preference is given to graduates of Iowa high schools.

Financial Data The stipend is $1,000.

Duration 1 year.

Number awarded 1 each year.

Deadline March of each year.

[248]
KAISER PERMANENTE NORTHWEST HEALTH CARE CAREER SCHOLARSHIPS

Kaiser Permanente Northwest
c/o Oregon Health Career Center
Attn: Scholarship Program Coordinator
25195 S.W. Parkway Avenue, Suite 204
Wilsonville, OR 97070
(503) 682-1300, ext. 113   Fax: (503) 682-1311
E-mail: kpnwscholarship@gmail.com
Web: www.kpnwscholarship.com

Summary To provide financial assistance to seniors (particularly Hispanic Americans or members of other minority groups underrepresented in the health professions) who are enrolled at more than 100 designated high schools in Oregon or Washington and plan to attend college in any state to prepare for a career as a health care professional.

Eligibility This program is open to seniors graduating from approved high schools in Oregon and Washington and planning to enroll full time at a college or university in any state. Applicants must be planning to prepare for a career as a medical or dental health care professional. They must be a U.S. citizen, national, or permanent resident and have a GPA of 2.5 or higher. Preference is given to students who 1) can demonstrate financial need; 2) are the first member of their family to attend college; 3) are bilingual; or 4) are a member of an ethnic or racial group underrepresented in the health professions.

Financial Data The stipend is $2,000 per year.

Duration 1 year (the freshman year of college); recipients may apply for 1 additional year (the junior year of college) of funding.

Additional data This program, which began in 2008, is offered jointly by Kaiser Permanente Northwest and the Oregon Health Career Center at the Oregon Health & Science University.

Number awarded At least 1 at each of the 113 approved high schools.

Deadline January of each year.

[249]
KANSAS ETHNIC MINORITY SCHOLARSHIP PROGRAM

Kansas Board of Regents
Attn: Student Financial Assistance
1000 S.W. Jackson Street, Suite 520
Topeka, KS 66612-1368
(785) 296-3518   Fax: (785) 296-0983
E-mail: dlindeman@ksbor.org
Web: www.kansasregents.org/scholarships_and_grants

Summary To provide financial assistance to Hispanic Americans and other minority students in Kansas who are interested in attending college in the state.

Eligibility Eligible to apply are Kansas residents who fall into 1 of these minority groups: American Indian, Alaskan Native, African American, Asian, Pacific Islander, or Hispanic. Applicants may be current college students (enrolled in community colleges, colleges, or universities in Kansas), but high school seniors graduating in the current year receive priority consideration. Minimum academic requirements include 1 of the following: 1) ACT score of 21 or higher or combined mathematics and critical reading SAT score of 990 or higher; 2) cumulative GPA of 3.0 or higher; 3) high school rank in upper 33%; 4) completion of the Kansas Scholars Curriculum (4 years of English, 3 years of mathematics, 3 years of science, 3 years of social studies, and 2 years of foreign language); 5) selection by the National Merit Corporation in any category; or 6) selection by the College Board as a Hispanic Scholar. Selection is based primarily on financial need.

Financial Data A stipend of up to $1,850 is provided, depending on financial need and availability of state funds.

Duration 1 year; may be renewed for up to 3 additional years (4 additional years for designated 5-year programs), provided the recipient maintains a 2.0 cumulative GPA and has financial need.

Additional data There is a $12 application fee.

Number awarded Approximately 200 each year.

Deadline April of each year.

[250]
KANSAS SPJ MINORITY STUDENT SCHOLARSHIP

Society of Professional Journalists-Kansas Professional
  Chapter
c/o Denise Neil, Scholarship Committee
Wichita Eagle
825 East Douglas Avenue
P.O. Box 820
Wichita, KS 67201-0820
(316) 268-6327   E-mail: dneil@wichitaeagle.com

Summary To provide financial assistance to Hispanic American and other minority residents of any state who are enrolled at colleges and universities in Kansas and interested in a career in journalism.

Eligibility This program is open to residents of any state who are members of a racial or ethnic minority group and entering their junior or senior year at colleges and universities in Kansas. Applicants do not have to be journalism or communication majors, but they must demonstrate a strong and sincere interest in print journalism, broadcast journalism, online journalism, or photojournalism. They must have a GPA of 2.5 or higher. Along with their application, they must submit a professional resume, 4 to 6 examples of their best work (clips or stories, copies of photographs, tapes or transcripts of broadcasts, printouts of web pages) and a 1-page cover letter about themselves, how they came to be interested in journalism, their professional goals, and (if appropriate) their financial need for this scholarship.

Financial Data The stipend is $1,000.

Duration 1 year.

Number awarded 1 each year.

Deadline March of each year.

[251]
KATHY MANN MEMORIAL SCHOLARSHIP

Wisconsin Education Association Council
Attn: Scholarship Committee
33 Nob Hill Drive
P.O. Box 8003
Madison, WI 53708-8003
(608) 276-7711   Toll Free: (800) 362-8034, ext. 278
Fax: (608) 276-8203   E-mail: BrisackM@weac.org
Web: www.weac.org

Summary To provide financial assistance to Hispanic American and other minority high school seniors whose parent is a member of the Wisconsin Education Association Council (WEAC) and who plan to study education at a college in any state.

Eligibility This program is open to high school seniors whose parent is an active WEAC member, an active retired member, or a person who died while holding a WEAC membership. Applicants must be members of a minority group (American Indian, Eskimo or Aleut, Hispanic, Asian or Pacific Islander, or Black). They must rank in the top 25% of their graduating class or have a GPA of 3.0 or higher, plan to major or minor in education at a college in any state, and intend to teach in Wisconsin. Along with their application, they must submit a 300-word essay on why they want to enter the education profession and what they hope to accomplish. Selection is based primarily on that essay, GPA, letters of recommendation, and school and community activities. Secondary consideration may be given to other factors, including financial need.

Financial Data The stipend is $1,450 per year.

Duration 4 years, provided the recipient maintains a GPA of 3.0 or higher.

Number awarded 1 each year.

Deadline February of each year.

[252]
KATU THOMAS R. DARGAN SCHOLARSHIP

KATU-TV
Attn: Human Resources
2153 N.E. Sandy Boulevard
P.O. Box 2
Portland, OR 97207-0002
(503) 231-4222
Web: www.katu.com/about/scholarship

Summary To provide financial assistance to Hispanic American and other minority students from Oregon and Washington who are studying broadcasting or communications in college.

Eligibility This program is open to minority (Asian, Black/African American, Hispanic or Latino, Native Hawaiian or Pacific Islander, American Indian or Alaska Native) U.S. citizens, currently enrolled as a sophomore or higher at a 4-year college or university or an accredited community college in Oregon or Washington. Residents of Oregon or Washington enrolled at a school in any state are also eligible. Applicants must be majoring in broadcasting or communications and have a GPA of 3.0 or higher. Community college students must be enrolled in a broadcast curriculum that is transferable to a 4-year accredited university. Finalists are interviewed. Selection is based on financial need, academic achievement, and an essay on personal and professional goals.

Financial Data The stipend is $6,000. Funds are sent directly to the recipient's school.

Duration 1 year; recipients may reapply if they have maintained a GPA of 3.0 or higher.

Additional data Winners are also eligible for a paid internship in selected departments at Fisher Broadcasting/KATU in Portland, Oregon.

Number awarded 1 each year.

Deadline April of each year.

[253]
KENNEDY CENTER AMERICAN COLLEGE THEATER FESTIVAL LATINO PLAYWRITING AWARD

John F. Kennedy Center for the Performing Arts
Education Department
Attn: Kennedy Center American College Theater Festival
2700 F Street, N.W.
Washington, DC 20566
(202) 416-8857　　　　　　　Fax: (202) 416-8860
E-mail: KCACTF@kennedy-center.org
Web: www.kcactf.org

Summary To recognize and reward outstanding plays by Latino student playwrights.

Eligibility Latino students at any accredited junior or senior college in the United States are eligible to compete, provided their college agrees to participate in the Kennedy Center American College Theater Festival (KCACTF). Undergraduate students must be carrying at least 6 semester hours, graduate students must be enrolled in at least 3 semester hours, and continuing part-time students must be enrolled in a regular degree or certificate program. This award is presented to the best student-written play by a Latino.

Financial Data The prizes are $1,000 for first place and $500 for second place.

Duration The award is presented annually.

Additional data This award, first presented in 2000, is part of the Michael Kanin Playwriting Awards Program. The sponsoring college or university must pay a registration fee of $275 for each production.

Number awarded 2 each year.

Deadline November of each year.

[254]
KENTUCKY LIBRARY ASSOCIATION SCHOLARSHIP FOR MINORITY STUDENTS

Kentucky Library Association
c/o Executive Secretary
1501 Twilight Trail
Frankfort, KY 40601
(502) 223-5322　　　　　　　Fax: (502) 223-4937
E-mail: info@kylibasn.org
Web: www.klaonline.org/scholarships965.cfm

Summary To provide financial assistance to Hispanic Americans and other minorities who are residents of Kentucky or attending school there and are working on an undergraduate or graduate degree in library science.

Eligibility This program is open to members of minority groups (defined as American Indian, Alaskan Native, Black, Hispanic, Pacific Islander, or other ethnic group) who are entering or continuing at a graduate library school accredited by the American Library Association (ALA) or an undergraduate library program accredited by the National Council of Teacher Education (NCATE). Applicants must be residents of Kentucky or a student in a library program in the state. Along with their application, they must submit a statement of their career objectives, why they have chosen librarianship as a career, and their reasons for applying for this scholarship. Selection is based on that statement, cumulative undergraduate and graduate GPA (if applicable), academic merit and potential, and letters of recommendation. U.S. citizenship or permanent resident status is required.

Financial Data The stipend is $1,000.

Duration 1 year; nonrenewable.

Number awarded 1 or more each year.

Deadline June of each year.

[255]
KENTUCKY MINORITY EDUCATOR RECRUITMENT AND RETENTION SCHOLARSHIPS

Kentucky Department of Education
Attn: Minority Educator Recruitment and Retention
500 Mero Street, 8th Floor
Frankfort, KY 40601
(502) 564-1479, ext. 4014　　　　Fax: (502) 564-6952
TDD: (502) 564-4970
E-mail: monica.davis@education.ky.gov
Web: www.education.ky.gov

Summary To provide funding to Hispanic American and other minority undergraduate and graduate students enrolled in Kentucky public institutions who want to become teachers.

Eligibility This program is open to residents of Kentucky who are undergraduate or graduate students pursuing initial teacher certification at a public university or community college in the state. Applicants must have a GPA of 2.5 or higher and either maintain full-time enrollment or be a part-time student within 18 semester hours of receiving a teacher education degree. They must be U.S. citizens and meet the Kentucky definition of a minority student.

Financial Data Stipends are $5,000 per year at the 8 state universities in Kentucky or $2,000 per year at community and technical colleges. This is a scholarship/loan program. Recipients are required to teach 1 semester in Kentucky for each semester or summer term the scholarship is received. If they fail to fulfill that requirement, the scholarship converts to a loan with severe penalties for non-payment.

Duration 1 year; may be renewed up to 3 additional years.

Additional data The Kentucky General Assembly established this program in 1992.

Number awarded Varies each year.

Deadline Each state college of teacher education sets its own deadline.

[256]
KIMBALL OFFICE SCHOLARSHIP

International Interior Design Association
Attn: IIDA Foundation
222 Merchandise Mart, Suite 567
Chicago, IL 60654
(312) 467-1950   Toll Free: (888) 799-4432
Fax: (312) 467-0779   E-mail: iidahq@iida.org
Web: www.iida.org

Summary To provide financial assistance to Hispanic American and other minority students enrolled in the senior year of an interior design program.

Eligibility This program is open to college seniors of African, Asian, Latino, or Native American heritage. Applicants must be working on a degree in interior design. Selection is based on excellence in academics and promising design talent.

Financial Data The stipend is $4,000.

Duration 1 year.

Additional data This program began in 2006 by Kimball Office, a unit of Kimball International, Inc.

Number awarded 1 each year.

Deadline Deadline not specified.

[257]
KINESIS SCHOLARSHIPS

Kinesis Foundation
89 de Diego Avenue
PMB 607, Suite 105
San Juan, PR 00927
(787) 772-8269   E-mail: info@kinesispr.org
Web: kinesispr.org/becasuperior.html

Summary To provide financial assistance to residents of Puerto Rico who are entering an undergraduate or graduate program at a college outside the Commonwealth.

Eligibility This program is open to high school seniors and graduates who have been residents of Puerto Rico for at least 2 years. Applicants must be entering a bachelor's, master's, or doctoral degree program at a university on the mainland or in another country. They must have a GPA of 3.5 or higher and be able to demonstrate financial need. Along with their application, they must submit a 200-word essay on their academic goals and how they can contribute to the future of Puerto Rico.

Financial Data Stipends average $5,000. Funds are disbursed directly to the recipient's university.

Duration 1 year; may be renewed, provided the recipient continues to meet eligibility requirements.

Number awarded Approximately 100 each year.

Deadline May of each year.

[258]
LA BECA GUADALUPANA

National Association of Pastoral Musicians
Attn: NPM Scholarships
962 Wayne Avenue, Suite 210
Silver Spring, MD 20910-4461
(240) 247-3000   Toll Free: (855) 207-0293
Fax: (240) 247-3001   E-mail: npmsing@npm.org
Web: www.npm.org/Membership/scholarship.htm

Summary To provide financial assistance to Latino/a undergraduate or graduate student members of the National Association of Pastoral Musicians.

Eligibility This program is open to Latino/a members of the association who are enrolled part or full time in an undergraduate or graduate degree program. They must be studying in a field related to pastoral music, be able to demonstrate financial need, and be intending to work for at least 2 years in the field of pastoral music following graduation. Applicants must submit 1) documentation of financial need; 2) a 5-minute performance CD of themselves or the choir-ensemble they direct; and 3) a brief essay explaining their definition of the term "pastoral musician."

Financial Data The stipend is $2,000 per year. Funds must be used to pay for tuition, registration, fees, or books.

Duration 1 year; recipients may reapply.

Additional data The English version of this award is Guadalupe Scholarship.

Number awarded 1 each year.

Deadline March of each year.

[259]
LA PLAZA SCHOLARSHIP FUND

Central Indiana Community Foundation
Attn: Scholarship Program
615 North Alabama Street, Suite 119
Indianapolis, IN 46204-1431
(317) 634-2423   Fax: (317) 684-0943
E-mail: scholarships@cicf.org
Web: www.cicf.org/scholarships

Summary To provide financial assistance to residents of Indiana, especially Hispanics, who are interested in attending college in the state.

Eligibility This program is open to seniors graduating from high schools in Indiana and students already enrolled at a college or university in the state. Preference is given to students of Hispanic descent. Applicants must have a GPA of 2.7 or higher. Along with their application, they must submit 1-page essays on 1) their desire to further their education and their career goals; and 2) their current involvement in the Hispanic community and why it is important to them. Selection is based on academic promise, determination and/or self-motivation, and financial need.

Financial Data The stipend is at least $1,000.

Duration 1 year.

Additional data This program began in 1997.

Number awarded Varies each year; recently, 7 of these scholarships were awarded.

Deadline February of each year.

[260]
LA UNIDAD LATINA SCHOLARSHIPS

La Unidad Latina Foundation, Inc.
132 East 43rd Street, Suite 358
New York, NY 10017
E-mail: info@lulfoundation.org
Web: www.lulfoundation.org

Summary To provide financial assistance to Hispanic students who are working on a bachelor's or master's degree in any field.

Eligibility This program is open to students of Hispanic background who have completed at least 1 year of full-time undergraduate study or 1 semester of full-time graduate work. Undergraduates must have a GPA of 2.8 or higher. Applicants must be enrolled at an accredited 4-year college or university in the United States and working on a bachelor's or master's degree. Along with their application, they must submit brief essays on their financial need, their academic plans and career goals, an instance in which they have demonstrated exceptional leadership during their college or graduate experience, the impact they have had or plan to have on improving or supporting their Latino/Hispanic community, their extracurricular activities, any honors or awards they have received, and their special interests or hobbies.

Financial Data Stipends range from $250 to $1,000.

Duration 1 year.

Number awarded Varies each year.

Deadline February of each year for spring semester; October of each year for fall semester.

[261]
LAGRANT FOUNDATION UNDERGRADUATE SCHOLARSHIPS

Lagrant Foundation
Attn: Senior Programs and Outreach Manager
600 Wilshire Boulevard, Suite 1520
Los Angeles, CA 90017
(323) 469-8680, ext. 223   Fax: (323) 469-8683
E-mail: erickainiguez@lagrant.com
Web: www.lagrantfoundation.org

Summary To provide financial assistance to Hispanic American and other minority college students who are interested in majoring in advertising, public relations, or marketing.

Eligibility This program is open to African Americans, Asian Americans/Pacific Islanders, Hispanics/Latinos, and Native Americans/American Indians who are full-time students at a 4-year accredited institution. Applicants must have a GPA of 2.75 or higher and be either majoring in advertising, marketing, or public relations or minoring in communications with plans to prepare for a career in advertising, marketing, or public relations. Along with their application, they must submit 1) a 1- to 2-page essay outlining their career goals; what steps they will take to increase ethnic representation in the fields of advertising, marketing, and public relations; and the role of an advertising, marketing, or public relations practitioner; 2) a paragraph describing the college and/or community activities in which they are involved; 3) a brief paragraph describing any honors and awards they have received; 4) a letter of reference; 5) a resume; and 6) an official transcript. U.S. citizenship or permanent resident status is required.

Financial Data The stipend is $5,000.

Duration 1 year.

Number awarded Varies each year; recently, 16 of these scholarships were awarded.

Deadline February of each year.

[262]
LAMBDA THETA NU SORORITY LATINA SCHOLARSHIP PROGRAM

Lambda Theta Nu Sorority, Inc.
Attn: Director of Community Service
1220 Rosecrans, Suite 543
San Diego, CA 92106
E-mail: community@lambdathetanu.org
Web: www.lambdathetanu.org

Summary To provide financial assistance for college to female high school seniors with a connection to the Latino community.

Eligibility This program is open to female graduating high school seniors who are either of Latino heritage or able to demonstrate dedication to community service and empowerment of the Latino community. Applicants must be planning to attend an accredited community college, university, or vocational/technical school. Along with their application, they must submit a personal statement that covers their family background, academic achievements, educational and career goals, commitment to the Latino community, and financial need.

Financial Data A stipend is awarded (amount not specified).

Duration 1 year.

Number awarded Approximately 35 each year (1 selected by each chapter of the sorority).

Deadline April of each year.

[263]
LANDMARK SCHOLARS PROGRAM

Landmark Media Enterprises LLC
c/o Ann Morris, Managing Editor
Greensboro News & Record
200 East Market Street
Greensboro, NC 27401
(540) 981-3211   Toll Free: (800) 346-1234
E-mail: amorris@news-record.com
Web: company.news-record.com/intern.htm

Summary To provide financial aid and work experience to Hispanic American and other minority undergraduates who are interested in preparing for a career in journalism.

Eligibility This program is open to minority (Asian, Hispanic, African American, Native American) college sophomores, preferably those with ties to the mid-Atlantic states (Delaware, Maryland, North Carolina, South Carolina, Virginia, and Washington, D.C.). Applicants must be full-time students with a GPA of 2.5 or higher in a 4-year degree program. They must be interested in preparing for a career in print journalism and participating in an internship in news, features, sports, copy editing, photography, or graphics/illustration. U.S. citizenship or permanent resident status is required. Selection is based on grades, work samples, recommendations, targeted selection interview skills, and financial need.

Financial Data The stipend is $5,000 per year. During the summers following their sophomore and junior years, recipients are provided with paid internships. Following graduation, they are offered a 1-year internship with full benefits and the possibility of continued employment.

Duration 2 years (the junior and senior years of college).

Additional data The internships are offered at the *News & Record* in Greensboro, North Carolina, the *Virginian-Pilot* in Norfolk, Virginia, or the *Roanoke Times* in Roanoke, Virginia.

Number awarded 1 or more each year.

Deadline January of each year.

[264]
LAPIZ FAMILY SCHOLARSHIP

Asian Pacific Fund
Attn: Scholarship Coordinator
San Francisco, CA 94104
(415) 395-9985 E-mail: scholarship@asianpacificfund.org
Web: www.asianpacificfund.org

Summary To provide financial assistance to students enrolled at campuses of the University of California (UC) who are children of farm workers.

Eligibility This program is open to residents of California who will be enrolled as a full time undergraduate at a UC campus in the following fall. Preference is given to students at UC Davis and UC Santa Cruz. Applicants may be of any ethnic or racial background but they must be a farm worker or the child of farm or migrant workers. They must have a GPA of 3.0 or higher and be able to demonstrate financial need. Along with their application, they must submit essays of 250 to 500 words each on 1) their experience as a farm worker or child of a farm worker and how that experience relates to their educational and career goals; 2) a project, experience, or person related to their academic and career goals that inspired them; and 3) any unusual family or personal circumstances that have affected their achievement in school, work, or extracurricular activities. U.S. citizenship or permanent resident status is required.

Financial Data The stipend is $1,000 per year.

Duration 1 year; may be renewed up to 3 additional years.

Number awarded 2 each year.

Deadline March of each year.

[265]
LARRY W. MCCORMICK COMMUNICATIONS SCHOLARSHIP FOR UNDERREPRESENTED STUDENTS

The Lullaby Guild, Inc.
Attn: Scholarship Committee
6709 La Tijera, Suite 116
Los Angeles, CA 90045
(310) 335-5655   E-mail: mail@lullabyguild.org
Web: www.lullabyguild.org

Summary To provide financial assistance to Hispanic American and other underrepresented upper-division students who are working on a degree in a field related to mass communications.

Eligibility This program is open to underrepresented (e.g., African American, Hispanic American, Native American, Alaskan American, Pacific Islander, Asian) students entering their junior or senior year at an accredited college or university. Applicants must be working on a degree in a field related to mass communications, including audiovisual and electronic and print journalism. Along with their application, they must submit a personal statement regarding their volunteer services, official transcripts, 3 letters of recommendation, 3 samples of their journalistic work, and a 500-word personal statement about their interest in journalism or mass communication. Selection is based on academic achievement, letters of recommendation, journalistic experience and/or evidence of journalistic talent, clarity of purpose in plans and goals for a future in journalism or mass communications, and involvement in volunteer community service.

Financial Data The stipend is $2,500.

Duration 1 year.

Number awarded 1 each year.

Deadline February of each year.

[266]
LATIN AMERICAN EDUCATIONAL FOUNDATION SCHOLARSHIPS

Latin American Educational Foundation
Attn: Scholarship Selection Committee
561 Santa Fe Drive
Denver, CO 80204
(303) 446-0541   Fax: (303) 446-0526
E-mail: info@laef.org
Web: www.laef.org/Scholarship

Summary To provide financial assistance to Hispanic American undergraduate students in Colorado who plan to attend college in any state.

Eligibility This program is open to Colorado residents who are of Hispanic heritage and/or actively involved in the Hispanic community. Applicants must be attending or accepted at an accredited college, university, or vocational school in any state. They must have a cumulative GPA of 3.0 or higher. Along with their application, they must submit a 1-page essay on their interests and career goals, how they anticipate achieving their goals, and what has motivated them to pursue higher education; their essay must demonstrate how their Hispanic heritage or involvement in their community has influenced their life. Selection is based on the essay, community service and extracurricular activities, academic achievement, letters of recommendation, and financial need.

Financial Data The amount of the award depends on the need of the recipient, ranging from $500 to $3,000 and averaging nearly $1,500. Scholarships may be used at Colorado colleges and universities or at out-of-state institutions. Most colleges and universities within Colorado participate in the Colorado Higher Education Partnership; member institutions provide additional funds to match the award granted by this foundation.

Duration 1 year; recipients may reapply.

Additional data This program began in 1949. Recipients are required to perform 10 hours of community service during the academic year.

Number awarded Varies each year; recently, 110 of these scholarships, with a value of nearly $150,000, were awarded.

Deadline March of each year.

[267]
LATINOS AND PLANNING DIVISION SCHOLARSHIP

American Planning Association
Attn: Planning and the Black Community Division
205 North Michigan Avenue, Suite 1200
Chicago, IL 60601
(312) 431-9100   Fax: (312) 786-6700
Web: www.planning.org/divisions/latinos/scholarships

Summary To provide financial assistance to Latinos interested in working on an undergraduate or graduate degree in planning.

Eligibility This program is open to Latinos who are 1) undergraduate students in the third or fourth year of an accredited planning program; or 2) graduate students in the first or second year of an accredited planning program. Applicants must submit a 1- to 2-page personal statement on their interest in a career in planning and the impact they want to make on planning in Latino communities. Selection is based on that statement, a letter of recommendation, academic achievement, and/or service or impacts made in the Latino community or the planning profession.

Financial Data The stipend is $500 per semester.

Duration 1 year.

Number awarded 1 each year.

Deadline January of each year.

[268]
LATINOS FOR DENTAL CAREERS SCHOLARSHIPS

California Dental Association
Attn: CDA Foundation, Grants Administrator
1201 K Street, Suite 1511
Sacramento, CA 95814
(916) 554-4929   Toll Free: (800) 232-7645
Fax: (916) 498-6182   E-mail: Jolene.Murray@cda.org
Web: www.cdafoundation.org/receive/scholarships-awards

Summary To provide financial assistance to dental and dental hygiene students of Latino descent in California.

Eligibility This program is open to students of Latino descent who are accepted or enrolled full time at a California dental school. Applicants may be dental students, dental hygiene students, or international students. Along with their application, they must submit descriptions of 1) their extracurricular activities; 2) how their Latino heritage has contributed to who they are today; and 3) their career goals and why they may be deserving of a scholarship. Financial need is also considered in the selection process.

Financial Data The stipend is $1,000. Funds are paid directly to the recipient's university account.

Duration 1 year; may be renewed.

Additional data This program is sponsored by the organization, Latinos for Dental Careers, which began as USC Hispanics for Dental Careers. In 2005, that organization expanded to include all dental schools in California.

Number awarded Varies each year; recently, 4 of these scholarships were awarded.

Deadline July of each year.

[269]
LAUNCHING LEADERS UNDERGRADUATE SCHOLARSHIP

JPMorgan Chase
Campus Recruiting
Attn: Launching Leaders
277 Park Avenue, Second Floor
New York, NY 10172
(212) 270-6000
E-mail: bronwen.x.baumgardner@jpmorgan.com
Web: careers.jpmorgan.com

Summary To provide financial assistance and work experience to Hispanic American and other underrepresented minority undergraduate students interested in a career in financial services.

Eligibility This program is open to Black, Hispanic, and Native American students enrolled as sophomores or juniors and interested in financial services. Applicants must have a GPA of 3.5 or higher. Along with their application, they must submit 500-word essays on 1) why they should be considered potential candidates for CEO of the sponsoring bank in 2020; and 2) the special background and attributes they would contribute to the sponsor's diversity agenda. They must be interested in a summer associate position in the sponsor's investment banking, sales and trading, or research divisions.

Financial Data The stipend is $5,000 for recipients accepted as sophomores or $10,000 for recipients accepted as juniors. For students accepted as sophomores and whose scholarship is renewed for a second year, the stipend is $15,000. The summer internship is a paid position.

Duration 1 year; may be renewed 1 additional year if the recipient successfully completes the 10-week summer intern program and maintains a GPA of 3.5 or higher.

Number awarded Approximately 12 each year.

Deadline October of each year.

[270]
LAURENCE R. FOSTER MEMORIAL SCHOLARSHIPS

Oregon Student Access Commission
Attn: Grants and Scholarships Division
1500 Valley River Drive, Suite 100
Eugene, OR 97401-2146
(541) 687-7395   Toll Free: (800) 452-8807, ext. 7395
Fax: (541) 687-7414   TDD: (800) 735-2900
E-mail: awardinfo@osac.state.or.us
Web: www.oregonstudentaid.gov/scholarships.aspx

Summary To provide financial assistance to Hispanic Americans and other residents of Oregon who come from a diverse environment and are enrolled at a college or graduate school in any state to prepare for a public health career.

Eligibility This program is open to residents of Oregon who are enrolled at least half time at a 4-year college or university in any state to prepare for a career in public health (not private practice). Preference is given first to applicants from diverse environments; second to persons employed in, or graduate students working on a degree in, public health; and third to juniors and seniors majoring in a health program (e.g., nursing, medical technology, physician assistant). Applicants must be able to demonstrate financial need. Along with their application, they must submit essays of 250 to 350 words on 1) what public health means to them; 2) the public health aspect they intend to practice and the health and population issues impacted by that aspect; and 3) their experience living or working in diverse environments.

Financial Data Stipends for scholarships offered by the Oregon Student Access Commission (OSAC) range from $200 to $10,000 but recently averaged $2,300.

Duration 1 year.

Additional data This program is administered by the OSAC with funds provided by the Oregon Community Foundation.

Number awarded Varies each year; recently, 6 of these scholarships were awarded.

Deadline February of each year.

[271]
LEADERSHIP FOR DIVERSITY SCHOLARSHIP

California School Library Association
Attn: CSL Foundation
6444 East Spring Street, Number 237
Long Beach, CA 90815-1553
Toll Free: (888) 655-8480   Fax: (888) 655-8480
E-mail: info@csla.net
Web: www.csla.net

Summary To provide financial assistance to Hispanic American and other students who reflect the diversity of California's population and are interested in earning a credential as a library media teacher in the state.

Eligibility This program is open to students who are members of a traditionally underrepresented group enrolled in a college or university library media teacher credential program in California. Applicants must intend to work as a library media teacher in a California school library media center for a minimum of 3 years. Along with their application, they must submit a 250-word statement on their school library media career interests and goals, why they should be considered, what they can contribute, their commitment to serving the needs of multicultural and multilingual students, and their financial situation.

Financial Data The stipend is $1,500.

Duration 1 year.

Number awarded 1 each year.

Deadline May of each year.

[272]
LEAGUE OF MEXICAN AMERICAN WOMEN SCHOLARSHIP

League of Mexican American Women
Attn: Scholarship Chair
P.O. Box 26522
Tucson, AZ 85726-6522
(520) 744-0476
E-mail: info@leagueofmexicanamericanwomen.org
Web: www.leagueofmexicanamericanwomen.org/id8.html

Summary To provide financial assistance to Mexican American and other students interested in attending a college or university in Arizona.

Eligibility Applicants must be U.S. citizens and entering or continuing at a college or university in Arizona as a full-time student. Preference is given to Mexican American applicants. The immediate family of the League of Mexican American

Women members are not eligible to apply. Financial need is considered in the selection process.

Financial Data A stipend is awarded (amount not specified).

Duration 1 year.

Number awarded Varies each year.

Deadline April for the summer session; May for the fall or spring sessions.

[273]
LEDC LATINO SCHOLARSHIP

Latino Economic Development Center
Attn: Membership Services Coordinator
1516 East Lake Street, Suite 201
Minneapolis, MN 55407
(612) 724-5332   Fax: (612) 729-5342
E-mail: info@ledc-mn.org
Web: www.ledc-mn.org/scholarships.php

Summary To provide financial assistance to Latino high school seniors and Mexican college freshmen in Minnesota who are interested in attending college in the state.

Eligibility This program is open to 1) seniors of Latino descent (1 or both parents must have been born outside of the United States in a Latin American country and immigrated to the United States) graduating from high schools in Minnesota; and 2) students from Mexico enrolled in their first year of study at an institution of postsecondary education in Minnesota. Latino high school seniors must have a GPA of 2.5 or higher; Mexican college freshmen must have a GPA of 3.0 or higher. Selection is based on academic performance, educational goals, leadership in the Latino community, and financial need. Preference is given to students who are ineligible for local or federal government funds for college.

Financial Data The stipend is $2,350.

Duration 1 year; nonrenewable.

Additional data This program, which began in 2006, includes the George G.W. Linares Scholarship, the Garcia-Urzua Scholarship, and the Ramiro Hernández Márquez Scholarship.

Number awarded Varies each year; recently, 5 of these scholarships were awarded: 3 to Latino high school seniors and 2 to Mexican college freshmen.

Deadline March of each year.

[274]
LEGACY PARK FOUNDATION SCHOLARSHIPS

Legacy Park Foundation
Attn: Scholarship Director
5240 Tennyson Parkway, Suite 207
Plano, TX 75024
E-mail: info@legacyparkfoundation.org
Web: www.legacyparkfoundation.org

Summary To provide financial assistance to Hispanic American and other minority or economically disadvantaged high school seniors who plan to attend college and major in any field.

Eligibility This program is open to graduating high school seniors who qualify as members of minority or other economically disadvantaged groups. Applicants must be U.S. citizens or permanent residents planning to enroll at a college or university in any state and major in any field. They must have a

GPA of 3.7 or higher and scores of at least 2000 on the SAT or 29 on the ACT. Selection is based on academic achievement, extracurricular and community participation, and financial need.

Financial Data The stipend is $1,000.

Duration 1 year.

Additional data This program began in 2007.

Number awarded 5 each year.

Deadline April of each year.

[275]
LEONARD M. PERRYMAN COMMUNICATIONS SCHOLARSHIP FOR ETHNIC MINORITY STUDENTS

United Methodist Communications
Attn: Communications Resourcing Team
810 12th Avenue South
P.O. Box 320
Nashville, TN 37202-0320
(615) 742-5481   Toll Free: (888) CRT-4UMC
Fax: (615) 742-5485   E-mail: scholarships@umcom.org
Web: crt.umc.org/interior.asp?ptid=44&mid=10270

Summary To provide financial assistance to Hispanic American and other minority students at United Methodist colleges who are interested in careers in religious communications.

Eligibility This program is open to United Methodist ethnic minority students enrolled in accredited institutions of higher education as juniors or seniors. Applicants must be interested in preparing for a career in religious communications. For the purposes of this program, "communications" is meant to cover audiovisual, electronic, and print journalism. Selection is based on Christian commitment and involvement in the life of the United Methodist church, academic achievement, journalistic experience, clarity of purpose, and professional potential as a religion communicator.

Financial Data The stipend is $2,500 per year.

Duration 1 year.

Additional data The scholarship may be used at any accredited institution of higher education.

Number awarded 1 each year.

Deadline March of each year.

[276]
LEROY APKER AWARD

American Physical Society
Attn: Honors Program
One Physics Ellipse
College Park, MD 20740-3844
(301) 209-3268   Fax: (301) 209-0865
E-mail: honors@aps.org
Web: www.aps.org/programs/honors/awards/apker.cfm

Summary To recognize and reward undergraduate students (particularly Hispanic Americans, other underrepresented minorities, and women) for outstanding work in physics.

Eligibility This program is open to undergraduate students at colleges and universities in the United States. Nominees should have completed or be completing the requirements for an undergraduate degree with an excellent academic record and should have demonstrated exceptional potential for sci-

entific research by making an original contribution to physics. Each department of physics in the United States may nominate only 1 student. Each nomination packet should include the student's academic transcript, a description of the original contribution written by the student (such as a manuscript or reprint of a research publication or senior thesis), a 1,000-word summary, and 2 letters of recommendation. Nominations of qualified women and members of underrepresented minority groups are especially encouraged.

Financial Data The award consists of a $5,000 honorarium for the student, a certificate citing the work and school of the recipient, and an allowance for travel expenses to the meeting of the American Physical Society (APS) at which the prize is presented. Each of the finalists receives an honorarium of $2,000 and a certificate. Each of the physics departments whose nominees are selected as recipients and finalists receives a certificate and an award; the departmental award is $5,000 for recipients and $1,000 for finalists.

Duration The award is presented annually.

Additional data This award was established in 1978.

Number awarded 2 recipients each year: 1 to a student at a Ph.D. granting institution and 1 at a non-Ph.D. granting institution.

Deadline June of each year.

[277]
LEROY SCHMIDT MINORITY 150-HOUR UNDERGRADUATE ACCOUNTING SCHOLARSHIP

Wisconsin Institute of Certified Public Accountants
Attn: WICPA Educational Foundation
235 North Executive Drive, Suite 200
Brookfield, WI 53005
(262) 785-0445, ext. 3025
Toll Free: (800) 772-6939 (within WI)
Fax: (262) 785-0838   E-mail: jessica@wicpa.org
Web: www.wicpa.org

Summary To provide financial assistance to Hispanic American and other underrepresented minority residents of Wisconsin who are enrolled at a college or university in the state and working to meet the requirements to sit for the Certified Public Accountant (C.P.A.) examination.

Eligibility This program is open to residents of Wisconsin who are African American, Native American/Alaskan Native, of Pacific Island races, or of Hispanic ethnic origin. Applicants must be entering the fifth year of academic work leading to an undergraduate degree in accounting at a college or university in the state. They must be working full time to complete the 150-hour accounting education requirement to sit for the C.P.A. examination. Along with their application, they must submit a 1-page personal statement on their career objectives, most significant accomplishment, and strongest personal attribute. Selection is based on that statement, honors and awards, academic achievement, extracurricular and volunteer activities, work experience, and letters of recommendation. U.S. citizenship is required.

Financial Data The stipend is $2,500.

Duration 1 year.

Number awarded 1 or more each year.

Deadline February of each year.

[278]
LIFE TECHNOLOGIES SCHOLARSHIPS

Society of Women Engineers
Attn: Scholarship Selection Committee
203 North LaSalle Street, Suite 1675
Chicago, IL 60601-1269
(312) 596-5223　　　　　Toll Free: (877) SWE-INFO
Fax: (312) 644-8557　　　E-mail: scholarships@swe.org
Web: societyofwomenengineers.swe.org

Summary To provide financial assistance to Hispanic American and other undergraduate women who are majoring in designated engineering specialties.

Eligibility This program is open to society members who are entering their sophomore, junior, or senior year at an ABET-accredited 4-year college or university. Applicants must be working full time on a degree in computer science or biomedical, chemical, civil, computer, electrical, industrial, manufacturing, materials, mechanical, or software engineering and have a GPA of 3.0 or higher. They must be U.S. citizens or permanent residents. Selection is based on merit. Preference is given to groups underrepresented in computer science and engineering.

Financial Data The stipend is $7,500 or $2,500.

Duration 1 year.

Number awarded 3 each year: 1 at $7,500 and 2 at $2,500.

Deadline February of each year.

[279]
LIN MEDIA MINORITY SCHOLARSHIP AND TRAINING PROGRAM

LIN Television Corporation
Attn: Vice President, Human Resources
One West Exchange Street, Suite 5A
Providence, RI 02903-1064
(401) 454-2880　　　　　Fax: (401) 454-6990
Web: www.linmedia.com

Summary To provide funding to Hispanic American and other minority undergraduates interested in earning a degree in a field related to broadcast journalism and working at a station owned by LIN Television Corporation.

Eligibility This program is open to U.S. citizens and permanent residents of non-white origin who are enrolled as a sophomore or higher at a college or university. Applicants must have a declared major in broadcast journalism, digital multimedia, mass/speech/digital communication, television production, or marketing and a GPA of 3.0 or higher. Along with their application, they must submit a list of organizations and activities in which they have held leadership positions, 3 references, a 50-word description of their career goals, a list of personal achievements and honors, and a 500-word essay about themselves. Financial need is not considered in the selection process.

Financial Data The program pays for tuition and fees, books, and room and board, to a maximum of $10,000 per year. Recipients must sign an employment agreement that guarantees them part-time employment as an intern during school and a 2-year regular position at a television station owned by LIN Television Corporation following graduation. If they fail to honor the employment agreement, they must repay all scholarship funds received.

Duration 2 years.

Additional data LIN Television Corporation owns 28 television stations in 17 media markets in the United States. Recipients of these scholarships must work at a station selected by LIN management.

Number awarded 2 each year: 1 for a student in broadcast television and 1 for a student in digital media.

Deadline March of each year.

[280]
LLAVE SCHOLARSHIPS

Llave Scholarship Committee
P.O. Box 841
Albuquerque, NM 87103-0841
(505) 241-4716
Web: www.llave-nm.org/scholarship.html

Summary To provide financial assistance to Hispanic American (primarily) and other residents of New Mexico who are interested in attending college or graduate school in any state.

Eligibility This program is open to Hispanic and other residents of New Mexico who are enrolled or accepted for enrollment at an accredited college, university, community college, or vocational school in any state as a full-time undergraduate or graduate student. Nontraditional and returning students are also eligible. Applicants must have a GPA of 2.0 or higher. Along with their application, they must submit a 1-page personal statement that covers their career goals and aspirations, their involvement with volunteerism and/or community service, how this scholarship will impact their educational goals, and special circumstances. Selection is based on commitment to diversity and higher education, involvement in local community groups or organizations, personal qualities and strengths, demonstrations of overcoming unique obstacles in obtaining an education, academic achievement (if applicable to category), and financial need.

Financial Data The stipend is $1,000.

Duration 1 year.

Additional data This program, which began in 1992, is funded by the PNM Resources Foundation, the nonprofit affiliate of the electric utility based in Albuquerque, and administered in cooperation with the Albuquerque Hispano Chamber of Commerce.

Number awarded Varies each year; recently, 10 of these scholarships were awarded.

Deadline March of each year.

[281]
LOCKHEED MARTIN/HENAAC SCHOLARS PROGRAM

Great Minds in STEM
Attn: HENAAC Scholars Program
602 Monterey Pass Road
Monterey Park, CA 91754
(323) 262-0997　　　　　Fax: (323) 262-0946
E-mail: gcruz@greatmindsinstem.org
Web: www.greatmindsinstem.org

Summary To provide financial assistance to Hispanic undergraduate students majoring in designated fields of engineering or computer science.

Eligibility This program is open to Hispanic students who are working full time on an undergraduate degree in computer science, computer engineering, or electrical engineering at a 4-year college or university. Applicants must be of Hispanic origin and/or must significantly participate in and promote organizations and activities in the Hispanic community. They must have a GPA of 3.2 or higher and be able to work in the United States. Along with their application, they must submit a 700-word essay on a topic that changes annually. Selection is based on leadership, academic achievements, and campus and community activities; financial need is not considered.

Financial Data Stipends range from $500 to $10,000.

Duration 1 year; recipients may reapply.

Additional data The Hispanic Engineer National Achievement Awards Conference (HENAAC) was established in 1989 and initiated a scholarship program in 2000. In 2010, the sponsoring organization officially adopted its current name, but it continues to hold the annual HENAAC conference, at which the scholarships are presented. This program is sponsored by Lockheed Martin Corporation. Recipients must attend the conference to accept their scholarship.

Number awarded Varies each year; recently, 7 of these scholarships were awarded.

Deadline April of each year.

[282]
LOUIS B. RUSSELL, JR. MEMORIAL SCHOLARSHIP

Indiana State Teachers Association
Attn: Scholarships
150 West Market Street, Suite 900
Indianapolis, IN 46204-2875
(317) 263-3369   Toll Free: (800) 382-4037
Fax: (800) 777-6128   E-mail: mshoup@ista-in.org
Web: www.ista-in.org/dynamic.aspx?id=1038

Summary To provide financial assistance to Hispanic American and other minority high school seniors in Indiana who are interested in attending vocational school in any state.

Eligibility This program is open to ethnic minority high school seniors in Indiana who are interested in continuing their education in the area of industrial arts, vocational education, or technical preparation at an accredited postsecondary institution in any state. Selection is based on academic achievement, leadership ability as expressed through co-curricular activities and community involvement, recommendations, and a 300-word essay on their educational goals and how they plan to use this scholarship.

Financial Data The stipend is $1,000.

Duration 1 year; may be renewed for 1 additional year, provided the recipient maintains a GPA of "C+" or higher.

Number awarded 1 each year.

Deadline February of each year.

[283]
LOUISE MORITZ MOLITORIS LEADERSHIP AWARD

Women's Transportation Seminar
Attn: WTS Foundation
1701 K Street, N.W., Suite 800
Washington, DC 20006
(202) 955-5085   Fax: (202) 955-5088
E-mail: wts@wtsinternational.org
Web: www.wtsinternational.org/education/scholarships

Summary To provide financial assistance to undergraduate women (particularly minority women) who are interested in a career in transportation.

Eligibility This program is open to women who are working on an undergraduate degree in transportation or a transportation-related field (e.g., transportation engineering, planning, finance, or logistics). Applicants must have a GPA of 3.0 or higher. Along with their application, they must submit a 500-word statement about their career goals after graduation and why they think they should receive the scholarship award; their statement should specifically address the issue of leadership. Applications must be submitted first to a local chapter; the chapters forward selected applications for consideration on the national level. Minority women are especially encouraged to apply. Selection is based on transportation involvement and goals, job skills, academic record, and leadership potential; financial need is not considered.

Financial Data The stipend is $5,000.

Duration 1 year.

Additional data Local chapters may also award additional funding to winners for their area.

Number awarded 1 each year.

Deadline Applications must be submitted by November to a local WTS chapter.

[284]
LTK SCHOLARSHIP

Conference of Minority Transportation Officials
Attn: National Scholarship Program
1875 I Street, N.W., Suite 500
Washington, DC 20006
(703) 234-4072   Fax: (202) 318-0364
Web: www.comto.org/?page=Scholarships

Summary To provide financial assistance to Hispanic American and other minority upper-division and graduate students in engineering or other fields related to transportation.

Eligibility This program is open to full-time minority juniors, seniors, and graduate students in engineering of other technical transportation-related disciplines. Applicants must have a GPA of 3.0 or higher. Along with their application, they must submit a cover letter with a 500-word statement of career goals. Financial need is not considered in the selection process. U.S. citizenship or legal resident status is required.

Financial Data The stipend is $6,000. Funds are paid directly to the recipient's college or university.

Duration 1 year.

Additional data The Conference of Minority Transportation Officials (COMTO) was established in 1971 to promote, strengthen, and expand the roles of minorities in all aspects of transportation. This program is sponsored by LTK Engineering Services. Recipients are required to become members of COMTO if they are not already members and attend the COMTO National Scholarship Luncheon.

Number awarded 1 or more each year.

Deadline May of each year.

[285]
LUBRIZOL CORPORATION SCHOLARSHIP PROGRAM

College Now Greater Cleveland, Inc.
Attn: Managed Scholarships
200 Public Square, Suite 3820
Cleveland, OH 44114
(216) 241-5587   Fax: (216) 241-6184
E-mail: info@collegenowgc.org
Web: www.collegenowgc.org

Summary To provide financial assistance to Hispanic Americans, other minorities, and women who are working on a degree in specified fields of science and business at college in any state.

Eligibility This program is open to members of minority ethnic groups (American Indians, African Americans, Asian Pacific Americans, and Hispanic Americans) and women. Applicants must be enrolled full time at a 4-year college or university in any state and majoring in chemistry, computer information systems, computer science, engineering (chemical, computer, or mechanical), business, marketing, accounting, or finance. They must have a GPA of 3.0 or higher and be able to demonstrate financial need. Along with their application, they must submit a 500-word essay describing their academic and career goals.

Financial Data The stipend is $4,000 per year.

Duration 1 year; may be renewed, provided the recipient maintains a GPA of 3.0 or higher.

Additional data This program is sponsored by the Lubrizol Corporation.

Number awarded Varies each year.

Deadline March of each year.

[286]
LULAC GENERAL AWARDS

League of United Latin American Citizens
Attn: LULAC National Education Service Centers
1133 19th Street, N.W., Suite 1000
Washington, DC 20036
(202) 835-9646   Fax: (202) 835-9685
E-mail: scholarships@lnesc.org
Web: www.lnesc.org/site/296/Scholarships

Summary To provide financial assistance to Hispanic American undergraduate and graduate students.

Eligibility This program is open to Hispanic Americans who are U.S. citizens or permanent residents currently enrolled or planning to enroll at an accredited college or university as a graduate or undergraduate student. Although grades are considered in the selection process, emphasis is placed on the applicant's motivation, sincerity, and community involvement, as revealed through a personal interview and in an essay on their personal and career goals. Need, community involvement, and leadership activities are also considered. Candidates must live near a participating local council of the League of United Latin American Citizens (LULAC) and must apply directly to that council.

Financial Data The stipend ranges from $250 to $1,000 per year, depending on the need of the recipient.

Duration 1 year.

Additional data This program represents an attempt to forge a partnership between the corporate world and the community. Under its fundsharing concept, LULAC's National Education Service Center gathers contributions nationally from corporations, while LULAC councils raise money locally. The total corporate donations are then apportioned back to the councils according to effort. Applications must be obtained directly from participating LULAC councils; for a list, contact the sponsor.

Number awarded Varies; approximately 500 each year.

Deadline March of each year.

[287]
LULAC HONORS AWARDS

League of United Latin American Citizens
Attn: LULAC National Education Service Centers
1133 19th Street, N.W., Suite 1000
Washington, DC 20036
(202) 835-9646   Fax: (202) 835-9685
E-mail: scholarships@lnesc.org
Web: www.lnesc.org/site/296/Scholarships

Summary To provide financial assistance to Hispanic American undergraduate and graduate students who are doing well in school.

Eligibility This program is open to Hispanic Americans who are U.S. citizens or permanent residents currently enrolled or planning to enroll at an accredited college or university as a graduate or undergraduate student. Applicants who are already in college must have a GPA of 3.25 or higher. Entering freshmen must have ACT scores of 23 or higher or SAT scores of 1100 or higher. In addition, applicants must demonstrate motivation, sincerity, and community involvement through a personal interview and in an essay on their personal and career goals. Need, community involvement, and leadership activities are also considered. Candidates must live near a participating local council of the League of United Latin American Citizens (LULAC) and must apply directly to that council.

Financial Data The stipend ranges from $500 to $2,000 per year, depending on the need of the recipient.

Duration 1 year.

Additional data This program represents an attempt to forge a partnership between the corporate world and the community. Under its fundsharing concept, LULAC's National Education Service Center gathers contributions nationally from corporations, while LULAC councils raise money locally. The total corporate donations are then apportioned back to the councils according to effort. Applications must be obtained directly from participating LULAC councils; for a list, send a self-addressed stamped envelope to the sponsor.

Number awarded Varies each year.

Deadline March of each year.

[288]
LULAC NATIONAL SCHOLASTIC ACHIEVEMENT AWARDS

League of United Latin American Citizens
Attn: LULAC National Education Service Centers
1133 19th Street, N.W., Suite 1000
Washington, DC 20036
(202) 835-9646   Fax: (202) 835-9685
E-mail: scholarships@lnesc.org
Web: www.lnesc.org/site/296/Scholarships

Summary To provide financial assistance to academically outstanding Hispanic American undergraduate and graduate students.

Eligibility This program is open to Hispanic Americans who are U.S. citizens or permanent residents currently enrolled or planning to enroll at an accredited college or university as a graduate or undergraduate student. Applicants who are already in college must have a GPA of 3.5 or higher. Entering freshmen must have ACT scores of 29 or higher or SAT scores of 1350 or higher. In addition, applicants must demonstrate motivation, sincerity, and community involvement through a personal interview and in an essay on their personal and career goals. Need, community involvement, and leadership activities are also considered. Candidates must live near a participating local council of the League of United Latin American Citizens (LULAC) and must apply directly to that council.

Financial Data Stipends are at least $2,000 per year.

Duration 1 year.

Additional data This program represents an attempt to forge a partnership between the corporate world and the community. Under its fundsharing concept, LULAC's National Education Service Center gathers contributions nationally from corporations, while LULAC councils raise money locally. The total corporate donations are then apportioned back to the councils according to effort. Applications must be obtained directly from participating LULAC councils; for a list, send a self-addressed stamped envelope to the sponsor.

Number awarded Varies each year.

Deadline March of each year.

[289]
MABEL SMITH MEMORIAL SCHOLARSHIP

Wisconsin Women of Color Network, Inc.
Attn: Scholarship Committee
P.O. Box 2337
Madison, WI 53701-2337
E-mail: contact@womenofcolornetwork-wis.org
Web: www.womenofcolornetwork-wis.org/scholarship.html

Summary To provide financial assistance for vocational/technical school or community college to Hispanic American and other minority residents of Wisconsin.

Eligibility This program is open to residents of Wisconsin who are high school or GED-equivalent graduating seniors planning to continue their education at a vocational/technical school or community college in any state. Applicants must be a member of 1 of the following groups: African American, Asian, American Indian, Latina, or biracial. They must have a GPA of 2.0 or higher and be able to demonstrate financial need. Along with their application, they must submit a 1-page

essay on how this scholarship will help them accomplish their educational goal. U.S. citizenship is required.

Financial Data A stipend is awarded (amount not specified).

Duration 1 year.

Additional data This program began in 1990.

Number awarded 1 each year.

Deadline May of each year.

[290]
MAINE SECTION ASCE HIGH SCHOOL SCHOLARSHIP

American Society of Civil Engineers-Maine Section
c/o Leslie L. Corrow, Scholarship Chair
Kleinschmidt Associates
75 Main Street
P.O. Box 576
Pittsfield, ME 04967
(207) 487-3328   Fax: (207) 487-3124
E-mail: scholarships@maineasce.org
Web: www.maineasce.org

Summary To provide financial assistance to high school seniors in Maine (particularly Hispanic Americans, other minorities, and women) who are interested in studying civil engineering in college.

Eligibility This program is open to graduating high school seniors who are Maine residents and who intend to study civil engineering in college. Women and minorities are especially encouraged to apply. Applicants must submit a 200-word statement describing why they have chosen civil engineering as a career and what they hope to accomplish by being a civil engineer. Selection is based on the statement, academic performance, extracurricular activities, and letters of recommendation.

Financial Data The stipend is $2,000.

Duration 1 year; nonrenewable.

Number awarded 1 each year.

Deadline January of each year.

[291]
MARATHON OIL CORPORATION COLLEGE SCHOLARSHIP PROGRAM OF THE HISPANIC SCHOLARSHIP FUND

Hispanic Scholarship Fund
Attn: Selection Committee
1411 West 190th Street, Suite 325
Gardena, CA 90248
Toll Free: (877) HSF-INFO   E-mail: scholar1@hsf.net
Web: www.hsf.net

Summary To provide financial assistance to Hispanic American and other minority upper-division and graduate students working on a degree in a field related to the oil and gas industry.

Eligibility This program is open to U.S. citizens and permanent residents (must have a permanent resident card or a passport stamped I-551) who are of Hispanic American, African American, Asian Pacific Islander American, or American Indian/Alaskan Native heritage. Applicants must be currently enrolled full time at an accredited 4-year college or university in the United States, Puerto Rico, Guam, or the U.S. Virgin Islands with a GPA of 3.0 or higher. They must be 1) sophomores majoring in accounting, chemical engineering, computer engineering, computer science, electrical engineering, environmental engineering, geology, geosciences, information technology/management information systems, mechanical engineering, or petroleum engineering; or 2) seniors planning to work on a master's degree in geology, geosciences, or petroleum engineering. Selection is based on academic achievement, personal strengths, interest and commitment to a career in the oil and gas industry, leadership, and financial need.

Financial Data The stipend is $15,000 per year.

Duration 2 years (the junior and senior undergraduate years or the first 2 years of a master's degree program).

Additional data This program is jointly sponsored by Marathon Oil Corporation and the Hispanic Scholarship Fund (HSF). Recipients may be offered a paid 8- to 10-week summer internship at various Marathon Oil Corporation locations.

Number awarded 1 or more each year.

Deadline September of each year.

[292]
MARCIA SILVERMAN MINORITY STUDENT AWARD

Public Relations Student Society of America
Attn: Vice President of Member Services
33 Maiden Lane, 11th Floor
New York, NY 10038-5150
(212) 460-1474   Fax: (212) 995-0757
E-mail: prssa@prsa.org
Web: www.prssa.org/scholarships_competitions/individual

Summary To provide financial assistance to Hispanic American and other minority college seniors who are interested in preparing for a career in public relations.

Eligibility This program is open to minority (African American/Black, Hispanic/Latino, Asian, Native American, Alaskan Native, or Pacific Islander) students who are entering their senior year at an accredited 4-year college or university. Applicants must have a GPA of 3.0 or higher and be working on a degree in public relations, journalism, or other field to prepare for a career in public relations. Along with their application, they must submit an essay on their view of the public relations profession and their public relations career goals. Selection is based on academic achievement, demonstrated leadership, practical experience, commitment to public relations, writing skills, and letters of recommendation.

Financial Data The stipend is $5,000.

Duration 1 year.

Additional data This program began in 2010.

Number awarded 1 each year.

Deadline June of each year.

[293]
MARIA ELENA SALINAS SCHOLARSHIP PROGRAM

National Association of Hispanic Journalists
Attn: Scholarship Committee
1050 Connecticut Avenue, N.W., Tenth Floor
Washington, DC 20036
(202) 662-7145   Toll Free: (888) 346-NAHJ
Fax: (202) 662-7144   E-mail: nahj@nahj.org
Web: www.nahj12.com/scholarships

Summary To provide financial assistance and work experience to student members of the National Association of Hispanic Journalists (NAHJ) who are interested in preparing for a career as a journalist in Spanish-language radio or television.

Eligibility This program is open to undergraduates and first-year graduate students who are NAHJ members. Applicants must demonstrate a sincere desire to prepare for a career as a journalist in Spanish-language television or radio. They must be enrolled full time at a college or university in the United States or Puerto Rico. Along with their application, they must submit 1) transcripts; 2) a 1-page resume; 3) 2 letters of recommendation; 4) work samples; 5) a 1,000-word autobiographical essay that includes why they are interested in a career in journalism, what inspired them to prepare for a career in the field, what hardships or obstacles they have experienced while trying to realize their goal of becoming a journalist, and the role Latino journalists play in the news industry; and 6) an essay written in the third person as a news story in Spanish on why they seek a career as a Spanish-language broadcast journalist. Selection is based on commitment to the field of journalism, academic achievement, awareness of the Latino community, and financial need.

Financial Data The stipend is $5,000 per year; the program also provides funding for an internship during the summer.

Duration 2 years.

Additional data This program, which began in 2002, is sponsored by Univision. The recipient participates in a summer internship with either the news division of the Univision network or a Univision affiliate near them.

Number awarded Varies each year; recently, 3 of these scholarships were awarded.

Deadline January of each year.

[294]
MARJORIE BOWENS-WHEATLEY SCHOLARSHIPS

Unitarian Universalist Association
Attn: UU Women's Federation
25 Beacon Street
Boston, MA 02108-2800
(617) 948-4692   Fax: (617) 742-2402
E-mail: uuwf@uua.org
Web: www.uuwf.org

Summary To provide financial assistance to Hispanic American and other women of color who are working on an undergraduate or graduate degree to prepare for Unitarian Universalist ministry or service.

Eligibility This program is open to women of color who are either 1) aspirants or candidates for the Unitarian Universalist ministry; or 2) candidates in the Unitarian Universalist Association's professional religious education or music leadership credentialing programs. Applicants must submit a 1- to 2-page narrative that covers their call to UU ministry, religious education, or music leadership; their passions; how their racial/ethnic/cultural background influences their goals for their calling; and how the work of the program's namesake relates to their dreams and plans for their UU service.

Financial Data Stipends from $1,500 to $2,000.

Duration 1 year.

Additional data This program began in 2009.

Number awarded Varies each year; recently, 4 of these scholarships were awarded.

Deadline March of each year.

[295]
MARRIOTT SCHOLARS PROGRAM

Hispanic College Fund
Attn: Scholarship Processing
1300 L Street, N.W., Suite 975
Washington, DC 20005
(202) 296-5400   Toll Free: (800) 644-4223
Fax: (202) 296-3774   E-mail: hcf-info@hispanicfund.org
Web: scholarships.hispanicfund.org/applications

Summary To provide financial assistance to Hispanic American undergraduate students who are interested in preparing for a career in the hospitality industry.

Eligibility This program is open to U.S. citizens and permanent residents of Hispanic background (at least 1 grandparent must be 100% Hispanic) who are enrolled full time at an accredited 4-year college or university in the 50 states or Puerto Rico or planning to transfer from a community college to a 4-year school. Applicants must be entering their freshman or sophomore year and working on or planning to work on a degree within the hospitality management, hotel management, culinary, or food and beverage field. They must have a GPA of 3.0 or higher and be able to demonstrate financial need.

Financial Data Stipends provide for full payment of tuition, to a maximum of $9,000 per year.

Duration 4 years.

Additional data This program is sponsored by the J. Willard and Alice S. Marriott Foundation. All applications must be submitted online; no paper applications are available.

Number awarded Varies each year.

Deadline February of each year.

[296]
MARTHA GUERRA-ARTEAGA SCHOLARSHIP

National Organization of Professional Hispanic Natural
   Resources Conservation Service Employees
c/o Jessie Howard, Scholarship and Endowment
   Committee
Natural Resources Conservation Service
Bedford Service Center
1031 Turnpike Road
Bedford, VA 24523
(540) 586-9195   Fax: (540) 586-4638
E-mail: scholarships@nophnrcse.org
Web: www.nophnrcse.org

Summary To provide financial assistance to Hispanic women interested in working on a bachelor's degree in a field related to public affairs or natural resources conservation.

Eligibility This program is open to Hispanic women who are graduating high school seniors or current full-time college students with at least 1 year remaining before graduation. Applicants must be interested in working on a bachelor's degree in public affairs, communications, or natural resources conservation. They must have a GPA of 2.75 or higher. Along with their application, they must submit a personal statement (in English) of 350 to 500 words on their background, name of

school they attend or plan to attend, personal and career goals, extracurricular activities, and interest in preparing for a career related to natural resources conservation. Financial need is not considered in the selection process. U.S. citizenship is required.

Financial Data The stipend is $1,000.

Duration 1 year.

Additional data The National Organization of Professional Hispanic Natural Resources Conservation Service Employees (NOPRNRCSE) is comprised of Hispanic employees of the Natural Resources Conservation Service of the U.S. Department of Agriculture (USDA-NRCS).

Number awarded 1 each year.

Deadline February of each year.

[297]
MARY HILL DAVIS ETHNIC/MINORITY STUDENT SCHOLARSHIP PROGRAM

Baptist General Convention of Texas
Attn: Institutional Ministries Department
333 North Washington
Dallas, TX 75246-1798
(214) 828-5252   Toll Free: (888) 244-9400
Fax: (214) 828-5261   E-mail: institutions@bgct.org
Web: texasbaptists.org

Summary To provide financial assistance for college to Hispanic American and other ethnic minority residents of Texas who are members of Texas Baptist congregations.

Eligibility This program is open to members of Texas Baptist congregations who are of African American, Hispanic, Native American, or other intercultural heritage. Applicants must be attending or planning to attend a university affiliated with the Baptist General Convention of Texas to work on a bachelor's degree as preparation for service as a future lay or vocational ministry leader in a Texas Baptist ethnic/minority church. They must have been active in their respective ethnic/minority community. Along with their application, they must submit a letter of recommendation from their pastor and transcripts. Students still in high school must have a GPA of at least 3.0; students previously enrolled in a college must have at least a 2.0 GPA. U.S. citizenship or permanent resident status is required.

Financial Data Stipends are $800 per semester ($1,600 per year) for full-time students or $400 per semester ($800 per year) for part-time students.

Duration 1 semester; may be renewed up to 7 additional semesters.

Additional data The scholarships are funded through the Week of Prayer and the Mary Hill Davis Offering for state missions sponsored annually by Women's Missionary Union of Texas. The eligible institutions are Baptist University of The Americas, Baylor University, Dallas Baptist University, East Texas Baptist University, Hardin Simmons University, Houston Baptist University, Howard Payne University, University of Mary Hardin Baylor, and Wayland Baptist University.

Number awarded Varies each year.

Deadline April of each year.

[298]
MARYLAND SEA GRANT RESEARCH EXPERIENCES FOR UNDERGRADUATES

Maryland Sea Grant College
c/o University of Maryland
4321 Hartwick Road, Suite 300
College Park, MD 20740
(301) 405-7500   Fax: (301) 314-5780
E-mail: mallen@mdsg.umd.edu
Web: www.mdsg.umd.edu

Summary   To provide undergraduate students (particularly minority and disadvantaged students) with an opportunity to conduct summer research on Chesapeake Bay in fields related to marine biology.

Eligibility   This program is open to undergraduate students who have completed at least 2 years of study towards a bachelor's degree. Applicants must be interested in conducting individual research projects (under the mentorship of scientists at laboratories of the University of Maryland Center for Environmental Sciences on Chesapeake Bay) in biology, chemistry, ecology, environmental science, engineering, marine science, mathematics, or physics. U.S. citizenship or permanent resident status is required. Selection is based on a 1-page description of interests, course work and grades, letters of recommendation, and the potential benefits students will gain from the research experience. Preference is given to rising seniors. Students from underrepresented groups and from institutions with limited research opportunities are especially encouraged to apply.

Financial Data   Fellows receive a stipend of $6,000, payment of dormitory costs, round-trip travel expenses, and funding to assist in publishing or presenting the results of summer research.

Duration   12 weeks during the summer.

Additional data   This program is supported by the National Science Foundation as part of the Research Experiences for Undergraduates Program.

Number awarded   14 each year.

Deadline   February of each year.

[299]
MAS FAMILY SCHOLARSHIP PROGRAM

Jorge Mas Canosa Freedom Foundation
Attn: Scholarship Coordinator
1312 S.W. 27th Avenue
Miami, FL 33145
(305) 529-7768   E-mail: info@canf.org
Web: jorgemascanosa.org/wordpress

Summary   To provide financial assistance to students of Cuban descent who are working on an undergraduate or graduate degree in selected subject areas.

Eligibility   This program is open to students who are direct descendants of those who left Cuba or were born in Cuba themselves. Applicants must have a GPA of 3.5 or higher and an SAT test score of at least 1500. They must be able to meet federal standards of financial need. At least 1 parent or 2 grandparents must have been born in Cuba. Both undergraduate and graduate students may apply, provided they are working on a degree in 1 of the following subjects: engineering, business, international relations, economics, communications, pediatric nursing, law, or journalism. Selection is

based on academic performance, leadership qualities, financial need, potential to contribute to the advancement of a free society, and likelihood of succeeding in their chosen field. Finalists may be interviewed.

Financial Data   The stipend ranges up to $8,000 per year.

Duration   1 year; may be renewed up to 3 additional years.

Additional data   This program, established in 1997, was previously offered by the Cuban American National Foundation.

Number awarded   Varies each year; since this program was established, it has provided support to more than 100 students.

Deadline   January of each year.

[300]
MASSMUTUAL SCHOLARS PROGRAM

Massachusetts Mutual Life Insurance Company
1295 State Street
Springfield, MA 01111-0001
Toll Free: (800) 542-6767
Web: www.act.org/massmutual

Summary   To provide financial assistance to Hispanic American and other minority undergraduates preparing for a career in the insurance and financial services industry.

Eligibility   This program is open to full-time students of African American, Asian/Pacific Islander, or Hispanic descent who are entering their sophomore, junior, senior, or fifth-year senior year at an accredited college or university in the United States, Puerto Rico, U.S. Virgin Islands, or Guam. Applicants must be U.S. citizens or permanent residents and have a GPA of 3.0 or higher. They may be majoring in any field, but preference is given to students who demonstrate 1) an interest in preparing for a career in the insurance and financial services industry; and 2) leadership and participation in extracurricular activities. Financial need is considered in the selection process.

Financial Data   The stipend is $5,000.

Duration   1 year.

Number awarded   30 each year.

Deadline   May of each year.

[301]
MAUREEN L. AND HOWARD N. BLITMAN, P.E. SCHOLARSHIP TO PROMOTE DIVERSITY IN ENGINEERING

National Society of Professional Engineers
Attn: NSPE Educational Foundation
1420 King Street
Alexandria, VA 22314-2794
(703) 684-2833   Toll Free: (888) 285-NSPE
Fax: (703) 836-4875   E-mail: education@nspe.org
Web: www.nspe.org/Students/Scholarships/index.html

Summary   To provide financial assistance for college to Hispanic Americans and members of other underrepresented ethnic minority groups who are interested in preparing for a career in engineering.

Eligibility   This program is open to members of underrepresented ethnic minorities (African Americans, Hispanics, or Native Americans) who are high school seniors accepted into an ABET-accredited engineering program at a 4-year college or university. Applicants must have a GPA of 3.5 or higher, verbal SAT score of 600 or higher, and math SAT score of 700 or higher (or English ACT score of 29 or higher and math ACT score of 29 or higher). They must submit brief essays on 4 assigned topics. Selection is based on those essays, GPA, internship/co-op experience and community involvement, 2 faculty recommendations, and honors/scholarships/awards. U.S. citizenship is required.

Financial Data   The stipend is $5,000 per year; funds are paid directly to the recipient's institution.

Duration   1 year; nonrenewable.

Number awarded   1 each year.

Deadline   February of each year.

[302]
ME ENCANTA SCHOLARSHIP PROGRAM

Hispanic College Fund
Attn: Scholarship Processing
1300 L Street, N.W., Suite 975
Washington, DC 20005
(202) 296-5400   Toll Free: (800) 644-4223
Fax: (202) 296-3774   E-mail: hcf-info@hispanicfund.org
Web: scholarships.hispanicfund.org/applications

Summary   To provide financial assistance to Hispanic American high school seniors from designated states who plan to attend college in the United States or Puerto Rico.

Eligibility   This program is open to U.S. citizens and permanent residents of Hispanic background (at least 1 grandparent must be 100% Hispanic) who are seniors graduating from high schools in the District of Columbia, Maryland, Virginia, or West Virginia. Applicants must be planning to enroll full time at a college or university in the United States or Puerto Rico and major in any field. They must have a GPA of 3.0 or higher and be able to demonstrate financial need.

Financial Data   This stipend is $1,500. Funds are paid directly to the recipient's college or university to help cover tuition and fees.

Duration   1 year.

Additional data   This program is sponsored by McDonald's. All applications must be submitted online; no paper applications are available.

Number awarded   1 or more each year.

Deadline   February of each year.

[303]
MEDICAL COLLEGE OF WISCONSIN DIVERSITY SUMMER HEALTH-RELATED RESEARCH EDUCATION PROGRAM

Medical College of Wisconsin
Attn: Office of Student Diversity Affairs
8701 Watertown Plank Road
Milwaukee, WI 53226
(414) 955-8735   Fax: (414) 955-0129
E-mail: studentdiversity@mcw.edu
Web: www.mcw.edu

Summary   To provide an opportunity for Hispanic American and other undergraduate residents of any state who come from diverse backgrounds to participate in a summer research training program at the Medical College of Wisconsin.

Eligibility   This program is open to U.S. citizens and permanent residents who come from an ethnically, economically,

and/or educationally disadvantaged backgrounds. The program targets African Americans, Mexican-Americans, Native Americans (American Indians, Alaska Natives, and Native Hawaiians), Pacific Islanders, Hmong, mainland Puerto Ricans, and individuals with disabilities. Applicants must be interested in participating in a summer research training program at the Medical College of Wisconsin. They must have completed at least 1 year of undergraduate study at an accredited college or university (or be a community college student enrolled in at least 3 courses per academic term) and have a GPA of 3.4 or higher.

Financial Data   The stipend is $10 per hour for a 40-hour week. Housing is provided for students who live outside Milwaukee County and travel expenses are paid for those who live outside Wisconsin.

Duration   10 weeks during the summer.

Additional data   Students are "matched" with a full-time faculty investigator to participate in a research project addressing the causes, prevention, and treatment of cardiovascular, pulmonary, or hematological diseases. This program is funded by the National Heart, Lung, and Blood Institute (NHLBI) of the National Institutes of Health (NIH). Participants are required to prepare an abstract of their research and make a brief oral presentation of their project at the conclusion of the summer.

Number awarded   Approximately 12 each year.

Deadline   February of each year.

[304]
MEDICAL SCIENTIST TRAINING PROGRAM

University of California at San Diego
Attn: School of Medicine
Summer Undergraduate Research Fellowship Program
9500 Gilman Drive, MC 0661
La Jolla, CA 92093-0661
(858) 822-5631   Toll Free: (800) 925-8704
Fax: (858) 822-3067   E-mail: mstp@ucsd.edu
Web: mstp.ucsd.edu/surf/Pages/default.aspx

Summary   To provide an opportunity for Hispanic Americans and other college students from underrepresented groups to work during the summer on a research project in the biomedical sciences at the University of California at San Diego (UCSD).

Eligibility   This program is open to undergraduate students at colleges in any state who are members of an underrepresented group (racial and ethnic groups that have been shown to be underrepresented in health-related sciences, individuals with disabilities, or individuals from a disadvantaged background). Applicants must be interested in working on a research project in the laboratory of a UCSD faculty member in the biomedical sciences. They must be U.S. citizens, permanent residents, or nationals. Along with their application, they must submit brief essays on 1) why they consider themselves an individual from a disadvantaged ethnicity or background or are underrepresented in the biomedical sciences; 2) their past research experiences; 3) the areas of research they wish to pursue in the program; 4) their educational and career plans and how this program will advance them towards their goals; and 5) anything else that might help to evaluate their application.

Financial Data   The program provides a stipend of $1,600 per month, room (but not board), and a $500 travel allowance.

Duration 8 weeks during the summer.

Additional data This program is sponsored by the National Heart, Lung, and Blood Institute (NHLBI) of the National Institutes of Health (NIH).

Number awarded Varies each year; recently, 11 students participated in this program.

Deadline January of each year.

[305]
MERITER MINORITY HEALTH CAREERS SCHOLARSHIP

Meriter Health Services
Attn: Human Resources
202 South Park Street
Madison, WI 53715-1596
(608) 417-6567   E-mail: rthrall@meriter.com
Web: www.meriter.com/wordpress/?p=2241

Summary To provide financial assistance to Hispanic Americans and members of other minority groups who are preparing for a career in a health care occupation.

Eligibility This program is open to members of minority groups (African American, Hispanic, Asian or Pacific Islander, and Native American) who are U.S. citizens or permanent residents. Applicants must have completed at least 1 semester in a college or technical school and be working on a college degree, professional degree, or certification in a health care occupation. Along with their application, they must submit a 2-page essay on their reasons for selecting a health career, any unique experiences that have prepared them for such a career, and how their contributions to the health care field can enhance the fabric of life in our community. Selection is based on demonstrated history of academic success and demonstrated commitment to community service.

Financial Data The stipend is $4,000. Funds are paid directly to the student for assistance with tuition.

Duration 1 year.

Number awarded 1 or more each year.

Deadline April of each year.

[306]
MEXICAN AMERICAN DREAM SCHOLARSHIPS

Council of Mexican Federations
125 Paseo de La Plaza, Suite 500
Los Angeles, CA 90012
(213) 417-8380   Toll Free: (866) 77-COFEM
Fax: (213) 625-0909   E-mail: scholarships@cofem.org
Web: www.cofem.org/programs/scholarships.html

Summary To provide financial assistance to undergraduate and graduate students who are either 1) members or family of members of a federation or club affiliated with the Council of Mexican Federations (COFEM) or 2) AB 540 students.

Eligibility This program is open to undergraduate and graduate students enrolled or planning to enroll full time at a 2- or 4-year college or university in any state. Applicants must be either 1) an AB 540 student; or 2) a member or relative of a member of a federation or club affiliated with COFEM. They must have a GPA of 3.0 or higher, be able to demonstrate financial need, and have a record of involvement in the community or work experience. AB 540 students must submit a 2-page essay on how they can help their community become stronger and more engaged on issues impacting their community. COFEM members must submit a 2-page essay on how they can help their club or federation become a stronger organization. All applicants must submit essays on 1) why they should receive this scholarship; and 2) how they believe this scholarship will help them contribute to the fulfillment of COFEM's mission through their intended career.

Financial Data Stipends are $500 for students at community colleges, $1,000 for students at 4-year colleges and universities, or $2,000 for graduate students.

Duration 1 year.

Number awarded Varies each year.

Deadline October of each year.

[307]
MEXICAN AMERICAN ENGINEERS AND SCIENTISTS SCHOLARSHIP PROGRAM

Society of Mexican American Engineers and Scientists
Attn: Scholarship Program
2437 Bay Area Boulevard, Suite 100
Houston, TX 77058
(281) 557-3677   Fax: (281) 715-5100
E-mail: questions@mymaes.org
Web: www.mymaes.org/program-item/maes-scholarships

Summary To provide financial assistance to undergraduate and graduate student members of the Society of Mexican American Engineers and Scientists (MAES).

Eligibility This program is open to MAES student members who are full-time undergraduate or graduate students at a college or university in the United States and have a GPA of 2.0 or higher. Community college students must be enrolled in majors that can transfer to a 4-year institution offering a baccalaureate degree. All applicants must be majoring in a field of science, technology, engineering, or mathematics. U.S. citizenship or permanent resident status is required. Along with their application, they must submit a personal statement that includes information on their family background, involvement in school and community activities, MAES involvement, and financial need.

Financial Data Stipends range from $1,000 to $4,000.

Duration 1 year.

Additional data This program includes Padrino/Madrina Scholarships at $4,000, graduate student scholarships at $3,000, the Founder's Scholarship at $2,500, the Presidential Scholarship at $2,500, the Pipeline Scholarships at $1,000, and general scholarships at $1,000 or $2,000. The Padrino/Madrina Scholarships are sponsored by Lockheed Martin; the Presidential and Pipeline Scholarships are sponsored by ExxonMobil; other scholarships are sponsored by various professional chapters of MAES. Recipients must attend the MAES International Symposium's Medalla de Oro Banquet in December.

Number awarded Varies each year; recently, available scholarships included 3 Padrino/Madrina Scholarships, 1 graduate scholarship, 1 Founder's Scholarship, 1 Presidential Scholarship, 2 Pipeline Scholarships, and up to 10 general scholarships.

Deadline September of each year.

[308]
MEXICAN AMERICAN GROCERS ASSOCIATION SCHOLARSHIP PROGRAM

Mexican American Grocers Association
405 North San Fernando Road
Los Angeles, CA 90031-1798
(323) 227-1565   Fax: (323) 227-6935
E-mail: maga727@sbcglobal.net
Web: www.maga.org/scholarships

Summary To provide financial assistance to Latino/Hispanic students interested in preparing for a business career.

Eligibility This program is open to Latino/Hispanic students who are attending or planning to attend a community college or a 4-year accredited college or university. Applicants must have a GPA of 2.8 or higher and a major in business administration or a business-related field (e.g., finance, economics, international business). They must demonstrate genuine financial need. Along with their application, they must submit a 1-page essay that includes a statement of what sets them apart from other applicants, their goals during school and upon completion, why they should receive this scholarship, and how they plan to give back to their community after college.

Financial Data Stipends range from $500 to $1,000.

Duration 1 year; may be renewed for up to 2 additional years.

Additional data To date, more than $500,000 has been distributed through this program. Recipients from southern California must attend the scholarship awards banquet in September.

Number awarded Varies; generally more than 50 each year.

Deadline July of each year.

[309]
MEXICAN FIESTA SCHOLARSHIPS

Wisconsin Hispanic Scholarship Foundation, Inc.
2997 South 20th Street
Milwaukee, WI 53215
(414) 383-7066   Fax: (414) 383-6677
E-mail: info@mexicanfiesta.org
Web: www.mexicanfiesta.org/scholarships.php

Summary To provide financial assistance to Hispanic American students in Wisconsin who are interested in attending college or graduate school in the state.

Eligibility This program is open to Wisconsin residents who are of at least 25% Hispanic descent and entering or enrolled at a 2- or 4-year college or university or graduate school in the state. Applicants must complete at least 20 hours of volunteer service during the Mexican Fiesta festival in Milwaukee during August of each year. Along with their application, they must submit an essay on how they plan to assist or help the Hispanic community after their receive their degree. U.S. citizenship or permanent resident status is required.

Financial Data Stipends range from $250 to $2,000.

Duration 1 year; recipients may reapply.

Additional data The sponsor is an affiliate of the League of United Latin American Citizens (LULAC) Wisconsin Councils 319 and 322.

Number awarded More than 100 each year.

Deadline March of each year.

[310]
MEXICAN SCHOLARSHIP FUND

Central Indiana Community Foundation
Attn: Scholarship Program
615 North Alabama Street, Suite 119
Indianapolis, IN 46204-1431
(317) 634-2423   Fax: (317) 684-0943
E-mail: scholarships@cicf.org
Web: www.cicf.org/scholarships

Summary To provide financial assistance to residents of Indiana, especially Mexican Americans, who are interested in attending college in any state.

Eligibility This program is open to residents of Indiana who are enrolled or planning to enroll at a college, university, or vocational/technical school in any state. Preference is given to students of Mexican descent. Applicants must have a GPA of 3.0 or higher. Along with their application, they must submit a 1-page essay either on what their Mexican heritage means to them or on their involvement with the Hispanic community. Financial need is considered in the selection process.

Financial Data The stipend is $2,000.

Duration 1 year.

Additional data The Mexican Consulate in Indianapolis established this program in 2005. The program includes an award funded by the Ambassador Randall L. Tobias and Dr. Marianne W. Tobias Endowed Scholarship Fund. The Tobias Scholars are expected to submit semi-annual letters written in Spanish about their academic progress.

Number awarded Varies each year; recently, 10 of these scholarships were awarded.

Deadline February of each year.

[311]
MICHAEL BAKER CORPORATION SCHOLARSHIP PROGRAM FOR DIVERSITY IN ENGINEERING

Association of Independent Colleges and Universities of Pennsylvania
101 North Front Street
Harrisburg, PA 17101-1405
(717) 232-8649   Fax: (717) 233-8574
E-mail: info@aicup.org
Web: www.aicup.org/fundraising

Summary To provide financial assistance to Hispanic Americans, other minorities, and women from any state enrolled at member institutions of the Association of Independent Colleges and Universities of Pennsylvania (AICUP) who are majoring in designated fields of engineering.

Eligibility This program is open to full-time undergraduate students from any state enrolled at designated AICUP colleges and universities who are women and/or members of the following minority groups: American Indians, Alaska Natives, Asians, Blacks/African Americans, Hispanics/Latinos, Native Hawaiians, or Pacific Islanders. Applicants must be juniors majoring in architectural, civil, or environmental engineering with a GPA of 3.0 or higher. Along with their application, they must submit a 2-page essay on what they believe will be the greatest challenge facing the engineering profession over the next decade, and why.

Financial Data The stipend is $2,500 per year.

Duration 1 year; may be renewed 1 additional year if the recipient maintains appropriate academic standards.

Additional data This program, sponsored by the Michael Baker Corporation, is available at the 83 private colleges and universities in Pennsylvania that comprise the AICUP.

Number awarded 1 each year.

Deadline April of each year.

[312]
MICHIGAN CHAPTER AABE SCHOLARSHIPS

American Association of Blacks in Energy-Michigan
  Chapter
Attn: Sheila Patterson
Consumers Energy
One Energy Plaza 7-253
Jackson, MI 49201
(517) 788-1893 E-mail: sheila.patterson@cmsenergy.com
Web: www.aabe.org/index.php?component=pages&id=572

Summary To provide financial assistance to Hispanic Americans and members of other underrepresented minority groups who are high school seniors in Michigan and planning to major in an energy-related field at a college in any state.

Eligibility This program is open to seniors graduating from high schools in Michigan and planning to work on a bachelor's degree at a college or university in any state. Applicants must be African Americans, Hispanics, or Native Americans who have a GPA of 3.0 or higher and are able to demonstrate financial need. Their intended major must be a field of business, engineering, physical science, mathematics, or technology related to energy. Along with their application, they must submit a 350-word statement on why they should receive this scholarship, their professional career objectives, and any other relevant information.

Financial Data The stipend is $1,000.

Duration 1 year; nonrenewable.

Additional data Winners are eligible to compete for regional and national scholarships.

Number awarded At least 1 each year.

Deadline February of each year.

[313]
MICHIGAN STEERING COMMITTEE MINORITY SCHOLARSHIPS

Michigan Association of Certified Public Accountants
Attn: Michigan Accountancy Foundation
5480 Corporate Drive, Suite 200
Troy, MI 48098-2642
(248) 267-3723   Toll Free: (888) 877-4CPE (within MI)
Fax: (248) 267-3737   E-mail: macpa@michcpa.org
Web: www.michcpa.org/Content/22461.aspx

Summary To provide financial assistance to Hispanic American and other students at Michigan colleges and universities who are working on a degree in accounting.

Eligibility This program is open to members of minority groups enrolled full time at accredited Michigan colleges and universities with a declared concentration in accounting. Applicants must be seniors planning to enter the fifth or graduate year of their school's program. They must intend to or have successfully passed the Michigan C.P.A. examination and intend to practice public accounting in the state. Along

with their application, they must submit a 500-word statement about their educational and career aspirations, including internships and/or other employment, volunteer and community activities, professional affiliations, and full-time employment. Documentation of financial need may also be included. U.S. citizenship or eligibility for permanent employment in the United States is required.

Financial Data The stipend is $4,000; funds are disbursed directly to the recipient's college or university.

Duration 1 year.

Number awarded Varies each year; recently, 5 of these scholarships were awarded.

Deadline January of each year.

[314]
MIGRANT FARMWORKER BACCALAUREATE SCHOLARSHIP

Geneseo Migrant Center
Attn: Scholarship Funds
3 Mt. Morris-Leicester Road
Leicester, NY 14481
(585) 658-7960   Toll Free: (800) 245-5681
Fax: (585) 658-7969   E-mail: dkatter@gvboces.org
Web: www.migrant.net/migrant/scholarships/index.htm

Summary To provide financial assistance to migrant farmworkers who are currently enrolled in college.

Eligibility This program is open to migrant farmworker students with a history of migrating for employment in agriculture. Applicants must have completed at least 1 year of college. Along with their application, they must submit a personal essay of at least 500 words on their background, career and personal goals, and why they should receive this assistance; 3 letters of recommendation; a college transcript; a copy of their Migrant Education Certificate of Eligibility (COE), and documentation of financial need. U.S. citizenship is not required.

Financial Data The stipend is $20,000 per year. These funds are intended to be in addition to any that the student receives through federal, state, or other scholarship assistance as an undergraduate. The same annual amount is available for graduate study or loan repayment.

Duration 1 year; may be renewed for an additional 2 years of undergraduate study. Recipients also have the option of an additional 2 years of graduate support or 3 years of loan repayment.

Additional data Following completion of their baccalaureate degree, recipients may apply for additional support as a graduate student or for assistance in repayment of educational loans.

Number awarded 1 each year.

Deadline June of each year.

[315]
MIGRANT HEALTH SCHOLARSHIP

National Center for Farmworker Health, Inc.
Attn: Migrant Health Scholarship
1770 FM 967
Buda, TX 78610
(512) 312-2700   Toll Free: (800) 531-5120
Fax: (512) 312-2600   E-mail: info@ncfh.org
Web: www.ncfh.org/?pid=232

Summary　To provide financial assistance to people working in the migrant health field, especially those with a farmworker background, who are interested in additional education.

Eligibility　This program is open to staff in clinical, administrative, and support positions at community and migrant health centers who are interested in obtaining additional education at the undergraduate or graduate level. Applicants must submit a 1-page personal statement discussing such issues as why they are interested in migrant health, personal experiences and achievements, future career goals, and commitment to migrant health. Financial need is also considered in the selection process. Preference is given to applicants with a farmworker background.

Financial Data　The stipend is $1,000.

Duration　1 year.

Additional data　This program began in 1984.

Number awarded　Varies each year; recently, 12 of these scholarships were awarded. Since the program was established, it has awarded 188 of these scholarships.

Deadline　March of each year.

[316]
MIGRANT STUDENT LEADERSHIP AND ACADEMIC SCHOLARSHIPS

Washington Apple Education Foundation
Attn: Scholarship Committee
2900 Euclid Avenue
Wenatchee, WA 98801
(509) 663-7713　　　　　　　　　　Fax: (509) 663-7469
E-mail: waef@waef.org
Web: www.waef.org/index.php?page_id=238

Summary　To provide financial assistance to residents of Washington whose families engage in migrant labor and who are interested in attending college in any state.

Eligibility　This program is open to residents of Washington who are current or former high school seniors or students already enrolled at a 2- or 4-year college, university, or trade/technical school in any state. Applicants must have moved across school boundaries for family employment in agriculture or fishing seasonal work, meeting federal eligibility criteria of the Title 1 Migrant Education Program. They must be able to demonstrate a high degree of community service involvement or an ability to be a positive role model for migrant youth. Along with their application, they must submit an official transcript, their SAT or ACT scores, 2 letters of reference, and an essay on an assigned topic. Financial need is also considered in the selection process.

Financial Data　The stipend is $1,000.

Duration　1 year.

Number awarded　2 each year.

Deadline　February of each year.

[317]
MILE HIGH CHAPTER SCHOLARSHIP AWARDS PROGRAM

American GI Forum-Mile High Chapter
Attn: Education Committee
1717 Federal Boulevard
Denver, CO 80204
(303) 455-3304
Web: www.agifmilehigh.org/EduComm.html

Summary　To provide financial assistance to Hispanic residents of Colorado who are attending or planning to attend college in any state.

Eligibility　This program is open to Colorado residents who are high school seniors, high school graduates, GED recipients, or continuing college students. Applicants must be of Hispanic background or involved with the Hispanic community or veteran's organizations. They must have a GPA of 2.0 or higher and be attending or planning to attend college in any state. Along with their application, they must submit an essay of 250 to 500 words on their educational and career goals, their financial need, and why they should be selected to receive a scholarship award. Selection is based on that essay, academic potential, community service and extracurricular activities, and financial need. Preference is given to applicants who have an association with the Mile High Chapter of the American GI Forum.

Financial Data　A stipend is awarded (amount not specified).

Duration　1 year.

Additional data　Recipients must provide 4 hours of volunteer service to the Mile High Chapter during the year they receive the award.

Number awarded　Up to 10 each year.

Deadline　July of each year.

[318]
MILLERCOORS CHICAGO/COLORADO SCHOLARSHIP

¡Adelante! U.S. Education Leadership Fund
8415 Datapoint Drive, Suite 400
San Antonio, TX 78229
(210) 692-1971　　　　　　　　Toll Free: (877) 692-1971
Fax: (210) 692-1951　　　　　E-mail: info@adelantefund.org
Web: www.adelantefund.org/#!scholarships/crij

Summary　To provide financial assistance to Hispanic upper-division students entering or enrolled at a college in Colorado or the Chicago metropolitan area, especially those majoring in designated fields.

Eligibility　This program is open to full-time incoming juniors and seniors at colleges and universities in Colorado or the Chicago metropolitan area. Applicants may be studying any field, but preference is given to those majoring in business, computer science, biochemistry, electrical engineering, or mechanical engineering. They must be of Hispanic descent, have a GPA of 3.0 or higher, be U.S. citizens or permanent residents, agree to attend the Adelante Leadership Institute, and provide 2 letters of recommendation.

Financial Data　The stipend is $3,000.

Duration　1 year.

Additional data　This fund was established by the Hispanic Association of Colleges and Universities in 1997 and became a separate organization in 1999. This program is sponsored by MillerCoors.

Number awarded Varies each year.

Deadline May of each year.

[319]
MILLERCOORS ENGINEERING AND SCIENCE SCHOLARSHIP

¡Adelante! U.S. Education Leadership Fund
8415 Datapoint Drive, Suite 400
San Antonio, TX 78229
(210) 692-1971   Toll Free: (877) 692-1971
Fax: (210) 692-1951   E-mail: info@adelantefund.org
Web: www.adelantefund.org/#!scholarships/crij

Summary To provide financial assistance to upper-division Hispanic students majoring in specified fields of engineering and science at designated universities.

Eligibility This program is open to Hispanic students entering their junior or senior year as full-time students at any of 76 designated partner colleges and universities. Applicants must be working on a degree in biochemistry, computer science, electrical engineering, or mechanical engineering. They must have a GPA of 3.0 or higher, be U.S. citizens or permanent residents, agree to attend the Adelante Leadership Institute, and provide 2 letters of recommendation.

Financial Data The stipend is $3,000.

Duration 1 year.

Additional data This fund was established by the Hispanic Association of Colleges and Universities in 1997 and became a separate organization in 1999. For a list of the 76 partner institutions, contact the fund. This program is sponsored by MillerCoors.

Number awarded Varies each year.

Deadline May of each year.

[320]
MILLERCOORS NATIONAL SCHOLARSHIP

¡Adelante! U.S. Education Leadership Fund
8415 Datapoint Drive, Suite 400
San Antonio, TX 78229
(210) 692-1971   Toll Free: (877) 692-1971
Fax: (210) 692-1951   E-mail: info@adelantefund.org
Web: www.adelantefund.org/#!scholarships/crij

Summary To provide financial assistance to upper-division Hispanic students majoring in fields related to business at designated universities.

Eligibility This program is open to Hispanic students entering their junior or senior year as full-time students at any of 76 designated partner colleges and universities. Applicants must be working on a degree in accounting, general business, general communications, economics, finance, international business, marketing, public relations, or sales. They must have a GPA of 3.0 or higher, be U.S. citizens or permanent residents, agree to attend the Adelante Leadership Institute, and provide 2 letters of recommendation.

Financial Data The stipend is $3,000.

Duration 1 year.

Additional data This fund was established by the Hispanic Association of Colleges and Universities in 1997 and became a separate organization in 1999. For a list of the 76 partner

institutions, contact the fund. This program is sponsored by MillerCoors.

Number awarded Varies each year.

Deadline May of each year.

[321]
MINORITIES IN GOVERNMENT FINANCE SCHOLARSHIP

Government Finance Officers Association
Attn: Scholarship Committee
203 North LaSalle Street, Suite 2700
Chicago, IL 60601-1210
(312) 977-9700   Fax: (312) 977-4806
Web: www.gfoa.org

Summary To provide financial assistance to Hispanic American and other minority upper-division and graduate students who are preparing for a career in state and local government finance.

Eligibility This program is open to upper-division and graduate students who are preparing for a career in public finance by working on a degree in public administration, accounting, finance, political science, economics, or business administration (with a specific focus on government or nonprofit management). Applicants must be members of a minority group, citizens or permanent residents of the United States or Canada, and able to provide a letter of recommendation from a representative of their school. Selection is based on career plans, academic record, plan of study, letters of recommendation, and GPA. Financial need is not considered.

Financial Data The stipend is $5,000.

Duration 1 year.

Additional data This program defines minorities as Blacks or African Americans, American Indians or Alaskan Natives, Hispanics or Latinos, Native Hawaiians or other Pacific Islanders, or Asians.

Number awarded 1 or more each year.

Deadline February of each year.

[322]
MINORITIES IN HOSPITALITY SCHOLARS PROGRAM

International Franchise Association
Attn: IFA Educational Foundation
1501 K Street, N.W., Suite 350
Washington, DC 20005
(202) 662-0784   Fax: (202) 628-0812
E-mail: mbrewer@franchise.org
Web: www.franchise.org/Scholarships.aspx

Summary To provide financial assistance to Hispanic American and other minority students working on an undergraduate degree related to hospitality.

Eligibility This program is open to college sophomores, juniors, and seniors who are U.S. citizens and members of a minority group (defined as African Americans, American Indians, Hispanic Americans, and Asian Americans). Applicants must be working on a degree in a field related to the hospitality industry. Along with their application, they must submit a 500-word essay on why they should be selected to receive this scholarship. Financial need is not considered in the selection process.

Financial Data The stipend is $2,000.

Duration 1 year.

Additional data This program is cosponsored by the IFA Educational Foundation and Choice Hotels International.

Number awarded 1 or more each year.

Deadline January of each year.

[323]
MINORITY AFFAIRS COMMITTEE AWARD FOR OUTSTANDING SCHOLASTIC ACHIEVEMENT

American Institute of Chemical Engineers
Attn: Minority Affairs Committee
Three Park Avenue
New York, NY 10016-5991
(646) 495-1348   Fax: (646) 495-1504
E-mail: awards@aiche.org
Web: www.aiche.org

Summary To recognize and reward Hispanic American and other underrepresented minority students majoring in chemical engineering who serve as role models for other minority students.

Eligibility Members of the American Institute of Chemical Engineers (AIChE) may nominate any chemical engineering student who serves as a role model for minority students in that field. Nominees must be members of a minority group that is underrepresented in chemical engineering (i.e., African American, Hispanic, Native American, Alaskan Native). They must have a GPA of 3.0 or higher. Along with their application, they must submit a 300-word essay on their immediate plans after graduation, areas of chemical engineering of most interest, and long-range career plans. Selection is based on that essay, academic record, participation in AIChE student chapter and professional or civic activities, and financial need.

Financial Data The award consists of a plaque and a $1,500 honorarium.

Duration The award is presented annually.

Additional data This award was first presented in 1996.

Number awarded 1 each year.

Deadline Nominations must be submitted by May of each year.

[324]
MINORITY AND "AT RISK" STUDENT SCHOLARSHIP

Idaho State Board of Education
Len B. Jordan Office Building
650 West State Street, Room 307
P.O. Box 83720
Boise, ID 83720-0037
(208) 332-1574   Fax: (208) 334-2632
E-mail: scholarshiphelp@osbe.idaho.gov
Web: www.boardofed.idaho.gov/scholarship/minority.asp

Summary To provide financial assistance to Hispanic Americans and other "at risk" high school seniors in Idaho who plan to attend college in the state.

Eligibility This program is open to residents of Idaho who are graduates of high schools in the state. Applicants must meet at least 3 of the following 5 requirements: 1) have a disability; 2) be a member of an ethnic minority group historically underrepresented in higher education in Idaho (Native Americans, African Americans, Hispanic Americans); 3) have sub-

stantial financial need; 4) be a first-generation college student; 5) be a migrant farm worker or a dependent of a farm worker. U.S. citizenship is required.

Financial Data The maximum stipend is $3,000 per year.

Duration 1 year; may be renewed for up to 3 additional years.

Additional data This program began in 1991 by the Idaho state legislature. Information is also available from high school counselors and financial aid offices of colleges and universities in Idaho. Recipients must plan to attend or be attending 1 of 11 participating colleges and universities in the state on a full-time basis. For a list of those schools, write to the State of Idaho Board of Education.

Number awarded Approximately 40 each year.

Deadline Deadline not specified.

[325]
MINORITY AND UNDERREPRESENTED ENVIRONMENTAL LITERACY PROGRAM

Missouri Department of Higher Education
Attn: Minority and Underrepresented Environmental
  Literacy Program
205 Jefferson Street
P.O. Box 1469
Jefferson City, MO 65102-1469
(573) 751-2361   Toll Free: (800) 473-6757
Fax: (573) 751-6635   E-mail: info@dhe.mo.gov
Web: dhe.mo.gov/ppc/grants/muelp_0310_final.php

Summary To provide financial assistance to Hispanic American and other underrepresented students from Missouri who are or will be working on a bachelor's or master's degree in an environmental field.

Eligibility This program is open to residents of Missouri who are high school seniors or current undergraduate or graduate students enrolled or planning to enroll full time at a college or university in the state. Priority is given to members of the following underrepresented minority ethnic groups: African Americans, Hispanic or Latino Americans, Native Americans and Alaska Natives, and Native Hawaiians and Pacific Islanders. Applicants must be working on or planning to work on a bachelor's or master's degree in 1) engineering (civil, chemical, environmental, mechanical, or agricultural); 2) environmental studies (geology, biology, wildlife management, natural resource planning, natural resources, or a closely-related course of study); 3) environmental chemistry; or 4) environmental law enforcement. They must be U.S. citizens or permanent residents or otherwise lawfully present in the United States. Graduating high school seniors must have a GPA of 3.0 or higher; students currently enrolled in college or graduate school must have a GPA of 2.5 or higher. Along with their application, they must submit a 1-page essay on their environmental education and career goals, 3 letters of recommendation, a resume of school and community activities, and transcripts that include SAT or ACT scores. Financial need is not considered in the selection process.

Financial Data Stipends vary each year; recently, they averaged approximately $3,996 per year.

Duration 1 year; may be renewed if the recipient maintains a GPA of 2.5 or higher and full-time enrollment.

Additional data This program was established by the Missouri Department of Natural Resources but transferred to the Department of Higher Education in 2009.

Number awarded Varies each year.

Deadline May of each year.

[326]
MINORITY LEAP SCHOLARSHIPS

Missouri Society of Certified Public Accountants
Attn: LEAP Program
540 Maryville Centre Drive, Suite 200
P.O. Box 419042
St. Louis, MO 63141-9042
(314) 997-7966, ext. 125
Toll Free: (800) 264-7966, ext. 125 (within MO)
Fax: (314) 997-2592   E-mail: lsimpson@mocpa.org
Web: www.mocpa.org/students/scholarships

Summary To provide financial assistance to Hispanic American and other minority residents of Missouri who are working on an undergraduate or graduate degree in accounting at a university in the state.

Eligibility This program is open to members of minority groups underrepresented in the accounting profession (Black/African American, Hispanic/Latino, Native American, Asian American) who are currently working full time on an undergraduate or graduate degree in accounting at a college or university in Missouri. Applicants must either be residents of Missouri or the children of members of the Missouri Society of Certified Public Accountants (MSCPA). They must be U.S. citizens, have completed at least 30 semester hours of college work, have a GPA of 3.3 or higher, and be student members of the MSCPA. Selection is based on the GPA, involvement in MSCPA, educator recommendations, and leadership potential. Financial need is not considered.

Financial Data The stipend is $1,250 per year.

Duration 1 year; may be renewed.

Additional data These scholarships are offered through the sponsor's Lead and Enhance the Accounting Profession (LEAP) program, established in 2001.

Number awarded Varies each year; recently, 2 of these scholarships were awarded.

Deadline February of each year.

[327]
MINORITY NURSE MAGAZINE SCHOLARSHIP PROGRAM

Minority Nurse Magazine
c/o Alloy Education
2 LAN Drive, Suite 100
Westford, MA 01886
Toll Free: (877) ASK-ALLO
E-mail: editor@minoritynurse.com
Web: www.minoritynurse.com

Summary To provide financial assistance to Hispanic Americans and members of other minority groups who are working on a bachelor's or master's degree in nursing.

Eligibility This program is open to students currently enrolled in 1) the third or fourth year of an accredited B.S.N. program; 2) an accelerated program leading to a B.S.N. degree (e.g., R.N. to B.S.N., B.A. to B.S.N.); or 3) an accelerated master's entry nursing program (e.g., B.A. to M.S.N.) for students with bachelor's degrees in fields other than nursing. Graduate students who already have a bachelor's degree in nursing are not eligible. Along with their application, they must submit a 250-word essay on their academic and personal accomplishments, community service, and goals for their future nursing career. Selection is based on academic excellence (GPA of 3.0 or higher), demonstrated commitment of service to the student's minority community, and financial need. U.S. citizenship of permanent resident status is required.

Financial Data The stipends are $3,000 or $1,000.

Duration 1 year.

Additional data This program began in 2000. Winners are announced in the summer issue of *Minority Nurse* magazine.

Number awarded 3 each year: 1 at $3,000 and 2 at $1,000.

Deadline January of each year.

[328]
MINORITY SCHOLARSHIP AWARD FOR ACADEMIC EXCELLENCE IN PHYSICAL THERAPY

American Physical Therapy Association
Attn: Honors and Awards Program
1111 North Fairfax Street
Alexandria, VA 22314-1488
(703) 684-APTA   Toll Free: (800) 999-APTA
Fax: (703) 684-7343   TDD: (703) 683-6748
E-mail: honorsandawards@apta.org
Web: www.apta.org

Summary To provide financial assistance to Hispanic American and other minority students who are interested in becoming a physical therapist or physical therapy assistant.

Eligibility This program is open to U.S. citizens and permanent residents who are members of the following minority groups: African American or Black, Asian, Native Hawaiian or other Pacific Islander, American Indian or Alaska Native, or Hispanic/Latino. Applicants must be in the final year of a professional physical therapy or physical therapy assistant education program. They must submit a personal essay outlining their professional goals and minority service. U.S. citizenship or permanent resident status is required. Selection is based on 1) demonstrated evidence of contributions in the area of minority affairs and services with an emphasis on contributions made while enrolled in a physical therapy program; 2) potential to contribute to the profession of physical therapy; and 3) scholastic achievement.

Financial Data The stipend varies; recently, minimum awards were $6,000 for physical therapy students or $2,500 for physical therapy assistant students.

Duration 1 year.

Number awarded Varies each year; recently, 7 of these awards were granted.

Deadline November of each year.

[329]
MINORITY SCHOLARSHIP AWARDS FOR COLLEGE STUDENTS IN CHEMICAL ENGINEERING

American Institute of Chemical Engineers
Attn: Minority Affairs Committee
Three Park Avenue
New York, NY 10016-5991
(646) 495-1348   Fax: (646) 495-1504
E-mail: awards@aiche.org
Web: www.aiche.org

Summary   To provide financial assistance for the undergraduate study of chemical engineering to Hispanic American and other underrepresented minority college student members of the American Institute of Chemical Engineers (AIChE).

Eligibility   This program is open to undergraduate student AIChE members who are also members of a minority group that is underrepresented in chemical engineering (African Americans, Hispanics, Native Americans, and Alaskan Natives). They must have a GPA of 3.0 or higher. Along with their application, they must submit a 300-word essay on their immediate plans after graduation, areas of chemical engineering of most interest, and long-range career plans. Selection is based on that essay, academic record, participation in AIChE student chapter and professional or civic activities, and financial need.

Financial Data   The stipend is $1,000.

Duration   1 year; nonrenewable.

Number awarded   Approximately 10 each year.

Deadline   June of each year.

[330]
MINORITY SCHOLARSHIP AWARDS FOR INCOMING COLLEGE FRESHMEN IN CHEMICAL ENGINEERING

American Institute of Chemical Engineers
Attn: Minority Affairs Committee
Three Park Avenue
New York, NY 10016-5991
(646) 495-1348   Fax: (646) 495-1504
E-mail: awards@aiche.org
Web: www.aiche.org

Summary   To provide financial assistance to Hispanic American and other incoming minority freshmen interested in studying science or engineering in college.

Eligibility   Eligible are members of a minority group that is underrepresented in chemical engineering (African Americans, Hispanics, Native Americans, and Alaskan Natives). Applicants must be graduating high school seniors planning to enroll at a 4-year university with a major in science or engineering. They must be nominated by an American Institute of Chemical Engineers (AIChE) local section. Selection is based on academic record (including a GPA of 3.0 or higher), participation in school and work activities, a 300-word letter outlining the reasons for choosing science or engineering, and financial need.

Financial Data   The stipend is $1,000.

Duration   1 year; nonrenewable.

Number awarded   Approximately 10 each year.

Deadline   Nominations must be submitted by June of each year.

[331]
MINORITY SCHOLARSHIP IN CLASSICS AND CLASSICAL ARCHAEOLOGY

American Philological Association
Attn: Executive Director
University of Pennsylvania
220 South 40th Street, Suite 201E
Philadelphia, PA 19104-3512
(215) 898-4975   Fax: (215) 573-7874
E-mail: apaclassics@sas.upenn.edu
Web: www.apaclassics.org

Summary   To provide Hispanic American and other minority undergraduates with summer training as preparation for advanced work in the classics or classical archaeology.

Eligibility   Eligible to apply are minority (African American, Hispanic American, Asian American, and Native American) undergraduate students who wish to engage in summer study as preparation for graduate work in the classics or classical archaeology. Applicants may propose participation in summer programs in Italy, Greece, Egypt, or other classical centers; language training at institutions in the United States, Canada, or Europe; or other relevant courses of study. Selection is based on academic qualifications, especially in classics; demonstrated ability in at least 1 classical language; quality of the proposal for study with respect to preparation for a career in classics; and financial need. Applications must be endorsed by a member of the American Philological Association (APA).

Financial Data   The maximum award is $4,000.

Duration   1 summer.

Additional data   This program includes 1 scholarship supported by the Gladys Krieble Delmas Foundation.

Number awarded   2 each year.

Deadline   December of each year.

[332]
MINORITY TEACHERS OF ILLINOIS SCHOLARSHIP PROGRAM

Illinois Student Assistance Commission
Attn: Scholarship and Grant Services
1755 Lake Cook Road
Deerfield, IL 60015-5209
(847) 948-8550   Toll Free: (800) 899-ISAC
Fax: (847) 831-8549   TDD: (800) 526-0844
E-mail: isac.studentservices@isac.illinois.gov
Web: www.collegeillinois.org

Summary   To provide funding to Hispanic American and other minority students in Illinois who plan to become teachers at the preschool, elementary, or secondary level.

Eligibility   Applicants must be Illinois residents, U.S. citizens or eligible noncitizens, members of a minority group (African American/Black, Hispanic American, Asian American, or Native American), and high school graduates or holders of a General Educational Development (GED) certificate. They must be enrolled at least half time as an undergraduate or graduate student, have a GPA of 2.5 or higher, not be in default on any student loan, and be enrolled or accepted for enrollment in a teacher education program.

Financial Data Grants up to $5,000 per year are awarded. This is a scholarship/loan program. Recipients must agree to teach full time 1 year for each year of support received. The teaching agreement may be fulfilled at a public, private, or parochial preschool, elementary school, or secondary school in Illinois; at least 30% of the student body at those schools must be minority. It must be fulfilled within the 5-year period following the completion of the undergraduate program for which the scholarship was awarded. The time period may be extended if the recipient serves in the U.S. armed forces, enrolls full time in a graduate program related to teaching, becomes temporarily disabled, is unable to find employment as a teacher at a qualifying school, or takes additional courses on at least a half-time basis to obtain certification as a teacher in Illinois. Recipients who fail to honor this work obligation must repay the award with 5% interest.

Duration 1 year; may be renewed for a total of 8 semesters or 12 quarters.

Number awarded Varies each year.

Deadline Priority consideration is given to applications received by February of each year.

[333]
MIRIAM WEINSTEIN PEACE AND JUSTICE EDUCATION AWARD

Philanthrofund Foundation
Attn: Scholarship Committee
1409 Willow Street, Suite 109
Minneapolis, MN 55403-2241
(612) 870-1806   Toll Free: (800) 435-1402
Fax: (612) 871-6587   E-mail: Info@PfundOnline.org
Web: www.pfundonline.org/scholarships.html

Summary To provide financial assistance to Hispanic American and other minority students from Minnesota who have supported gay, lesbian, bisexual, and transgender (GLBT) activities and are interested in working on a degree in education.

Eligibility This program is open to residents of Minnesota and students attending a Minnesota educational institution who are members of a religious, racial, or ethnic minority. Applicants must be self-identified as GLBT or from a GLBT family and have demonstrated a commitment to peace and justice issues. They may be attending or planning to attend trade school, technical college, college, or university (as an undergraduate or graduate student). Preference is given to students who have completed at least 2 years of college and are working on a degree in education. Selection is based on the applicant's 1) affirmation of GLBT or allied identity; 2) evidence of experience and skills in service and leadership; and 3) evidence of service, leading, and working for change in GLBT communities, including serving as a role model, mentor, and/or adviser.

Financial Data The stipend is $3,000. Funds must be used for tuition, books, fees, or dissertation expenses.

Duration 1 year.

Number awarded 1 each year.

Deadline January of each year.

[334]
MISSISSIPPI CHAPTER AABE SCHOLARSHIPS

American Association of Blacks in Energy-Mississippi Chapter
Attn: Scholarship Committee Chair
P.O. Box 986
Jackson, MS 39205
E-mail: rkent@entergy.com
Web: www.aabe.org/index.php?component=pages&id=387

Summary To provide financial assistance to Hispanic Americans and members of other underrepresented minority groups who are high school seniors in Mississippi and planning to major in an energy-related field at a college in any state.

Eligibility This program is open to seniors graduating from high schools in Mississippi and planning to attend a 4-year college or university in any state. Applicants must be African Americans, Hispanics, or Native Americans who have a GPA of 3.0 or higher and are able to demonstrate financial need. Their intended major must be computer technology, engineering, technology, mathematics, the physical sciences (chemistry, geology, meteorology, or physics only), or other energy-related field. Along with their application, they must submit a 350-word statement on why they should receive this scholarship, how their professional career objectives relate to energy, and any other relevant information.

Financial Data Stipends are $2,000 or $1,000.

Duration 1 year.

Additional data Winners are eligible to compete for regional and national scholarships.

Number awarded 4 or more each year: 1 at $2,000 and 3 or more at $1,000.

Deadline March of each year.

[335]
MISSOURI MINORITY TEACHING SCHOLARSHIP PROGRAM

Missouri Department of Higher Education
Attn: Student Financial Assistance
205 Jefferson Street
P.O. Box 1469
Jefferson City, MO 65102-1469
(573) 526-7958   Toll Free: (800) 473-6757
Fax: (573) 751-6635   E-mail: info@dhe.mo.gov
Web: www.dhe.mo.gov/ppc/grants/minorityteaching.php

Summary To provide scholarships and other funding to Hispanic American and other minority high school seniors, high school graduates, and college students in Missouri who are interested in preparing for a teaching career in mathematics or science.

Eligibility This program is open to Missouri residents who are African American, Asian American, Hispanic American, or Native American. Applicants must be 1) high school seniors, college students, or returning adults (without a degree) who rank in the top 25% of their high school class and scored at or above the 75th percentile on the ACT or SAT examination (recently, that meant a composite score of 24 or higher on the ACT or 1340 or higher on the composite critical reading and mathematics SAT); 2) individuals who have completed 30 college hours and have a cumulative GPA of 3.0 or better; or 3) baccalaureate degree-holders who are returning to an approved mathematics or science teacher education program. They must be a U.S. citizen or permanent resident or otherwise lawfully present in the United States. All applicants must be enrolled full time in an approved teacher education program at a community college, 4-year college, or university in Missouri. Selection is based on high school class rank, ACT or SAT scores, school and community activities, career interest in teaching, leadership skills, employment experience, and recommendations.

Financial Data The stipend is $3,000 per year, of which $2,000 is provided by the state as a forgivable loan and $1,000 is provided by the school as a scholarship. Recipients must commit to teaching in a Missouri public elementary or secondary school for 5 years following graduation. If they fail to fulfill that obligation, they must repay the state portion of the scholarship with interest at 9.5%.

Duration Up to 4 years.

Number awarded Up to 100 each year.

Deadline June of each year.

[336]
MONSIGNOR PHILIP KENNEY SCHOLARSHIP FUND

New Hampshire Charitable Foundation
37 Pleasant Street
Concord, NH 03301-4005
(603) 225-6641   Toll Free: (800) 464-6641
Fax: (603) 225-1700   E-mail: info@nhcf.org
Web: www.nhcf.org/page.aspx?pid=482

Summary To provide financial assistance for college to minority students from New Hampshire, especially Hispanics.

Eligibility This program is open to all minority residents of New Hampshire, but first preference is given to Hispanics. Applicants may be planning to attend a local community college, enroll in a 4-year degree program, or study part time, but they must be in a degree or recognized certification program. Both traditional college-age and adult students are eligible. Their family income must be less than $27,930 for a family of 1, rising to $94,710 for a family of 8. Selection is based on academic achievement, involvement in school and community activities, work experience, and financial need.

Financial Data The stipend ranges from $500 to $2,500 per year.

Duration 1 year; recipients may reapply.

Additional data This program was established by Monsignor Philip Kenney in 1986 with the award funds he received as Manchester's Citizen of the Year.

Number awarded 8 to 10 each year.

Deadline April of each year.

[337]
MONTGOMERY SUMMER RESEARCH DIVERSITY FELLOWSHIPS

American Bar Foundation
Attn: Summer Research Diversity Fellowship
750 North Lake Shore Drive
Chicago, IL 60611-4403
(312) 988-6515   Fax: (312) 988-6579
E-mail: fellowships@abfn.org
Web: www.americanbarfoundation.org

Summary To provide an opportunity for Hispanic American and other undergraduate students from diverse backgrounds to work on a summer research project in the field of law and social science.

Eligibility This program is open to U.S. citizens and permanent residents who are African Americans, Hispanic/Latinos, Asians, Puerto Ricans, Native Americans, or other individuals who will add diversity to the field of law and social science. Applicants must be sophomores or juniors in college, have a GPA of 3.0 or higher, be majoring in the social sciences or humanities, and be willing to consider an academic or research career. Along with their application, they must submit a 200-word essay on their future plans and why this fellowship would contribute to them, another essay on an assigned topic, official transcripts, and a letter of recommendation from a faculty member familiar with their work.

Financial Data Participants receive a stipend of $3,600.

Duration 35 hours per week for 8 weeks during the summer.

Additional data Students are assigned to an American Bar Foundation Research Professor who involves the student in the design and conduct of the professor's research project and who acts as mentor during the student's tenure.

Number awarded 4 each year.

Deadline February of each year.

[338]
MOSS ADAMS FOUNDATION SCHOLARSHIP

Educational Foundation for Women in Accounting
Attn: Foundation Administrator
136 South Keowee Street
Dayton, OH 45402
(937) 424-3391   Fax: (937) 222-5749
E-mail: info@efwa.org
Web: www.efwa.org/scholarships_MossAdams.php

Summary To provide financial support to women (preference given to Hispanic American and other minority women) who are working on an accounting degree.

Eligibility This program is open to women who are enrolled in an accounting degree program at an accredited college or university. Applicants must meet 1 of the following criteria: 1) women pursuing a fifth-year requirement either through general studies or within a graduate program; 2) women returning to school as current or reentry juniors or seniors; or 3) minority women. Selection is based on aptitude for accounting and business, commitment to the goal of working on a degree in accounting (including evidence of continued commitment after receiving this award), clear evidence that the candidate has established goals and a plan for achieving those goals (both personal and professional), financial need, and a demonstration of how the scholarship will impact her life. U.S. citizenship is required.

Financial Data The stipend is $1,000.

Duration 1 year.

Additional data This program was established by Rowling, Dold & Associates LLP, a woman-owned C.P.A. firm based in San Diego. It was renamed when that firm merged with Moss Adams LLP.

Number awarded 1 each year.

Deadline April of each year.

[339]
MSCPA/ALPFA SCHOLARSHIPS

Massachusetts Society of Certified Public Accountants
Attn: MSCPA Educational Foundation
105 Chauncy Street, Tenth Floor
Boston, MA 02111
(617) 556-4000   Toll Free: (800) 392-6145
Fax: (617) 556-4126   E-mail: info@mscpaonline.org
Web: www.cpatrack.com/scholarships

Summary To provide financial assistance to members of the Association of Latino Professionals in Finance and Accounting (ALPFA) from Massachusetts working on an undergraduate degree in accounting at a college or university in the state.

Eligibility This program is open to student members of the Boston chapter of ALPFA who are enrolled at a college or university in Massachusetts. Applicants must have completed at least the first semester of their sophomore year and be able to demonstrate financial need, academic excellence, and an intention to prepare for a career as a Certified Public Accountant (C.P.A.) at a firm in Massachusetts.

Financial Data The stipend is $2,500.

Duration 1 year.

Additional data This program is sponsored by ALPFA-Boston and the Massachusetts Society of Certified Public Accountants (MSCPA).

Number awarded 2 each year.

Deadline March of each year.

[340]
M&T BANK SCHOLARSHIP PROGRAM

Hispanic College Fund
Attn: Scholarship Processing
1300 L Street, N.W., Suite 975
Washington, DC 20005
(202) 296-5400   Toll Free: (800) 644-4223
Fax: (202) 296-3774   E-mail: hcf-info@hispanicfund.org
Web: scholarships.hispanicfund.org/applications

Summary To provide financial assistance to Hispanic American undergraduate and graduate students from designated areas who plan to work on a degree in a field related to banking at a school in the United States or Puerto Rico.

Eligibility This program is open to U.S. citizens and permanent residents of Hispanic background (at least 1 grandparent must be 100% Hispanic) who reside in the Washington, D.C. region, New York, or Pennsylvania. Applicants must be enrolled or planning to enroll full time at a college or university in the United States or Puerto Rico and work on an undergraduate or graduate degree in a field related to banking, including accounting, business, or finance. They must have a GPA of 3.0 or higher and be able to demonstrate financial need. Preference is given to applicants who have a strong record of community service.

Financial Data This stipend ranges from $2,000 to $3,000. Funds are paid directly to the recipient's college or university to help cover tuition and fees.

Duration 1 year.

Additional data This program is sponsored by M&T Bank. All applications must be submitted online; no paper applications are available.

Number awarded 1 or more each year.
Deadline February of each year.

[341]
MUTUAL OF OMAHA ACTUARIAL SCHOLARSHIP FOR MINORITY STUDENTS

Mutual of Omaha
Attn: Strategic Staffing-Actuarial Recruitment
Mutual of Omaha Plaza
Omaha, NE 68175
(402) 351-3300   E-mail: diversity@mutualofomaha.com
Web: www.mutualofomaha.com

Summary To provide financial aid and work experience to Hispanic American and other minority undergraduate students who are preparing for an actuarial career.

Eligibility This program is open to members of minority groups (African American, Hispanic, Native American, Asian or Pacific Islander, or Alaskan Eskimo) who have completed at least 24 semester hours of full-time study. Applicants must be working on an actuarial or mathematics-related degree with the goal of preparing for an actuarial career. They must have a GPA of 3.0 or higher and have passed at least 1 actuarial examination. Prior to accepting the award, they must be available to complete a summer internship at the sponsor's home office in Omaha, Nebraska. Along with their application, they must submit a 1-page personal statement on why they are interested in becoming an actuary and how they are preparing themselves for an actuarial career. Status as a U.S. citizen, permanent resident, asylee, or refugee must be established.

Financial Data The scholarship stipend is $5,000 per year. Funds are paid directly to the student. For the internship, students receive an hourly rate of pay, subsidized housing, and financial incentives for successful examination results received during the internship period.

Duration 1 year. Recipients may reapply if they maintain a cumulative GPA of 3.0 or higher.

Number awarded Varies each year.

Deadline October of each year.

[342]
NACME PRE-ENGINEERING STUDENT SCHOLARSHIPS

National Action Council for Minorities in Engineering
Attn: Pre-Engineering Department
440 Hamilton Avenue, Suite 302
White Plains, NY 10601-1813
(914) 539-4010   Fax: (914) 539-4032
E-mail: scholarships@nacme.org
Web: www.nacmebacksme.org/NBM_C.aspx?pageid=153

Summary To provide financial assistance to Hispanic American and other underrepresented minority high school seniors interested in studying engineering in college.

Eligibility This program is open to African American, Latino, and American Indian high school seniors who have participated in an Academy of Engineering or other pre-college or high school program focused on mathematics, science, and engineering. Applicants must have been accepted as a full-time student at 1 of 51 ABET-accredited engineering programs at universities that have partnered with this sponsor. They must have a GPA of 3.0 or higher and minimum scores of 1650 on the SAT (including 550 on mathematics) or 24 on the ACT composite (including 24 on the mathematics section). Along with their application, they must submit documentation of financial need and 2 brief essays on assigned topics. U.S. citizenship or permanent resident status is required.

Financial Data The stipend is $2,500. Funds are sent directly to the recipient's university.

Duration 1 year; nonrenewable.

Additional data For a list of the 51 partner institutions, contact the sponsor.

Number awarded Varies each year; recently, 95 of these scholarships were awarded.

Deadline March of each year.

[343]
NACOPRW SCHOLARSHIP AWARD

National Conference of Puerto Rican Women-Miami
  Chapter
c/o Elizabeth Baez, President
13381 S.W. 77th Street
Miami, FL 33183
(305) 338-1844   E-mail: NACOPRW.MIAMI@gmail.com
Web: www.nacoprwmiami.org/ScholarshipApp.htm

Summary To provide financial assistance for college to Puerto Rican women.

Eligibility This program is open to women who are Puerto Rican by birth or descent. Applicants must have been admitted to an accredited college or university in the United States or Puerto Rico. They must have a GPA of 3.0 or higher and be able to demonstrate financial need.

Financial Data The stipend is approximately $1,000.

Duration 1 year.

Additional data The National Conference of Puerto Rican Women (NACOPRW) "promotes the full participation of Puerto Rican and other Hispanic women in the economic, social and political life of the United States and Puerto Rico."

Number awarded 1 or more each year.

Deadline April of each year.

[344]
NAHJ FORD MOTOR COMPANY SCHOLARSHIPS

National Association of Hispanic Journalists
Attn: Scholarship Committee
1050 Connecticut Avenue, N.W., Tenth Floor
Washington, DC 20036
(202) 662-7145   Toll Free: (888) 346-NAHJ
Fax: (202) 662-7144   E-mail: nahj@nahj.org
Web: www.nahj12.com/scholarships

Summary To provide financial assistance to undergraduate and graduate student members of the National Association of Hispanic Journalists (NAHJ) who are interested in preparing for careers in the media.

Eligibility This program is open to Hispanic American high school seniors, undergraduates, and graduate students who are interested in preparing for a career in print, broadcast (radio or television), online, or visual journalism. Applicants must be enrolled full time at a college or university in the United States or Puerto Rico. They must have a GPA of 2.0 or higher and be NAHJ members. Along with their application, they must submit transcripts, a 1-page resume, 2 letters of recommendation, work samples, and a 1,000-word autobiographical essay that includes why they are interested in a career in journalism, what inspired them to prepare for a career in the field, what hardships or obstacles they have experienced while trying to realize their goal of becoming a journalist, and the role Latino journalists play in the news industry. Selection is based on commitment to the field of journalism, academic achievement, awareness of the Latino community, and financial need.

Financial Data Stipends range up to $2,500.

Duration 1 year; may be renewed until completion of a college degree.

Additional data This program is sponsored by Ford Motor Company.

Number awarded Varies each year; recently, 8 of these scholarships were awarded.

Deadline January of each year.

[345]
NAJERA CONSULTING GROUP/HENAAC SCHOLARS PROGRAM

Great Minds in STEM
Attn: HENAAC Scholars Program
602 Monterey Pass Road
Monterey Park, CA 91754
(323) 262-0997   Fax: (323) 262-0946
E-mail: gcruz@greatmindsinstem.org
Web: www.greatmindsinstem.org

Summary To provide financial assistance to Hispanic undergraduate students majoring in civil engineering at designated universities.

Eligibility This program is open to Hispanic students who are working on an undergraduate degree in civil engineering at the University of Illinois, University of Michigan, Michigan State University, University of Southern California, or Texas Tech University. Applicants must be of Hispanic origin and/or must significantly participate in and promote organizations and activities in the Hispanic community. They must have a GPA of 3.0 or higher. Along with their application, they must submit a 700-word essay on a topic that changes annually. Selection is based on leadership, academic achievements, and campus and community activities; financial need is not considered.

Financial Data Stipends range from $500 to $10,000.

Duration 1 year; recipients may reapply.

Additional data The Hispanic Engineer National Achievement Awards Conference (HENAAC) was established in 1989 and initiated a scholarship program in 2000. In 2010, the sponsoring organization officially adopted its current name, but it continues to hold the annual HENAAC conference, at which the scholarships are presented. This program is sponsored by Najera Consulting Group, Inc. Recipients must attend the conference to accept their scholarship.

Number awarded 1 or more each year.

Deadline April of each year.

[346]
NASA JOHNSON SPACE CENTER SCHOLARSHIPS

Great Minds in STEM
Attn: HENAAC Scholars Program
602 Monterey Pass Road
Monterey Park, CA 91754
(323) 262-0997   Fax: (323) 262-0946
E-mail: gcruz@greatmindsinstem.org
Web: www.greatmindsinstem.org

Summary To provide financial assistance to Hispanic undergraduate students from any state who are enrolled at universities in southern California and majoring in designated fields of engineering or computer science.

Eligibility This program is open to Hispanic undergraduate students from any state who are majoring in computer science or engineering (aerospace, biomedical, computer, electrical, or mechanical) at a college or university in southern California. Applicants must be of Hispanic origin and/or must significantly participate in and promote organizations and activities in the Hispanic community. They must have a GPA of 3.0 or higher. Along with their application, they must submit a 700-word essay on a topic that changes annually. Selection is based on leadership, academic achievements, and campus and community activities; financial need is not considered.

Financial Data Stipends range from $500 to $10,000.

Duration 1 year; recipients may reapply.

Additional data The Hispanic Engineer National Achievement Awards Conference (HENAAC) was established in 1989 and initiated a scholarship program in 2000. In 2010, the sponsoring organization officially adopted its current name, but it continues to hold the annual HENAAC conference, at which the scholarships are presented. This program is sponsored by the Johnson Space Center of the National Aeronautics and Space Administration (NASA). Recipients must attend the conference to accept their scholarship.

Number awarded Varies each year; recently, 9 of these scholarships were awarded.

Deadline April of each year.

[347]
NASA UNDERGRADUATE STUDENT RESEARCH PROGRAM

Universities Space Research Association
Attn: NASA USRP Project Administrator
2101 NASA Parkway, AE2 Education Office
Houston, TX 77058
(281) 244-2036   E-mail: garza@epo.usra.edu
Web: usrp.usra.edu

Summary To provide an opportunity for undergraduate students (particularly those who represented diversity) to participate in a research project at centers of the U.S. National Aeronautics and Space Administration (NASA).

Eligibility This program is open to sophomores, juniors, and seniors enrolled full time at accredited U.S. colleges and universities. Applicants must have a GPA of 3.0 or higher with an academic major or demonstrated course work concentration in engineering, mathematics, computer science, or physical/life sciences. They must be interested in participating in a mentored research experience at a designated NASA center. The program seeks participation from students who repre-

sent America's rich and diverse population: female and male students of all races, creeds, colors, national origins, ages, and disabilities. U.S. citizenship is required.

Financial Data The stipend is $6,500 for the summer session or $9,500 for the fall or spring semester. Participants also receive round-trip airfare or ground transportation costs to and from the NASA host center.

Duration 10 weeks during the summer or 15 weeks during the fall or spring semester.

Additional data The participating NASA centers include Ames Research Center (Moffett Field, California), Dryden Flight Research Center (Edwards, California), Glenn Research Center (Cleveland, Ohio), Goddard Space Flight Center (Greenbelt, Maryland), Jet Propulsion Laboratory (Pasadena, California), Johnson Space Center (Houston, Texas), Kennedy Space Center (Florida), Langley Research Center (Hampton, Virginia), Marshall Space Flight Center (Huntsville, Alabama), Stennis Space Center (Mississippi), Wallops Flight Facility (Virginia), and White Sands Test Facility (Las Cruces, New Mexico).

Number awarded Approximately 330 each year.

Deadline Deadline not specified.

[348]
NASCAR/WENDELL SCOTT AWARD

Hispanic Association of Colleges and Universities
Attn: National Scholarship Program
8415 Datapoint Drive, Suite 400
San Antonio, TX 78229
(210) 692-3805   Fax: (210) 692-0823
TDD: (800) 855-2880   E-mail: scholarship@hacu.net
Web: www.hacu.net/hacu/Scholarships.asp

Summary To provide financial assistance to undergraduate and graduate students majoring in specified fields at member institutions of the Hispanic Association of Colleges and Universities (HACU) in designated states.

Eligibility This program is open to full-time undergraduate and graduate students at 4-year HACU member institutions in Florida, Georgia, or North Carolina. Applicants must be working on a degree in business, engineering, management, marketing, mass media, public relations, sports marketing, or technology. They must have a GPA of 3.0 or higher and be able to demonstrate financial need. Along with their application, they must submit an essay that focuses on their personal motivation for applying to this scholarship program, their academic and/or career goals, and the skills they could bring to an employer.

Financial Data The stipend is $2,200.

Duration 1 year.

Additional data This program is sponsored by NASCAR and administered by HACU.

Number awarded 1 or more each year.

Deadline June of each year.

[349]
NATIONAL ASSOCIATION OF HISPANIC JOURNALISTS BROADCAST SCHOLARSHIPS

National Association of Hispanic Journalists
Attn: Scholarship Committee
1050 Connecticut Avenue, N.W., Tenth Floor
Washington, DC 20036
(202) 662-7145   Toll Free: (888) 346-NAHJ
Fax: (202) 662-7144   E-mail: nahj@nahj.org
Web: www.nahj12.com/scholarships

Summary To provide financial assistance to undergraduate and graduate student members of the National Association of Hispanic Journalists (NAHJ) who are interested in preparing for a career in television broadcast journalism.

Eligibility This program is open to Hispanic American undergraduate and graduate students who are interested in preparing for a career in television broadcast journalism. Applicants must be enrolled full time at a college or university in the United States or Puerto Rico. They must be NAHJ members. Along with their application, they must submit transcripts, a 1-page resume, 2 letters of recommendation, work samples, and a 1,000-word autobiographical essay that includes why they are interested in a career in journalism, what inspired them to prepare for a career in the field, what hardships or obstacles they have experienced while trying to realize their goal of becoming a journalist, and the role Latino journalists play in the news industry. Selection is based on commitment to the field of journalism, academic achievement, awareness of the Latino community, and financial need.

Financial Data The stipend ranges up to $5,000.

Duration 1 year.

Additional data This program includes the Soledad O'Brien Scholarship and the Jane Velez-Mitchell Scholarship.

Number awarded 2 each year.

Deadline January of each year.

[350]
NATIONAL ASSOCIATION OF HISPANIC NURSES SCHOLARSHIPS

National Association of Hispanic Nurses
Attn: National Awards and Scholarship Committee Chair
1455 Pennsylvania Avenue, N.W., Suite 400
Washington, DC 20004
(202) 387-2477   Fax: (202) 483-7183
E-mail: info@thehispanicnurses.org
Web: www.nahnnet.org/NAHNScholarships.html

Summary To provide financial assistance for nursing education to members of the National Association of Hispanic Nurses (NAHN).

Eligibility Eligible are members of the association enrolled in associate, diploma, baccalaureate, graduate, or practical/vocational nursing programs at NLN-accredited schools of nursing. Applicants must have a GPA of 3.0 or higher. Along with their application, they must submit a letter of recommendation; a 300-word essay that reflects their qualifications and potential for leadership in nursing in the Hispanic community; a resume that includes earned certificates, awards, and special honors; information on their financial status; and an official transcript. U.S. citizenship or permanent resident status is required.

Financial Data The stipend is $2,500.

Duration 1 year.

Additional data Support for this program is provided by Lilly USA, LLC.

Number awarded Varies each year; recently, 4 of these scholarships were awarded.

Deadline June of each year.

[351]
NATIONAL HISPANIC BUSINESS WOMEN ASSOCIATION EDUCATIONAL SCHOLARSHIPS

National Hispanic Business Women Association
2024 North Broadway, Suite 100
Santa Ana, CA 92706
(714) 836-4042
Web: nationalhbwa.com/main/?page_id=367

Summary To provide financial assistance to women in California who are working on an undergraduate or graduate degree at a school in any state and submit an essay related to Latinas in education.

Eligibility This program is open to female residents of California who are currently enrolled as undergraduate or graduate students at a school in any state. Applicants must have a GPA of 3.0 or higher and be able to demonstrate financial need. They must also have a record of participation in some form of community service. Along with their application, they must submit 2 essays of 2 pages each on 1) their academic and professional goals; and 2) the importance or value of obtaining a higher education, the potential impacts or influences of a growing Latino population in relation to their field of interest, or the specific challenges faced by Latinas in pursuit of higher education.

Financial Data Stipends range from $500 to $1,000.

Duration 1 year.

Number awarded Varies each year; recently, 13 of these scholarships were awarded.

Deadline March of each year.

[352]
NATIONAL HISPANIC CAUCUS OF SCHOOL BOARD MEMBERS SCHOLARSHIPS

National School Boards Association
Attn: National Hispanic Caucus of School Board Members
1680 Duke Street
Alexandria, VA 22314-3493
(703) 838-6722   Fax: (703) 683-7590
E-mail: Hispanic_Caucus@nsba.org
Web: www.nsba.org

Summary To provide financial assistance for college to Hispanic high school seniors.

Eligibility This program is open to public high school seniors of Hispanic origin who have been accepted to an accredited 4-year college or university. Applicants must have a GPA of 2.5 or higher and be able to demonstrate financial need. Along with their application, they must submit a 600-word autobiographical statement that includes a paragraph about their financial need. Selection is based on academic record, extracurricular activities, personal qualities, and financial need; special consideration is given to education majors.

Financial Data The stipend is $1,000.

Duration 1 year.

Additional data This program, established in 1998, is currently funded by Washington Mutual Bank, Sodexo School Services, ARAMARK, VisionIT, and Vanguard Charitable Endowment Program.

Number awarded 10 each year: 2 per region of the sponsoring organization.

Deadline February of each year.

[353]
NATIONAL HISPANIC HEALTH PROFESSIONAL STUDENT SCHOLARSHIP

National Hispanic Medical Association
Attn: National Hispanic Health Foundation
1411 K Street, Suite 1100
Washington, DC 20005
(202) 628-5895   Fax: (202) 628-5898
E-mail: scholarship@nhmamd.org
Web: www.nhmafoundation.org/scholarshipprogram.html

Summary To provide financial assistance to Hispanic students from California, Connecticut, New Jersey, and New York who are working on a health-related degree at a school in their home state.

Eligibility This program is open to residents of California, Connecticut, New Jersey, and New York. Applicants must be currently enrolled full time at a dental, medical, nursing, public health, or health policy school in their home state. They are not required to be Hispanic, but they must be able to demonstrate an affinity for the health of Hispanic communities. Along with their application, they must submit a letter of recommendation, transcripts, a personal statement that includes their career goals, and a current curriculum vitae. Students in pre-health professional program are not eligible. Selection is based on academic performance, leadership, and commitment to their Hispanic community.

Financial Data Stipends are $5,000 or $2,000.

Duration 1 year.

Additional data This program began in 2005 in affiliation with the Robert F. Wagner Graduate School of Public Service at New York University.

Number awarded 20 each year: 16 at $5,000 and 4 at $2,000.

Deadline September of each year for students from California; October of each year for students from Connecticut, New Jersey, and New York.

[354]
NATIONAL OCEANIC AND ATMOSPHERIC ADMINISTRATION EDUCATIONAL PARTNERSHIP PROGRAM WITH MINORITY SERVING INSTITUTIONS UNDERGRADUATE SCHOLARSHIPS

National Oceanic and Atmospheric Administration
Attn: Office of Education
1315 East-West Highway
SSMC3, Room 10703
Silver Spring, MD 20910
(301) 713-9437, ext. 150   Fax: (301) 713-9465
E-mail: studentscholarshipprograms@noaa.gov
Web: www.epp.noaa.gov/ssp_undergrad_page.html

Summary To provide financial aid and research experience to undergraduate students at Minority Serving Institutions who are majoring in scientific fields of interest to the National Oceanic and Atmospheric Administration (NOAA).

Eligibility This program is open to full-time juniors at Minority Serving Institutions, including Hispanic Serving Institutions (HSIs), Historically Black Colleges and Universities (HBCUs), and Tribal Colleges and Universities (TCUs). Applicants must have a GPA of 3.0 or higher and a major in atmospheric science, biology, computer science, engineering, environmental science, geography, hydrology, mathematics, oceanography, physical science, physics, remote sensing, social science, or other field that supports NOAA's programs and mission. They must also be interested in participating in a research internship at an NOAA site. Selection is based on relevant course work (30%), education plan and statement of career interest (40%), recommendations (20%), and additional experience related to diversity of education, extracurricular activities, honors and awards, non-academic and volunteer work, and communication skills (10%). U.S. citizenship is required.

Financial Data This program provides payment of tuition and fees (to a maximum of $8,000 per year) and a stipend during the internship of $650 per week.

Duration 2 academic years and 2 summer internships.

Number awarded Up to 15 each year.

Deadline February of each year.

[355]
NATIONAL PRESS CLUB SCHOLARSHIP FOR JOURNALISM DIVERSITY

National Press Club
Attn: Executive Director's Office
529 14th Street, N.W., 13th Floor
Washington, DC 20045
(202) 662-7599
Web: www.press.org/about/students

Summary To provide funding to Hispanic Americans and other high school seniors who are planning to major in journalism in college and who will bring diversity to the field.

Eligibility This program is open to high school seniors who have been accepted to college and plan to prepare for a career in journalism. Applicants must submit 1) a 500-word essay explaining how they would add diversity to U.S. journalism; 2) up to 5 work samples demonstrating an ongoing interest in journalism through work on a high school newspaper or other media; 3) letters of recommendation from 3 people; 4) a copy of their high school transcript; 5) documentation of financial need; 6) a letter of acceptance from the college or university of their choice; and 7) a brief description of how they have pursued journalism in high school.

Financial Data The stipend is $2,000 for the first year and $2,500 for each subsequent year. The program also provides an additional $500 book stipend, designated the Ellen Masin Persina Scholarship, for the first year.

Duration 4 years.

Additional data The program began in 1990.

Number awarded 1 each year.

Deadline February of each year.

[356]
NATIONAL SPACE GRANT COLLEGE AND FELLOWSHIP PROGRAM

National Aeronautics and Space Administration
Attn: Office of Education
300 E Street, S.W.
Mail Suite 6M35
Washington, DC 20546-0001
(202) 358-1069   Fax: (202) 358-7097
E-mail: Diane.D.DeTroye@nasa.gov
Web: www.nasa.gov

Summary   To provide financial assistance to undergraduate and graduate students (particularly Hispanic Americans, other underrepresented minorities, and women) who are interested in preparing for a career in a space-related field.

Eligibility   This program is open to undergraduate and graduate students at colleges and universities that participate in the National Space Grant program of the U.S. National Aeronautics and Space Administration (NASA) through their state consortium. Applicants must be interested in a program of study and/or research in a field of science, technology, engineering, or mathematics (STEM) related to space. A specific goal of the program is to recruit and train U.S. citizens, especially underrepresented minorities, women, and persons with disabilities, for careers in aerospace science and technology. Financial need is not considered in the selection process.

Financial Data   Each consortium establishes the terms of the fellowship program in its state.

Additional data   NASA established the Space Grant program in 1989. It operates through 52 consortia in each state, the District of Columbia, and Puerto Rico. Each consortium includes selected colleges and universities in that state as well as other affiliates from industry, museums, science centers, and state and local agencies.

Number awarded   Varies each year.

Deadline   Each consortium sets its own deadlines.

[357]
NATIONWIDE HISPANIC SCHOLARSHIPS OF THE INDEPENDENT COLLEGE FUND OF MARYLAND

Independent College Fund of Maryland
Attn: Director of Programs and Scholarships
3225 Ellerslie Avenue, Suite C-160
Baltimore, MD 21218-3519
(443) 997-5700   Fax: (443) 997-2740
E-mail: Ifund@jhu.edu
Web: i-fundinfo.org/scholarships/minority-scholarships.html

Summary   To provide financial assistance to upper-division Hispanic students from any state at member institutions of the Independent College Fund of Maryland who are majoring in business.

Eligibility   This program is open to Hispanic students from any state currently entering their junior, or senior year at member institutions. Applicants must be enrolled full time and majoring in or be able to demonstrate a career interest in business, particularly financial services. They must have a GPA of 3.0 or higher.

Financial Data   The stipend is $2,000.

Duration   1 year.

Additional data   The member institutions are Notre Dame of Maryland University, Goucher College, Hood College, Johns Hopkins University, Loyola University of Maryland, McDaniel College, Mount St. Mary's University, St. John's College, Stevenson University, and Washington College.

Number awarded   1 or more each year.

Deadline   Deadline not specified.

[358]
NAVSEA/SPAWAR SCHOLARS PROGRAM

Great Minds in STEM
Attn: HENAAC Scholars Program
602 Monterey Pass Road
Monterey Park, CA 91754
(323) 262-0997   Fax: (323) 262-0946
E-mail: gcruz@greatmindsinstem.org
Web: www.greatmindsinstem.org

Summary   To provide financial assistance to Hispanic high school seniors majoring in a field of science, technology, engineering, or mathematics (STEM) at an Hispanic-serving institution (HSI).

Eligibility   This program is open to Hispanic high school seniors who plan to enroll at an HSI and work on an undergraduate degree in a field of STEM. Applicants must be of Hispanic origin and/or must significantly participate in and promote organizations and activities in the Hispanic community. They must have a GPA of 3.0 or higher and a record of activity in school and community organizations. Along with their application, they must submit a 700-word essay on a topic that changes annually. Selection is based on leadership, academic achievements, campus and community activities, and financial need.

Financial Data   The stipend is $10,000.

Duration   1 year; recipients may reapply.

Additional data   The Hispanic Engineer National Achievement Awards Conference (HENAAC) was established in 1989 and initiated a scholarship program in 2000. In 2010, the sponsoring organization officially adopted its current name, but it continues to hold the annual HENAAC conference, at which the scholarships are presented. This program is sponsored by the Naval Sea Systems Command (NAVSEA) and the Space and Naval Warfare Systems Command (SPAWAR). Recipients must attend the conference to accept their scholarship.

Number awarded   1 each year.

Deadline   April of each year.

[359]
NAVY/MARINE CORPS JROTC SCHOLARSHIP

National Naval Officers Association-Washington, D.C.
  Chapter
c/o LCDR Stephen Williams
P.O. Box 30784
Alexandria, VA 22310
(703) 566-3840   Fax: (703) 566-3813
E-mail: Stephen.Williams@navy.mil
Web: dcnnoa.memberlodge.com

Summary   To provide financial assistance to Hispanic American and other minority high school seniors from the Washington, D.C. area who have participated in Navy or

Marine Corps Junior Reserve Officers Training Corps (JROTC) and are planning to attend college in any state.

Eligibility This program is open to minority seniors graduating from high schools in the Washington, D.C. metropolitan area who have participated in Navy or Marine Corps JROTC. Applicants must be planning to enroll full time at an accredited 2- or 4-year college or university in any state. They must have a GPA of 2.5 or higher. Selection is based on academic achievement, community involvement, and financial need. U.S. citizenship or permanent resident status is required.

Financial Data The stipend is $1,000.

Duration 1 year; nonrenewable.

Additional data Recipients are not required to join or affiliate with the military in any way after college.

Number awarded 1 each year.

Deadline March of each year.

[360]
NCLR-BEST BUY EMERGING LATINO LEADERS SCHOLARSHIP PROGRAM

National Council of La Raza
Attn: Lideres Initiative
Raul Yzaguirre Building
1126 16th Street, N.W., Suite 600
Washington, DC 20036-4845
(202) 785-1670   Fax: (202) 776-1792
E-mail: dpernick@nclr.org
Web: lideres.nclr.org/section/opportunities

Summary To recognize and reward, with college scholarships, Hispanic high school seniors who submit outstanding essays on topics related to leadership activities.

Eligibility This competition is open to graduating high school seniors who are of Hispanic descent and have a GPA of 2.0 or higher. Applicants must submit an essay, in English, from 850 to 1,500 words in length, on a topic that changes annually but relates to their leadership activities. Recently, students were asked to describe their efforts to provide 50 hours of volunteer service to projects that increase educational opportunities for the Latino community and to refer 200 students to this program. Selection is based on the quality of the essay (creativity, vocabulary, and clarity) as well as the applicant's community service, leadership, and financial need.

Financial Data Awards are $15,000 (for the grand prize winner), $5,000, or $2,500. Funds are paid directly to the college or university that the recipient will be attending in the fall following the competition.

Duration The competition is held annually.

Additional data This competition, first held in 2007, is administered by the National Council of La Raza (NCLR) with support from the Best Buy Children's Foundation.

Number awarded 4 each year: 1 at $15,000, 1 at $5,000, and 2 at $2,500.

Deadline May of each year.

[361]
NELLIE STONE JOHNSON SCHOLARSHIP

Nellie Stone Johnson Scholarship Program
P.O. Box 40309
St. Paul, MN 55104
(651) 738-1404   Toll Free: (866) 738-5238
E-mail: info@nelliestone.org
Web: www.nelliestone.org

Summary To provide financial assistance to Hispanic American and other minority union members or their families who are interested in working on an undergraduate or graduate degree in any field at a Minnesota state college or university.

Eligibility This program is open to students in undergraduate and graduate programs at a 2- or 4-year institution that is a component of Minnesota State Colleges and Universities (MnSCU). Applicants must be a minority (Asian, American Indian, Alaska Native, Black/African American, Hispanic/Latino, Native Hawaiian, or Pacific Islander) union member or the child, grandchild, or spouse of a minority union member. They must submit a 2-page essay about their background, educational goals, career goals, and other activities that may impact the cause of human or civil rights. Undergraduates must have a GPA of 2.0 or higher; graduate students must have a GPA of 3.0 or higher. Preference is given to Minnesota residents. Selection is based on the essay, commitment to human or civil rights, extracurricular activities, volunteer activities, community involvement, academic standing, and financial need.

Financial Data Stipends range from $500 to $2,000 per year.

Duration 1 year; may be renewed up to 3 additional years for students working on a bachelor's degree, 1 additional year for students working on a master's degree, or 1 additional year for students in a community or technical college program.

Number awarded Varies each year; recently, 18 of these scholarships were awarded.

Deadline April of each year.

[362]
NEW MEXICO ALLIANCE FOR HISPANIC EDUCATION SCHOLARSHIPS

New Mexico Alliance for Hispanic Education
Attn: Program Director
P.O. Box 25806
Albuquerque, NM 87125
(505) 342-3504
Web: www.nmalliance.org/scholarships.html

Summary To provide financial assistance to Hispanic residents of New Mexico who are interested in attending college or graduate school in any state.

Eligibility This program is open to residents of New Mexico who are of Hispanic heritage and interested enrolling full time at an accredited 2- or 4-year college or university in the United States, Puerto Rico, the U.S. Virgin Islands, or Guam. Applicants must have a GPA of 3.0 or higher and be working on or planning to work on an undergraduate or graduate degree. They must be U.S. citizens, permanent residents, or visitors with a passport stamped I-551. In addition to submitting the application, they must apply for federal financial aid by completing the Free Application for Federal Student Aid (FAFSA).

Financial Data Stipends range from $1,000 to $2,500.

Duration 1 year.

Number awarded Varies each year.

Deadline February of each year.

[363]
NIDDK/OMHRC SUMMER INTERNSHIP PROGRAM FOR UNDERREPRESENTED GROUPS

National Institute of Diabetes and Digestive and Kidney Diseases
Attn: Office of Minority Health Research Coordination
6707 Democracy Boulevard, Room 906A
Bethesda, MD 20892-5454
(301) 435-2988   Fax: (301) 594-9358
E-mail: MartinezW@mail.nih.gov
Web: www2.niddk.nih.gov/Funding

Summary <PP>To provide Hispanic American and other underrepresented minority undergraduate students with an opportunity to conduct research in the laboratory of a National Institute of Diabetes and Digestive and Kidney Diseases (NIDDK) intramural scientist during the summer.

Eligibility This program is open to undergraduate students who are members of underrepresented minority groups (African Americans, Hispanic Americans, Native Americans, Native Hawaiians, other Pacific Islanders, and Alaska Natives). Applicants must be interested in participating in a research project conducted at an intramural research laboratory of NIDDK in Bethesda, Maryland or Phoenix, Arizona. They must have completed at least 1 year at an accredited institution and have a GPA of 3.0 or higher. Along with their application, they must submit a 2-page personal statement of their research interest, career goals, and reasons for applying to training at NIDDK. U.S. citizenship or permanent resident status is required.

Financial Data Students receive a stipend of $2,500, housing, and (for those who live outside the Washington metropolitan area or the state of Arizona) a travel allowance of $500.

Duration 10 weeks during the summer.

Number awarded Varies each year.

Deadline February of each year.

[364]
NLGJA/KAY LONGCOPE SCHOLARSHIP AWARD

National Lesbian & Gay Journalists Association
2120 L Street, N.W., Suite 850
Washington, DC 20037
(202) 588-9888   Fax: (202) 588-1818
E-mail: info@nlgfa.org
Web: www.nlgja.org/students/longcope

Summary To provide financial assistance to Hispanic American and other lesbian, gay, bisexual, and transgender (LGBT) undergraduate and graduate students of color who are interested in preparing for a career in journalism.

Eligibility This program is open to LGBT students of color who are 1) high school seniors accepted to a U.S. community college or 4-year university and planning to enroll full time; 2) full-time undergraduate students at U.S. community colleges and 4-year universities; or 3) undergraduate students who

have been accepted for their first year at a U.S. graduate school. Applicants must be planning a career in journalism and be committed to furthering the sponsoring organization's mission of fair and accurate coverage of the LGBT community. They must demonstrate an awareness of the issues facing the LGBT community and the importance of fair and accurate news coverage. For undergraduates, a declared major in journalism and/or communications is desirable but not required; non-journalism majors may demonstrate their commitment to a journalism career through work samples, internships, and work on a school news publication, online news service, or broadcast affiliate. Graduate students must be enrolled in a journalism program. Along with their application, they must submit a 1-page resume, 5 work samples, official transcripts, 3 letters of recommendation, and a 750-word news story on a designated subject involving the LGBT community. U.S. citizenship or permanent resident status is required. Selection is based on journalistic and scholastic ability.

Financial Data The stipend is $3,000.

Duration 1 year.

Additional data This program began in 2008.

Number awarded 1 each year.

Deadline June of each year.

[365]
NOPRNRCSE SCHOLARSHIPS

National Organization of Professional Hispanic Natural Resources Conservation Service Employees
c/o Jessie Howard, Scholarship and Endowment Committee
Natural Resources Conservation Service
Bedford Service Center
1031 Turnpike Road
Bedford, VA 24523
(540) 586-9195   Fax: (540) 586-4638
E-mail: scholarships@nophnrcse.org
Web: www.nophnrcse.org

Summary To provide financial assistance to Hispanic high seniors and college students interested in working on a bachelor's degree in a field related to natural resources or conservation.

Eligibility This program is open to Hispanic high school seniors and full-time college students who are attending or planning to attend an accredited 4-year college or university. Applicants must be planning to work on a bachelor's degree in an agricultural, natural resources, or natural resources conservation-related field of study. They must have a GPA of 2.75 or higher. Along with their application, they must submit a personal statement (in English) of 350 to 500 words on their background, name of school they attend or plan to attend, personal and career goals, extracurricular activities, and interest in preparing for a career related to natural resources conservation. Financial need is not considered in the selection process. U.S. citizenship is required.

Financial Data The stipend is $1,000.

Duration 1 year.

Additional data The National Organization of Professional Hispanic Natural Resources Conservation Service Employees (NOPRNRCSE) is comprised of Hispanic employees of the Natural Resources Conservation Service of the U.S. Department of Agriculture (USDA-NRCS).

Number awarded Varies each year; recently, 3 of these scholarships were awarded.

Deadline April of each year.

[366]
NORA STONE SMITH SCHOLARSHIP

Seattle Foundation
Attn: Scholarship Administrator
1200 Fifth Avenue, Suite 1300
Seattle, WA 98101-3151
(206) 622-2294   Fax: (206) 622-7673
E-mail: scholarships@seattlefoundation.org
Web: www.seattlefoundation.org

Summary To provide financial assistance for college to high school seniors who have been enrolled in English as a Second Language/English Language Learners (ESL/ELL) programs.

Eligibility This program is open to seniors graduating from high schools who are current or former ESL/ELL students, regardless of their citizenship status. Applicants must be planning to enroll full time at a 2- or 4-year college, university, or vocational/trade school. Along with their application, they must submit a 250-word essay about themselves, where they are from, how they came to be here, their educational achievements, and their future goals. Financial need is considered in the selection process.

Financial Data The maximum stipend is $2,000 per year.

Duration 1 year; may be renewed up to 3 additional years.

Number awarded 10 each year.

Deadline February of each year.

[367]
NORTH CAROLINA CHAPTER AABE SCHOLARSHIPS

American Association of Blacks in Energy-North Carolina
   Chapter
Attn: Scholarship Committee
P.O. Box 207
Raleigh, NC 27602-0207
E-mail: jgraves73@gmail.com
Web: www.aabe.org/index.php?component=pages&id=416

Summary To provide financial assistance to Hispanic Americans and members of other underrepresented minority groups who are high school seniors in North Carolina and planning to major in an energy-related field at a college in any state.

Eligibility This program is open to seniors graduating from high schools in North Carolina and planning to work on a bachelor's degree at a college or university in any state. Applicants must be African Americans, Hispanics, or Native Americans who have a GPA of 3.0 or higher and are able to demonstrate financial need. Their intended major must be a field of business, engineering, physical science, mathematics, or technology related to energy. Along with their application, they must submit a 350-word statement on why they should receive this scholarship, their professional career objectives, and any other relevant information.

Financial Data The stipend is $1,000.

Duration 1 year; nonrenewable.

Additional data Winners are eligible to compete for regional and national scholarships.

Number awarded 1 or more each year.

Deadline February of each year.

[368]
NORTH CAROLINA CPA FOUNDATION OUTSTANDING MINORITY ACCOUNTING STUDENT SCHOLARSHIPS

North Carolina Association of Certified Public
   Accountants
Attn: North Carolina CPA Foundation, Inc.
3100 Gateway Centre Boulevard
P.O. Box 80188
Raleigh, NC 27623-0188
(919) 469-1040, ext. 130   Toll Free: (800) 722-2836
Fax: (919) 378-2000   E-mail: jtahler@ncacpa.org
Web: ncacpa.org

Summary To provide financial assistance to Hispanic American and other minority undergraduate and graduate students working on a degree in accounting at colleges and universities in North Carolina.

Eligibility This program is open to North Carolina residents who have completed at least 36 semester hours, including at least 4 accounting courses, at a college or university in the state. Applicants must be members of a minority group, defined as Black, Native American/Alaskan Native, Middle-Eastern, Asian or Pacific Islander, or Hispanic. They must be enrolled full time in an academic program leading to a degree in accounting or its equivalent and have a GPA of 3.0 or higher. Along with their application, they must submit a 500-word essay on 1 of the following questions: 1) what the profession can do to educate minorities about understanding the impact of and ways to survive the national financial crisis; 2) how they will impact minority communities by becoming a C.P.A.; or 3) the challenges that minority C.P.A.s face in the profession. Selection is based on GPA (30%), extracurricular activities (20%), essay content (25%), and essay grammar (25%).

Financial Data Stipends are $2,000 or $1,000.

Duration 1 year; may be renewed up to 2 additional years.

Number awarded 2 each year: 1 at $2,000 and 1 at $1,000.

Deadline March of each year.

[369]
NORTH CAROLINA HISPANIC COLLEGE FUND SCHOLARSHIPS

North Carolina Society of Hispanic Professionals
Attn: North Carolina Hispanic College Fund
8450 Chapel Hill Road, Suite 209
Cary, NC 27513
(919) 467-8424   Fax: (919) 469-1785
E-mail: mailbox@thencshp.org
Web: thencshp.org/programs/nc-hispanic-college-fund

Summary To provide financial assistance to Hispanic students from North Carolina who are interested in attending college in any state.

Eligibility This program is open to residents of North Carolina who are of Hispanic background (both parents are at least half Hispanic or 1 parent is fully Hispanic) and either 1) are graduating high school seniors; or 2) graduated from high school within the past 2 years. Applicants must be enrolled or planning to enroll at a community college or a 2- or 4-year college or university in any state and be committed to public service and community development. They must have a high school GPA of 2.5 or higher. Along with their application, they must submit a 500-word essay on why their Hispanic parentage and family background are important to them, personal and/or academic achievements, academic plans and career goals, and past and current efforts (as well as future plans) towards making a difference in their community. Preference is given to foreign-born applicants and the native-born children of foreign-born parents. Selection is based on academic achievement, community involvement, volunteerism, leadership, and family economic need.

Financial Data Stipends range from $500 to $2,500 per year. Funds are paid directly to the college or university.

Duration 1 year; may be renewed up to 3 additional years.

Number awarded Varies each year; recently 15 of these scholarships were awarded.

Deadline January of each year.

[370]
NORTHROP GRUMMAN/HENAAC SCHOLARS PROGRAM

Great Minds in STEM
Attn: HENAAC Scholars Program
602 Monterey Pass Road
Monterey Park, CA 91754
(323) 262-0997   Fax: (323) 262-0946
E-mail: gcruz@greatmindsinstem.org
Web: www.greatmindsinstem.org

Summary To provide financial assistance to Hispanic undergraduate students majoring in designated engineering or computer science at selected universities.

Eligibility This program is open to Hispanic students who are majoring in computer engineering, computer science, electrical engineering, software engineering, or systems engineering at 12 selected universities. Applicants must be of Hispanic origin and/or must significantly participate in and promote organizations and activities in the Hispanic community. They must have a GPA of 3.0 or higher. Along with their application, they must submit a 700-word essay on a topic that changes annually. Financial need is not considered. U.S. citizenship is required.

Financial Data Stipends range from $500 to $5,000.

Duration 1 year; recipients may reapply.

Additional data The Hispanic Engineer National Achievement Awards Conference (HENAAC) was established in 1989 and initiated a scholarship program in 2000. In 2010, the sponsoring organization officially adopted its current name, but it continues to hold the annual HENAAC conference, at which the scholarships are presented. This program is sponsored by Northrop Grumman. The 12 selected universities are California Polytechnic State University at San Luis Obispo, California State Polytechnic University at Pomona, University of California at Irvine, University of California at Los Angeles, University of Southern California, University of Maryland at College Park, University of Maryland-Baltimore, George Mason University, North Carolina A&T State University, North Carolina State University, Pennsylvania State University, and Virginia Polytechnic Institute and State University. Recipients must attend the conference to accept their scholarship.

Number awarded Varies each year; recently, 5 of these scholarships were awarded.

Deadline April of each year.

[371]
NORTHWEST JOURNALISTS OF COLOR SCHOLARSHIP AWARDS

Northwest Journalists of Color
c/o Caroline Li
1433 12th Avenue, Suite A1
Seattle, WA 98122
E-mail: Caroline@SoMuchGoodMusic.com
Web: www.aajaseattle.org/scholarships

Summary To provide financial assistance to Hispanic American and other minority students from Washington state who are interested in careers in journalism.

Eligibility This program is open to members of minority groups (Asian American, African American, Native American, and Latino) who are 1) residents of Washington attending an accredited college or university in any state; 2) residents of any state attending a Washington college or university; or 3) seniors graduating from Washington high schools and planning to attend an accredited college in any state. Applicants must be planning a career in broadcast, photo, or print journalism. Along with their application, they must submit 1) a 500-word essay about their interest in a career as a journalist; 2) a current resume; 3) up to 3 work samples; 4) reference letters; and 5) documentation of financial need.

Financial Data Stipends range up to $2,500 per year.

Duration 1 year; may be renewed.

Additional data This program, established in 1986, is sponsored by the Seattle chapters of the Asian American Journalists Association, the Native American Journalists Association, the National Association of Black Journalists, and the Latino Media Association. It includes the Walt and Milly Woodward Memorial Scholarship donated by the Western Washington Chapter of the Society of Professional Journalists.

Number awarded Varies each year.

Deadline April of each year.

[372]
NSCA MINORITY SCHOLARSHIPS

National Strength and Conditioning Association
Attn: Grants and Scholarships Program
1885 Bob Johnson Drive
Colorado Springs, CO 80906-4000
(719) 632-6722, ext. 152   Toll Free: (800) 815-6826
Fax: (719) 632-6367   E-mail: foundation@nsca-lift.org
Web: www.nsca-lift.org/Foundation/grants-and-scholarships

Summary To provide financial assistance to Hispanic Americans and other minorities who are interested in working on an undergraduate or graduate degree in strength training and conditioning.

Eligibility This program is open to Blacks, Hispanics, Asian Americans, and Native Americans who are 17 years of age and older. Applicants must have been accepted into an accredited postsecondary institution to work on an undergraduate or graduate degree in the strength and conditioning field. Along with their application, they must submit a 500-word essay on their personal and professional goals and how receiving this scholarship will assist them in achieving those goals. Selection is based on that essay, academic achievement, strength and conditioning experience, honors and awards, community involvement, letters of recommendation, and involvement in the National Strength and Conditioning Association (NSCA).

Financial Data The stipend is $1,500.

Duration 1 year.

Additional data The NSCA is a nonprofit organization of strength and conditioning professionals, including coaches, athletic trainers, physical therapists, educators, researchers, and physicians. This program was first offered in 2003.

Number awarded Varies each year; recently, 9 of these scholarships were awarded.

Deadline March of each year.

[373]
NSNA/BREAKTHROUGH TO NURSING SCHOLARSHIPS

National Student Nurses' Association
Attn: Foundation
45 Main Street, Suite 606
Brooklyn, NY 11201
(718) 210-0705   Fax: (718) 797-1186
E-mail: nsna@nsna.org
Web: www.nsna.org

Summary To provide financial assistance to Hispanic American and other minority undergraduate and graduate students who wish to prepare for careers in nursing.

Eligibility This program is open to students currently enrolled in state-approved schools of nursing or pre-nursing associate degree, baccalaureate, diploma, generic master's, generic doctoral, R.N. to B.S.N., R.N. to M.S.N., or L.P.N./L.V.N. to R.N. programs. Graduating high school seniors are not eligible. Support for graduate education is provided only for a first degree in nursing. Applicants must be members of a racial or ethnic minority underrepresented among registered nurses (American Indian or Alaska Native, Hispanic or Latino, Native Hawaiian or other Pacific Islander, Black or African American, or Asian). They must be committed to providing quality health care services to underserved populations. Along with their application, they must submit a 200-word description of their professional and educational goals and how this scholarship will help them achieve those goals. Selection is based on academic achievement, financial need, and involvement in student nursing organizations and community health activities. U.S. citizenship or permanent resident status is required.

Financial Data Stipends range from $1,000 to $2,500.

Duration 1 year.

Additional data Applications must be accompanied by a $10 processing fee.

Number awarded Varies each year; recently, 13 of these scholarships were awarded: 10 sponsored by the American Association of Critical-Care Nurses and 3 sponsored by the Mayo Clinic.

Deadline January of each year.

[374]
NUESTRA GENTE SCHOLARSHIP

La Raza Youth Leadership Institute
P.O. Box 8571
Denver, CO 90201
(303) 556-6730   E-mail: scholarships@larazayouth.org
Web: www.larazayouth.org/lryli-gente-scholarship

Summary To provide financial assistance to high school seniors in Colorado who participate in the La Raza Youth Leadership Conference and plan to attend college in any state.

Eligibility This program is open to seniors graduating from high schools in Colorado who participate in the annual La Raza Youth Leadership Conference. Applicants must be planning to enroll at an accredited community college or 4-year college or university in any state. They must have a GPA of 2.5 or higher. Along with their application, they must submit a 1-page essay that describes their community involvement and leadership experience, their educational and career goals, what they will do to accomplish those goals, and how they relate the theme of the conference to their own personal and professional goals. Financial need is not considered in the selection process.

Financial Data The stipend is $1,000.

Duration 1 year.

Additional data The La Raza Youth Leadership Conference began in 1991 as a program to expose Latino males to "the importance of higher education, career planning, self-esteem building and developing leadership skills." Recently, approximately 1,500 Latino males and females from throughout Colorado have participated in the 1-day Conference.

Number awarded 1 or more each year.

Deadline March of each year.

[375]
NUESTRA JUVENTUD SCHOLARSHIPS

WUVC Univision 40
Attn: Nuestra Juventud Program
4505 Falls of The Neuse Road, Suite 660
Raleigh, NC 27609
(919) 872-7440   E-mail: juventud40@univision.net

Summary To provide financial assistance to Hispanic high school seniors in North Carolina who plan to attend college in any state.

Eligibility This program is open to seniors of Hispanic background who are graduating from high schools in North Carolina and planning to attend a 2- or 4-year college or university in any state. Selection is based on academic achievement, leadership qualities, and character.

Financial Data The stipend is $1,000.

Duration 1 year.

Additional data This program operates in cooperation with the North Carolina Society of Hispanic Professionals. Funding is provided by Golden Corral.

Number awarded 7 each year.

Deadline October of each year.

[376]
NWA/DAVID SANKEY MINORITY SCHOLARSHIP IN METEOROLOGY

National Weather Association
Attn: Executive Director
228 West Millbrook Road
Raleigh, NC 27609-4304
(919) 845-1546   Fax: (919) 845-2956
E-mail: exdir@nwas.org
Web: www.nwas.org

Summary To provide financial assistance to Hispanic Americans and other members of minority groups who are working on an undergraduate or graduate degree in meteorology.

Eligibility This program is open to members of minority ethnic groups who are either entering their sophomore or higher year of undergraduate study or enrolled as graduate students. Applicants must be working on a degree in meteorology. Along with their application, they must submit a 1-page statement explaining why they are applying for this scholarship. Selection is based on that statement, academic achievement, and 2 letters of recommendation.

Financial Data The stipend is $1,000.

Duration 1 year.

Additional data This program began in 2002.

Number awarded 1 each year.

Deadline April of each year.

[377]
OHIO HIGH SCHOOL ATHLETIC ASSOCIATION ETHNIC MINORITY SCHOLARSHIPS

Ohio High School Athletic Association
Attn: Foundation
4080 Roselea Place
Columbus, OH 43214
(614) 267-2502   Fax: (614) 267-1677
Web: www.ohsaa.org/members/scholar/application.htm

Summary To provide financial assistance to Hispanic American and other minority high school seniors in Ohio who have participated in athletics and plan to attend college in any state.

Eligibility This program is open to minority seniors graduating from high schools in Ohio that are members of the Ohio High School Athletic Association (OHSAA). Applicants must have received at least 3 varsity letters in 1 sport or 4 letters in 2 sports and have a GPA of 3.25 or higher. They must be planning to attend a college or university in any state. Along with their application, they must submit a 1-page essay on the role that interscholastic athletics has played in their life and how such participation will benefit them in the future. Selection is based on that essay, GPA, ACT and SAT scores, varsity letters earned, and athletic honors.

Financial Data The stipend is $1,000.

Duration 1 year.

Additional data Recipients of athletic scholarships in NCAA Division I or II institutions or appointees to military academies are not eligible to apply for this scholarship.

Number awarded 6 each year: 1 in each OHSSA District.

Deadline March of each year.

[378]
OHIO NEWSPAPERS FOUNDATION MINORITY SCHOLARSHIPS

Ohio Newspapers Foundation
Attn: Foundation
1335 Dublin Road, Suite 216-B
Columbus, OH 43215-7038
(614) 486-6677, ext. 1010   Fax: (614) 486-4940
E-mail: ariggs@ohionews.org
Web: www.ohionews.org/foundation/scholarships

Summary To provide financial assistance to Hispanic American and other minority high school seniors in Ohio planning to attend college in the state to prepare for a career in journalism.

Eligibility This program is open to high school seniors in Ohio who are members of minority groups (African American, Hispanic, Asian American, or American Indian) and planning to prepare for a career in newspaper journalism. Applicants must have a high school GPA of 2.5 or higher and demonstrate writing ability in an autobiography of 750 to 1,000 words that describes their academic and career interests, awards, extracurricular activities, and journalism-related activities. They must be planning to attend a college or university in Ohio.

Financial Data The stipend is $1,500.

Duration 1 year; nonrenewable.

Additional data This program began in 1990.

Number awarded 1 each year.

Deadline March of each year.

[379]
ONEONTA TRADING CORPORATION/ COOPRIDER SCHOLARSHIPS

Washington Apple Education Foundation
Attn: Scholarship Committee
2900 Euclid Avenue
Wenatchee, WA 98801
(509) 663-7713   Fax: (509) 663-7469
E-mail: waef@waef.org
Web: www.waef.org/scholarships

Summary To provide financial assistance to Hispanics whose parents are employed within the Washington tree fruit industry and who are interested in attending a public college in the state and participating in college sports.

Eligibility This program is open to Hispanic students who are enrolled or entering college and whose parents are involved in Washington's tree fruit industry. Applicants must be interested in participating in college sports at a Washington state public college or university. Along with their application, they must submit an official transcript, their SAT or ACT scores, 2 letters of reference, and an essay on an assigned topic. Financial need is also considered in the selection process. Preference is given to students at Wenatchee Valley College.

Financial Data The stipend is $3,000.

Duration 1 year.

Additional data This program is sponsored by Oneonta Trading Corporation to honor Sandy Cooprider, a physical education instructor at Wenatchee Valley College.

Number awarded 4 each year.

Deadline February of each year.

[380]
OPERATION JUMP START III SCHOLARSHIPS

American Association of Advertising Agencies
Attn: AAAA Foundation
1065 Avenue of the Americas, 16th Floor
New York, NY 10018
(212) 262-2500   E-mail: ameadows@aaaa.org
Web: www.aaaa.org

Summary To provide financial assistance to Hispanic American and other multicultural art directors and copywriters interested in working on an undergraduate or graduate degree in advertising.

Eligibility This program is open to African Americans, Asian Americans, Hispanic Americans, and Native Americans who are U.S. citizens or permanent residents. Applicants must be incoming graduate students at 1 of 6 designated portfolio schools or full-time juniors at 1 of 2 designated colleges. They must be able to demonstrate extreme financial need, creative talent, and promise. Along with their application, they must submit 10 samples of creative work in their respective field of expertise.

Financial Data The stipend is $5,000 per year.

Duration Most awards are for 2 years.

Additional data Operation Jump Start began in 1997 and was followed by Operation Jump Start II in 2002. The current program began in 2006. The 6 designated portfolio schools are the AdCenter at Virginia Commonwealth University, the Creative Circus in Atlanta, the Portfolio Center in Atlanta, the Miami Ad School, the University of Texas at Austin, and Pratt Institute. The 2 designated colleges are the Minneapolis College of Art and Design and the Art Center College of Design at Pasadena, California.

Number awarded 20 each year.

Deadline Deadline not specified.

[381]
ORACLE/HENAAC SCHOLARS PROGRAM

Great Minds in STEM
Attn: HENAAC Scholars Program
602 Monterey Pass Road
Monterey Park, CA 91754
(323) 262-0997   Fax: (323) 262-0946
E-mail: gcruz@greatmindsinstem.org
Web: www.greatmindsinstem.org

Summary To provide financial assistance to Hispanic undergraduate students majoring in computer science or information technology.

Eligibility This program is open to Hispanic students who are working on an undergraduate degree in computer science or information technology. Applicants must be of Hispanic origin and/or must significantly participate in and promote organizations and activities in the Hispanic community. They must have a GPA of 3.6 or higher. Along with their application, they must submit a 700-word essay on a topic that changes annually. Selection is based on leadership, academic achievements, and campus and community activities; financial need is not considered.

Financial Data Stipends range from $500 to $10,000.

Duration 1 year; recipients may reapply.

Additional data The Hispanic Engineer National Achievement Awards Conference (HENAAC) was established in 1989 and initiated a scholarship program in 2000. In 2010, the sponsoring organization officially adopted its current name, but it continues to hold the annual HENAAC conference, at which the scholarships are presented. This program is sponsored by Oracle Corporation. Recipients must attend the conference to accept their scholarship.

Number awarded Varies each year.

Deadline April of each year.

[382]
OREGON ASSOCIATION OF LATINO ADMINISTRATORS SCHOLARSHIP

Confederation of Oregon School Administrators
Attn: Youth Development Program
707 13th Street, S.E., Suite 100
Salem, OR 97301-4035
(503) 581-3141   Fax: (503) 581-9840
Web: www.cosa.k12.or.us

Summary To provide financial assistance to Latino high school seniors in Oregon who are interested in attending a community college, college, or university in the state.

Eligibility This program is open to graduating high school seniors in Oregon who are of Latino descent. Applicants must be interested in attending a community college, college, or university in the state. They must have been active in community and school affairs, have at least a 3.5 GPA, and be able to enroll in the fall term after graduating from high school. Along with their application, they must submit a 1-page autobiography (that includes their personal goals), the name of the school they plan to attend, and the endorsement of a member of the Confederation of Oregon School Administrators (COSA). Financial need is not considered in the selection process.

Financial Data The stipend is $1,000. Funds are paid directly to the recipient.

Duration 1 year; nonrenewable.

Number awarded 1 each year.

Deadline February of each year.

[383]
PAGE EDUCATION FOUNDATION GRANTS

Page Education Foundation
P.O. Box 581254
Minneapolis, MN 55458-1254
(612) 332-0406   E-mail: info@page-ed.org
Web: www.page-ed.org

Summary To provide funding to Hispanic Americans and other high school seniors of color in Minnesota who plan to attend college in the state.

Eligibility This program is open to students of color who are graduating from high schools in Minnesota and planning to enroll full time at a postsecondary school in the state. Applicants must submit a 500-word essay that deals with why they believe education is important, their plans for the future, and the service-to-children project they would like to complete in the coming school year. Selection is based on the essay, 3 letters of recommendation, and financial need.

Financial Data Stipends range from $1,000 to $2,500 per year.

Duration 1 year; may be renewed up to 3 additional years.

Additional data This program was founded in 1988 by Alan Page, a former football player for the Minnesota Vikings. While attending college, the Page Scholars fulfill a 50-hour service-to-children contract that brings them into contact with K-8 students of color.

Number awarded Varies each year; recently, 503 Page Scholars (210 new recipients and 293 renewals) were enrolled, of whom 260 were African American, 141 Asian American, 70 Chicano/Latino, 13 American Indian, and 19 biracial or multiracial.

Deadline April of each year.

[384]
PARSONS BRINCKERHOFF ENGINEERING SCHOLARSHIP

Conference of Minority Transportation Officials
Attn: National Scholarship Program
1875 I Street, N.W., Suite 500
Washington, DC 20006
(703) 234-4072   Fax: (202) 318-0364
Web: www.comto.org/?page=Scholarships

Summary To provide financial assistance to Hispanic Americans and other members of the Conference of Minority Transportation Officials (COMTO) who are working on an undergraduate degree in engineering.

Eligibility This program is open to undergraduate students who have been members of COMTO for at least 1 year. Applicants must be working on a degree in engineering with a GPA of 3.0 or higher. Along with their application, they must submit a cover letter with a 500-word statement of career goals. Financial need is not considered in the selection process. U.S. citizenship or legal resident status is required.

Financial Data The stipend is $2,500. Funds are paid directly to the recipient's college or university.

Duration 1 year.

Additional data COMTO was established in 1971 to promote, strengthen, and expand the roles of minorities in all aspects of transportation. This program is sponsored by Parsons Brinckerhoff, Inc. Recipients are expected to attend the COMTO National Scholarship Luncheon.

Number awarded 2 each year.

Deadline May of each year.

[385]
PARSONS BRINCKERHOFF GOLDEN APPLE SCHOLARSHIP

Conference of Minority Transportation Officials
Attn: National Scholarship Program
1875 I Street, N.W., Suite 500
Washington, DC 20006
(703) 234-4072   Fax: (202) 318-0364
Web: www.comto.org/?page=Scholarships

Summary To provide financial assistance to Hispanic American and other members of the Conference of Minority Transportation Officials (COMTO) and their children who are high school seniors planning to attend college to prepare for a career in the business aspects of the transportation industry.

Eligibility This program is open to graduating high school seniors who are members of COMTO or whose parents are members. Applicants must be planning to attend an accredited college, university, or vocational/technical institution to prepare for a career in transportation in the fields of communications, finance, or marketing. They must have a GPA of 2.0 or higher. Along with their application, they must submit a cover letter with a 500-word statement of career goals. Financial need is not considered in the selection process. U.S. citizenship or legal resident status is required.

Financial Data The stipend is $2,500. Funds are paid directly to the recipient's college or university.

Duration 1 year.

Additional data COMTO was established in 1971 to promote, strengthen, and expand the roles of minorities in all aspects of transportation. This program is sponsored by Parsons Brinckerhoff, Inc. Recipients are expected to attend the COMTO National Scholarship Luncheon.

Number awarded 1 each year.

Deadline May of each year.

[386]
PDA FOUNDATION DIVERSITY SCHOLARSHIP

Pennsylvania Dietetic Association
Attn: Foundation
96 Northwoods Boulevard, Suite B2
Columbus, OH 43235
(614) 436-6136   Fax: (614) 436-6181
E-mail: padafoundation@eatrightpa.org
Web: www.eatrightpa.org/scholarshipapp.cfm

Summary To provide financial assistance to Hispanic American and other minority members of the Pennsylvania Dietetic Association (PDA) who are working on an associate or bachelor's degree in dietetics.

Eligibility This program is open to PDA members who are Black, Hispanic, Asian or Pacific Islander, or Native American (Alaskan Native, American Indian, or Hawaiian Native). Applicants must be 1) enrolled in the first year of study in an accredited dietetic technology program; or 2) enrolled in the third year of study in an accredited undergraduate or coordinated program in dietetics. They must have a GPA of 2.5 or higher. Along with their application, they must submit a letter indicating their intent and the reason they are applying for the scholarship, including a description of their personal financial situation. Selection is based on academic achievement (20%), commitment to the dietetic profession (30%), leadership ability (30%), and financial need (20%).

Financial Data The stipend is $1,000.

Duration 1 year.

Additional data The Pennsylvania Dietetic Association is the Pennsylvania affiliate of the Academy of Nutrition and Dietetics.

Number awarded 1 or more each year.

Deadline March of each year.

[387]
PDEF MICKEY WILLIAMS MINORITY STUDENT SCHOLARSHIPS

Society of Nuclear Medicine and Molecular Imaging
Attn: Grants and Awards
1850 Samuel Morse Drive
Reston, VA 20190-5316
(703) 708-9000, ext. 1253   Fax: (703) 708-9015
E-mail: kpadleyh@snmmi.org
Web: www.snm.org/index.cfm?pageid=1083

Summary To provide financial support to Hispanic American and other minority students working on an associate or bachelor's degree in nuclear medicine technology.

Eligibility This program is open to students accepted or enrolled in a baccalaureate or associate degree program in nuclear medicine technology. Applicants must be members of a minority group: African American, Native American (including American Indian, Eskimo, Hawaiian, and Samoan), Hispanic American, Asian American, or Pacific Islander. They must have a cumulative GPA of 2.5 or higher and be able to demonstrate financial need. Along with their application, they must submit an essay on their reasons for entering the nuclear medicine technology field, their career goals, and their financial need. U.S. citizenship or permanent resident status is required.

Financial Data The stipend is $2,500.

Duration 1 year; may be renewed for 1 additional year.

Additional data This program is supported by corporate sponsors of the Professional Development and Education Fund (PDEF) of the Society of Nuclear Medicine and Molecular Imaging Technologist Section (SNMMITS).

Number awarded Varies each year; recently, 2 of these scholarships were awarded.

Deadline April of each year.

[388]
PDK/DR. JO ANN OTA FUJIOKA SCHOLARSHIP

Phi Delta Kappa International
Attn: PDK Educational Foundation
320 West Eighth Street, Suite 216
P.O. Box 7888
Bloomington, IN 47407-7888
(812) 339-1156   Toll Free: (800) 766-1156
Fax: (812) 339-0018   E-mail: scholarships@pdkintl.org
Web: pdkintl.org

Summary To provide financial assistance to Hispanic American and other high school seniors of color who plan to study education at a college in any state and have a connection to Phi Delta Kappa (PDK).

Eligibility This program is open to high school seniors of color who are planning to major in education and can meet 1 of the following criteria: 1) is a member of a Future Educators Association (FEA) chapter; 2) is the child or grandchild of a PDK member; 3) has a reference letter written by a PDK member; or 4) is selected to represent the local PDK chapter. Applicants must submit a 500-word essay on a topic related to education that changes annually; recently, they were invited to explain what caused them to choose a career in education, what they hope to accomplish during their career as an educator, and how they will measure their success. Selection is based on the essay, academic standing, letters of recommendation, service activities, educational activities, and leadership activities; financial need is not considered.

Financial Data The stipend depends on the availability of funds; recently, it was $2,000.

Duration 1 year.

Additional data This program began in 2006.

Number awarded 1 each year.

Deadline March of each year.

[389]
PEERMUSIC LATIN SCHOLARSHIP

Broadcast Music Inc.
Attn: BMI Foundation, Inc.
7 World Trade Center
250 Greenwich Street
New York, NY 10007-0030
(212) 220-3000
E-mail: latinscholarship@bmifoundation.org
Web: www.bmifoundation.org

Summary To recognize and reward students at colleges and universities who submit outstanding songs or instrumental works in a Latin genre.

Eligibility This competition is open to students between 16 and 24 years of age enrolled at colleges and universities in the United States and Puerto Rico. Applicants may not have had any musical work commercially recorded or distributed. They must submit an original song or instrumental work in a Latin genre. The entry must be submitted on CD or MP3, accompanied by 3 typed copies of the lyric.

Financial Data The award is $5,000.

Duration The award is presented annually.

Additional data This award, first presented in 2003, is sponsored by peermusic Companies.

Number awarded 1 each year.

Deadline February of each year.

[390]
PEPSICO SCHOLARSHIPS OF THE NATIONAL ASSOCIATION OF HISPANIC JOURNALISTS

National Association of Hispanic Journalists
Attn: Scholarship Committee
1050 Connecticut Avenue, N.W., Tenth Floor
Washington, DC 20036
(202) 662-7145   Toll Free: (888) 346-NAHJ
Fax: (202) 662-7144   E-mail: nahj@nahj.org
Web: www.nahj12.com/scholarships

Summary To provide financial assistance to undergraduate and graduate student members of the National Association of Hispanic Journalists (NAHJ) who are interested in preparing for careers in the media.

Eligibility This program is open to Hispanic American high school seniors, undergraduates, and graduate students who are interested in preparing for a career in print, broadcast (radio or television), online, or visual journalism. Applicants must be enrolled full time at a college or university in the United States or Puerto Rico. They must have a GPA of 2.0 or higher and be NAHJ members. Along with their application, they must submit transcripts, a 1-page resume, 2 letters of recommendation, work samples, and a 1,000-word autobiographical essay that includes why they are interested in a career in journalism, what inspired them to prepare for a career in the field, what hardships or obstacles they have experienced while trying to realize their goal of becoming a journalist, and the role Latino journalists play in the news industry. Selection is based on commitment to the field of journalism, academic achievement, awareness of the Latino community, and financial need.

Financial Data Stipends range up to $2,500.

Duration 1 year; may be renewed until completion of a college degree.

Additional data   This program is sponsored by PepsiCo.
Number awarded   Varies each year.
Deadline   January of each year.

[391]
PFATS-NFL CHARITIES MINORITY SCHOLARSHIPS

Professional Football Athletic Trainers Society
c/o Britt Brown, ATC, Associate Athletic Trainer
Dallas Cowboys
One Cowboys Parkway
Irving, TX 75063
(972) 497-4992   E-mail: bbrown@dallascowboys.net
Web: www.pfats.com/about/scholarships

Summary   To provide financial assistance to Hispanic American and other minority undergraduate and graduate students working on a degree in athletic training.

Eligibility   This program is open to ethnic minority students who are working on an undergraduate or graduate degree in athletic training. Applicants must have a GPA of 2.5 or higher. Along with their application, they must submit a cover letter, a curriculum vitae, and a letter of recommendation from their supervising athletic trainer.

Financial Data   A stipend is awarded (amount not specified).

Duration   1 year.

Additional data   Recipients also have an opportunity to work at summer training camp of a National Football League (NFL) team. Support for this program, which began in 1993, is provided by NFL Charities.

Number awarded   1 or more each year.

Deadline   March of each year.

[392]
PHILIP ARREOLA RETURNING STUDENT SCHOLARSHIPS

Hispanic Chamber of Commerce-Wisconsin
Attn: Scholarship Committee
1021 West National Avenue
Milwaukee, WI 53204
(414) 643-6963   Fax: (414) 643-6994
E-mail: eagosto@hccw.org
Web: www.hccw.org

Summary   To provide financial assistance to Hispanic students who are reentering colleges and universities in Wisconsin after a lapse of time.

Eligibility   This program is open to Hispanic students currently enrolled full time at a college or university in Wisconsin after at least a 1-year lapse in their undergraduate education. Applicants must be residents of Wisconsin, have a high school diploma or GED, have a record of participation in school and/or community activities, and be U.S. citizens or permanent residents. Along with their application, they must submit a 3-page essay covering their strengths that should be considered for this scholarship, career plans, current and future commitment to the Hispanic community, and financial need.

Financial Data   The stipend is $1,000.

Duration   1 year; nonrenewable.

Number awarded   Varies each year; recently, 2 of these scholarships were awarded.

Deadline   April of each year.

[393]
PHILIP ARREOLA SCHOLARSHIPS

Hispanic Chamber of Commerce-Wisconsin
Attn: Scholarship Committee
1021 West National Avenue
Milwaukee, WI 53204
(414) 643-6963   Fax: (414) 643-6994
E-mail: eagosto@hccw.org
Web: www.hccw.org

Summary   To provide financial assistance to Hispanic high school seniors in Wisconsin who plan to attend college in the state.

Eligibility   This program is open to Hispanic students graduating from high school in Wisconsin and planning to attend an accredited college or university in the state. Applicants must be residents of Wisconsin; have a history of academic achievement, participation in school activities, and involvement in community activities; be able to demonstrate financial need; and be U.S. citizens or permanent residents. Along with their application, they must submit a 3-page essay covering their strengths that should be considered for this scholarship, career plans, current and future commitment to the Hispanic community, and financial need.

Financial Data   The stipend is $2,500 per year.

Duration   4 years, provided the recipient remains enrolled full time with a GPA of 2.5 or higher and volunteers for 20 hours of community service work annually.

Number awarded   Varies each year; recently, 3 of these scholarships were awarded.

Deadline   April of each year.

[394]
PHILLIP D. REED UNDERGRADUATE ENDOWMENT FELLOWSHIP

National Action Council for Minorities in Engineering
Attn: University Programs
440 Hamilton Avenue, Suite 302
White Plains, NY 10601-1813
(914) 539-4010   Fax: (914) 539-4032
E-mail: scholarships@nacme.org
Web: www.nacme.org/NACME_D.aspx?pageid=105

Summary   To provide financial assistance to Hispanic American and other underrepresented minority college sophomores majoring in engineering or related fields.

Eligibility   This program is open to African American, Latino, and American Indian college sophomores who have a GPA of 3.0 or higher and have demonstrated academic excellence, leadership skills, and a commitment to science and engineering as a career. Applicants must be enrolled full time at an ABET-accredited engineering program. Fields of study include all areas of engineering as well as computer science, materials science, mathematics, operations research, or physics.

Financial Data   The stipend is $5,000 per year. Funds are sent directly to the recipient's university.

Duration   Up to 3 years.

Number awarded 1 each year.

Deadline April of each year.

[395]
PHYLLIS G. MEEKINS SCHOLARSHIP

Ladies Professional Golf Association
Attn: LPGA Foundation
100 International Golf Drive
Daytona Beach, FL 32124-1082
(386) 274-6200 Fax: (386) 274-1099
E-mail: foundation.scholarships@lpga.com
Web: www.lpgafoundation.org/scholarships?

Summary To provide financial assistance to Hispanic American and other minority female graduating high school seniors who played golf in high school and plan to continue to play in college.

Eligibility This program is open to female high school seniors who are members of a recognized minority group. Applicants must have a GPA of 3.0 or higher and a background in golf. They must be planning to enroll full time at a college or university in the United States and play competitive golf. Along with their application, they must submit a letter that describes how golf has been an integral part of their lives and includes their personal, academic, and professional goals; their chosen discipline of study; and how this scholarship will be of assistance. Financial need is considered in the selection process. U.S. citizenship or legal resident status is required.

Financial Data The stipend is $1,250.

Duration 1 year.

Additional data This program began in 2006.

Number awarded 1 each year.

Deadline May of each year.

[396]
PHYSICAL AND LIFE SCIENCES DIRECTORATE INTERNSHIPS

Lawrence Livermore National Laboratory
Physical and Life Sciences Directorate
Attn: Education Coordinator
7000 East Avenue, L-418
Livermore, CA 94550
(925) 422-0455 E-mail: hutcheon3@llnl.gov
Web: www-pls.llnl.gov

Summary To provide an opportunity for undergraduate and graduate students (particularly Hispanic Americans, other minorities, and women) to work on summer research projects within the Physical and Life Sciences Directorate (PLS) of Lawrence Livermore National Laboratory (LLNL).

Eligibility This program is open to full-time undergraduate and graduate students who are interested in working on research projects within the PLS Directorate of LLNL. Openings are currently available in chemistry (organic, inorganic, synthetic, analytical, computational, nuclear, and environmental) and materials science (theory, simulation and modeling, synthesis and processing, materials under extreme conditions, dynamic materials science, metallurgy, nuclear fuels, optical materials, and surface science). Applicants must have a GPA of 3.0 or higher. Selection is based on academic record, aptitude, research interests, and recommendations of instructors. Women and minorities are encouraged to apply.

Financial Data The stipend is $14 to $20 per hour for undergraduates or $4,100 to $4,900 per month for graduate students. Living accommodations and arrangements are the responsibility of the intern.

Duration 2 or 3 months, during the summer.

Number awarded Varies each year.

Deadline February of each year.

[397]
P.O. PISTILLI SCHOLARSHIPS

Design Automation Conference
c/o Andrew B. Kahng, Scholarship Director
University of California at San Diego-Jacobs School of Engineering
Jacobs Hall, EBU3B, Rpp, 2134
9500 Gilman Drive
La Jolla, CA 92093-0404
(858) 822-4884 Fax: (858) 534-7029
E-mail: abk@cs.ucsd.edu
Web: www.dac.com

Summary To provide financial assistance to Hispanic Americans, other minorities, females, and individuals with disabilities who are high school seniors and interested in preparing for a career in computer science or electrical engineering.

Eligibility This program is open to graduating high school seniors who are members of underrepresented groups: women, African Americans, Hispanics, Native Americans, and persons with disabilities. Applicants must be interested in preparing for a career in electrical engineering, computer engineering, or computer science. They must have at least a 3.0 GPA, have demonstrated high achievements in math and science courses, have demonstrated involvement in activities associated with the underrepresented group they represent, and be able to demonstrate significant financial need. U.S. citizenship is not required, but applicants must be U.S. residents when they apply and must plan to attend an accredited U.S. college or university. Along with their application, they must submit 3 letters of recommendation, official transcripts, ACT/SAT and/or PSAT scores, a personal statement outlining future goals and why they think they should receive this scholarship, and documentation of financial need.

Financial Data Stipends are $4,000 per year. Awards are paid each year in 2 equal installments.

Duration 1 year; may be renewed up to 4 additional years.

Additional data This program is funded by the Design Automation Conference of the Association for Computing Machinery's Special Interest Group on Design Automation.

Number awarded 2 to 7 each year.

Deadline January of each year.

[398]
PRAXAIR SCHOLARSHIPS

Society of Women Engineers
Attn: Scholarship Selection Committee
203 North LaSalle Street, Suite 1675
Chicago, IL 60601-1269
(312) 596-5223 Toll Free: (877) SWE-INFO
Fax: (312) 644-8557 E-mail: scholarships@swe.org
Web: societyofwomenengineers.swe.org

Summary To provide financial assistance to undergraduate women (particularly Hispanic Americans and other underrepresented minorities) who are majoring in chemical or mechanical engineering.

Eligibility This program is open to society members who are entering their sophomore, junior, or senior year at an ABET-accredited 4-year college or university. Applicants must be working full time on a degree in computer science or chemical or mechanical engineering and have a GPA of 3.2 or higher. Selection is based on merit. Preference is given to groups underrepresented in computer science and engineering.

Financial Data The stipend is $1,000.

Duration 1 year.

Additional data This program began in 2011 by Praxair, Inc.

Number awarded 10 each year.

Deadline February of each year.

[399]
PRE-MED ENRICHMENT PROGRAM FOR UNDERREPRESENTED MINORITY UNDERGRADUATES

University of Pennsylvania
Perelman School of Medicine
Attn: Center of Excellence for Diversity in Health
  Education and Research
3508 Market Street, Suite 234
Philadelphia, PA 19104-3357
(215) 898-3980   Fax: (215) 573-2793
E-mail: tyeshiak@mail.med.upenn.edu
Web: www.uphs.upenn.edu/coeomh/premed.htm

Summary To provide an opportunity for Hispanic American and other underrepresented minority undergraduates to gain research experience in medicine during a summer program at the University of Pennsylvania.

Eligibility This program is open to undergraduate students who are members of ethnic or racial groups underrepresented in medicine. Applicants must have completed at least 60 credits of a pre-medical program and have a GPA of 2.75 or higher. They must be interested in participating in a program at the University of Pennsylvania that includes research, clinical observations, classroom exercises, and teaching observation designed to stimulate and cultivate their interest in academic medicine. U.S. citizenship or permanent resident status is required.

Financial Data The program provides a stipend (amount not specified), housing, and 2 meals per day.

Duration 10 weeks during the summer.

Additional data This program, which began in 1993, is sponsored by the Bureau of Health Professions of the U.S. Health Resources and Services Administration.

Number awarded 10 to 12 each year.

Deadline January of each year.

[400]
PRINCETON SUMMER UNDERGRADUATE RESEARCH EXPERIENCE

Princeton University
Attn: Graduate School
Office of Academic Affairs and Diversity
Clio Hall
Princeton, NJ 08544-0255
(609) 258-2066   E-mail: diverse@princeton.edu
Web: www.princeton.edu

Summary To provide an opportunity for Hispanic American and other minority or disadvantaged students to assist Princeton faculty in any area during the summer.

Eligibility This program is open to full-time sophomores and juniors at all colleges and universities in the United States who are majoring in any academic discipline and have a GPA of 3.5 or higher in their major. Current college freshmen and graduating seniors are not eligible. Applicants must be interested in working during the summer with a Princeton faculty member. They should have a goal of continuing on for a Ph.D. and preparing for a career in college or university teaching and research. Students in the sciences and engineering normally work in a laboratory group on an aspect of the faculty member's current research. Students in the humanities and social sciences might assist a faculty member engaged in a particular research, editing, bibliographical, or course-preparation project; alternatively, they may work on a research paper under faculty supervision. Members of racial and ethnic minority groups underrepresented in doctoral research programs, students from socioeconomically disadvantaged backgrounds, and students at small liberal arts colleges are especially encouraged to apply.

Financial Data Participants receive a stipend of $3,750, housing in a campus dormitory, a $150 meal card, and up to $500 in reimbursement of travel costs.

Duration 8 weeks during the summer.

Number awarded Up to 20 each year.

Deadline January of each year.

[401]
PROCTER & GAMBLE PROFESSIONAL ORAL CARE–HDA FOUNDATION SCHOLARSHIPS

Hispanic Dental Association
Attn: HDA Foundation
1111 14th Street, N.W., Suite 1100
Washington, DC 20005
(202) 629-3628   Fax: (202) 629-3802
E-mail: scholarships@hdassoc.org
Web: www.hdassoc.org

Summary To provide financial assistance to members of the Hispanic Dental Association (HDA) interested in preparing for a career in a dental profession.

Eligibility This program is open to HDA members who are entering as first- or second-year full-time students at an accredited dental, dental hygiene, dental assisting, or dental technician program. Applicants must be permanent U.S. residents. They must have a GPA of 3.0 or higher. Along with their application, they must submit an essay on why they want to be a dental professional and how they will help to improve their community when they have reached their goal. Selection is based on scholastic achievement, community service, leadership skills, and commitment to improving the oral health of the Hispanic community.

Financial Data The stipend is $1,000.

Duration 1 year.

Additional data This program, which began in 1994, is sponsored by Procter & Gamble Company.

Number awarded Varies each year; recently, 6 of these scholarships were awarded.

Deadline June of each year.

[402]
PROFESSIONAL GOLF MANAGEMENT DIVERSITY SCHOLARSHIP

Professional Golfers' Association of America
Attn: PGA Foundation
100 Avenue of the Champions
Palm Beach Gardens, FL 33418
Toll Free: (888) 532-6661
Web: www.pgafoundation.com

Summary To provide financial assistance to Hispanic Americans, other minorities, and women who are interested in attending a designated college or university to prepare for a career as a golf professional.

Eligibility This program is open to women and minorities interested in becoming a licensed PGA Professional. Applicants must be interested in attending 1 of 20 colleges and universities that offer the Professional Golf Management (PGM) curriculum sanctioned by the PGA.

Financial Data The stipend is $3,000 per year.

Duration 1 year; may be renewed.

Additional data This program began in 1993. Programs are offered at 20 designated universities; for a list, contact the PGA.

Number awarded Varies each year; recently, 20 of these scholarships were awarded.

Deadline Deadline not specified.

[403]
PROGRESS ENERGY HISPANIC ENGINEERING SCHOLARSHIP

North Carolina Society of Hispanic Professionals
Attn: North Carolina Hispanic College Fund
8450 Chapel Hill Road, Suite 209
Cary, NC 27513
(919) 467-8424   Fax: (919) 469-1785
E-mail: mailbox@thencshp.org
Web: thencshp.org/programs/nc-hispanic-college-fund

Summary To provide financial assistance to Hispanic residents of North Carolina who are interested in majoring in specified fields of engineering at colleges in the state.

Eligibility This program is open to residents of North Carolina who are of Hispanic background (both parents are at least half Hispanic or 1 parent is fully Hispanic) and either 1) are graduating high school seniors; or 2) graduated from high school within the past 2 years. Applicants must be enrolled or planning to enroll at a university or community college in the state and study chemical, civil, electrical, mechanical, or nuclear engineering. They must have a high school GPA of 2.5 or higher. Along with their application, they must submit a 500-word essay on why their Hispanic parentage and family background are important to them, personal and/or academic

achievements, academic plans and career goals, and past and current efforts (as well as future plans) towards making a difference in their community. Preference is given to foreign-born applicants and the native-born children of foreign-born parents. Selection is based on academic achievement, community involvement, volunteerism, leadership, and family economic need.

Financial Data Stipends range from $500 to $2,500 per year. Funds are paid directly to the college or university.

Duration 1 year; may be renewed up to 3 additional years.

Additional data This program is sponsored by Progress Energy Foundation.

Number awarded 1 or more each year.

Deadline January of each year.

[404]
PRSSA DIVERSITY MULTICULTURAL SCHOLARSHIPS

Public Relations Student Society of America
Attn: Vice President of Member Services
33 Maiden Lane, 11th Floor
New York, NY 10038-5150
(212) 460-1474   Fax: (212) 995-0757
E-mail: prssa@prsa.org
Web: www.prssa.org/scholarships_competitions/individual

Summary To provide financial assistance to Hispanic American and other minority college students who are interested in preparing for a career in public relations.

Eligibility This program is open to minority (African American/Black, Hispanic/Latino, Asian, Native American, Alaskan Native, or Pacific Islander) students who are at least juniors at an accredited 4-year college or university. Applicants must be enrolled full time, be able to demonstrate financial need, and have a GPA of 3.0 or higher. Membership in the Public Relations Student Society of America is preferred but not required. A major or minor in public relations is preferred; students who attend a school that does not offer a public relations degree or program must be enrolled in a communications degree program (e.g., journalism, mass communications).

Financial Data The stipend is $1,500.

Duration 1 year.

Additional data This program began in 1989.

Number awarded 2 each year.

Deadline May of each year.

[405]
PUGET SOUND CHAPTER/HORACE AND SUSIE REVELS CAYTON SCHOLARSHIP

Public Relations Society of America-Puget Sound
  Chapter
c/o Amy Turner
EnviroIssues
101 Stewart Street, Suite 1200
Seattle, WA 98101
(206) 269-5041   Fax: (206) 269-5046
E-mail: prsascholarship@asi-seattle.net
Web: www.prsapugetsound.org/Page.aspx?cid=127

Summary To provide financial assistance to Hispanic American and other minority upperclassmen from Washington who are interested in preparing for a career in public relations.

Eligibility This program is open to U.S. citizens who are members of minority groups, defined as African Americans, Asian Americans, Hispanic/Latino Americans, Native Americans, and Pacific Islanders. Applicants must be full-time juniors or seniors attending a college in Washington or Washington students (who graduated from a Washington high school or whose parents live in the state year-round) attending college elsewhere. They must be able to demonstrate aptitude in public relations and related courses, activities, and/or internships.

Financial Data The stipend is $2,500.

Duration 1 year.

Additional data This program began in 1992.

Number awarded 1 each year.

Deadline April of each year.

[406]
PUGET SOUND CHAPTER SHARON D. BANKS MEMORIAL UNDERGRADUATE SCHOLARSHIP

Women's Transportation Seminar-Puget Sound Chapter
c/o Jennifer Barnes, Scholarship Co-Chair
Heffron Transportation, Inc.
532 27th Avenue
Seattle, WA 98122
(206) 324-3623   Fax: (877) 314-9959
E-mail: jennifer@hefftrans.com
Web: www.wtsinternational.org

Summary To provide financial assistance to women (especially Hispanic American and other minority women) who are undergraduate students from Washington working on a degree related to transportation.

Eligibility This program is open to women who are residents of Washington, studying at a college in the state, or working as an intern in the state. Applicants must be currently enrolled in an undergraduate degree program in a transportation-related field, such as engineering, planning, finance, or logistics. They must have a GPA of 3.0 or higher and plans to prepare for a career in a transportation-related field. Minority women are especially encouraged to apply. Along with their application, they must submit a 500-word statement about their career goals after graduation and why they think they should receive this scholarship award. Selection is based on that statement, academic record, and transportation-related activities or job skills. Financial need is not considered.

Financial Data The stipend is $4,000.

Duration 1 year.

Additional data The winner is also nominated for scholarships offered by the national organization of the Women's Transportation Seminar.

Number awarded 1 each year.

Deadline November of each year.

[407]
RAUL YZAGUIRRE SCHOLARSHIP

Adelante
c/o Frito-Lay, Inc.
Attn: M. Ochoa-Dennis
7701 Legacy Drive
Mail drop 4A-197
Plano, TX 75024-4099

Summary To provide financial assistance for college to Hispanic students who have been activists for their community.

Eligibility This program is open to Hispanic students who are entering or enrolled at a 2- or 4-year college or university. Applicants must have an activist vision of equality that advances the inclusion and progress of the Hispanic community. They must have a GPA of 2.5 or higher. Along with their application, they must submit an essay of 1 to 2 pages that answers 1 of the following questions: what person or circumstance has most impacted their life, what legacy do they wish to leave behind, or what have they done to make a difference in their community.

Financial Data Stipends are $6,000, $3,000, or $1,000.

Duration 1 year.

Additional data The sponsoring organization is the Latino/Hispanic employee resource group of PepsiCo.

Number awarded 3 each year: 1 each at $6,000, $3,000, and $1,000.

Deadline May of each year.

[408]
RAY AND CARMELLA MELLADO SCHOLARSHIP

Great Minds in STEM
Attn: HENAAC Scholars Program
602 Monterey Pass Road
Monterey Park, CA 91754
(323) 262-0997   Fax: (323) 262-0946
E-mail: gcruz@greatmindsinstem.org
Web: www.greatmindsinstem.org

Summary To provide financial assistance to Hispanic undergraduate and graduate students who are enrolled at a university in any state and working on a degree in a field of science, technology, engineering, or mathematics (STEM).

Eligibility This program is open to Hispanic undergraduate and graduate students who are working on a degree in a field of STEM at colleges and universities in any state. Applicants must be of Hispanic origin and/or must significantly participate in and promote organizations and activities in the Hispanic community. They must have a GPA of 3.0 or higher. There is no citizenship requirement. Along with their application, they must submit a 700-word essay on a topic that changes annually. Selection is based on leadership, academic achievements, and campus and community activities; financial need is not considered.

Financial Data Stipends range from $500 to $10,000.

Duration 1 year; recipients may reapply.

Additional data The Hispanic Engineer National Achievement Awards Conference (HENAAC) was established in 1989 and initiated a scholarship program in 2000. In 2010, the sponsoring organization officially adopted its current name, but it continues to hold the annual HENAAC conference, at which the scholarships are presented. Recipients must attend the conference to accept their scholarship.

Number awarded 1 or more each year.

Deadline April of each year.

[409]
RDW GROUP, INC. MINORITY SCHOLARSHIP FOR COMMUNICATIONS

Rhode Island Foundation
Attn: Funds Administrator
One Union Station
Providence, RI 02903
(401) 427-4017   Fax: (401) 331-8085
E-mail: lmonahan@rifoundation.org
Web: www.rifoundation.org

Summary To provide financial assistance to Hispanic Americans and other residents of color from Rhode Island who are working on a undergraduate or graduate degree in communications in any state.

Eligibility This program is open to undergraduate and graduate students at colleges and universities in any state who are Rhode Island residents of color. Applicants must intend to work on a degree in communications (including computer graphics, art, cinematography, or other fields that would prepare them for a career in advertising). They must be able to demonstrate financial need and a commitment to a career in communications. Along with their application, they must submit an essay (up to 300 words) on the impact they would like to have on the communications field.

Financial Data The stipend is approximately $2,000 per year.

Duration 1 year; recipients may reapply.

Additional data This program is sponsored by the RDW Group, Inc.

Number awarded 1 each year.

Deadline April of each year.

[410]
RESEARCH AND ENGINEERING APPRENTICESHIP PROGRAM (REAP) FOR HIGH SCHOOL STUDENTS

Academy of Applied Science
Attn: REAP
1 Maple Street
Concord, NH 03301
(603) 228-4520   Fax: (603) 228-0210
E-mail: renie@aas-world.org
Web: www.aas-world.org/interest-pages/for-students.html

Summary To provide an opportunity for Hispanic American and other high school students from groups historically underrepresented in science, technology, engineering, and science (STEM) who want to participate in a summer research apprenticeship.

Eligibility This program is open to high school students from groups historically underrepresented or underserved in STEM; that includes 1) Blacks/African Americans; 2) Hispanics; 3) Native Americans/Alaskan Natives; 4) low-income according to federal TRIO criteria; and 5) women in physical science, computer science, mathematics, or engineering. Applicants must be interested in working as an apprentice on a research project in the laboratory of a mentor scientist at a college or university near their home. Selection is based on demonstrated interests in STEM research and demonstrated potential for a successful career in STEM. They must be at least 16 years of age.

Financial Data The stipend is $1,300.

Duration Summer months.

Additional data The program provides intensive summer training for high school students in the laboratories of scientists. The program, established in 1980, is funded by a grant from the U.S. Army Research Office. Students must live at home while they participate in the program and must live in the area of an approved college or university. The program does not exist in every state.

Number awarded Varies; recently, approximately 120 students were funded at 44 universities nationwide.

Deadline February of each year.

[411]
RESEARCH EXPERIENCES FOR UNDERGRADUATES PROGRAM IN SOLAR AND SPACE PHYSICS

University of Colorado
Attn: Laboratory for Atmospheric and Space Physics
1234 Innovation Drive
Boulder, CO 80303-7814
(303) 735-2143   E-mail: martin.snow@lasp.colorado.edu
Web: lasp.colorado.edu/home/education/reu

Summary To provide an opportunity for upper-division students (particularly Hispanic Americans, other minorities, women, and students with disabilities) to work on research projects related to solar and space physics at laboratories in Boulder, Colorado during the summer.

Eligibility This program is open to students currently enrolled as sophomores and juniors at colleges and universities in any state. Applicants must be interested in participating on a research project related to solar and space physics at a participating laboratory in Boulder, Colorado. They must be U.S. citizens, nationals, or permanent residents. Applications are especially encouraged from underrepresented minorities, persons with disabilities, and women.

Financial Data The stipend is $500 per week. Students also receive dormitory housing, a food allowance, and a travel stipend of $500.

Duration 8 weeks, starting in June.

Additional data The participating laboratories are the Laboratory for Atmospheric and Space Physics (LASP) of the University of Colorado, the High Altitude Observatory (HAO) of the National Center for Atmospheric Research (NCAR), the Space Weather Prediction Center (SWPC) of the National Oceanic and Atmospheric Administration (NOAA), the Planetary Science Directorate of the Southwest Research Institute (SwRI), and NorthWest Research Associates (NWRA). This program is funded by the National Science Foundation as part of its Research Experiences for Undergraduates (REU) Program.

Number awarded Varies each year; recently, 16 of these internships were awarded.

Deadline January of each year.

[412]
RESEARCH IN SCIENCE AND ENGINEERING PROGRAM

Rutgers University
Attn: Graduate School
25 Bishop Place
New Brunswick, NJ 08901-1181
(848) 932-6584   Fax: (732) 932-7407
E-mail: rise@rci.rutgers.edu
Web: rise.rutgers.edu/index.php

Summary To provide an opportunity for undergraduate students from any state (particularly Hispanic Americans and members of other underrepresented or disadvantaged groups) to work on a summer research project in science, mathematics, or engineering at Rutgers University in New Jersey.

Eligibility This program is open to undergraduates majoring in science (especially the biomedical sciences), mathematics, or engineering at a college or university in any state. Applicants must be interested in participating in a summer research project under the guidance of a faculty member at the graduate school of Rutgers University in New Brunswick. They should have completed at least the sophomore year and have a GPA of 3.0 or higher. Applications are especially encouraged from members of groups underrepresented in the sciences, mathematics, or engineering; students from economically or educationally disadvantaged backgrounds; members of the first generation in their family to attend college; undergraduates attending schools that do not offer opportunities for independent research or mentoring by research-active faculty; nontraditional students; and individuals who have faced life challenges. U.S. citizenship or permanent residents status is required.

Financial Data The program provides a stipend of $4,000, free housing, and up to $500 of reimbursement for travel expenses.

Duration 8 or 10 weeks during the summer.

Additional data This program is administered by the Rutgers University Graduate School. Support is provided by many sponsors, including the National Science Foundation, the Federation of American Societies for Experimental Biology, Merck Research Laboratories, Public Service Electric and Gas, the New Jersey Space Grant Consortium, the New Jersey Commission on Cancer Research, and the McNair Scholars Program.

Number awarded 20 to 25 each year.

Deadline Applications are accepted on a rolling basis; selection begins in January and continues until all places are filled.

[413]
RHODE ISLAND LATINO DOLLARS SCHOLARSHIPS

Latino Dollars for Scholars of Rhode Island
P.O. Box 6764
Providence, RI 02940
(401) 495-5052   E-mail: ladori.dfs@gmail.com
Web: latinodollarsforscholars.org

Summary To provide financial assistance to Latino residents of Rhode Island who are interested in attending college in any state.

Eligibility This program is open to Latino residents (at least 1 parent must be of Latino descent) of Rhode Island who are enrolled or planning to enroll at a college or university in any state. Applicants must be able to demonstrate financial need. Selection is based on academic excellence and commitment to improving the community.

Financial Data A stipend is awarded (amount not specified).

Duration 1 year.

Additional data This program began in 1993.

Number awarded Varies each year; recently, 18 of these scholarships were awarded. Since the program was established, it has awarded 290 scholarships.

Deadline April of each year.

[414]
RICHARD B. FISHER SCHOLARSHIP

Morgan Stanley
Attn: Diversity Recruiting
1585 Broadway
New York, NY 10036
(212) 762-0211   Toll Free: (888) 454-3965
Fax: (212) 507-4972
E-mail: richardbfisherprogram@morganstanley.com
Web: www.morganstanley.com

Summary To provide financial aid and work experience to Hispanic Americans and members of other underrepresented groups who are preparing for a career in technology within the financial services industry.

Eligibility This program is open to African American, Hispanic, Native American and lesbian/gay/bisexual/transgender students who are enrolled in their sophomore or junior year of college (or the third or fourth year of a 5-year program). Applicants must be enrolled full time and have a GPA of 3.4 or higher. They must be willing to commit to a paid summer internship in the Morgan Stanley Information Technology Division. All majors and disciplines are eligible, but preference is given to students preparing for a career in technology within the financial services industry. Along with their application, they must submit 1-page essays on 1) why they are applying for this scholarship and why they should be selected as a recipient; 2) a technical project on which they worked, either through a university course or previous work experience, their role in the project, and how they contributed to the end result; and 3) a software, hardware, or new innovative application of existing technology that they would create if they could and the impact it would have. Financial need is not considered in the selection process.

Financial Data The stipend is $7,500 per year.

Duration 1 year (the junior year); may be renewed for the senior year.

Additional data The program, established in 1993, includes a paid summer internship in the Morgan Stanley Information Technology Division in the summer following the time of application.

Number awarded 1 or more each year.

Deadline December of each year.

[415]
RICHARD HECKERT FELLOWSHIP

National Action Council for Minorities in Engineering
Attn: University Programs
440 Hamilton Avenue, Suite 302
White Plains, NY 10601-1813
(914) 539-4010   Fax: (914) 539-4032
E-mail: scholarships@nacme.org
Web: www.nacme.org/NACME_D.aspx?pageid=105

Summary To provide financial assistance to Hispanic Americans and other underrepresented minority high school seniors interested in studying engineering or related fields in college.

Eligibility This program is open to African American, Latino, and American Indian high school seniors who are in the top 10% of their graduating class, have a GPA of 3.0 or higher, and have demonstrated academic excellence, leadership skills, and a commitment to science and engineering as a career. Candidates must have been accepted as a full-time student at an ABET-accredited engineering program. They must be nominated by their school (each high school may nominate only 1 student). Fields of study include all areas of engineering as well as computer science, materials science, mathematics, operations research, or physics. Letters of nomination must be accompanied by a transcript, SAT or ACT report form, resume, and 100-word statement of why the student should receive this scholarship.

Financial Data The stipend is $5,000 per year. Funds are sent directly to the recipient's university.

Duration 4 years.

Number awarded 1 each year.

Deadline April of each year.

[416]
RICHARD S. SMITH SCHOLARSHIP

United Methodist Church
Attn: General Board of Discipleship
Young People's Ministries
P.O. Box 340003
Nashville, TN 37203-0003
(615) 340-7184   Toll Free: (877) 899-2780, ext. 7184
Fax: (615) 340-7063   E-mail: ypm@gbod.org
Web: globalyoungpeople.org

Summary To provide financial assistance to Hispanic American and other minority high school seniors who wish to prepare for a Methodist church-related career.

Eligibility This program is open to graduating high school seniors who are members of racial/ethnic minority groups and have been active members of a United Methodist Church for at least 1 year. Applicants must have been admitted to an accredited college or university to prepare for a church-related career. They must have maintained at least a "C" average throughout high school and be able to demonstrate financial need. Along with their application, they must submit brief essays on their participation in church projects and activities, a leadership experience, the role their faith plays in their life, the church-related vocation to which God is calling them, and their extracurricular interests and activities. U.S. citizenship or permanent resident status is required.

Financial Data The stipend is $1,000.

Duration 1 year; nonrenewable.

Additional data This program began in 1997. Recipients must enroll full time in their first year of undergraduate study.

Number awarded 2 each year.

Deadline May of each year.

[417]
RIXIO MEDINA & ASSOCIATES SCHOLARSHIP FOR HISPANICS IN SAFETY

American Society of Safety Engineers
Attn: ASSE Foundation
Scholarship Award Program
1800 East Oakton Street
Des Plaines, IL 60018
(847) 699-2929   Fax: (847) 768-3434
E-mail: bzylstra@asse.org
Web: www.asse.org

Summary To provide financial assistance to Hispanic upper-division and graduate students working on a degree related to occupational safety.

Eligibility This program is open to ASSE student members who are working on an undergraduate or graduate degree in occupational safety, health, environment, industrial hygiene, occupational health nursing, or a closely-related field (e.g., industrial or environmental engineering). Applicants must be bilingual (Spanish-English); Hispanic ethnicity is preferred. Students enrolled in an ASAC/ABET-accredited safety program also receive preference. They must be full-time students who have completed at least 60 semester hours with a GPA of 3.0 or higher as undergraduates or at least 9 semester hours as graduate students. U.S. citizenship is not required. Membership in the American Society of Safety Engineers (ASSE) is not required, but preference is given to members.

Financial Data The stipend is $4,000 per year.

Duration 1 year; recipients may reapply.

Additional data This program began in 2005.

Number awarded 1 each year.

Deadline November of each year.

[418]
ROBERT T. CHAPA SR. MEMORIAL SCHOLARSHIPS

Hispanic Scholarship Consortium
Attn: Scholarship Selection Committee
1107 South Eighth Street
Austin, TX 78704
(512) 368-2956   Fax: (512) 692-1831
E-mail: scholarships@hispanicscholar.org
Web: www.hispanicscholar.org

Summary To provide financial assistance to high school seniors of Hispanic heritage from Texas who plan to attend college in any state.

Eligibility This program is open to seniors graduating from high schools in Texas who are of Hispanic heritage and have a GPA of 3.0 or higher. Applicants must be planning to enroll full time at an accredited 2- or 4-year college or university in the United States. Selection is based on academic record, community service, financial need, and a personal interview. U.S. citizenship or permanent resident status is required.

Financial Data The stipend is $2,000 per year.

Duration 1 year; may be renewed, provided the recipient remains enrolled full time, maintains a GPA of 3.0 or higher, and participates in at least 25 hours of community service per semester.

Additional data This program is sponsored by the Fiesta de Independencia Foundation.

Number awarded 1 or more each year.

Deadline August of each year.

[419]
ROCKWELL AUTOMATION SCHOLARSHIPS

Society of Women Engineers
Attn: Scholarship Selection Committee
203 North LaSalle Street, Suite 1675
Chicago, IL 60601-1269
(312) 596-5223   Toll Free: (877) SWE-INFO
Fax: (312) 644-8557   E-mail: scholarships@swe.org
Web: societyofwomenengineers.swe.org

Summary To provide financial assistance to upper-division women (particularly Hispanic Americans and other underrepresented minorities) who are majoring in computer science or selected engineering specialties.

Eligibility This program is open to women who are entering their junior year at an ABET-accredited college or university. Applicants must be working full time on a degree in computer science or computer, electrical, industrial, manufacturing, mechanical, or software engineering and have a GPA of 3.0 or higher. Selection is based on merit and demonstrated leadership potential. Preference is given to students attending designated universities and to members of groups underrepresented in computer science and engineering.

Financial Data The stipend is $2,500.

Duration 1 year.

Additional data This program, established in 1991, is supported by Rockwell Automation, Inc. For a list of the preferred universities, check the web site of the Society of Women Engineers.

Number awarded 2 each year.

Deadline February of each year.

[420]
ROCKWELL COLLINS SWE SCHOLARSHIPS

Society of Women Engineers
Attn: Scholarship Selection Committee
203 North LaSalle Street, Suite 1675
Chicago, IL 60601-1269
(312) 596-5223   Toll Free: (877) SWE-INFO
Fax: (312) 644-8557   E-mail: scholarships@swe.org
Web: societyofwomenengineers.swe.org

Summary To provide financial assistance to undergraduates (particularly Hispanic Americans and other underrepresented minorities) who are members of the Society of Women Engineers (SWE) and majoring in computer science or selected engineering specialties.

Eligibility This program is open to members of the society who are entering their sophomore or junior year at a 4-year ABET-accredited college or university. Applicants must be working full time on a degree in computer science or computer, electrical, or software engineering and have a GPA of 3.0 or higher. Selection is based on merit. They must be available to accepted 1 Rockwell Collins co-op or internship prior

to completing their degree. Preference is given to members of groups underrepresented in computer science and engineering.

Financial Data The stipend is $2,500.

Duration 1 year.

Additional data This program, established in 1991, is supported by Rockwell Collins, Inc.

Number awarded 3 each year.

Deadline February of each year.

[421]
ROSA L. PARKS SCHOLARSHIPS

Conference of Minority Transportation Officials
Attn: National Scholarship Program
1875 I Street, N.W., Suite 500
Washington, DC 20006
(703) 234-4072   Fax: (202) 318-0364
Web: www.comto.org/?page=Scholarships

Summary To provide financial assistance for college to children of members of the Conference of Minority Transportation Officials (COMTO) and to other students interested in working on a bachelor's or master's degree in transportation.

Eligibility This program is open to 1) college-bound high school seniors whose parent has been a COMTO member for at least 1 year; 2) undergraduates who have completed at least 60 semester credit hours in a transportation discipline; and 3) students working on a master's degree in transportation who have completed at least 15 credits. Applicants must have a GPA of 3.0 or higher. Along with their application, they must submit a cover letter with a 500-word statement of career goals. Financial need is not considered in the selection process. U.S. citizenship or legal resident status is required.

Financial Data The stipend is $4,500. Funds are paid directly to the recipient's college or university.

Duration 1 year.

Additional data COMTO was established in 1971 to promote, strengthen, and expand the roles of minorities in all aspects of transportation. Recipients are expected to attend the COMTO National Scholarship Luncheon.

Number awarded 1 each year.

Deadline May of each year.

[422]
ROYCE OSBORN MINORITY STUDENT SCHOLARSHIPS

American Society of Radiologic Technologists
Attn: ASRT Education and Research Foundation
15000 Central Avenue, S.E.
Albuquerque, NM 87123-3909
(505) 298-4500, ext. 2541
Toll Free: (800) 444-2778, ext. 2541
Fax: (505) 298-5063   E-mail: foundation@asrt.org
Web: www.asrtfoundation.org

Summary To provide financial assistance to Hispanic American and other minority students enrolled in entry-level radiologic sciences programs.

Eligibility This program is open to Blacks or African Americans, American Indians or Alaska Natives, Hispanics or Latinos, Asians, and Native Hawaiians or other Pacific Islanders who are enrolled in an accredited entry-level program in radiography, sonography, magnetic resonance, or nuclear medicine. Applicants must be able to finish their degree or certificate in the year for which they are applying. They must be U.S. citizens, nationals, or permanent residents have a GPA of 3.0 or higher. Along with their application, they must submit 9 essays of 200 words each on assigned topics related to their personal situation and interest in a career in radiologic science. Selection is based on those essays, academic and professional achievements, recommendations, and financial need.

Financial Data The stipend is $4,000. Funds are paid directly to the recipient's institution.

Duration 1 year.

Number awarded 5 each year.

Deadline January of each year.

[423]
RTDNF/CAROLE SIMPSON SCHOLARSHIP

Radio Television Digital News Foundation
Attn: Programs, Awards, and Membership Manager
529 14th Street, N.W., Suite 425
Washington, DC 20045
(202) 725-8318   Fax: (202) 223-4007
E-mail: katies@rtdna.org
Web: www.rtdna.org/pages/education/scholarship-info.php

Summary To provide financial assistance to Hispanic American and other minority undergraduate students who are interested in preparing for a career in electronic journalism.

Eligibility This program is open to sophomore or more advanced minority undergraduate students enrolled in an electronic journalism sequence at an accredited or nationally-recognized college or university. Applicants must submit 1 to 3 examples of their journalistic skills on audio CD or DVD (no more than 15 minutes total, accompanied by scripts); a description of their role on each story and a list of who worked on each story and what they did; a 1-page statement explaining why they are preparing for a career in electronic journalism with reference to their specific career preference (radio, television, online, reporting, producing, or newsroom management); a resume; and a letter of reference from their dean or faculty sponsor explaining why they are a good candidate for the award and certifying that they have at least 1 year of school remaining.

Financial Data The stipend is $2,000, paid in semiannual installments of $1,000 each.

Duration 1 year.

Additional data The Radio Television Digital News Foundation (RTDNF) also provides an all-expense paid trip to the Radio Television Digital News Association (RTDNA) annual international conference. The RTDNF was formerly the Radio and Television News Directors Foundation (RTNDF). Previous winners of any RTDNF scholarship or internship are not eligible.

Number awarded 1 each year.

Deadline May of each year.

[424]
RUBEN SALAZAR SCHOLARSHIPS

National Association of Hispanic Journalists
Attn: Scholarship Committee
1050 Connecticut Avenue, N.W., Tenth Floor
Washington, DC 20036
(202) 662-7145   Toll Free: (888) 346-NAHJ
Fax: (202) 662-7144   E-mail: nahj@nahj.org
Web: www.nahj12.com/scholarships

Summary To provide financial assistance to undergraduate and graduate student members of the National Association of Hispanic Journalists (NAHJ) who are interested in preparing for careers in the media.

Eligibility This program is open to Hispanic American high school seniors, undergraduates, and graduate students who are interested in preparing for a career in English- or Spanish-language print, broadcast (radio or television), online, or photojournalism; students majoring in other fields must be able to demonstrate a strong interest in preparing for a career in journalism. Applicants must be enrolled full time at a college or university in the United States or Puerto Rico. They must be NAHJ members. Along with their application, they must submit transcripts, a 1-page resume, 2 letters of recommendation, work samples, and a 1,000-word autobiographical essay that includes why they are interested in a career in journalism, what inspired them to prepare for a career in the field, what hardships or obstacles they have experienced while trying to realize their goal of becoming a journalist, and the role Latino journalists play in the news industry. Selection is based on commitment to the field of journalism, academic achievement, awareness of the Latino community, and financial need.

Financial Data Stipends are $2,000 or $1,000.

Duration 1 year.

Number awarded Varies each year; recently, 10 of these scholarships were awarded: 5 at $2,000 and 5 at $1,000.

Deadline January of each year.

[425]
RUBINOS-MESIA SCHOLARSHIP

Structural Engineers Association of Illinois
Attn: Structural Engineers Foundation
134 North LaSalle Street, Suite 1910
Chicago, IL 60602
(312) 726-4165   Fax: (312) 277-1991
E-mail: office@seaol.org
Web: www.seaoi.org/sef.htm

Summary To provide financial assistance to upper-division and graduate students of Hispanic descent interested in a career in structural engineering.

Eligibility This program is open to students of Hispanic descent who are 1) entering their third or higher year of an undergraduate program; or 2) entering or continuing a graduate program. Applicants must be enrolled in a civil or architectural engineering program and planning to continue with a structural engineering specialization. Students enrolled in structural engineering technology programs are also eligible if they are qualified to take the Fundamentals of Engineering and Principles and Practice licensure examinations in their home state upon graduation. U.S. citizenship or permanent resident status is required. Students enrolled in military academies or ROTC programs are not eligible. Selection is based on a statement giving reasons why the applicant should receive the award (including plans for continued formal education), academic performance, and potential for development and leadership. Financial need is not considered.

Financial Data   The stipend is $2,000.

Duration   1 year; nonrenewable.

Number awarded   1 or more each year.

Deadline   April of each year.

[426]
RUDY PEREZ SONGWRITING SCHOLARSHIP

American Society of Composers, Authors and Publishers
Attn: ASCAP Foundation
ASCAP Building
One Lincoln Plaza
New York, NY 10023-7142
(212) 621-6329   Fax: (212) 621-6236
E-mail: concertmusic@ascap.com
Web: www.ascap.com

Summary   To provide financial assistance to Latino students interested in studying songwriting at designated schools.

Eligibility   This program is open to Latino students currently enrolled at 1 of the following institutions: University of Miami, Conservatory of Music of Puerto Rico, The Julliard School, University of Texas at San Antonio, or Los Angeles County High School for the Arts. Applicants must be interested in studying songwriting. They must be able to demonstrate potential to produce creative and original work and financial need.

Financial Data   A stipend is awarded (amount not specified).

Duration   1 year.

Additional data   This program began in 2003.

Number awarded   1 each year.

Deadline   Deadline not specified.

[427]
SADCO SCHOLARSHIP PROGRAM

Sociedad Amigos de Colombia
Attn: Scholarship Selection Committee
P.O. Box 1141
Carmel, IN 46082
(317) 767-7927   E-mail: information@sadco.org
Web: www.sadco.org/sadco-scholarship-program

Summary   To provide financial assistance to Hispanic residents of Indiana who are attending or planning to attend college in any state.

Eligibility   This program is open to high school seniors and college freshmen, sophomores, and juniors who are Indiana residents and Hispanics of first, second, or third generation. Applicants must be attending or planning to attend an accredited college or university in any state to work on an associate or bachelor's degree. Achievement awards are available to students who have a GPA of 3.6 or higher and a record of positive leadership ability, community service, and demonstrated responsibility. Need awards are available to students who have a GPA of 3.0 or higher and are able to demonstrate financial need or verifiable, unique, unusual, or mitigating circumstances.

Financial Data   Stipends vary but recently were $2,000 for awards based on need or $1,000 for awards based on achievement.

Duration   1 year.

Additional data   Sponsors of this program include Lumina Foundation for Education, Dow AgroSciences, Cummins, USA Funds, and Key Bank.

Number awarded   Varies each year; recently, 22 of these scholarships were awarded: 4 based on achievement and 18 based on need.

Deadline   April of each year.

[428]
SANDISK SCHOLARS PROGRAM

SanDisk Foundation
951 SanDisk Drive
Milpitas, CA 97034-7933
(408) 801-1240   Fax: (408) 801-8657
E-mail: Mike.wong@sandisk.com
Web: www.sandisk.com

Summary   To provide financial assistance to Latinos, African Americans, and women who are interested in attending college to study a field of science, technology, engineering, or mathematics (STEM).

Eligibility   This program is open to women, African Americans, and Latinos who are high school seniors or freshmen, sophomores, or juniors at a 2- or 4-year college or university. Applicants must be interested in working full time on an undergraduate degree in a field of STEM. Selection is based on academic achievements and records, community involvement, an essay, and financial need.

Financial Data   The stipend is $2,500 per year.

Duration   1 year; may be renewed up to 3 additional years.

Additional data   This program, which began in 2012, is offered in partnership with the United Negro College Fund (UNCF), the Hispanic Scholarship Fund (HSF), the Silicon Valley Community Foundation (SVCF), and International Scholarship and Tuition Services (ISTS). The program also offers scholarships to dependents of SanDisk employees and provides grants to specified universities for their scholarships.

Number awarded   Varies each year; recently, 29 of these scholarships were awarded to the general public.

Deadline   March of each year.

[429]
SANDRA R. SPAULDING MEMORIAL SCHOLARSHIPS

California Nurses Association
Attn: California Nurses Foundation
2030 Franklin Street, Suite 610
Oakland, CA 94612
(510) 622-8311   Fax: (510) 663-4825
E-mail: info@calnursesfoundation.org
Web: www.nationalnursesunited.org/pages/1074

Summary   To provide financial assistance to Hispanic Americans and other students from diverse ethnic backgrounds who are enrolled in an associate degree in nursing (A.D.N.) program in California.

Eligibility   This program is open to students who have been admitted to a second-year accredited A.D.N. program in California and plan to complete the degree within 2 years. Along with their application, they must submit a 1-page essay describing their personal and professional goals. Selection is based on that essay, commitment and active participation in nursing and health-related organizations, professional vision and direction, and financial need. A goal of this scholarship program is to encourage ethnic and socioeconomic diversity in nursing.

Financial Data   A stipend is awarded (amount not specified).

Duration   1 year; nonrenewable.

Additional data   This program began in 1985.

Number awarded   1 or more each year.

Deadline   July of each year.

[430]
SAO SUMMER INTERN PROGRAM

Harvard-Smithsonian Center for Astrophysics
Attn: Summer Intern Program
60 Garden Street, Mail Stop 70
Cambridge, MA 02138
(617) 496-7063   E-mail: intern-at-cfa@harvard.edu
Web: hea-www.harvard.edu/REU/REU.html

Summary   To enable undergraduates (particularly Hispanic Americans, other underrepresented minorities, women, and students with disabilities) who are interested in a physical science career or science education to obtain research experience at the Smithsonian Astrophysical Observatory (SAO) at Harvard University.

Eligibility   This program is open to U.S. citizens, nationals, and permanent residents enrolled in a program leading to a bachelor's degree. Applicants must be interested in a career in astronomy, astrophysics, physics, or related physical sciences. Along with their application, they must submit an essay of 600 to 800 words describing academic and career goals, scientific interests, relevant work experience, why they would like to be in the program, and why they would be a good candidate. Graduating seniors are not eligible. Applications are especially encouraged from underrepresented minorities, persons with disabilities, and women.

Financial Data   The stipend is $4,500. Housing and travel expenses are provided.

Duration   10 weeks during the summer.

Additional data   Each intern works with a scientist on an individual research project. Potential areas of research include observational and theoretical cosmology, extragalactic and galactic astronomy, interstellar medium and star formation, laboratory astrophysics, supernovae and supernova remnants, planetary science, and solar and stellar astrophysics. Also included in the program are weekly lectures, field trips, and workshops specifically designed for the participants. This program is supported by the National Science Foundation as part of its Research Experiences for Undergraduates (REU) Program.

Number awarded   10 each year.

Deadline   January of each year.

[431]
SCHOLARSHIPS FOR MINORITY ACCOUNTING STUDENTS

American Institute of Certified Public Accountants
Attn: Academic and Career Development Division
220 Leigh Farm Road
Durham, NC 27707-8110
(919) 402-4931   Fax: (919) 419-4705
E-mail: scholarships@aicpa.org
Web: www.aicpa.org

Summary   To provide financial assistance to Hispanic Americans and other minorities interested in studying accounting at the undergraduate or graduate school level.

Eligibility   This program is open to minority undergraduate and graduate students, enrolled full time, who have a GPA of 3.3 or higher (both cumulatively and in their major) and intend to pursue a C.P.A. credential. The program defines minority students as those whose heritage is Black or African American, Hispanic or Latino, Native American, or Asian American. Undergraduates must have completed at least 30 semester hours, including at least 6 semester hours of a major in accounting. Graduate students must be working on a master's degree in accounting, finance, taxation, or a related program. Applicants must be U.S. citizens or permanent residents and student affiliate members of the American Institute of Certified Public Accountants (AICPA). Along with their application, they must submit 500-word essays on 1) why they want to become a C.P.A. and how attaining that licensure will contribute to their goals; and 2) how they would spread the message about accounting and the C.P.A. profession in their community and school. In the selection process, some consideration is given to financial need.

Financial Data   Stipends range from $1,500 to $3,000 per year. Funds are disbursed directly to the recipient's school.

Duration   1 year; may be renewed up to 3 additional years or until completion of a bachelor's or master's degree, whichever is earlier.

Additional data   This program began in 1969.

Number awarded   Varies each year; recently, 78 students received funding through this program.

Deadline   March of each year.

[432]
SCHOLARSHIPS FOR RACIAL JUSTICE

Higher Education Consortium for Urban Affairs
Attn: Student Services
2233 University Avenue West, Suite 210
St. Paul, MN 55114-1698
(651) 287-3300   Toll Free: (800) 554-1089
Fax: (651) 659-9421   E-mail: hecua@hecua.org
Web: www.hecua.org/programs/scholarships

Summary   To provide financial assistance to Hispanic American and other students of color who are enrolled in programs of the Higher Education Consortium for Urban Affairs (HECUA) at participating colleges and universities and are committed to undoing institutionalized racism.

Eligibility   This program is open to students at member colleges and universities who are participating in HECUA programs. Applicants must be a student of color who can demonstrate a commitment to undoing institutionalized racism. Along with their application, they must submit a reflective essay on the personal, social, or political influences in their lifetime that have motivated them to work on racial justice issues.

Financial Data The stipend is $4,000. Funds are applied as a credit to the student's HECUA program fees for the semester.

Duration 1 semester.

Additional data This program began in 2006. Consortium members include Augsburg College (Minneapolis, Minnesota), Augustana College (Sioux Falls, South Dakota), Carleton College (Northfield, Minnesota), College of Saint Scholastica (Duluth, Minnesota), Colorado College (Colorado Springs, Colorado), Denison University (Granville, Ohio), Gustavus Adolphus College (St. Peter, Minnesota), Hamline University (St. Paul, Minnesota), Macalester College (St. Paul, Minnesota), Saint Mary's University (Winona, Minnesota), Saint Catherine University (St. Paul, Minnesota), Saint Olaf College (Northfield, Minnesota), Swarthmore College (Swarthmore, Pennsylvania), University of Minnesota (Twin Cities, Duluth, Morris, Crookston, Rochester), University of Saint Thomas (St. Paul, Minnesota), and Viterbo University (La Crosse, Wisconsin).

Number awarded Several each year.

Deadline April of each year for summer and fall programs; November of each year for January and spring programs.

[433]
SCHOLARSHIPS SUPPORTING POST-SECONDARY EDUCATION FOR A CAREER IN THE AUDIOVISUAL INDUSTRY

InfoComm International
International Communications Industries Foundation
11242 Waples Mill Road, Suite 200
Fairfax, VA 22030
(703) 273-7200   Toll Free: (800) 659-7469
Fax: (703) 278-8082   E-mail: jhardwick@infocomm.org
Web: www.infocomm.org

Summary To provide financial assistance to undergraduate and graduate students (particularly Hispanic Americans, other minorities, and women) who are interested in preparing for a career in the audiovisual (AV) industry.

Eligibility This program is open to second-year students at 2-year colleges, juniors and seniors at 4-year institutions, and graduate students. Applicants must have a GPA of 2.75 or higher and be majoring or planning to major in audiovisual subjects or related fields, including audio, video, audiovisual, radio/television/film, or other field related to a career in the audiovisual industry. Students in other programs, such as journalism, may be eligible if they can demonstrate a relationship to career goals in the AV industry. Along with their application, they must submit 1) an essay of 150 to 200 words on the career path they plan to pursue in the audiovisual industry in the next 5 years; and 2) an essay of 250 to 300 words on the experience or person influencing them the most in selecting the audiovisual industry as their career of choice. Minority and women candidates are especially encouraged to apply. Selection is based on the essays, presentation of the application, GPA, AV-related experience, work experience, and letters of recommendation.

Financial Data The stipend is $4,000. Funds are sent directly to the school.

Duration 1 year.

Additional data InfoComm International, formerly the International Communications Industries Association, established the International Communications Industries Foundation (ICIF) to manage its charitable and educational activities.

Number awarded Varies each year.

Deadline April of each year.

[434]
SCIENCE LEADERSHIP SCHOLARSHIPS

Washington Science Teachers Association
c/o Sonia Siegel Vexler
Pacific Science Center
200 Second Avenue North
Seattle, WA 98109
(206) 443-2001   Fax: (206) 443-3631
TDD: (206) 443-2887   E-mail: ssiegelvexler@pacsci.org
Web: www.wsta.net/awards

Summary To provide financial assistance to upper-division students and teachers in Washington (particularly Hispanic Americans, other underrepresented minorities, and women) who are interested in training in science education.

Eligibility This program is open to juniors and seniors at colleges and universities in Washington who are working on certification in science education or in elementary education with an emphasis on science. Preference is given to African Americans, Hispanics, Native Americans, and women. Applicants must submit a 1-page essay on why they are applying for this scholarship.

Financial Data The stipend is $2,000.

Duration 1 year; nonrenewable.

Additional data This program began in 2003 as the Peggy Vatter Memorial Scholarships.

Number awarded 1 or more each year.

Deadline June of each year.

[435]
SEATTLE CHAPTER AWIS SCHOLARSHIPS

Association for Women in Science-Seattle Chapter
c/o Fran Solomon, Scholarship Committee Chair
5805 16th Avenue, N.E.
Seattle, WA 98105
(206) 522-6441   E-mail: scholarship@seattleawis.org
Web: seattleawis.org/award/scholarships

Summary To provide financial assistance to Hispanic American and other women undergraduates from any state majoring in science, mathematics, or engineering at colleges and universities in Washington.

Eligibility This program is open to women from any state entering their junior or senior year at a 4-year college or university in Washington. Applicants must have a declared major in science (e.g., biological sciences, environmental science, biochemistry, chemistry, pharmacy, geology, computer science, physics), mathematics, or engineering. Along with their application, they must submit essays on the events that led to their choice of a major, their current career plans and long-term goals, and their volunteer and community activities. Selection is based on academic excellence, motivation to prepare for a science-based career, record of giving back to their communities, and financial need. At least 1 scholarship is reserved for a woman from a group that is underrepresented in science, mathematics, and engineering careers, including Native American Indians and Alaska Natives, Black/African Americans, Mexican Americans/Chicanas/Latinas, Native Pacific Islanders (Polynesians, Melanesians, and Micronesians), adult learners (returning students), and women with disabilities.

Financial Data Stipends range from $1,000 to $1,500.

Duration 1 year.

Additional data This program includes the following named awards: the Virginia Badger Scholarship, the Angela Paez Memorial Scholarship, and the Fran Solomon Scholarship. Support for the program is provided by several sponsors, including the American Chemical Society, Iota Sigma Pi, Rosetta Inpharmatics, and ZymoGenetics, Inc.

Number awarded 4 to 6 each year.

Deadline April of each year.

[436]
SHARON D. BANKS MEMORIAL UNDERGRADUATE SCHOLARSHIP

Women's Transportation Seminar
Attn: WTS Foundation
1701 K Street, N.W., Suite 800
Washington, DC 20006
(202) 955-5085   Fax: (202) 955-5088
E-mail: wts@wtsinternational.org
Web: www.wtsinternational.org/education/scholarships

Summary To provide financial assistance to undergraduate women (particularly Hispanic Americans and other minorities) who are interested in a career in transportation.

Eligibility This program is open to women who are working on an undergraduate degree in transportation or a transportation-related field (e.g., transportation engineering, planning, finance, or logistics). Applicants must have a GPA of 3.0 or higher and be interested in a career in transportation. Along with their application, they must submit a 500-word statement about their career goals after graduation and why they think they should receive the scholarship award. Applications must be submitted first to a local chapter; the chapters forward selected applications for consideration on the national level. Minority women are especially encouraged to apply. Selection is based on transportation involvement and goals, job skills, and academic record; financial need is not considered.

Financial Data The stipend is $5,000.

Duration 1 year.

Additional data This program began in 1992. Local chapters may also award additional funding to winners in their area.

Number awarded 1 each year.

Deadline Applications must be submitted by November to a local WTS chapter.

[437]
SHAW INDUSTRIES ACHIEVEMENT SCHOLARSHIP

Society of Hispanic Professional Engineers Foundation, Inc.
Attn: Advancing Hispanic Excellence in Technology, Engineering, Math and Science
13181 Crossroads Parkway North, Suite 450
P.O. Box 93577
City of Industry, CA 91715
(323) 725-3970, ext. 118   Fax: (323) 622-1046
E-mail: shpefoundation@shpe.org
Web: www.shpefoundation.org

Summary To provide financial assistance to undergraduate members of the Society of Hispanic Professional Engineers (SHPE) who are working on a degree in designated fields of engineering and are members of underrepresented groups at universities in selected southern states.

Eligibility This program is open to full-time students who are sophomores or juniors working on a 4-year degree in the following fields of engineering: chemical, electrical, industrial, material science (especially polymer and fiber materials concentration), mechanical, systems, or textile. Applicants must be SHPE members enrolled at a university in Alabama, Georgia, Kentucky, Mississippi, North Carolina, South Carolina, Tennessee, or Virginia. They must have a GPA of 3.0 or higher and be a female and/or minority student currently underrepresented at their university. If at any time female and/or minority students are no longer underrepresented at their university, or if in a given year no qualified female and/or minority students apply for the scholarship, it will be open to any student who meets all other criteria. Along with their application, they must submit a 500-word personal statement covering their community involvement, leadership, academic achievements, research internship and co-op experiences, and short-term and long-term goals and aspirations. Selection is based on that statement, academic merit and potential, leadership and communication skills, and financial need. U.S. citizenship or permanent resident status is required.

Financial Data A stipend is awarded (amount not specified).

Duration 1 year.

Additional data Advancing Hispanic Excellence in Technology, Engineering, Math and Science (AHETEMS) was established in 2004 by SHPE as an independent nonprofit foundation. This program is sponsored by Shaw Industries.

Number awarded 1 or more each year.

Deadline April of each year.

[438]
SHELL INCENTIVE FUND SCHOLARSHIPS

Shell Oil Company
Attn: Scholarship Administrator
910 Louisiana, Suite 4476C
Houston, TX 77002
(713) 241-6314   E-mail: terry.garland@shell.com
Web: www.shell.us

Summary To provide financial assistance to Hispanic American and other underrepresented minority students majoring in specified engineering and geosciences fields at designated universities.

Eligibility This program is open to students enrolled full time as sophomores, juniors, or seniors at 22 participating universities. Applicants must be U.S. citizens or authorized to work in the United States and members of a race or ethnicity underrepresented in the technical and scientific academic areas (Black, Hispanic/Latino, American Indian, or Alaskan Native). They must have a GPA of 3.2 or higher with a major in engineering (chemical, civil, electrical, geological, geophysical, mechanical, or petroleum) or geosciences (geology, geophysics, or physics). Along with their application, they must submit a 100-word essay on the kind of work they plan to be doing in 10 years, both in their career and in their community. Financial need is not considered in the selection process.

Financial Data The stipend is $5,000 per year.

Duration 1 year; may be renewed up to 3 additional years, provided the recipient remains qualified and accepts a Shell Oil Company internship (if offered).

Additional data This program is administered by Educational Testing Service, Scholarship and Recognition Programs, P.O. Box 6730, Princeton, NJ 08541, (609) 771-7878. The participating institutions are Colorado School of Mines, Cornell University, Florida A&M University, Georgia Institute of Technology, Louisiana State University, Massachusetts Institute of Technology, Michigan State University, North Carolina A&T State University, Ohio State University, Pennsylvania State University, Prairie View A&M University, Purdue University, Rice University, Stanford University, Texas A&M University, University of Colorado at Boulder, University of Houston, University of Illinois at Urbana-Champaign, University of Michigan, University of Oklahoma, University of Texas at Austin, and University of Texas at El Paso.

Number awarded Approximately 20 each year.

Deadline May of each year.

[439]
SHPE ACCENTURE SCHOLARSHIP

Society of Hispanic Professional Engineers Foundation, Inc.
Attn: Advancing Hispanic Excellence in Technology, Engineering, Math and Science
13181 Crossroads Parkway North, Suite 450
P.O. Box 93577
City of Industry, CA 91715
(323) 725-3970, ext. 118   Fax: (323) 622-1046
E-mail: shpefoundation@shpe.org
Web: www.shpefoundation.org

Summary To provide financial assistance to undergraduate members of the Society of Hispanic Professional Engineers (SHPE) who are working on a degree in engineering or related fields.

Eligibility This program is open to full-time students who are sophomores, juniors, or seniors working on a degree in engineering (any field), computer science, management information systems, or decision science. Applicants must be SHPE members enrolled at a 2- or 4-year college or university in the United States or Puerto Rico. They must have a GPA of 3.0 or higher. Along with their application, they must submit a 500-word personal statement covering their community involvement, leadership, academic achievements, research internship and co-op experiences, and short-term

and long-term goals and aspirations. Selection is based on merit. U.S. citizenship is required.

Financial Data The stipend is $2,000.

Duration 1 year.

Additional data Advancing Hispanic Excellence in Technology, Engineering, Math and Science (AHETEMS) was established in 2004 by SHPE as an independent nonprofit foundation. This program is sponsored by Accenture.

Number awarded 5 each year.

Deadline April of each year.

[440]
SMITHSONIAN MINORITY AWARDS PROGRAM

Smithsonian Institution
Attn: Office of Fellowships and Internships
470 L'Enfant Plaza, Suite 7102
P.O. Box 37012, MRC 902
Washington, DC 20013-7012
(202) 633-7070   Fax: (202) 633-7069
E-mail: siofi@si.edu
Web: www.smithsonianofi.com

Summary To provide funding to Hispanic American and other minority undergraduate and graduate students who are interested in conducting research at the Smithsonian Institution.

Eligibility This program is open to members of U.S. minority groups underrepresented in the Smithsonian's scholarly programs. Applicants must be undergraduates or beginning graduate students interested in conducting research in the Institution's disciplines and in the museum field. They must be U.S. citizens or permanent residents and have a GPA of 3.0 or higher.

Financial Data Students receive a grant of $600 per week.

Duration Up to 10 weeks.

Additional data Recipients must carry out independent research projects in association with the Smithsonian's research staff. Eligible fields of study currently include animal behavior, ecology, and environmental science (including an emphasis on the tropics); anthropology (including archaeology); astrophysics and astronomy; earth sciences and paleobiology; evolutionary and systematic biology; history of science and technology; history of art (especially American, contemporary, African, Asian, and 20th-century art); American crafts and decorative arts; social and cultural history of the United States; and folk life. Students are required to be in residence at the Smithsonian for the duration of the fellowship.

Number awarded Varies each year; recently, 25 of these awards were granted: 2 for fall, 19 for summer, and 4 for spring.

Deadline January of each year for summer and fall residency; September of each year for spring residency.

[441]
SOUTH CAROLINA CHAPTER JOSIE K. CLAIBORNE MEMORIAL SCHOLARSHIPS

American Association of Blacks in Energy-South Carolina Chapter
Attn: Scholarship Committee
P.O. Box 7696
Columbia, SC 29202
(803) 933-7252　　E-mail: mpriester-clarke@scana.com
Web: www.aabe.org/index.php?component=pages&id=920

Summary To provide financial assistance to Hispanic Americans and members of other underrepresented minority groups who are high school seniors in South Carolina and planning to major in an energy-related field at a college in any state.

Eligibility This program is open to seniors graduating from high schools in South Carolina and planning to work on a bachelor's degree at a college or university in any state. Applicants must be African Americans, Hispanics, or Native Americans who have a GPA of 3.0 or higher and are able to demonstrate financial need. Their intended major must be a field of business, engineering, physical science (e.g., astronomy, chemistry, geology, mineralogy, meteorology, physics), mathematics, or technology related to energy. Along with their application, they must submit a 350-word statement on why they should receive this scholarship, their professional career objectives, and any other relevant information.

Financial Data The stipend is $1,000.

Duration 1 year; nonrenewable.

Additional data Winners are eligible to compete for regional and national scholarships.

Number awarded Up to 2 each year.

Deadline February of each year.

[442]
SOUTHERN CALIFORNIA EDISON/HENAAC SCHOLARS PROGRAM

Great Minds in STEM
Attn: HENAAC Scholars Program
602 Monterey Pass Road
Monterey Park, CA 91754
(323) 262-0997　　　　　　Fax: (323) 262-0946
E-mail: gcruz@greatmindsinstem.org
Web: www.greatmindsinstem.org

Summary To provide financial assistance to Hispanic undergraduate students from any state who are enrolled at universities in southern California and majoring in civil or electrical engineering.

Eligibility This program is open to Hispanic undergraduate students from any state who are working on a degree in civil or electrical engineering at colleges and universities in southern California. Applicants must be of Hispanic origin and/or must significantly participate in and promote organizations and activities in the Hispanic community. They must have a GPA of 3.0 or higher. Along with their application, they must submit a 700-word essay on a topic that changes annually. Selection is based on leadership, academic achievements, and campus and community activities; financial need is not considered. U.S. citizenship is required.

Financial Data Stipends range from $500 to $10,000.

Duration 1 year; recipients may reapply.

Additional data The Hispanic Engineer National Achievement Awards Conference (HENAAC) was established in 1989 and initiated a scholarship program in 2000. In 2010, the sponsoring organization officially adopted its current name, but it continues to hold the annual HENAAC conference, at which the scholarships are presented. This program is sponsored by Southern California Edison. Recipients must attend the conference to accept their scholarship.

Number awarded Varies each year; recently, 5 of these scholarships were awarded.

Deadline April of each year.

[443]
SPANISH BAPTIST CONVENTION OF NEW MEXICO SCHOLARSHIP

Baptist Convention of New Mexico
Attn: Missions Mobilization Team
5325 Wyoming Boulevard, N.E.
P.O. Box 94485
Albuquerque, NM 87199-4485
(505) 924-2315　　　　　　Toll Free: (800) 898-8544
Fax: (505) 924-2320　　　　E-mail: cpairett@bcnm.com
Web: www.bcnm.com

Summary To provide financial assistance to Hispanic Baptist students from New Mexico interested in attending college or seminary in any state.

Eligibility This program is open to college and seminary students who are active members of churches affiliated with the Baptist Convention of New Mexico. Applicants must be of Hispanic background and committed to full-time Christian service. They must be attending college or seminary in any state.

Financial Data A stipend is awarded (amount not specified).

Duration 1 year; may be renewed.

Number awarded 1 or more each year.

Deadline April of each year.

[444]
SPHINX COMPETITION AWARDS

Sphinx Organization
Attn: Screening Committee
400 Renaissance Center, Suite 2550
Detroit, MI 48243
(313) 877-9100　　　　　　Fax: (313) 877-0164
E-mail: Competition@sphinxmusic.org
Web: www.sphinxmusic.org

Summary To recognize and reward outstanding junior high, high school, and college-age Latino and Black string instrumentalists.

Eligibility This competition is open to Black and Latino instrumentalists in 2 divisions: junior, for participants who are younger than 18 years of age, and senior, for participants who are between 18 and 27 years of age. All entrants must be current U.S. residents who can compete in the instrumental categories of violin, viola, cello, and double bass. Along with their applications, they must submit a preliminary audition tape that includes all of the required preliminary repertoire for their instrument category. Based on those tapes, qualifiers are invited to participate in the semifinals and finals competitions, held at sites in Detroit and Ann Arbor, Michigan.

Financial Data   In the senior division, the first-place winner receives a $10,000 cash prize, solo appearances with major orchestras, and a performance with the Sphinx Symphony; the second-place winner receives a $5,000 cash prize and a performance with the Sphinx Symphony; the third-place winner receives a $3,500 cash prize and a performance with the Sphinx Symphony. In the junior division, the first-place winner receives a $5,000 cash prize, solo appearances with major orchestras, a national radio debut, and 2 performances with the Sphinx Symphony; the second-place winner receives a $3,500 cash prize and a performance with the Sphinx Symphony; the third-place winner receives a $2,000 cash prize and a performance with the Sphinx Symphony. All semifinalists receive scholarships to attend designated summer programs. They also receive full tuition scholarships for their instrumental studies at selected colleges and universities from the Sphinx Music Assistance Fund (MAF) of the League of American Orchestras.

Duration   The competition is held annually.

Additional data   The sponsoring organization was incorporated in 1996 to hold this competition, first conducted in 1998. The Sphinx Symphony is an all African American and Latino orchestra that performs at Orchestra Hall in Detroit. The MAF program was established by the New York Philharmonic in 1965, transferred to the American Symphony Orchestra League in 1994, and to the League of American Orchestras in 2001. In 2002, it partnered with the Sphinx Organization to provide scholarships to all 18 semifinalists. Applications must be accompanied by a $35 fee. That fee may be waived from both divisions and all instrumental categories if demonstrable need is shown.

Number awarded   18 semifinalists (9 from each age division) are selected each year. Of those, 3 junior and 3 senior competitors win cash prizes.

Deadline   November of each year.

[445]
SPIE SCHOLARSHIP PROGRAM

SPIE-The International Society for Optical Engineering
Attn: Scholarship Committee
1000 20th Street
P.O. Box 10
Bellingham, WA 98227-0010
(360) 676-3290   Toll Free: (888) 504-8171
Fax: (360) 647-1445   E-mail: scholarships@spie.org
Web: spie.org/x7236.xml

Summary   To provide financial assistance to entering or continuing undergraduate and graduate student members of SPIE-The International Society for Optical Engineering (particularly Hispanic Americans, other minorities, women, and veterans) who are preparing for a career in optical science or engineering.

Eligibility   This program is open to high school seniors planning to attend college, current undergraduate students, and current graduate students. Applicants must be society members majoring or planning to enroll full or part time and major in optics, optoelectronics, photonics, imaging, or a related discipline (e.g., physics, electrical engineering) at a college or university anywhere in the world. Along with their application, they must submit a 500-word essay on their academic work, career objectives, how this scholarship would help them attain their goals, and what they have achieved and

learned through their studies and activities. Financial need is not considered in the selection process. Women, minorities, and veterans are encouraged to apply.

Financial Data   Stipends range from $2,000 to $11,000. Special awards include the D.J. Lovell Scholarship at $11,000; the John Kiel Scholarship at $10,000; the Laser Technology, Engineering, and Applications Scholarship at $5,000; the Optical Design and Engineering Scholarship at $5,000, and the BACUS Scholarship at $5,000.

Duration   1 year.

Additional data   The International Society for Optical Engineering was founded in 1955 as the Society of Photo-Optical Instrumentation Engineers (SPIE). This program includes the following special named scholarships: the D.J. Lovell Scholarship, sponsored by SPIE (the most prestigious of the scholarships); the John Kiel Scholarship, awarded for a student's potential for long-term contribution to the field of optics and optical engineering; the Optical Design and Engineering Scholarship in Optical Engineering, established to honor Bill Price and Warren Smith and awarded to a full-time graduate or undergraduate student in the field of optical design and engineering; the Laser Technology, Engineering, and Applications Scholarship (formerly the F-MADE Scholarship), sponsored by the Forum for Military Applications of Directed Energy (F-MADE) in recognition of a student's scholarly achievement in laser technology, engineering, or applications; and the BACUS Scholarship, awarded to a full-time undergraduate or graduate student in the field of microlithography with an emphasis on optical tooling and/or semiconductor manufacturing technologies, sponsored by BACUS (SPIE's photomask international technical group).

Number awarded   Varies each year; recently, this program awarded 140 scholarships with a value of $353,000. Since the program was established, it has awarded more than $3.8 million to nearly 2,000 students in 86 countries.

Deadline   February of each year.

[446]
STAN BECK FELLOWSHIP

Entomological Society of America
Attn: Entomological Foundation
9332 Annapolis Road, Suite 210
Lanham, MD 20706-3150
(301) 459-9082   Fax: (301) 459-9084
E-mail: melodie@entfdn.org
Web: www.entfdn.org/awards_education.php

Summary   To assist "needy" students working on an undergraduate or graduate degree in entomology who are nominated by members of the Entomological Society of America (ESA).

Eligibility   This program is open to students working on an undergraduate or graduate degree in entomology at a college or university in Canada, Mexico, or the United States. Candidates must be nominated by members of the society. They must be "needy" students; for the purposes of this program, need may be based on physical limitations, or economic, minority, or environmental conditions.

Financial Data   The stipend is $2,000 per year.

Duration   1 year; may be renewed up to 3 additional years.

Additional data   This fellowship was first awarded in 1996. Recipients are expected to be present at the society's annual meeting, where the award will be presented.

Number awarded 1 each year.
Deadline June of each year.

[447]
STANFORD SUMMER RESEARCH PROGRAM/ AMGEN SCHOLARS PROGRAM

Stanford University
School of Medicine
Attn: Office of Graduate Education
M.S.O.B. Second Floor
251 Campus Drive
Stanford, CA 94305-5421
(650) 725-8791   E-mail: ssrpmail@stanford.edu
Web: ssrp.stanford.edu

Summary To provide Hispanic American and other underrepresented minority undergraduate students with a summer research experience at Stanford University in biological and biomedical sciences.

Eligibility This program is open to sophomores, juniors, and non-graduating seniors at 4-year colleges and universities in the United States, Puerto Rico, and U.S. territories. Students from all ethnic backgrounds are eligible, but the program especially encourages applications from African Americans, Latino/Hispanic Americans, Native Americans, Pacific Islanders, and other undergraduates who, by reason of their culture, class, race, ethnicity, background, work and life experiences, skills, and interests would bring diversity to graduate study in the biological and biomedical sciences (biochemistry, bioengineering, biology, biomedical informatics, biophysics, cancer biology, chemical and systems biology, developmental biology, genetics, immunology, microbiology, molecular and cellular physiology, neurosciences, stem cell and regenerative medicine, and structural biology). Applicants must have at least 1 year of undergraduate education remaining before graduation and should be planning to prepare for and enter a Ph.D. program in the biological or biomedical sciences. They must have a GPA of 3.2 or higher. U.S. citizenship or permanent resident status is required.

Financial Data The program provides a stipend of $3,500, housing, meals, and transportation to and from the San Francisco Bay area.

Duration 9 weeks during the summer.

Additional data This program currently serves as the Stanford component of the Amgen Scholars Program, which operates at 9 other U.S. universities and is funded by the Amgen Foundation.

Number awarded Up to 25 each year.

Deadline January of each year.

[448]
STATE REPRESENTATIVE IRMA RANGEL MEMORIAL SCHOLARSHIPS

Hispanic Scholarship Consortium
Attn: Scholarship Selection Committee
1107 South Eighth Street
Austin, TX 78704
(512) 368-2956   Fax: (512) 692-1831
E-mail: scholarships@hispanicscholar.org
Web: www.hispanicscholar.org

Summary To provide financial assistance to Hispanic residents of Texas who are pre-law students at designated universities in the state or law students in any state.

Eligibility This program is open to residents of Texas who are of Hispanic heritage and are either 1) rising juniors or seniors at Concordia University, St. Edward's University, Southwestern University, Texas State University, or the University of Texas at Austin; or 2) students enrolled at a law school in any state. Rising seniors must be planning to take the LSAT examination in the current academic year and rising juniors must be planning to take that examination in the following academic year. Applicants must submit a 500-word essay on why they would like to become an attorney. They must have a GPA of 3.0 or higher. Selection is based on academic record, community service, financial need, and a personal interview. U.S. citizenship or permanent resident status is required.

Financial Data The stipend is $2,000.

Duration 1 year.

Additional data This program is sponsored by the Hispanic Bar Association of Austin College Fund.

Number awarded 1 or more each year.

Deadline August of each year.

[449]
STATEWIDE HISPANIC CHAMBER OF COMMERCE OF NEW JERSEY SCHOLARSHIPS

Statewide Hispanic Chamber of Commerce of New Jersey
Attn: Scholarship Selection Committee
One Gateway Center, Suite 2409
Newark, NJ 07102
(973) 900-5886   Fax: (866) 226-1828
E-mail: chamber@shccnj.org
Web: www.shccnj.org/scholarship

Summary To provide financial assistance to Hispanic residents of New Jersey who intend to major in a business-related field at a college or university in the state.

Eligibility This program is open to residents of New Jersey who are Hispanic (at least 1 parent must be fully Hispanic) and U.S. citizens or permanent residents. Applicants must be full-time college freshmen or high school seniors with a GPA of 3.0 or higher. They must be intending to major in business or a business technology-related program at a 2- or 4-year college in New Jersey. Along with their application, they must submit short answers to questions about their community and the environment in which they have lived during the past 4 years, their high school experience and an important aspect of their high school career, their involvement in extracurricular activities in school and/or their community, their family and how it has shaped their development, and their willingness to participate in internship and mentoring activities that may be available through the scholarship program. They must also submit an essay of 750 to 1,000 words on their choice of 3 topics that relate to Hispanics and business. Financial need is considered in the selection process.

Financial Data The stipend is $2,000 per year.

Duration 4 years.

Additional data This program began in 2003.

Number awarded 45 each year.

Deadline June of each year.

[450]
STEM AWARD

TELACU Education Foundation
Attn: College Success Program
5400 East Olympic Boulevard, Suite 300
Los Angeles, CA 90022
(323) 721-1655   Fax: (323) 721-3560
E-mail: collegesuccess@telacu.com
Web: www.telacu.com

Summary To provide financial assistance to Latino students from eligible communities in California, Texas, Illinois, and New York who are interested in studying fields of science, technology, engineering, or mathematics (STEM) at colleges and universities in any state.

Eligibility This program is open to Latino residents of selected communities in southern California, selected cities in Texas, the Greater Chicagoland area of Illinois, or the state of New York. Applicants must 1) be a first-generation college student; 2) be from a low-income family; and 3) have a GPA of 2.5 or higher. They must be enrolled or planning to enroll full time at a college or university in any state and major in a field of STEM. Selection is based on leadership potential, professional and extracurricular achievement, commitment to the development and economic empowerment of communities, and financial need. Priority is given to students attending institutions that provide matching funds (for a list, contact the sponsor).

Financial Data Stipends range from $500 to $5,000 per year.

Duration 1 year; may be renewed up to 3 additional years, provided the recipient remains enrolled full time, maintains a GPA of 2.75 or higher, and volunteers for at least 20 hours of community service.

Additional data The eligible areas in California include underserved communities in Los Angeles, Orange, and San Bernardino counties such as unincorporated areas of east Los Angeles and the cities of Baldwin Park, Bell Gardens, Commerce, Huntington Park, Los Angeles, Montebello, Ontario, Pico Rivera, Pomona, San Bernardino, Santa Ana, and South Gate. The cities in Texas are Austin, Edinburg, Laredo, Rio Grande City, San Antonio.

Number awarded 1 or more each year.

Deadline March of each year.

[451]
STOP & SHOP AND COCA-COLA LIVE POSITIVELY SCHOLARSHIP PROGRAM

Hispanic Scholarship Fund
Attn: Selection Committee
1411 West 190th Street, Suite 325
Gardena, CA 90248
Toll Free: (877) HSF-INFO   E-mail: scholar1@hsf.net
Web: www.hsf.net

Summary To provide financial assistance to Hispanic high school seniors in designated northeastern states who plan to attend college in the United States or designated territories.

Eligibility This program is open to Hispanic seniors who are graduating from high schools in Connecticut, Massachusetts, New Jersey, New York, or Rhode Island and have a GPA of 3.0 or higher. Applicants must be U.S. citizens or permanent residents (must have a permanent resident card or a passport stamped I-551). They must be planning to enroll full

time at an accredited 2- or 4-year college or university in the United States, Puerto Rico, the U.S. Virgin Islands, or Guam. Their proposed major may be in any field. Selection is based on academic achievement, personal strengths, leadership, and financial need.

Financial Data The stipend is $5,000.

Duration 1 year.

Additional data This program is jointly sponsored by Stop & Shop Supermarket Company, Coca-Cola, and the Hispanic Scholarship Fund (HSF).

Number awarded 4 each year.

Deadline December of each year.

[452]
STUDENT OPPORTUNITY SCHOLARSHIPS OF THE PRESBYTERIAN CHURCH (USA)

Presbyterian Church (USA)
Attn: Office of Financial Aid for Studies
100 Witherspoon Street, Room M-052
Louisville, KY 40202-1396
(502) 569-5224   Toll Free: (800) 728-7228, ext. 5224
Fax: (502) 569-8766   TDD: (800) 833-5955
E-mail: finaid@pcusa.org
Web: gamc.pcusa.org

Summary To provide financial assistance to Presbyterian college students, especially Hispanic Americans and other racial/ethnic minorities.

Eligibility This program is open to active members of the Presbyterian Church (USA) who are entering their sophomore, junior, or senior year of college as full-time students. Preference is given to applicants who are members of racial/ethnic minority groups (Asian American, African American, Hispanic American, Native American, Alaska Native). Applicants must have a GPA of 2.5 or higher and be able to demonstrate financial need.

Financial Data Stipends range up to $2,000 per year, depending upon the financial need of the recipient.

Duration 1 year; may be renewed for up to 3 additional years if the recipient continues to need financial assistance and demonstrates satisfactory academic progress.

Number awarded Varies each year.

Deadline May of each year.

[453]
SUMMER HONORS UNDERGRADUATE RESEARCH PROGRAM

Harvard Medical School
Attn: Division of Medical Sciences
Diversity Programs Office
260 Longwood Avenue, Room 432
Boston, MA 02115-5720
(617) 432-1342   Toll Free: (800) 367-9019
Fax: (617) 432-2644   E-mail: SHURP@hms.harvard.edu
Web: www.hms.harvard.edu/dms/diversity/shurp

Summary To provide an opportunity for underrepresented minority students to engage in research at Harvard Medical School during the summer.

Eligibility This program at Harvard Medical School is open to undergraduate students belonging to minority groups that are underrepresented in the sciences. Applicants must have had at least 1 summer (or equivalent) of experience in a research laboratory and have taken at least 1 upper-level biology course that includes molecular biology. They should be considering a career in biological or biomedical research. U.S. citizenship or permanent resident status is required.

Financial Data The program provides a stipend of $420 per week, dormitory housing, travel costs, a meal card, and health insurance if it is needed.

Duration 10 weeks during the summer.

Number awarded Varies each year.

Deadline January of each year.

[454]
SUMMER RESEARCH OPPORTUNITIES PROGRAM (SROP)

Committee on Institutional Cooperation
Attn: Academic and International Programs
1819 South Neil Street, Suite D
Champaign, IL 61820-7271
(217) 333-8475 Fax: (217) 244-7127
E-mail: cic@staff.cic.net
Web: www.cic.net/Home/Students/SROP/Home.aspx

Summary To provide an opportunity for Hispanic Americans and other undergraduates from diverse backgrounds to gain research experience at member institutions of the Committee on Institutional Cooperation (CIC) during the summer.

Eligibility This program is open to students currently enrolled in a degree-granting program at a college or university who have a GPA of 3.0 or higher and an interest in continuing on to graduate school. Applicants must be interested in conducting a summer research project under the supervision of a faculty mentor at a CIC member institution. The program is designed to increase educational access for students from diverse backgrounds; members of racial and ethnic minority groups and low-income first-generation students are especially encouraged to apply. U.S. citizenship or permanent resident status is required.

Financial Data Participants are paid a stipend that depends on the participating CIC member institution, but ranges from $3,000 to $6,000. Faculty mentors receive a $500 research allowance for the cost of materials.

Duration 8 to 10 weeks during the summer.

Additional data Participants work directly with faculty mentors at the institution of their choice and also engage in other enrichment activities, such as workshops and social gatherings. In July, all participants come together at 1 of the CIC campuses for the annual SROP conference. The participating CIC member institutions are University of Illinois at Urbana-Champaign, University of Iowa, University of Michigan, University of Minnesota, University of Nebraska at Lincoln, University of Wisconsin at Madison, Michigan State University, Northwestern University, Ohio State University, Pennsylvania State University, and Purdue University. Students are required to write a paper and an abstract describing their projects and to present the results of their work at a campus symposium.

Number awarded Varies each year.

Deadline February of each year.

[455]
SUMMER UNDERGRADUATE RESEARCH FELLOWSHIPS IN ORGANIC CHEMISTRY

American Chemical Society
Division of Organic Chemistry
1155 16th Street, N.W.
Washington, DC 20036
(202) 872-4401 Toll Free: (800) 227-5558, ext. 4401
E-mail: division@acs.org
Web: www.organicdivision.org/?nd=p_surf_program

Summary To provide an opportunity for college juniors (particularly Hispanic Americans and other minorities) to work on a research project in organic chemistry during the summer.

Eligibility This program is open to students who are currently enrolled as juniors at a college or university in the United States and are nominated by their school. Nominees must be interested in conducting a research project in organic chemistry at the home institution during the following summer. The project must be mentored by a member of the Organic Division of the American Chemical Society. Along with their application, students must submit brief statements on the project they propose to undertake, their background that has prepared them to do this work, their proposed methodology, and how a summer research project fits into their long-range plans. U.S. citizenship or permanent resident status is required. Selection is based on demonstrated interest and talent in organic chemistry, merit and feasibility of the research project, commitment of a faculty mentor to support the student, academic record (particularly in organic chemistry and related sciences), and importance of the award in facilitating the personal and career plans of the student. Applications from minorities are especially encouraged.

Financial Data Grants range up to $5,000. The program also covers the costs of a trip by all participants to an industrial campus in the fall for a dinner, award session, scientific talks, a tour of the campus, and a poster session where the results of the summer research investigations are presented.

Duration Summer months.

Additional data Current corporate sponsors of this program include Pfizer, Merck, and Genentech.

Number awarded 12 each year.

Deadline February of each year.

[456]
SURETY AND FIDELITY INDUSTRY SCHOLARSHIP PROGRAM

The Surety Foundation
Attn: Scholarship Program for Minority Students
1101 Connecticut Avenue, N.W., Suite 800
Washington, DC 20036
(202) 463-0600 Fax: (202) 463-0606
E-mail: scarradine@surety.org
Web: www.thesuretyfoundation.org

Summary To provide financial assistance to Hispanic American and other minority undergraduates working on a degree in a field related to insurance.

Eligibility This program is open to full-time undergraduates who are U.S. citizens and members of a minority group (Black, Native American/Alaskan Native, Asian/Pacific Islander, Hispanic). Applicants must have completed at least

30 semester hours of study at an accredited 4-year college or university and have a declared major in insurance/risk management, accounting, business, or finance. They must have a GPA of 3.0 or higher and be able to demonstrate financial need. Along with their application, they must submit an essay of 500 to 1,000 words on the role of surety bonding and the surety industry in public sector construction.

Financial Data   The stipend is $2,500 per year.

Duration   1 year; recipients may reapply.

Additional data   This program, established in 2003 by The Surety & Fidelity Association of America, includes the Adrienne Alexander Scholarship and the George W. McClellan Scholarship.

Number awarded   Varies each year.

Deadline   April of each year.

[457]
SYNOD OF LAKES AND PRAIRIES RACIAL ETHNIC SCHOLARSHIPS

Synod of Lakes and Prairies
Attn: Committee on Racial Ethnic Ministry
2115 Cliff Drive
Eagen, MN 55122-3327
(651) 357-1140   Toll Free: (800) 328-1880, ext. 202
Fax: (651) 357-1141   E-mail: mkes@lakesandprairies.org
Web: www.lakesandprairies.org

Summary   To provide financial assistance to Hispanic American and other minority residents of the Presbyterian Church (USA) Synod of Lakes and Prairies who are working on an undergraduate or graduate degree at a college or seminary in any state in preparation for service to the church.

Eligibility   This program is open to members of Presbyterian churches who reside within the Synod of Lakes and Prairies (Iowa, Minnesota, Nebraska, North Dakota, South Dakota, and Wisconsin). Applicants must be members of ethnic minority groups studying at least half time for service in the Presbyterian Church (USA) as a teaching elder, ordained minister, commissioned ruling elder, lay professional, or volunteer. They must be in good academic standing, making progress toward an undergraduate or graduate degree, and able to demonstrate financial need. Along with their application, they must submit essays of 200 to 500 words on 1) what the church needs to do to be faithful to its mission in the world today; and 2) the people, practices, or events that influence their commitment to Christ in ways that renew their fair and strengthen their service.

Financial Data   Stipends range from $850 to $3,500.

Duration   1 year.

Number awarded   Varies each year; recently, 9 of these scholarships were awarded.

Deadline   September of each year.

[458]
SYNOD OF THE TRINITY RACIAL ETHNIC EDUCATIONAL SCHOLARSHIPS

Synod of the Trinity
Attn: Scholarships
3040 Market Street
Camp Hill, PA 17011-4599
(717) 737-0421, ext. 233
Toll Free: (800) 242-0534, ext. 233
Fax: (717) 737-8211   E-mail: mhumer@syntrinity.org
Web: www.syntrinity.org

Summary   To provide financial assistance to Hispanic American and other ethnic minority students in Pennsylvania, West Virginia, and designated counties in Ohio who are interested in attending college in any state.

Eligibility   This program is open to members of a racial minority group (African American, Asian, Hispanic, Latino, Middle Eastern, or Native American) who are enrolled or planning to enroll full time at an accredited college or vocational school in any state. Applicants may be of any religious denomination, but they must be residents of the area covered by the Presbyterian Church (USA) Synod of the Trinity, which covers all of Pennsylvania; West Virginia except for the counties of Berkeley, Grant, Hampshire, Hardy, Jefferson, Mineral, Morgan, and Pendleton; and the Ohio counties of Belmont, Columbiana, Harrison, Jefferson, and Monroe. They must have total income of less than $85,000 for a family of 4. U.S. citizenship or permanent resident status is required.

Financial Data   Awards range from $100 to $1,000 per year, depending on the need of the recipient.

Duration   1 year; recipients may reapply.

Number awarded   Varies each year.

Deadline   April of each year.

[459]
TELACU SCHOLARSHIPS

TELACU Education Foundation
Attn: College Success Program
5400 East Olympic Boulevard, Suite 300
Los Angeles, CA 90022
(323) 721-1655   Fax: (323) 721-3560
E-mail: collegesuccess@telacu.com
Web: www.telacu.com

Summary   To provide financial assistance to Latino students from eligible communities in California, Texas, Illinois, and New York who are interested in attending college in any state.

Eligibility   This program is open to Latino residents of selected communities in southern California, selected cities in Texas, the Greater Chicagoland area of Illinois, or the state of New York. Applicants must 1) be a first-generation college student; 2) be from a low-income family; and 3) have a GPA of 2.5 or higher. They must be enrolled or planning to enroll full time at a college or university in any state. Selection is based on leadership potential, professional and extracurricular achievement, commitment to the development and economic empowerment of communities, and financial need. Priority is given to students attending institutions that provide matching funds (for a list, contact the sponsor).

Financial Data   Stipends range from $500 to $5,000 per year.

Duration Both 1-year and continuing scholarships are available. Continuing scholarships may be renewed for a total of 4 years, provided the recipient attends all sessions of the College Advisement and Leadership Program each year, maintains a GPA of 2.75 or higher, and volunteers 20 hours of service annually to the TELACU Education Foundation or other community organization.

Additional data The eligible areas in California include underserved communities in Los Angeles, Orange, and San Bernardino counties such as unincorporated areas of east Los Angeles and the cities of Baldwin Park, Bell Gardens, Commerce, Huntington Park, Los Angeles, Montebello, Ontario, Pico Rivera, Pomona, San Bernardino, Santa Ana, and South Gate. The cities in Texas are Austin, Edinburg, Laredo, Rio Grande City, San Antonio.

Number awarded Varies each year; the program supports approximately 500 students annually.

Deadline March of each year.

[460]
TENNESSEE MINORITY TEACHING FELLOWS PROGRAM

Tennessee Student Assistance Corporation
Parkway Towers
404 James Robertson Parkway, Suite 1510
Nashville, TN 37243-0820
(615) 741-1346   Toll Free: (800) 342-1663
Fax: (615) 741-6101   E-mail: TSAC.Aidinfo@tn.gov
Web: www.tn.gov

Summary To provide funding to Hispanic American and other minority residents of Tennessee who wish to attend college in the state to prepare for a career in the teaching field.

Eligibility This program is open to minority residents of Tennessee who are either high school seniors planning to enroll full time at a college or university in the state or continuing college students at a Tennessee college or university. High school seniors must have a GPA of 2.75 or higher and an ACT score of at least 18 or a combined mathematics and critical reading SAT score of at least 860. Continuing college students must have a college GPA of 2.5 or higher. All applicants must agree to teach at the K-12 level in a Tennessee public school following graduation from college. Along with their application, they must submit a 250-word essay on why they chose teaching as a profession. U.S. citizenship is required.

Financial Data The scholarship/loan is $5,000 per year. Recipients incur an obligation to teach at the preK-12 level in a Tennessee public school 1 year for each year the award is received.

Duration 1 year; may be renewed for up to 3 additional years, provided the recipient maintains full-time enrollment and a cumulative GPA of 2.5 or higher.

Additional data This program began in 1989.

Number awarded 20 new awards are granted each year.

Deadline April of each year.

[461]
THE TOMORROW FUND FOR HISPANIC STUDENTS

Triangle Community Foundation
Attn: Scholarships and Community Outreach Coordinator
324 Blackwell Street, Suite 1220
Durham, NC 27701
(919) 474-8370, ext. 4025   Fax: (919) 941-9208
E-mail: gina@trianglecf.org
Web: www.trianglecf.org/grants_support/view_scholarships

Summary To provide financial assistance to Hispanic residents of North Carolina enrolled at a college or university in the state.

Eligibility This program is open to residents of North Carolina who self-identify as an Hispanic/Latino immigrant or first-generation U.S. citizen and who attended high school in the state for at least 2 years. Applicants must be enrolled full time at a college, university, or community college in the state and must be nominated by their institution. They must come from a low-income family background, have a GPA of 2.5 or higher, be a first-generation U.S. college student in their family, and already be receiving some financial assistance from their postsecondary institution.

Financial Data The stipend ranges from $2,000 to $15,000. Funds are sent directly to the educational institution to be used for tuition, required fees, books, room and board, or other expenses (such as a laptop) with prior approval.

Duration 1 year.

Additional data This program began in 2009 by making grants to institutions. In 2011, it was converted to a scholarship fund.

Number awarded 1 or more each year.

Deadline May of each year.

[462]
THOMAS G. NEUSOM SCHOLARSHIPS

Conference of Minority Transportation Officials
Attn: National Scholarship Program
1875 I Street, N.W., Suite 500
Washington, DC 20006
(703) 234-4072   Fax: (202) 318-0364
Web: www.comto.org/?page=Scholarships

Summary To provide financial assistance for college or graduate school to Hispanic American and other members of the Conference of Minority Transportation Officials (COMTO).

Eligibility This program is open to undergraduate and graduate students who have been members of COMTO for at least 1 year. Applicants must be working (either full or part time) on a degree in a field related to transportation and have a GPA of 2.5 or higher. Along with their application, they must submit a cover letter with a 500-word statement of career goals. Financial need is not considered in the selection process. U.S. citizenship or legal resident status is required.

Financial Data The stipend is $5,500. Funds are paid directly to the recipient's college or university.

Duration 1 year.

Additional data COMTO was established in 1971 to promote, strengthen, and expand the roles of minorities in all aspects of transportation. Recipients are expected to attend the COMTO National Scholarship Luncheon.

Number awarded 1 each year.

Deadline May of each year.

[463]
TRAILBLAZER SCHOLARSHIP

Conference of Minority Transportation Officials
Attn: National Scholarship Program
1875 I Street, N.W., Suite 500
Washington, DC 20006
(703) 234-4072　　　　　　　　Fax: (202) 318-0364
Web: www.comto.org/?page=Scholarships

Summary To provide financial assistance to Hispanic American and other minority undergraduate and graduate students working on a degree in a field related to transportation.

Eligibility This program is open to minority undergraduate and graduate students who are working (either full or part time) on a degree in a field related to transportation and have a GPA of 2.5 or higher. Along with their application, they must submit a cover letter with a 500-word statement of career goals. Financial need is not considered in the selection process. U.S. citizenship or legal resident status is required.

Financial Data The stipend is $2,500. Funds are paid directly to the recipient's college or university.

Duration 1 year.

Additional data The Conference of Minority Transportation Officials (COMTO) was established in 1971 to promote, strengthen, and expand the roles of minorities in all aspects of transportation. Recipients are expected to attend the COMTO National Scholarship Luncheon.

Number awarded 1 each year.

Deadline May of each year.

[464]
TRAVELERS SCHOLARSHIP

Hispanic Association of Colleges and Universities
Attn: National Scholarship Program
8415 Datapoint Drive, Suite 400
San Antonio, TX 78229
(210) 692-3805　　　　　　　　Fax: (210) 692-0823
TDD: (800) 855-2880　　　E-mail: scholarship@hacu.net
Web: www.hacu.net/hacu/Scholarships.asp

Summary To provide financial assistance to undergraduate students majoring in designated fields at member institutions of the Hispanic Association of Colleges and Universities (HACU).

Eligibility This program is open to full-time undergraduate students at 4-year HACU member institutions. Applicants must be working on a degree in accounting, computer engineering, computer science, finance, general business, general management, or human resources. They must have a GPA of 3.0 or higher.

Financial Data The stipend is $5,000.

Duration 1 year.

Additional data This program is sponsored by Travelers Insurance and administered by HACU.

Number awarded 1 or more each year.

Deadline June of each year.

[465]
UNDERGRADUATE STUDENT RESEARCH EXPERIENCES AT FDA

National Science Foundation
Directorate for Engineering
Attn: Division of Chemical, Bioengineering,
　Environmental, and Transport Systems
4201 Wilson Boulevard, Room 565S
Arlington, VA 22230
(703) 292-7942　　　　　　　　Fax: (703) 292-9098
TDD: (800) 281-8749　　　E-mail: lesterow@nsf.gov
Web: www.nsf.gov/funding/pgm_summ.jsp?pims_id=5605

Summary To provide an opportunity for undergraduate students (particularly Hispanic Americans, other underrepresented minorities, and students with disabilities) to be part of research studies at an intramural laboratory of the U.S. Food and Drug Administration (FDA).

Eligibility This program is open to undergraduate students in science, engineering, and mathematics fields of interest to the National Science Foundation (NSF). Applicants must be U.S. citizens, nationals, or permanent residents. They must be proposing a program of full- or part-time work at an FDA laboratory in an area related to their academic program under the guidance of an academic adviser and an FDA mentor. The program encourages applications from all citizens, including women and men, underrepresented minorities, and persons with disabilities.

Financial Data Undergraduate students may receive stipends up to $450 per week; they may also receive some assistance with housing or travel expenses, or both. No indirect costs are allowed. The total award may be up to $8,000 for a fellowship for a single student. FDA provides office space, research facilities, research costs in the form of expendable and minor equipment purchases in the host laboratory, and the time of its research staff.

Duration Support may be provided for a summer project, or for 1 or 2 semesters of part- or full-time work.

Additional data This program is also offered by the NSF Directorate for Computer and Information Science and Engineering.

Number awarded A total of 3 to 10 grants for all FDA programs is awarded each year; total funding is approximately $500,000.

Deadline March of each year.

[466]
UNITED METHODIST ETHNIC MINORITY SCHOLARSHIPS

United Methodist Church
Attn: General Board of Higher Education and Ministry
Office of Loans and Scholarships
1001 19th Avenue South
P.O. Box 340007
Nashville, TN 37203-0007
(615) 340-7344　　　　　　　　Fax: (615) 340-7367
E-mail: umscholar@gbhem.org
Web: www.gbhem.org

Summary To provide financial assistance to Hispanic Americans and other undergraduate Methodist students of ethnic minority ancestry.

Eligibility This program is open to full-time undergraduate students at accredited colleges and universities in the United States who have been active, full members of a United Methodist Church for at least 1 year prior to applying. Applicants must have at least 1 parent who is African American, Hispanic, Asian, Native American, or Pacific Islander. They must have a GPA of 2.5 or higher and be able to demonstrate financial need. U.S. citizenship, permanent resident status, or membership in a central conference of the United Methodist Church is required. Selection is based on church membership, involvement in church and community activities, GPA, and financial need.

Financial Data Stipends range from $500 to $1,000.

Duration 1 year; recipients may reapply.

Number awarded Varies each year.

Deadline February of each year.

[467]
UNITED PARCEL SERVICE SCHOLARSHIP FOR MINORITY STUDENTS

Institute of Industrial Engineers
Attn: Scholarship Coordinator
3577 Parkway Lane, Suite 200
Norcross, GA 30092
(770) 449-0461, ext. 105   Toll Free: (800) 494-0460
Fax: (770) 441-3295   E-mail: bcameron@iienet.org
Web: www.iienet2.org/Details.aspx?id=857

Summary To provide financial assistance to Hispanic American and other minority undergraduates who are studying industrial engineering at a school in the United States, Canada, or Mexico.

Eligibility Eligible to be nominated are minority undergraduate students enrolled at any school in the United States or its territories, Canada, or Mexico, provided the school's engineering program is accredited by an agency recognized by the Institute of Industrial Engineers (IIE) and the student is pursuing a full-time course of study in industrial engineering with a GPA of at least 3.4. Nominees must have at least 5 full quarters or 3 full semesters remaining until graduation. Students may not apply directly for these awards; they must be nominated by the head of their industrial engineering department. Nominees must be IIE members. Selection is based on scholastic ability, character, leadership, and potential service to the industrial engineering profession.

Financial Data The stipend is $4,000.

Duration 1 year.

Additional data Funding for this program is provided by the UPS Foundation.

Number awarded 1 each year.

Deadline Schools must submit nominations by November of each year.

[468]
UNIVERSITY OF CALIFORNIA AT BERKELEY AMGEN SCHOLARS PROGRAM

University of California at Berkeley
Attn: Amgen Scholars Program
158 Barrows Hall
MC 2990
Berkeley, CA 94720-2990
(510) 642-0280   Fax: (510) 643-6762
E-mail: amgenscholars@berkeley.edu
Web: amgenscholars.berkeley.edu

Summary To provide undergraduate students (particularly Hispanic Americans and others from diverse backgrounds) with a summer research experience at the University of California at Berkeley in biological and biomedical sciences.

Eligibility This program is open to sophomores, juniors, and non-graduating seniors at 4-year colleges and universities in the United States, Puerto Rico, and U.S. territories. Applicants must be interested in a summer research experience at UC Berkeley in biochemistry, bioengineering, biophysics, cell and developmental biology, chemical biology, chemical and biomedical engineering, chemistry, computational biology, genetics, genomics and development, immunology, integrative biology, microbiology, molecular and cell biology, neuroscience, plant and microbial biology, structural biology, or synthetic biology. They must have a GPA of 3.2 or higher and an interest in continuing on to a Ph.D. or M.D./Ph.D. (but not M.D.) program. Applications are especially encouraged from students from diverse populations and backgrounds. U.S. citizenship or permanent resident status is required.

Financial Data Housing, travel to and from Berkeley, meals, and a stipend of $4,000 are provided.

Duration 10 weeks during the summer.

Additional data This program serves as the UC Berkeley component of the Amgen Scholars Program, which operates at 9 other U.S. universities and is funded by the Amgen Foundation.

Number awarded 25 each year.

Deadline January of each year.

[469]
UNIVERSITY OF CALIFORNIA AT SAN FRANCISCO SUMMER RESEARCH OPPORTUNITIES

University of California at San Francisco
Office of Graduate Outreach
Attn: Outreach and Student Programs Coordinator
1675 Owens Street, Room 310
Box 0523
San Francisco, CA 94143-0523
(415) 514-3510   Fax: (415) 514-0844
E-mail: gdsummerprogram@ucsf.edu
Web: graduate.ucsf.edu

Summary To provide undergraduate students (particularly Hispanic Americans and others from diverse backgrounds) with a summer research experience at the University of California at San Francisco in biological and biomedical sciences.

Eligibility This activity consists of 3 separate programs, but they operate together and have a common application and requirements. The 3 programs are the Amgen Scholars

Program, the Molecular Biosciences Research Experiences for Undergraduates (REU), and the Summer Research Training Program (SRTP). The activity is open to sophomores, juniors, and non-graduating seniors at 4-year colleges and universities in the United States, Puerto Rico, and U.S. territories. Applicants must be interested in a summer research experience at UC San Francisco in biochemistry, bioengineering, bioinformatics, biology (molecular, cell, and developmental), biopsychology, biotechnology, chemical and biomedical engineering, chemistry, immunology, medical pharmacology, microbiology, molecular genetics, molecular medicine, molecular pharmacology, neurobiology, neuroscience, pathology, physiological psychology, physiological science, statistics, or toxicology. They must be U.S. citizens, nationals, or permanent residents. The Amgen Scholars Program requires a GPA of 3.2 or higher but the other 2 components have no minimum GPA requirement; all programs require an interest in continuing on to a Ph.D. or M.D./Ph.D. (but not M.D.) program. Applications are especially encouraged from underrepresented minority, socioeconomically disadvantaged, and first-generation college students and from students with limited access to research laboratories.

Financial Data The program provides a stipend of $4,000, a $500 allowance for travel to and from San Francisco, housing in the city, health insurance, and a public transportation pass.

Duration 10 weeks during the summer.

Additional data This program is comprised of 1) the UC San Francisco component of the Amgen Scholars Program, which operates at 9 other U.S. universities and is funded by the Amgen Foundation; 2) the REU program, funded by the National Science Foundation; and 3) the SRTP, which is a UCSF program with supplemental funding from Genentech and the Howard Hughes Medical Institute.

Number awarded Approximately 60 each year.

Deadline January of each year.

[470]
USHCC-WELLS FARGO SCHOLARSHIPS

Hispanic Scholarship Fund
Attn: Selection Committee
1411 West 190th Street, Suite 325
Gardena, CA 90248
Toll Free: (877) HSF-INFO   E-mail: scholar1@hsf.net
Web: www.hsf.net

Summary To provide financial assistance for college or graduate school to dependents and relatives of members of the U.S. Hispanic Chamber of Commerce (USHCC).

Eligibility This program is open to U.S. citizens and permanent residents (must have a permanent resident card or a passport stamped I-551) who are of Hispanic heritage. Applicants must be enrolling as a full-time undergraduate or graduate student at a 4-year college or university in the United States and have a GPA of 3.0 or higher. They must be a dependent or relative of a USHCC member or employee or a former USHCC BizFest participant. Selection is based on academic achievement, personal strengths, leadership, and financial need.

Financial Data The stipend is $2,500.

Duration 1 year.

Additional data This program is funded by Wells Fargo Bank.

Number awarded 57 each year.

Deadline January of each year.

[471]
VANGUARD MINORITY SCHOLARSHIP PROGRAM

Scholarship America
Attn: Scholarship Management Services
One Scholarship Way
P.O. Box 297
St. Peter, MN 56082
(507) 931-1682   Toll Free: (800) 537-4180
Fax: (507) 931-9168
Web: sms.scholarshipamerica.org/vanguard/index.html

Summary To provide financial assistance to Hispanic American and other minority students working on an undergraduate degree in specified fields.

Eligibility This program is open to U.S. citizens and permanent residents who are members of racial or ethnic minorities. Applicants must be entering their junior or senior year as a full-time student at an accredited 4-year college or university in the United States and have a GPA of 3.0 or higher. They must be working on a degree in accounting, business, economics, or finance. Selection is based on academic record, demonstrated leadership and participation in school and community activities, honors, work experience, a statement of goals and aspirations, unusual personal or family circumstances, recommendations, and a resume; financial need is not considered. Students who attended a 2-year college while working on a bachelor's degree are not eligible.

Financial Data The stipend ranges up to $10,000.

Duration 1 year; nonrenewable.

Additional data This program, established in 2004, is sponsored by Vanguard Group, Inc.

Number awarded Up to 10 each year.

Deadline November of each year.

[472]
VERIZON/HENAAC SCHOLARS PROGRAM

Great Minds in STEM
Attn: HENAAC Scholars Program
602 Monterey Pass Road
Monterey Park, CA 91754
(323) 262-0997   Fax: (323) 262-0946
E-mail: gcruz@greatmindsinstem.org
Web: www.greatmindsinstem.org

Summary To provide financial assistance to Hispanic undergraduate students from any state who are enrolled at designated universities and majoring in selected fields of science or engineering.

Eligibility This program is open to Hispanic undergraduate students from any state who are enrolled at 1 of 12 designated colleges or universities. Applicants must be of Hispanic origin and/or must significantly participate in and promote organizations and activities in the Hispanic community. They must have a GPA of 3.0 or higher and be majoring in computer information systems, computer engineering, computer science, electrical engineering, or information technology. Along with their application, they must submit a 700-word essay on a topic that changes annually. Selection is based on leadership, academic achievements, and campus and community activities; financial need is not considered. U.S. citizenship is required.

Financial Data Stipends range from $500 to $10,000.

Duration 1 year; recipients may reapply.

Additional data The Hispanic Engineer National Achievement Awards Conference (HENAAC) was established in 1989 and initiated a scholarship program in 2000. In 2010, the sponsoring organization officially adopted its current name, but it continues to hold the annual HENAAC conference, at which the scholarships are presented. This program is sponsored by Verizon. The designated universities are City University of New York-City College, Cornell University, Georgia Institute of Technology, University of Illinois, Ohio State University, Pennsylvania State University, University of Puerto Rico, Purdue University, Rutgers University, University of South Florida, University of Southern California, and Villanova University. Recipients must attend the conference to accept their scholarship.

Number awarded Varies each year; recently, 5 of these scholarships were awarded.

Deadline April of each year.

[473]
VETERANS OF FOREIGN WARS OF MEXICAN ANCESTRY SCHOLARSHIP PROGRAM

Veterans of Foreign Wars of the United States of Mexican
  Ancestry
c/o Mike Palomo
1309 West Mission Boulevard, Apartment 27
Ontario, CA 91762-6843

Summary To provide financial assistance for college to Mexican American high school students (especially children of veterans) in California.

Eligibility This program is open to high school seniors of Mexican descent who reside in California. They must have earned a GPA of 3.5 or higher and need financial assistance to attend college. Preference is given to the children of veterans.

Financial Data Stipends range from $500 to $1,000.

Duration 1 year.

Additional data Students who live in northern California should contact Robert Gonzalez, 3210 Santa Maria Avenue, Santa Clara, CA 95051-1622, (408) 248-1677.

Number awarded Varies each year.

Deadline March of each year.

[474]
VICTORIA ALEGRIA TRACY SCHOLARSHIP

Great Minds in STEM
Attn: HENAAC Scholars Program
602 Monterey Pass Road
Monterey Park, CA 91754
(323) 262-0997   Fax: (323) 262-0946
E-mail: gcruz@greatmindsinstem.org
Web: www.greatmindsinstem.org

Summary To provide financial assistance to Hispanic women from any state who are enrolled at universities in southern California and majoring in a field of science, technology, engineering, or mathematics (STEM).

Eligibility This program is open to female Hispanic undergraduate students from any state who are working on a

degree in a field of STEM at colleges and universities in southern California. Applicants must be of Hispanic origin and/or must significantly participate in and promote organizations and activities in the Hispanic community. They must have a GPA of 2.5 or higher. Along with their application, they must submit a 700-word essay on a topic that changes annually. Selection is based on leadership, academic achievements, and campus and community activities; financial need is not considered.

Financial Data Stipends range from $500 to $10,000.

Duration 1 year; recipients may reapply.

Additional data The Hispanic Engineer National Achievement Awards Conference (HENAAC) was established in 1989 and initiated a scholarship program in 2000. In 2010, the sponsoring organization officially adopted its current name, but it continues to hold the annual HENAAC conference, at which the scholarships are presented. This program was first offered in 2008. Recipients must attend the conference to accept their scholarship.

Number awarded Varies each year; recently, 5 of these scholarships were awarded.

Deadline April of each year.

[475]
VIRGINIA CHAPTER AABE SCHOLARSHIPS

American Association of Blacks in Energy-Virginia
  Chapter
Attn: Scholarship Committee
120 Tredegar Street
Richmond, VA 23219
E-mail: aabe@dom.com
Web: www.aabe.org

Summary To provide financial assistance to Hispanic Americans and members of other underrepresented minority groups who are high school seniors in Virginia and planning to major in an energy-related field at a college in any state.

Eligibility This program is open to seniors graduating from high schools in Virginia and planning to attend a college or university in any state. Applicants must be African Americans, Hispanics, or Native Americans who have a GPA of 3.0 or higher and who can demonstrate financial need. Their intended major must be business, engineering, technology, mathematics, the physical sciences, or other energy-related field. Along with their application, they must submit a 350-word statement on why they should receive this scholarship, how their professional career objectives relate to energy, and any other relevant information.

Financial Data The stipend is $1,000.

Duration 1 year.

Additional data The winner is eligible to compete for regional and national scholarships.

Number awarded 4 each year.

Deadline February of each year.

[476]
VIRGINIA LATINO HIGHER EDUCATION NETWORK SCHOLARSHIP

Virginia Latino Higher Education Network
c/o Monica Gomez, Scholarship Co-Chair
Northern Virginia Community College
Loudon/Reston Center, Room 332
1831 Wiehle Avenue
Reston, VA 20190
(703) 948-7593   E-mail: scholarships@valhen.org
Web: www.valhen.org/scholarship

Summary   To provide financial assistance to Latino residents of Virginia who are interested in attending college in the state.

Eligibility   This program is open to residents of Virginia who are of Latino/Hispanic heritage and either high school seniors or students currently enrolled full time at an institution of higher education in the state. Applicants must submit a 500-word essay on what being Latino in America means to them.

Financial Data   Stipends are $1,000 or $500.

Duration   1 year.

Additional data   This program includes 3 scholarships of $500 each sponsored by Liberty Tax Service through its Una Familia Sin Fronteras program.

Number awarded   Varies each year; recently, 7 of these scholarships were awarded.

Deadline   July of each year.

[477]
VIRGINIA NURSE PRACTITIONER/NURSE MIDWIFE SCHOLARSHIP PROGRAM

Virginia Department of Health
Attn: Office of Minority Health and Public Health Policy
109 Governor Street, Suite 1016 East
Richmond, VA 23219
(804) 864-7435   Fax: (804) 864-7440
E-mail: IncentivePrograms@vdh.virginia.gov
Web: www.vdh.virginia.gov

Summary   To provide funding to nursing students in Virginia (particularly Hispanic Americans and other minorities) who are willing to work as nurse practitioners and/or midwives in the state following graduation.

Eligibility   This program is open to residents of Virginia who are enrolled or accepted for enrollment full or part time at a nurse practitioner program in the state or a nurse midwifery program in Virginia or a nearby state. Applicants must have a cumulative GPA of at least 3.0 in undergraduate and/or graduate courses. Preference is given to 1) residents of designated medically underserved areas of Virginia; 2) students enrolled in family practice, obstetrics and gynecology, pediatric, adult health, and geriatric nurse practitioner programs; and 3) minority students. Selection is based on scholastic achievement, character, and stated commitment to postgraduate employment in a medically underserved area of Virginia.

Financial Data   The stipend is $5,000 per year. Recipients must agree to serve in a designated medically underserved area of Virginia for a period of years equal to the number of years of scholarship support received. The required service must begin within 2 years of the recipient's graduation and must be in a facility that provides services to persons who are

unable to pay for the service and that participates in all government-sponsored insurance programs designed to assure full access to medical care service for covered persons. If the recipient fails to complete the course of study, or pass the licensing examination, or provide the required service, all scholarship funds received must be repaid with interest and a penalty.

Duration   1 year; may be renewed for 1 additional year.

Number awarded   Up to 5 each year.

Deadline   June of each year.

[478]
VSCPA MINORITY ACCOUNTING SCHOLARSHIPS

Virginia Society of Certified Public Accountants
Attn: Educational Foundation
4309 Cox Road
Glen Allen, VA 23060
(804) 612-9427   Toll Free: (800) 733-8272
Fax: (804) 273-1741   E-mail: info@vscpafoundation.com
Web: www.vscpa.com

Summary   To provide financial assistance to Hispanic American and other minority students enrolled in an undergraduate accounting program in Virginia.

Eligibility   Applicants must be minority students (African American or Black, Hispanic or Latino, American Indian or Native Alaskan, Asian, Native Hawaiian or other Pacific Islander) currently enrolled in a Virginia college or university undergraduate accounting program. They must be U.S. citizens, be majoring in accounting, have completed at least 3 hours of accounting, be currently registered for 3 more credit hours of accounting and have a GPA of 3.0 or higher. Along with their application, they must submit a 500-word essay on assigned topics. Selection is based on the essay, their most recent transcript, a current resume, a faculty letter of recommendation, and financial need.

Financial Data   The stipend is $1,000.

Duration   1 year.

Number awarded   Varies each year; recently, 2 of these scholarships were awarded.

Deadline   March of each year.

[479]
WAKE FOREST UNIVERSITY SCHOOL OF MEDICINE EXCELLENCE IN CARDIOVASCULAR SCIENCES SUMMER RESEARCH PROGRAM

Wake Forest University School of Medicine
Attn: Hypertension and Vascular Research Center
Medical Center Boulevard
Winston-Salem, NC 27157-1032
(336) 716-1080   Fax: (336) 716-2456
E-mail: nsarver@wakehealth.edu
Web: www.wakehealth.edu

Summary   To provide Hispanic American and other underrepresented or disadvantaged students with an opportunity to engage in a summer research project in cardiovascular science at Wake Forest University in Winston-Salem, North Carolina.

Eligibility   This program is open to undergraduates and master's degree students who are members of underrepresented minority groups (African Americans, Alaskan Natives,

Asian Americans, Native Americans, Pacific Islanders, and Hispanics) or who come from disadvantaged backgrounds (e.g., rural areas, first-generation college students). Applicants must be interested in participating in a program of summer research in the cardiovascular sciences that includes "hands-on" laboratory research, a lecture series by faculty and guest speakers, and a research symposium at which students present their research findings. U.S. citizenship or permanent resident status is required.

Financial Data The stipend is $1,731 per month, housing in a university dormitory, and round-trip transportation expense.

Duration 2 months during the summer.

Additional data This program is sponsored by the National Heart, Lung, and Blood Institute (NHLBI) of the National Institutes of Health (NIH).

Number awarded Approximately 12 each year.

Deadline February of each year.

[480]
WARNER NORCROSS & JUDD PARALEGAL ASSISTANT SCHOLARSHIP

Grand Rapids Community Foundation
Attn: Education Program Officer
185 Oakes Street S.W.
Grand Rapids, MI 49503-4008
(616) 454-1751, ext. 103   Fax: (616) 454-6455
E-mail: rbishop@grfoundation.org
Web: www.grfoundation.org/scholarshipslist

Summary To provide financial assistance to Hispanic and other minority residents of Michigan who are interested in working on a paralegal studies degree at an institution in the state.

Eligibility This program is open to residents of Michigan who are students of color attending or planning to attend an accredited public or private 2- or 4-year college or university in the state. Applicants must have a declared major in paralegal/legal assistant studies. They must be U.S. citizens or permanent residents and have a GPA of 2.5 or higher. Financial need is considered in the selection process.

Financial Data The stipend is $2,000. Funds are paid directly to the recipient's institution.

Duration 1 year.

Additional data Funding for this program is provided by the law firm Warner Norcross & Judd LLP.

Number awarded 1 each year.

Deadline March of each year.

[481]
WASA/PEMCO 21ST CENTURY EDUCATOR SCHOLARSHIP

Washington Association of School Administrators
825 Fifth Avenue, S.E.
Olympia, WA 98501
(360) 943-5717   Toll Free: (800) 859-9272
Fax: (360) 352-2043   E-mail: admin@wasa-oly.org
Web: www.wasa-oly.org

Summary To provide financial assistance to minority and other high school seniors in the state of Washington who are interested in majoring in education in college.

Eligibility This program is open to high school seniors who are enrolled in a Washington public or accredited private school, have a GPA of 3.0 or higher, and intend to major and prepare for a career in K-12 education. Applicants must submit a completed application form, a criteria essay, a goals essay, 3 reference letters, and an official grades transcript. They compete in 3 applicant pools: eastern Washington, western Washington, and minority. Along with their application, they must submit a 1-page essay on why they have chosen K-12 education as their future profession. Selection is based on that essay, leadership, community service, honors and awards, and student activities.

Financial Data The stipend is $1,000 per year.

Duration 4 years.

Additional data This program is sponsored jointly by the Washington Association of School Administrators (WASA) and the PEMCO Foundation.

Number awarded 3 each year: 1 to a student from eastern Washington, 1 to a student from western Washington, and 1 to a minority student.

Deadline March of each year.

[482]
WASHINGTON ADMIRAL'S FUND SCHOLARSHIP

National Naval Officers Association-Washington, D.C.
   Chapter
c/o LCDR Stephen Williams
P.O. Box 30784
Alexandria, VA 22310
(703) 566-3840   Fax: (703) 566-3813
E-mail: Stephen.Williams@navy.mil
Web: dcnnoa.memberlodge.com

Summary To provide financial assistance to Hispanic American and other minority high school seniors from the Washington, D.C. area who are interested in attending a college or university in any state and enrolling in the Navy Reserve Officers Training Corps (NROTC) program.

Eligibility This program is open to minority seniors graduating from high schools in the Washington, D.C. metropolitan area who plan to enroll full time at an accredited 2- or 4-year college or university in any state. Applicants must be planning to enroll in the NROTC program. They must have a GPA of 2.5 or higher and be U.S. citizens or permanent residents. Selection is based on academic achievement, community involvement, and financial need.

Financial Data The stipend is $1,000.

Duration 1 year; nonrenewable.

Additional data If the recipient fails to enroll in the NROTC unit, all scholarship funds must be returned.

Number awarded 1 each year.

Deadline March of each year.

[483]
WASHINGTON DC AREA SUPPLY OFFICERS SCHOLARSHIP

National Naval Officers Association-Washington, D.C.
   Chapter
c/o LCDR Stephen Williams
P.O. Box 30784
Alexandria, VA 22310
(703) 566-3840   Fax: (703) 566-3813
E-mail: Stephen.Williams@navy.mil
Web: dcnnoa.memberlodge.com

Summary To provide financial assistance to Hispanic American and other minority high school seniors from the Washington, D.C. area who are interested in attending college in any state.

Eligibility This program is open to minority seniors graduating from high schools in the Washington, D.C. metropolitan area who plan to enroll full time at an accredited 2- or 4-year college or university in any state. Applicants must have a GPA of 3.0 or higher and be U.S. citizens or permanent residents. Selection is based on academic achievement, community involvement, and financial need.

Financial Data The stipend is $3,000.

Duration 1 year; nonrenewable.

Number awarded 1 each year.

Deadline March of each year.

[484]
WASHINGTON DC METROPOLITAN AREA CHAPTER AABE SCHOLARSHIPS

American Association of Blacks in Energy-Washington
   DC Metropolitan Area Chapter
Attn: Scholarship Committee
P.O. Box 77263
Washington, DC 20013
E-mail: dcaabeschl@aol.com
Web: www.aabe.org

Summary To provide financial assistance to Hispanic Americans and members of other underrepresented minority groups who are high school seniors in the Washington, D.C. metropolitan area and planning to major in an energy-related field at a college in any state.

Eligibility This program is open to seniors graduating from high schools in the Washington, D.C. metropolitan area who are planning to work on a bachelor's degree at a college or university in any state. Applicants must be African Americans, Hispanics, or Native Americans who have a GPA of 3.0 or higher and who can demonstrate financial need. Their intended major must be a field of business, engineering, physical science, mathematics, or technology related to energy. Along with their application, they must submit a 350-word statement on why they should receive this scholarship, their professional career objectives, and any other relevant information.

Financial Data Stipends range from $1,500 to $2,500.

Duration 1 year; nonrenewable.

Additional data Winners are eligible to compete for regional and national scholarships.

Number awarded 3 each year: 1 each at $2,500, $2,000, and $1,500.

Deadline February of each year.

[485]
WASHINGTON UNIVERSITY AMGEN SCHOLARS PROGRAM

Washington University
Division of Biology and Biomedical Sciences
Attn: Summer Research Admissions
660 South Euclid Avenue
Campus Box 8226
St. Louis, MO 63110-1093
(314) 362-7963   Toll Free: (800) 852-9074
E-mail: DBBS-summerresearch@wusm.wustl.edu
Web: dbbs.wustl.edu

Summary To provide undergraduate students (particularly Hispanic Americans, other underrepresented minorities, women, and students with disabilities) with a summer research experience at Washington University in St. Louis in biological and biomedical sciences.

Eligibility This program is open to sophomores, juniors, and non-graduating seniors at 4-year colleges and universities in the United States, Puerto Rico, and U.S. territories. Applicants must be interested in a summer research experience at Washington University in biochemistry, bioengineering, bioinformatics, biology (molecular, cell, and developmental), biopsychology, biotechnology, chemical and biomedical engineering, chemistry, immunology, medical pharmacology, microbiology, molecular genetics, molecular medicine, molecular pharmacology, neurobiology, neuroscience, pathology, physiological psychology, physiological science, statistics, or toxicology. They must have a GPA of 3.2 or higher and an interest in continuing on to a Ph.D. or M.D./Ph.D. (but not M.D.) program. Applications are especially encouraged from students from economically disadvantaged backgrounds, those who attend small liberal arts colleges, and from members of groups traditionally underrepresented in biomedical research (African Americans, Hispanic Americans, Native Americans, Pacific Islanders, women, and people with disabilities). U.S. citizenship or permanent resident status is required.

Financial Data Housing, travel to and from St. Louis, meals, and a stipend of $4,000 are provided.

Duration 10 weeks during the summer.

Additional data This program serves as the Washington University component of the Amgen Scholars Program, which operates at 9 other U.S. universities and is funded by the Amgen Foundation.

Number awarded 25 each year.

Deadline January of each year.

[486]
WATSON MIDWIVES OF COLOR SCHOLARSHIP

American College of Nurse-Midwives
Attn: ACNM Foundation, Inc.
8403 Colesville Road, Suite 1550
Silver Spring, MD 20910-6374
(240) 485-1850   Fax: (240) 485-1818
E-mail: fdn@acnm.org
Web: www.midwife.org

Summary To provide financial assistance for midwifery education to Hispanic Americans and other students of color who belong to the American College of Nurse-Midwives (ACNM).

Eligibility This program is open to ACNM members of color (African Americans, Asian Americans, Hispanic Americans, and Native Americans). They must be interested in preparing for a career as a midwife and working on an undergraduate or graduate degree.

Financial Data The stipend is $3,000.

Duration 1 year.

Number awarded Varies each year; recently, 3 of these scholarships were awarded.

Deadline March of each year.

[487]
WAYNE D. CORNILS SCHOLARSHIP

Idaho State Broadcasters Association
1674 West Hill Road, Suite 3
Boise, ID 83702
(208) 345-3072   Fax: (208) 343-8946
E-mail: isba@qwestoffice.net
Web: bestinbroadcasting.com

Summary To provide financial assistance to Hispanic Americans and other less advantaged students at Idaho colleges and universities who are preparing for a career in the broadcasting field.

Eligibility This program is open to full-time students at Idaho schools who are preparing for a career in broadcasting, including business administration, sales, journalism, or engineering. Applicants must have a GPA of at least 2.0 for the first 2 years of school or 2.5 for the last 2 years. Along with their application, they must submit a letter of recommendation from the general manager of a broadcasting station that is a member of the Idaho State Broadcasters Association and a 1-page essay describing their career plans and why they want the scholarship. Applications are encouraged from a broad and diverse student population. This scholarship is reserved for a less advantaged applicant.

Financial Data The amount of the stipend depends on the need of the recipient.

Duration 1 year.

Number awarded 1 each year.

Deadline March of each year.

[488]
WEISMAN SCHOLARSHIPS

Connecticut Office of Financial and Academic Affairs for
  Higher Education
Attn: Student Financial Aid
61 Woodland Street
Hartford, CT 06105-2326
(860) 947-1853   Toll Free: (800) 842-0229 (within CT)
Fax: (860) 947-1314   E-mail: mtip@ctdhe.org
Web: www.ctohe.org/SFA/default.htm

Summary To provide financial assistance to Hispanic Americans and other minority upper-division college students from any state who are enrolled at a college in Connecticut and interested in teaching mathematics or science at public middle and high schools in the state.

Eligibility This program is open to residents of any state who are enrolled full time as juniors or seniors at Connecticut colleges and universities and preparing to become a mathematics or science teacher at the middle or high school level. Applicants must be members of a minority group, defined as African American, Hispanic/Latino, Asian American, or Native American. They must be nominated by the education dean at their institution.

Financial Data The maximum stipend is $5,000 per year. In addition, if recipients complete a credential and begin teaching mathematics or science at a public school in Connecticut within 16 months of graduation, they may receive up to $2,500 per year, for up to 4 years, to help pay off college loans.

Number awarded Varies each year.

Deadline October of each year.

[489]
WELLS FARGO SCHOLARSHIP PROGRAM OF THE HISPANIC SCHOLARSHIP FUND

Hispanic Scholarship Fund
Attn: Selection Committee
1411 West 190th Street, Suite 325
Gardena, CA 90248
Toll Free: (877) HSF-INFO   E-mail: scholar1@hsf.net
Web: www.hsf.net

Summary To provide financial assistance to Hispanic high school seniors and community college transfer students entering a 4-year college or university to work on a degree in any field.

Eligibility This program is open to U.S. citizens and permanent residents (must have a permanent resident card or a passport stamped I-551) who are of Hispanic heritage. Applicants must be 1) enrolling as a full-time freshman at a 4-year college or university in the United States, Puerto Rico, the U.S. Virgin Islands, or Guam; or 2) transferring from a community or junior college to a 4-year institution. They may be majoring in any field but must have a GPA of 3.0 or higher. Selection is based on academic achievement, personal strengths, leadership, and financial need.

Financial Data The stipend ranges from $1,000 to $5,000.

Duration 1 year.

Additional data This program is funded by Wells Fargo Bank.

Number awarded 1 or more each year.

Deadline January of each year.

[490]
WESTERN UNION FOUNDATION FAMILY SCHOLARSHIP PROGRAM

Western Union Foundation
c/o Institute of International Education
1400 K Street, N.W., Suite 700
Washington, DC 20005
(202) 326-7861   Fax: (202) 326-7696
E-mail: wufoundaton@iie.org
Web: foundation.westernunion.com

Summary To provide financial assistance to pairs of students from the same family of immigrants in designated cities, both of whom wish to attend college in any state.

Eligibility Applications to this program must be submitted jointly by 2 students who are members of the same family (parent and child, siblings). Both applicants must be 18 years of age or older, have been born outside of the United States, have been in this country for 7 years or less, and be planning to attend an accredited institution of higher education or nonprofit training institute in any state. They must be residents of Chicago, Denver, Los Angeles, Miami, New York, San Francisco, or Washington, D.C. Funding is available for college or university tuition, language acquisition classes, technical or skill training, and/or financial literacy; graduate study is not supported.

Financial Data   Stipends range from $1,000 to $5,000 per family. Funds are paid directly to the educational institution.

Duration   1 year.

Additional data   This program began in 2009.

Number awarded   Varies each year.

Deadline   October of each year.

[491]
WILLIAM K. SCHUBERT M.D. MINORITY NURSING SCHOLARSHIP PROGRAM

Cincinnati Children's Hospital Medical Center
Attn: Office of Diversity and Inclusion, MLC 9008
3333 Burnet Avenue
Cincinnati, OH 45229-3039
(513) 803-6416   Toll Free: (800) 344-2462
Fax: (513) 636-5643   TDD: (513) 636-4900
E-mail: diversity@cchmc.org
Web: www.cincinnatichildrens.org

Summary   To provide financial assistance to Hispanic Americans and members of other underrepresented groups who are interested in working on a bachelor's or master's degree in nursing to prepare for licensure in Ohio.

Eligibility   This program is open to members of groups underrepresented in the nursing profession (males, American Indians or Alaska Natives, Blacks or African Americans, Hawaiian Natives or other Pacific Islanders, Hispanics or Latinos, or Asians). Applicants must be enrolled or accepted in a professional bachelor's or master's registered nurse program at an accredited school of nursing to prepare for initial licensure in Ohio. They must have a GPA of 2.75 or higher. Along with their application, they must submit a 750-word essay that covers 1) their long-range personal, educational, and professional goals; 2) why they chose nursing as a profession; 3) how their experience as a member of an underrepresented group has influenced a major professional and/or personal decision in their life; 4) any unique qualifications, experiences, or special talents that demonstrate their creativity; and 5) how their work experience has contributed to their personal development.

Financial Data   The stipend is $2,750 per year.

Duration   1 year. May be renewed up to 3 additional years for students working on a bachelor's degree or 1 additional year for students working on a master's degree; renewal requires that students maintain a GPA of 2.75 or higher.

Number awarded   1 or more each year.

Deadline   April of each year.

[492]
WILLIAM RANDOLPH HEARST ENDOWMENT SCHOLARSHIPS

National Action Council for Minorities in Engineering
Attn: University Programs
440 Hamilton Avenue, Suite 302
White Plains, NY 10601-1813
(914) 539-4010   Fax: (914) 539-4032
E-mail: scholarships@nacme.org
Web: www.nacme.org/NACME_D.aspx?pageid=105

Summary   To provide financial assistance to Hispanic American and other underrepresented minority college freshmen or sophomores majoring in engineering or related fields.

Eligibility   This program is open to African American, Latino, and American Indian college freshmen and sophomores who have a GPA of 2.8 or higher and have demonstrated academic excellence, leadership skills, and a commitment to science and engineering as a career. Applicants must be enrolled full time at an ABET-accredited engineering program. Fields of study include all areas of engineering as well as computer science, materials science, mathematics, operations research, or physics.

Financial Data   The stipend is $2,500 per year. Funds are sent directly to the recipient's university.

Duration   Up to 4 years.

Additional data   This program was established by the William Randolph Hearst Foundation.

Number awarded   2 each year.

Deadline   April of each year.

[493]
WILLIAM TOWNSEND PORTER FELLOWSHIP FOR MINORITY INVESTIGATORS

Marine Biological Laboratory
Attn: Chief Academic and Scientific Officer
7 MBL Street
Woods Hole, MA 02543-1015
(508) 289-7173   Fax: (508) 457-1924
E-mail: casoofice@mbl.edu
Web: hermes.mbl.edu

Summary   To support Hispanic Americans and other underrepresented minorities who wish to conduct research during the summer at the Marine Biological Laboratory (MBL) in Woods Hole, Massachusetts.

Eligibility   This program is open to young scientists (undergraduates, senior graduate students, and postdoctoral trainees) who are from an underrepresented minority group (African American, Hispanic American, or Native American), are U.S. citizens or permanent residents, and are interested in conducting research with senior investigators at MBL. Applicants must submit a statement of the potential impact of this award on their career development. Fields of study include, but are not limited to, cell biology, developmental biology, ecology, evolution, microbiology, neurobiology, physiology, regenerative biology, and tissue engineering.

Financial Data   Grants range from $5,000 to $25,000, typically to cover laboratory rental and/or housing costs. Awardees are responsible for other costs, such as supplies, shared resource usage, affiliated staff who accompany them, or travel.

Duration   8 to 10 weeks during the summer.

Additional data This fellowship was first awarded in 1921. Funding is provided by the Harvard Apparatus Foundation.

Number awarded 1 or more each year.

Deadline December of each year.

[494]
WISCONSIN MINORITY TEACHER LOANS

Wisconsin Higher Educational Aids Board
131 West Wilson Street, Suite 902
P.O. Box 7885
Madison, WI 53707-7885
(608) 267-2212   Fax: (608) 267-2808
E-mail: deanna.schulz@wisconsin.gov
Web: heab.state.wi.us/programs.html

Summary To provide funding to Hispanic Americans and other minorities in Wisconsin who are interested in teaching in Wisconsin school districts with large minority enrollments.

Eligibility This program is open to residents of Wisconsin who are African Americans, Hispanic Americans, American Indians, or southeast Asians (students who were admitted to the United States after December 31, 1975 and who are a former citizen of Laos, Vietnam, or Cambodia or whose ancestor was a citizen of 1 of those countries). Applicants must be enrolled at least half time as juniors, seniors, or graduate students at an independent or public institution in the state in a program leading to teaching licensure and have a GPA of 2.5 or higher. They must agree to teach in a Wisconsin school district in which minority students constitute at least 29% of total enrollment or in a school district participating in the interdistrict pupil transfer program. Financial need is not considered in the selection process.

Financial Data Loans are provided up to $2,500 per year. For each year the student teaches in an eligible school district, 25% of the loan is forgiven; if the student does not teach in an eligible district, the loan must be repaid at an interest rate of 5%.

Duration 1 year; may be renewed 1 additional year.

Additional data Eligible students should apply through their school's financial aid office.

Number awarded Varies each year.

Deadline Deadline dates vary by institution; check with your school's financial aid office.

[495]
WISCONSIN MINORITY UNDERGRADUATE RETENTION GRANTS

Wisconsin Higher Educational Aids Board
131 West Wilson Street, Suite 902
P.O. Box 7885
Madison, WI 53707-7885
(608) 267-2212   Fax: (608) 267-2808
E-mail: deanna.schulz@wisconsin.gov
Web: heab.state.wi.us/programs.html

Summary To provide financial assistance to Hispanic Americans and other minorities in Wisconsin who are currently enrolled at a college in the state.

Eligibility This program is open to residents of Wisconsin who are African Americans, Hispanic Americans, American Indians, or southeast Asians (students who were admitted to the United States after December 31, 1975 and who are a former citizen of Laos, Vietnam, or Cambodia or whose ancestor

was a citizen of 1 of those countries). Applicants must be enrolled at least half time as sophomores, juniors, seniors, or fifth-year undergraduates at a Wisconsin technical college, tribal college, or independent college or university in the state. They must be nominated by their institution and be able to demonstrate financial need.

Financial Data Stipends range from $250 to $2,500 per year, depending on the need of the recipient.

Duration Up to 4 years.

Additional data The Wisconsin Higher Educational Aids Board administers this program for students at private nonprofit institutions, technical colleges, and tribal colleges. The University of Wisconsin has a similar program for students attending any of the branches of that system. Eligible students should apply through their school's financial aid office.

Number awarded Varies each year.

Deadline Deadline dates vary by institution; check with your school's financial aid office.

[496]
WISCONSIN TALENT INCENTIVE PROGRAM (TIP) GRANTS

Wisconsin Higher Educational Aids Board
131 West Wilson Street, Suite 902
P.O. Box 7885
Madison, WI 53707-7885
(608) 266-1665   Fax: (608) 267-2808
E-mail: colettem1.brown@wi.gov
Web: heab.state.wi.us/programs.html

Summary To provide financial assistance for college to Hispanic Americans and other needy and educationally disadvantaged students in Wisconsin.

Eligibility This program is open to residents of Wisconsin entering a college or university in the state who meet the requirements of both financial need and educational disadvantage. Financial need qualifications include 1) family contribution (a dependent student whose expected parent contribution is $200 or less or an independent student whose maximum academic year contribution is $200 or less); 2) Temporary Assistance to Needy Families (TANF) or Wisconsin Works (W2) benefits (a dependent student whose family is receiving TANF or W2 benefits or an independent student who is receiving TANF or W2 benefits); or 3) unemployment (a dependent student whose parents are ineligible for unemployment compensation and have no current income from employment, or an independent student and spouse, if married, who are ineligible for unemployment compensation and have no current income from employment). Educational disadvantage qualifications include students who are 1) minorities (African American, Native American, Hispanic, or southeast Asian); 2) enrolled in a special academic support program due to insufficient academic preparation; 3) a first-generation college student (neither parent graduated from a 4-year college or university); 4) disabled according to the Department of Workforce Development, the Division of Vocational Rehabilitation, or a Wisconsin college or university that uses the Americans with Disabilities Act definition; 5) currently or formerly incarcerated in a correctional institution; or 6) from an environmental and academic background that deters the pursuit of educational plans. Students already in college are not eligible.

Financial Data Stipends range up to $1,800 per year.

Duration 1 year; may be renewed up to 4 additional years, provided the recipient continues to be a Wisconsin resident enrolled at least half time in a degree or certificate program, makes satisfactory academic progress, demonstrates financial need, and remains enrolled continuously from semester to semester and from year to year. If recipients withdraw from school or cease to attend classes for any reason (other than medical necessity), they may not reapply.

Number awarded Varies each year.

Deadline Deadline not specified.

[497]
WOMEN OF ALPFA DELOITTE STUDENT ESSAY COMPETITION

Association of Latino Professionals in Finance and
Accounting
Attn: Student Essay Contest
801 South Grand Avenue, Suite 650
Los Angeles, CA 90017
(213) 243-0004   Fax: (213) 243-0006
Web: www.alpfa.org

Summary To recognize and reward, with scholarships for further study, female members of the Association of Latino Professionals in Finance and Accounting (ALPFA) who submit outstanding essays on topics related to business.

Eligibility This competition is open to women who are members of ALPFA and working full time on an undergraduate or master's degree in accounting, business, finance, or a related field at a college or university in the United States or Puerto Rico. Applicants must have a GPA of 3.0 or higher. They must submit an essay, approximately 800 words in length, in response to an assigned problem related to professional development in business-related fields. Their essay should include descriptions and explanations of their ability to demonstrate leadership, strategize and problem solve effectively, overcome team doubt, and show strength derived from their culture. U.S. citizenship or permanent resident status is required.

Financial Data The award is a $1,200 scholarship. The winner also receives complimentary registration, airfare, and accommodations for the ALPFA annual convention.

Duration The competition is held annually.

Additional data This competition is sponsored by Deloitte LLP.

Number awarded 1 each year.

Deadline May of each year.

[498]
WOMEN'S TRANSPORTATION SEMINAR JUNIOR COLLEGE SCHOLARSHIP

Women's Transportation Seminar
Attn: WTS Foundation
1701 K Street, N.W., Suite 800
Washington, DC 20006
(202) 955-5085   Fax: (202) 955-5088
E-mail: wts@wtsinternational.org
Web: www.wtsinternational.org/education/scholarships

Summary To provide financial assistance to women (particularly minority women) who are enrolled at a community college or trade school to prepare for a career in transportation.

Eligibility This program is open to women who are working on an associate or technical degree in transportation or a transportation-related field (e.g., transportation engineering, planning, finance, or logistics). Applicants must have a GPA of 3.0 or higher. Along with their application, they must submit a 500-word statement about their career goals after graduation and why they think they should receive the scholarship award. Applications must be submitted first to a local chapter; the chapters forward selected applications for consideration on the national level. Minority women are especially encouraged to apply. Selection is based on transportation involvement and goals, job skills, academic record, and leadership potential; financial need is not considered.

Financial Data The stipend is $1,000.

Duration 1 year.

Additional data Local chapters may also award additional funding to winners for their area.

Number awarded 1 each year.

Deadline Applications must be submitted by November to a local WTS chapter.

[499]
XEROX TECHNICAL MINORITY SCHOLARSHIP PROGRAM

Xerox Corporation
Attn: Technical Minority Scholarship Program
150 State Street, Fourth Floor
Rochester, NY 14614
(585) 422-7689   E-mail: GlobalCareers@xerox.com
Web: www.xerox.com/jobs/minority-scholarships/enus.html

Summary To provide financial assistance to Hispanic Americans and other minorities interested in undergraduate or graduate education in the sciences and/or engineering.

Eligibility This program is open to minorities (people of African American, Asian, Pacific Islander, Native American, Native Alaskan, or Hispanic descent) working full time on a bachelor's, master's, or doctoral degree in chemistry, computing and software systems, engineering (chemical, computer, electrical, imaging, manufacturing, mechanical, optical, or software), information management, laser optics, materials science, physics, or printing management science. Applicants must be U.S. citizens or permanent residents with a GPA of 3.0 or higher and attending a 4-year college or university.

Financial Data Stipends range from $1,000 to $10,000.

Duration 1 year.

Number awarded Varies each year, recently, 130 of these scholarships were awarded.

Deadline September of each year.

[500]
ZANNONI INDIVIDUAL SUMMER UNDERGRADUATE RESEARCH FELLOWSHIPS

American Society for Pharmacology and Experimental
Therapeutics
9650 Rockville Pike
Bethesda, MD 20814-3995
(301) 634-7060   Fax: (301) 634-7061
E-mail: djordan@aspet.org
Web: www.aspet.org/awards/SURF

Summary To provide funding to undergraduate students (particularly Hispanic Americans, other minorities, and women) who are interested in participating in a summer research project at a laboratory affiliated with the American Society for Pharmacology and Experimental Therapeutics (ASPET).

Eligibility This program is open to undergraduate students interested in working during the summer in the laboratory of a society member who must agree to act as a sponsor. Applications must be submitted jointly by the student and the sponsor, and they must include 1) a letter from the sponsor with a brief description of the proposed research, a statement of the qualifications of the student, the degree of independence the student will have, a description of complementary activities available to the student, and a description of how the student will report on the research results; 2) a letter from the student indicating the nature of his or her interest in the project and a description of future plans; 3) a copy of the sponsor's updated curriculum vitae; and 4) copies of all the student's undergraduate transcripts. Selection is based on the nature of the research opportunities provided, student and sponsor qualifications, and the likelihood the student will prepare for a career in pharmacology. Applications from underrepresented minorities and women are particularly encouraged.

Financial Data The stipend is $2,800. Funds are paid directly to the institution but may be used only for student stipends.

Duration 10 weeks during the summer.

Additional data Some of these awards are funded through the Glenn E. Ullyot Fund; those recipients are designated as the Ullyot Fellows.

Number awarded Varies each year; recently, 4 of these fellowships were awarded.

Deadline February of each year.

Graduate Students

Listed alphabetically by program title and described in detail here are 420 fellowships, forgivable loans, grants, awards, and other sources of "free money" set aside for Hispanic Americans who are incoming, continuing, or returning graduate students working on a master's, doctoral, or professional degree. This funding is available to support study, training, research, and/or creative activities in the United States.

[501]
ABA LEGAL OPPORTUNITY SCHOLARSHIP

American Bar Association
Attn: Fund for Justice and Education
321 North Clark Street, 21st Floor
Chicago, IL 60654-7598
(312) 988-5927   Fax: (312) 988-6392
E-mail: legalosf@staff.abanet.org
Web: www.americanbar.org

Summary To provide financial assistance to Hispanic Americans and other racial and ethnic minority students who are interested in attending law school.

Eligibility This program is open to racial and ethnic minority college graduates who are interested in attending an ABA-accredited law school. Only students beginning law school may apply; students who have completed 1 or more semesters of law school are not eligible. Applicants must have a cumulative GPA of 2.5 or higher and be citizens or permanent residents of the United States. Along with their application, they must submit a 1,000-word statement describing their personal and family background, community service activities, and other connections to their racial and ethnic minority community. Financial need is also considered in the selection process.

Financial Data The stipend is $5,000 per year.

Duration 1 year; may be renewed for 2 additional years if satisfactory performance in law school has been achieved.

Additional data This program began in the 2000-01 academic year.

Number awarded Approximately 20 each year.

Deadline February of each year.

[502]
ABC LATINO MINISTRIES SCHOLARSHIP

American Baptist Churches USA
Attn: American Baptist Home Mission Societies
National Coordinator for Intercultural Ministries
P.O. Box 851
Valley Forge, PA 19482-0851
(610) 768-2421   Toll Free: (800) ABC-3USA, ext. 2421
Fax: (610) 768-2453
E-mail: Salvador.Orellana@abc-usa.org
Web: www.abhms.org

Summary To provide financial assistance to Latinos who are interested in preparing for or furthering a church career in the American Baptist Church (ABC).

Eligibility This program is open to Latino members of the ABC or its recognized institutions who demonstrate financial need. They must be enrolled full time at an accredited institution, working on an undergraduate degree or first professional degree in a seminary. Applicants must be currently serving or planning to serve in a vocation with the church or with its recognized institutions. They must be U.S. citizens who have been a member of an American Baptist Church for at least 1 year.

Financial Data The stipends range from $500 to $3,000 per year.

Duration 1 year; may be renewed.

Number awarded Varies each year.

Deadline May of each year.

[503]
ACA/MARTIN LUTHER KING JR. SCHOLARSHIP AWARDS

American Correctional Association
Attn: Scholarship Award Committee
206 North Washington Street, Suite 200
Alexandria, VA 22314
(703) 224-0000   Toll Free: (800) ACA-JOIN
Fax: (703) 224-0179   E-mail: jenniferb@aca.org
Web: www.aca.org/pastpresentfuture/awards.asp

Summary To provide financial assistance for undergraduate or graduate study to Hispanic Americans and other minorities interested in a career in the criminal justice field.

Eligibility Members of the American Correctional Association (ACA) may nominate a minority person for these awards. Nominees do not need to be ACA members, but they must have been accepted to or be enrolled in an undergraduate or graduate program in criminal justice at a 4-year college or university. Along with the nomination package, they must submit a 250-word essay describing their reflections on the ideals and philosophies of Dr. Martin Luther King and how they have attempted to emulate those qualities in their lives. They must provide documentation of financial need, academic achievement, and commitment to the principles of Dr. King.

Financial Data A stipend is awarded (amount not specified). Funds are paid directly to the recipient's college or university.

Number awarded 1 each year.

Deadline May of each year.

[504]
ACADEMY OF NUTRITION AND DIETETICS GRADUATE SCHOLARSHIPS

Academy of Nutrition and Dietetics
Attn: Foundation
120 South Riverside Plaza, Suite 2000
Chicago, IL 60606-6995
(312) 899-0040   Toll Free: (800) 877-1600, ext. 1133
Fax: (312) 899-4817   E-mail: scholarships@eatright.org
Web: www.eatright.org/Foundation/scholarships

Summary To provide financial assistance to Hispanic American and other graduate student members of the Academy of Nutrition and Dietetics.

Eligibility This program is open to members of the academy who are enrolled in the second year of a master's or doctoral degree program in dietetics. Applicants who are currently completing a dietetic internship or preprofessional practice program that is combined with a graduate program may also apply. The graduate scholarships are available only to U.S. citizens and permanent residents. Applicants should intend to practice in the field of dietetics. Some scholarships require specific areas of study (e.g., public health nutrition, food service administration) and status as a registered dietitian. Others may require membership in a specific dietetic practice group, residency in a specific state, or underrepresented minority group status. The same application form can be used for all categories.

Financial Data Stipends normally range from $500 to $3,000; recently, they averaged approximately $1,870.

Duration 1 year.

Additional data The Academy of Nutrition and Dietetics was formerly the American Dietetic Association.

Number awarded Approximately 60 each year.

Deadline February of each year.

[505]
ACOUSTICAL SOCIETY OF AMERICA MINORITY FELLOWSHIP

Acoustical Society of America
Attn: Office Manager
2 Huntington Quadrangle, Suite 1NO1
Melville, NY 11747-4502
(516) 576-2360   Fax: (516) 576-2377
E-mail: asa@aip.org
Web: www.acousticalsociety.org

Summary To provide financial assistance to Hispanic Americans and other underrepresented minorities who are working on a graduate degree involving acoustics.

Eligibility This program is open to U.S. and Canadian citizens and permanent residents who are members of a minority group that is underrepresented in the sciences (Hispanic, African American, or Native American). Applicants must be enrolled in or accepted to a graduate degree program as a full-time student. Their program of study may be in any field of pure or applied science and engineering directly related to acoustics, including acoustical oceanography, architectural acoustics, animal bioacoustics, biomedical ultrasound, bioresponse to vibration, engineering acoustics, musical acoustics, noise, physical acoustics, psychological acoustics, physiological acoustics, signal processing in acoustics, speech communication, structural acoustics and vibration, and underwater acoustics. Along with their application, student must submit a statement on why they are enrolled in their present academic program, including how they intend to use their graduate education to develop a career and how the study of acoustics is relevant to their career objectives.

Financial Data The stipend is $20,000 per year. The sponsor strongly encourages the host educational institution to waive all tuition costs and assessed fees. Fellows also receive $1,000 for travel to attend a national meeting of the sponsor.

Duration 1 year; may be renewed for 1 additional year if the recipient is making normal progress toward a degree and is enrolled full time.

Additional data This program began in 1992.

Number awarded 1 each year.

Deadline March of each year.

[506]
ACS/ORGANIC CHEMISTRY GRADUATE STUDENT FELLOWSHIPS

American Chemical Society
Division of Organic Chemistry
1155 16th Street, N.W.
Washington, DC 20036
(202) 872-4401   Toll Free: (800) 227-5558, ext. 4401
E-mail: division@acs.org
Web: www.organicdivision.org/?nd=graduate_fellowship

Summary To provide funding for research to members (particularly minority and female members) of the Division of Organic Chemistry of the American Chemical Society (ACS) who are working on a doctoral degree in organic chemistry.

Eligibility This program is open to members of the division who are entering the third or fourth year of a Ph.D. program in organic chemistry. Applicants must submit 3 letters of recommendation, a resume, and a short essay on a research area of their choice. U.S. citizenship or permanent resident status is required. Selection is based primarily on evidence of research accomplishment. Applications from women and minorities are especially encouraged.

Financial Data The stipend is $26,000; that includes $750 for travel support to present a poster of their work at the National Organic Symposium.

Duration 1 year.

Additional data This program began in 1982. It includes the Emmanuil Troyansky Fellowship. Current corporate sponsors include Genentech, Organic Syntheses, Boehringer Ingelheim, and Amgen.

Number awarded Varies each year; recently, 8 of these fellowships were awarded.

Deadline May of each year.

[507]
ADDIE B. MORRIS SCHOLARSHIP

American Association of Railroad Superintendents
P.O. Box 200
La Fox, IL 60147
(630) 762-0754   E-mail: aars@supt.org
Web: www.railroadsuperintendents.org/Scholarships

Summary To provide financial assistance to undergraduate and graduate students, with preference given to Hispanic Americans and other minorities working on a degree in transportation.

Eligibility This program is open to full-time undergraduate and graduate students enrolled at accredited colleges and universities in Canada or the United States. Applicants must have completed enough credits to have standing as a sophomore and must have a GPA of 2.75 or higher. Preference is given to minority students enrolled in the transportation field who can demonstrate financial need.

Financial Data The stipend is $1,000. Funds are sent directly to the recipient's institution.

Duration 1 year.

Number awarded 1 or more each year.

Deadline May of each year.

[508]
ADLER POLLOCK & SHEEHAN DIVERSITY SCHOLARSHIP

Adler Pollock & Sheehan P.C.
Attn: Diversity Committee Chair
175 Federal Street
Boston, MA 02110-2210
(617) 482-0600   Fax: (617) 482-0604
E-mail: Diversitycomm@apslaw.com
Web: www.apslaw.com/firm-diversity.html

Summary To provide financial assistance to Hispanic Americans and other residents of Massachusetts and Rhode Island who are members of diverse groups and plan to attend law school in any state.

Eligibility This program is open to residents of Massachusetts and Rhode Island who are members of a diverse group, including African American, American Indian, Hispanic, Asian/Pacific Islander, gay/lesbian, or other minority group. Applicants must be entering their first year at an ABA-accredited law school in the United States. They must be able to demonstrate academic achievement, a desire to work and reside in Massachusetts or Rhode Island after graduation, a demonstrated commitment to the community, a vision of contributions to the profession and community after graduation, and financial need.

Financial Data The stipend is $10,000.

Duration 1 year.

Number awarded 1 each year.

Deadline May of each year.

[509]
ADRIENNE M. AND CHARLES SHELBY ROOKS FELLOWSHIP FOR RACIAL AND ETHNIC THEOLOGICAL STUDENTS

United Church of Christ
Attn: Local Church Ministries
700 Prospect Avenue East
Cleveland, OH 44115-1100
(216) 736-3865   Toll Free: (866) 822-8224, ext. 3865
Fax: (216) 736-3783   E-mail: lcm@ucc.org
Web: www.ucc.org/seminarians/ucc-scholarships-for.html

Summary To provide financial assistance to Hispanic American and other minority students who are either enrolled at an accredited seminary preparing for a career of service in the United Church of Christ (UCC) or working on a doctoral degree in the field of religion.

Eligibility This program is open to members of underrepresented ethnic groups (African American, Hispanic American, Asian American, Native American Indian, or Pacific Islander) who have been a member of a UCC congregation for at least 1 year. Applicants must be either 1) enrolled in an accredited school of theology in the United States or Canada and working on an M.Div. degree with the intent of becoming a pastor or teacher within the UCC; or 2) doctoral (Ph.D., Th.D., or Ed.D.) students within a field related to religious studies. Seminary students must have a GPA in all postsecondary work of 3.0 or higher and must have begun the in-care process; preference is given to students who have demonstrated leadership (through a history of service to the church) and scholarship (through exceptional academic performance). For doctoral students, preference is given to applicants who have demonstrated academic excellence, teaching effectiveness, and commitment to the UCC and who intend to become professors in colleges, seminaries, or graduate schools.

Financial Data Grants range from $500 to $5,000 per year.

Duration 1 year; may be renewed.

Number awarded Varies each year; recently, 16 of these scholarships, including 10 for M.Div. students and 6 for doctoral students, were awarded.

Deadline February of each year.

[510]
ADVANCING HISPANIC EXCELLENCE IN TECHNOLOGY, ENGINEERING, MATH AND SCIENCE (AHETEMS) DISSERTATION SCHOLARSHIPS

Society of Hispanic Professional Engineers Foundation, Inc.
Attn: Advancing Hispanic Excellence in Technology, Engineering, Math and Science
13181 Crossroads Parkway North, Suite 450
P.O. Box 93577
City of Industry, CA 91715
(323) 725-3970, ext. 118   Fax: (323) 622-1046
E-mail: shpefoundation@shpe.org
Web: www.shpefoundation.org

Summary To provide funding for dissertation research to doctoral candidates of Hispanic descent who are preparing for a career in science, technology, engineering, mathematics (STEM), or a related field.

Eligibility This program is open to doctoral candidates of Hispanic descent who are enrolled at an accredited university in the United States or Puerto Rico and are members of the Society of Hispanic Professional Engineers (SHPE). Applicants must be working on a Ph.D. or Eng.D. degree in a STEM or related field and have completed all work except the dissertation. They must have a GPA of 3.5 or higher. Along with their application, they must submit a 500-word personal statement covering their community involvement, leadership, academic achievements, research internship and co-op experiences, and short-term and long-term goals and aspirations. Financial need is considered in the selection process.

Financial Data The grant is $5,000.

Duration 1 year.

Number awarded 1 or more each year.

Deadline April of each year.

[511]
ADVANCING HISPANIC EXCELLENCE IN TECHNOLOGY, ENGINEERING, MATH AND SCIENCE (AHETEMS) GENERAL SCHOLARSHIPS

Society of Hispanic Professional Engineers Foundation, Inc.
Attn: Advancing Hispanic Excellence in Technology, Engineering, Math and Science
13181 Crossroads Parkway North, Suite 450
P.O. Box 93577
City of Industry, CA 91715
(323) 725-3970, ext. 118   Fax: (323) 622-1046
E-mail: shpefoundation@shpe.org
Web: www.shpefoundation.org

Summary To provide financial assistance to undergraduate and graduate students of Hispanic descent who are preparing for a career in science, technology, engineering, mathematics (STEM), or a related field.

Eligibility This program is open to students of Hispanic descent who are accepted into or attending an accredited 2- or 4-year college or university in the United States or Puerto Rico and are members of the Society of Hispanic Professional Engineers (SHPE). Applicants must be working or planning to work full time on a degree in a STEM or related field. High school seniors and undergraduates must have a

GPA of 2.75 or higher; graduate students must have a GPA of 3.0 or higher. Along with their application, they must submit a 500-word personal statement covering their community involvement, leadership, academic achievements, research internship and co-op experiences, and short-term and long-term goals and aspirations. Both merit-based and need-based scholarships are available. U.S. citizenship or permanent resident status is not required.

Financial Data Stipends range from $1,000 to $3,000.

Duration 1 year.

Additional data Advancing Hispanic Excellence in Technology, Engineering, Math and Science (AHETEMS) was established in 2004 by the Society of Hispanic Professional Engineers (SHPE) as an independent nonprofit foundation.

Number awarded 1 or more each year.

Deadline April of each year.

[512]
ADVANCING HISPANIC EXCELLENCE IN TECHNOLOGY, ENGINEERING, MATH AND SCIENCE (AHETEMS) PROFESSIONAL SCHOLARSHIPS

Society of Hispanic Professional Engineers Foundation, Inc.
Attn: Advancing Hispanic Excellence in Technology, Engineering, Math and Science
13181 Crossroads Parkway North, Suite 450
P.O. Box 93577
City of Industry, CA 91715
(323) 725-3970, ext. 118   Fax: (323) 622-1046
E-mail: shpefoundation@shpe.org
Web: www.shpefoundation.org

Summary To provide financial assistance to Hispanic professionals working on a graduate degree in science, technology, engineering, or mathematics.

Eligibility This program is open to members of the Society of Hispanic Professional Engineers (SHPE) who are employed full time in the United States or Puerto Rico in a technical career field. Applicants must be enrolled at least half time in a science, technology, engineering, or mathematics (STEM) degree program in the United States or Puerto Rico. They must have a GPA of 3.25 or higher. Along with their application, they must submit a 500-word personal statement covering their community involvement, leadership, academic achievements, research internship and co-op experiences, and short-term and long-term goals and aspirations. Selection is based on merit. U.S. citizenship or permanent resident status is not required.

Financial Data The stipend is $2,000.

Duration 1 year.

Additional data Advancing Hispanic Excellence in Technology, Engineering, Math and Science (AHETEMS) was established in 2004 by SHPE as an independent nonprofit foundation.

Number awarded 1 or more each year.

Deadline April of each year.

[513]
AETNA FOUNDATION-NMF HEALTHCARE LEADERSHIP PROGRAM

National Medical Fellowships, Inc.
Attn: Scholarship Program
347 Fifth Avenue, Suite 510
New York, NY 10016
(212) 483-8880, ext. 304   Toll Free: (877) NMF-1DOC
Fax: (212) 483-8897   E-mail: mbrito@nmfonline.org
Web: www.nmfonline.org/programs/aetna-foundation

Summary To provide financial assistance to Hispanic Americans and other underrepresented minorities who are medical students at schools in selected states.

Eligibility This program is open to members of underrepresented minority groups (African American, Hispanic/Latino, American Indian, Native Hawaiian, Alaska Native, Vietnamese, Cambodian, or Native Pacific Islander) who are currently enrolled in their second or third year of medical school. U.S. citizenship is required. Applicants must be attending medical school in southern California (particularly Los Angeles), Connecticut, Illinois (particularly Chicago), New Jersey, New York City, or Philadelphia. Along with their application, they must submit an essay of 500 to 1,000 words on what leadership means for physicians. Selection is based on that essay, letters of recommendation, community service and leadership activities, and financial need.

Financial Data The stipend is $5,000.

Duration 1 year.

Additional data Funding for this program, which is administered by National Medical Fellowships (NMF), is provided by the Aetna Foundation.

Number awarded 10 each year.

Deadline February of each year for Illinois; March of each year for Connecticut, New Jersey, New York City, and Philadelphia; or April of each year for southern California.

[514]
AFRL/DAGSI OHIO STUDENT-FACULTY RESEARCH FELLOWSHIP PROGRAM

Dayton Area Graduate Studies Institute
3155 Research Boulevard, Suite 205
Kettering, OH 45420
(937) 781-4001   Fax: (937) 781-4005
E-mail: kelam@dagsi.org
Web: www.dagsi.org/pages/osrfp_proinforeq.html

Summary To provide funding to faculty and graduate students (particularly Hispanic Americans and other minorities, women, and individuals with disabilities) at designated universities in Ohio who are from any state and interested in conducting research in aerospace technologies of interest to the U.S. Air Force.

Eligibility This program is open to research teams of full-time graduate students and faculty at 18 designated Ohio universities. Applicants must be interested in conducting research that will utilize the facilities of the Air Force Research Laboratory (AFRL) at Wright-Patterson Air Force Base. All 6 directorates at the AFRL (air vehicles, propulsion, sensors, materials and manufacturing, human effectiveness, and information) participate in this program. Applications from Ph.D. candidates must be developed and written largely by the student, with support, guidance, and input as necessary from the faculty partner. For master's projects, the proposal can be developed and written jointly by the faculty member and the student. All participants (faculty and student) must be U.S. citizens. Underrepresented minorities, women, and persons with disabilities are strongly urged to apply.

Financial Data Grants provide stipends of $23,500 for students who have a master's degree and are working on a Ph.D. or $18,500 for students who have a bachelor's degree and are working on a master's; student's tuition for 1 academic year; a faculty stipend of $11,000; student and faculty allowances of $3,000 each for program-related travel or other approved expenses; and overhead at a maximum off-campus rate of 26% of student and faculty stipends and miscellaneous allowances.

Duration 1 year; may be renewed for 1 additional year by master's students and for 2 additional years by Ph.D. candidates. Students are expected to spend 8 consecutive weeks conducting research at AFRL and faculty members are expected to spend at least 1 month conducting research at AFRL.

Additional data DAGSI was established in 1994 as a consortium of graduate engineering schools at the University of Dayton, Wright State University, and the Air Force Institute of Technology. The Ohio State University and the University of Cincinnati joined as affiliated members in 1996 and Miami University and Ohio University joined as associate members in 2001. Students from the following universities are also eligible to participate in this program: University of Akron, Bowling Green State University, Central State University, Cleveland State University, Kent State University, Shawnee State University, University of Toledo, Youngstown State University, Medical College of Ohio, Northeastern Ohio Universities College of Medicine, and Case Western Reserve University.

Number awarded At least 20 each year.

Deadline January of each year.

[515]
AGA INVESTING IN THE FUTURE STUDENT RESEARCH FELLOWSHIPS

American Gastroenterological Association
Attn: AGA Research Foundation
Research Awards Manager
4930 Del Ray Avenue
Bethesda, MD 20814-2512
(301) 222-4012   Fax: (301) 654-5920
E-mail: awards@gastro.org
Web: www.gastro.org/aga-foundation/grants

Summary To provide funding for research on digestive diseases or nutrition to undergraduate and medical students who are Hispanic Americans or from other underrepresented minority groups.

Eligibility This program is open to undergraduate and medical students at accredited U.S. institutions who are African Americans, Hispanic/Latino Americans, Alaska Natives, American Indians, or Natives of the U.S. Pacific Islands. Applicants must be interested in conducting research on digestive diseases or nutrition. They may not hold similar salary support awards from other agencies (e.g., American Liver Foundation, Crohn's and Colitis Foundation). Research must be conducted under the supervision of a preceptor who is a full-time faculty member at an institution in a state other than the student's, directing a research project in a gastroenterol-

ogy-related area, and a member of the American Gastroenterological Association (AGA).

Financial Data Fellowships provide payment of housing, travel, and a stipend of $5,000.

Duration 8 to 10 weeks. The work may take place at any time during the year.

Number awarded 10 each year.

Deadline February of each year.

[516]
AGING RESEARCH DISSERTATION AWARDS TO INCREASE DIVERSITY

National Institute on Aging
Attn: Office of Extramural Affairs
7201 Wisconsin Avenue, Suite 2C-218
Bethesda, MD 20814
(301) 402-4158   Fax: (301) 402-2945
TDD: (301) 451-0088   E-mail: hunterc@nia.nih.gov
Web: www.grants.nih.gov

Summary To provide financial assistance to doctoral candidates from underrepresented groups (particularly Hispanic Americans, other minorities, and students with disabilities) who wish to conduct research on aging.

Eligibility This program is open to doctoral candidates conducting research on a dissertation with an aging-related focus, including the basic biology of aging; chronic, disabling, and degenerative diseases of aging, with a particular focus on Alzheimer's Disease; multiple morbidities; individual behavioral and social changes with aging; caregiving; longevity; and the consequences for society of an aging population. Applicants must be 1) members of an ethnic or racial group underrepresented in biomedical or behavioral research (African Americans, Hispanic Americans, American Indians, Alaska Natives, Native Hawaiians, and other Pacific Islanders); 2) individuals with disabilities; or 3) individuals from socially, culturally, economically, or educationally disadvantaged backgrounds that have inhibited their ability to prepare for a career in health-related research. They must be U.S. citizens, nationals, or permanent residents.

Financial Data Grants provide $22,032 per year for stipend and up to $20,000 for additional expenses. No funds may be used to pay for tuition or fees associated with completion of doctoral studies. The institution may receive up to 8% of direct costs as facilities and administrative costs per year.

Duration Up to 2 years.

Number awarded Up to 5 each year.

Deadline Applications must be submitted by February, June, or October of each year.

[517]
AHRQ GRANTS FOR HEALTH SERVICES RESEARCH DISSERTATIONS

Agency for Healthcare Research and Quality
Attn: Office of Extramural Research, Education, and
  Priority Populations
540 Gaither Road
Rockville, MD 20850
(301) 427-1869   Fax: (301) 427-1561
TDD: (301) 451-0088 E-mail: Ali.Azadegan@ahrq.hhs.gov
Web: grants.nih.gov/grants/guide/pa-files/PA-12-256.html

Summary To provide funding to doctoral candidates (particularly Hispanic Americans, other underrepresented minorities, and students with disabilities) who are engaged in research for a dissertation that examines an aspect of the health care system.

Eligibility This program is open to citizens, nationals, and permanent residents who are enrolled full time in an accredited research doctoral degree program at an institution in the United States. Applicants must have completed all requirements for the doctoral degree except for the dissertation in such fields as the social or behavioral sciences, mathematics, engineering, health services, nursing, epidemiology, biostatistics, health policy, or health informatics. Their proposed dissertation topic must relate to the strategic goals of the Agency for Healthcare Research and Quality (AHRQ): 1) reducing the risk of harm from health care services by promoting the delivery of appropriate care that achieves the best quality outcomes; 2) achieving wider access to effective health care services and reducing health care costs; and 3) assuring that providers and consumers/patients use beneficial and timely health care information to make informed decisions. Priority is given to proposals that address health services research issues critical to such priority population as individuals living in inner city and rural (including frontier) areas; low-income and minority groups; women, children, and the elderly; and individuals with special health care needs, including those with disabilities and those who need chronic or end-of-life health care. Members of underrepresented racial and ethnic groups, individuals from disadvantaged backgrounds, and individuals with disabilities are especially encouraged to apply.

Financial Data Up to $40,000 is awarded for the investigator's salary, direct project expenses (travel, data purchasing, data processing, and supplies), and matriculation fees. The institution will receive facilities and administrative costs of 8% of total allowable direct costs, exclusive of tuition and related fees, health insurance, and expenditures for equipment.

Duration 9 to 17 months.

Number awarded Up to 30 each year.

Deadline January, April, July, or October of each year.

[518]
AICPA FELLOWSHIPS FOR MINORITY DOCTORAL STUDENTS

American Institute of Certified Public Accountants
Attn: Academic and Career Development Division
220 Leigh Farm Road
Durham, NC 27707-8110
(919) 402-4931   Fax: (919) 419-4705
E-mail: scholarships@aicpa.org
Web: www.aicpa.org

Summary To provide financial assistance to Hispanic American and other underrepresented minority doctoral students who wish to prepare for a career teaching accounting at the college level.

Eligibility This program is open to underrepresented minority students who have applied to and/or been accepted into a doctoral program with a concentration in accounting. Applicants must have earned a master's degree or completed a minimum of 3 years of full-time work in accounting. They must be attending or planning to attend school full time and agree not to work full time in a paid position, teach more than 1 course as a teaching assistant, or work more than 25% as a research assistant. U.S. citizenship or permanent resident status is required. Preference is given to applicants who have attained a C.P.A. designation and/or are members of the American Institute of Certified Public Accountants (AICPA) and those who perform AICPA committee service. For purposes of this program, the AICPA defines minority students as those whose heritage is Black or African American, Hispanic or Latino, or Native American. Selection is based on academic and professional achievement, commitment to earning an accounting doctoral degree, and financial need.

Financial Data The stipend is $12,000 per year.

Duration 1 year; may be renewed up to 4 additional years.

Number awarded Varies each year; recently, 21 of these fellowships were awarded.

Deadline March of each year.

[519]
AIR FORCE SUMMER FACULTY FELLOWSHIP PROGRAM

American Society for Engineering Education
Attn: AFSFF Program
1818 N Street, N.W., Suite 600
Washington, DC 20036-2479
(202) 649-3834   Fax: (202) 265-8504
E-mail: sffp@asee.org
Web: sffp.asee.org

Summary To provide funding to science and engineering faculty and graduate students (particularly Hispanic Americans and other underrepresented minorities) who are interested in conducting research during the summer at Air Force facilities.

Eligibility This program is open to U.S. citizens and permanent residents who have a full-time faculty appointment at a U.S. college or university in a field of engineering or science of interest to the Air Force. Applicants must be interested in conducting a research project, under the direction of an Air Force research adviser, at an Air Force Research Laboratory, the U.S. Air Force Academy, or the Air Force Institute of Technology. A graduate student may accompany the faculty member. Faculty and students at Historically Black Colleges and Universities ((HBCUs), Minority Institutions (MIs), American Indian Tribal Colleges and Universities (TCUs), and Hispanic Serving Institutions (HSIs) are especially encouraged to apply.

Financial Data Stipends are $1,700 per week for full professors, $1,500 per week for associate professors, $1,300 per week for assistant professors, $884 per week for graduate students working on a master's degree, or $1,037 per week for graduate students working on a doctoral degree. Relocation reimbursement and a daily expense allowance of $50 (for fellows with a commute distance greater than 50 miles) are also available.

Duration 8 to 12 weeks during the summer. May be renewed for a second and third summer, but recipients may not reapply for 2 years after completing a third summer.

Additional data This program first operated in 2005. Research must be conducted in residence at an Air Force facility.

Number awarded Approximately 100 each year.

Deadline December of each year.

[520]
ALA SPECTRUM SCHOLARSHIP PROGRAM

American Library Association
Attn: Office for Diversity
50 East Huron Street
Chicago, IL 60611-2795
(312) 280-5048   Toll Free: (800) 545-2433, ext. 5048
Fax: (312) 280-3256   TDD: (888) 814-7692
E-mail: spectrum@ala.org
Web: www.ala.org/offices/diversity/spectrum

Summary   To provide financial assistance to Hispanic American and other minority students interested in working on a degree in librarianship.

Eligibility   This program is open to ethnic minority students (African American or Black, Asian, Native Hawaiian or other Pacific Islander, Latino or Hispanic, and American Indian or Alaska Native). Applicants must be U.S. or Canadian citizens or permanent residents who have completed no more than a third of the requirements for a master's or school library media degree. They must be enrolled full or part time at an ALA-accredited school of library and information studies or an ALA-recognized NCATE school library media program. Selection is based on academic leadership, outstanding service, commitment to a career in librarianship, statements indicating the nature of the applicant's library and other work experience, letters of reference, and personal presentation.

Financial Data   The stipend is $5,000.

Duration   1 year; nonrenewable.

Additional data   This program began in 1998. It is administered by a joint committee of the American Library Association (ALA).

Number awarded   Varies each year; recently, 69 of these scholarships were awarded.

Deadline   February of each year.

[521]
ALAO DIVERSITY SCHOLARSHIP

Academic Library Association of Ohio
c/o Diane Kolosionek, Diversity Committee Chair
Cleveland State University, Michael Schwartz Library
2121 Euclid Avenue
RT 110D
Cleveland, OH 44115-2214
(216) 802-3358   E-mail: d.kolosionek44@csuohio.edu
Web: www.alaoweb.org

Summary   To provide financial assistance to Hispanic American and other residents of Ohio who are working on a master's degree in library science at a school in any state and will contribute to diversity in the profession.

Eligibility   This program is open to residents of Ohio who are enrolled or entering an ALA-accredited program for a master's degree in library science, either on campus or via distance education. Applicants must be able to demonstrate how they will contribute to diversity in the profession, including (but not limited to) race or ethnicity, sexual orientation, life experience, physical ability, and a sense of commitment to those and other diversity issues. Along with their application, they must submit 1) a list of participation in honor societies or professional organizations, awards, scholarships, prizes, honors, or class offices; 2) a list of their community, civic, organizational, or volunteer experiences; and 3) an essay on their understanding of and commitment to diversity in libraries, including how they, as library school students and future professionals, might address the issue.

Financial Data   The stipend is $1,500.

Duration   1 year.

Number awarded   1 each year.

Deadline   March of each year.

[522]
ALAS/HOUGHTON MIFFLIN HARCOURT SCHOLARSHIP

Association of Latino Administrators & Superintendents
65 West Boston Post Road, Suite 200
Marlborough, MA 01752
(508) 486-4536   Fax: (508) 624-6565
E-mail: alasheadquarters@gmail.com
Web: www.alasedu.net/Scholarships.aspx

Summary   To provide financial assistance to members of the Association of Latino Administrators & Superintendents (ALAS) who are interested in working on an advanced degree in educational administration.

Eligibility   This program is open to members of ALAS who are interested in working on an advanced degree in education with the goal of becoming a superintendent. Applicants must submit a 500-word essay on how an advanced degree will help them achieve their goals and further the goals of ALAS.

Financial Data   The stipend is $10,000. An honorable mention scholarship of $2,000 may also be awarded.

Duration   1 year.

Additional data   This scholarship, first awarded in 2006, is supported by Houghton Mifflin Harcourt.

Number awarded   1 or 2 each year.

Deadline   September of each year.

[523]
ALBERT W. DENT STUDENT SCHOLARSHIP

American College of Healthcare Executives
Attn: Scholarship Committee
One North Franklin Street, Suite 1700
Chicago, IL 60606-3529
(312) 424-2800   Fax: (312) 424-0023
E-mail: geninfo@ache.org
Web: www.ache.org

Summary   To provide financial assistance for college to Hispanic American and other minority graduate student members of the American College of Healthcare Executives (ACHE).

Eligibility   This program is open to ACHE student associates entering their final year of classroom work in a health care management master's degree program. Applicants must be minority students, enrolled full time, able to demonstrate financial need, and U.S. or Canadian citizens. Along with their application, they must submit an 1- to 2-page essay describing their leadership abilities and experiences, their community and volunteer involvement, their goals as a health care executive, and how this scholarship can help them achieve their career goals.

Financial Data   The stipend is $5,000.

Duration   1 year.

Additional data The program was established and named in honor of Dr. Albert W. Dent, the foundation's first African American fellow and president emeritus of Dillard University.

Number awarded Varies each year; the sponsor awards up to 20 scholarships through this and its other scholarship program.

Deadline March of each year.

[524]
AMA FOUNDATION MINORITY SCHOLARS AWARDS

American Medical Association
Attn: AMA Foundation
515 North State Street
Chicago, IL 60610
(312) 464-4193   Fax: (312) 464-4142
E-mail: amafoundation@ama-assn.org
Web: www.ama-assn.org

Summary To provide financial assistance to medical school students who are Hispanic American or members of other underrepresented minority groups.

Eligibility This program is open to first- and second-year medical students who are members of the following minority groups: African American, American Indian, Native Hawaiian, Alaska Native, or Hispanic. Only nominations are accepted. Each medical school is invited to submit 2 nominees. U.S. citizenship or permanent resident status is required.

Financial Data The stipend is $10,000.

Duration 1 year.

Additional data This program is offered by the AMA Foundation of the American Medical Association in collaboration with the Minority Affairs Consortium (MAC) and with support from the Pfizer Medical Humanities Initiative.

Number awarded Up to 12 each year.

Deadline April of each year.

[525]
AMELIA KEMP MEMORIAL SCHOLARSHIP

Women of the Evangelical Lutheran Church in America
Attn: Scholarships
8765 West Higgins Road
Chicago, IL 60631-4101
(773) 380-2741   Toll Free: (800) 638-3522, ext. 2741
Fax: (773) 380-2419   E-mail: valora.starr@elca.org
Web: www.womenoftheelca.org

Summary To provide financial assistance to Hispanic American and other lay women of color who are members of Evangelical Lutheran Church of America (ELCA) congregations and who wish to study on the undergraduate, graduate, professional, or vocational school level.

Eligibility This program is open to ELCA lay women of color who are at least 21 years of age and have experienced an interruption of at least 2 years in their education since high school. Applicants must have been admitted to an educational institution to prepare for a career in other than ordained ministry. U.S. citizenship is required.

Financial Data The maximum stipend is $1,000.

Duration Up to 2 years.

Number awarded 1 or more each year.

Deadline February of each year.

[526]
AMERICAN ANTHROPOLOGICAL ASSOCIATION MINORITY DISSERTATION FELLOWSHIP PROGRAM

American Anthropological Association
Attn: Director of Academic Relations
2200 Wilson Boulevard, Suite 600
Arlington, VA 22201-3357
(703) 528-1902   Fax: (703) 528-3546
E-mail: academic@aaanet.org
Web: www.aaanet.org/cmtes/minority/Minfellow.cfm

Summary To provide funding to Hispanic Americans and other minorities who are working on a Ph.D. dissertation in anthropology.

Eligibility This program is open to Native American, African American, Latino(a), Pacific Islander, and Asian American doctoral students who have been admitted to degree candidacy in anthropology. Applicants must be U.S. citizens, enrolled in a full-time academic program leading to a doctoral degree in anthropology, and members of the American Anthropological Association. They must have a record of outstanding academic success, have had their dissertation proposal approved by their dissertation committee prior to application, be writing a dissertation in an area of anthropological research, and need funding to complete the dissertation. Along with their application, they must submit a cover letter, a research plan summary, a curriculum vitae, a statement regarding employment, a disclosure statement providing information about other sources of available and pending financial support, 3 letters of recommendation, and an official transcript from their doctoral program. Selection is based on the quality of the submitted information and the judged likelihood that the applicant will have a good chance of completing the dissertation.

Financial Data The grant is $10,000. Funds are sent in 2 installments (in September and in January) directly to the recipient.

Duration 1 year; nonrenewable.

Number awarded 1 each year.

Deadline February of each year.

[527]
AMERICAN ASSOCIATION OF UNIVERSITY WOMEN CAREER DEVELOPMENT GRANTS

American Association of University Women
Attn: AAUW Educational Foundation
301 ACT Drive, Department 60
P.O. Box 4030
Iowa City, IA 52243-4030
(319) 337-1716, ext. 60   Fax: (319) 337-1204
E-mail: aauw@act.org
Web: www.aauw.org

Summary To provide financial assistance to Hispanic American and other women who are seeking career advancement, career change, or reentry into the workforce.

Eligibility This program is open to women who are U.S. citizens or permanent residents, have earned a bachelor's degree, received their most recent degree more than 4 years ago, and are making career changes, seeking to advance in current careers, or reentering the workforce. Applicants must be interested in working toward a master's degree, second bachelor's or associate degree, professional degree (e.g., M.D., J.D.), certification program, or technical school certificate. They must be planning to undertake course work at an accredited 2- or 4-year college or university (or a technical school that is licensed, accredited, or approved by the U.S. Department of Education). Primary consideration is given to women of color and women pursuing their first advanced degree or credentials in nontraditional fields. Support is not provided for prerequisite course work or for Ph.D. course work or dissertations. Selection is based on demonstrated commitment to education and equity for women and girls, reason for seeking higher education or technical training, degree to which study plan is consistent with career objectives, potential for success in chosen field, documentation of opportunities in chosen field, feasibility of study plans and proposed time schedule, validity of proposed budget and budget narrative (including sufficient outside support), and quality of written proposal.

Financial Data Grants range from $2,000 to $12,000. Funds may be used for tuition, fees, books, supplies, local transportation, dependent child care, or purchase of a computer required for the study program.

Duration 1 year, beginning in July; nonrenewable.

Additional data The filing fee is $35.

Number awarded Varies each year; recently, 63 of these grants, with a value of $670,000, were awarded.

Deadline December of each year.

[528]
AMERICAN EDUCATIONAL RESEARCH ASSOCIATION DISSERTATION GRANTS PROGRAM

American Educational Research Association
1430 K Street, N.W., Suite 1200
Washington, DC 20005
(202) 238-3200   Fax: (202) 238-3250
E-mail: fellowships@aera.net
Web: www.aera.net

Summary To provide funding to doctoral students (particularly Hispanic Americans and other underrepresented minorities) who are writing their dissertation on educational policy.

Eligibility This program is open to advanced graduate students who are writing their dissertations in such disciplines as (but not limited to) education, sociology, economics, psychology, demography, statistics, or psychometrics. Applicants may be U.S. citizens, U.S. permanent residents, or non-U.S. citizens working at a U.S. institution. Underrepresented minority researchers are strongly encouraged to apply. Dissertation topics may cover a wide range of policy-related issues, but priority is given to proposals that 1) develop or benefit from new quantitative measures or methodological approaches for addressing education issues; 2) incorporate subject matter expertise, especially when studying science, technology, engineering, or mathematics (STEM) learning; 3) analyze TIMSS, PISA, or other international data resources; or 4) include the integration and analysis of more than 1 data set. The research project must include the analysis of data from at least 1 of the large-scale nationally or internationally representative data sets, such as those of the National Science Foundation (NSF), National Center for Education Statistics (NCES), or National Institutes of Health (NIH). Selection is based on the importance of the proposed policy issue,

strength of the methodological model and proposed statistical analysis of the study, and relevant experience or research record of the applicant.

Financial Data The maximum grant is $20,000 per year. No support is provided for indirect costs to institutions. Funding is linked to approval of the recipient's progress report and final report. Grantees receive one-third of the total award at the beginning of the grant period, one-third upon acceptance of the progress report, and one-third upon acceptance of the final report. Funds can be sent either to the recipients or to their institutions.

Duration 1 year; nonrenewable.

Additional data Funding for this program is provided by the NSF and the NCES. Grantees must submit a brief (3 to 6 pages) progress report midway through the grant period. A final report must be submitted at the end of the grant period. The final report may be either an article suitable for publication in a scholarly journal or a copy of the dissertation.

Number awarded Approximately 15 each year.

Deadline January, March, or August of each year.

[529]
AMERICAN GEOPHYSICAL UNION GRADUATE FELLOWSHIP IN THE HISTORY OF SCIENCE

American Geophysical Union
Attn: History of Geophysics
2000 Florida Avenue, N.W.
Washington, DC 20009-1277
(202) 462-6900   Toll Free: (800) 966-2481
Fax: (202) 328-0566
E-mail: HistoryofGeophysics@agu.org
Web: www.agu.org/about/history/fellowship.shtml

Summary To provide funding to doctoral candidates (particularly Hispanic Americans, other minorities, women, and students with disabilities) who are conducting dissertation research in the history of geophysics.

Eligibility This program is open to doctoral candidates at U.S. institutions who have passed all preliminary examinations. Applicants must be completing a dissertation in the history of the geophysical sciences, including topics related to atmospheric sciences, biogeosciences, geodesy, geomagnetism and paleomagnetism, hydrology, ocean sciences, planetary sciences, seismology, space physics, aeronomy, tectonophysics, volcanology, geochemistry, and petrology. They must submit a cover letter with a vita, undergraduate and graduate transcripts, a 10-page description of the dissertation topic and proposed research plan, and 3 letters of recommendation. U.S. citizenship or permanent resident status is required. Applications are encouraged from women, minorities, and students with disabilities who are traditionally underrepresented in the geophysical sciences.

Financial Data The grant is $5,000; funds are to be used to assist with the costs of travel to obtain archival or research materials.

Number awarded 1 each year.

Deadline August of each year.

[530]
AMERICAN HEALTH INFORMATION MANAGEMENT ASSOCIATION FOUNDATION DIVERSITY SCHOLARSHIPS

American Health Information Management Association
Attn: AHIMA Foundation
233 North Michigan Avenue, 21st Floor
Chicago, IL 60601-5809
(312) 233-1175   Fax: (312) 233-1475
E-mail: info@ahimafoundation.org
Web: www.ahimafoundation.org

Summary To provide financial assistance to members of the American Health Information Management Association (AHIMA) who are interested in working on an undergraduate or graduate degree in health information management (HIM) or health information technology (HIT) and who will contribute to diversity in the profession.

Eligibility This program is open to AHIMA members who are enrolled at least half time in a program accredited by the Commission on Accreditation for Health Informatics and Information Management Education (CAHIM). Applicants must be working on a degree in HIM or HIT at the associate, bachelor's, post-baccalaureate, master's, or doctoral level. They must have a GPA of 3.5 or higher and at least 1 full semester remaining after the date of the award. To qualify for this support, applicants must demonstrate how they will contribute to diversity in the health information management profession; diversity is defined as differences in race, ethnicity, nationality, gender, sexual orientation, socioeconomic status, age, physical capabilities, and religious beliefs. Selection is based on GPA and academic achievement, volunteer and work experience, commitment to the HIM profession, quality and relevance of references, and completeness and clarity of thought.

Financial Data Stipends are $1,000 for associate degree students, $1,500 for bachelor's degree or post-baccalaureate certificate students, $2,000 for master's degree students, or $2,500 for doctoral degree students.

Duration 1 year.

Number awarded Varies each year; recently, 9 of these scholarships were awarded: 6 to undergraduates and 3 to graduate students.

Deadline September of each year.

[531]
AMERICAN METEOROLOGICAL SOCIETY GRADUATE FELLOWSHIP IN THE HISTORY OF SCIENCE

American Meteorological Society
Attn: Development and Student Program Manager
45 Beacon Street
Boston, MA 02108-3693
(617) 227-2426, ext. 3907   Fax: (617) 742-8718
E-mail: dFernandez@ametsoc.org
Web: www.ametsoc.org

Summary To provide funding to graduate students (particularly Hispanic Americans, other minorities, women, and individuals with disabilities) who are members of the American Meteorological Society (AMS) and interested in conducting dissertation research on the history of meteorology.

Eligibility This program is open to AMS members and student members who are planning to complete a doctoral dissertation on the history of the atmospheric or related oceanic or hydrologic sciences. Applicants must be U.S. citizens or permanent residents and working on a degree at a U.S. institution. Fellowships may be used to support research at a location away from the student's institution, provided the plan is approved by the student's thesis adviser. In such an instance, an effort is made to place the student into a mentoring relationship with a member of the society at an appropriate institution. The sponsor specifically encourages applications from women, minorities, and students with disabilities who are traditionally underrepresented in the atmospheric and related oceanic sciences.

Financial Data The stipend is $15,000.

Duration 1 year.

Number awarded 1 each year.

Deadline February of each year.

[532]
AMERICAN PEDIATRIC SOCIETY/SOCIETY FOR PEDIATRIC RESEARCH STUDENT RESEARCH PROGRAM

American Pediatric Society/Society for Pediatric Research
3400 Research Forest Drive, Suite B-7
The Woodlands, TX 77381
(281) 419-0052   Fax: (281) 419-0082
E-mail: student-research@aps-spr.org
Web: www.aps-spr.org/get-involved/student-research

Summary To provide financial assistance to medical students (particularly Hispanic Americans and members of other underrepresented groups) who are considering careers in research related to pediatrics.

Eligibility This program is open to students seeking a pediatric research opportunity at an institution (in the United States or Canada) other than their own medical school. Applicants must be enrolled in a medical school in good standing at the time of their application. If they already have a medical degree, they are ineligible. Letters of recommendation are required. Members of underrepresented groups are encouraged to apply.

Financial Data The stipend is $61.20 per day, to a maximum of $5,508.

Duration 2 to 3 months.

Additional data Participants choose or are assigned to 1 of more than 300 leading research laboratories in the United States or Canada to work under the direct supervision of experienced scientists in the field of pediatrics.

Number awarded Varies each year.

Deadline January of each year.

[533]
AMERICAN PLANNING ASSOCIATION/JUDITH MCMANUS PRICE SCHOLARSHIPS

American Planning Association
Attn: Leadership Affairs Associate
205 North Michigan Avenue, Suite 1200
Chicago, IL 60601
(312) 431-9100   Fax: (312) 786-6700
E-mail: fellowship@planning.org
Web: www.planning.org/scholarships/apa

Summary To provide financial assistance to Hispanic Americans, other underrepresented minority students, and women enrolled in undergraduate or graduate degree programs at recognized planning schools.

Eligibility This program is open to undergraduate and graduate students in urban and regional planning who are women or members of the following minority groups: African American, Hispanic American, or Native American. Applicants must be citizens of the United States and able to document financial need. They must intend to work as practicing planners in the public sector. Along with their application, they must submit a 2-page personal and background statement describing how their education will be applied to career goals and why they chose planning as a career path. Selection is based (in order of importance), on: 1) commitment to planning as reflected in their personal statement and on their resume; 2) academic achievement and/or improvement during the past 2 years; 3) letters of recommendation; 4) financial need; and 5) professional presentation.

Financial Data Stipends range from $2,000 to $4,000 per year. The money may be applied to tuition and living expenses only. Payment is made to the recipient's university and divided by terms in the school year.

Duration 1 year; recipients may reapply.

Additional data This program began in 2002.

Number awarded Varies each year; recently, 3 of these scholarships were awarded.

Deadline April of each year.

[534]
AMERICAN POLITICAL SCIENCE ASSOCIATION MINORITY FELLOWS PROGRAM

American Political Science Association
Attn: APSA Minority Fellows Program
1527 New Hampshire Avenue, N.W.
Washington, DC 20036-1206
(202) 349-9362   Fax: (202) 483-2657
E-mail: sragland@apsanet.org
Web: www.apsanet.org/content_3284.cfm

Summary To provide financial assistance to Hispanic Americans and other underrepresented minorities interested in working on a doctoral degree in political science.

Eligibility This program is open to African Americans, Asian Pacific Americans, Latino(a)s, and Native Americans who are in their senior year at a college or university or currently enrolled in a master's degree program. Applicants must be planning to enroll in a doctoral program in political science to prepare for a career in teaching and research. They must be U.S. citizens and able to demonstrate financial need. Along with their application, they must submit a 500-word personal statement that includes why they are interested in attending graduate school in political science, what specific fields within the discipline they plan to study, and how they intend to contribute to research within the discipline. Selection is based on interest in teaching and potential for research in political science.

Financial Data The stipend is $2,000 per year.

Duration 2 years.

Additional data In addition to the fellows who receive stipends from this program, students who are selected as fellows without stipend are recommended for admission and financial support to every doctoral political science program in the country. This program was established in 1969.

Number awarded Up to 12 fellows receive stipends each year.

Deadline October of each year.

[535]
AMERICAN PSYCHOLOGICAL ASSOCIATION PREDOCTORAL FELLOWSHIP IN MENTAL HEALTH AND SUBSTANCE ABUSE SERVICES

American Psychological Association
Attn: Minority Fellowship Program
750 First Street, N.E.
Washington, DC 20002-4242
(202) 336-6127   Fax: (202) 336-6012
TDD: (202) 336-6123   E-mail: mfp@apa.org
Web: www.apa.org

Summary To provide financial assistance to doctoral students (particularly Hispanic Americans and members of other ethnic minority groups) who are committed to providing mental health and substance abuse services to ethnic minority populations.

Eligibility Applicants must be U.S. citizens, nationals, or permanent residents, enrolled full time in an accredited doctoral program, and committed to a career in psychology related to ethnic minority mental health and substance abuse services. Members of ethnic minority groups (African Americans, Hispanics/Latinos, American Indians, Alaskan Natives, Asian Americans, Native Hawaiians, and other Pacific Islanders) are especially encouraged to apply. Preference is given to students specializing in clinical, school, and counseling psychology. Selection is based on commitment to ethnic minority behavioral health services or policy, knowledge of ethnic minority behavioral health services, the fit between career goals and training environment selected, potential as a future leader in ethnic minority psychology as demonstrated through accomplishments and goals, scholarship and grades, and letters of recommendation.

Financial Data The stipend varies but is based on the amount established by the National Institutes of Health for predoctoral students; recently that was $22,032 per year.

Duration 1 academic or calendar year; may be renewed for up to 2 additional years.

Additional data Funding is provided by the U.S. Substance Abuse and Mental Health Services Administration.

Number awarded Varies each year.

Deadline January of each year.

[536]
AMERICAN SOCIETY OF CRIMINOLOGY FELLOWSHIPS FOR ETHNIC MINORITIES

American Society of Criminology
Attn: Awards Committee
1314 Kinnear Road, Suite 212
Columbus, OH 43212-1156
(614) 292-9207   Fax: (614) 292-6767
E-mail: asc@asc41.com
Web: www.asc41.com/awards/GradMinorityFellowship.html

Summary To provide financial assistance to Hispanic American and other ethnic minority doctoral students in criminology and criminal justice.

Eligibility This program is open to students of color, especially members of ethnic groups underrepresented in the field of criminology and criminal justice, including (but not limited to) Asians, Blacks, Indigenous peoples, and Hispanics. Applicants must have been accepted into a doctoral program in the field. Along with their application, they must submit an up-to-date curriculum vitae; an indication of race or ethnicity; copies of undergraduate and graduate transcripts; a statement of need and prospects for other financial assistance; a letter describing career plans, salient experiences, and nature of interest in criminology and criminal justice; and 3 letters of reference.

Financial Data The stipend is $6,000.

Duration 1 year.

Additional data This fellowship was first awarded in 1989.

Number awarded 3 each year.

Deadline February of each year.

[537]
AMERICAN SOCIOLOGICAL ASSOCIATION MINORITY FELLOWSHIP PROGRAM GENERAL FELLOWSHIP

American Sociological Association
Attn: Minority Affairs Program
1430 K Street, N.W., Suite 600
Washington, DC 20005-2504
(202) 383-9005, ext. 322   Fax: (202) 638-0882
TDD: (202) 638-0981 E-mail: minority.affairs@asanet.org
Web: www.asanet.org/funding/mfp.cfm

Summary To provide financial assistance to doctoral students in sociology who are Hispanic American or members of other minority groups.

Eligibility This program is open to U.S. citizens, permanent residents, and noncitizen nationals who are Blacks/African Americans, Latinos (e.g., Mexican Americans, Puerto Ricans, Cubans), American Indians or Alaskan Natives, Asian Americans (e.g., southeast Asians, Japanese, Chinese, Koreans), or Pacific Islanders (e.g., Filipinos, Samoans, Hawaiians, Guamanians). Applicants must be entering or continuing students in sociology at the doctoral level. Along with their application, they must submit 3-page essays on 1) the reasons why they decided to undertake graduate study in sociology, their primary research interests, and why they hope to do with a Ph.D. in sociology; and 2) what led them to select the doctoral program they attend or hope to attend and how they see that doctoral program preparing them for a professional career in sociology. Selection is based on commitment to research, focus of research experience, academic achievement, writing ability, research potential, and financial need.

Financial Data The stipend is $18,000 per year.

Duration 1 year; may be renewed up to 2 additional years.

Additional data This program, which began in 1974, is supported by individual members of the American Sociological Association (ASA) and by several affiliated organizations (Alpha Kappa Delta, Sociologists for Women in Society, the Association of Black Sociologists, the Midwest Sociological Society, and the Southwestern Sociological Association).

Number awarded Varies each year; since the program began, approximately 500 of these fellowships have been awarded.

Deadline January of each year.

[538]
AMERICAN SPEECH-LANGUAGE-HEARING FOUNDATION SCHOLARSHIP FOR MINORITY STUDENTS

American Speech-Language-Hearing Foundation
Attn: Programs Administrator
2200 Research Boulevard
Rockville, MD 20850-3289
(301) 296-8703   Fax: (301) 296-8567
E-mail: foundationprograms@asha.org
Web: www.ashfoundation.org/grants/GraduateScholarships

Summary To provide financial assistance to Hispanic American and other minority graduate students in communication sciences and disorders programs.

Eligibility This program is open to full-time graduate students who are enrolled in communication sciences and disorders programs, with preference given to U.S. citizens who are members of a racial or ethnic minority group. Applicants must submit an essay, up to 5 pages in length, on a topic that relates to the future of leadership in the discipline. Selection is based on academic promise and outstanding academic achievement.

Financial Data The stipend is $5,000. Funds must be used for educational support (e.g., tuition, books, school living expenses), not for personal or conference travel.

Duration 1 year.

Number awarded 1 each year.

Deadline June of each year.

[539]
AMS GRADUATE FELLOWSHIPS

American Meteorological Society
Attn: Development and Student Program Manager
45 Beacon Street
Boston, MA 02108-3693
(617) 227-2426, ext. 3907   Fax: (617) 742-8718
E-mail: dFernandez@ametsoc.org
Web: www.ametsoc.org

Summary To encourage students (particularly Hispanic Americans, other minorities, women, and individuals with disabilities) who are entering their first year of graduate school to work on an advanced degree in the atmospheric and related oceanic and hydrologic sciences.

Eligibility This program is open to students entering their first year of graduate study and planning to work on an advanced degree in the atmospheric or related oceanic or hydrologic sciences. Applicants must be U.S. citizens or permanent residents and have a GPA of 3.25 or higher. Along with their application, they must submit 200-word essays on 1) their most important achievements that qualify them for this scholarship; and 2) their career goals in the atmospheric or related sciences. Selection is based on academic record as an undergraduate. The sponsor specifically encourages applications from women, minorities, and students with disabilities who are traditionally underrepresented in the atmospheric and related sciences.

Financial Data The stipend is $24,000 per academic year.

Duration 9 months.

Additional data This program was initiated in 1991. It is funded by high-technology firms and government agencies.

Number awarded Varies each year; recently, 13 of these scholarships were awarded.

Deadline January of each year.

[540]
ANAPATA DIVERSITY SCHOLARSHIP CONTEST

Ms. JD
Attn: Chief Financial Officer
3207 Jackson Street
Houston, TX 77004
E-mail: staff@ms-jd.org
Web: ms-jd.org/anapata-student-scholarship

Summary To provide financial assistance to law students who are Hispanic American or members of other groups traditionally underrepresented in the legal profession.

Eligibility This program is open to students currently enrolled at ABA-approved law schools in the United States. Members of groups traditionally underrepresented in the legal profession are especially encouraged to apply. They must submit a resume, transcript, personal introduction paragraph, 2 recommendations, and a 750-word essay demonstrating their personal philosophy regarding diversity in the legal profession. Selection is based on academic achievement, leadership ability, writing and interpersonal skills, and interest in promoting diversity in the legal profession.

Financial Data The stipend is $1,000.

Duration 1 year.

Additional data This program is offered by Ms. JD in partnership with Anapata, Inc.

Number awarded 1 or more each year.

Deadline February of each year.

[541]
ANL LABORATORY–GRADUATE RESEARCH APPOINTMENTS

Argonne National Laboratory
Division of Educational Programs
Attn: Graduate Student Program Office
9700 South Cass Avenue/DEP 223
Argonne, IL 60439-4845
(630) 252-3366   Fax: (630) 252-3193
E-mail: lisareed@anl.gov
Web: www.dep.anl.gov/p_graduate/labgrad.htm

Summary To offer opportunities for qualified graduate students (particularly Hispanic Americans, other underrepresented minorities, and women) to carry out their master's or doctoral thesis research at the Argonne National Laboratory (ANL).

Eligibility Appointments are available for graduate students at U.S. universities who wish to carry out their thesis research under the co-sponsorship of an Argonne National Laboratory staff member and a faculty member. Research may be conducted in the basic physical and life sciences, mathematics, computer science, and engineering, as well as in a variety of applied areas relating to energy, conservation, environmental impact and technology, nanomaterials, and advanced nuclear energy systems. Applicants must be U.S. citizens or permanent residents. The laboratory encourages applications from all qualified persons, especially women and members of underrepresented minority groups.

Financial Data Support consists of a stipend, tuition payments up to $5,000 per year, and payment of certain travel expenses. In addition, the student's faculty sponsor may receive payment for limited travel expenses.

Duration 1 year; may be renewed.

Additional data This program, which is also referred to as the Lab–Grad Program, is sponsored by the U.S. Department of Energy. In certain cases, students may be awarded support for pre-thesis studies on campus, provided that they intend to carry out their thesis research at Argonne.

Number awarded Varies each year.

Deadline Applications may be submitted at any time, but a complete application should be submitted at least 2 months prior to the proposed starting date.

[542]
APAGS COMMITTEE ON ETHNIC MINORITY AFFAIRS GRANT PROGRAM

American Psychological Association
Attn: American Psychological Association of Graduate Students
750 First Street, N.E.
Washington, DC 20002-4242
(202) 336-6014   Fax: (202) 336-5694
E-mail: apags@apa.org
Web: www.apa.org

Summary To provide funding to graduate students (particularly Hispanic Americans and other ethnic minorities) who are members of the American Psychological Association of Graduate Students (APAGS) and who wish to develop a project that increases membership and participation of ethnic minority students within the association.

Eligibility This program is open to members of APAGS who are enrolled at least half time in a master's or doctoral program at an accredited university. Applicants must be interested in developing a project to increase the membership and participation of ethnic minority graduate students within APAGS, advertise education and training opportunities for ethnic minorities, and enhance the recruitment and retention efforts for ethnic minority students in psychology. Examples include, but are not limited to, workshops, conferences, speaker series, mentorship programs, and the development of student organizations with a focus on multiculturalism or ethnic minority concerns.

Financial Data The grant is $1,000.

Duration The grant is presented annually.

Additional data This grant was first awarded in 1997.

Number awarded 5 each year.

Deadline Deadline not specified.

[543]
APF/COGDOP GRADUATE RESEARCH SCHOLARSHIPS

American Psychological Foundation
750 First Street, N.E.
Washington, DC 20002-4242
(202) 336-5843   Fax: (202) 336-5812
E-mail: foundation@apa.org
Web: www.apa.org/apf/funding/cogdop.aspx

Summary To provide funding for research to graduate students (particularly Hispanic Americans and other diverse students) who are working on a graduate degree in psychology.

Eligibility Each department of psychology that is a member in good standing of the Council of Graduate Departments of Psychology (COGDOP) may nominate up to 3 candidates for these scholarships. Nominations must include a completed application form, a letter of nomination from the department chair or director of graduate studies, a letter of recommendation from the nominee's graduate research adviser, a transcript of all graduate course work completed by the nominee, a curriculum vitae, and a brief outline of the nominee's thesis or dissertation research project. Selection is based on the context for the research, the clarity and comprehensibility of the research question, the appropriateness of the research design, the general importance of the research, and the use of requested funds. The sponsor encourages applications from individuals who represent diversity in race, ethnicity, gender, age, disability, and sexual orientation.

Financial Data Awards range from $1,000 to $5,000 per year. A total of $28,000 is available for these scholarships each year.

Duration 1 year.

Additional data The highest rated nominees receive the Harry and Miriam Levinson Scholarship of $5,000 and the William and Dorothy Bevan Scholarship of $5,000. The next highest rated nominee receives the Ruth G. and Joseph D. Matarazzo Scholarship of $3,000. The next highest rated nominee receives the Clarence Rosecrans Scholarship of $2,000. The next highest rated nominees receive the William C. Howell Scholarship and the Peter and Malina James and Dr. Louis P. James Legacy Scholarship of $1,000 each. Another 9 scholarships of $1,000 each are also awarded.

Number awarded 15 each year: 2 at $5,000, 1 at $3,000, 1 at $2,000, and 11 at $1,000.

Deadline June of each year.

[544]
AP-GOOGLE JOURNALISM AND TECHNOLOGY SCHOLARSHIP PROGRAM

Online News Association
Attn: Scholarship Manager
P.O. Box 65741
Washington, DC 20035
(646) 290-7900   E-mail: irving@journalists.org
Web: journalists.org/next-gen/ap-google-scholarship

Summary To recognize and reward undergraduate and graduate students (especially Hispanic Americans and those from other diverse backgrounds) who propose outstanding projects "at the intersection of journalism and technology."

Eligibility This program is open to full-time undergraduates (at least sophomores) and graduate students at U.S. institutions who have at least 1 year of study remaining and a GPA of 3.0 or higher. Students from diverse backgrounds (defined as ethnic and racial minorities, members of the lesbian, gay, bisexual, and transgender (LGBT) community, and students with disabilities) and those attending rural area institutions are strongly encouraged to apply. Some scholarships are reserved for students who can demonstrate financial need. Applicants must develop original journalistic content with computer science elements; they should explain how their strategy moves digital journalism forward or provides

valuable lessons or outcomes. Examples include data visualization, data mining, mobile devices and applications, 3-D storytelling, digital ethics, or microcomputers. In the selection process, emphasis is placed on innovation and creativity. U.S. citizenship is required.

Financial Data The award is a $20,000 scholarship, of which half is paid to the winner's institution at the beginning of the first semester and half at the beginning of the second semester, provided the recipient earns a GPA of 3.0 or higher for the first semester.

Duration The competition is held annually.

Additional data This competition is supported by Google.

Number awarded 6 each year.

Deadline February of each year.

[545]
ARENT FOX DIVERSITY SCHOLARSHIPS

Arent Fox LLP
Attn: Attorney Recruitment and Professional Development Coordinator
1717 K Street, N.W.
Washington, DC 20036
(202) 857-6000   Fax: (202) 857-6395
E-mail: dcattorneyrecruit@arentfox.com
Web: www.arentfox.com

Summary To provide financial aid and work experience to Hispanic American and other minority law students.

Eligibility This program is open to first-year law students who are members of a diverse population that historically has been underrepresented in the legal profession. Applicants must be U.S. citizens or otherwise authorized to work in the United States. They must also be willing to work as a summer intern at the sponsoring law firm's offices in Los Angeles, New York City, or Washington, D.C. Along with their application, they must submit a resume, an undergraduate transcript and law school grades when available, a 5- to 10-page legal writing sample, 3 letters of recommendation, and an essay on how their background, skills, experience, and interest equip them to meet the sponsor's goal of commitment to diversity. Selection is based on academic performance during college and law school, oral and writing communication skills, leadership qualities, and community involvement.

Financial Data The scholarship stipend is $15,000. The summer salary is $2,500 per week.

Duration 1 year.

Additional data These scholarships were first offered in 2006. Recipients are also offered summer internships with Arent Fox: 1 in Los Angeles, 1 in New York City, and 1 in Washington, D.C. Students interested in the summer program in Los Angeles should contact Attorney Recruitment Manager, 555 West Fifth Street, 48th Floor, Los Angeles, CA 90013, (213) 629-7400, Fax: (213) 629-7401, E-mail: laattorneyrecruit@arentfox.com. Students interested in the summer program in New York should contact Attorney Recruitment Coordinator, 1675 Broadway, New York, NY 10019, (212) 484-3983, Fax: (212) 484-3990, E-mail: nyattorneyrecruit@arentfox.com.

Number awarded 3 each year.

Deadline January of each year.

[546]
ASCA FOUNDATION SCHOLARSHIPS

American School Counselor Association
Attn: ASCA Foundation
1101 King Street, Suite 625
Alexandria, VA 22314
(703) 683-ASCA   Toll Free: (800) 306-4722
Fax: (703) 683-1619   E-mail: asca@schoolcounselor.org
Web: www.schoolcounselor.org/content.asp?contentid=176

Summary To provide financial assistance for graduate school to members of the American School Counselor Association (ASCA), especially Hispanic Americans, other minorities, and males.

Eligibility This program is open to ASCA members working full time on a master's degree in school counseling. Applicants must submit a 2-page essay on a topic that changes annually but relates to the role of counselors in schools. Males and minorities are especially encouraged to apply.

Financial Data The stipend is $1,000.

Duration 1 year.

Additional data Support for this program is provided by Anheuser-Busch.

Number awarded Up to 10 each year.

Deadline October of each year.

[547]
ASME GRADUATE TEACHING FELLOWSHIP

ASME International
Attn: Centers Administrator
Two Park Avenue
New York, NY 10016-5675
(212) 591-8131   Toll Free: (800) THE-ASME
Fax: (212) 591-7143   E-mail: LefeverB@asme.org
Web: www.asme.org

Summary To provide funding to members of the American Society of Mechanical Engineers (ASME) who are working on a doctorate in mechanical engineering (particularly those who are Hispanic Americans, other minority group members, and female).

Eligibility This program is open to U.S. citizens or permanent residents who have an undergraduate degree from an ABET-accredited program, belong to the society as a student member, are currently employed as a teaching assistant with lecture responsibility, and are working on a Ph.D. in mechanical engineering. Along with their application, they must submit a statement about their interest in a faculty career. Applications from women and minorities are particularly encouraged.

Financial Data Fellowship stipends are $5,000 per year.

Duration Up to 2 years.

Additional data Recipients must teach at least 1 lecture course.

Number awarded Up to 4 each year.

Deadline February of each year.

[548]
ASSOCIATION OF CUBAN ENGINEERS SCHOLARSHIPS

Association of Cuban Engineers
c/o Dr. Helena Solo-Gabriele
University of Miami, College of Engineering
1251 Memorial Drive, EB252
Coral Gables, FL 33146
(305) 284-2908   Fax: (305) 284-3492
E-mail: hmsolo@miami.edu
Web: aic-ace.com

Summary To provide financial assistance to undergraduate and graduate students of Cuban American heritage who are interested in preparing for a career in engineering.

Eligibility This program is open to U.S. citizens and legal residents who have completed at least 30 units of college work in the United States and are working on an undergraduate or graduate degree in engineering. Applicants must be attending an ABET-accredited college or university within the United States or Puerto Rico as a full-time student and have a GPA of 3.0 or higher. They must be of Cuban or other Hispanic heritage (at least 1 grandparent Cuban or other Hispanic nationality). Along with their application, they must submit brief essays on their family history, professional goals, extracurricular activities, work experience, and how they will help other Cuban and Hispanic engineering students in the future. Financial need is not considered in the selection process.

Financial Data Stipends range from $500 to $2,000.

Duration 1 year; may be renewed.

Additional data This program also includes the Pedro O. Martinez Scholarship and the Luciano de Goicochea Award (for students at the University of Miami), the Antonio Choy Award (for a student at the University of Florida), and the Noel Betancourt Award (for a student at Florida International University).

Number awarded Varies each year; recently, 10 of these scholarships were awarded.

Deadline November of each year.

[549]
BAKER DONELSON DIVERSITY SCHOLARSHIPS

Baker, Donelson, Bearman, Caldwell & Berkowitz, P.C.
Attn: Director of Attorney Recruiting
3414 Peachtree Road N.E., Suite 1600
Atlanta, GA 30326
(404) 577-6000   Fax: (404) 221-6501
E-mail: lklein@bakerdonelson.com
Web: www.bakerdonelson.com

Summary To provide financial assistance to law students who are Hispanic American or members of other groups underrepresented at large law firms.

Eligibility This program is open to students who have completed the first year at an ABA-accredited law school. Applicants must be members of a group traditionally underrepresented at large law firms (American Indian or Alaskan Native, Native Hawaiian or Pacific Islander, Hispanic or Latino, Black, or Asian). Along with their application, they must submit a 10-page legal writing sample and a 1-page personal statement on challenges they have faced in pursuit of their legal career that have helped them to understand the value of diversity and its inclusion in the legal profession. Finalists are interviewed.

Financial Data The stipend is $10,000.

Duration 1 year.

Additional data Recipients are also offered summer internships at Baker Donelson offices in Atlanta (Georgia), Baton Rouge (Louisiana), Birmingham (Alabama), Chattanooga (Tennessee), Jackson (Mississippi), Johnson City (Tennessee), Knoxville (Tennessee), Memphis (Tennessee), Nashville (Tennessee), and New Orleans (Louisiana).

Number awarded 3 each year.

Deadline June of each year.

[550]
BAKERHOSTETLER DIVERSITY FELLOWSHIP PROGRAM

BakerHostetler LLP
Attn: Attorney Recruitment and Development Manager
PNC Center
1900 East Ninth Street, Suite 3200
Cleveland, OH 44114-3482
(216) 621-0200   Fax: (216) 696-0740
E-mail: ddriscole@bakerlaw.com
Web: www.bakerlaw.com/diversityfellowshipprogram

Summary To provide financial aid and summer work experience to Hispanic American and other minority law school students who are interested in employment with Baker-Hostetler.

Eligibility This program is open to full-time second-year students at ABA-accredited law schools who are members of underrepresented groups (Black/African American, Hispanic, Asian American/Pacific Islander, American Indian/Alaskan Native, 2 or more races, or gay, lesbian, bisexual, transgender). Applicants must be interested in a summer associate position with BakerHostetler and possible full-time employment following graduation. They must be U.S. citizens or otherwise authorized to work in the United States. Along with their application, they must submit a 500-word personal statement presenting their views of or experience with diversity, including why they are interested in Baker Hostetler and how they will be able to contribute to the diversity objectives of the firm. Selection is based on academic performance in college and law school, personal achievements, community involvement, oral and written communication skills, demonstrated leadership achievements, and a sincere interest and commitment to join BakerHostetler.

Financial Data The stipend is $25,000, of which $10,000 is paid within the first 30 days of starting a summer associate position with the firm and the remaining $15,000 is contingent upon receiving and accepting a full-time offer with the firm.

Duration Summer associate positions are for 8 weeks.

Additional data Summer associate positions may be performed at any of the firm's offices in Chicago, Cincinnati, Cleveland, Columbus, Costa Mesa, Denver, Houston, Los Angeles, New York, Orlando, or Washington, D.C.

Number awarded 1 or more each year.

Deadline October of each year.

[551]
BALFOUR PHI DELTA PHI MINORITY SCHOLARSHIP PROGRAM

Phi Delta Phi International Legal Fraternity
1426 21st Street, N.W., First Floor
Washington, DC 20036
(202) 223-6801   Toll Free: (800) 368-5606
Fax: (202) 223-6808   E-mail: info@phideltaphi.org
Web: www.phideltaphi.org

Summary To provide financial assistance to Hispanic Americans and other minorities who are members of Phi Delta Phi International Legal Fraternity.

Eligibility This program is open to ethnic minority members of the legal fraternity. Applicants must affirm that they intend to practice law in inner-cities of the United States, especially in New England. They must submit a 750-word essay on why they consider themselves qualified to serve as role models for minority youth. Selection is based on participation, ethics, and scholastics.

Financial Data The stipend is $3,000.

Duration 1 year.

Additional data This program began in 1997 with funding from the Lloyd G. Balfour Foundation.

Number awarded 1 each year.

Deadline October of each year.

[552]
BARBARA JORDAN MEMORIAL SCHOLARSHIPS

Association of Texas Professional Educators
Attn: ATPE Foundation
305 East Huntland Drive, Suite 300
Austin, TX 78752-3792
Toll Free: (800) 777-ATPE   Fax: (512) 302-5884
E-mail: admin@atpefoundation.org
Web: www.atpefoundation.org/scholarships.asp

Summary To provide financial assistance to upper-division and graduate students from any state who are enrolled in educator preparation programs at predominantly ethnic minority institutions in Texas.

Eligibility This program is open to juniors, seniors, and graduate students from any state who are enrolled in educator preparation programs at predominantly ethnic minority institutions in Texas. Applicants must submit a 2-page essay on their personal educational philosophy, why they want to become an educator, who influenced them the most in making their career decision, and why they are applying for the scholarship. Financial need is not considered in the selection process.

Financial Data The stipend is $1,500.

Duration 1 year.

Additional data The qualifying institutions are Huston-Tillotson College, Jarvis Christian College, Our Lady of the Lake University, Paul Quinn College, Prairie View A&M University, St. Mary's University of San Antonio, Sul Ross State University, Sul Ross State University Rio Grande College, Texas A&M International University, Texas A&M University at Kingsville, Texas Southern University, University of Houston, University of Houston-Downtown, University of Texas at Brownsville and Texas Southmost College, University of Texas at El Paso, University of Texas at San Antonio, University of Texas-

Pan American, University of the Incarnate Word, and Wiley College.

Number awarded Up to 6 each year.

Deadline May of each year.

[553]
BEHAVIORAL SCIENCES STUDENT FELLOWSHIPS IN EPILEPSY

Epilepsy Foundation
Attn: Research Department
8301 Professional Place
Landover, MD 20785-2353
(301) 459-3700   Toll Free: (800) EFA-1000
Fax: (301) 577-2684   TDD: (800) 332-2070
E-mail: grants@efa.org
Web: www.epilepsyfoundation.org

Summary To provide funding to undergraduate and graduate students (particularly Hispanic Americans, other minorities, women, and students with disabilities) who are interested in working on a summer research project in a behavioral science field relevant to epilepsy.

Eligibility This program is open to undergraduate and graduate students in a behavioral science program relevant to epilepsy research or clinical care, including, but not limited to, sociology, social work, psychology, anthropology, nursing, economics, vocational rehabilitation, counseling, or political science. Applicants must be interested in working on an epilepsy research project under the supervision of a qualified mentor. Because the program is designed as a training opportunity, the quality of the training plans and environment are considered in the selection process. Other selection criteria include the quality of the proposed project, the relevance of the proposed work to epilepsy, the applicant's interest in the field of epilepsy, the applicant's qualifications, and the mentor's qualifications (including his or her commitment to the student and the project), and the quality of the training environment for research related to epilepsy. U.S. citizenship is not required, but the project must be conducted in the United States. Applications from women, members of minority groups, and people with disabilities are especially encouraged. The program is not intended for students working on a dissertation research project.

Financial Data The grant is $3,000.

Duration 3 months during the summer.

Additional data This program is supported by the American Epilepsy Society, Abbott Laboratories, Ortho-McNeil Pharmaceutical Corporation, and Pfizer Inc.

Number awarded Varies each year.

Deadline March of each year.

[554]
BELFER CENTER FOR SCIENCE AND INTERNATIONAL AFFAIRS FELLOWSHIPS

Harvard University
John F. Kennedy School of Government
Belfer Center for Science and International Affairs
Attn: Fellowship Coordinator
79 John F. Kennedy Street, Mailbox 53
Cambridge, MA 02138
(617) 495-8806   Fax: (617) 495-8963
E-mail: bcsia_fellowships@hks.harvard.edu
Web: belfercenter.ksg.harvard.edu/fellowships

Summary To provide funding to professionals, postdoctorates, and doctoral students (particularly Hispanic Americans, other minorities, and women) who are interested in conducting research in areas of concern to the Belfer Center for Science and International Affairs at Harvard University in Cambridge, Massachusetts.

Eligibility The postdoctoral fellowship is open to recent recipients of the Ph.D. or equivalent degree, university faculty members, and employees of government, military, international, humanitarian, and private research institutions who have appropriate professional experience. Applicants for predoctoral fellowships must have passed their general examinations. Lawyers, economists, political scientists, those in the natural sciences, and others of diverse disciplinary backgrounds are also welcome to apply. The program especially encourages applications from women, minorities, and citizens of all countries. All applicants must be interested in conducting research in 1 of the 2 major program areas of the center: 1) the International Security Program (ISP), which addresses U.S. defense and foreign policy, security policy, nuclear proliferation, terrorism, internal and ethnic conflict, and related topics; and 2) the Science, Technology, and Public Policy Program (STPP), including technology and innovation, information and communications technology, water-energy nexus, managing the atom, energy technology innovation policy, China and environmental sustainability, geoengineering and climate policy, geopolitics of energy, and geospatial policy and management.

Financial Data The stipend is $34,000 for postdoctoral research fellows or $20,000 for predoctoral research fellows. Health insurance is also provided.

Duration 10 months.

Number awarded A limited number each year.

Deadline January of each year.

[555]
BENTON-MEIER NEUROPSYCHOLOGY SCHOLARSHIPS

American Psychological Foundation
750 First Street, N.E.
Washington, DC 20002-4242
(202) 336-5843   Fax: (202) 336-5812
E-mail: foundation@apa.org
Web: www.apa.org/apf/funding/benton-meier.aspx

Summary To provide research funding to graduate students (particularly Hispanic Americans and other students from diverse groups) who are completing a dissertation related to neuropsychology.

Eligibility This program is open to students who have been admitted to candidacy for a doctoral degree in the area of neuropsychology. Applicants must submit statements documenting their research competence and area commitment, a budget and justification, and how the scholarship money will be used. Selection is based on conformance with stated program goals and the applicant's demonstrated scholarship and research competence. The sponsor encourages applications from individuals who represent diversity in race, ethnicity, gender, age, disability, and sexual orientation.

Financial Data The grant is $2,500.

Duration 1 year.

Additional data This program replaces the Henry Hécaen Scholarship, first awarded in 1994, and the Manfred Meier Scholarship, first awarded in 1997.

Number awarded 2 each year.

Deadline May of each year.

[556]
BETTY LEA STONE RESEARCH FELLOWSHIP

American Cancer Society-New England Division
30 Speen Street
Framingham, MA 01701
(508) 270-3109   Toll Free: (800) 952-7664, ext. 3109
Fax: (508) 270-4607   E-mail: koconnor@cancer.org
Web: www.cancer.org

Summary To provide funding for cancer research during the summer to medical students (particularly Hispanic American and other minority students) in New England.

Eligibility This program is open to first-year students at medical schools in New England. Applicants must be interested in working on a summer research project under the supervision of a faculty sponsor. Minority students and those with American Cancer Society volunteer experience are encouraged to apply.

Financial Data The grant is $5,000.

Duration 10 weeks during the summer.

Number awarded 1 or more each year.

Deadline January of each year.

[557]
BILL BERNBACH DIVERSITY SCHOLARSHIPS

American Association of Advertising Agencies
Attn: AAAA Foundation
1065 Avenue of the Americas, 16th Floor
New York, NY 10018
(212) 262-2500   E-mail: bbscholarship@ddb.com
Web: www.aaaa.org

Summary To provide financial assistance to Hispanic American and other multicultural students who are interested in working on an undergraduate or graduate degree in advertising at designated schools.

Eligibility This program is open to African Americans, Asian Americans, Hispanic Americans, and Native Americans (including American Indians, Alaska Natives, Native Hawaiians, and other Pacific Islanders) who are interested in studying the advertising creative arts at designated institutions as a full-time student. Applicants must be working on or have already received an undergraduate degree and be able to demonstrate creative talent and promise. They must be U.S. citizens, nationals, or permanent residents. Along with

their application, they must submit 10 samples of creative work in their respective field of expertise.

Financial Data The stipend is $5,000.

Duration 1 year.

Additional data This program, which began in 1998, is currently sponsored by DDB Worldwide. The participating schools are the Art Center College of Design (Pasadena, California), Creative Circus (Atlanta, Georgia), Miami Ad School (Miami Beach, Florida), University of Texas at Austin, VCU Brandcenter (Richmond, Virginia), Savannah College of Art and Design (Savannah, Georgia), University of Oregon (Eugene), City College of New York, School of Visual Arts (New York, New York), Fashion Institute of Technology (New York, New York), and Brigham Young University (Provo, Utah).

Number awarded 3 each year.

Deadline October of each year.

[558]
BISHOP THOMAS HOYT, JR. FELLOWSHIP

St. John's University
Attn: Collegeville Institute for Ecumenical and Cultural
  Research
2475 Ecumenical Drive
P.O. Box 2000
Collegeville, MN 56321-2000
(320) 363-3366   Fax: (320) 363-3313
E-mail: staff@CollegevilleInstitute.org
Web: collegevilleinstitute.org

Summary To provide funding to Hispanic Americans and other students of color who wish to complete their doctoral dissertation while in residence at the Collegeville Institute for Ecumenical and Cultural Research of St. John's University in Collegeville, Minnesota.

Eligibility This program is open to people of color completing a doctoral dissertation in ecumenical and cultural research. Applicants must be interested in a residency at the Collegeville Institute for Ecumenical and Cultural Research of St. John's University. Along with their application, they must submit a 1,000-word description of the research project they plan to complete while in residence at the Institute.

Financial Data The stipend covers the residency fee of $2,000, which includes housing and utilities.

Duration 1 year.

Additional data Residents at the Institute engage in research, publication, and education on the important intersections between faith and culture. They seek to discern and communicate the meaning of Christian identity and unity in a religiously and culturally diverse world.

Number awarded 1 each year.

Deadline October of each year.

[559]
BROWN AND CALDWELL MINORITY SCHOLARSHIP

Brown and Caldwell
Attn: Scholarship Program
201 North Civic Drive, Suite 115
P.O. Box 8045
Walnut Creek, CA 94596
(925) 937-9010　　　　　　　　Fax: (925) 937-9026
E-mail: scholarships@brwncald.com
Web: www.brownandcaldwell.com/scholarships.asp

Summary To provide financial assistance to Hispanic American and other minority students working on an undergraduate or graduate degree in an environmental or engineering field.

Eligibility This program is open to members of minority groups (African Americans, Hispanics, Asians, Pacific Islanders, Native Americans, or Alaska Natives) who are full-time juniors, seniors, or graduate students at an accredited 4-year college or university. Applicants must have a GPA of 3.0 or higher and a declared major in civil, chemical, or environmental engineering or an environmental science (e.g., biology, ecology, geology, hydrogeology). They must be U.S. citizens or permanent residents. Along with their application, they must submit an essay (up to 250 words) on their future career goals in environmental science. Financial need is not considered in the selection process.

Financial Data The stipend is $5,000.

Duration 1 year.

Number awarded 4 each year.

Deadline April of each year.

[560]
BULLIVANT HOUSER BAILEY LAW STUDENT DIVERSITY FELLOWSHIP PROGRAM

Bullivant Houser Bailey PC
Attn: Manager of Professional Development, Recruitment
　and Diversity
888 S.W. Fifth Avenue, Suite 300
Portland, OR 97204-2017
(503) 228-6351　　　　　　　Toll Free: (800) 654-8972
Fax: (503) 295-0915　　E-mail: jill.valentine@bullivant.com
Web: www.bullivant.com/diversity

Summary To provide financial aid and work experience to Hispanic American and other law students who come from a minority or disadvantaged background.

Eligibility This program is open to first-year law students who are members of a minority group (including any group underrepresented in the legal profession) and/or students coming from a disadvantaged educational or economic background. Applicants must have 1) a record of academic achievement and leadership in college and law school; 2) a willingness to complete a 12-week summer associateship at an office of the firm; and 3) a record of contributions to the community that promote diversity within society, the legal community, and/or law school.

Financial Data The program provides a salaried associate position at an office of the firm during the summer following the first year of law school and a stipend of $7,500 for the second year.

Duration 1 year.

Number awarded 2 each year: 1 assigned to an associateship in the Sacramento office and 1 assigned to an associateship in the Portland office.

Deadline January of each year.

[561]
BUTLER RUBIN DIVERSITY SCHOLARSHIP

Butler Rubin Saltarelli & Boyd LLP
Attn: Diversity Partner
70 West Madison Street, Suite 1800
Chicago, IL 60602
(312) 242-4120　　　　　　　Fax: (312) 444-9294
E-mail: kborg@butlerrubin.com
Web: www.butlerrubin.com

Summary To provide financial aid and summer work experience to Hispanic American and other diverse law students who are interested in the area of business litigation.

Eligibility This program is open to law students of racial and ethnic backgrounds that will contribute to diversity in the legal profession. Applicants must be interested in the private practice of law in the area of business litigation and in a summer associateship in that field with Butler Rubin Saltarelli & Boyd in Chicago. Selection is based on academic performance and achievement, intention to remain in the Chicago area following graduation, and interpersonal and communication skills.

Financial Data The stipend is $10,000 per year; funds are to be used for tuition and other expenses associated with law school. For the summer associateship, a stipend is paid.

Duration 1 year; may be renewed.

Additional data This program began in 2006.

Number awarded 1 each year.

Deadline Deadline not specified.

[562]
C. CLYDE FERGUSON LAW SCHOLARSHIP

New Jersey Commission on Higher Education
Attn: Educational Opportunity Fund
20 West State Street, Fourth Floor
P.O. Box 542
Trenton, NJ 08625-0542
(609) 984-2709　　　　　　　Fax: (609) 292-7225
E-mail: audrey.bennerson@njhe.state.nj.us
Web: www.state.nj.us/highereducation/EOF/index.html

Summary To provide financial assistance to Hispanic Americans and other disadvantaged or minority students from New Jersey who want to study law in the state.

Eligibility This program is open to students who 1) fall within specified income guidelines (currently, less than $21,660 for a family of 1 rising to $74,020 for a family of 8); 2) minority or disadvantaged students with financial need; or 3) former or current recipients of a New Jersey Educational Opportunity Fund undergraduate or graduate grant, or who would have been eligible to receive the grant as an undergraduate. Applicants must have been New Jersey residents for at least 12 months before receiving the award and must plan to enroll full time in the Minority Student Program at law schools in New Jersey (Rutgers University School of Law at Newark, Rutgers University School of Law at Camden, or Seton Hall Law School).

Financial Data Awards are based on financial need. In no case, however, can awards exceed the maximum amount of tuition, fees, room, and board charged at Rutgers University School of Law at Newark.

Duration 1 year; may be renewed.

Number awarded 1 or more each year.

Deadline Deadline not specified.

[563]
CALIFORNIA BAR FOUNDATION DIVERSITY SCHOLARSHIPS

State Bar of California
Attn: California Bar Foundation
180 Howard Street
San Francisco, CA 94105-1639
(415) 856-0780   Fax: (415) 856-0788
E-mail: scholarships@calbarfoundation.org
Web: www.calbarfoundation.org/diversity-scholarship.html

Summary To provide financial assistance to Hispanic Americans and other underrepresented minorities from any state who are entering law school in California.

Eligibility This program to open to residents of any state who are entering their first year at a law school in California. Applicants must self-identify as being from a racial or ethnic group that historically has been underrepresented in the legal profession (Latino, African American, Asian and Pacific Islander, and Native American). They must be committed to making an impact in the community through leadership. Along with their application, they must submit a 500-word essay describing their commitment to serving the community and, if applicable, any significant obstacles or hurdles they have overcome to attend law school. Financial need is considered in the selection process.

Financial Data The stipend is $7,500.

Duration 1 year.

Additional data This program began in 2008. Each year, the foundation grants awards named after sponsors that donate funding for the scholarships. Recipients are required to attend a reception in their honor in October of the year of their award and to submit a report on their progress at the end of that year.

Number awarded Varies each year; recently, 19 of these scholarships were awarded.

Deadline June of each year.

[564]
CALIFORNIA STATE UNIVERSITY CHANCELLOR'S DOCTORAL INCENTIVE PROGRAM

California State University
Office of the Chancellor
Attn: Human Resources
401 Golden Shore, Fourth Floor
Long Beach, CA 90802-4210
(562) 951-4425   Fax: (562) 951-4954
E-mail: forgivableloan@calstate.edu
Web: www.calstate.edu/hr/cdip

Summary To provide funding to Hispanic Americans and other graduate students who can help increase the diversity of persons qualified to compete for instructional faculty positions at campuses of the California State University (CSU) system.

Eligibility This program is open to new and continuing full-time students enrolled in a doctoral program anywhere in the United States, whether affiliated with a CSU campus or not. Applicants must present a plan of support from a full-time CSU faculty sponsor who has agreed to advise and support the candidate throughout doctoral study. Selection is based on the applicant's academic record; professional qualifications; and relevant background, experience, skills, and motivation to educate a diverse student body in the CSU system. The factors considered include experience working with persons with a wide range of backgrounds and perspectives, research interests related to educating an increasingly diverse student body, and experience in a variety of cultural environments. Primary consideration is given to candidates whose proposed area of study falls where CSU campuses anticipate the greatest difficulty in filling instructional faculty positions.

Financial Data Participants receive up to $10,000 per year or a maximum of $30,000 over 5 years. The loans are converted to fellowships at the rate of 20% of the total loan amount for each postdoctoral year that the program participant teaches, for up to 5 years. Thus, the entire loan will be forgiven after the recipient has taught full time for 5 years on a CSU campus. Recipients who do not teach on a CSU campus or who discontinue full-time studies will be required to repay the total loan amount within a 15-year period at the rate established for other student loans.

Duration Up to 5 years.

Additional data This program began in 1987 as the California State University Forgivable Loan Program. It has loaned $46 million to 1,965 doctoral students enrolled in universities throughout the nation and abroad. Participants included 17.6% African American, 13.3% Asian, 26.2% Hispanic, 4.1% American Indian, and 32.1% White.

Number awarded Varies each year; recently, 60 new participants were admitted to the program.

Deadline The deadline varies at different CSU campuses but typically falls in February of each year.

[565]
CANFIT PROGRAM GRADUATE SCHOLARSHIPS

Communities-Adolescents-Nutrition-Fitness
Attn: Scholarship Program
2140 Shattuck Avenue, Suite 610
Berkeley, CA 94704
(510) 644-1533   Toll Free: (800) 200-3131
Fax: (510) 644-1535   E-mail: info@canfit.org
Web: www.canfit.org/scholarships

Summary To provide financial assistance to Hispanic American and other minority graduate students who are working on a degree in nutrition, physical education, or public health in California.

Eligibility This program is open to American Indians, Alaska Natives, African Americans, Asian Americans, Pacific Islanders, and Latinos/Hispanics from California who are enrolled in 1) an approved master's or doctoral program in nutrition, public health, or physical education in the state; or 2) a preprofessional practice program approved by the American Dietetic Association at an accredited university in the state. Applicants must have completed 12 to 15 units of graduate course work and have a cumulative GPA of 3.0 or higher. Along with their application, they must submit 1) documentation of financial need; 2) letters of recommendation from 2 individuals; 3) a 1- to 2-page letter describing their academic goals and involvement in community nutrition and/or physical education activities; and 4) an essay of 500 to 1,000 words on a topic related to healthy foods for youth from low-income communities of color.

Financial Data A stipend is awarded (amount not specified).

Number awarded 1 or more each year.

Deadline March of each year.

[566]
CAREFIRST BLUECROSS BLUESHIELD SCHOLARSHIP PROGRAM

Hispanic College Fund
Attn: Scholarship Processing
1300 L Street, N.W., Suite 975
Washington, DC 20005
(202) 296-5400   Toll Free: (800) 644-4223
Fax: (202) 296-3774   E-mail: hcf-info@hispanicfund.org
Web: scholarships.hispanicfund.org/applications

Summary To provide financial assistance to Hispanic American students working on an undergraduate or graduate degree in a field related to health care, science, or business.

Eligibility This program is open to undergraduate and graduate students of Hispanic background (at least 1 grandparent must be 100% Hispanic) who are enrolled or planning to enroll full time at an accredited college or university in any state or Puerto Rico. Applicants must have a GPA of 3.0 or higher; be interested in working on a degree in a field related to health care, science, or business; and be able to demonstrate financial need. They must either 1) be U.S. citizens or permanent residents; or 2) have graduated from a high school in the United States after having attended for at least 3 years. Preference is given to applicants who reside or attend college in Maryland, the District of Columbia, or northern Virginia.

Financial Data Stipends range from $500 to $5,000, depending on need and academic achievement. Funds are paid directly to the recipient's college or university to help cover tuition and fees.

Duration 1 year; recipients may reapply.

Additional data This program is sponsored by CareFirst BlueCross BlueShield, which provides health insurance in Maryland, the District of Columbia, and portions of northern Virginia. All applications must be submitted online; no paper applications are available.

Number awarded Varies each year.

Deadline February of each year.

[567]
CARLOS M. CASTANEDA JOURNALISM SCHOLARSHIP

Carlos M. Castañeda Educational Foundation
Attn: FECMC Journalism Scholarship
1925 Brickell Avenue, Suite D-1108
Miami, FL 33129
(305) 859-9617
E-mail: fundacion_educativa_cmc@yahoo.com
Web: fecmc.tripod.com

Summary To provide financial assistance to Spanish-speaking graduate students and journalists working on a master's degree in journalism.

Eligibility This program is open to Spanish-speaking students and journalists from any country (including the United States) who have been accepted into a graduate program in journalism at a university in the United States. Applicants must have completed a 4-year undergraduate degree with a GPA of 3.0 or higher. They are not required to have majored in journalism as an undergraduate, but their curriculum must have included courses in history and liberal arts. A knowledge of and interest in Hispanic culture and an awareness of current events in Latin America are also required. Along with their application, they must submit a curriculum vitae, a cover letter, 3 reference letters, a portfolio with 3 stories published by professional or school publications in Spanish, and a 2,000-word essay (in Spanish) on the work of Carlos M. Castañeda as a champion of freedom of the press and human rights. Financial need is considered in the selection process.

Financial Data The stipend is $7,000.

Duration 1 year; may be renewed 1 additional year if the recipient maintains a GPA of 3.0 or higher.

Additional data This program began in 2005.

Number awarded 1 or more each year.

Deadline April of each year.

[568]
CARMEN E. TURNER SCHOLARSHIPS

Conference of Minority Transportation Officials
Attn: National Scholarship Program
1875 I Street, N.W., Suite 500
Washington, DC 20006
(703) 234-4072   Fax: (202) 318-0364
Web: www.comto.org/?page=Scholarships

Summary To provide financial assistance for college or graduate school to Hispanic American and other members of the Conference of Minority Transportation Officials (COMTO).

Eligibility This program is open to undergraduate and graduate students who have been members of COMTO for at least 1 year. Applicants must be working on a degree in a field related to transportation and have a GPA of 2.5 or higher. They must be enrolled at least half time. Along with their application, they must submit a cover letter with a 500-word statement of career goals. Financial need is not considered in the selection process. U.S. citizenship or legal resident status is required.

Financial Data The stipend is $3,500. Funds are paid directly to the recipient's college or university.

Duration 1 year.

Additional data COMTO was established in 1971 to promote, strengthen, and expand the roles of minorities in all aspects of transportation. Recipients are expected to attend the COMTO National Scholarship Luncheon.

Number awarded 1 each year.

Deadline May of each year.

[569]
CATHY L. BROCK MEMORIAL SCHOLARSHIP

Institute for Diversity in Health Management
Attn: Education Specialist
155 North Wacker Avenue, Suite 400
Chicago, IL 60606
(312) 422-2658   Toll Free: (800) 233-0996
Fax: (312) 895-4511   E-mail: cbiddle@aha.org
Web: www.diversityconnection.org

Summary To provide financial assistance to Hispanic American and other minority graduate students in health care management, especially financial operations.

Eligibility This program is open to members of ethnic minority groups who are enrolled in the first or second year of an accredited graduate program in health care administration. Applicants must have a GPA of 3.0 or higher. They must demonstrate commitment to a career in health care finance. Along with their application, they must submit 1) a personal statement of 1 to 2 pages on their interest in health care management and their career goals; 2) an essay on what they see as the most challenging issue facing America's hospitals and health systems; and 3) a 500-word essay on their interest and background in health care finance. Selection is based on academic achievement, commitment to a career in health care finance, and financial need. U.S. citizenship is required.

Financial Data The stipend is $1,000.

Duration 1 year.

Number awarded 1 each year.

Deadline January of each year.

[570]
CENTRAL FLORIDA CHAPTER NBMBAA SCHOLARSHIPS

National Black MBA Association-Central Florida Chapter
Attn: Scholarship Committee Chair
P.O. Box 692696
Orlando, FL 32869-2696
(321) 578-8305   E-mail: scholarships@cflblackmba.org
Web: www.cflblackmba.org

Summary To provide financial assistance to Hispanic Americans or members of another minority group who are residents of any state working on a degree in business at a university in Florida.

Eligibility This program is open to members of the following groups from any state: African American/Black, American Indian/Alaska Native, Asian American/Pacific Islander, or Hispanic/Latino. Applicants must be enrolled in a business program at an AACSB-accredited college or university in Florida. They must have a GPA of 3.0 or higher. Along with their application, they must submit a 2-page essay on a topic that changes annually but relates to minorities and business. Selection is based on that essay, transcripts, a resume, and extracurricular activities. The highest-ranked applicant

receives a named scholarship sponsored by Darden Restaurants.

Financial Data The Darden Named Scholarship is $5,000; a total of $10,000 in scholarships is awarded each year.

Duration 1 year.

Number awarded Varies each year.

Deadline October of each year.

[571]
CESAR E. CHAVEZ DISSERTATION FELLOWSHIP FOR U.S. LATINA/O SCHOLARS

Dartmouth College
Attn: Office of Graduate Studies
6062 Wentworth Hall, Room 304
Hanover, NH 03755-3526
(603) 646-2106   Fax: (603) 646-8762
Web: graduate.dartmouth.edu/funding/fellowships/cem.html

Summary To provide funding to Latino/a and other doctoral students who are interested in working on their dissertation at Dartmouth College.

Eligibility This program is open to doctoral candidates who have completed all requirements for the Ph.D. except the dissertation and are planning a career in higher education. Applicants must be Latina/os or other graduate students with a demonstrated commitment and ability to advance educational diversity. They must be interested in working on their dissertation at Dartmouth College. All academic fields that are taught in the Dartmouth undergraduate Arts and Sciences curriculum are eligible. Selection is based on academic achievement and promise; demonstrated commitment to increasing opportunities for underrepresented minorities and increasing cross-racial understanding; and potential for serving as an advocate and mentor for minority undergraduate and graduate students. U.S. citizenship is required.

Financial Data The stipend is $25,000. In addition, fellows receive office space, library privileges, and a $2,500 research allowance.

Duration 1 year, beginning in September.

Additional data The fellows are affiliated with a department or program at Dartmouth College. Fellows are expected to be in residence at Dartmouth College for the duration of the program and to complete their dissertation during that time. They are also expected to teach a course, either as the primary instructor or as part of a team.

Number awarded 1 each year.

Deadline January of each year.

[572]
CH2M HILL PARTNERSHIP SCHOLARSHIP

Women's Transportation Seminar
Attn: WTS Foundation
1701 K Street, N.W., Suite 800
Washington, DC 20006
(202) 955-5085   Fax: (202) 955-5088
E-mail: wts@wtsinternational.org
Web: www.wtsinternational.org/education/scholarships

Summary To provide financial assistance to women graduate students (particularly Hispanic American and other minority women) who are interested in preparing for a career in transportation.

Eligibility This program is open to women who are enrolled in a graduate degree program in a transportation-related field (e.g., transportation engineering, planning, finance, or logistics). Applicants must have at least a 3.0 GPA and be interested in a career in transportation. Along with their application, they must submit a 750-word statement about their career goals after graduation and why they think they should receive the scholarship award. Applications must be submitted first to a local chapter; the chapters forward selected applications for consideration on the national level. Minority women are particularly encouraged to apply. Selection is based on transportation involvement and goals, job skills, and academic record.

Financial Data The stipend is $10,000.

Duration 1 year.

Additional data This program is sponsored by CH2M Hill. Local chapters may also award additional funding to winners in their area.

Number awarded 1 each year.

Deadline Applications must be submitted by November to a local WTS chapter.

[573]
CHARLES B. RANGEL GRADUATE FELLOWSHIP PROGRAM

Howard University
Attn: Ralph J. Bunche International Affairs Center
2281 Sixth Street, N.W.
Washington, DC 20059
(202) 806-4367   Toll Free: (877) 633-0002
Fax: (202) 806-5424   E-mail: pscroggs@howard.edu
Web: www.rangelprogram.org

Summary To provide financial assistance for graduate study in a field related to the work of the Foreign Service, especially to Hispanic Americans and members of other underrepresented minority groups.

Eligibility This program is open to U.S. citizens who are either graduating college seniors or recipients of an undergraduate degree. Applicants must be planning to enter graduate school to work on a master's degree in international affairs or other area of interest to the Foreign Service of the U.S. Department of State (e.g., public administration, public policy, business administration, foreign languages, economics, political science, or communications). They must have a GPA of 3.2 or higher. Strong preference is given to members of minority groups historically underrepresented in the Foreign Service and those who can demonstrate financial need.

Financial Data The stipend is $35,000 per year.

Duration 2 years.

Additional data This program is offered jointly by Howard University and the U.S. Department of State. Fellows are provided an internship working on international issues for members of Congress during the summer after they are selected and before they begin graduate study. They are provided a second internship at a U.S. embassy overseas during the summer before their second year of graduate study. Fellows who complete the program and Foreign Service entry requirements receive appointments as Foreign Service Officers. Each fellow who obtains a master's degree is committed to at least 3 years of service as a Foreign Service Officer. If recipients do not complete the program successfully or do not fulfill the 3-year service obligation, they may be subject to a reimbursement obligation.

Number awarded 20 each year.

Deadline January of each year.

[574]
CHCI-UNITED HEALTH FOUNDATION SCHOLAR INTERN PROGRAM

Congressional Hispanic Caucus Institute, Inc.
911 Second Street, N.E.
Washington, DC 20002
(202) 543-1771   Toll Free: (800) EXCEL-DC
Fax: (202) 546-2143   E-mail: chci@chci.org
Web: www.chci.org/scholarships

Summary To provide an educational stipend and work experience at community health organizations to undergraduate and graduate students of Hispanic descent.

Eligibility This program is open to U.S. citizens and permanent residents who are of Hispanic descent and currently enrolled full time at an accredited community college, 4-year university, or graduate/professional program. Applicants must be working on a health-related degree, including (but not limited to) nursing, pre-medicine or medicine, dentistry, public health, nutrition, or other health care field. They must obtain a paid internship at a community-based health organization that will require a total of at least 80 hours of service. Financial need is considered in the selection process.

Financial Data Participants receive a salary from the health organization where they work; upon verification of completion of 80 hours of paid employment, they also receive an educational stipend of $1,000 from the Congressional Hispanic Caucus Institute (CHCI).

Duration The stipend supports 1 year of study.

Additional data Funding for this program is provided by United Health Foundation.

Number awarded Varies each year; recently, 18 of these scholarship/internships were awarded: 14 to undergraduates, and 4 to graduate students.

Deadline April of each year.

[575]
CHILDREN'S MERCY HOSPITALS PEDIATRIC NURSING SCHOLARSHIP

National Association of Hispanic Nurses
Attn: National Awards and Scholarship Committee Chair
1455 Pennsylvania Avenue, N.W., Suite 400
Washington, DC 20004
(202) 387-2477   Fax: (202) 483-7183
E-mail: info@thehispanicnurses.org
Web: www.nahnnet.org/NAHNScholarships.html

Summary To provide financial assistance to members of the National Association of Hispanic Nurses (NAHN) who are interested in preparing for a career in pediatric nursing.

Eligibility Eligible are members of the association enrolled in associate, diploma, baccalaureate, graduate, or practical/vocational nursing programs in pediatric nursing. Applicants must have a GPA of 3.0 or higher. Along with their application, they must submit a letter of recommendation; a 300-word essay that reflects their qualifications and potential for leadership in nursing in the Hispanic community; a resume that includes earned certificates, awards, and special honors;

information on their financial status; and an official transcript. U.S. citizenship or permanent resident status is required.

Financial Data The stipend is $2,500.

Duration 1 year.

Additional data Support for this program, which began in 2013, is provided by Children's Mercy Hospitals of Kansas City, Missouri.

Number awarded 1 or more each year.

Deadline June of each year.

[576]
CINTHYA FELIX SCHOLARSHIP

Latino Medical Student Association
c/o Amaranta Craig, Scholarship Vice President
1355 Willard, Apartment B
San Francisco, CA 94117
E-mail: VP_Scholarship@lmsa.net
Web: www.lmsa.net/default.asp?contentID=9

Summary To provide financial assistance to undergraduate and graduate student members of the Latino Medical Student Association (LMSA) in selected western states who are preparing for a career in medicine.

Eligibility This program is open to LMSA members who are 1) residents of or attending school in its western region (Arizona, California, Oregon, Utah, and Washington); 2) enrolled at least as sophomores at a 4-year university or in a graduate program; 3) able to demonstrate a desire to advance the state of health care and education in Latino communities through extracurricular activities and/or membership in civic organizations; and 4) committed to preparing for a professional career in medicine and dedicated to serving the Latino and underserved communities. Applicants are eligible regardless of their immigrant or citizenship status, as long as the university they attend allows them to enroll and register for classes. Along with their application, they must submit a 1-page personal statement describing their family and personal background, educational objectives, community involvement, financial need, and how they would assist LMSA in its mission to provide health care to the Latino and/or other underserved communities.

Financial Data A stipend is awarded (amount not specified).

Duration 1 year.

Additional data Until 2002, this organization was known as the Chicano/Latino Medical Student Association of California. This program was established in 2011.

Number awarded Varies each year.

Deadline November of each year.

[577]
CISCO DIVERSITY SCHOLARSHIPS

Society of Hispanic Professional Engineers Foundation, Inc.
Attn: Advancing Hispanic Excellence in Technology, Engineering, Math and Science
13181 Crossroads Parkway North, Suite 450
P.O. Box 93577
City of Industry, CA 91715
(323) 725-3970, ext. 118   Fax: (323) 622-1046
E-mail: shpefoundation@shpe.org
Web: www.shpefoundation.org

Summary To provide financial assistance to undergraduate and graduate student members of the Society of Hispanic Professional Engineers (SHPE) who are working on a degree in designated fields of science, technology, engineering or mathematics (STEM).

Eligibility This program is open to full-time students who are either 1) rising sophomores or juniors; or 2) entering first-year graduate students. Applicants must be working on a degree in computer information systems, computer science, engineering (computer, electrical, or systems), management information systems, mathematics, physics, or technology management. They must have a GPA of 3.0 or higher. Along with their application, they must submit a 500-word personal statement on the event or experience that has had the greatest influence in shaping their character. Selection is based on that statement, potential for a commitment to a career in technology, leadership and community involvement, participation in their SHPE chapter activities, and interest in an internship with Cisco Systems. U.S. citizenship or permanent resident status is required.

Financial Data The stipend is $5,000.

Duration 1 year.

Additional data Advancing Hispanic Excellence in Technology, Engineering, Math and Science (AHETEMS) was established in 2004 by SHPE as an independent nonprofit foundation. This program is sponsored by Cisco Systems.

Number awarded 5 each year.

Deadline April of each year.

[578]
CLA SCHOLARSHIP FOR MINORITY STUDENTS IN MEMORY OF EDNA YELLAND

California Library Association
2471 Flores Street
San Mateo, CA 94403
(650) 376-0886   Fax: (650) 539-2341
E-mail: info@cla-net.org
Web: www.cla-net.org

Summary To provide financial assistance to Hispanic American and other minority students in California who are attending graduate school in any state to prepare for a career in library or information science.

Eligibility This program is open to California residents who are members of ethnic minority groups (American Indian/Alaska Native, African American/Black, Latino/Hispanic, Asian American, or Pacific Islander). Applicants must have completed at least 1 course in a master's program at an accredited graduate library school in any state. Evidence of financial need and U.S. citizenship or permanent resident status must be submitted. Finalists are interviewed.

Financial Data The stipend is $2,500.

Duration 1 academic year.

Additional data This fellowship is named for the executive secretary of the California Library Association from 1947 to 1963 who worked to promote the goals of the California Library Association and the profession. Until 1985, it was named the Edna Yelland Memorial Scholarship.

Number awarded 3 each year.

Deadline July of each year.

[579]
CLINICAL RESEARCH PRE-DOCTORAL FELLOWSHIP PROGRAM

American Nurses Association
Attn: SAMHSA Minority Fellowship Programs
8515 Georgia Avenue, Suite 400
Silver Spring, MD 20910-3492
(301) 628-5247   Toll Free: (800) 274-4ANA
Fax: (301) 628-5339   E-mail: janet.jackson@ana.org
Web: www.emfp.org

Summary To provide financial assistance to Hispanic American and other minority nurses who are doctoral candidates interested in psychiatric, mental health, and substance abuse issues that impact the lives of ethnic minority people.

Eligibility This program is open to nurses who have a master's degree and are members of an ethnic or racial minority group, including but not limited to Blacks or African Americans, Hispanics or Latinos, American Indians and Alaska Natives, Asian Americans, and Native Hawaiians and other Pacific Islanders. Applicants must be able to demonstrate a commitment to a research career in nursing and psychiatric/ mental health issues affecting ethnic minority populations. They must be interested in a program of full-time doctoral study, with a research focus on such issues of concern to minority populations as child abuse, violence in intimate relationships, mental health disorders, substance abuse, mental health service utilization, and stigma as a barrier to mental health care and personal resilience. U.S. citizenship or permanent resident status and membership in the American Nurses Association are required. Selection is based on research potential, scholarship, writing ability, knowledge of broad issues in mental health nursing, and professional commitment to ethnic minority concerns.

Financial Data The program provides an annual stipend of $22,032 and tuition assistance.

Duration 3 to 5 years.

Additional data Funds for this program are provided by the Substance Abuse and Mental Health Services Administration (SAMHSA).

Number awarded 1 or more each year.

Deadline February of each year.

[580]
COLGATE-PALMOLIVE/HDA FOUNDATION SCHOLARSHIPS

Hispanic Dental Association
Attn: HDA Foundation
1111 14th Street, N.W., Suite 1100
Washington, DC 20005
(202) 629-3628   Fax: (202) 629-3802
E-mail: scholarships@hdassoc.org
Web: www.hdassoc.org

Summary To provide financial assistance to members of the Hispanic Dental Association (HDA) interested in working on a postgraduate degree in dentistry.

Eligibility This program is open to HDA members who are U.S. citizens or permanent residents. Applicants must be working on a master's degree or higher in a dentistry-related program. They must have an undergraduate or graduate degree in an oral health-related field (e.g., dental hygiene, dentistry) from an institution in the United States or abroad. Along with their application, they must submit an essay on why they want to have a master's degree or higher in a dentistry-related field and how they will help improve their community when they have reached their goal. Selection is based on scholastic achievement, community service, leadership skills, and commitment to improving the oral health of the Hispanic community.

Financial Data The stipend is $10,000.

Duration 1 year.

Additional data This program, which began in 2005, is sponsored by the Colgate-Palmolive Company.

Number awarded Varies each year; recently, 2 of these scholarships were awarded.

Deadline June of each year.

[581]
COMMITTEE ON ETHNIC MINORITY RECRUITMENT SCHOLARSHIP

United Methodist Church-California-Pacific Annual
  Conference
Attn: Board of Ordained Ministry
1720 East Linfield Street
Glendora, CA 91740
(626) 335-6629   Fax: (626) 335-5750
E-mail: cathy.adminbom@gmail.com
Web: www.calpacordainedministry.org/523451

Summary To provide financial assistance to Hispanic Americans and members of other ethnic minority groups in the California Pacific Annual Conference of the United Methodist Church (UMC) who are attending a seminary in any state to qualify for ordination as an elder or deacon.

Eligibility This program is open to members of ethnic minority groups in the UMC California-Pacific Annual Conference who are enrolled at a seminary in any state approved by the UMC University Senate. Applicants must have been approved as certified candidates by their district committee and be seeking Probationary Deacon or Elder's Orders. They may apply for 1 or more types of assistance: tuition scholarships, grants for books and school supplies (including computers), or emergency living expense grants.

Financial Data Tuition stipends are $1,000 per year; books and supplies grants range up to $1,000 per year; emergency living expense grants depend on need and the availability of funds.

Duration 1 year; may be renewed up to 2 additional years.

Additional data The California-Pacific Annual Conference includes churches in southern California, Hawaii, Guam, and Saipan.

Number awarded Varies each year.

Deadline August of each year for fall term; December of each year for spring term.

[582]
CONGRESSIONAL HISPANIC CAUCUS INSTITUTE SCHOLARSHIP AWARDS

Congressional Hispanic Caucus Institute, Inc.
911 Second Street, N.E.
Washington, DC 20002
(202) 543-1771   Toll Free: (800) EXCEL-DC
Fax: (202) 546-2143   E-mail: chci@chci.org
Web: www.chci.org/scholarships

Summary To provide financial assistance for college or graduate school to students of Hispanic descent.

Eligibility This program is open to U.S. citizens and permanent residents who are Hispanic as defined by the U.S. Census Bureau (individuals of Mexican, Puerto Rican, Cuban, Central and South American, and other Spanish and Latin American descent). Applicants must be attending or planning to attend an accredited community college, 4-year university, or professional or graduate program as a full-time student. Along with their application, they must submit a 1-page essay on the field of study they plan to pursue and how the Latino community will benefit. Selection is based on demonstrated financial need, consistent active participation in public and/or community service activities, and good writing skills. There are no GPA or academic major requirements.

Financial Data The stipend is $5,000 for graduate students, $2,500 for students at 4-year institutions, or $1,000 for students at 2-year community colleges. Funds are intended to cover tuition, room and board, textbooks, and other educational expenses associated with college enrollment. The stipend may be divided over the number of years required to complete a degree (e.g., a freshman entering a 4-year institution may receive $625 per year for 4 years).

Duration 1 year.

Number awarded Varies each year; recently, 130 of these scholarships were awarded: 10 to community college students, 114 to undergraduates, and 6 to graduate students.

Deadline April of each year.

[583]
CONNECTICUT HISPANIC BAR ASSOCIATION SCHOLARSHIPS

Connecticut Hispanic Bar Association
c/o Marilyn Diaz
940 Poquonock Avenue
Windsor, CT 06095
(860) 285-8058   E-mail: mdiazesq@sbcglobal.net
Web: www.ct-hba.org/for-students

Summary To provide financial assistance to students who are enrolled at law schools in Connecticut and have a connection to the Latino community.

Eligibility This program is open to students currently enrolled at law schools in Connecticut who have a strong connection to the Latino community. Applicants must submit a personal statement of 500 to 1,000 words discussing what they hope to achieve as a lawyer, especially their commitment to the Latino community.

Financial Data A stipend is awarded (amount not specified).

Duration 1 year.

Additional data This program, established in 1997, is offered through the Hartford Foundation for Public Giving.

Number awarded Varies each year; recently, 5 of these scholarships were awarded.

Deadline September of each year.

[584]
CONSORTIUM FOR GRADUATE STUDY IN MANAGEMENT FELLOWSHIPS

Consortium for Graduate Study in Management
229 Chesterfield Business Parkway
Chesterfield, MO 63005
(636) 681-5553   Fax: (636) 681-5499
E-mail: recruiting@cgsm.org
Web: www.cgsm.org

Summary To provide college funding and work experience to Hispanic Americans and other underrepresented racial minorities who are interested in preparing for a management career in business.

Eligibility This program is open to African Americans, Hispanic Americans (Chicanos, Cubans, Dominicans, and Puerto Ricans), and Native Americans who have graduated from college and are interested in preparing for a career in business. Other U.S. citizens and permanent residents who can demonstrate a commitment to the sponsor's mission of enhancing diversity in business education are also eligible. An undergraduate degree in business or economics is not required. Applicants must be planning to work on an M.B.A. degree at 1 of the consortium's 18 schools.

Financial Data The fellowship pays full tuition and required fees. Summer internships with the consortium's cooperative sponsors, providing paid practical experience, are also offered.

Duration Up to 4 semesters.

Additional data This program began in 1966. The participating schools are Carnegie Mellon University, Cornell University, Dartmouth College, Emory University, Georgetown University, Indiana University, University of Michigan, New York University, University of California at Berkeley, University of California at Los Angeles, University of North Carolina at Chapel Hill, University of Rochester, University of Southern California, University of Texas at Austin, University of Virginia, Washington University, University of Wisconsin at Madison, and Yale University. Fellowships are tenable at member schools only. Application fees are $150 for students applying to 1 or 2 schools, $200 for 3 schools, $240 for 4 schools, $275 for 5 schools, or $300 for 6 schools.

Number awarded Varies each year; recently, more than 380 of these fellowships were awarded.

Deadline March of each year.

[585]
CONSTANGY, BROOKS & SMITH DIVERSITY SCHOLARS AWARD

Constangy, Brooks & Smith LLC
Attn: Chair, Diversity Council
200 West Forsyth Street, Suite 1700
Jacksonville, FL 32202-4317
(904) 356-8900   Fax: (904) 356-8200
E-mail: mzabijaka@constangy.com
Web: www.constangy.com/f-4.html

Summary To provide financial assistance to Hispanic Americans and other diverse students who are enrolled in law schools in selected states.

Eligibility This program is open to second-year students enrolled in accredited law schools located in 1 of 3 regions: South (Alabama, Florida, Georgia, South Carolina, Tennessee), Midwest/West Coast (California, Illinois, Kansas, Missouri, Texas, Wisconsin), or East (Massachusetts, New Jersey, North Carolina, Virginia/Washington D.C.). Applicants must submit a personal statement on why diversity is important to them personally and in the legal profession. They must have a GPA of 2.7 or higher. Selection is based on academic achievement, commitment to diversity, and personal achievement in overcoming obstacles.

Financial Data The stipend is $3,000.

Duration 1 year.

Number awarded 3 each year: 1 in each region.

Deadline November of each year.

[586]
CONSUELO W. GOSNELL MEMORIAL SCHOLARSHIPS

National Association of Social Workers
Attn: NASW Foundation
750 First Street, N.E., Suite 700
Washington, DC 20002-4241
(202) 408-8600, ext. 298   Fax: (202) 336-8292
E-mail: naswfoundation@naswdc.org
Web: www.naswfoundation.org/fellowships.asp

Summary To provide financial assistance to Hispanic Americans, Native Americans, and other students interested in working on a master's degree in social work.

Eligibility This program is open to students who have applied to or been accepted into an accredited M.S.W. program. Applicants must have demonstrated a commitment to work with, or have a special affinity with, American Indian, Alaska Native, or Hispanic/Latino populations in the United States. They must be members of the National Association of Social Workers (NASW), have the potential for completing an M.S.W. program, and have a GPA of 3.0 or higher. Applicants who have demonstrated a commitment to working with public or voluntary nonprofit agencies or with local grassroots groups in the United States are also eligible. Financial need is considered in the selection process.

Financial Data The stipends range up to $4,000 per year.

Duration Up to 1 year; may be renewed for 1 additional year.

Number awarded Up to 10 each year.

Deadline March of each year.

[587]
COOK/RUTLEDGE FELLOWSHIP

New Jersey Department of Health
Office of Minority and Multicultural Health
Attn: Executive Director
John Fitch Plaza, Room 501
P.O. Box 360
Trenton, NJ 08625-0360
(609) 292-6962   Fax: (609) 292-8713
Web: www.nj.gov/health/omh/professions.shtml

Summary To provide financial support to Hispanic American and other public health, law, and medical students in New Jersey who are interested in conducting research related to health disparities issues during the summer.

Eligibility This program is open to students in medical science, law, or master's of public health programs who are 1) residents of New Jersey attending school in the state or else-

where; or 2) residents of other states attending a college or university in New Jersey. Applicants must be interested in working on a supervised project at the New Jersey Department of Health in Trenton on current and relevant health equity/health disparity issues impacting the racial or ethnic minority populations in New Jersey. Along with their application, they must submit letters of recommendation from 1) a college instructor indicating their commitment to an understanding of the issues facing the racial or ethnic minority populations; or 2) a community-based or faith-based organization or public health organization where they volunteered, worked, or assisted with a health care initiative that directly impacted a racial or ethnic minority group.

Financial Data The stipend is $6,000.

Duration 8 to 10 weeks during the summer.

Number awarded 1 each year.

Deadline March of each year.

[588]
COOLEY DIVERSITY FELLOWSHIP PROGRAM

Cooley LLP
Attn: Attorney Recruiting Manager
4401 Eastgate Mall
San Diego, CA 92121-1909
(858) 550-6474   E-mail: diversityfellowship@cooley.com
Web: www.cooley.com/diversityfellowship

Summary To provide financial aid and work experience to Hispanic American and other law students who are committed to promoting diversity in their community and are interested in summer associateships and employment at an office of Cooley LLP.

Eligibility This program is open to students enrolled full time at an ABA-accredited law school and planning to graduate 2 years after applying. Applicants must submit a 3-page personal statement describing their demonstrated commitment to promoting diversity (e.g., ethnicity, gender, physical disability, and/or sexual orientation) in their community. They must be interested in a summer associateship. Selection is based on undergraduate and law school academic performance, personal achievements, leadership abilities, community service, and demonstrated commitment to promoting diversity.

Financial Data The award includes a stipend of $10,000 after completing a summer associateship after the first year of law school, another stipend of $10,000 after completing another summer associateship after the second year of law school, and another stipend of $10,000 after graduating from law school and joining the firm as a full-time associate.

Duration 3 years.

Additional data Summer associates may work in any of the firm's offices in California (Palo Alto, San Diego, or San Francisco), Colorado (Broomfield), Massachusetts (Boston), New York (New York), Virginia (Reston), Washington (Seattle), or Washington, D.C.

Number awarded 1 or more each year.

Deadline June of each year.

[589]
CORPORATE SCHOLARSHIP TEXAS INSTRUMENTS

Society of Hispanic Professional Engineers Foundation, Inc.
Attn: Advancing Hispanic Excellence in Technology, Engineering, Math and Science
13181 Crossroads Parkway North, Suite 450
P.O. Box 93577
City of Industry, CA 91715
(323) 725-3970, ext. 118   Fax: (323) 622-1046
E-mail: shpefoundation@shpe.org
Web: www.shpefoundation.org

Summary To provide financial assistance to undergraduate and graduate student members of the Society of Hispanic Professional Engineers (SHPE) who are working on a degree in specified fields of science, technology, engineering, or mathematics (STEM), especially at designated universities.

Eligibility This program is open to full-time undergraduate and graduate student members of SHPE. Preference is given to members working on a degree in computer or electrical engineering; alternate eligible fields include chemical engineering, computer science, electrical engineering technology, electronic technology, management information systems, materials science, mechanical engineering, microelectronics, or physics. Applicants must have a GPA of 3.0 or higher. They must be eligible to work in the United States. Along with their application, they must submit a 500-word personal statement covering their community involvement, leadership, academic achievements, research internship and co-op experiences, and short-term and long-term goals and aspirations. Selection is based on motivation and aptitude for a career in STEM. Preferred universities include Arizona State University, Georgia Tech University, Stanford University, Texas A&M University, Texas Tech University, University of Florida, University of Illinois, University of Maryland, University of Michigan, University of Texas at Austin, and University of Texas at Dallas. First priority is given to bachelor's degree students, although master's and doctoral candidates are also eligible.

Financial Data The stipend is $2,700.

Duration 1 year.

Additional data Advancing Hispanic Excellence in Technology, Engineering, Math and Science (AHETEMS) was established in 2004 by SHPE as an independent nonprofit foundation. This program is sponsored by Texas Instruments.

Number awarded 1 or more each year.

Deadline April of each year.

[590]
CORRIS BOYD SCHOLARSHIP

Association of University Programs in Health Administration
Attn: Prizes, Fellowships and Scholarships
2000 14th Street North, Suite 780
Arlington, VA 22201
(703) 894-0940, ext. 115   Fax: (703) 894-0941
E-mail: aupha@aupha.org
Web: www.aupha.org/i4a/pages/index.cfm?pageid=3541

Summary To provide financial assistance to Hispanic American and other minority students entering graduate schools affiliated with the Association of University Programs in Health Administration (AUPHA).

Eligibility This program is open to students of color (African Americans, American Indians, Alaska Natives, Asian Americans, Hispanic Americans, Native Hawaiians, and other Pacific Islanders) who have been accepted to a master's degree program in health care management at an AUPHA member institution. Applicants must be U.S. citizens or permanent residents and have a GPA of 3.0 or higher. Along with their application, they must submit a personal statement explaining why they are choosing to prepare for a career in health administration. Selection is based on leadership qualities, academic achievement, community involvement, and commitment to health care; financial need may be considered if all other factors are equal.

Financial Data The stipend is $40,000.

Duration 1 year.

Additional data This program began in 2006.

Number awarded 2 each year.

Deadline May of each year.

[591]
CRCNA RACE RELATIONS MULTIRACIAL STUDENT SCHOLARSHIP

Christian Reformed Church
Attn: Office of Race Relations
2850 Kalamazoo Avenue, S.E.
Grand Rapids, MI 49560-0200
(616) 224-5883   Toll Free: (877) 279-9994
Fax: (616) 224-0834   E-mail: elugo@crcna.org
Web: www.crcna.org/race/scholarships

Summary To provide financial assistance to Hispanic American and other minority undergraduate and graduate students who are interested in attending colleges related to the Christian Reformed Church in North America (CRCNA).

Eligibility This program is open to students of color in the United States and Canada. Normally, applicants are expected to be members of CRCNA congregations who plan to pursue their educational goals at Calvin Theological Seminary or any of the colleges affiliated with the CRCNA. They must be interested in training for the ministry of racial reconciliation in church and/or in society. Students who have no prior history with the CRCNA must attend a CRCNA-related college or seminary for a full academic year before they are eligible to apply for this program. Students entering their sophomore year must have earned a GPA of 2.0 or higher as freshmen; students entering their junior year must have earned a GPA of 2.3 or higher as sophomores; students entering their senior year must have earned a GPA of 2.6 or higher as juniors.

Financial Data First-year students receive $500 per semester. Other levels of students may receive up to $2,000 per academic year.

Duration 1 year.

Additional data This program was first established in 1971 and revised in 1991. Recipients are expected to train to engage actively in the ministry of racial reconciliation in church and in society. They must be able to work in the United States or Canada upon graduating and must consider working for 1 of the agencies of the CRCNA.

Number awarded Varies each year; recently, 31 students received a total of $21,000 in support.

Deadline March of each year.

[592]
CTA/MARTIN LUTHER KING, JR. MEMORIAL SCHOLARSHIP FUND

California Teachers Association
Attn: CTA Foundation for Teaching and Learning
1705 Murchison Drive
P.O. Box 921
Burlingame, CA 94011-0921
(650) 697-1400   E-mail: scholarships@cta.org
Web: www.cta.org

Summary To provide financial assistance for college or graduate school to Hispanic Americans and other racial and ethnic minorities who are members of the California Teachers Association (CTA), children of members, or members of the Student CTA.

Eligibility This program is open to members of racial or ethnic minority groups (African Americans, American Indians/Alaska Natives, Asians/Pacific Islanders, and Hispanics) who are 1) active CTA members; 2) dependent children of active, retired, or deceased CTA members; or 3) members of Student CTA. Applicants must be interested in preparing for a teaching career in public education or already engaged in such a career.

Financial Data Stipends vary each year; recently, they ranged from $1,000 to $4,000.

Duration 1 year.

Number awarded Varies each year; recently, 25 of these scholarships were awarded: 5 to CTA members, 10 to children of CTA members, and 10 to Student CTA members.

Deadline February of each year.

[593]
CUBAN AMERICAN BAR ASSOCIATION SCHOLARSHIPS

Cuban American Bar Association
c/o Meland Russin & Budwick, PA
200 South Biscayne Boulevard, Suite 3200
Miami, FL 33131
(786) 210-5984   Fax: (303) 646-0633
E-mail: info@cabaonline.com
Web: www.cabaonline.com/page/scholarships

Summary To provide financial assistance to law students who have a connection with the Cuban American community.

Eligibility This program is open to students currently enrolled at an accredited law school who 1) are Cuban Americans who have distinguished themselves academically and/or in service-oriented activities; or 2) have distinguished themselves in research, writing, community services, and/or activities of importance to the Cuban American community. Applicants must submit a 1,000-word essay focusing on and describing in detail the activities and achievements that qualify them for the award.

Financial Data Stipends range from $500 to $4,500.

Duration 1 year.

Additional data This program includes the Osvaldo Soto Scholarship and the Judge Margarita Esquiroz Scholarship.

Number awarded Varies each year; recently, 5 of these scholarships were awarded: 1 at $4,500, 3 at $2,500, and 1 at $500.

Deadline September of each year.

[594]
CUMMINS/HENAAC SCHOLARS PROGRAM

Great Minds in STEM
Attn: HENAAC Scholars Program
602 Monterey Pass Road
Monterey Park, CA 91754
(323) 262-0997   Fax: (323) 262-0946
E-mail: gcruz@greatmindsinstem.org
Web: www.greatmindsinstem.org

Summary To provide financial assistance to Hispanic undergraduate and graduate students working on a degree in a field of science, technology, engineering, or mathematics (STEM).

Eligibility This program is open to Hispanic students who are working on an undergraduate or graduate degree in a field of STEM. Applicants must be of Hispanic origin and/or must significantly participate in and promote organizations and activities in the Hispanic community. They must have a GPA of 3.0 or higher. Along with their application, they must submit a 700-word essay on a topic that changes annually. Selection is based on leadership, academic achievements, and campus and community activities; financial need is not considered. U.S. citizenship or permanent resident status is required.

Financial Data Stipends range from $500 to $10,000.

Duration 1 year; recipients may reapply.

Additional data The Hispanic Engineer National Achievement Awards Conference (HENAAC) was established in 1989 and initiated a scholarship program in 2000. In 2010, the sponsoring organization officially adopted its current name, but it continues to hold the annual HENAAC conference, at which the scholarships are presented. This program is sponsored by Cummins, Inc. Recipients must attend the conference to accept their scholarship.

Number awarded Varies each year; recently, 8 of these scholarships were awarded.

Deadline April of each year.

[595]
CUMMINS SCHOLARSHIPS

Society of Women Engineers
Attn: Scholarship Selection Committee
203 North LaSalle Street, Suite 1675
Chicago, IL 60601-1269
(312) 596-5223   Toll Free: (877) SWE-INFO
Fax: (312) 644-8557   E-mail: scholarships@swe.org
Web: societyofwomenengineers.swe.org

Summary To provide financial assistance to minority and other women working on an undergraduate or graduate degree in computer science or designated engineering specialties.

Eligibility This program is open to women who are sophomores, juniors, seniors, or graduate students at 4-year ABET-accredited colleges and universities. Applicants must be working full time on a degree in computer science or automotive, chemical, computer, electrical, industrial, manufacturing, materials, or mechanical engineering and have a GPA of 3.5 or higher. Preference is given to members of groups underrepresented in engineering or computer science. Selection is based on merit. U.S. citizenship or permanent resident status is required.

Financial Data The stipend is $1,000.

Duration 1 year.

Additional data This program is sponsored by Cummins, Inc.

Number awarded 2 each year.

Deadline February of each year.

[596]
DAISY PABON SCHOLARSHIP

Puerto Rican Civic Club, Inc.
Attn: Scholarship Committee
P.O. Box 765
San Jose, CA 95106
(408) 475-7722   E-mail: puertorros@hotmail.com
Web: www.puertoricancivicclub.org

Summary To provide financial assistance to residents of California who are of Puerto Rican ancestry and interested in working on an undergraduate or graduate degree in any field at a school in any state.

Eligibility This program is open to students of Puerto Rican descent who are residents of California enrolled or planning to enroll at a college or university in any state. Applicants must be high school seniors, high school graduates, GED recipients, undergraduates, or graduate students. They must have a GPA of 2.5 or higher. Selection is based on academic record, extracurricular activities, work experience, community service, an essay, and financial need.

Financial Data Stipends range from $500 to $1,000.

Duration 1 year.

Number awarded Varies each year; recently, 4 of these scholarships were awarded.

Deadline May of each year.

[597]
DALLAS HISPANIC LAW FOUNDATION SCHOLARSHIPS

Dallas Hispanic Law Foundation
c/o Ophelia Camina, President
Susman Godfrey L.L.P.
901 Main Street, Suite 5100
Dallas, TX 75202-3775
(214) 754-1900   Fax: (214) 754-1933
E-mail: dhlf.scholarships@gmail.com
Web: www.dallashispaniclawfoundation.com

Summary To provide financial assistance to residents of Texas attending law school in the state and planning to serve the Hispanic community.

Eligibility This program is open to residents of Texas attending law school in the state. Applicants must submit a 1-page statement on their career aspirations and how they intend to use their law degree to benefit the Hispanic community. Financial need is considered in the selection process.

Financial Data The stipend is at least $1,000.

Duration 1 year.

Additional data This program began in 2006.

Number awarded Varies each year; recently, 13 of these scholarships were awarded.

Deadline March of each year.

[598]
DAVID C. LIZARRAGA GRADUATE FELLOWSHIPS

TELACU Education Foundation
Attn: David Lizárraga Fellowship Program
5400 East Olympic Boulevard, Suite 300
Los Angeles, CA 90022
(323) 721-1655   Fax: (323) 721-3560
E-mail: jogarcia@telacu.com
Web: www.telacu.com

Summary To provide financial assistance to Latino students from designated communities who are working on a master's degree in business or engineering at a school in any state.

Eligibility This program is open to Latino residents of selected communities in southern California, selected cities in Texas, the Greater Chicagoland area of Illinois, or the state of New York. Applicants must be working full time on a master's degree in business administration or engineering at a university in any state; students working on other graduate degrees may be considered at the discretion of the sponsor. Priority is given to students in their last year of graduate study, although first-year graduate students may be considered. They must be a first-generation college student and have a GPA of 2.5 or higher. Selection is based on leadership potential, professional and extracurricular achievement, commitment to the development and economic empowerment of communities, and financial need.

Financial Data The stipend ranges from $500 to $5,000.

Duration 1 year.

Additional data This program is sponsored by Toyota. The eligible areas in California include underserved communities in Los Angeles, Orange, and San Bernardino counties such as unincorporated areas of east Los Angeles and the cities of Baldwin Park, Bell Gardens, Commerce, Huntington Park, Los Angeles, Montebello, Ontario, Pico Rivera, Pomona, San Bernardino, Santa Ana, and South Gate. The cities in Texas are Austin, Edinburg, Laredo, Rio Grande City, and San Antonio.

Number awarded Up to 6 each year.

Deadline March of each year.

[599]
DAVID HILLIARD EATON SCHOLARSHIP

Unitarian Universalist Association
Attn: Ministerial Credentialing Office
25 Beacon Street
Boston, MA 02108-2800
(617) 948-6403   Fax: (617) 742-2875
E-mail: mcoadministrator@uua.org
Web: www.uua.org

Summary To provide financial assistance to Hispanic American and other minority women preparing for the Unitarian Universalist (UU) ministry.

Eligibility This program is open to women from historically marginalized groups who are currently enrolled or planning to enroll full or at least half time in a UU ministerial training program with aspirant or candidate status. Applicants must be citizens of the United States or Canada. Priority is given first to those who have demonstrated outstanding ministerial ability and secondarily to students with the greatest financial need (especially persons of color).

Financial Data The stipend ranges from $1,000 to $15,000 per year.

Duration 1 year.

Number awarded 1 or 2 each year.

Deadline April of each year.

[600]
DAVID POHL SCHOLARSHIP

Unitarian Universalist Association
Attn: Ministerial Credentialing Office
25 Beacon Street
Boston, MA 02108-2800
(617) 948-6403   Fax: (617) 742-2875
E-mail: mcoadministrator@uua.org
Web: www.uua.org

Summary To provide financial assistance to seminary students (particularly Hispanic Americans and other persons of color) who are preparing for the Unitarian Universalist (UU) ministry.

Eligibility This program is open to seminary students who are enrolled full or at least half time in a UU ministerial training program with candidate status. Applicants must be citizens of the United States or Canada. Priority is given first to those who have demonstrated outstanding ministerial ability and secondarily to students with the greatest financial need (especially persons of color).

Financial Data The stipend ranges from $1,000 to $15,000 per year.

Duration 1 year.

Number awarded 1 each year.

Deadline April of each year.

[601]
DAVIS WRIGHT TREMAINE 1L DIVERSITY SCHOLARSHIP PROGRAM

Davis Wright Tremaine LLP
Attn: Diversity Scholarship Program
1201 Third Avenue, Suite 2200
Seattle, WA 98101-3045
(206) 757-8761   Toll Free: (877) 398-8416
Fax: (206) 757-7700   E-mail: BrookDormaier@dwt.com
Web: www.dwt.com/1LDiversityScholarship

Summary To provide financial aid and summer work experience to Hispanic American and other law students of color.

Eligibility This program is open to first-year law students of color and others of diverse backgrounds. Applicants must have a record of academic achievement as an undergraduate and in the first year of law school that demonstrates promise for a successful career in law, a commitment to civic involvement that promotes diversity and will continue after entering the legal profession, and a commitment to practicing in the Northwest after law school. Although demonstrated need may be taken into account, applicants need not disclose their financial circumstances.

Financial Data The award consists of a $7,500 stipend for second-year tuition and expenses and a paid summer clerkship.

Duration 1 academic year and summer.

Number awarded 2 each year: 1 in the Seattle office and 1 in the Portland office.

Deadline January of each year.

[602]
DENNY'S HUNGRY FOR EDUCATION SCHOLARSHIPS

Hispanic Association of Colleges and Universities
Attn: National Scholarship Program
8415 Datapoint Drive, Suite 400
San Antonio, TX 78229
(210) 692-3805   Fax: (210) 692-0823
TDD: (800) 855-2880   E-mail: scholarship@hacu.net
Web: www.hacu.net/hacu/Scholarships.asp

Summary To provide financial assistance to undergraduate and graduate students majoring in business or hospitality at member institutions of the Hispanic Association of Colleges and Universities (HACU) in designated states.

Eligibility This program is open to full- and part-time undergraduate and graduate students at 2- and 4-year HACU member institutions in Arizona, California, Colorado, Florida, Georgia, Illinois, Nevada, New Mexico, New York, South Carolina, Texas, or Washington, D.C. Applicants must be working on a degree in business or hospitality and have a GPA of 3.0 or higher. Along with their application, they must submit a 500-word essay on how Denny's can help in the fight against childhood hunger in the United States.

Financial Data The stipend is $1,000.

Duration 1 year.

Additional data This program is sponsored by Denny's and administered by HACU.

Number awarded 1 or more each year.

Deadline June of each year.

[603]
DEPARTMENT OF HOMELAND SECURITY SUMMER FACULTY AND STUDENT RESEARCH TEAM PROGRAM

Oak Ridge Institute for Science and Education
Attn: Science and Engineering Education
P.O. Box 117
Oak Ridge, TN 37831-0117
(865) 574-1447   Fax: (865) 241-5219
E-mail: Patti.Obenour@orau.gov
Web: see.orau.org

Summary To provide an opportunity for teams of students and faculty from minority-serving educational institutions to conduct research during the summer in areas of interest to the Department of Homeland Security (DHS).

Eligibility This program is open to teams of up to 2 students (undergraduate and/or graduate) and 1 faculty from Historically Black Colleges and Universities (HBCUs), Hispanic Serving Institutions (HSIs), Tribal Colleges and Universities (TCUs), Alaska Native Serving Institutions (ANSIs), and Native Hawaiian Serving Institutions (NHSIs). Applicants must be interested in conducting research at designated DHS Centers of Excellence in science, technology, engineering, or mathematics related to homeland security (HS-STEM), including explosives detection, mitigation, and response; social and behavioral sciences; risk, economics, and decision sciences; human factors; chemical threats and countermeasures; biological threats and countermeasures; community, commerce, and infrastructure resilience; food and agricultural security; transportation security; border security; immigration studies; maritime and port security; infrastructure protection;

natural disasters and related geophysical studies; emergency preparedness and response; communications and interoperability; or advanced data analysis and visualization. Faculty must have a full-time appointment at an eligible institution and have received a Ph.D. in an HS-STEM discipline no more than 7 years previously; at least 2 years of full-time research and/or teaching experience is preferred. Students must have a GPA of 3.0 or higher and be enrolled full time. Undergraduates must be entering their junior or senior year. U.S. citizenship is required. Selection is based on relevance and intrinsic merit of the research (40%), faculty applicant qualifications (30%), academic benefit to the faculty applicant and his/her institution (10%), and student applicant qualifications (20%).

Financial Data Stipends are $1,200 per week for faculty, $600 per week for graduate students, and $500 per week for undergraduates. Faculty members who live more than 50 miles from their assigned site may receive a housing allowance of $1,500 and travel expenses up to an additional $500. Limited travel expenses for 1 round trip are reimbursed for undergraduate and graduate students living more than 50 miles from their assigned site.

Duration 12 weeks during the summer.

Additional data This program is funded by DHS and administered by Oak Ridge Institute for Science and Education (ORISE). Recently, the available DHS Centers of Excellence were the Center for Advancing Microbial Risk Assessment (led by Michigan State University and Drexel University); the National Center for Risk and Economic Analysis of Terrorism Events (led by University of Southern California); the National Center for Food Protection and Defense (led by University of Minnesota); the Center of Excellence for Zoonotic and Animal Disease Defense (led by Texas A&M University and Kansas State University); the National Consortium for the Study of Terrorism and Responses to Terrorism (led by University of Maryland); the Center of Excellence for Awareness and Localization of Explosives-Related Threats (led by Northeastern University and University of Rhode Island); the National Center for Border Security and Immigration (led by the University of Arizona and the University of Texas at El Paso); the Center for Maritime, Island and Remote and Extreme Environment Security (led by the University of Hawaii and Stevens Institute of Technology); the Coastal Hazards Center of Excellence (led by the University of North Carolina at Chapel Hill and Jackson State University); the National Transportation Security Center of Excellence (consisting of 7 institutions); and the Center of Excellence in Command, Control, and Interoperability (led by Purdue University and Rutgers University).

Number awarded Approximately 12 teams are selected each year.

Deadline January of each year.

[604]
DEPARTMENT OF TRANSPORTATION/ EISENHOWER GRADUATE TRANSPORTATION FELLOWSHIPS

Department of Transportation
Federal Highway Administration
Attn: Universities and Grants Programs
4600 North Fairfax Drive, Suite 800
Arlington, VA 22203-1553
(703) 235-0538   Toll Free: (877) 558-6873
Fax: (703) 235-0593   E-mail: transportationedu@dot.gov
Web: www.fhwa.dot.gov/tpp/ddetfp.htm

Summary To provide financial assistance to graduate students (particularly at Minority Serving Institutions) who are working on a master's or doctoral degree in transportation-related fields.

Eligibility This program is open to students enrolled or planning to enroll full time to work on a master's or doctoral degree in a field of study directly related to transportation. Applicants must be planning to enter the transportation profession after completing their higher level education. They must be U.S. citizens or have an I-20 (foreign student) or I-551 (permanent resident) identification card. Selection is based on the proposed plan of study, academic records (class standing, GPA, and official transcripts), transportation work experience (including employer's endorsement), and recommendations. Students at Historically Black Colleges and Universities (HBCUs), Hispanic Serving Institutions (HSIs), and Tribal Colleges and Universities (TCUs) are especially encouraged to apply.

Financial Data Fellows receive tuition and fees (to a maximum of $10,000 per year), monthly stipends of $1,700 for master's degree students or $2,000 for doctoral students, and a 1-time allowance of up to $1,500 for travel to an annual meeting of the Transportation Research Board.

Duration For master's degree students, 24 months, and the degree must be completed within 3 years; for doctoral students, 36 months, and the degree must be completed within 5 years.

Number awarded Approximately 100 to 150 each year.

Deadline March of each year.

[605]
DEPARTMENT OF TRANSPORTATION/ EISENHOWER GRANTS FOR RESEARCH AND INTERN FELLOWSHIPS

Department of Transportation
Federal Highway Administration
Attn: Universities and Grants Programs
4600 North Fairfax Drive, Suite 800
Arlington, VA 22203-1553
(703) 235-0538   Toll Free: (877) 558-6873
Fax: (703) 235-0593   E-mail: transportationedu@dot.gov
Web: www.fhwa.dot.gov/tpp/ddetfp.htm

Summary To enable students (particularly those at Minority Serving Institutions) to participate in transportation-related research activities either at facilities of the U.S. Department of Transportation (DOT) Federal Highway Administration in the Washington, D.C. area or as interns for private or public organizations.

Eligibility This program is open to 1) students in their junior year of a baccalaureate program who will complete their junior year before being awarded a fellowship; 2) students in their senior year of a baccalaureate program; and 3) students who have completed their baccalaureate degree and are enrolled in a program leading to a master's, Ph.D., or equivalent degree. Applicants must be enrolled full time at an accredited U.S institution of higher education and planning to enter the transportation profession after completing their higher education. They must be U.S. citizens or have an I-20 (foreign student) or I-551 (permanent resident) identification card. For research fellowships, they select 1 or more projects from a current list of research activities underway at various DOT facilities; the research is conducted with academic supervision provided by a faculty adviser from their home university (which grants academic credit for the research project) and with technical direction provided by the DOT staff. Intern fellowships provide students with opportunities to perform transportation-related research, development, technology transfer, and other activities at public and private sector organizations. Specific requirements for the target projects vary; most require engineering backgrounds, but others involve transportation planning, information management, public administration, physics, materials science, statistical analysis, operations research, chemistry, economics, technology transfer, urban studies, geography, and urban and regional planning. The DOT encourages students at Historically Black Colleges and Universities (HBCUs), Hispanic Serving Institutions (HSIs), and Tribal Colleges and Universities (TCUs) to apply for these grants. Selection is based on match of the student's qualifications with the proposed research project (including the student's ability to accomplish the project in the available time), recommendation letters regarding the nominee's qualifications to conduct the research, academic records (including class standing, GPA, and transcripts), and transportation work experience (if any), including the employer's endorsement.

Financial Data Fellows receive full tuition and fees that relate to the academic credits for the approved research project (to a maximum of $10,000) and a monthly stipend of $1,450 for undergraduates, $1,700 for master's students, or $2,000 for doctoral students. An allowance for travel to and from the DOT facility where the research is conducted is also provided, but selectees are responsible for their own housing accommodations. Recipients are also provided with a 1-time allowance of up to $1,500 to attend the annual Transportation Research Board (TRB) meeting.

Duration Projects normally range from 3 to 12 months.

Number awarded Varies each year; recently, 9 students participated in this program.

Deadline Applications remain open until each project is filled.

[606]
DICKSTEIN SHAPIRO DIVERSITY SCHOLARSHIP

Dickstein Shapiro LLP
Attn: Director of Professional Development and Attorney Recruiting
1825 Eye Street, N.W.
Washington, DC 20006-5403
(202) 420-4880   Fax: (202) 420-2201
E-mail: careers@dicksteinshapiro.com
Web: www.dicksteinshapiro.com/careers/diversity

Summary To provide financial aid and summer work experience at Dickstein Shapiro in Washington, D.C. or New York City to Hispanic American and other diverse law students from any state.

Eligibility This program is open to second-year diverse law students, including 1) members of the lesbian, gay, bisexual, and transgender (LGBT) community; 2) members of minority ethnic and racial groups (Blacks, Hispanics and Latinos, Asians, American Indians and Native Alaskans, and Native Hawaiians and Pacific Islanders); and 3) students with disabilities. Applicants must be interested in a summer associateship with Dickstein Shapiro in Washington, D.C. or New York City. Selection is based on academic and professional experience as well as the extent to which they reflect the core values of the firm: excellence, loyalty, respect, initiative, and integrity.

Financial Data The stipend is $25,000, including $15,000 upon completion of the summer associate program and $10,000 upon acceptance of a full-time offer of employment following graduation.

Duration The associateship takes place during the summer following the second year of law school and the stipend covers the third year of law school.

Additional data This program began in 2006.

Number awarded 1 or more each year.

Deadline September of each year.

[607]
DINSMORE & SHOHL LLP DIVERSITY SCHOLARSHIP PROGRAM

Dinsmore & Shohl LLP
Attn: Manager of Legal Recruiting
255 East Fifth Street, Suite 1900
Cincinnati, OH 45202
(513) 977-8488   Fax: (513) 977-8141
E-mail: dinsmore.legalrecuiting@dinsmore.com
Web: www.dinsmorecareers.com

Summary To provide financial aid and summer work experience to Hispanic American and other law students from groups traditionally underrepresented in the legal profession.

Eligibility This program is open to first- and second-year law students who are members of groups traditionally underrepresented in the legal profession. Applicants must have a demonstrated record of academic or professional achievement and leadership qualities. They must also be interested in a summer associateship with Dinsmore & Shohl LLP. Along with their application, they must submit a 500-word personal statement explaining their interest in the scholarship program and how diversity has impacted their life.

Financial Data The program provides an academic scholarship of $5,000 to $10,000 and a paid associateship at the firm.

Duration The academic scholarship is for 1 year. The summer associateship is for 12 weeks.

Additional data Associateships are available at firm offices in Charleston (West Virginia), Cincinnati (Ohio), or Morgantown (West Virginia). The program includes 1 associateship in which the student spends 6 weeks as a clerk in the legal department of the Procter & Gamble Company's worldwide headquarters in Cincinnati and 6 weeks at Dinsmore & Shohl's Cincinnati office. All associates are assigned to an attorney with the firm who serves as a mentor.

Number awarded Varies each year.

Deadline September of each year for second-year students; December of each year for first-year students.

[608]
DISSERTATION FELLOWSHIPS OF THE CONSORTIUM FOR FACULTY DIVERSITY

Consortium for Faculty Diversity at Liberal Arts Colleges
c/o Gettysburg College
Provost's Office
300 North Washington Street
Campus Box 410
Gettysburg, PA 17325
(717) 337-6796   E-mail: sgockows@gettysburg.edu
Web: www.gettysburg.edu/about/offices/provost/cfd

Summary To provide an opportunity for Hispanic Americans and other doctoral candidates who will promote diversity to work on their dissertation while in residence at selected liberal arts colleges.

Eligibility This program is open to U.S. citizens and permanent residents who have completed all the requirements for the Ph.D. or M.F.A. except the dissertation. Applicants must be interested in a residency at a member institution of the Consortium for Faculty Diversity at Liberal Arts Colleges during which they will complete their dissertation. They must be able to contribute to diversity at the institution.

Financial Data Dissertation fellows receive a stipend based on the average salary paid to instructors at the participating college. Modest funds are made available to finance the fellow's proposed research, subject to the usual institutional procedures.

Duration 1 year.

Additional data The following schools are participating in the program: Allegheny College, Bard College, Bowdoin College, Bryn Mawr College, Carleton College, Centenary College of Louisiana, Centre College, College of Wooster, Colorado College, Denison University, DePauw University, Dickinson College, Gettysburg College, Goucher College, Grinnell College, Gustavus Adolphus College, Hamilton College, Haverford College, Hobart and William Smith Colleges, Lafayette College, Lawrence University, Luther College, Macalester College, Mount Holyoke College, Muhlenberg College, New College of Florida, Oberlin College, Pitzer College, Pomona College, Reed College, Rhodes College, University of Richmond, Ripon College, Scripps College, St. Olaf College, Skidmore College, Smith College, Southwestern University, Swarthmore College, Transylvania University, Trinity College, Vassar College, and Wellesley College. Fellows

are expected to teach at least 1 course, participate in departmental seminars, and interact with students.

Number awarded Varies each year.

Deadline October of each year.

[609]
DISSERTATION FELLOWSHIPS OF THE FORD FOUNDATION DIVERSITY FELLOWSHIP PROGRAM

National Research Council
Attn: Fellowships Office, Keck 576
500 Fifth Street, N.W.
Washington, DC 20001
(202) 334-2872   Fax: (202) 334-3419
E-mail: infofell@nas.edu
Web: sites.nationalacademies.org

Summary To provide funding for dissertation research to Hispanic Americans and other graduate students whose success will increase the racial and ethnic diversity of U.S. colleges and universities.

Eligibility This program is open to citizens, permanent residents, and nationals of the United States who are Ph.D. or Sc.D. degree candidates committed to a career in teaching and research at the college or university level. Applicants must be completing a degree in fields of the arts, sciences, humanities, and social sciences, but not for most practice-oriented areas, terminal master's degrees, other doctoral degrees (e.g., Ed.D., D.F.A., Psy.D.), professional degrees (e.g., medicine, law, public health), or joint degrees (e.g., M.D./Ph.D., J.D./Ph.D., M.F.A./Ph.D.). The following are considered as positive factors in the selection process: evidence of superior academic achievement; promise of continuing achievement as scholars and teachers; membership in a group whose underrepresentation in the American professoriate has been severe and longstanding, including Black/African Americans, Puerto Ricans, Mexican Americans/Chicanos/Chicanas, Native American Indians, Alaska Natives (Eskimos, Aleuts, and other indigenous people of Alaska), and Native Pacific Islanders (Hawaiians, Micronesians, or Polynesians); capacity to respond in pedagogically productive ways to the learning needs of students from diverse backgrounds; sustained personal engagement with communities that are underrepresented in the academy and an ability to bring this asset to learning, teaching, and scholarship at the college and university level; and likelihood of using the diversity of human experience as an educational resource in teaching and scholarship.

Financial Data The stipend is $21,000; stipend payments are made through fellowship institutions.

Duration 9 to 12 months.

Additional data The competition for this program is conducted by the National Research Council on behalf of the Ford Foundation. Fellows may not accept remuneration from another fellowship or similar external award while supported by this program; however, supplementation from institutional funds, educational benefits from the Department of Veterans Affairs, or educational incentive funds may be received concurrently with Ford Foundation support. Dissertation fellows are required to submit an interim progress report 6 months after the start of the fellowship and a final report at the end of the 12 month tenure.

Number awarded Approximately 35 each year.

Deadline November of each year.

[610]
DIVERSITY COMMITTEE SCHOLARSHIP

American Society of Safety Engineers
Attn: ASSE Foundation
Scholarship Award Program
1800 East Oakton Street
Des Plaines, IL 60018
(847) 699-2929   Fax: (847) 768-3434
E-mail: bzylstra@asse.org
Web: www.asse.org

Summary To provide financial assistance to Hispanic American and other diverse upper-division or graduate students who are working on a degree related to occupational safety.

Eligibility This program is open to students who are working on an undergraduate or graduate degree in occupational safety, health, environment, industrial hygiene, occupational health nursing, or a closely-related field (e.g., industrial or environmental engineering). Applicants must be full-time students who have completed at least 60 semester hours with a GPA of 3.0 or higher as undergraduates or at least 9 semester hours as graduate students. A goal of this program is to support individuals regardless of race, ethnicity, gender, religion, personal beliefs, age, sexual orientation, physical challenges, geographic location, university, or specific area of study. U.S. citizenship is not required. Membership in the American Society of Safety Engineers (ASSE) is not required, but preference is given to members.

Financial Data The stipend is $1,000 per year.

Duration 1 year; recipients may reapply.

Number awarded 1 each year.

Deadline November of each year.

[611]
DIVERSITY IN PLANNING AWARD

American Planning Association-California Chapter
Attn: California Planning Foundation
c/o Paul Wack
California Polytechnic State University at San Luis Obispo
City and Regional Planning Department
San Luis Obispo, CA 93407-0283
(805) 756-6331   Fax: (805) 756-1340
E-mail: pwack@calpoly.edu
Web: www.californiaplanningfoundation.org

Summary To provide financial assistance to Hispanic American and other undergraduate and graduate students in accredited planning programs at California universities who will increase diversity in the profession.

Eligibility This program is open to students entering their final year for an undergraduate or master's degree in an accredited planning program at a university in California. Applicants must be students who will increase diversity in the planning profession. Selection is based on academic performance, professional promise, and financial need.

Financial Data The stipend is $3,000. The award includes a 1-year student membership in the American Planning Association (APA) and payment of registration for the APA California Conference.

Duration 1 year.

Additional data The accredited planning programs are at 3 campuses of the California State University system (California State Polytechnic University at Pomona, California Polytechnic State University at San Luis Obispo, and San Jose State University), 3 campuses of the University of California (Berkeley, Irvine, and Los Angeles), and the University of Southern California.

Number awarded 1 each year.

Deadline March of each year.

[612]
DIVERSITY IN PSYCHOLOGY AND LAW RESEARCH AWARD

American Psychological Association
Attn: Division 41 (American Psychology-Law Society)
c/o Diane Sivasubramaniam, Minority Affairs Committee Chair
Swinburne University of Technology
Faculty of Life and Social Sciences
Mail H31
P.O. Box 218
Hawthorn, VIC 3122
Australia
61 3 9214 5858 E-mail: dsivasubramaniam@swin.edu.au
Web: www.ap-ls.org

Summary To provide funding to Hispanic American and other student members of the American Psychology-Law Society (AP-LS) who are interested in conducting a research project related to diversity.

Eligibility This program is open to undergraduate and graduate student members of AP-LS who are interested in conducting research on issues related to psychology, law, multiculturalism, and/or diversity (e.g., research pertaining to psycholegal issues on race, gender, culture, sexual orientation). Students from underrepresented groups are strongly encouraged to apply; underrepresented groups include, but are not limited to: racial and ethnic minorities; first-generation college students; lesbian, gay, bisexual, and transgender students; and physically disabled students. Applicants must submit a project description that includes a statement of the research problem, the project's likely impact on the field of psychology and law broadly, methodology, budget, and an overview of relevant literature. Selection is based on the impact of the project on diversity and multiculturalism and the expected completion within the allocated time.

Financial Data The grant is $1,000.

Duration The project must be completed within 1 year.

Number awarded Up to 4 each year.

Deadline November of each year.

[613]
DOCTORAL DISSERTATION IMPROVEMENT GRANTS IN THE DIRECTORATE FOR BIOLOGICAL SCIENCES

National Science Foundation
Directorate for Biological Sciences
Attn: Division of Environmental Biology
4201 Wilson Boulevard
Arlington, VA 22230
(703) 292-8480   TDD: (800) 281-8749
E-mail: ddig-deb@nsf.gov
Web: www.nsf.gov/funding/pgm_summ.jsp?pims_id=5234

Summary To provide partial support to students (especially Hispanic Americans, other underrepresented minorities, women, and students with disabilities) for dissertation research in selected areas supported by the National Science Foundation (NSF) Directorate for Biological Sciences (DBS).

Eligibility Applications may be submitted through regular university channels by dissertation advisers on behalf of graduate students who have advanced to candidacy and have begun or are about to begin dissertation research. Students must be enrolled at U.S. institutions but need not be U.S. citizens. Proposals should focus on the ecology, ecosystems, systematics, or population biology programs in the DBS Division of Environmental Biology, or the animal behavior programs in the DBS Division of Integrative Organismal Systems. In the selection process, consideration is given to the achievement of societally relevant outcomes, including full participation of women, persons with disabilities, and underrepresented minorities.

Financial Data Grants range up to $13,000; funds may be used for travel to specialized facilities or field research locations, specialized research equipment, purchase of supplies and services not otherwise available, fees for computerized or other forms of data, and rental of environmental chambers or other research facilities. Funding is not provided for stipends, tuition, textbooks, journals, allowances for dependents, travel to scientific meetings, publication costs, dissertation preparation or reproduction, or indirect costs.

Duration Normally 2 years.

Number awarded 100 to 120 each year; approximately $1,600,000 is available for this program each year.

Deadline October of each year.

[614]
DOCTORAL DIVERSITY FELLOWSHIPS IN SCIENCE, TECHNOLOGY, ENGINEERING, AND MATHEMATICS

State University of New York
Attn: Office of Diversity, Equity and Inclusion
State University Plaza
353 Broadway
Albany, NY 12246
(518) 320-1189
Web: www.suny.edu/provost/odee/programs.cfm

Summary To provide financial assistance to residents of any state (particularly Hispanic Americans and other underrepresented minorities) who are working on a doctoral degree in a field of science, technology, engineering, and mathematics (STEM) at campuses of the State University of New York (SUNY) and will contribute to the diversity of the student body.

Eligibility This program is open to U.S. citizens who are residents of any state and enrolled as doctoral students at any of the participating SUNY institutions. Applicants must be working on a degree in a field of STEM. They must be able to demonstrate how they will contribute to the diversity of the student body, primarily by having overcome a disadvantage or other impediment to success in higher education. Economic disadvantage, although not a requirement, may be the basis for eligibility. Membership in a racial or ethnic group that is underrepresented at the applicant's school or program may serve as a plus factor in making awards, but may not form the sole basis of selection.

Financial Data The stipend is $20,000 per year.

Duration 3 years; may be renewed for up to 2 additional years.

Number awarded Up to 3 each year.

Deadline January of each year.

[615]
DOCTORAL/POST-DOCTORAL FELLOWSHIP PROGRAM IN LAW AND SOCIAL SCIENCE

American Bar Foundation
Attn: Administrative Assistant for Academic Affairs and
    Research Administration
750 North Lake Shore Drive
Chicago, IL 60611-4403
(312) 988-6517   Fax: (312) 988-6579
E-mail: aehrhardt@abfn.org
Web: www.americanbarfoundation.org

Summary To provide research funding to scholars (particularly Hispanic Americans and other minorities) who are completing or have completed doctoral degrees in fields related to law, the legal profession, and legal institutions.

Eligibility This program is open to Ph.D. candidates in the social sciences who have completed all doctoral requirements except the dissertation. Applicants who have completed the dissertation are also eligible. Doctoral and proposed research must be in the general area of sociolegal studies or in social scientific approaches to law, the legal profession, or legal institutions and legal processes. Applications must include 1) a dissertation abstract or proposal with an outline of the substance and methods of the research; 2) 2 letters of recommendation; and 3) a curriculum vitae. Minority candidates are especially encouraged to apply.

Financial Data The stipend is $30,000. Fellows may request up to $1,500 to reimburse expenses associated with research, travel to meet with advisers, or travel to conferences at which papers are presented. Relocation expenses of up to $2,500 may be reimbursed on application.

Duration 12 months, beginning in September.

Additional data Fellows are offered access to the computing and word processing facilities of the American Bar Foundation and the libraries of Northwestern University and the University of Chicago. This program was established in 1996. Fellowships must be held in residence at the American Bar Foundation. Appointments to the fellowship are full time; fellows are not permitted to undertake other work.

Number awarded 1 or more each year.

Deadline December of each year.

[616]
DOLLARS FOR SCHOLARS PROGRAM

United Methodist Higher Education Foundation
Attn: Scholarships Administrator
60 Music Square East, Suite 350
P.O. Box 340005
Nashville, TN 37203-0005
(615) 649-3990   Toll Free: (800) 811-8110
Fax: (615) 649-3980
E-mail: umhefscholarships@umhef.org
Web: www.umhef.org/UMDFSapp.php

Summary To provide financial assistance to Hispanic American and other students at Methodist colleges, universities, and seminaries whose home churches agree to contribute to their support.

Eligibility The Double Your Dollars for Scholars program is open to students attending or planning to attend a United Methodist-related college, university, or seminary as a full-time student. Applicants must have been an active, full member of a United Methodist Church for at least 1 year prior to applying. Their home church must nominate them and agree to contribute to their support. Many of the United Methodist colleges and universities have also agreed to contribute matching funds for a Triple Your Dollars for Scholars Program, and a few United Methodist conference foundations have agreed to contribute additional matching funds for a Quadruple Your Dollars for Scholars Program. Awards are granted on a first-come, first-served basis. Some of the awards are designated for Hispanic, Asian, and Native American (HANA) students funded by the General Board of Higher Education and Ministry.

Financial Data The sponsoring church contributes $1,000 and the United Methodist Higher Education Foundation (UMHEF) contributes a matching $1,000. Students who attend a participating United Methodist college or university receive an additional $1,000 for the Triple Your Dollars for Scholars Program, and those from a participating conference receive a fourth $1,000 increment for the Quadruple Your Dollars for Scholars Program.

Duration 1 year; may be renewed as long as the recipients maintain satisfactory academic progress as defined by their institution.

Additional data Currently, participants in the Double Your Dollars for Scholars program include 1 United Methodist seminary and theological school, 1 professional school, 19 senior colleges and universities, and 1 2-year college. The Triple Your Dollars for Scholars program includes an additional 12 United Methodist seminaries and theological schools, 72 senior colleges and universities, and 4 2-year colleges (for a complete list, consult the UMHEF). The conference foundations participating in the Quadruple Your Dollars for Scholars Program are limited to the Alabama-West Florida United Methodist Foundation, the East Ohio United Methodist Foundation, the Kentucky United Methodist Foundation, the Missouri United Methodist Foundation (for students at Saint Paul School of Theology or Central Methodist University), the Nashville Area United Methodist Foundation, the North Carolina United Methodist Foundation (for students at Louisburg College, Methodist University, or North Carolina Wesleyan College), the Georgia United Methodist Foundation, the Oklahoma United Methodist Foundation (for students at Oklahoma City University), the United Methodist Foundation of Arkansas, and the United Methodist Foundation of Western North Carolina.

Number awarded 350 each year, including 25 designated for HANA students.

Deadline Local churches must submit applications in February of each year for senior colleges, universities, and seminaries or May of each year for 2-year colleges.

[617]
DOLORES NYHUS GRADUATE FELLOWSHIP

California Dietetic Association
Attn: CDA Foundation
7740 Manchester Avenue, Suite 102
Playa del Rey, CA 90293-8499
(310) 822-0177   Fax: (310) 823-0264
E-mail: patsmith@dietitian.org
Web: www.dietitian.org/d_cdaf/cdaf_outreach.html

Summary To provide financial assistance to members (particularly Hispanic Americans or other minorities, men, and members with disabilities) of the Academy of Nutrition and Dietetics (AND) who live in California and are interested in working on a graduate degree in dietetics or a related field at a school in any state.

Eligibility This program is open to California residents who are AND members and have a bachelor's degree and 3 to 5 years of professional experience. Applicants must be a registered dietitian (R.D.), be a registered dietetic technician (D.T.R.), or have a credential earned at least 6 months previously. They must be enrolled in or admitted to a graduate school in any state in the areas of public health, gerontology, or a community-related program with the intention of practicing in the field of dietetics. Along with their application, they must submit a letter of application that includes a discussion of their career goals. Selection is based on that letter (15%), academic ability (25%), work or volunteer experience (15%), letters of recommendation (15%), extracurricular activities (5%), and financial need (25%). Applications are especially encouraged from ethnic minorities, men, and people with physical disabilities.

Financial Data The stipend is normally $1,000.

Duration 1 year.

Additional data The California Dietetic Association is the California affiliate of the AND.

Number awarded 1 each year.

Deadline April of each year.

[618]
DOMINICAN BAR ASSOCIATION LAW SCHOOL SCHOLARSHIPS

Dominican Bar Association
Attn: Law School Scholarship Program
Canal Street Station
P.O. Box 203
New York, NY 10013
(917) 953-1285   E-mail: dominicanbarassoc@gmail.com
Web: www.dominicanbarassociation.org

Summary To provide financial assistance to Latino law students.

Eligibility This program is open to Latino students currently enrolled in their first, second, or third year of law school. Applicants must submit a cover letter that describes their reasons for studying law, their professional objectives, and their past involvement in activities that they believe have served or benefited the Latino community. Selection is based on academic and personal achievement, demonstrated involvement in and commitment to serve the Latino community through the legal profession, and financial need.

Financial Data The stipend is $3,000.

Duration 1 year.

Additional data This program began in 2003.

Number awarded 3 each year.

Deadline March of each year.

[619]
DONALD W. BANNER DIVERSITY SCHOLARSHIP

Banner & Witcoff, Ltd.
Attn: Christopher Hummel
1100 13th Street, N.W., Suite 1200
Washington, DC 20005-4051
(202) 824-3000   Fax: (202) 824-3001
E-mail: chummel@bannerwitcoff.com
Web: www.bannerwitcoff.com/about/diversity

Summary To provide financial assistance to Hispanic Americans and other law students who come from groups historically underrepresented in intellectual property law.

Eligibility This program is open to students enrolled in the first or second year of a J.D. program at an ABA-accredited law school in the United States. Applicants must come from a group historically underrepresented in intellectual property law; that underrepresentation may be the result of race, sex, ethnicity, sexual orientation, disability, education, culture, religion, age, or socioeconomic background. Selection is based on academic merit, commitment to the pursuit of a career in intellectual property law, written communication skills, oral communication skills (determined through an interview), leadership qualities, and community involvement.

Financial Data The stipend is $5,000 per year.

Duration 1 year (the second or third year of law school); students who accept and successfully complete the firm's summer associate program may receive an additional $5,000 for a subsequent semester of law school.

Number awarded 2 each year.

Deadline October of each year.

[620]
DORSEY & WHITNEY DIVERSITY FELLOWSHIPS

Dorsey & Whitney LLP
Attn: Recruiting Manager
50 South Sixth Street, Suite 1500
Minneapolis, MN 55402-1498
(612) 340-2600   Toll Free: (800) 759-4929
Fax: (612) 340-2868 E-mail: forsmark.claire@dorsey.com
Web: www.dorsey.com/diversity_fellowship_12111

Summary To provide financial assistance for law school to Hispanic Americans and other students from diverse backgrounds who are interested in working during the summer at offices of the sponsoring law firm.

Eligibility This program is open to first-year students at ABA-accredited law schools who have accepted a summer associate position at an office of the sponsor in Denver, Minneapolis, or Seattle. Applicants must be able to demonstrate academic achievement and a commitment to promoting

diversity in the legal community. Along with their application, they must submit a personal statement on the ways in which they have promoted and will continue to promote diversity in the legal community, what diversity means to them, and why they are interested in the sponsoring law firm.

Financial Data Fellows receive a stipend of $7,500 for the second year of law school and, if they complete a summer associate position in the following summer, another stipend of $7,500 for the third year of law school. If they join the firm following graduation, they receive an additional $5,000.

Duration 1 year; may be renewed for 1 additional year.

Additional data This program began in 2006.

Number awarded 1 or more each year.

Deadline January of each year.

[621]
DR. ALEJANDRO PEREZ SCHOLARSHIP

Arizona Hispanic School Administrators Association
Attn: Scholarship Committee
P.O. Box 18271
Phoenix, AZ 85005
(480) 753-3542
Web: azhsaa.org

Summary To provide financial assistance to members of the Arizona Hispanic School Administrators Association (AHSAA) who are working on a master's or doctoral degree in educational administration at a school in Arizona.

Eligibility This program is open to graduate students at colleges and universities in Arizona working on a master's or doctoral degree or certification in educational administration. Applicants must be members of AHSAA and planning to serve Latino communities in Arizona. They must have a GPA of 2.5 or higher. Along with their application, they must submit a 2-page essay on an assigned topic related to educational administration.

Financial Data The stipend is $5,000.

Duration 1 year.

Number awarded 1 or more each year.

Deadline September of each year.

[622]
DR. JUAN D. VILLARREAL–HDA FOUNDATION SCHOLARSHIPS

Hispanic Dental Association
Attn: HDA Foundation
1111 14th Street, N.W., Suite 1100
Washington, DC 20005
(202) 629-3628   Fax: (202) 629-3802
E-mail: scholarships@hdassoc.org
Web: www.hdassoc.org

Summary To provide financial assistance to members of the Hispanic Dental Association (HDA) at institutions in Texas.

Eligibility This program is open to HDA members who have been accepted or are currently enrolled at an accredited dental school or dental hygiene program in Texas as a full-time student. Applicants must have permanent resident status in the United States. Along with their application, they must submit a 250-word essay on why they want to be a dentist or dental hygienist and how they will help improve their community when they have reached their goal. Selection is based on commitment and dedication to improving the oral health of the Hispanic community, leadership skills, scholastic achievement, and community service.

Financial Data Stipends are $1,000 or $500.

Duration 1 year.

Additional data This program began in 1995.

Number awarded Varies each year; recently, 2 dental students and 1 dental hygiene student received these scholarships.

Deadline June of each year.

[623]
DR. NANCY FOSTER SCHOLARSHIP PROGRAM

National Oceanic and Atmospheric Administration
Attn: Office of Education
1315 East-West Highway
SSMC3, Room 11146
Silver Spring, MD 20910
(301) 713-9437, ext. 150   Fax: (301) 713-9465
E-mail: fosterscholars@noaa.gov
Web: fosterscholars.noaa.gov

Summary To provide financial assistance to graduate students (especially Hispanic Americans, other minorities, and women) who are interested in working on a degree in fields related to marine sciences.

Eligibility This program is open to U.S. citizens, particularly women and members of minority groups, currently working on or intending to work on a master's or doctoral degree in oceanography, marine biology, or maritime archaeology, including all science, engineering, and resource management of ocean and coastal areas. Applicants must submit a description of their academic, research, and career goals, and how their proposed course of study or research will help them to achieve those goals. They must be enrolled full time and have a GPA of 3.0 or higher. As part of their program, they must be interested in participating in a summer research collaboration at a facility of the National Oceanic and Atmospheric Administration (NOAA). Selection is based on academic record and the statement of career goals and objectives (25%); quality of project and applicability to program priorities (35%); recommendations and/or endorsements (15%); additional relevant experience related to diversity of education, extracurricular activities, honors and awards, written and oral communication skills, and interpersonal skills (15%); and financial need (10%).

Financial Data The program provides a stipend of $30,000 per academic year, a tuition allowance of up to $12,000 per academic year, and up to $10,000 of support for a 4- to 6-week research collaboration at a NOAA facility is provided.

Duration Master's degree students may receive up to 2 years of stipend and tuition support and 1 research collaboration (for a total of $94,000). Doctoral students may receive up to 4 years of stipend and tuition support and 2 research collaborations (for a total of $188,000).

Additional data This program began in 2001.

Number awarded Varies each year; recently, 3 of these fellowships were awarded.

Deadline February of each year.

[624]
DREAM ACT STUDENT ACTIVIST SCHOLARSHIP PROGRAM

Mexican American Legal Defense and Educational Fund
634 South Spring Street, 11th Floor
Los Angeles, CA 90014-1974
(213) 629-2512   Fax: (213) 629-0266
Web: www.maldef.org/leadership/scholarships/index.html

Summary To provide financial assistance for college or graduate school to Dream Act student activists.

Eligibility This program is open to undergraduate and graduate students who have been advocates for the Dream Act and all immigrant rights. Eligibility extends to students seeking to enroll in college for the first time or to re-enroll following a leave of absence. Applicants must submit 500-word essays on their 1) background and financial need; 2) activism in support of the Dream Act and immigrant rights; and 3) future plans.

Financial Data Stipends range up to $5,000.

Duration 1 year.

Number awarded 1 or more each year.

Deadline June of each year.

[625]
DRI LAW STUDENT DIVERSITY SCHOLARSHIP

DRI-The Voice of the Defense Bar
Attn: Deputy Executive Director
55 West Monroe Street, Suite 2000
Chicago, IL 60603
(312) 795-1101   Fax: (312) 795-0747
E-mail: dri@dri.org
Web: www.dri.org/About

Summary To provide financial assistance to Hispanic American, other minority, and female law students.

Eligibility This program is open to full-time students entering their second or third year of law school who are African American, Hispanic, Asian, Native American, or women. Applicants must submit an essay, up to 1,000 words, on a topic that changes annually but relates to the work of defense attorneys. Selection is based on that essay, demonstrated academic excellence, service to the profession, service to the community, and service to the cause of diversity. Students affiliated with the American Association for Justice as members, student members, or employees are not eligible. Finalists are invited to participate in personal interviews.

Financial Data The stipend is $10,000.

Duration 1 year.

Additional data This program began in 2004.

Number awarded 2 each year.

Deadline May of each year.

[626]
DWIGHT DAVID EISENHOWER TRANSPORTATION FELLOWSHIP PROGRAM FOR HISPANIC-SERVING INSTITUTIONS

Department of Transportation
Federal Highway Administration
Attn: Universities and Grants Programs
4600 North Fairfax Drive, Suite 800
Arlington, VA 22203-1553
(703) 235-0538   Toll Free: (877) 558-6873
Fax: (703) 235-0593   E-mail: transportationedu@dot.gov
Web: www.fhwa.dot.gov/tpp/ddetfp.htm

Summary To provide financial assistance to undergraduate and graduate students working on a degree in a transportation-related field at an Hispanic Serving Institution (HSI).

Eligibility This program is open to students working on a bachelor's, master's, or doctoral degree at a federally-designated 4-year HSI. Applicants must be working on a degree in a transportation-related field (e.g., engineering, business, aviation, architecture, public policy and analysis, urban and regional planning). They must be U.S. citizens or have an I-20 (foreign student) or I-551 (permanent resident) identification card. Undergraduates must be entering at least their junior year and have a GPA of 3.0 or higher. Graduate students must have a GPA of at least 3.25. Selection is based on their proposed plan of study, academic achievement (based on class standing, GPA, and transcripts), transportation work experience, and letters of recommendation.

Financial Data Fellows receive payment of full tuition and fees (to a maximum of $10,000) and a monthly stipend of $1,450 for undergraduates, $1,700 for master's students, or $2,000 for doctoral students. They are also provided with a 1-time allowance of up to $1,500 to attend the annual Transportation Research Board (TRB) meeting.

Duration 1 year.

Additional data This program is administered by the participating HSIs: California State University at Fullerton, California State University at Los Angeles, Polytechnic University of Puerto Rico, Texas A&M University at Kingsville, the University of Puerto Rico at Mayaguez, the University of Texas at El Paso, or the University of Texas at San Antonio.

Number awarded Varies each year.

Deadline January of each year.

[627]
EDWARD S. ROTH MANUFACTURING ENGINEERING SCHOLARSHIP

Society of Manufacturing Engineers
Attn: SME Education Foundation
One SME Drive
P.O. Box 930
Dearborn, MI 48121-0930
(313) 425-3300   Toll Free: (800) 733-4763, ext. 3300
Fax: (313) 425-3411   E-mail: foundation@sme.org
Web: www.smeef.org/scholarships

Summary To provide financial assistance to Hispanic Americans and other students enrolled or planning to work on a bachelor's or master's degree in manufacturing engineering at selected universities.

Eligibility This program is open to U.S. citizens who are graduating high school seniors or currently-enrolled under-

graduate or graduate students. Applicants must be enrolled or planning to enroll as a full-time student at 1 of 13 selected 4-year universities to work on a bachelor's or master's degree in manufacturing engineering. They must have a GPA of 3.0 or higher. Preference is given to 1) students demonstrating financial need; 2) minority students; and 3) students participating in a co-op program. Some preference may also be given to graduating high school seniors and graduate students. Along with their application, they must submit a 300-word essay that covers their career and educational objectives, how this scholarship will help them attain those objectives, and why they want to enter this field.

Financial Data Stipend amounts vary; recently, the value of all scholarships provided by this foundation averaged approximately $2,330.

Duration 1 year; may be renewed.

Additional data The eligible institutions are California Polytechnic State University at San Luis Obispo, California State Polytechnic State University at Pomona, University of Miami (Florida), Bradley University (Illinois), Central State University (Ohio), Miami University (Ohio), Boston University, Worcester Polytechnic Institute (Massachusetts), University of Massachusetts, St. Cloud State University (Minnesota), University of Texas-Pan American, Brigham Young University (Utah), and Utah State University.

Number awarded 2 each year.

Deadline January of each year.

[628]
ELIZABETH MUNSTERBERG KOPPITZ CHILD PSYCHOLOGY GRADUATE FELLOWSHIPS

American Psychological Foundation
750 First Street, N.E.
Washington, DC 20002-4242
(202) 336-5843   Fax: (202) 336-5812
E-mail: foundation@apa.org
Web: www.apa.org/apf/funding/koppitz.aspx

Summary To provide funding to doctoral students (particularly Hispanic Americans, other minorities, women, and students with disabilities) who are interested in conducting research in child psychology.

Eligibility This program is open to graduate students who have progressed academically through the qualifying examinations, usually after the third or fourth year of doctoral study. Applicants must be interested in conducting psychological research that promotes the advancement of knowledge and learning in the field of child psychology. Selection is based on conformance with stated program goals, magnitude of incremental contribution, quality of proposed work, and applicant's demonstrated scholarship and research competence. The sponsor encourages applications from individuals who represent diversity in race, ethnicity, gender, age, disability, and sexual orientation.

Financial Data The grant is $25,000 for fellows or $5,000 for runners-up.

Duration 1 year.

Additional data This fellowship was first awarded in 2003.

Number awarded Varies each year; recently, 6 fellows and 2 runners-up were selected.

Deadline November of each year.

[629]
ELLIOTT C. ROBERTS, SR. SCHOLARSHIP

Institute for Diversity in Health Management
Attn: Education Specialist
155 North Wacker Avenue, Suite 400
Chicago, IL 60606
(312) 422-2658   Toll Free: (800) 233-0996
Fax: (312) 895-4511   E-mail: cbiddle@aha.org
Web: www.diversityconnection.org

Summary To provide financial assistance to Hispanic American and other minority graduate students in health services management who have demonstrated outstanding community service.

Eligibility This program is open to members of ethnically diverse groups who are enrolled in the second year of a graduate program in health care administration. Applicants must have a GPA of 3.0 or higher. They must be able to demonstrate a commitment to community service. Along with their application, they must submit 1) a personal statement of 1 to 2 pages on their interest in health care management and their career goals; 2) an essay on what they see as the most challenging issue facing America's hospitals and health systems; and 3) a 500-word essay on how they currently serve their community beyond their academic career. Selection is based on academic achievement, commitment to community service, and financial need. U.S. citizenship is required.

Financial Data The stipend is $1,000.

Duration 1 year.

Number awarded 1 each year.

Deadline January of each year.

[630]
ENDOCRINE SOCIETY SUMMER RESEARCH FELLOWSHIPS

Endocrine Society
Attn: Summer Research Fellowships
8401 Connecticut Avenue, Suite 900
Chevy Chase, MD 20815
(301) 951-2616   Toll Free: (888) 363-6274
Fax: (301) 576-7787   E-mail: awards@endo-society.org
Web: www.endo-society.org

Summary To provide funding to undergraduate, medical, and graduate students (particularly Hispanic Americans and other underrepresented minorities) who are interested in conducting a research project during the summer in endocrinology.

Eligibility This program is open to full-time students who are undergraduates in the third year of study or higher, medical students beyond their first year of study, and first-year graduate students. Applicants must be interested in participating in a research project under the supervision of a mentor. The mentor must be an active member of the Endocrine Society. Each member may sponsor only 1 student. Projects must be relevant to an aspect of endocrinology and are expected to have clearly defined research goals; students should not function as aides or general research assistants. Applications on behalf of underrepresented minority students are especially encouraged.

Financial Data The grant of $4,000 provides funding for a stipend, fringe benefits, and indirect costs.

Duration 10 to 12 weeks during the summer.

Additional data At the conclusion of the fellowship period, students must submit a 1-page summary of their research project explaining how the fellowship affected their consideration of a career in endocrinology.

Number awarded 20 each year.

Deadline January of each year.

[631]
ESPERANZA SCHOLARSHIP

New York Women in Communications, Inc.
Attn: NYWICI Foundation
355 Lexington Avenue, 15th Floor
New York, NY 10017-6603
(212) 297-2133   Fax: (212) 370-9047
E-mail: nywicipr@nywici.org
Web: www.nywici.org/foundation/scholarships

Summary To provide financial assistance to Hispanic women who are residents of designated eastern states and interested in preparing for a career in communications at a college or graduate school in any state.

Eligibility This program is open to Hispanic women who are seniors graduating from high schools in New York, New Jersey, Connecticut, or Pennsylvania or undergraduate or graduate students who are permanent residents of those states; they must be attending or planning to attend a college or university in any state. Graduate students must be members of New York Women in Communications, Inc. (NYWICI). Also eligible are Hispanic women who reside outside the 4 states but are currently enrolled at a college or university within 1 of the 5 boroughs of New York City. All applicants must be working on a degree in a communications-related field (e.g., advertising, broadcasting, communications, English, film, journalism, marketing, digital media, public relations) and have a GPA of 3.2 or higher. Along with their application, they must submit a 2-page resume; a personal essay of 300 words on an assigned topic that changes annually; 2 letters of recommendation; and an official transcript. Selection is based on academic record, need, demonstrated leadership, participation in school and community activities, honors and other awards or recognition, work experience, goals and aspirations, and unusual personal and/or family circumstances. U.S. citizenship is required.

Financial Data The stipend ranges up to $10,000.

Duration 1 year.

Additional data This program is funded by Macy's and Bloomingdale's.

Number awarded 1 each year.

Deadline January of each year.

[632]
ESTHER KATZ ROSEN GRADUATE STUDENT FELLOWSHIPS

American Psychological Foundation
750 First Street, N.E.
Washington, DC 20002-4242
(202) 336-5843   Fax: (202) 336-5812
E-mail: foundation@apa.org
Web: www.apa.org/apf/funding/rosen.aspx

Summary To provide funding to graduate students (particularly Hispanic Americans, other minorities, and students with disabilities) who are interested in conducting research on psychological issues relevant to giftedness in children.

Eligibility This program is open to graduate students at universities in the United States and Canada who have advanced to candidacy. Applicants must be interested in conducting research on the psychological understanding of gifted and talented children and adolescents. Selection is based on conformance with stated program goals, magnitude of incremental contribution, quality of proposed work, and applicant's demonstrated scholarship and research competence. The sponsor encourages applications from individuals who represent diversity in race, ethnicity, gender, age, disability, and sexual orientation.

Financial Data The grant is $20,000. The fellow's home institution is expected to provide a tuition waiver.

Duration 1 year.

Additional data This fund was established in 1974.

Number awarded 1 each year.

Deadline April of each year.

[633]
ESTHER NGAN-LING CHOW AND MAREYJOYCE GREEN SCHOLARSHIP

Sociologists for Women in Society
Attn: Executive Officer
Southern Connecticut State University
Department of Sociology
501 Crescent Street
New Haven, CT 06515
(203) 392-7714   Fax: (203) 392-7715
E-mail: swseo@socwomen.org
Web: www.socwomen.org/awards.html

Summary To provide funding to Hispanic American and other women of color who are conducting dissertation research in sociology.

Eligibility This program is open to women from a racial/ethnic group that faces discrimination in the United States. Applicants must be in the early stages of writing a doctoral dissertation in sociology on a topic relating to the concerns that women of color face domestically and/or internationally. They must be able to demonstrate financial need. Both domestic and international students are eligible to apply. Along with their application, they must submit a personal statement that details their short- and long-term career and research goals; a resume or curriculum vitae; 2 letters of recommendation; and a 5-page dissertation proposal that includes the purpose of the research, the work to be accomplished through support from this scholarship, and a time line for completion.

Financial Data The stipend is $15,000. An additional grant of $500 is provided to enable the recipient to attend the winter meeting of Sociologists for Women in Society (SWS), and travel expenses to attend the summer meeting are reimbursed.

Duration 1 year.

Additional data This program began in 2007 and originally named the Women of Color Dissertation Scholarship.

Number awarded 1 each year.

Deadline March of each year.

[634]
ETS SUMMER INTERNSHIP PROGRAM FOR GRADUATE STUDENTS

Educational Testing Service
Attn: Fellowships
660 Rosedale Road
MS 19-T
Princeton, NJ 08541-0001
(609) 734-5543   Fax: (609) 734-5410
E-mail: internfellowships@ets.org
Web: www.ets.org/research/fellowships/summer

Summary To provide an opportunity for doctoral students (particularly Hispanic Americans and other underrepresented minorities) to conduct research during the summer under the guidance of senior staff at the Educational Testing Service (ETS).

Eligibility This program is open to doctoral students interested in working on a research project at ETS in 1 of the following areas: educational measurement and psychometrics, validity, natural language processing and speech technologies, cognitive psychology, learning theory, linguistics and computational linguistics, teaching and classroom research, statistics, or international large scale assessments. Applicants must have completed at least 2 years of full-time study for a Ph.D. or Ed.D. Selection is based on the scholarship of the applicant, match of applicant interests with participating ETS researchers, and the ETS affirmative action objectives. An explicit goal of the program is to increase the number of scholars and students from diverse backgrounds, especially such traditionally underrepresented groups as African Americans, Hispanic/Latino Americans, and American Indians, who are interested in conducting research in educational measurement and related fields.

Financial Data The award includes a salary of $6,000 and a $3,000 relocation and housing allowance for interns residing outside a 50-mile radius of the ETS campus.

Duration 8 weeks in the summer.

Additional data Fellows work with senior staff at ETS in Princeton, New Jersey.

Number awarded 15 to 20 each year.

Deadline January of each year.

[635]
EXXONMOBIL LOFT FELLOWSHIPS

Hispanic Heritage Foundation
1444 Duke Street
Alexandria, VA 22314
(202) 861-9797   Toll Free: (866) 665-2112
Fax: (202) 861-9799 E-mail: LOFT@hispanicheritage.org
Web: www.hispanicheritage.org/loft_int.php?sec=200

Summary To provide financial assistance to Hispanic undergraduate and graduate students who participate in the Latinos on Fast Track (LOFT) program.

Eligibility This program is open to Hispanic sophomores, juniors, seniors, and graduate students at 4-year colleges and universities who are U.S. citizens or permanent residents and fluent in English. Applicants must be working on a degree and preparing for a career in chemistry, engineering (chemical, civil, computer, electrical, environmental, industrial, materials, mechanical, or petroleum), geology, material sciences, mathematics, or physics. Their GPA must be at least

3.5. They must be participating in the LOFT program with an ExxonMobil engineer or scientist as mentor. Along with their application, they must submit an essay of 500 to 700 words that covers why they chose their major, how they intend to prepare for an active career related to their major, and why they should be considered for this program.

Financial Data Selected LOFT participants receive $1,000 scholarships.

Duration The scholarships are presented annually and are nonrenewable.

Additional data The LOFT program involves 5 meetings of 1 hour each with the mentor (virtually or in person), participation in an online ExxonMobil mentee program that introduces them to career opportunities with the company, the possibility to interview for ExxonMobil internships or full-time positions upon successful completion of the program, and the possibility of these scholarships.

Number awarded 20 each year.

Deadline Deadline not specified.

[636]
FACS GRADUATE FELLOWSHIPS

National Association of Teacher Educators for Family and
   Consumer Sciences
c/o Lela G. Goar, Fellowship Committee Chair
225 CR 207A
Burnet, TX 78611
(512) 715-8249   Fax: (512) 585-7606
E-mail: lkgoar@wildblue.net
Web: www.natefacs.org/scholarship.html

Summary To provide financial assistance to Hispanic American and other graduate students in family and consumer science education.

Eligibility This program is open to graduate students working on a master's or doctoral degree in family and consumer sciences education. Applicants must submit an autobiographical sketch (up to 3 pages in length) presenting their professional goals, including information on the institution where they are studying or planning to study, areas or emphases of study, possible research topic, and other pertinent information regarding their plans. Selection is based on likelihood of completing the degree, likelihood of contribution to family and consumer sciences education, previous academic work, professional association involvement, professional experience (including scholarly work), and references. At least 1 fellowship is reserved for a minority (African American, Hispanic American, Native American, or Asian American) candidate.

Financial Data Stipends range from $2,000 to $4,000.

Duration 1 year.

Additional data The sponsor is an affiliate of the Family and Consumer Sciences (FACS) Division of the Association for Career and Technical Education.

Number awarded Varies each year.

Deadline October of each year.

[637]
FAEGRE BAKER DANIELS DIVERSITY AND INCLUSION FELLOWSHIPS

Faegre Baker Daniels
Attn: Diversity and Pro Bono Coordinator
300 North Meridian Street, Suite 2700
Indianapolis, IN 46204
(317) 237-8298   Fax: (317) 237-1000
E-mail: brita.horvath@faegrebd.com
Web: www.faegrebd.com/fellowship

Summary To provide financial aid and summer work experience to Hispanic Americans and other students from diverse backgrounds entering the second year of law school.

Eligibility This program is open to residents of any state who are entering their second year at an accredited law school. Applicants must reflect diversity, defined to mean that they come from varied ethnic, racial, cultural, and lifestyle backgrounds, as well as those with disabilities or unique viewpoints. They must also be interested in a place in the sponsor's associate program during the summer between their second and third year of law school. Along with their application, they must submit a 2-page personal statement describing how or why they will contribute meaningfully to diversity and inclusion at the sponsoring firm and/or in the legal profession.

Financial Data The stipend is $10,000.

Duration 1 year.

Additional data This law firm was formerly Baker & Daniels LLP. Recipients of these fellowships may elect to conduct their associateship at offices in Boulder, Chicago, Denver, Des Moines, Fort Wayne, Indianapolis, Minneapolis, Silicon Valley (East Palo Alto), South Bend, and Washington, D.C.

Number awarded 4 each year.

Deadline September of each year.

[638]
FARM CREDIT EAST SCHOLARSHIPS

Farm Credit East
Attn: Scholarship Program
240 South Road
Enfield, CT 06082
(860) 741-4380   Toll Free: (800) 562-2235
Fax: (860) 741-4389
E-mail: specialoffers@famcrediteast.com
Web: www.farmcrediteast.com

Summary To provide financial assistance to Hispanic American and other residents of designated northeastern states who plan to attend school in any state to work on an undergraduate or graduate degree in a field related to agriculture, forestry, or fishing.

Eligibility This program is open to residents of Massachusetts, Connecticut, Rhode Island, New Jersey, and portions of New York and New Hampshire. Applicants must be working on or planning to work on an associate, bachelor's, or graduate degree in production agriculture, agribusiness, the forest products industry, or commercial fishing at a college or university in any state. They must submit a 200-word essay on why they wish to prepare for a career in agriculture, forestry, or fishing. Selection is based on the essay, extracurricular activities (especially farm work experience and activities indicative of an interest in preparing for a career in agriculture or agribusiness), and interest in agriculture. The program includes diversity scholarships reserved for members of minority groups (Black or African American, American Indian or Alaska Native, Asian, Native Hawaiian or other Pacific Islander, or Hispanic or Latino).

Financial Data The stipend is $1,500. Funds are paid directly to the student to be used for tuition, room and board, books, and other academic charges.

Duration 1 year; nonrenewable.

Additional data Recipients are given priority for an internship with the sponsor in the summer following their junior year. Farm Credit East was formerly named First Pioneer Farm Credit.

Number awarded Up to 28 each year, including several diversity scholarships.

Deadline April of each year.

[639]
FDA GRADUATE STUDENT FELLOWSHIPS

National Science Foundation
Directorate for Engineering
Attn: Division of Chemical, Bioengineering,
  Environmental, and Transport Systems
4201 Wilson Boulevard, Room 565S
Arlington, VA 22230
(703) 292-7942　　　　　　　　Fax: (703) 292-9098
TDD: (800) 281-8749　　　　　　E-mail: lesterow@nsf.gov
Web: www.nsf.gov/funding/pgm_summ.jsp?pims_id=5605

Summary To provide an opportunity for graduate students (particularly Hispanic Americans, other underrepresented minorities, women, and students with disabilities) to conduct research at an intramural laboratory of the U.S. Food and Drug Administration (FDA).

Eligibility This program is open to graduate students (preferably Ph.D. students) in science, engineering, and mathematics fields of interest to the National Science Foundation (NSF). Applicants must be U.S. citizens, nationals, or permanent residents. They must be proposing a program of full- or part-time work at an FDA intramural laboratory in an area related to their research, conducted under the guidance of an academic adviser and an FDA mentor. The program encourages applications from all citizens, including women and men, underrepresented minorities, and persons with disabilities.

Financial Data Graduate students may receive stipends $2,100 per month, plus transportation expenses. The faculty adviser may receive 10% of the total award for research-related expenses, excluding equipment. The academic institution receives an allowance of 15% of total direct costs for administrative expenses. The total award may be up to $35,000 for a fellowship for a single student. FDA provides office space, research facilities, research costs in the form of expendable and minor equipment purchases in the host laboratory, and the time of its research staff.

Duration 1 to 4 semesters.

Additional data This program is also offered by the NSF Directorate for Computer and Information Science and Engineering.

Number awarded A total of 3 to 10 grants for all FDA programs is awarded each year; total funding is approximately $500,000.

Deadline March of each year.

[640]
FERMILAB PH.D. FELLOWSHIP PROGRAM FOR MINORITY STUDENTS

Fermi National Accelerator Laboratory
Attn: Equal Opportunity and Diversity Office
MS 117
P.O. Box 500
Batavia, IL 60510-0500
(630) 840-4574　　　　　　　　Fax: (630) 840-5207
E-mail: scharles@fnal.gov
Web: www.fnal.gov/eeo/phd_fellowship.html

Summary To provide financial assistance for doctoral study in physics to Hispanic American and other underrepresented minority students at universities that are members of the Universities Research Association, Inc. (URA).

Eligibility This program is open to doctoral students who are members of minority groups historically underrepresented in physics (Hispanics, African Americans, and Native Americans). Applicants must be enrolled at 1 of the 82 universities in the United States that are URA members. They must be U.S. citizens or permanent residents. Along with their application, they must submit a statement on why they want to participate in this program, why they are considering physics as their course of study in graduate school, how they intend to use their physics training after they complete their education, and whether they plan to work or do postdoctoral study after completing their education. Selection is based on that statement, financial need, university transcripts, and a progress letter from the thesis adviser.

Financial Data The stipend depends on the availability of funds and the needs of the student.

Duration 1 year; may be renewed up to 6 additional years.

Additional data Fermilab scientists are assigned to all recipients as advisers to aid their progress in graduate school. In addition, students are encouraged to work summers at Fermilab under the supervision of a staff physicist. Funding support for this program is provided by the U.S. Department of Energy.

Number awarded Varies each year.

Deadline July of each year.

[641]
FINNEGAN HENDERSON DIVERSITY SCHOLARSHIP

Finnegan, Henderson, Farabow, Garrett & Dunner, LLP
Attn: Attorney Recruitment Manager
901 New York Avenue, N.W.
Washington, DC 20001-4413
(202) 408-4034　　　　　　　　Fax: (202) 408-4400
E-mail: diversityscholarship@finnegan.com
Web: www.finnegan.com/careers/summerprogram/overview

Summary To provide financial aid and work experience to Hispanic American and other law students from diverse groups who are interested in a career in intellectual property law.

Eligibility This program is open to law students who have demonstrated a commitment to a career in intellectual property law and are currently enrolled either as a first-year full-time student or second-year part-time student. Applicants must contribute to enhancing diversity; the sponsor defines diversity broadly, and has considered members of racial, ethnic, disabled, and sexual orientation groups that have been historically underrepresented in the legal profession. They must have earned an undergraduate degree in life sciences, engineering, or computer science, or have substantial prior trademark experience. Selection is based on academic performance at the undergraduate, graduate (if applicable), and law school level; relevant work experience; community service; leadership skills; and special accomplishments.

Financial Data The stipend is $15,000 per year.

Duration 1 year; may be renewed 1 additional year as long as the recipient completes a summer associateship with the sponsor and maintains of GPA of 3.0 or higher.

Additional data The sponsor, the world's largest intellectual property law firm, established this scholarship in 2003. Summer associateships are available at its offices in Washington, D.C., Atlanta, Boston, Palo Alto, or Reston.

Number awarded 1 each year.

Deadline February of each year.

[642]
FISH & RICHARDSON DIVERSITY FELLOWSHIP PROGRAM

Fish & Richardson P.C.
Recruiting Department
Attn: Manager of Diversity
12390 El Camino Real
San Diego, CA 92130
(858) 678-5070   Fax: (858) 678-5099
E-mail: diversity@fr.com
Web: www.fr.com/diversity

Summary To provide financial assistance for law school to Hispanic Americans and other students who will contribute to diversity in the legal profession.

Eligibility This program is open to students enrolled in the first year at a law school anywhere in the country. Applicants must be African American/Black, American Indian/Alaskan, Hispanic/Latino, Native Hawaiian/Pacific Islander, Asian, 2 or more races, disabled, or openly GLBT. Along with their application, they must submit a 500-word essay describing their background, what led them to the legal field, their interest in the sponsoring law firm, and what they could contribute to its practice and the profession. They must also indicate their first 3 choices of an office of the firm where they are interested in a summer associate clerkship.

Financial Data The stipend is $5,000.

Duration 1 year: the second year of law school.

Additional data Recipients are also offered a paid associate clerkship during the summer following their first year of law school at an office of the firm in the location of their choice in Atlanta, Austin, Boston, Dallas, Delaware, Houston, New York, San Diego, Silicon Valley, Twin Cities, or Washington, D.C. This program began in 2005.

Number awarded 1 or more each year.

Deadline January of each year.

[643]
FIVE COLLEGE FELLOWSHIP PROGRAM

Five Colleges, Incorporated
Attn: Five Colleges Fellowship Program Committee
97 Spring Street
Amherst, MA 01002-2324
(413) 542-4013   E-mail: ntherien@fivecolleges.edu
Web: www.fivecolleges.edu/faculty/fellowships

Summary To provide funding to Hispanic American and other graduate students from underrepresented groups who have completed all the requirements for the Ph.D. except the dissertation and are interested in teaching at selected colleges in Massachusetts.

Eligibility Fellows are chosen by the host department in each of the 4 participating liberal arts colleges (Amherst, Hampshire, Mount Holyoke, and Smith). Applicants must be graduate students at an accredited school who have completed all doctoral requirements except the dissertation and are interested in devoting full time to the completion of the dissertation. The chief goal of the program is to support scholars from underrepresented groups and/or scholars "with unique interests and histories whose engagement in the Academy will enrich scholarship and teaching."

Financial Data The program provides a stipend of $30,000, a research grant, health benefits, office space, library privileges, and housing assistance.

Duration 1 academic year; nonrenewable.

Additional data Although the primary goal is completion of the dissertation, each fellow also has many opportunities to experience working with students and faculty colleagues on the host campus as well as with those at the other colleges. The fellows are also given an opportunity to teach (generally as a team teacher, in a section of a core course, or in a component within a course). Fellows meet monthly with each other to share their experiences. At Smith College, this program is named Mendenhall Fellowships. The fifth institution that belongs to this organization, the University of Massachusetts at Amherst, does not participate in this program.

Number awarded 4 each year; 1 at each of the participating colleges.

Deadline January of each year.

[644]
F.J. MCGUIGAN DISSERTATION AWARD

American Psychological Foundation
750 First Street, N.E.
Washington, DC 20002-4242
(202) 336-5843   Fax: (202) 336-5812
E-mail: foundation@apa.org
Web: www.apa.org/apf/funding/mcguigan-dissertation.aspx

Summary To provide funding to doctoral candidates (particularly Hispanic Americans, other minorities, women, and students with disabilities) who are interested in conducting research on the materialistic understanding of the human mind.

Eligibility This program is open to graduate students enrolled full time in a psychology program at an accredited college or university in the United States or Canada. Applicants must be interested in conducting dissertation research that addresses an aspect of mental function (e.g., cognition, affect, motivation) and should utilize behavioral and/or neuroscientific methods. Selection is based on conformance with stated program goals, quality of proposed work, and applicant's demonstrated scholarship and research competence. The sponsor encourages applications from individuals who represent diversity in race, ethnicity, gender, age, disability, and sexual orientation.

Financial Data   The grant is $2,000.

Duration   1 year.

Additional data   This grant was first awarded in 2009.

Number awarded   1 each year.

Deadline   May of each year.

[645]
FLEMING/BLASZCAK SCHOLARSHIP

Society of Plastics Engineers
Attn: SPE Foundation
13 Church Hill Road
Newtown, CT 06740
(203) 740-5447   Fax: (203) 775-1157
E-mail: foundation@4spe.org
Web: www.4spe.org/spe-foundation

Summary   To provide financial assistance to Mexican American undergraduate and graduate students who have a career interest in the plastics industry.

Eligibility   This program is open to full-time undergraduate and graduate students of Mexican descent who are enrolled at a 4-year college or university. Applicants must be U.S. citizens or legal residents. They must be majoring in or taking courses that would be beneficial to a career in the plastics or polymer industry (e.g., plastics engineering, packaging, polymer sciences, chemistry, physics, chemical engineering, mechanical engineering, industrial engineering). Along with their application, they must submit 3 letters of recommendation; a high school and/or college transcript; a 1- to 2-page statement telling why they are applying for the scholarship, their qualifications, and their educational and career goals in the plastics industry; their employment history; a list of current and past school activities and community activities and honors; information on their financial need; and documentation of their Mexican heritage.

Financial Data   The stipend is $2,000. Funds are paid directly to the recipient's school.

Duration   1 year.

Number awarded   1 each year.

Deadline   February of each year.

[646]
FLORIDA LIBRARY ASSOCIATION MINORITY SCHOLARSHIPS

Florida Library Association
164 N.W. Madison Street, Suite 104
P.O. Box 1571
Lake City, FL 32056-1571
(386) 438-5795   Fax: (386) 438-5796
E-mail: fla.admin@comcast.net
Web: www.flalib.org/scholarships.php

Summary   To provide financial assistance to Hispanic American and other minority students working on a graduate degree in library and information science in Florida.

Eligibility   This program is open to residents of Florida who are working on a graduate degree in library and information

science at schools in the state. Applicants must be members of a minority group: Black/African American, American Indian/Alaska Native, Asian/Pacific Islander, or Hispanic/Latino. They must have some experience in a Florida library, must be a member of the Florida Library Association, and must commit to working in a Florida library for at least 1 year after graduation. Along with their application, they must submit 1) a list of activities, honors, awards, and/or offices held during college and outside college; 2) an essay of 1 to 2 pages on why they are entering librarianship; and 3) an essay of 1 to 2 pages on their career goals with respect to Florida libraries. Financial need is considered in the selection process.

Financial Data   The stipend is $2,000.

Duration   1 year.

Number awarded   1 each year.

Deadline   January of each year.

[647]
FOLEY & LARDNER DIVERSITY SCHOLARSHIP

Foley & Lardner LLP
Attn: Regional Legal Recruiting Coordinator
555 South Flower Street
Los Angeles, CA 90071-2411
(213) 972-4535   E-mail: enesbitt@foley.com
Web: www.foley.com/careers/lawstudents

Summary   To provide financial aid and work experience to Hispanic American and other first-year law students who will contribute to diversity in the legal profession.

Eligibility   This program is open to students completing the first year of full-time study at an ABA-accredited law school. Applicants must have demonstrated a commitment to promoting diversity and inclusion in the legal profession and the broader community. They must be interested in a summer associateship at an office of the sponsoring firm. Selection is based on involvement in diversity-related student organizations, involvement in community activities, undergraduate and law school academic achievement, and interest in employment with the sponsoring firm.

Financial Data   Upon completion of the associateship, participants receive a $20,000 fellowship.

Duration   1 summer and 1 academic year.

Additional data   This program began in 1998. The sponsoring firm has offices in Boston, Chicago, Detroit, Jacksonville, Los Angeles, Madison, Miami, Milwaukee, New York, Orlando, Sacramento, San Diego, San Francisco, Silicon Valley, Tallahassee, Tampa, and Washington, D.C.

Number awarded   2 each year.

Deadline   April of each year.

[648]
FORD BLUE OVAL NATION-WIDE GRADUATE SCHOLARSHIPS

Hispanic College Fund
Attn: Scholarship Processing
1300 L Street, N.W., Suite 975
Washington, DC 20005
(202) 296-5400   Toll Free: (800) 644-4223
Fax: (202) 296-3774   E-mail: hcf-info@hispanicfund.org
Web: scholarships.hispanicfund.org/applications

Summary To provide financial assistance to Hispanic American students working on a master's degree in business administration.

Eligibility This program is open to U.S. citizens and permanent residents of Hispanic background (at least 1 grandparent must be 100% Hispanic) who are enrolled or planning to enroll full time at an accredited college or university in any state. Applicants must have a GPA of 3.0 or higher and be able to demonstrate financial need. They may be working on a master's degree in business administration.

Financial Data Stipends range from $500 to $5,000, depending on need and academic achievement. Funds are paid directly to the recipient's college or university to help cover tuition and fees.

Duration 1 year; recipients may reapply.

Additional data This program is sponsored by Ford Motor Company. All applications must be submitted online; no paper applications are available.

Number awarded Varies each year.

Deadline February of each year.

[649]
FOURTH DISTRICT MOSAIC SCHOLARSHIP

American Advertising Federation-District 4
c/o Maria Lucas, Governor
Farah & Farah
10 West Adams Street
Jacksonville, FL 32202
(904) 807-3113   Toll Free: (800) 533-5555
Fax: (904) 355-5599 E-mail: mlucas@farahandfarah.com
Web: 4aaf.com/education/scholarships

Summary To provide financial assistance to Hispanic American and other minority undergraduate and graduate students from any state who are enrolled at colleges and universities in Florida and interested in entering the field of advertising.

Eligibility This program is open to undergraduate and graduate students from any state enrolled at accredited colleges and universities in Florida who are U.S. citizens or permanent residents of African, African American, Hispanic, Hispanic American, Indian, Native American, Asian, Asian American, or Pacific Islander descent. Applicants must be working on a bachelor's or master's degree in advertising, marketing, communications, public relations, art, graphic arts, or a related field. They must have an overall GPA of 3.0 or higher. Along with their application, they must submit a 250-word essay on why multiculturalism, diversity, and inclusion are important in the advertising, marketing, and communications industry today. Preference is given to members of the American Advertising Federation.

Financial Data The stipend is $1,000.

Duration 1 year.

Number awarded 1 or more each year.

Deadline February of each year.

[650]
FRAMELINE COMPLETION FUND

Frameline
Attn: Completion Fund
145 Ninth Street, Suite 300
San Francisco, CA 94103
(415) 703-8650   Fax: (415) 861-1404
E-mail: info@frameline.org
Web: www.frameline.org/filmmaker-support

Summary To provide funding to lesbian, gay, bisexual, and transgender (LGBT) film/video artists (particularly Hispanic Americans, other film/video artists of color, and women).

Eligibility This program is open to LGBT artists who are in the last stages of the production of documentary, educational, narrative, animated, or experimental projects about or of interest to LGBT people and their communities. Applicants may be independent artists, students, producers, or nonprofit corporations. They must be interested in completion work and must have 90% of the production completed; projects in development, script-development, pre-production, or production are not eligible. Student projects are eligible only if the student maintains artistic and financial control of the project. Women and people of color are especially encouraged to apply. Selection is based on financial need, the contribution the grant will make to completing the project, assurances that the project will be completed, and the statement the project makes about LGBT people and/or issues of concern to them and their communities.

Financial Data Grants range from $1,000 to $5,000.

Duration These are 1-time grants.

Additional data This program began in 1990.

Number awarded Varies each year; recently, 5 of these grants were awarded. Since this program was established, it has provided $389,200 in support to 118 films.

Deadline October of each year.

[651]
FRANCHISE LAW DIVERSITY SCHOLARSHIP AWARD

International Franchise Association
Attn: President, Educational Foundation
1501 K Street, N.W., Suite 350
Washington, DC 20005
(202) 662-0764   Fax: (202) 628-0812
E-mail: jreynolds@franchise.org
Web: www.franchise.org/files/Scholarships.aspx

Summary To provide financial assistance to Hispanic American and other law students from diverse groups who are interested in taking courses related to franchise law.

Eligibility This program is open to second- and third-year students who are enrolled at ABA-accredited law schools and a member of a diverse group (defined as African Americans, American Indians, Hispanic Americans, Asian Americans, or gays/lesbians). Applicants must be enrolled in at least 1 course oriented toward franchise law (e.g., torts, unfair trade practices, trade secrets, antitrust, trademarks, contracts, agency, or securities). Along with their application, they must submit a current transcript, an essay explaining their interest in franchise law, and 2 letters of recommendation.

Financial Data The stipend is $4,000. Funds are paid to the recipient's law school and are to be used for tuition.

Duration 1 year.

Additional data This award is cosponsored by the IFA Educational Foundation and DLA Piper US LLP. It may not be used by the recipient's law school to reduce the amount of any institutionally-awarded financial aid.

Number awarded 1 or more each year.

Deadline December of each year.

[652]
FRANCIS M. KEVILLE MEMORIAL SCHOLARSHIP

Construction Management Association of America
Attn: CMAA Foundation
7926 Jones Branch Drive, Suite 800
McLean, VA 22101-3303
(703) 356-2622   Fax: (703) 356-6388
E-mail: foundation@cmaanet.org
Web: www.cmaafoundation.org

Summary To provide financial assistance to minority and female undergraduate and graduate students working on a degree in construction management.

Eligibility This program is open to women and members of minority groups who are enrolled as full-time undergraduate or graduate students. Applicants must have completed at least 1 year of study and have at least 1 full year remaining for a bachelor's or master's degree in construction management or a related field. Along with their application, they must submit essays on why they are interested in a career in construction management and why they should be awarded this scholarship. Selection is based on that essay (20%), academic performance (40%), recommendation of the faculty adviser (15%), and extracurricular activities (25%); a bonus of 5% is given to student members of the Construction Management Association of America (CMAA).

Financial Data The stipend is $3,000. Funds are disbursed directly to the student's university.

Duration 1 year.

Number awarded 1 each year.

Deadline June of each year.

[653]
FRANK T. MARTIN LEADERSHIP SCHOLARSHIP

Conference of Minority Transportation Officials
Attn: National Scholarship Program
1875 I Street, N.W., Suite 500
Washington, DC 20006
(703) 234-4072   Fax: (202) 318-0364
Web: www.comto.org/?page=Scholarships

Summary To provide financial assistance to Hispanic American and other minority undergraduate and graduate students working on a degree in transportation or a related field.

Eligibility This program is open to full-time undergraduate and graduate students who are working on a degree in transportation, engineering, planning, or a related discipline. They must be able to demonstrate leadership and active commitment to community service. Along with their application, they must submit a cover letter with a 500-word statement of career goals. Financial need is not considered in the selection process. U.S. citizenship or legal resident status is required.

Financial Data The stipend is $3,000. Funds are paid directly to the recipient's college or university.

Duration 1 year.

Additional data The Conference of Minority Transportation Officials (COMTO) was established in 1971 to promote, strengthen, and expand the roles of minorities in all aspects of transportation. This program is sponsored by Atkins North America. Recipients are expected to attend the COMTO National Scholarship Luncheon.

Number awarded 1 each year.

Deadline May of each year.

[654]
FREDRIKSON & BYRON FOUNDATION MINORITY SCHOLARSHIP

Fredrikson & Byron Foundation
Attn: Attorney Recruiting Administrator
200 South Sixth Street, Suite 4000
Minneapolis, MN 55402-1425
(612) 492-7141   Fax: (612) 492-7077
E-mail: glarson@fredlaw.com
Web: www.fredlaw.com/firm/scholarship.htm

Summary To provide financial aid and summer work experience to Hispanic American and other minority law students from any state who are interested in practicing in the Twin Cities area of Minnesota.

Eligibility This program is open to African American, Asian American, Pacific Islander, Hispanic, Native American, and Alaska Native students enrolled in their first year of law school. Applicants must be interested in practicing law in the Minneapolis-St. Paul area. Along with their application, they must submit brief statement on their expectations and objectives in applying for this scholarship; the factors they will use to measure success in their legal career; what they see as potential issues, obstacles, and opportunities facing new lawyers in a large private practice firm; and their interest in a summer associate position in private practice, including their interest in practicing law in the Minneapolis-St. Paul area. Financial need is not considered.

Financial Data The fellowship stipend is $10,000. The internship portion of the program provides a $1,000 weekly stipend.

Duration 1 year.

Additional data Fellows are also eligible to participate in an internship at the firm's offices in Minneapolis.

Number awarded 1 each year.

Deadline March of each year.

[655]
FUND FOR LATINO SCHOLARSHIP

American Political Science Association
Attn: Centennial Center Visiting Scholars Program
1527 New Hampshire Avenue, N.W.
Washington, DC 20036-1206
(202) 483-2512   Fax: (202) 483-2657
E-mail: center@apsanet.org
Web: www.apsanet.org/content_3471.cfm

Summary To provide funding for travel or research to members of the American Political Science Association (APSA) and other students and scholars who are involved with Latinos.

Eligibility Applications for this assistance should involve activities that 1) provide professional opportunities and financial assistance to Latino/a graduate students in political science programs; 2) support the teaching, research, and publishing activities of junior-level, tenure-track Latino/a political science faculty; or 3) support activities that advance our knowledge of Latino/a politics. Latino/a scholars (whatever their research field) and all scholars (including non-Latinos/as) who are studying Latino politics in the United States are eligible.

Financial Data Travel grants and most research grants are $500. Under exceptional circumstances, a grant of up to $1,000 may be awarded. Funding is intended for travel assistance to attend the APSA annual meeting, conduct field research, attend another scholarly conference, or participate in a program at the APSA Centennial Center for Political Science and Public Affairs.

Duration These are 1-time grants.

Additional data The APSA launched its Centennial Center for Political Science and Public Affairs in 2003 to commemorate the centennial year of the association.

Number awarded 1 or more each year.

Deadline May of each year.

[656]
GAIUS CHARLES BOLIN DISSERTATION AND POST-MFA FELLOWSHIPS

Williams College
Attn: Dean of the Faculty
880 Main Street
Hopkins Hall, Third Floor
P.O. Box 141
Williamstown, MA 01267
(413) 597-4351   Fax: (413) 597-3553
E-mail: gburda@williams.edu
Web: dean-faculty.williams.edu

Summary To provide financial assistance to Hispanic Americans and members of other underrepresented groups who are interested in teaching courses at Williams College while working on their doctoral dissertation or building their post-M.F.A. professional portfolio.

Eligibility This program is open to members of underrepresented groups, including ethnic minorities, first-generation college students, women in predominantly male fields, and scholars with disabilities. Applicants must be 1) doctoral candidates in any field who have completed all work for a Ph.D. except for the dissertation; or 2) artists who completed an M.F.A. degree within the past 2 years and are building their professional portfolio. They must be willing to teach a course at Williams College. Along with their application, they must submit a full curriculum vitae, a graduate school transcript, 3 letters of recommendation, a copy of their dissertation prospectus or samples of their artistic work, and a description of their teaching interests within a department or program at Williams College. U.S. citizenship or permanent resident status is required.

Financial Data Fellows receive $36,000 for the academic year, plus housing assistance, office space, computer and library privileges, and a research allowance of up to $4,000.

Duration 2 years.

Additional data Bolin fellows are assigned a faculty adviser in the appropriate department. This program was

established in 1985. Fellows are expected to teach a 1-semester course each year. They must be in residence at Williams College for the duration of the fellowship.

Number awarded 3 each year.

Deadline November of each year.

[657]
GE HISPANIC FORUM SCHOLARSHIP PROGRAM

Hispanic Scholarship Fund
Attn: Selection Committee
1411 West 190th Street, Suite 325
Gardena, CA 90248
Toll Free: (877) HSF-INFO   E-mail: scholar1@hsf.net
Web: www.hsf.net/Scholarship-Programs.aspx

Summary To provide financial assistance to Hispanic undergraduate and graduate students from designated states and communities who are working on a degree in specified fields.

Eligibility This program is open to U.S. citizens and permanent residents (must have a permanent resident card or a passport stamped I-551) who are of Hispanic heritage. Applicants must be enrolled as full-time sophomores, juniors, seniors, fifth-year undergraduates, or master's degree students at a 4-year college or university and have a GPA of 3.0 or higher. They must be working on a degree in accounting, aeronautics/aviation, aerospace engineering, biochemistry, bioengineering/biotechnology, biology, business administration, chemical engineering, chemistry, civil engineering, computational biology/bioinformatics, computer engineering, computer sciences, cybernetics/robotics, economics, electrical engineering, engineering, finance, industrial engineering/technology, information technology/management information systems, international business, management, manufacturing engineering, marketing, materials science/engineering, mathematics/statistics, mechanical engineering, neuroscience, nuclear engineering, petroleum engineering, physics, science, supply chain management, telecommunications. The program is limited to students who reside in and attend school in 1) the states of Arizona or New Hampshire; 2) Puerto Rico; or 3) the metropolitan areas of Atlanta, Austin, Boston, Chicago, Cincinnati, Dallas, Denver, Detroit, Erie (Pennsylvania), Fairfield County (Connecticut), Greenville, Hartford, Houston, Jacksonville, Kansas City (Missouri), Los Angeles, Louisville, Miami, Milwaukee, New York, Philadelphia (including southern New Jersey), Salt Lake City, San Antonio, San Francisco, Seattle, Schenectady, Twin Cities (Minnesota), Tampa Bay, or Wilmington (North Carolina). Selection is based on academic achievement, personal strengths, leadership, and financial need.

Financial Data The stipend is $2,500.

Duration 1 year.

Additional data This program is funded by the GE Hispanic Forum, which provides mentors to recipients.

Number awarded 1 or more each year.

Deadline January of each year.

[658]
GEM M.S. ENGINEERING FELLOWSHIP PROGRAM

National Consortium for Graduate Degrees for Minorities
in Engineering and Science (GEM)
Attn: Manager, Fellowships Administration
1430 Duke Street
Alexandria, VA 22314
(703) 562-3646   Fax: (202) 207-3518
E-mail: info@gemfellowship.org
Web: www.gemfellowship.org/gem-fellowship

Summary To provide financial aid and summer work experience to Hispanic American and other underrepresented minority students interested in working on a master's degree in engineering or computer science.

Eligibility This program is open to U.S. citizens and permanent residents who are members of ethnic groups underrepresented in engineering: American Indians/Native Americans, Blacks/African Americans, or Latinos/Hispanic Americans. Applicants must be a senior or graduate of an ABET-accredited engineering or computer science program and have an academic record that indicates the ability to pursue graduate studies in engineering (including a GPA of 2.8 or higher). They must agree to apply to at least 3 of the 102 GEM member universities that offer a master's degree and to intern during summers with a sponsoring GEM employer.

Financial Data Fellows receive 1) a stipend of $4,000 per semester; 2) full tuition and fees at the GEM member university; and 3) a salary during the summer work assignment as a GEM summer intern.

Duration Up to 4 semesters, plus summer work internships lasting 10 to 14 weeks for up to 2 summers.

Additional data During the summer internship, each fellow is assigned an engineering project in a research setting. Each project is based on the fellow's interest and background and is carried out under the supervision of an experienced engineer. At the conclusion of the internship, each fellow writes a project report. Recipients must work on a master's degree in the same engineering discipline as their baccalaureate degree.

Number awarded Approximately 300 each year.

Deadline November of each year.

[659]
GEM PH.D. ENGINEERING FELLOWSHIP PROGRAM

National Consortium for Graduate Degrees for Minorities
in Engineering and Science (GEM)
Attn: Manager, Fellowships Administration
1430 Duke Street
Alexandria, VA 22314
(703) 562-3646   Fax: (202) 207-3518
E-mail: info@gemfellowship.org
Web: www.gemfellowship.org/gem-fellowship

Summary To provide financial aid and summer work experience to Hispanic American and other underrepresented minority students interested in obtaining a Ph.D. degree in engineering.

Eligibility This program is open to U.S. citizens and permanent residents who are members of ethnic groups underrepresented in engineering: American Indians/Native Ameri-

cans, Blacks/African Americans, and Latinos/Hispanic Americans. Applicants must be college seniors, master's degree students, or graduates of an ABET-accredited program in engineering and have an academic record that indicates the ability to work on a doctoral degree in engineering (including a GPA of 3.0 or higher). They must agree to apply to at least 3 of the 102 GEM member universities that offer a doctoral degree in engineering and to intern during summer with a sponsoring GEM employer.

Financial Data The stipend is $16,000 for the first year; in subsequent years, fellows receive full payment of tuition and fees plus a stipend and assistantship from their university that is equivalent to funding received by other doctoral students in their department.

Duration 3 to 5 years for the fellowship; 12 weeks during the summer immediately after sponsorship for the internship.

Additional data This program is valid only at 1 of the 102 participating GEM member universities; contact GEM for a list. The fellowship award is designed to support the student in the first year of the doctoral program without working. Subsequent years are subsidized by the respective universities and will usually include either a teaching or research assistantship. Recipients must participate in the GEM summer internship; failure to agree to accept the internship cancels the fellowship.

Number awarded Approximately 50 each year.

Deadline November of each year.

[660]
GEM PH.D. SCIENCE FELLOWSHIP PROGRAM

National Consortium for Graduate Degrees for Minorities
in Engineering and Science (GEM)
Attn: Manager, Fellowships Administration
1430 Duke Street
Alexandria, VA 22314
(703) 562-3646   Fax: (202) 207-3518
E-mail: info@gemfellowship.org
Web: www.gemfellowship.org/gem-fellowship

Summary To provide financial aid and summer work experience to Hispanic American and other underrepresented minority students interested in working on a Ph.D. degree in the life sciences, mathematics, or physical sciences.

Eligibility This program is open to U.S. citizens and permanent residents who are members of ethnic groups underrepresented in the natural sciences: American Indians/Native Americans, Blacks/African Americans, and Latinos/Hispanic Americans. Applicants must be college seniors, master's degree students, or recent graduates in the biological sciences, mathematics, or physical sciences (chemistry, computer science, environmental sciences, and physics) with an academic record that indicates the ability to pursue doctoral studies (including a GPA of 3.0 or higher). They must agree to apply to at least 3 of the 102 GEM member universities that offer a doctoral degree in science and to intern during summer with a sponsoring GEM employer.

Financial Data The stipend is $16,000 for the first year; in subsequent years, fellows receive full payment of tuition and fees plus a stipend and assistantship from their university that is equivalent to funding received by other doctoral students in their department.

Duration 3 to 5 years for the fellowship; 12 weeks during the summer immediately after sponsorship for the internship.

Additional data This program is valid only at 1 of 102 participating GEM member universities; contact GEM for a list. The fellowship award is designed to support the student in the first year of the doctoral program without working. Subsequent years are subsidized by the respective university and will usually include either a teaching or research assistantship. Recipients must participate in the GEM summer internship; failure to agree to accept the internship cancels the fellowship. Recipients must enroll in the same scientific discipline as their undergraduate major.

Number awarded Approximately 40 each year.

Deadline November of each year.

[661]
GEOLOGICAL SOCIETY OF AMERICA GRADUATE STUDENT RESEARCH GRANTS

Geological Society of America
Attn: Program Officer-Grants, Awards and Recognition
3300 Penrose Place
P.O. Box 9140
Boulder, CO 80301-9140
(303) 357-1028   Toll Free: (800) 472-1988, ext. 1028
Fax: (303) 357-1070   E-mail: awards@geosociety.org
Web: www.geosociety.org/grants/gradgrants.htm

Summary To provide funding to graduate student members (particularly Hispanic Americans, other minorities, women, and students with disabilities) of the Geological Society of America (GSA) who are interested in conducting research at universities in the United States, Canada, Mexico, or Central America.

Eligibility This program is open to GSA members working on a master's or doctoral degree at a university in the United States, Canada, Mexico, or Central America. Applicants must be interested in conducting geological research. Minorities, women, and persons with disabilities are strongly encouraged to apply. Selection is based on the scientific merits of the proposal, the capability of the investigator, and the reasonableness of the budget.

Financial Data Grants range up to $4,000 and recently averaged $1,829. Funds can be used for the cost of travel, room and board in the field, services of a technician or field assistant, funding of chemical and isotope analyses, or other expenses directly related to the fulfillment of the research contract. Support is not provided for the purchase of ordinary field equipment, for maintenance of the families of the grantees and their assistants, as reimbursement for work already accomplished, for institutional overhead, for adviser participation, or for tuition costs.

Duration 1 year.

Additional data In addition to general grants, GSA awards a number of specialized grants: the Gretchen L. Blechschmidt Award for women (especially in the fields of biostratigraphy and/or paleoceanography); the John T. Dillon Alaska Research Award for earth science problems particular to Alaska; the Robert K. Fahnestock Memorial Award for the field of sediment transport or related aspects of fluvial geomorphology; the Lipman Research Award for volcanology and petrology; the Bruce L. "Biff" Reed Award for studies in the tectonic and magmatic evolution of Alaska; the Alexander Sisson Award for studies in Alaska and the Caribbean; the Harold T. Stearns Fellowship Award for work on the geology of the Pacific Islands and the circum-Pacific region; the Parke

D. Snavely, Jr. Cascadia Research Fund Award for studies of the Pacific Northwest convergent margin; the Alexander and Geraldine Wanek Fund Award for studies of coal and petroleum; the Charles A. and June R.P. Ross Research Fund Award for stratigraphy; and the John Montagne Fund Award for research in the field of quaternary geology or geomorphology.

Number awarded Varies each year; recently, the society awarded more than 300 grants worth more than $550,000 through this and all of its specialized programs.

Deadline January of each year.

[662]
GEOPHYSICAL FLUID DYNAMICS FELLOWSHIPS

Woods Hole Oceanographic Institution
Attn: Academic Programs Office
Clark Laboratory, MS 31
266 Woods Hole Road
Woods Hole, MA 02543-1541
(508) 289-2950   Fax: (508) 457-2188
E-mail: gfd@whoi.edu
Web: www.whoi.edu/gfd

Summary To provide summer research and study opportunities at Woods Hole Oceanographic Institution (WHOI) to pre- and postdoctoral scholars (particularly Hispanic Americans, other underrepresented minorities, and women) who are interested in geophysical fluid dynamics.

Eligibility This program is open to pre- and postdoctorates who are interested in pursuing research or study opportunities in a field that involves non-linear dynamics of rotating, stratified fluids. Fields of specialization include classical fluid dynamics, physical oceanography, meteorology, geophysical fluid dynamics, astrophysics, planetary atmospheres, hydromagnetics, physics, and applied mathematics. Applications from women and members of underrepresented groups are particularly encouraged.

Financial Data Participants receive a stipend of $5,600 and an allowance for travel expenses within the United States.

Duration 10 weeks during the summer.

Additional data Each summer, the program at WHOI revolves around a central theme. A recent theme related to shear turbulence. The main components of the summer program are a series of principal lectures, a set of supplementary research seminars, and research projects conducted by the student fellows with the active support of the staff. Funding for this program, which began in 1959, is provided by the National Science Foundation and Office of Naval Research.

Number awarded Up to 10 graduate students are supported each year.

Deadline February of each year.

[663]
GEORGE A. STRAIT MINORITY SCHOLARSHIP ENDOWMENT

American Association of Law Libraries
Attn: Chair, Scholarships Committee
105 West Adams Street, Suite 3300
Chicago, IL 60603
(312) 939-4764   Fax: (312) 431-1097
E-mail: scholarships@aall.org
Web: www.aallnet.org

Summary To provide financial assistance to Hispanic American and other minority college seniors or college graduates who are interested in becoming law librarians.

Eligibility This program is open to college graduates with meaningful law library experience who are members of minority groups and intend to have a career in law librarianship. Applicants must be degree candidates at an ALA-accredited library school or an ABA-accredited law school. Along with their application, they must submit a personal statement that discusses their interest in law librarianship, reason for applying for this scholarship, career goals as a law librarian, and any other pertinent information.

Financial Data The stipend is $3,500.

Duration 1 year.

Additional data This program, established in 1990, is currently supported by Thomson Reuters.

Number awarded Varies each year; recently, 5 of these scholarships were awarded.

Deadline March of each year.

[664]
GEORGE V. POWELL DIVERSITY SCHOLARSHIP

Lane Powell PC
Attn: Manager of Attorney Recruiting
1420 Fifth Avenue, Suite 4200
P.O. Box 91302
Seattle, WA 98111-9402
(206) 223-6123   Fax: (206) 223-7107
E-mail: rodenl@lanepowell.com
Web: www.lanepowell.com/422/diversity-scholarship

Summary To provide financial aid and work experience to Hispanic Americans and other law students who will contribute to the diversity of the legal community.

Eligibility This program is open to second-year students in good standing at an ABA-accredited law school. Applicants must be able to contribute meaningfully to the diversity of the legal community and have a demonstrated desire to work, live, and eventually practice law in Seattle or Portland. They must submit a cover letter that includes a statement indicating eligibility to participate in the program, a resume, a current copy of law school transcript, a legal writing sample, and a list of 2 or 3 professional or academic references. Selection is based on academic achievement and record of leadership abilities, community service, and involvement in community issues.

Financial Data The program provides a stipend of $7,500 for the third year of law school and a paid summer associate clerkship.

Duration 1 year, including the summer.

Additional data This program began in 2005. Clerkships are provided at the offices of the sponsor in Seattle or Portland.

Number awarded 1 each year.

Deadline August of each year.

[665]
GERALDO RIVERA SCHOLARSHIP

National Association of Hispanic Journalists
Attn: Scholarship Committee
1050 Connecticut Avenue, N.W., Tenth Floor
Washington, DC 20036
(202) 662-7145   Toll Free: (888) 346-NAHJ
Fax: (202) 662-7144   E-mail: nahj@nahj.org
Web: www.nahj12.com/scholarships

Summary To provide financial assistance to college senior and graduate student members of the National Association of Hispanic Journalists (NAHJ) who are interested in preparing for a career in television broadcast journalism.

Eligibility This program is open to Hispanic American college seniors and graduate students who are interested in preparing for a career in English- or Spanish-language television broadcast journalism. Applicants must be enrolled full time at a college or university in the United States or Puerto Rico. They must be NAHJ members. Along with their application, they must submit transcripts, a 1-page resume, 2 letters of recommendation, work samples, and a 1,000-word autobiographical essay that includes why they are interested in a career in journalism, what inspired them to prepare for a career in the field, what hardships or obstacles they have experienced while trying to realize their goal of becoming a journalist, and the role Latino journalists play in the news industry. Selection is based on commitment to the field of journalism, academic achievement, awareness of the Latino community, and financial need.

Financial Data The stipend ranges up to $5,000.

Duration 1 year.

Number awarded 1 each year.

Deadline January of each year.

[666]
GILBERT RIOS MEMORIAL AWARD

Los Padres Foundation
P.O. Box 305
Nassau, DE 19969
(302) 644-1124   Toll Free: (800) 528-4105
Fax: (866) 810-1361
E-mail: lpfadmin@lospadresfoundation.com
Web: www.lospadresfoundation.org

Summary To provide financial assistance to graduate students from low-income Puerto Rican/Latino families.

Eligibility This program is open to graduate students who are the first in their family to attend college and whose family meets the federal low-income guidelines. Applicants must be U.S. citizens or permanent residents of Puerto Rican/Latino origin planning to attend an accredited college or university. They must have a GPA of 3.0 or higher and a record of at least 100 hours of non-faith based volunteer community service each year they were enrolled in undergraduate school. Along with their application, they must submit 250-word personal essays on 1) their future objectives and goals; 2) the volunteer community service projects which with they have been involved as an undergraduate; 3) the issue or problem that was the focus of each organization with which they were a volunteer; 4) the influence or impact of this activity or program on their community; and 5) what they consider to be the major issue affecting their community. Males and females are considered separately.

Financial Data The stipend is $5,000.

Duration 1 year.

Additional data This program began in 2005.

Number awarded 2 each year: 1 to a male and 1 to a female.

Deadline May of each year.

[667]
GOALI GRADUATE STUDENT INDUSTRIAL FELLOWSHIPS/TRAINEESHIPS

National Science Foundation
Directorate for Engineering
Attn: Division of Industrial Innovation and Partnerships
4201 Wilson Boulevard, Room 550S
Arlington, VA 22230
(703) 292-7082   Fax: (703) 292-9056
TDD: (800) 281-8749   E-mail: dsenich@nsf.gov
Web: www.nsf.gov

Summary To provide an opportunity for graduate students (particularly Hispanic Americans, other minorities, women, and students with disabilities) to work or conduct research in industry as part of the Grant Opportunities for Academic Liaison with Industry (GOALI) program of the National Science Foundation (NSF).

Eligibility This program is open to graduate students (preferably Ph.D. students) in science, engineering, and mathematics fields of interest to NSF. Applicants must be U.S. citizens, nationals, or permanent residents. They must be proposing a program of full- or part-time work in industry in an area related to their research under the guidance of an academic adviser and an industrial mentor. In the selection process, consideration is given to the achievement of societally relevant outcomes, including full participation of women, persons with disabilities, and underrepresented minorities.

Financial Data Graduate students may receive stipends from $1,500 to $1,800 per month, plus transportation expenses. The faculty adviser may receive 10% of the total award for research-related expenses, excluding equipment. No indirect costs are allowed. The total award may be up to $30,000 for a fellowship for a single student.

Duration Up to 1 year.

Additional data This program is also offered by most other NSF directorates. Check the web site for a name and e-mail address of the contact person in each directorate.

Number awarded A total of 60 to 80 grants for all GOALI programs is awarded each year; total funding is approximately $5 million.

Deadline Applications may be submitted at any time.

[668]
GOLDMAN SACHS MBA FELLOWSHIP

Goldman Sachs
Attn: Human Capital Management
200 West Street, 25th Floor
New York, NY 10282
E-mail: Iris.Birungi@gs.com
Web: www.goldmansachs.com

Summary To provide financial aid and work experience to Hispanic American and other underrepresented minority students interested in working on an M.B.A. degree.

Eligibility This program is open to graduate students of Black, Latino, or Native American descent who are interested in working on an M.B.A. degree. Applicants must be preparing for a career in the financial services industry. Along with their application, they must submit 2 essays of 500 words or less on the following topics: 1) why they are preparing for a career in the financial services industry; and 2) their current involvement with a community-based organization. Selection is based on analytical skills and the ability to identify significant problems, gather facts, and analyze situations in depth; interpersonal skills, including, but not limited to, poise, confidence, and professionalism; academic record; evidence of hard work and commitment; ability to work well with others; and commitment to community involvement.

Financial Data Fellows receive $15,000 toward payment of tuition and living expenses for the first year of business school; an internship at a domestic office of Goldman Sachs during the summer after the first year of business school; and (after successful completion of the summer internship and acceptance of an offer to return to the firm after graduation as a full-time regular employee) either payment of tuition costs for the second year of business school or an additional $15,000 toward tuition and living costs.

Duration Up to 2 years.

Additional data This program was initiated in 1997.

Number awarded 1 or more each year.

Deadline November of each year.

[669]
GOOGLE SCHOLARSHIP PROGRAM

Hispanic College Fund
Attn: Scholarship Processing
1300 L Street, N.W., Suite 975
Washington, DC 20005
(202) 296-5400   Toll Free: (800) 644-4223
Fax: (202) 296-3774   E-mail: hcf-info@hispanicfund.org
Web: scholarships.hispanicfund.org/applications

Summary To provide financial assistance to Hispanic American upper-division and graduate students who are interested in preparing for a career in computer science or computer engineering.

Eligibility This program is open to U.S. citizens and permanent residents of Hispanic background (at least 1 grandparent must be 100% Hispanic) who are entering their junior or senior year of college or who are enrolled in graduate school. Applicants must be working on a bachelor's, master's, or Ph.D. degree in computer science or computer engineering and have a cumulative GPA of 3.0 or higher. They must be enrolled at an accredited college or university in the 50 states or Puerto Rico as a full-time student. Financial need is considered in the selection process.

Financial Data This stipend is $10,000. Funds are paid directly to the recipient's college or university to help cover tuition and fees.

Duration 1 year; recipients may reapply.

Additional data This program is sponsored by Google. All applications must be submitted online; no paper applications are available.

Number awarded Varies each year.

Deadline February of each year.

[670]
GRADUATE TRAINING IN DISPARITIES RESEARCH

Susan G. Komen Breast Cancer Foundation
Attn: Grants Department
5005 LBJ Freeway, Suite 250
Dallas, TX 75244
(972) 855-1616   Toll Free: (866) 921-9678
Fax: (972) 855-1640
E-mail: helpdesk@komengrantsaccess.org
Web: ww5.komen.org

Summary To provide funding for training to minority and other graduate students interested in conducting research related to disparities in breast cancer outcomes.

Eligibility This program provides support to students enrolled in a master's, combined master's/doctoral, or doctoral degree program. Applications must be submitted by a full-time faculty member at their institution who is currently conducting research on disparities in breast cancer outcomes. Neither the students nor the faculty mentors are required to be U.S. citizens or residents. The application must describe a training program that combines didactic course work and hands-on laboratory, clinical, and/or public health research. The training program must ensure that all students at all levels will develop the analytic, research, scientific, clinical, and public health skills critical for them to effectively explore the basis for differences in breast cancer outcomes and to develop and translate research discoveries into clinical and public health practice to eliminate those disparities. Strong preference is given to involving trainees from populations adversely affected by disparities in breast cancer outcomes.

Financial Data The grant is $45,000 per student per year for direct costs only.

Duration 2 years; a third year may be approved, based on an assessment of first-year progress.

Additional data This program was formerly known as the Post-Baccalaureate Training in Disparities Research Grants.

Number awarded Varies each year; recently, 5 of these grants were awarded.

Deadline Pre-applications must be submitted by early September of each year; full applications are due in October.

[671]
GREENSPOON MARDER DIVERSITY SCHOLARSHIP

Community Foundation of Sarasota County
Attn: Grants and Scholarships Coordinator
2635 Fruitville Road
P.O. Box 49587
Sarasota, FL 34230-6587
(941) 556-7114   Fax: (941) 952-7115
E-mail: eyoung@cfsarasota.org
Web: www.cfsarasota.org/Default.aspx?tabid=263

Summary To provide financial assistance to Hispanic American and other minority students from any state attending designated law schools (most of which are in Florida).

Eligibility This program is open to racial and ethnic minority students from any state who are members of groups traditionally underrepresented in the legal profession. Applicants must be entering their second year of full-time study at the University of Florida Levin College of Law, Florida State University College of Law, Stetson University College of Law, Nova Southeastern University Shepard Broad Law Center, St. Thomas University School of Law, Florida A&M University College of Law, Howard University College of Law, Texas Southern University Thurgood Marshall School of Law, Florida Coastal School of Law, or Florida International University College of Law. They must have a GPA of 2.6 or higher. Along with their application, they must submit a 1,000-word personal statement that describes their personal strengths, their contributions through community service, any special or unusual circumstances that may have affected their academic performance, or their personal and family history of educational or socioeconomic disadvantage; it should include aspects of their minority racial or ethnic identity that are relevant to their application. Applicants may also include information about their financial circumstances if they wish to have those considered in the selection process. U.S. citizenship or permanent resident status is required.

Financial Data The stipend is $2,500 per semester.

Duration 1 semester (the spring semester of the second year of law school); may be renewed 1 additional semester (the fall semester of the third year).

Additional data This program was established by the Florida law firm Ruden McClosky, which was acquired by the firm Greenspoon Marder in 2011. It is administered by the Community Foundation of Sarasota County, but the law firm selects the recipients.

Number awarded 1 or more each year.

Deadline July of each year.

[672]
HANA SCHOLARSHIPS

United Methodist Church
Attn: General Board of Higher Education and Ministry
Office of Loans and Scholarships
1001 19th Avenue South
P.O. Box 340007
Nashville, TN 37203-0007
(615) 340-7344   Fax: (615) 340-7367
E-mail: umscholar@gbhem.org
Web: www.gbhem.org

Summary To provide financial assistance to upper-division and graduate Methodist students who are of Hispanic, Asian, Native American, or Pacific Islander ancestry.

Eligibility This program is open to full-time juniors, seniors, and graduate students at accredited colleges and universities in the United States who have been active, full members of a United Methodist Church (UMC) for at least 1 year prior to applying. Applicants must have at least 1 parent who is Hispanic, Asian, Native American, or Pacific Islander. They must be able to demonstrate involvement in their Hispanic, Asian, or Native American (HANA) community in the UMC. Selection is based on that involvement, academic ability (GPA of at least 2.85), and financial need. U.S. citizenship or permanent resident status is required.

Financial Data The maximum stipend is $3,000 for undergraduates or $5,000 for graduate students.

Duration 1 year; recipients may reapply.

Number awarded 50 each year.

Deadline February of each year.

[673]
HARRIETT G. JENKINS PREDOCTORAL FELLOWSHIP PROGRAM

United Negro College Fund Special Programs
  Corporation
6402 Arlington Boulevard, Suite 600
Falls Church, VA 22042
(703) 205-7625   Toll Free: (800) 530-6232
Fax: (703) 205-7645
E-mail: sheryl.karpowicz@uncfsp.org
Web: www.uncfsp.org

Summary To provide financial aid and work experience to Hispanic Americans, other minorities, women, and people with disabilities working on a graduate degree in a field of interest to the National Aeronautics and Space Administration (NASA).

Eligibility This program is open to members of groups underrepresented in science, technology, engineering, or mathematics (STEM), including women, minorities, and people with disabilities. Applicants must be full-time graduate students entering or in the first 3 years of a program leading to a master's or doctoral degree in a NASA-related discipline (aeronautics, aerospace engineering, astronomy, atmospheric science, bioengineering, biology, chemistry, computer science, earth sciences, engineering, environmental sciences, life sciences, materials sciences, mathematics, meteorology, neuroscience, physics, or robotics). They must be U.S. citizens and have a GPA of 3.0 or higher. Doctoral students who have advanced to candidacy are ineligible.

Financial Data The stipend is $24,000 per year for doctoral fellows or $18,000 per year for master's degree students. The tuition offset is at least $8,500. Fellows who are also selected for a mini research award at a NASA Center or the Jet Propulsion Laboratory receive an additional grant of $8,000.

Duration 3 years.

Additional data This program, established in 2001, is funded by NASA and administered by the United Negro College Fund Special Programs Corporation. Fellows may also compete for a mini research award to engage in a NASA research experience that is closely aligned with the research conducted at the fellow's institution. The participating NASA facilities are Ames Research Center (Moffett Field, California), Jet Propulsion Laboratory (Pasadena, California), Dryden Flight Research Center (Edwards, California), Johnson Space Center (Houston, Texas), Stennis Space Center (Stennis Space Center, Mississippi), Marshall Space Flight Center (Marshall Space Flight Center, Alabama), Glenn Research Center (Cleveland, Ohio), Kennedy Space Center (Kennedy Space Center, Florida), Langley Research Center (Hampton, Virginia), and Goddard Space Flight Center (Greenbelt, Maryland).

Number awarded Approximately 20 each year.

Deadline April of each year.

[674]
HBAPA LEGAL EDUCATION FUND SCHOLARSHIPS

Hispanic Bar Association of Pennsylvania
Attn: Legal Education Fund
P.O. Box 58399
Philadelphia, PA 19102-8399
(215) 686-4292   E-mail: pahbanews@gmail.com
Web: www.hbapa.com/legal-ed-fund.php

Summary To provide financial assistance to Hispanic residents of any state attending law school in Pennsylvania or the Delaware Valley.

Eligibility This program is open to students of Hispanic background from any state who are currently enrolled at a law school located in Pennsylvania or the Delaware Valley (defined to include Burlington, Camden, Cumberland, Gloucester, and Salem counties in New Jersey; New Castle County in Delaware; and Cecil County in Maryland). Applicants must submit a personal statement of 1 to 3 pages that covers their background, achievements, career goals, geographic area where they will consider practicing, involvement in community activities, involvement in law school organizations and/or activities, and financial need.

Financial Data The stipend is $1,250.

Duration 1 year.

Number awarded 1 or more each year.

Deadline September of each year.

[675]
HEALTH RESEARCH AND EDUCATIONAL TRUST SCHOLARSHIPS

New Jersey Hospital Association
Attn: Health Research and Educational Trust
760 Alexander Road
P.O. Box 1
Princeton, NJ 08543-0001
(609) 275-4224   Fax: (609) 452-8097
Web: www.njha.com/education/scholarships

Summary To provide financial assistance to New Jersey residents (particularly Hispanic Americans, other minorities, and women) who are working on an undergraduate or graduate degree in a field related to health care administration at a school in any state.

Eligibility This program is open to residents of New Jersey enrolled in an upper-division or graduate program in hospital or health care administration, public administration, nursing, or other allied health profession at a school in any state. Graduate students working on an advanced degree to prepare to teach nursing are also eligible. Applicants must have a GPA of 3.0 or higher and be able to demonstrate financial need. Along with their application, they must submit a 2-page essay (on which 50% of the selection is based) describing their academic plans for the future. Minorities and women are especially encouraged to apply.

Financial Data   The stipend is $2,000.

Duration   1 year.

Additional data   This program began in 1983.

Number awarded   Varies each year; recently, 3 of these scholarships were awarded.

Deadline   July of each year.

[676]
HEALTH SCIENCES STUDENT FELLOWSHIPS IN EPILEPSY

Epilepsy Foundation
Attn: Research Department
8301 Professional Place
Landover, MD 20785-2353
(301) 459-3700   Toll Free: (800) EFA-1000
Fax: (301) 577-2684   TDD: (800) 332-2070
E-mail: grants@efa.org
Web: www.epilepsyfoundation.org

Summary   To provide financial assistance to medical and health science graduate students (particularly Hispanic Americans, other minorities, women, and students with disabilities) who are interested in working on an epilepsy project during the summer.

Eligibility   This program is open to students enrolled, or accepted for enrollment, in a medical school, a doctoral program, or other graduate program. Applicants must have a defined epilepsy-related study or research plan to be carried out under the supervision of a qualified mentor. Because the program is designed as a training opportunity, the quality of the training plans and environment are considered in the selection process. Other selection criteria include the quality of the proposed project, the relevance of the proposed work to epilepsy, the applicant's interest in the field of epilepsy, the applicant's qualifications, the mentor's qualifications (including his or her commitment to the student and the project), and the quality of the training environment for research related to epilepsy. U.S. citizenship is not required, but the project must be conducted in the United States. Applications from women, members of minority groups, and people with disabilities are especially encouraged. The program is not intended for students working on a dissertation research project.

Financial Data   Stipends are $3,000.

Duration   3 months during the summer.

Additional data   Support for this program is provided by many individuals, families, and corporations, especially the American Epilepsy Society, Abbott Laboratories, Ortho-McNeil Pharmaceutical, and Pfizer Inc.

Number awarded   Varies each year; recently, 3 of these fellowships were awarded.

Deadline   March of each year.

[677]
HELENE M. OVERLY MEMORIAL GRADUATE SCHOLARSHIP

Women's Transportation Seminar
Attn: WTS Foundation
1701 K Street, N.W., Suite 800
Washington, DC 20006
(202) 955-5085   Fax: (202) 955-5088
E-mail: wts@wtsinternational.org
Web: www.wtsinternational.org/education/scholarships

Summary   To provide financial assistance to women graduate students (particularly Hispanic American and other minority women) who are interested in preparing for a career in transportation.

Eligibility   This program is open to women who are enrolled in a graduate degree program in a transportation-related field (e.g., transportation engineering, planning, finance, or logistics). Applicants must have at least a 3.0 GPA and be interested in a career in transportation. Along with their application, they must submit a 750-word statement about their career goals after graduation and why they think they should receive the scholarship award. Applications must be submitted first to a local chapter; the chapters forward selected applications for consideration on the national level. Minority women are particularly encouraged to apply. Selection is based on transportation involvement and goals, job skills, and academic record.

Financial Data   The stipend is $10,000.

Duration   1 year.

Additional data   This program began in 1981. Local chapters may also award additional funding to winners in their area.

Number awarded   1 each year.

Deadline   Applications must be submitted by November to a local WTS chapter.

[678]
HENAAC STUDENT LEADERSHIP AWARDS

Great Minds in STEM
Attn: HENAAC Scholars Program
602 Monterey Pass Road
Monterey Park, CA 91754
(323) 262-0997   Fax: (323) 262-0946
E-mail: gcruz@greatmindsinstem.org
Web: www.greatmindsinstem.org

Summary   To provide financial assistance to Hispanic undergraduate and graduate students working on a degree in fields of science, technology, engineering, or mathematics (STEM).

Eligibility   This program is open to Hispanic undergraduate and graduate students who are enrolled at a college or university and working on a degree in a STEM field. Applicants must be of Hispanic origin and/or must significantly participate in and promote organizations and activities in the Hispanic community. They must have a GPA of 3.0 or higher. Along with their application, they must submit a 700-word essay on a topic that changes annually; recently, students were asked to write on how they see their academic major contributing to global efforts and technology and how they, in their field of study, will contribute to global progress as well as actively contribute to their local communities. Selection is based on leadership, academic achievements, and campus and community activities; financial need is not considered.

Financial Data The stipend is $10,000.

Duration 1 year.

Additional data The Hispanic Engineer National Achievement Awards Conference (HENAAC) was established in 1989 and initiated a scholarship program in 2000. In 2010, the sponsoring organization officially adopted its current name, but it continues to hold the annual HENAAC conference, at which the scholarships are presented. Recipients must attend the conference to accept their scholarship.

Number awarded 2 each year: 1 undergraduate and 1 graduate student.

Deadline April of each year.

[679]
HENRY DAVID RESEARCH GRANT IN HUMAN REPRODUCTIVE BEHAVIOR AND POPULATION STUDIES

American Psychological Foundation
750 First Street, N.E.
Washington, DC 20002-4242
(202) 336-5843   Fax: (202) 336-5812
E-mail: foundation@apa.org
Web: www.apa.org/apf/funding/david.aspx

Summary To provide funding to young psychologists (particularly Hispanic Americans, other minorities, women, and individuals with disabilities) who are interested in conducting research on reproductive behavior.

Eligibility This program is open to doctoral students in psychology working on a dissertation and young psychologists who have no more than 7 years of postgraduate experience. Applicants must be interested in conducting research on human reproductive behavior or an area related to population concerns. Along with their application, they must submit a current curriculum vitae, 2 letters of recommendation, and an essay of 1 to 2 pages on their interest in human reproductive behavior or in population studies. The sponsor encourages applications from individuals who represent diversity in race, ethnicity, gender, age, disability, and sexual orientation.

Financial Data The grant is $1,500.

Duration The grant is presented annually.

Number awarded 1 each year.

Deadline February of each year.

[680]
HERBERT W. NICKENS MEDICAL STUDENT SCHOLARSHIPS

Association of American Medical Colleges
Attn: Division of Diversity Policy and Programs
2450 N Street, N.W.
Washington, DC 20037-1126
(202) 862-6203   Fax: (202) 828-1125
E-mail: nickensawards@aamc.org
Web: www.aamc.org/initiatives/awards/nickens-student

Summary To provide financial assistance to Hispanic American and other medical students who have demonstrated efforts to address the health-care needs of minorities.

Eligibility This program is open to U.S. citizens and permanent residents entering their third year of study at a U.S. allopathic medical school. Each medical school may nominate 1 student for these awards. The letter must describe the nominee's 1) academic achievement through the first and second year, including special awards and honors, clerkships or special research projects, and extracurricular activities in which the student has shown leadership abilities; 2) leadership efforts to eliminate inequities in medical education and health care; 3) demonstrated leadership efforts in addressing the educational, societal, and health-care needs of minorities; and 4) awards and honors, special research projects, and extracurricular activities in which the student has shown leadership abilities. Nominees must submit a curriculum vitae and a 2-page essay that discusses their leadership efforts in eliminating inequities in medical education and health care for minorities.

Financial Data The stipend is $5,000.

Duration 1 year.

Number awarded 5 each year.

Deadline April of each year.

[681]
HILLIS CLARK MARTIN & PETERSON DIVERSITY FELLOWSHIP

Hillis Clark Martin & Peterson P.S.
Attn: Recruiting Coordinator
1221 Second Avenue, Suite 500
Seattle, WA 98101-2925
(206) 470-7647   Fax: (206) 623-7789
E-mail: Brenda@hcmp.com
Web: www.hcmp.com/index.php?p=1_144

Summary To provide financial aid and work experience to Hispanic American and other students whose background and life experiences will contribute to the diversity of the legal community.

Eligibility This program is open to students enrolled in the first year at an ABA-accredited law school. Applicants must have a background and life experiences that will contribute meaningfully to the diversity of the legal community. Along with their application, they must submit a resume, transcripts, a personal statement of 1 to 2 pages describing their background and addressing the selection criteria, a legal writing sample, and a list of 3 references. Selection is based on distinction in academic performance, accomplishments and activities, commitment to community service, leadership ability, and financial need.

Financial Data The stipend is $7,500.

Duration 1 year.

Additional data The program includes a salaried summer associate position following the first year of law school.

Number awarded 1 or more each year.

Deadline January of each year.

[682]
HISPANIC BAR ASSOCIATION OF NEW JERSEY SCHOLARSHIP

Hispanic Bar Association of New Jersey
c/o J. Andres Mayor, Scholarship Committee Chair
Day Pitney LLP
One Jefferson Road
Parsippany, NJ 07054
(973) 966-8203   E-mail: amayor@daypitney.com
Web: www.njhba.org

Summary To provide financial assistance to Hispanic law students from New Jersey.
Eligibility This program is open to students of Hispanic ancestry (at least 1 parent of Hispanic descent) who are enrolled in the first, second, or third year of study at an ABA-approved law school in the United States. Applicants must be or have been residents of New Jersey. Along with their application, they must submit a statement describing their recent community and/or law school activities and how they, after graduating as a lawyer, intend to contribute to the advancement of the Hispanic community and Bar. Financial need is considered in the selection process.

Financial Data The stipend is $3,000.

Duration 1 year.

Number awarded 1 or more each year.

Deadline April of each year.

[683]
HISPANIC HIGHER EDUCATION SCHOLARSHIP FUND

New Jersey Mental Health Institute
Attn: Debra Wentz, Executive Director
The Neuman Building
3575 Quakerbridge Road, Suite 102
Mercerville, NJ 08619
(609) 838-5488, ext. 292   Fax: (609) 838-5480
E-mail: dwentz@njmhi.org
Web: www.njmhi.org/scholarshipfunds.html

Summary To provide financial assistance to Hispanic students working on a master's degree in social work at New Jersey universities.
Eligibility This program is open to U.S. citizens and permanent residents of Hispanic background who have a baccalaureate degree. Applicants must be interested in working on a master's degree in social work at a university in New Jersey. They must be bilingual (English and Spanish) in both their verbal and written communications. Along with their application, they must submit a brief personal statement explaining why they believe they should receive this scholarship and a 1-page essay on why they are entering the field of social work and how they plan to contribute to the field. Selection is based on information in the application, a personal interview, and an in-person written and verbal communications skills test.

Financial Data A stipend is awarded (amount not specified).

Duration 1 year.

Additional data This program began in 2002.

Number awarded 1 each year.

Deadline April of each year.

[684]
HISPANIC LEADERSHIP DEVELOPMENT FUND

United Methodist Church
General Board of Global Ministries
Attn: United Methodist Committee on Relief
Health and Welfare Ministries
475 Riverside Drive, Room 330
New York, NY 10115
(212) 870-3871   Toll Free: (800) UMC-GBGM
E-mail: jyoung@gbgm-umc.org
Web: new.gbgm-umc.org/umcor/work/health/scholarships

Summary To provide financial assistance to Methodists and other Christians of Hispanic descent who are preparing for a career in a health-related field.
Eligibility This program is open to undergraduate and graduate students who are U.S. citizens or permanent residents of Hispanic descent. Applicants must be professed Christians, preferably United Methodists. They must be working on an undergraduate or graduate degree to enter or continue in a health-related field. Financial need is considered in the selection process.

Financial Data The stipend is $2,000.

Duration 1 year.

Additional data This program began in 1986.

Number awarded Varies each year.

Deadline June of each year.

[685]
HISPANIC METROPOLITAN CHAMBER SCHOLARSHIPS

Hispanic Metropolitan Chamber
Attn: Scholarship Committee
333 S.W. Fifth Avenue, Suite 100
P.O. Box 1837
Portland, OR 97207
(503) 222-0280   Fax: (503) 243-5597
E-mail: hmcc@qwest.net
Web: www.hmccoregon.com/scholarships

Summary To provide financial assistance to Hispanic residents of Oregon and Clark County, Washington who are interested in attending college or graduate school in any state.
Eligibility This program is open to residents of Oregon and Clark County, Washington who are of Hispanic ancestry. Applicants must have a GPA of 3.0 or higher and be enrolled or planning to enroll in an accredited community college, 4-year university, or graduate school in any state. Along with their application, they must submit 250-word essays on how their heritage has influenced their life and long-term goals, and either why they should be selected to receive another scholarship (for renewal applicants) or a community activity in which they have participated and how it has benefited the Latino community in the past year (for first-time applicants). If they wish to be considered for a scholarship for low-income families, they may also submit documentation of financial need. U.S. citizenship or permanent resident status is required.

Financial Data Stipends range from $2,000 to $5,500.

Duration 1 year; may be renewed.

Additional data Matching funds are provided to students who choose to attend George Fox University, Lewis and Clark College, Linfield College, Oregon State University, Portland State University, University of Oregon, University of Portland, Western Oregon University, Whitman College, or Willamette University.

Number awarded Varies each year; recently, 50 of these scholarships were awarded: 1 at $5,500, 1 at $5,000, 2 at $4,500, 2 at $3,250, 3 at $3,000, 10 at $2,500, and 31 at $2,000.

Deadline January of each year.

[686]
HISPANIC PROFESSIONALS OF GREATER MILWAUKEE ADVANCED DEGREE SCHOLARSHIPS

Hispanic Professionals of Greater Milwaukee
Attn: Advanced Degree Scholarship Program
P.O. Box 510545
Milwaukee, WI 53203
(414) 384-3700, ext. 208
E-mail: Griselda.aldrete@hpgm.org
Web: www.hpgm.org

Summary To provide financial assistance to residents of Wisconsin who are of Hispanic heritage and working on an advanced degree in any state.

Eligibility This program is open to residents of Wisconsin who are U.S. citizens of Hispanic heritage. Applicants must be enrolled at least half time at an accredited college or institute in any state and working on an advanced degree (e.g., M.B.A., M.A., M.S., Ph.D.). Along with their application, they must submit a 1,000-word essay on a time when they did something unexpected in their professional and/or educational career. Selection is based on that essay, academic record, community service, and academic plans and career goals.

Financial Data Stipends are $2,500 for students who have a GPA of at least 3.0 or $10,000 if their GPA is 3.5 or higher.

Duration 1 year.

Additional data Recipients are required to volunteer at 1 event held by the sponsoring organization.

Number awarded At least 4 each year.

Deadline June of each year.

[687]
HISPANIC SCHOLARSHIP FUND GENERAL COLLEGE SCHOLARSHIPS

Hispanic Scholarship Fund
Attn: Selection Committee
1411 West 190th Street, Suite 325
Gardena, CA 90248
Toll Free: (877) HSF-INFO   E-mail: scholar1@hsf.net
Web: www.hsf.net

Summary To provide financial assistance for college or graduate school to Hispanic American students.

Eligibility This program is open to U.S. citizens and permanent residents (must have a permanent resident card or a passport stamped I-551). Applicants must be of Hispanic heritage and enrolled or planning to enroll full time in a degree program at an accredited community college, 4-year university, or graduate school in the United States, Puerto Rico, Guam, or the U.S. Virgin Islands. They must have a GPA of 3.0 or higher and have applied for federal financial aid. Selection is based on academic achievement, personal strengths, leadership, and financial need.

Financial Data Stipends normally range from $1,000 to $5,000 per year.

Duration 1 year; recipients may reapply.

Additional data Since this program began in 1975, more than $334 million has been awarded to nearly 100,000 Hispanic students.

Number awarded Varies each year; recently, this program awarded more than $29 million in scholarships to more than 4,300 students.

Deadline December of each year.

[688]
HOLLY A. CORNELL SCHOLARSHIP

American Water Works Association
Attn: Scholarship Coordinator
6666 West Quincy Avenue
Denver, CO 80235-3098
(303) 794-7771   Toll Free: (800) 926-7337
Fax: (303) 347-0804   E-mail: lmoody@awwa.org
Web: www.awwa.org

Summary To provide financial assistance to outstanding minority and female students interested in working on an master's degree in the field of water supply and treatment.

Eligibility This program is open to minority and female students working on a master's degree in the field of water supply and treatment at a college or university in Canada, Guam, Mexico, Puerto Rico, or the United States. Students who have been accepted into graduate school but have not yet begun graduate study are encouraged to apply. Applicants must submit a 2-page resume, official transcripts, 3 letters of recommendation, a proposed curriculum of study, a 1-page statement of educational plans and career objectives demonstrating an interest in the drinking water field, and a 3-page proposed plan of research. Selection is based on academic record and potential to provide leadership in the field of water supply and treatment.

Financial Data The stipend is $7,500.

Duration 1 year; nonrenewable.

Additional data Funding for this program comes from the consulting firm CH2M Hill.

Number awarded 1 each year.

Deadline January of each year.

[689]
HOWARD MAYER BROWN FELLOWSHIP

American Musicological Society
6010 College Station
Brunswick, ME 04011-8451
(207) 798-4243   Toll Free: (877) 679-7648
Fax: (207) 798-4254   E-mail: ams@ams-net.org
Web: www.ams-net.org/fellowships/hmb.php

Summary To provide financial assistance to Hispanic American and other minority students who are working on a doctoral degree in the field of musicology.

Eligibility This program is open to members of minority groups historically underrepresented in the field of musicology. In the United States, that includes African Americans, Native Americans, Hispanic Americans, and Asian Americans. In Canada, it refers to visible minorities. Applicants must have completed at least 1 year of full-time academic work at an institution with a graduate program in musicology and be planning to complete a Ph.D. degree in the field. There are no restrictions on research area, age, or sex. Candidates must submit a personal statement summarizing their musical and academic background and stating why they wish to work on an advanced degree in musicology, letters of support from 3 faculty members, a curriculum vitae, and samples of their work (such as term papers or published material). U.S. or Canadian citizenship or permanent resident status is required.

Financial Data The stipend is $20,000.

Duration 1 year; nonrenewable.

Additional data This fellowship was first awarded in 1995.

Number awarded 1 each year.

Deadline November of each year.

[690]
HUGH J. ANDERSEN MEMORIAL SCHOLARSHIPS

National Medical Fellowships, Inc.
Attn: Scholarship Program
347 Fifth Avenue, Suite 510
New York, NY 10016
(212) 483-8880   Toll Free: (877) NMF-1DOC
Fax: (212) 483-8897 E-mail: scholarships@nmfonline.org
Web: www.nmfonline.org

Summary To provide financial assistance to Hispanic American and other underrepresented minority medical students who reside or attend school in Minnesota.

Eligibility This program is open to African Americans, Hispanics/Latinos, Native Americans, Vietnamese, Cambodians, and Pacific Islanders who are entering the second or third year of medical school. Applicants must be Minnesota residents enrolled in an accredited U.S. medical school or residents of other states attending medical school in Minnesota. Selection is based on leadership, community service, and financial need.

Financial Data The award is $2,500.

Duration 1 year.

Additional data This program began in 1982.

Number awarded Up to 5 each year.

Deadline September of each year.

[691]
IBM PHD FELLOWSHIP PROGRAM

IBM Corporation
Attn: University Relations
1133 Westchester Avenue
White Plains, NY 10604
Toll Free: (800) IBM-4YOU   TDD: (800) IBM-3383
E-mail: phdfellow@us.ibm.com
Web: www.research.ibm.com

Summary To provide funding and work experience to students (particularly minorities, women, and others who contribute to diversity) who are working on a Ph.D. in a research area of broad interest to IBM.

Eligibility Students nominated for this fellowship should be enrolled full time at an accredited college or university in any country and should have completed at least 1 year of graduate study in computer science or engineering, electrical or mechanical engineering, physical sciences (chemistry, material sciences, physics), mathematical sciences, public sector and business sciences, or service science, management, and engineering (SSME). Focus areas that receive special consideration include technology that creates new business or social value, innovative software, new types of computers, or interdisciplinary projects that create social and business value. Applicants should be planning a career in research.

Nominations must be made by a faculty member and endorsed by the department head. The program values diversity, and encourages nominations of women, minorities, and others who contribute to that diversity. Selection is based on the applicants' potential for research excellence, the degree to which their technical interests align with those of IBM, and academic progress to date. Preference is given to students who have had an IBM internship or have closely collaborated with technical or services people from IBM.

Financial Data Fellowships pay tuition, fees, and a stipend of $17,500 per year.

Duration 1 year; may be renewed up to 2 additional years, provided the recipient is renominated, interacts with IBM's technical community, and demonstrates continued progress and achievement.

Additional data Recipients are offered an internship at 1 of the IBM Research Division laboratories and are given an IBM computer.

Number awarded Varies each year; recently, 57 of these scholarships were awarded.

Deadline October of each year.

[692]
ILLINOIS NURSES FOUNDATION CENTENNIAL SCHOLARSHIP

Illinois Nurses Association
Attn: Illinois Nurses Foundation
105 West Adams Street, Suite 1420
Chicago, IL 60603
(312) 419-2900   Fax: (312) 419-2920
E-mail: inf@illinoisnurses.com
Web: www.illinoisnurses.com

Summary To provide financial assistance to nursing undergraduate and graduate students who are Hispanic American or members of other underrepresented groups.

Eligibility This program is open to students working on an associate, bachelor's, or master's degree at an accredited NLNAC or CCNE school of nursing. Applicants must be members of a group underrepresented in nursing (African Americans, Hispanics, American Indians, Asians, and males). Undergraduates must have earned a passing grade in all nursing courses taken to date and have a GPA of 2.85 or higher. Graduate students must have completed at least 12 semester hours of graduate work and have a GPA of 3.0 or higher. All applicants must be willing to 1) act as a spokesperson to other student groups on the value of the scholarship to continuing their nursing education; and 2) be profiled in any media or marketing materials developed by the Illinois Nurses Foundation. Along with their application, they must submit a narrative of 250 to 500 words on how they, as nurses, plan to affect policy at either the state or national level that impacts on nursing or health care generally, or how they believe they will impact the nursing profession in general.

Financial Data A stipend is awarded (amount not specified).

Duration 1 year.

Number awarded 1 or more each year.

Deadline March of each year.

[693]
INITIATIVE TO RECRUIT A DIVERSE WORKFORCE

Association of Research Libraries
Attn: Director of Diversity Programs
21 Dupont Circle, N.W., Suite 800
Washington, DC 20036
(202) 296-2296   Fax: (202) 872-0884
E-mail: mpuente@arl.org
Web: www.arl.org/diversity/init/index.shtml

Summary   To provide financial assistance to Hispanic Americans and other minorities who are interested in preparing for a career as an academic or research librarian.

Eligibility   This program is open to members of racial and ethnic minority groups that are underrepresented as professionals in academic and research libraries (American Indian or Alaska Native, Asian, Black or African American, Native Hawaiian or other Pacific Islander, or Hispanic or Latino). Preference is given to students who have an academic background in a discipline of science, technology, engineering, or mathematics (STEM). Applicants must be interested in working on an M.L.I.S. degree at an ALA-accredited program. They must be citizens or permanent residents of the United States (including Puerto Rico) or Canada. Along with their application, they must submit a 400-word essay on what attracts them to a career in a research library. The essays are judged on clarity and content of form, clear goals and benefits, enthusiasm, potential growth perceived, and professional goals.

Financial Data   The stipend is $5,000 per year.

Duration   2 years.

Additional data   This program began in 2000. Funding is currently provided by the Institute of Museum and Library Services and by the contributions of 52 libraries that are members of the Association of Research Libraries (ARL). Recipients who do not have academic training in STEM disciplines must take additional course work to prepare them for a career in those fields.

Number awarded   Varies each year; recently, 14 of these scholarships were awarded.

Deadline   April of each year.

[694]
INSTITUTE FOR SUPPLY MANAGEMENT DOCTORAL DISSERTATION GRANT PROGRAM

Institute for Supply Management
Attn: Director, Education and Training
2055 East Centennial Circle
P.O. Box 22160
Tempe, AZ 85285-2160
(480) 752-6276, ext. 3092
Toll Free: (800) 888-6276, ext. 3092
Fax: (480) 752-7890   E-mail: cmendoza@ism.ws
Web: www.ism.ws

Summary   To provide financial support to doctoral candidates (particularly Hispanic Americans, other minorities, women, and students with disabilities) who are conducting dissertation research in purchasing or related fields.

Eligibility   This program is open to doctoral candidates who are working on a Ph.D. or D.B.A. in supply management, supply chain management, business, management, logistics, economics, industrial engineering, or a related field at an accredited university in the United States. International applicants are accepted. Examples of research projects that could be funded include: purchasing and supply management models, methodologies, measurement, supply networks, operations and logistics integration, produce/service innovation, supply relationships, supply's role in corporate success, or strategic development of supply. The research proposal (up to 25 pages) must discuss hypotheses, significance of the study, research methodology, and value of the research to the field of purchasing. The program encourages applications from a diverse population, regardless of gender, race, creed, age, ethnic or national origin, sexual orientation, or disability.

Financial Data   Grants range up to $6,000.

Duration   1 year.

Additional data   The sponsoring organization was previously known as the National Association of Purchasing Management.

Number awarded   Up to 4 each year.

Deadline   January of each year.

[695]
INTEL CORPORATION SCHOLARSHIPS

Society of Women Engineers
Attn: Scholarship Selection Committee
203 North LaSalle Street, Suite 1675
Chicago, IL 60601-1269
(312) 596-5223   Toll Free: (877) SWE-INFO
Fax: (312) 644-8557   E-mail: scholarships@swe.org
Web: societyofwomenengineers.swe.org

Summary   To provide financial assistance to women (particularly Hispanic American and other minority women) who are members of the Society of Women Engineers (SWE) and working on a graduate degree in computer science or specified fields of engineering.

Eligibility   This program is open to SWE members working full time on a graduate degree in computer science or chemical, computer, electrical, industrial, manufacturing, materials, or mechanical engineering. Applicants must have a GPA of 3.5 or higher. Selection is based on merit and financial need. Preference is given to members of groups underrepresented in computer science and engineering and to residents of Arizona, California, Colorado, Massachusetts, New Mexico, Oregon, and Washington. U.S. citizenship or permanent residents status is required.

Financial Data   The stipend is $5,000.

Duration   1 year.

Additional data   This program is sponsored by Intel Corporation.

Number awarded   2 each year.

Deadline   February of each year.

[696]
INTELLECTUAL PROPERTY LAW SECTION WOMEN AND MINORITY SCHOLARSHIP

State Bar of Texas
Attn: Intellectual Property Law Section
c/o Syed K. Fareed, Scholarship Selection Committee
Vinson & Elkins LLP
2801 Via Fortuna, Suite 100
Austin, TX 78746
(512) 542-8400   Fax: (512) 542-8612
E-mail: sfareed@velaw.com
Web: texasbariplaw.org

Summary To provide financial assistance to Hispanic Americans, other minorities, and females who are enrolled at law schools in Texas and plan to practice intellectual property law.

Eligibility This program is open to women and members of minority groups (African Americans, Hispanics, Asian Americans, and Native Americans) from any state who are currently enrolled at an ABA-accredited law school in Texas. Applicants must be planning to practice intellectual property law in Texas. Along with their application, they must submit a 2-page essay explaining why they plan to prepare for a career in intellectual property law in Texas, any qualifications they believe are relevant for their consideration for this scholarship, and (optionally) any issues of financial need they wish to have considered.

Financial Data The stipend is $2,500.

Duration 1 year.

Number awarded 2 each year: 1 to a women and 1 to a minority.

Deadline April of each year.

[697]
INTERFAITH SPIRITUALITY SCHOLARSHIP

Unitarian Universalist Association
Attn: Ministerial Credentialing Office
25 Beacon Street
Boston, MA 02108-2800
(617) 948-6403   Fax: (617) 742-2875
E-mail: mcoadministrator@uua.org
Web: www.uua.org

Summary To provide financial assistance to seminary students (particularly Hispanic Americans and other students of color) who are preparing for the Unitarian Universalist (UU) ministry and are interested in interfaith understanding.

Eligibility This program is open to seminary students who are enrolled full or at least half time in a UU ministerial training program with aspirant or candidate status. Applicants must have demonstrated 1) an interest in and desire to integrate interfaith understanding into their ministry; and 2) a commitment to guiding others on their own spiritual path. Priority is given first to those who have demonstrated outstanding ministerial ability and secondarily to students with the greatest financial need (especially persons of color).

Financial Data The stipend ranges from $1,000 to $15,000 per year.

Duration 1 year.

Number awarded 1 each year.

Deadline April of each year.

[698]
INTERMOUNTAIN SECTION AWWA DIVERSITY SCHOLARSHIP

American Water Works Association-Intermountain
   Section
Attn: Member Services Coordinator
3430 East Danish Road
Sandy, UT 94093
(801) 712-1619, ext. 2   Fax: (801) 487-6699
E-mail: nicoleb@ims-awwa.org
Web: ims-awwa.site-ym.com/group/StudentPO

Summary To provide financial assistance to Hispanic Americans, other minorities, and women who are interested in working on an undergraduate or graduate degree in the field of water quality, supply, and treatment at a university in Idaho or Utah.

Eligibility This program is open to 1) women; and 2) students who identify as Hispanic or Latino, Black or African American, Native Hawaiian or other Pacific Islander, Asian, or American Indian or Alaska Native. Applicants must be entering or enrolled in an undergraduate or graduate program at a college or university in Idaho or Utah that relates to water quality, supply, or treatment. Along with their application, they must submit a 2-page essay on their academic interests and career goals and how those relate to water quality, supply, or treatment. Selection is based on that essay, letters of recommendation, and potential to contribute to the field of water quality, supply, and treatment in the Intermountain West.

Financial Data The stipend is $1,000. The winner also receives a 1-year student membership in the Intermountain Section of the American Water Works Association (AWWA) and a 1-year subscription to *Journal AWWA*.

Duration 1 year; nonrenewable.

Number awarded 1 each year.

Deadline October of each year.

[699]
ISAAC J. "IKE" CRUMBLY MINORITIES IN ENERGY GRANT

American Association of Petroleum Geologists
   Foundation
Attn: Grants-in-Aid Program
1444 South Boulder Avenue
P.O. Box 979
Tulsa, OK 74101-0979
(918) 560-2644   Toll Free: (855) 302-2743
Fax: (918) 560-2642   E-mail: foundation@aapg.org
Web: foundation.aapg.org/gia/crumbly.cfm

Summary To provide funding to Hispanic Americans, other minorities, and women who are in graduate school and interested in conducting research related to earth science aspects of the petroleum industry.

Eligibility This program is open to women and ethnic minorities (Black, Hispanic, Asian, or Native American, including American Indian, Eskimo, Hawaiian, or Samoan) who are working on a master's or doctoral degree. Applicants must be interested in conducting research related to the search for and development of petroleum and energy-minerals resources and to related environmental geology issues. Selection is based on student's academic and employment history (10 points), scientific merit of proposal (30 points), suitability to program objectives (30 points), financial merit of proposal (20 points), and endorsement by faculty or department adviser (10 points).

Financial Data Grants range from $500 to $3,000. Funds are to be applied to research-related expenses (e.g., a summer of field work). They may not be used to purchase capital equipment or to pay salaries, tuition, room, or board.

Duration 1 year. Doctoral candidates may receive a 1-year renewal.

Number awarded 1 each year.

Deadline February of each year.

[700]
JAMES B. MORRIS SCHOLARSHIPS

James B. Morris Scholarship Fund
Attn: Scholarship Selection Committee
P.O. Box 12145
Des Moines, IA 50312
(515) 864-0922
Web: www.morrisscholarship.org

Summary To provide financial assistance to Hispanic American and other minority undergraduate, graduate, and law students from Iowa.

Eligibility This program is open to minority students (African Americans, Asian/Pacific Islanders, Hispanics, or Native Americans) who are interested in working on an undergraduate or graduate degree. Applicants must be either Iowa residents attending a college or university anywhere in the United States or non-Iowa residents who are attending a college or university in Iowa. Along with their application, they must submit an essay of 250 to 500 words on why they are applying for this scholarship, activities or organizations in which they are involved, and their future plans. Selection is based on the essay, academic achievement (GPA of 2.5 or higher), community service, and financial need. U.S. citizenship is required.

Financial Data The stipend ranges from $1,000 to $2,500 per year.

Duration 1 year; may be renewed.

Additional data This fund was established in 1978 in honor of the J.B. Morris family, who founded the Iowa branch of the National Association for the Advancement of Colored People and published the *Iowa Bystander* newspaper. The program includes the Ann Chapman Scholarships, the Vincent Chapman, Sr. Scholarships, and the Brittany Hall Memorial Scholarships.

Number awarded Varies each year; recently, 19 of these scholarships were awarded.

Deadline March of each year.

[701]
JAMES CARLSON MEMORIAL SCHOLARSHIP

Oregon Student Access Commission
Attn: Grants and Scholarships Division
1500 Valley River Drive, Suite 100
Eugene, OR 97401-2146
(541) 687-7395　　Toll Free: (800) 452-8807, ext. 7395
Fax: (541) 687-7414　　TDD: (800) 735-2900
E-mail: awardinfo@osac.state.or.us
Web: www.oregonstudentaid.gov/scholarships.aspx

Summary To provide financial assistance to Oregon residents from diverse environments (including Hispanic Americans) who are majoring in education on the undergraduate or graduate school level at a school in any state.

Eligibility This program is open to residents of Oregon who are U.S. citizens or permanent residents and enrolled at a college or university in any state. Applicants must be either 1) college seniors or fifth-year students majoring in elementary or secondary education; or 2) graduate students working on an elementary or secondary certificate. Full-time enrollment and financial need are required. Priority is given to 1) students who come from diverse environments and submit an essay of 250 to 350 words on their experience living or working in diverse environments; 2) dependents of members of the Oregon Education Association; and 3) applicants committed to teaching autistic children.

Financial Data Stipends for scholarships offered by the Oregon Student Access Commission (OSAC) range from $200 to $10,000 but recently averaged $2,300.

Duration 1 year.

Additional data This program is administered by the OSAC with funds provided by the Oregon Community Foundation.

Number awarded Varies each year; recently, 3 of these scholarships were awarded.

Deadline February of each year.

[702]
JAMES W. STOUDT SCHOLARSHIPS

Pennsylvania Bar Association
Attn: Foundation
100 South Street
P.O. Box 186
Harrisburg, PA 17108-0186
(717) 213-2501　　Toll Free: (888) 238-3036
Fax: (717) 213-2548　　E-mail: info@pabarfoundation.org
Web: www.pabarfoundation.org

Summary To provide financial assistance to Hispanic American and other residents of Pennsylvania who are attending law school in the state.

Eligibility This program is open to residents of Pennsylvania who are currently enrolled in the second year (or third year of a 4- or 5-year law school program) at a law school in the state. Applicants must be members of the Pennsylvania Bar Association student division. Some of the awards are reserved for students who are members of groups historically underrepresented in the legal profession (African Americans, Hispanic Americans, and Native Americans). Along with their application, they must submit a 500-word essay explaining how they plan to demonstrate their potential for making a contribution to society and the legal profession. Selection is based on that essay, academic achievement, and financial need.

Financial Data The stipend is $3,000.

Duration 1 year.

Number awarded 4 each year, of which 2 are reserved for underrepresented minority students.

Deadline November of each year.

[703]
JEANNE SPURLOCK RESEARCH FELLOWSHIP IN SUBSTANCE ABUSE AND ADDICTION FOR MINORITY MEDICAL STUDENTS

American Academy of Child and Adolescent Psychiatry
Attn: Department of Research, Training, and Education
3615 Wisconsin Avenue, N.W.
Washington, DC 20016-3007
(202) 587-9663   Fax: (202) 966-5894
E-mail: training@aacap.org
Web: www.aacap.org

Summary To provide funding to Hispanic American and other minority medical students who are interested in working during the summer on the topics of drug abuse and addiction with a child and adolescent psychiatrist researcher-mentor.

Eligibility This program is open to African American, Asian American, Native American, Alaska Native, Mexican American, Hispanic, and Pacific Islander students in accredited U.S. medical schools. Applicants must present a plan for a program of research training in drug abuse and addiction that involves significant contact with a mentor who is an experienced child and adolescent psychiatrist researcher. The plan should include program planning discussions; instruction in research planning and implementation; regular meetings with the mentor, laboratory director, and research group; and assigned readings. The mentor must be a member of the American Academy of Child and Adolescent Psychiatry (AACAP). Research assignments may include responsibility for part of the observation or evaluation, developing specific aspects of the research mechanisms, conducting interviews or tests, using rating scales, and psychological or cognitive testing of subjects. The training plan also should include discussion of ethical issues in research, such as protocol development, informed consent, collection and storage of raw data, safeguarding data, bias in analyzing data, plagiarism, protection of patients, and ethical treatment of animals. U.S. citizenship or permanent resident status is required.

Financial Data The stipend is $4,000. Fellows also receive reimbursement of travel expenses to attend the annual meeting of the American Academy of Child and Adolescent Psychiatry.

Duration 12 weeks during the summer.

Additional data Upon completion of the training program, the student is required to submit a brief paper summarizing the research experience. The fellowship pays expenses for the fellow to attend the academy's annual meeting and present this paper. This program is co-sponsored by the National Institute on Drug Abuse.

Number awarded Up to 5 each year.

Deadline February of each year.

[704]
JIM MCKAY SCHOLARSHIP PROGRAM

National Collegiate Athletic Association
Attn: Jim McKay Scholarship Program Staff Liaison
700 West Washington Street
P.O. Box 6222
Indianapolis, IN 46206-6222
(317) 917-6222   Fax: (317) 917-6888
E-mail: lthomas@ncaa.org
Web: www.ncaa.org

Summary To provide financial assistance to student-athletes (particularly Hispanic Americans, other minorities, and women) who are interested in attending graduate school to prepare for a career in sports communications.

Eligibility This program is open to college seniors planning to enroll full time in a graduate degree program and to students already enrolled full time in graduate study at an institution that is a member of the National Collegiate Athletic Association (NCAA). Applicants must have competed in intercollegiate athletics as a member of a varsity team at an NCAA member institution and have an overall undergraduate cumulative GPA of 3.5 or higher. They must be preparing for a career in the sports communications industry. Women and minorities are especially encouraged to apply. Neither financial need nor U.S. citizenship are required. Nominations must be submitted by the faculty athletics representative or chief academic officer at the institution in which the student is or was an undergraduate.

Financial Data The stipend is $10,000.

Duration 1 year; nonrenewable.

Additional data This program began in 2008.

Number awarded 2 each year: 1 female and 1 male.

Deadline January of each year.

[705]
JOHN A. MAYES SCHOLARSHIP

National Athletic Trainers' Association
Attn: Ethnic Diversity Advisory Committee
2952 Stemmons Freeway, Suite 200
Dallas, TX 75247-6103
(214) 532-8802   Toll Free: (800) 879-6282
Fax: (214) 637-2206
Web: www.nata.org/edac/John-A-Mayes-Scholarship

Summary To provide financial aid to Hispanic American and other ethnically diverse graduate students who are preparing for a career as an athletic trainer.

Eligibility This program is open to members of ethnically diverse groups who have been accepted into an entry-level master's athletic training degree program or into a doctoral-level athletic training and/or sports medicine degree program. Applicants must be sponsored by a certified athletic trainer who is a member of the National Athletic Trainers' Association (NATA). They must have a cumulative GPA of 3.2 or higher. First priority is given to a student working on an entry-level athletic training master's degree; second priority is given to a student entering the second year of an athletic training master's degree program; third priority is given to a student working on a doctoral degree in athletic training or sports medicine. Special consideration is given to applicants who have been members of NATA for at least 2 years.

Financial Data The stipend is $2,300.

Duration 1 year.

Additional data This program began in 2009.

Number awarded 1 each year.

Deadline February of each year.

[706]
JOHN AND MURIEL LANDIS SCHOLARSHIPS

American Nuclear Society
Attn: Scholarship Coordinator
555 North Kensington Avenue
La Grange Park, IL 60526-5535
(708) 352-6611   Toll Free: (800) 323-3044
Fax: (708) 352-0499   E-mail: outreach@ans.org
Web: www.new.ans.org/honors/scholarships

Summary To provide financial assistance to undergraduate or graduate students (particularly Hispanic Americans, other minorities, and women) who are interested in preparing for a career in nuclear-related fields and can demonstrate financial need.

Eligibility This program is open to undergraduate and graduate students at colleges or universities located in the United States who are preparing for, or planning to prepare for, a career in nuclear science, nuclear engineering, or a nuclear-related field. Qualified high school seniors are also eligible. Applicants must have greater than average financial need and have experienced circumstances that render them disadvantaged. Along with their application, they must submit an essay on their academic and professional goals, experiences that have affected those goals, etc. Selection is based on that essay, academic achievement, letters of recommendation, and financial need. Women and members of minority groups are especially urged to apply. U.S. citizenship is not required.

Financial Data The stipend is $5,000, to be used to cover tuition, books, fees, room, and board.

Duration 1 year; nonrenewable.

Number awarded Up to 9 each year.

Deadline January of each year.

[707]
JOHN HOPE FRANKLIN DISSERTATION FELLOWSHIP

American Philosophical Society
Attn: Committee on Research
104 South Fifth Street
Philadelphia, PA 19106-3387
(215) 440-3429   Fax: (215) 440-3436
E-mail: LMusumeci@amphilsoc.org
Web: www.amphilsoc.org/grants/johnhopefranklin

Summary To provide funding to Hispanic American and other underrepresented minority graduate students conducting research for a doctoral dissertation.

Eligibility This program is open to African American, Hispanic American, and Native American graduate students working on a degree at a Ph.D. granting institution in the United States. Other talented students who have a demonstrated commitment to eradicating racial disparities and enlarging minority representation in academia are also eligible. Applicants must have completed all course work and examinations preliminary to the doctoral dissertation and be able to devote full-time effort, with no teaching obligations, to researching or writing their dissertation. The proposed research should relate to a topic in which the holdings of the Library of the American Philosophical Society (APS) are particularly strong: quantum mechanics, nuclear physics, computer development, the history of genetics and eugenics, the history of medicine, Early American political and cultural history, natural history in the 18th and 19th centuries, the development of cultural anthropology, or American Indian culture and linguistics.

Financial Data The grant is $25,000; an additional grant of $5,000 is provided to support the cost of residency in Philadelphia.

Duration 12 months, to begin at the discretion of the grantee.

Additional data This program began in 2005. Recipients are expected to spend a significant amount of time in residence at the APS Library.

Number awarded 1 each year.

Deadline March of each year.

[708]
JOHN MCLENDON MEMORIAL MINORITY POSTGRADUATE SCHOLARSHIP AWARD

National Association of Collegiate Directors of Athletics
Attn: NACDA Foundation
24651 Detroit Road
Westlake, OH 44145
(440) 788-7475   Fax: (440) 892-4007
E-mail: jbouyer@nacda.com
Web: www.nacda.com/mclendon/scholarship.html

Summary To provide financial assistance to Hispanic American and other minority college seniors who are interested in working on a graduate degree in athletics administration.

Eligibility This program is open to minority college students who are seniors, are attending school on a full-time basis, have a GPA of 3.2 or higher, intend to attend graduate school to earn a degree in athletics administration, and are involved in college or community activities. Also eligible are college graduates who have at least 2 years' experience in an athletics administration position. Candidates must be nominated by an official of a member institution of the National Association of Collegiate Directors of Athletics (NACDA) or (for college graduates) a supervisor.

Financial Data The stipend is $10,000.

Duration 1 year.

Additional data Recipients must maintain full-time status during the senior year to retain their eligibility. They must attend NACDA-member institutions.

Number awarded 5 each year.

Deadline Nominations must be submitted by April of each year.

[709]
JOHN STANFORD MEMORIAL WLMA SCHOLARSHIP

Washington Library Media Association
c/o Susan Kaphammer, Scholarship Chair
521 North 24th Avenue
Yakima, WA 98902
(509) 972-5999   E-mail: kaphammers@wvsd208.org
Web: www.wlma.org/scholarships

Summary To provide financial assistance to Hispanic Americans and other ethnic minorities in Washington who are interested in attending a school in any state to prepare for a library media career.

Eligibility This program is open to residents of Washington who are working toward a library media endorsement or graduate degree in the field at a school in any state. Applicants must be members of an ethnic minority group. They must be working or planning to work in a school library. Along with their application, they must submit a 3-page letter that includes a description of themselves and their achievements to date, their interest and work in the library field, their personal and professional activities, their goals and plans for further education and professional development, how they expect the studies funded by this award to impact their professional practice and contributions to the Washington school library community, and their financial need.

Financial Data The stipend is $1,000.

Duration 1 year.

Number awarded 1 each year.

Deadline April of each year.

[710]
JOHNSON & JOHNSON-AMERICAN ASSOCIATION OF COLLEGES OF NURSING MINORITY NURSE FACULTY SCHOLARS PROGRAM

American Association of Colleges of Nursing
One Dupont Circle, N.W., Suite 530
Washington, DC 20036
(202) 463-6930 Fax: (202) 785-8320
E-mail: scholarship@aacn.nche.edu
Web: www.aacn.nche.edu/students/scholarships

Summary To provide funding to Hispanic American and other minority students who are working on a graduate degree in nursing to prepare for a career as a faculty member.

Eligibility This program is open to members of racial and ethnic minority groups (Alaska Native, American Indian, Black or African American, Native Hawaiian or other, Pacific Islander, Hispanic or Latino, or Asian American) who are enrolled full time at a school of nursing. Applicants must be working on 1) a doctoral nursing degree (e.g., Ph.D., D.N.P.); or 2) a clinically-focused master's degree in nursing (e.g., M.S.N., M.S.). They must commit to 1) serve in a teaching capacity at a nursing school for a minimum of 1 year for each year of support they receive; 2) provide 6-month progress reports to the American Association of Colleges of Nursing (AACN) throughout the entire funding process and during the payback period; 3) agree to work with an assigned mentor throughout the period of the scholarship grant; and 4) attend an annual leadership training conference to connect with their mentor, fellow scholars, and colleagues. Selection is based on ability to contribute to nursing education; leadership potential; development of goals reflecting education, research, and professional involvement; ability to work with a mentor/adviser throughout the award period; proposed research and/or practice projects that are significant and show commitment to improving nursing education and clinical nursing practice in the United States; proposed research and/or clinical education professional development plan that exhibits quality, feasibility, and innovativeness; and evidence of commitment to a career in nursing education and to recruiting, mentoring, and retaining future underrepresented minority nurses. Preference is given to students enrolled in doctoral nursing programs. Applicants must be U.S. citizens, permanent residents, refugees, or qualified immigrants.

Financial Data The stipend is $18,000 per year. The award includes $1,500 that is held in escrow to cover the costs for the recipient to attend the leadership training conference. Recipients are required to sign a letter of commitment that they will provide 1 year of service in a teaching capacity at a nursing school in the United States for each year of support received; if they fail to complete that service requirement, they must repay all funds received.

Duration 1 year; may be renewed 1 additional year.

Additional data This program, established in 2007, is sponsored by the Johnson & Johnson Campaign for Nursing's Future.

Number awarded 5 each year.

Deadline April of each year.

[711]
JOSE MARTI SCHOLARSHIP CHALLENGE GRANT FUND

Florida Department of Education
Attn: Office of Student Financial Assistance
325 West Gaines Street
Tallahassee, FL 32399-0400
(850) 410-5160 Toll Free: (888) 827-2004
Fax: (850) 487-1809 E-mail: osfa@fldoe.org
Web: www.floridastudentfinancialaid.org

Summary To provide financial assistance to Hispanic American high school seniors and graduate students in Florida.

Eligibility This program is open to Florida residents of Spanish culture who were born in, or whose natural parent was born in, Mexico or a Hispanic country of the Caribbean, Central America, or South America. Applicants must be citizens or eligible noncitizens of the United States, be enrolled or planning to enroll as full-time undergraduate or graduate students at an eligible postsecondary school in Florida, be able to demonstrate financial need as determined by a nationally-recognized needs analysis service, and have earned a cumulative GPA of 3.0 or higher in high school or, if a graduate school applicant, in undergraduate course work.

Financial Data The maximum grant is $2,000 per academic year. Available funds are contingent upon matching contributions from private sources.

Duration 1 year; may be renewed if the student maintains full-time enrollment and a GPA of 3.0 or higher and continues to demonstrate financial need.

Number awarded Varies each year; recently, this program awarded 11 new and 27 renewal grants.

Deadline March of each year.

[712]
JOSEPH B. GITTLER AWARD

American Psychological Foundation
750 First Street, N.E.
Washington, DC 20002-4242
(202) 336-5843 Fax: (202) 336-5812
E-mail: foundation@apa.org
Web: www.apa.org/apf/funding/gittler.aspx

Summary To recognize and reward scholars and graduate students in psychology (particularly Hispanic Americans, other minorities, women, and individuals with disabilities) whose work has transformed the philosophical foundations of the discipline.

Eligibility This award is available to scholars and graduate students whose body of work or whose individual work has transformed the philosophical foundations of psychological knowledge. Self-nominations are welcome. Selection is based on conformance with stated program goals and magnitude of contributions The sponsor encourages nominations of individuals who represent diversity in race, ethnicity, gender, age, disability, and sexual orientation.

Financial Data The award is $10,000.

Duration The award is presented annually.

Additional data This award was first presented in 2008.

Number awarded 1 each year.

Deadline Nominations must be submitted by May of each year.

[713]
JOSEPH L. FISHER DOCTORAL DISSERTATION FELLOWSHIPS

Resources for the Future
Attn: Coordinator for Academic Programs
1616 P Street, N.W., Suite 600
Washington, DC 20036-1400
(202) 328-5020   Fax: (202) 939-3460
E-mail: fisher-award@rff.org
Web: www.rff.org

Summary To provide funding to doctoral candidates in economics (particularly Hispanic Americans, other minorities, and women) who are interested in conducting dissertation research on issues related to the environment, natural resources, or energy.

Eligibility This program is open to graduate students in their final year of research on a dissertation related to the environment, natural resources, or energy. Applicants must submit a brief letter of application and a curriculum vitae, a graduate transcript, a 1-page abstract of the dissertation, a technical summary of the dissertation (up to 2,500 words), a letter from their department chair, and 2 letters of recommendation from faculty members on the student's dissertation committee. The technical summary should describe clearly the aim of the dissertation, its significance in relation to the existing literature, and the research methods to be used. Women and minority candidates are strongly encouraged to apply. Non-citizens are eligible if they have proper work and residency documentation.

Financial Data The stipend is $18,000.

Duration 1 academic year.

Additional data It is expected that recipients will not hold other employment during the fellowship period. Recipients must notify Resources for the Future of any financial assistance they receive from any other source for support of doctoral work.

Number awarded 1 to 3 each year.

Deadline February of each year.

[714]
JOSEPHINE AND BENJAMIN WEBBER TRUST SCHOLARSHIPS

Arizona Association of Family and Consumer Sciences
Attn: Webber Trusts Committee
Kathryn L. Hatch
4843 North Via Sonrisa
Tucson, AZ 85718-5724
(502) 577-6109   E-mail: klhatch@u.arizona.edu
Web: ag.arizona.edu/webbertrusts

Summary To provide financial assistance to Hispanic women from mining towns in Arizona who are interested in working on an undergraduate or graduate degree in a field related to family and consumer sciences at a school in the state.

Eligibility This program is open to Hispanic women who reside in the following Arizona mining towns: Ajo, Arizona City, Bisbee, Clifton, Douglas, Duncan, Globe, Green Valley, Hayden, Kingman, Kearny, Mammoth, Morenci, Prescott, Safford, Sahuarita, San Manuel, Seligman, Superior, or Winkelman. If too few female Hispanic residents of those towns apply, the program may be open to 1) non-Hispanic women who live in those towns; and/or 2) Hispanic women who currently live elsewhere in Arizona and whose parents or grandparents had lived or continue to live in those communities. Applicants must be enrolled or planning to enroll at a college or university in Arizona to work on an undergraduate or graduate degree. Eligible fields of study include those in the following categories: foods, nutrition, and/or dietetics; restaurant and food service management; culinary arts; family studies; interior design; family and consumer science education; dietetic education; early childhood education; or apparel and clothing. Financial need is considered in the selection process.

Financial Data Funding at public colleges and universities provides for payment of tuition and fees, books, educational supplies, housing, food, and transportation to and from campus. At private institutions, stipend amounts are equivalent to those at public schools.

Duration 1 year; may be renewed for a total of 8 semesters and 2 summers of undergraduate study or 4 semesters and 2 summers of graduate study.

Additional data This program began in 1980.

Number awarded Varies each year; recently, 5 of these scholarships were awarded.

Deadline March of each year.

[715]
JOSEPHINE FORMAN SCHOLARSHIP

Society of American Archivists
Attn: Chair, Awards Committee
17 North State Street, Suite 1425
Chicago, IL 60602-4061
(312) 606-0722   Toll Free: (866) 722-7858
Fax: (312) 606-0728   E-mail: info@archivists.org
Web: www.archivists.org/recognition

Summary To provide financial assistance to Hispanic American and other minority graduate students working on a degree in archival science.

Eligibility This program is open to members of minority groups (American Indian/Alaska Native, Asian, Black/African

American, Hispanic/Latino, or Native Hawaiian/other Pacific Islander) currently enrolled in or accepted to a graduate program or a multi-course program in archival administration. The program must offer at least 3 courses in archival science and students may have completed no more than half of the credit requirements toward their graduate degree. Selection is based on potential for scholastic and personal achievement and commitment both to the archives profession and to advancing diversity concerns within it. U.S. citizenship or permanent resident status is required.

Financial Data The stipend is $10,000.

Duration 1 year.

Additional data Funding for this program, established in 2011, is provided by the General Commission on Archives and History of the United Methodist Church.

Number awarded 1 each year.

Deadline February of each year.

[716]
JOSIAH MACY JR. FOUNDATION SCHOLARSHIPS

National Medical Fellowships, Inc.
Attn: Scholarship Program
347 Fifth Avenue, Suite 510
New York, NY 10016
(212) 483-8880   Toll Free: (877) NMF-1DOC
Fax: (212) 483-8897 E-mail: scholarships@nmfonline.org
Web: www.nmfonline.org

Summary To provide financial assistance to Hispanic Americans and other underrepresented minority medical students who demonstrate financial need.

Eligibility This program is open to African Americans, Hispanics/Latinos, Native Americans, Vietnamese, Cambodians, and Pacific Islanders who are entering their second or third year of medical school. Selection is based on academic achievement, leadership, community service, and financial need.

Financial Data A stipend is awarded (amount not specified).

Duration 1 year.

Additional data This program is sponsored by the Josiah Macy Jr. Foundation.

Number awarded 4 each year.

Deadline September of each year.

[717]
KALA SINGH MEMORIAL SCHOLARSHIP

American Speech-Language-Hearing Foundation
Attn: Programs Administrator
2200 Research Boulevard
Rockville, MD 20850-3289
(301) 296-8703   Fax: (301) 296-8567
E-mail: foundationprograms@asha.org
Web: www.ashfoundation.org/grants/GraduateScholarships

Summary To provide financial assistance to Hispanic Americans, other minorities, and international students who are interested in working on a graduate degree in communication sciences and disorders.

Eligibility This program is open to full-time international and minority graduate students who are enrolled in communication sciences and disorders programs. Applicants must

submit an essay, up to 5 pages in length, on a topic that relates to the future of leadership in the discipline. Selection is based on academic promise and outstanding academic achievement.

Financial Data The stipend is $5,000. Funds must be used for educational support (e.g., tuition, books, school living expenses), not for personal or conference travel.

Duration The award is granted annually.

Number awarded 1 each year.

Deadline June of each year.

[718]
KATTEN MUCHIN ROSENMAN MINORITY SCHOLARSHIPS

Katten Muchin Rosenman LLP
Attn: Attorney Recruiting Manager
525 West Monroe Street
Chicago, IL 60661-3693
(312) 902-5200   Fax: (312) 902-1060
E-mail: nicole.morden@kattenlaw.com
Web: www.kattenlaw.com/minority-scholarship

Summary To provide financial aid and summer work experience in Chicago or New York City to Hispanic American and other minority law students from any state.

Eligibility This program is open to minority students from any state who have completed their first year of law school. Applicants must have applied for and been accepted as a summer associate at the sponsoring law firm's Chicago or New York office. Along with their application, they must submit 250-word statements on 1) their strongest qualifications for this award; 2) their reasons for preparing for law as a profession; and 3) their views on diversity and how their personal experience and philosophy will be an asset to the firm. Selection is based on academic achievement, leadership experience, and personal qualities that reflect the potential for outstanding contributions to the firm and the legal profession.

Financial Data Participants receive the standard salary for the summer internship and a stipend of $15,000 for the academic year.

Duration 1 year.

Number awarded 2 each year; 1 for an internship in Chicago and 1 for an internship in New York City.

Deadline September of each year.

[719]
KEGLER, BROWN, HILL & RITTER MINORITY MERIT SCHOLARSHIP

Kegler, Brown, Hill & Ritter
Attn: Human Resources Manager
Capitol Square, Suite 1800
65 East State Street
Columbus, OH 43215
(614) 462-5467   Toll Free: (800) 860-7885
Fax: (614) 464-2634
E-mail: ctammaro@keglerbrown.com
Web: www.keglerbrown.com

Summary To provide financial aid and summer work experience at Kegler, Brown, Hill & Ritter in Columbus, Ohio to Hispanic American and other minority students at law schools in any state.

Eligibility This program is open to first-year students of minority descent at law schools in any state. Applicants must be interested in a summer clerkship with the firm following their first year of law school. Along with their application, they must submit brief essays on 1) a major accomplishment that has shaped their life, how it influenced their decision to prepare for a career in law, and how it prepared them for a future as a lawyer; 2) what diversity means to them; 3) why they have applied for the scholarship; and 4) any training and/or experience they believe to be relevant to the clerkship. Selection is based on academic performance, accomplishments, activities, and potential contributions to the legal community.

Financial Data The program provides a $5,000 stipend for law school tuition and a paid summer clerkship position.

Duration 1 year.

Additional data This program began in 2004.

Number awarded 2 each year.

Deadline January of each year.

[720]
KENNEDY CENTER AMERICAN COLLEGE THEATER FESTIVAL LATINO PLAYWRITING AWARD

John F. Kennedy Center for the Performing Arts
Education Department
Attn: Kennedy Center American College Theater Festival
2700 F Street, N.W.
Washington, DC 20566
(202) 416-8857   Fax: (202) 416-8860
E-mail: KCACTF@kennedy-center.org
Web: www.kcactf.org

Summary To recognize and reward outstanding plays by Latino student playwrights.

Eligibility Latino students at any accredited junior or senior college in the United States are eligible to compete, provided their college agrees to participate in the Kennedy Center American College Theater Festival (KCACTF). Undergraduate students must be carrying at least 6 semester hours, graduate students must be enrolled in at least 3 semester hours, and continuing part-time students must be enrolled in a regular degree or certificate program. This award is presented to the best student-written play by a Latino.

Financial Data The prizes are $1,000 for first place and $500 for second place.

Duration The award is presented annually.

Additional data This award, first presented in 2000, is part of the Michael Kanin Playwriting Awards Program. The sponsoring college or university must pay a registration fee of $275 for each production.

Number awarded 2 each year.

Deadline November of each year.

[721]
KENTUCKY LIBRARY ASSOCIATION SCHOLARSHIP FOR MINORITY STUDENTS

Kentucky Library Association
c/o Executive Secretary
1501 Twilight Trail
Frankfort, KY 40601
(502) 223-5322   Fax: (502) 223-4937
E-mail: info@kylibasn.org
Web: www.klaonline.org/scholarships965.cfm

Summary To provide financial assistance to Hispanic Americans and other minorities who are residents of Kentucky or attending school there and are working on an undergraduate or graduate degree in library science.

Eligibility This program is open to members of minority groups (defined as American Indian, Alaskan Native, Black, Hispanic, Pacific Islander, or other ethnic group) who are entering or continuing at a graduate library school accredited by the American Library Association (ALA) or an undergraduate library program accredited by the National Council of Teacher Education (NCATE). Applicants must be residents of Kentucky or a student in a library program in the state. Along with their application, they must submit a statement of their career objectives, why they have chosen librarianship as a career, and their reasons for applying for this scholarship. Selection is based on that statement, cumulative undergraduate and graduate GPA (if applicable), academic merit and potential, and letters of recommendation. U.S. citizenship or permanent resident status is required.

Financial Data The stipend is $1,000.

Duration 1 year; nonrenewable.

Number awarded 1 or more each year.

Deadline June of each year.

[722]
KENTUCKY MINORITY EDUCATOR RECRUITMENT AND RETENTION SCHOLARSHIPS

Kentucky Department of Education
Attn: Minority Educator Recruitment and Retention
500 Mero Street, 8th Floor
Frankfort, KY 40601
(502) 564-1479, ext. 4014   Fax: (502) 564-6952
TDD: (502) 564-4970
E-mail: monica.davis@education.ky.gov
Web: www.education.ky.gov

Summary To provide funding to Hispanic American and other minority undergraduate and graduate students enrolled in Kentucky public institutions who want to become teachers.

Eligibility This program is open to residents of Kentucky who are undergraduate or graduate students pursuing initial teacher certification at a public university or community college in the state. Applicants must have a GPA of 2.5 or higher and either maintain full-time enrollment or be a part-time student within 18 semester hours of receiving a teacher education degree. They must be U.S. citizens and meet the Kentucky definition of a minority student.

Financial Data Stipends are $5,000 per year at the 8 state universities in Kentucky or $2,000 per year at community and technical colleges. This is a scholarship/loan program. Recipients are required to teach 1 semester in Kentucky for each semester or summer term the scholarship is received. If they fail to fulfill that requirement, the scholarship converts to a loan with severe penalties for non-payment.

Duration 1 year; may be renewed up to 3 additional years.

Additional data The Kentucky General Assembly established this program in 1992.

Number awarded Varies each year.

Deadline Each state college of teacher education sets its own deadline.

[723]
KINESIS SCHOLARSHIPS

Kinesis Foundation
89 de Diego Avenue
PMB 607, Suite 105
San Juan, PR 00927
(787) 772-8269   E-mail: info@kinesispr.org
Web: kinesispr.org/becasuperior.html

Summary To provide financial assistance to residents of Puerto Rico who are entering an undergraduate or graduate program at a college outside the Commonwealth.

Eligibility This program is open to high school seniors and graduates who have been residents of Puerto Rico for at least 2 years. Applicants must be entering a bachelor's, master's, or doctoral degree program at a university on the mainland or in another country. They must have a GPA of 3.5 or higher and be able to demonstrate financial need. Along with their application, they must submit a 200-word essay on their academic goals and how they can contribute to the future of Puerto Rico.

Financial Data Stipends average $5,000. Funds are disbursed directly to the recipient's university.

Duration 1 year; may be renewed, provided the recipient continues to meet eligibility requirements.

Number awarded Approximately 100 each year.

Deadline May of each year.

[724]
KING & SPALDING DIVERSITY FELLOWSHIP PROGRAM

King & Spalding
Attn: Diversity Fellowship Program
1180 Peachtree Street
Atlanta, GA 30309
(404) 572-4643   Fax: (404) 572-5100
E-mail: fellowship@kslaw.com
Web: www.kslaw.com/careers/Law-Students

Summary To provide financial aid and summer work experience at U.S. offices of King & Spalding to Hispanic American and other law students who will contribute to the diversity of the legal community.

Eligibility This program is open to second-year law students who 1) come from a minority ethnic or racial group (American Indian/Alaskan Native, Asian American/Pacific Islander, Black/African American, Hispanic, or multi-racial); 2) are a member of the gay, lesbian, bisexual, or transgender (GLBT) community; or 3) have a disability. Applicants must receive an offer of a clerkship at a U.S. office of King & Spalding during their second-year summer. Along with their application, they must submit a 500-word personal statement that

describes their talents, qualities, and experiences and how they would contribute to the diversity of the firm.

Financial Data Fellows receive a stipend of $10,000 for their second year of law school and a paid summer associate clerkship at a U.S. office of the firm during the following summer.

Duration 1 year.

Additional data The firm's U.S. offices are located in Atlanta, Austin, Charlotte, Houston, New York, San Francisco, Silicon Valley, and Washington.

Number awarded Up to 4 each year.

Deadline August of each year.

[725]
KIRKLAND & ELLIS LLP DIVERSITY FELLOWSHIP PROGRAM

Kirkland & Ellis LLP
Attn: Attorney Recruiting Manager
333 South Hope Street
Los Angeles, CA 90071
(213) 680-8436   Fax: (213) 680-8500
E-mail: cherie.beffa@kirkland.com
Web: www.kirkland.com

Summary To provide financial assistance and summer work experience at an office of Kirkland & Ellis to Hispanic American and other minority law students from any state.

Eligibility This program is open to second-year students at ABA-accredited law schools who meet the racial and ethnic categories established by the Equal Employment Opportunity Commission. Applicants must have been accepted as summer associates at a domestic office of the sponsoring law firm (Chicago, Los Angeles, New York, Palo Alto, San Francisco, Washington, D.C.) and be likely to practice at 1 of those offices after graduation. Along with their application, they must submit a 1-page personal statement that describes ways in which they have promoted and will continue to promote diversity in the legal community, along with their interest in the firm. Selection is based on merit.

Financial Data Fellows receive a salary during their summer associateship and a $25,000 stipend at the conclusion of the summer. Stipend funds are to be used for payment of educational expenses during the third year of law school.

Duration 1 year.

Additional data This program, which replaced the Kirkland & Ellis Minority Fellowship Program, was established at 14 law schools in 2004. In 2006, it began accepting applications from students at all ABA-accredited law schools.

Number awarded Varies each year; recently, 10 of these fellowships were awarded. Since the program began, it has awarded 121 fellowships worth more than $1.9 million.

Deadline August of each year.

[726]
KPMG MINORITY ACCOUNTING DOCTORAL SCHOLARSHIPS

KPMG Foundation
Attn: Scholarship Administrator
Three Chestnut Ridge Road
Montvale, NJ 07645-0435
(201) 307-7161 Fax: (201) 624-7763
E-mail: us-kpmgfoundation@kpmg.com
Web: www.kpmgfoundation.org/foundinit.asp

Summary To provide funding to Hispanic American and other underrepresented minority students working on a doctoral degree in accounting.

Eligibility Applicants must be African Americans, Hispanic Americans, or Native Americans. They must be U.S. citizens or permanent residents and accepted or enrolled in a full-time accounting doctoral program. Along with their application, they must submit a brief letter explaining their reason for working on a Ph.D. in accounting.

Financial Data The stipend is $10,000 per year.

Duration 1 year; may be renewed up to 4 additional years.

Additional data These funds are not intended to replace funds normally made available by the recipient's institution. The foundation recommends that the recipient's institution also award, to the recipient, a $5,000 annual stipend, a teaching or research assistantship, and a waiver of tuition and fees.

Number awarded 12 each year.

Deadline April of each year.

[727]
LA BECA GUADALUPANA

National Association of Pastoral Musicians
Attn: NPM Scholarships
962 Wayne Avenue, Suite 210
Silver Spring, MD 20910-4461
(240) 247-3000 Toll Free: (855) 207-0293
Fax: (240) 247-3001 E-mail: npmsing@npm.org
Web: www.npm.org/Membership/scholarship.htm

Summary To provide financial assistance to Latino/a undergraduate or graduate student members of the National Association of Pastoral Musicians.

Eligibility This program is open to Latino/a members of the association who are enrolled part or full time in an undergraduate or graduate degree program. They must be studying in a field related to pastoral music, be able to demonstrate financial need, and be intending to work for at least 2 years in the field of pastoral music following graduation. Applicants must submit 1) documentation of financial need; 2) a 5-minute performance CD of themselves or the choir-ensemble they direct; and 3) a brief essay explaining their definition of the term "pastoral musician."

Financial Data The stipend is $2,000 per year. Funds must be used to pay for tuition, registration, fees, or books.

Duration 1 year; recipients may reapply.

Additional data The English version of this award is Guadalupe Scholarship.

Number awarded 1 each year.

Deadline March of each year.

[728]
LA UNIDAD LATINA SCHOLARSHIPS

La Unidad Latina Foundation, Inc.
132 East 43rd Street, Suite 358
New York, NY 10017
E-mail: info@lulfoundation.org
Web: www.lulfoundation.org

Summary To provide financial assistance to Hispanic students who are working on a bachelor's or master's degree in any field.

Eligibility This program is open to students of Hispanic background who have completed at least 1 year of full-time undergraduate study or 1 semester of full-time graduate work. Undergraduates must have a GPA of 2.8 or higher. Applicants must be enrolled at an accredited 4-year college or university in the United States and working on a bachelor's or master's degree. Along with their application, they must submit brief essays on their financial need, their academic plans and career goals, an instance in which they have demonstrated exceptional leadership during their college or graduate experience, the impact they have had or plan to have on improving or supporting their Latino/Hispanic community, their extracurricular activities, any honors or awards they have received, and their special interests or hobbies.

Financial Data Stipends range from $250 to $1,000.

Duration 1 year.

Number awarded Varies each year.

Deadline February of each year for spring semester; October of each year for fall semester.

[729]
LAGRANT FOUNDATION GRADUATE SCHOLARSHIPS

Lagrant Foundation
Attn: Senior Programs and Outreach Manager
600 Wilshire Boulevard, Suite 1520
Los Angeles, CA 90017
(323) 469-8680, ext. 223 Fax: (323) 469-8683
E-mail: erickainiguez@lagrant.com
Web: www.lagrantfoundation.org

Summary To provide financial assistance to Hispanic American and other minority graduate students who are working on a degree in advertising, public relations, or marketing.

Eligibility This program is open to African Americans, Asian American/Pacific Islanders, Hispanics/Latinos, and Native Americans/American Indians who are full-time graduate students at an accredited institution. Applicants must have a GPA of 3.2 or higher and be working on a master's degree in advertising, marketing, or public relations. They must have at least 2 academic semesters remaining to complete their degree. Along with their application, they must submit 1) a 1- to 2-page essay outlining their career goals; why it is important to increase ethnic representation in the fields of advertising, marketing, and public relations; and the role of an advertising, marketing, or public relations practitioner; 2) a paragraph describing the graduate school and/or community activities in which they are involved; 3) a brief paragraph describing any honors and awards they have received; 4) a letter of reference; 5) a resume; and 6) an official transcript. U.S. citizenship or permanent resident status is required.

Financial Data   The stipend is $10,000 per year.
Duration   1 year.
Number awarded   Varies each year; recently, 7 of these scholarships were awarded.
Deadline   February of each year.

[730]
LATHAM & WATKINS DIVERSITY SCHOLARS PROGRAM

Latham & Watkins LLP
Attn: Diversity Committee Co-Chair
885 Third Avenue
New York, NY 10022-4834
(212) 906-1332   Fax: (212) 751-4864
E-mail: sharon.bowen@lw.com
Web: www.lw.com/AboutUs/Diversity

Summary   To provide financial assistance to Hispanic American and other minority law students interested in working for a global law firm.

Eligibility   Applicants must be second-year law students at an ABA-accredited law school and plan to practice law in a major city in the United States. Students who have received a similar scholarship from another sponsor are not eligible to apply. Applicants must submit a 500-word personal statement that describes their ability to contribute to the diversity objectives of global law firms; the life experiences that have shaped their values and that provide them with a unique perspective, including any obstacles or challenges they have overcome; their academic and/or leadership achievements; and their intent to practice in a global law firm environment.

Financial Data   The stipend is $10,000.
Duration   1 year; nonrenewable.
Additional data   This program began in 2005. Recipients are not required to work for Latham & Watkins after graduation.
Number awarded   6 each year.
Deadline   September of each year.

[731]
LATINA LAWYERS BAR ASSOCIATION SCHOLARSHIPS

Latina Lawyers Bar Association
Attn: Scholarship Committee
P.O. Box 86488
Los Angeles, CA 90086
E-mail: office@llbalaw.org
Web: www.llbalaw.org/content/scholarship

Summary   To provide financial assistance for tuition or bar review courses to students, especially Latinas, currently enrolled at law schools in California or preparing for the state bar examination.

Eligibility   This program is open to students currently enrolled at California law schools and current candidates for the California State Bar examination. Preference is given to Latina law students. Applicants must be able to demonstrate community service, commitment to the Latina community, potential to succeed, and financial need. Along with their application, they must submit a 1,000-word statement that includes information regarding their background, reasons for pursuing further education, challenges they face outside of school, legal field of interest, career goals, special circumstances, and financial need.

Financial Data   A stipend is awarded (amount not specified).
Duration   Funds provide 1 year of support at a California law school or a 1-time grant for bar examination assistance.
Number awarded   1 or more each year.
Deadline   April of each year.

[732]
LATINOS AND PLANNING DIVISION SCHOLARSHIP

American Planning Association
Attn: Planning and the Black Community Division
205 North Michigan Avenue, Suite 1200
Chicago, IL 60601
(312) 431-9100   Fax: (312) 786-6700
Web: www.planning.org/divisions/latinos/scholarships

Summary   To provide financial assistance to Latinos interested in working on an undergraduate or graduate degree in planning.

Eligibility   This program is open to Latinos who are 1) undergraduate students in the third or fourth year of an accredited planning program; or 2) graduate students in the first or second year of an accredited planning program. Applicants must submit a 1- to 2-page personal statement on their interest in a career in planning and the impact they want to make on planning in Latino communities. Selection is based on that statement, a letter of recommendation, academic achievement, and/or service or impacts made in the Latino community or the planning profession.

Financial Data   The stipend is $500 per semester.
Duration   1 year.
Number awarded   1 each year.
Deadline   January of each year.

[733]
LATINOS FOR DENTAL CAREERS SCHOLARSHIPS

California Dental Association
Attn: CDA Foundation, Grants Administrator
1201 K Street, Suite 1511
Sacramento, CA 95814
(916) 554-4929   Toll Free: (800) 232-7645
Fax: (916) 498-6182   E-mail: Jolene.Murray@cda.org
Web: www.cdafoundation.org/receive/scholarships-awards

Summary   To provide financial assistance to dental and dental hygiene students of Latino descent in California.

Eligibility   This program is open to students of Latino descent who are accepted or enrolled full time at a California dental school. Applicants may be dental students, dental hygiene students, or international students. Along with their application, they must submit descriptions of 1) their extracurricular activities; 2) how their Latino heritage has contributed to who they are today; and 3) their career goals and why they may be deserving of a scholarship. Financial need is also considered in the selection process.

Financial Data   The stipend is $1,000. Funds are paid directly to the recipient's university account.
Duration   1 year; may be renewed.

Additional data This program is sponsored by the organization, Latinos for Dental Careers, which began as USC Hispanics for Dental Careers. In 2005, that organization expanded to include all dental schools in California.

Number awarded Varies each year; recently, 4 of these scholarships were awarded.

Deadline July of each year.

[734]
LAUNCHING LEADERS MBA SCHOLARSHIP

JPMorgan Chase
Campus Recruiting
Attn: Launching Leaders
277 Park Avenue, Second Floor
New York, NY 10172
(212) 270-6000
E-mail: bronwen.x.baumgardner@jpmorgan.com
Web: careers.jpmorgan.com

Summary To provide financial assistance and work experience to underrepresented minority students enrolled in the first year of an M.B.A. program.

Eligibility This program is open to Black, Hispanic, and Native American students enrolled in the first year of an M.B.A. program. Applicants must have a demonstrated commitment to working in financial services. Along with their application, they must submit essays on 1) a hypothetical proposal on how to use $50 million from a donor to their school to benefit all of its students; and 2) the special background and attributes they would contribute to the sponsor's diversity agenda and their motivation for applying to this scholarship program. They must be interested in a summer associate position in the sponsor's investment banking, sales and trading, or research divisions.

Financial Data The stipend is $40,000 for the first year of study; a paid summer associate position is also provided.

Duration 1 year; may be renewed 1 additional year if the recipient successfully completes the 10-week summer associate program.

Number awarded Varies each year.

Deadline October of each year.

[735]
LAURENCE R. FOSTER MEMORIAL SCHOLARSHIPS

Oregon Student Access Commission
Attn: Grants and Scholarships Division
1500 Valley River Drive, Suite 100
Eugene, OR 97401-2146
(541) 687-7395   Toll Free: (800) 452-8807, ext. 7395
Fax: (541) 687-7414   TDD: (800) 735-2900
E-mail: awardinfo@osac.state.or.us
Web: www.oregonstudentaid.gov/scholarships.aspx

Summary To provide financial assistance to Hispanic Americans and other residents of Oregon who come from a diverse environment and are enrolled at a college or graduate school in any state to prepare for a public health career.

Eligibility This program is open to residents of Oregon who are enrolled at least half time at a 4-year college or university in any state to prepare for a career in public health (not private practice). Preference is given first to applicants from diverse environments; second to persons employed in, or graduate students working on a degree in, public health; and third to juniors and seniors majoring in a health program (e.g., nursing, medical technology, physician assistant). Applicants must be able to demonstrate financial need. Along with their application, they must submit essays of 250 to 350 words on 1) what public health means to them; 2) the public health aspect they intend to practice and the health and population issues impacted by that aspect; and 3) their experience living or working in diverse environments.

Financial Data Stipends for scholarships offered by the Oregon Student Access Commission (OSAC) range from $200 to $10,000 but recently averaged $2,300.

Duration 1 year.

Additional data This program is administered by the OSAC with funds provided by the Oregon Community Foundation.

Number awarded Varies each year; recently, 6 of these scholarships were awarded.

Deadline February of each year.

[736]
LEADERSHIP FOR DIVERSITY SCHOLARSHIP

California School Library Association
Attn: CSL Foundation
6444 East Spring Street, Number 237
Long Beach, CA 90815-1553
Toll Free: (888) 655-8480   Fax: (888) 655-8480
E-mail: info@csla.net
Web: www.csla.net

Summary To provide financial assistance to Hispanic American and other students who reflect the diversity of California's population and are interested in earning a credential as a library media teacher in the state.

Eligibility This program is open to students who are members of a traditionally underrepresented group enrolled in a college or university library media teacher credential program in California. Applicants must intend to work as a library media teacher in a California school library media center for a minimum of 3 years. Along with their application, they must submit a 250-word statement on their school library media career interests and goals, why they should be considered, what they can contribute, their commitment to serving the needs of multicultural and multilingual students, and their financial situation.

Financial Data The stipend is $1,500.

Duration 1 year.

Number awarded 1 each year.

Deadline May of each year.

[737]
LEADERSHIP LEGACY SCHOLARSHIP FOR GRADUATES

Women's Transportation Seminar
Attn: WTS Foundation
1701 K Street, N.W., Suite 800
Washington, DC 20006
(202) 955-5085   Fax: (202) 955-5088
E-mail: wts@wtsinternational.org
Web: www.wtsinternational.org/education/scholarships

Summary To provide financial assistance to graduate women (particularly Hispanic Americans and other minorities) who are interested in a career in transportation.

Eligibility This program is open to women who are working on a graduate degree in transportation or a transportation-related field (e.g., transportation engineering, planning, business management, finance, or logistics). Applicants must have a GPA of 3.0 or higher and be interested in a career in transportation. Along with their application, they must submit a 1,000-word statement about their vision of how their education will give them the tools to better serve their community's needs and transportation issues. Applications must be submitted first to a local chapter; the chapters forward selected applications for consideration on the national level. Minority women are especially encouraged to apply. Selection is based on transportation involvement and goals, job skills, and academic record; financial need is not considered.

Financial Data The stipend is $5,000.

Duration 1 year.

Additional data This program began in 2008. Each year, it focuses on women with a special interest; recently, it was reserved for women who have a specific interest in addressing the impact of transportation on sustainability, land use, environmental impact, security, and quality of life issues internationally.

Number awarded 1 each year.

Deadline Applications must be submitted by November to a local WTS chapter.

[738]
LEONARD AND HELEN R. STULMAN ENDOWED SCHOLARS GRANTS

Central Scholarship Bureau
1700 Reisterstown Road, Suite 220
Baltimore, MD 21208
(410) 415-5558   Toll Free: (855) 276-0239
Fax: (410) 415-5501
E-mail: gohigher@central-scholarship.org
Web: www.central-scholarship.org/scholarships/overview

Summary To provide financial assistance to bilingual residents of Maryland working on a graduate degree in mental health or social work.

Eligibility This program is open to residents of Maryland who are bilingual; strong preference is given to Spanish speakers. Applicants must be enrolled in a graduate program in mental health or social work. They must be able to demonstrate financial need (family income less than $90,000). Along with their application, they must submit a 500-word essay on their achievements, career and educational goals, and personal or family circumstances demonstrating exceptional merit or need. U.S. citizenship or permanent resident status is required.

Financial Data The stipend is $5,000.

Duration 1 year.

Number awarded 1 or more each year.

Deadline March of each year.

[739]
LEROY SCHMIDT MINORITY MASTER'S ACCOUNTING SCHOLARSHIP

Wisconsin Institute of Certified Public Accountants
Attn: WICPA Educational Foundation
235 North Executive Drive, Suite 200
Brookfield, WI 53005
(262) 785-0445, ext. 3025
Toll Free: (800) 772-6939 (within WI)
Fax: (262) 785-0838   E-mail: jessica@wicpa.org
Web: www.wicpa.org

Summary To provide financial assistance to Hispanic American and other underrepresented minority residents of Wisconsin who are working on a master's degree at a college or university in the state.

Eligibility This program is open to residents of Wisconsin who are African American, Native American/Alaskan Native, of Pacific Island races, or of Hispanic ethnic origin. Applicants must be working on a master's degree in accounting at a college or university in the state by completing the 150-hour accounting education requirement to sit for the C.P.A. examination. Along with their application, they must submit a 1-page personal statement on their career objectives, most significant accomplishment, and strongest personal attribute. Selection is based on that statement, honors and awards, academic achievement, extracurricular and volunteer activities, work experience, and letters of recommendation. U.S. citizenship is required.

Financial Data The stipend is $5,000.

Duration 1 year.

Number awarded 1 or more each year.

Deadline February of each year.

[740]
LIBRARY AND INFORMATION TECHNOLOGY ASSOCIATION MINORITY SCHOLARSHIPS

American Library Association
Attn: Library and Information Technology Association
50 East Huron Street
Chicago, IL 60611-2795
(312) 280-4270   Toll Free: (800) 545-2433, ext. 4270
Fax: (312) 280-3257   TDD: (888) 814-7692
E-mail: lita@ala.org
Web: www.ala.org/lita/awards

Summary To provide financial assistance to Hispanic American and other minority graduate students interested in preparing for a career in library automation.

Eligibility This program is open to U.S. or Canadian citizens who are interested in working on a master's degree in library/information science and preparing for a career in the field of library and automated systems. Applicants must be a member of 1 of the following ethnic groups: American Indian, Alaskan Native, Asian, Pacific Islander, African American, or Hispanic. They may not have completed more than 12 credit hours of course work for their degree. Selection is based on academic excellence, leadership potential, evidence of a commitment to a career in library automation and information technology, and prior activity and experience in those fields. Financial need is considered when all other factors are equal.

Financial Data Stipends are $3,000 or $2,500. Funds are paid directly to the recipient.

Duration 1 year.

Additional data This program includes scholarships funded by Online Computer Library Center (OCLC) and by Library Systems & Services, Inc. (LSSI).

Number awarded 2 each year: 1 at $3,000 (funded by OCLC) and 1 at $2,500 (funded by LSSI).

Deadline February of each year.

[741]
LILLIAN MARRERO SCHOLARSHIP AWARD

REFORMA-Northeast Chapter
c/o Louis Muñoz, Scholarship Committee Chair
Brooklyn Public Library
Languages and Literature Division
10 Grand Army Plaza
Brooklyn, NY 11238
(718) 230-2100　　　E-mail: louismunoz@yahoo.com
Web: reforma-northeast.org/scholarship.html

Summary To provide financial assistance to members of the Northeast Chapter of REFORMA who are working on a graduate degree in library science and are committed to serving the Spanish-speaking community.

Eligibility This program is open to members of the Northeast Chapter of REFORMA, an association committed to serving the Latino community in Connecticut, Massachusetts, New Jersey, New York, Pennsylvania, and Rhode Island. Applicants must be working on a master's or doctoral degree in library science and be able to demonstrate an understanding of and desire to serve the Spanish-speaking community. They are not required to be enrolled full time, but they must be U.S. citizens or permanent residents. In the selection process, special attention is paid to participation in chapter activities.

Financial Data The stipend is $1,000.

Duration 1 year.

Number awarded 1 each year.

Deadline November of each year.

[742]
LIONEL C. BARROW MINORITY DOCTORAL STUDENT SCHOLARSHIP

Association for Education in Journalism and Mass
　Communication
Attn: Communication Theory and Methodology Division
234 Outlet Pointe Boulevard, Suite A
Columbia, SC 29210-5667
(803) 798-0271　　　　　　Fax: (803) 772-3509
E-mail: aejmc@aejmc.org
Web: aejmc.net

Summary To provide financial assistance to Hispanic Americans and other minorities who are interested in working on a doctorate in mass communication.

Eligibility This program is open to minority students enrolled in a Ph.D. program in journalism and/or mass communication. Applicants must submit 2 letters of recommendation, a resume, and a brief letter outlining their research interests and career plans. Membership in the association is not required, but applicants must be U.S. citizens or permanent residents. Selection is based on the likelihood that the applicant's work will contribute to communication theory and/or methodology.

Financial Data The stipend is $1,400.

Duration 1 year.

Additional data This program began in 1972.

Number awarded 1 each year.

Deadline May of each year.

[743]
LIZETTE PETERSON-HOMER INJURY PREVENTION RESEARCH GRANT

American Psychological Foundation
750 First Street, N.E.
Washington, DC 20002-4242
(202) 336-5843　　　　　　Fax: (202) 336-5812
E-mail: foundation@apa.org
Web: www.apa.org/apf/funding/peterson-homer.aspx

Summary To provide funding to graduate students and faculty (particularly Hispanic Americans, other minorities, women, and individuals with disabilities) who are interested in conducting research related to the prevention of injuries in children.

Eligibility This program is open to graduate students and faculty interested in conducting research that focuses on the prevention of physical injury in children and young adults through accidents, violence, abuse, or suicide. Applicants must submit a 100-word abstract, description of the project, detailed budget, curriculum vitae, and letter from the supporting faculty supervisor (if the applicant is a student). Selection is based on conformance with stated program goals, magnitude of incremental contribution, quality of proposed work, and applicant's demonstrated scholarship and research competence. The sponsor encourages applications from individuals who represent diversity in race, ethnicity, gender, age, disability, and sexual orientation.

Financial Data Grants up to $5,000 are available.

Additional data This program began in 1999 as the Rebecca Routh Coon Injury Research Award. The current name was adopted in 2003. It is supported by Division 54 (Society of Pediatric Psychology) of the American Psychological Association and the American Psychological Foundation.

Number awarded 1 each year.

Deadline September of each year.

[744]
LLAVE SCHOLARSHIPS

Llave Scholarship Committee
P.O. Box 841
Albuquerque, NM 87103-0841
(505) 241-4716
Web: www.llave-nm.org/scholarship.html

Summary To provide financial assistance to Hispanic American (primarily) and other residents of New Mexico who are interested in attending college or graduate school in any state.

Eligibility This program is open to Hispanic and other residents of New Mexico who are enrolled or accepted for enrollment at an accredited college, university, community college, or vocational school in any state as a full-time undergraduate or graduate student. Nontraditional and returning students are also eligible. Applicants must have a GPA of 2.0 or higher. Along with their application, they must submit a 1-page personal statement that covers their career goals and aspirations, their involvement with volunteerism and/or community service, how this scholarship will impact their educational goals, and special circumstances. Selection is based on commitment to diversity and higher education, involvement in local community groups or organizations, personal qualities and strengths, demonstrations of overcoming unique obstacles in obtaining an education, academic achievement (if applicable to category), and financial need.

Financial Data The stipend is $1,000.

Duration 1 year.

Additional data This program, which began in 1992, is funded by the PNM Resources Foundation, the nonprofit affiliate of the electric utility based in Albuquerque, and administered in cooperation with the Albuquerque Hispano Chamber of Commerce.

Number awarded Varies each year; recently, 10 of these scholarships were awarded.

Deadline March of each year.

[745]
LLOYD M. JOHNSON, JR. SCHOLARSHIP PROGRAM

United Negro College Fund
Attn: Scholarships and Grants Department
8260 Willow Oaks Corporate Drive
P.O. Box 10444
Fairfax, VA 22031-8044
(703) 205-3466   Toll Free: (800) 331-2244
Fax: (703) 205-3574
Web: www.uncf.org

Summary To provide financial assistance to Hispanic Americans and other law students from disadvantaged backgrounds who are interested in corporate law and will contribute to diversity in the legal profession.

Eligibility Applicants must be U.S. citizens, have a strong academic record (an undergraduate GPA of 3.2 or higher), have been accepted to an ABA-accredited law school, be able to demonstrate community service and leadership qualities, have an interest in diversity, be financially disadvantaged, plan to study on a full-time basis, and have an interest in corporate law, including working in a corporate law department and/or law firm. Applicants must submit a current transcript, a resume, 2 letters of recommendation, a personal statement, and a diversity essay. All students are eligible, but the sponsor expects that most recipients will contribute to diversity in the legal profession.

Financial Data The stipend is $10,000 for the first year and varying amounts for subsequent years.

Duration 1 year; may be renewed up to 2 additional years.

Additional data The Minority Corporate Counsel Association first began this program in 2005 and now cosponsors it with the United Negro College Fund. Mentoring and internship experiences are also offered to the winners.

Number awarded Approximately 10 each year.

Deadline May of each year.

[746]
LTK SCHOLARSHIP

Conference of Minority Transportation Officials
Attn: National Scholarship Program
1875 I Street, N.W., Suite 500
Washington, DC 20006
(703) 234-4072   Fax: (202) 318-0364
Web: www.comto.org/?page=Scholarships

Summary To provide financial assistance to Hispanic American and other minority upper-division and graduate students in engineering or other fields related to transportation.

Eligibility This program is open to full-time minority juniors, seniors, and graduate students in engineering of other technical transportation-related disciplines. Applicants must have a GPA of 3.0 or higher. Along with their application, they must submit a cover letter with a 500-word statement of career goals. Financial need is not considered in the selection process. U.S. citizenship or legal resident status is required.

Financial Data The stipend is $6,000. Funds are paid directly to the recipient's college or university.

Duration 1 year.

Additional data The Conference of Minority Transportation Officials (COMTO) was established in 1971 to promote, strengthen, and expand the roles of minorities in all aspects of transportation. This program is sponsored by LTK Engineering Services. Recipients are required to become members of COMTO if they are not already members and attend the COMTO National Scholarship Luncheon.

Number awarded 1 or more each year.

Deadline May of each year.

[747]
LULAC GENERAL AWARDS

League of United Latin American Citizens
Attn: LULAC National Education Service Centers
1133 19th Street, N.W., Suite 1000
Washington, DC 20036
(202) 835-9646   Fax: (202) 835-9685
E-mail: scholarships@lnesc.org
Web: www.lnesc.org/site/296/Scholarships

Summary To provide financial assistance to Hispanic American undergraduate and graduate students.

Eligibility This program is open to Hispanic Americans who are U.S. citizens or permanent residents currently enrolled or planning to enroll at an accredited college or university as a graduate or undergraduate student. Although grades are considered in the selection process, emphasis is placed on the applicant's motivation, sincerity, and community involvement, as revealed through a personal interview and in an essay on their personal and career goals. Need, community involvement, and leadership activities are also considered. Candidates must live near a participating local council of the League of United Latin American Citizens (LULAC) and must apply directly to that council.

Financial Data The stipend ranges from $250 to $1,000 per year, depending on the need of the recipient.

Duration 1 year.

Additional data This program represents an attempt to forge a partnership between the corporate world and the community. Under its fundsharing concept, LULAC's National Education Service Center gathers contributions nationally from corporations, while LULAC councils raise money locally. The total corporate donations are then apportioned back to the councils according to effort. Applications must be obtained directly from participating LULAC councils; for a list, contact the sponsor.

Number awarded Varies; approximately 500 each year.

Deadline March of each year.

[748]
LULAC HONORS AWARDS

League of United Latin American Citizens
Attn: LULAC National Education Service Centers
1133 19th Street, N.W., Suite 1000
Washington, DC 20036
(202) 835-9646 Fax: (202) 835-9685
E-mail: scholarships@lnesc.org
Web: www.lnesc.org/site/296/Scholarships

Summary To provide financial assistance to Hispanic American undergraduate and graduate students who are doing well in school.

Eligibility This program is open to Hispanic Americans who are U.S. citizens or permanent residents currently enrolled or planning to enroll at an accredited college or university as a graduate or undergraduate student. Applicants who are already in college must have a GPA of 3.25 or higher. Entering freshmen must have ACT scores of 23 or higher or SAT scores of 1100 or higher. In addition, applicants must demonstrate motivation, sincerity, and community involvement through a personal interview and in an essay on their personal and career goals. Need, community involvement, and leadership activities are also considered. Candidates must live near a participating local council of the League of United Latin American Citizens (LULAC) and must apply directly to that council.

Financial Data The stipend ranges from $500 to $2,000 per year, depending on the need of the recipient.

Duration 1 year.

Additional data This program represents an attempt to forge a partnership between the corporate world and the community. Under its fundsharing concept, LULAC's National Education Service Center gathers contributions nationally from corporations, while LULAC councils raise money locally. The total corporate donations are then apportioned back to the councils according to effort. Applications must be obtained directly from participating LULAC councils; for a list, send a self-addressed stamped envelope to the sponsor.

Number awarded Varies each year.

Deadline March of each year.

[749]
LULAC NATIONAL SCHOLASTIC ACHIEVEMENT AWARDS

League of United Latin American Citizens
Attn: LULAC National Education Service Centers
1133 19th Street, N.W., Suite 1000
Washington, DC 20036
(202) 835-9646 Fax: (202) 835-9685
E-mail: scholarships@lnesc.org
Web: www.lnesc.org/site/296/Scholarships

Summary To provide financial assistance to academically outstanding Hispanic American undergraduate and graduate students.

Eligibility This program is open to Hispanic Americans who are U.S. citizens or permanent residents currently enrolled or planning to enroll at an accredited college or university as a graduate or undergraduate student. Applicants who are already in college must have a GPA of 3.5 or higher. Entering freshmen must have ACT scores of 29 or higher or SAT scores of 1350 or higher. In addition, applicants must demonstrate motivation, sincerity, and community involvement through a personal interview and in an essay on their personal and career goals. Need, community involvement, and leadership activities are also considered. Candidates must live near a participating local council of the League of United Latin American Citizens (LULAC) and must apply directly to that council.

Financial Data Stipends are at least $2,000 per year.

Duration 1 year.

Additional data This program represents an attempt to forge a partnership between the corporate world and the community. Under its fundsharing concept, LULAC's National Education Service Center gathers contributions nationally from corporations, while LULAC councils raise money locally. The total corporate donations are then apportioned back to the councils according to effort. Applications must be obtained directly from participating LULAC councils; for a list, send a self-addressed stamped envelope to the sponsor.

Number awarded Varies each year.

Deadline March of each year.

[750]
MALDEF LAW SCHOOL SCHOLARSHIP PROGRAM

Mexican American Legal Defense and Educational Fund
634 South Spring Street, 11th Floor
Los Angeles, CA 90014-1974
(213) 629-2512 Fax: (213) 629-0266
Web: www.maldef.org/leadership/scholarships/index.html

Summary To provide financial assistance to Latino students who are attending or interested in attending law school.

Eligibility This program is open to Latino students entering their first, second, or third year of law school. Applicants must be enrolled full time. Along with their application, they must submit a 750-word personal statement detailing their background, history of service to the Latino community, and interest in law. Selection is based upon past achievement and potential for achievement, commitment to advancing Latino civil rights, and financial need.

Financial Data Stipends range up to $5,000.

Duration 1 year.

Number awarded Varies each year; recently, 10 of these scholarships were awarded.

Deadline December of each year.

[751]
MARATHON OIL CORPORATION COLLEGE SCHOLARSHIP PROGRAM OF THE HISPANIC SCHOLARSHIP FUND

Hispanic Scholarship Fund
Attn: Selection Committee
1411 West 190th Street, Suite 325
Gardena, CA 90248
Toll Free: (877) HSF-INFO   E-mail: scholar1@hsf.net
Web: www.hsf.net

Summary To provide financial assistance to Hispanic American and other minority upper-division and graduate students working on a degree in a field related to the oil and gas industry.

Eligibility This program is open to U.S. citizens and permanent residents (must have a permanent resident card or a passport stamped I-551) who are of Hispanic American, African American, Asian Pacific Islander American, or American Indian/Alaskan Native heritage. Applicants must be currently enrolled full time at an accredited 4-year college or university in the United States, Puerto Rico, Guam, or the U.S. Virgin Islands with a GPA of 3.0 or higher. They must be 1) sophomores majoring in accounting, chemical engineering, computer engineering, computer science, electrical engineering, environmental engineering, geology, geosciences, information technology/management information systems, mechanical engineering, or petroleum engineering; or 2) seniors planning to work on a master's degree in geology, geosciences, or petroleum engineering. Selection is based on academic achievement, personal strengths, interest and commitment to a career in the oil and gas industry, leadership, and financial need.

Financial Data The stipend is $15,000 per year.

Duration 2 years (the junior and senior undergraduate years or the first 2 years of a master's degree program).

Additional data This program is jointly sponsored by Marathon Oil Corporation and the Hispanic Scholarship Fund (HSF). Recipients may be offered a paid 8- to 10-week summer internship at various Marathon Oil Corporation locations.

Number awarded 1 or more each year.

Deadline September of each year.

[752]
MARIA ELENA SALINAS SCHOLARSHIP PROGRAM

National Association of Hispanic Journalists
Attn: Scholarship Committee
1050 Connecticut Avenue, N.W., Tenth Floor
Washington, DC 20036
(202) 662-7145   Toll Free: (888) 346-NAHJ
Fax: (202) 662-7144   E-mail: nahj@nahj.org
Web: www.nahj12.com/scholarships

Summary To provide financial assistance and work experience to student members of the National Association of Hispanic Journalists (NAHJ) who are interested in preparing for a career as a journalist in Spanish-language radio or television.

Eligibility This program is open to undergraduates and first-year graduate students who are NAHJ members. Applicants must demonstrate a sincere desire to prepare for a career as a journalist in Spanish-language television or radio.

They must be enrolled full time at a college or university in the United States or Puerto Rico. Along with their application, they must submit 1) transcripts; 2) a 1-page resume; 3) 2 letters of recommendation; 4) work samples; 5) a 1,000-word autobiographical essay that includes why they are interested in a career in journalism, what inspired them to prepare for a career in the field, what hardships or obstacles they have experienced while trying to realize their goal of becoming a journalist, and the role Latino journalists play in the news industry; and 6) an essay written in the third person as a news story in Spanish on why they seek a career as a Spanish-language broadcast journalist. Selection is based on commitment to the field of journalism, academic achievement, awareness of the Latino community, and financial need.

Financial Data The stipend is $5,000 per year; the program also provides funding for an internship during the summer.

Duration 2 years.

Additional data This program, which began in 2002, is sponsored by Univision. The recipient participates in a summer internship with either the news division of the Univision network or a Univision affiliate near them.

Number awarded Varies each year; recently, 3 of these scholarships were awarded.

Deadline January of each year.

[753]
MARJORIE BOWENS-WHEATLEY SCHOLARSHIPS

Unitarian Universalist Association
Attn: UU Women's Federation
25 Beacon Street
Boston, MA 02108-2800
(617) 948-4692   Fax: (617) 742-2402
E-mail: uuwf@uua.org
Web: www.uuwf.org

Summary To provide financial assistance to Hispanic American and other women of color who are working on an undergraduate or graduate degree to prepare for Unitarian Universalist ministry or service.

Eligibility This program is open to women of color who are either 1) aspirants or candidates for the Unitarian Universalist ministry; or 2) candidates in the Unitarian Universalist Association's professional religious education or music leadership credentialing programs. Applicants must submit a 1- to 2-page narrative that covers their call to UU ministry, religious education, or music leadership; their passions; how their racial/ethnic/cultural background influences their goals for their calling; and how the work of the program's namesake relates to their dreams and plans for their UU service.

Financial Data Stipends from $1,500 to $2,000.

Duration 1 year.

Additional data This program began in 2009.

Number awarded Varies each year; recently, 4 of these scholarships were awarded.

Deadline March of each year.

[754]
MARK T. BANNER SCHOLARSHIP FOR LAW STUDENTS

Richard Linn American Inn of Court
c/o Matthew Walch, Scholarship Chair
Latham & Watkins LLP
233 South Wacker Drive, Suite 5800
Chicago, IL 60606
(312) 876-7603   E-mail: matthew.walch@lw.com
Web: www.linninn.org/marktbanner.htm

Summary To provide financial assistance to Hispanic American and other law students who are members of historically underrepresented groups and interested in specializing in intellectual property law.

Eligibility This program is open to students at ABA-accredited law schools in the United States who are members of groups historically underrepresented (by race, sex, ethnicity, sexual orientation, or disability) in intellectual property law. Applicants must submit a 3-page statement on how they have focused on ethics, civility, and professionalism have been their focus; how diversity has impacted them; and their commitment to a career in intellectual property law.

Financial Data The stipend is $5,000.

Duration 1 year.

Number awarded 1 each year.

Deadline November of each year.

[755]
MARRIAGE AND FAMILY THERAPY MASTER'S STUDENT MINORITY SCHOLARSHIP

American Association for Marriage and Family Therapy
Attn: AAMFT Research and Education Foundation
112 South Alfred Street
Alexandria, VA 22314-3061
(703) 838-9808   Fax: (703) 838-9805
Web: www.aamft.org

Summary To provide financial assistance to Hispanic American and other minority students enrolled in master's and post-degree training programs in marriage and family therapy.

Eligibility This program is open to minority students (including African Americans, Hispanics, Native Americans, Asian Americans, and Pacific Islanders) enrolled in master's degree programs or post-degree institutes that provide training in marriage and family therapy. Applicants must be members of the American Association for Marriage and Family Therapy (AAMFT). They must be citizens or permanent residents of the United States or Canada and show promise in and commitment to a career in marital and family therapy education, research, or practice. Along with their application, they must submit a personal statement explaining how their racial or ethnic background has had an impact on them and their career decision; the statement should include their professional interests, goals, and commitment to the field of marriage and family therapy.

Financial Data The stipend is $2,000. Awardees also receive a plaque and funding up to $750 to attend the association's annual conference.

Duration 1 year.

Additional data This program began in 1986.

Number awarded Up to 3 each year.

Deadline January of each year.

[756]
MARTHA AND ROBERT ATHERTON MINISTERIAL SCHOLARSHIP

Unitarian Universalist Association
Attn: Ministerial Credentialing Office
25 Beacon Street
Boston, MA 02108-2800
(617) 948-6403   Fax: (617) 742-2875
E-mail: mcoadministrator@uua.org
Web: www.uua.org

Summary To provide financial assistance minority and other seminary students preparing for the Unitarian Universalist (UU) ministry.

Eligibility This program is open to second- or third-year seminary students currently enrolled full or at least half time in a UU ministerial training program with aspirant or candidate status. Applicants must respect hard work as a foundation of a full life and appreciate the freedom, political system, and philosophical underpinnings of our country. They should be citizens of the United States or Canada. Priority is given first to those who have demonstrated outstanding ministerial ability and secondarily to students with the greatest financial need (especially persons of color).

Financial Data The stipend ranges from $1,000 to $15,000 per year.

Duration 1 year.

Additional data This program began in 1997.

Number awarded 1 or 2 each year.

Deadline April of each year.

[757]
MAS FAMILY SCHOLARSHIP PROGRAM

Jorge Mas Canosa Freedom Foundation
Attn: Scholarship Coordinator
1312 S.W. 27th Avenue
Miami, FL 33145
(305) 529-7768   E-mail: info@canf.org
Web: jorgemascanosa.org/wordpress

Summary To provide financial assistance to students of Cuban descent who are working on an undergraduate or graduate degree in selected subject areas.

Eligibility This program is open to students who are direct descendants of those who left Cuba or were born in Cuba themselves. Applicants must have a GPA of 3.5 or higher and an SAT test score of at least 1500. They must be able to meet federal standards of financial need. At least 1 parent or 2 grandparents must have been born in Cuba. Both undergraduate and graduate students may apply, provided they are working on a degree in 1 of the following subjects: engineering, business, international relations, economics, communications, pediatric nursing, law, or journalism. Selection is based on academic performance, leadership qualities, financial need, potential to contribute to the advancement of a free society, and likelihood of succeeding in their chosen field. Finalists may be interviewed.

Financial Data The stipend ranges up to $8,000 per year.

Duration 1 year; may be renewed up to 3 additional years.

Additional data This program, established in 1997, was previously offered by the Cuban American National Foundation.

Number awarded Varies each year; since this program was established, it has provided support to more than 100 students.

Deadline January of each year.

[758]
MCANDREWS DIVERSITY IN PATENT LAW FELLOWSHIP

McAndrews, Held & Malloy, Ltd.
Attn: Diversity Fellowship
500 West Madison Street, Suite 3400
Chicago, IL 60661
(312) 775-8000   Fax: (312) 775-8100
E-mail: info@mcandrews-ip.com
Web: www.mcandrews-ip.com/diversity_fellowship.html

Summary To provide financial aid and work experience to Hispanic American and other law students who come from a diverse background and are interested in patent law.

Eligibility This program is open to first-year students at ABA-accredited law schools who come from a diverse background. Applicants must have a degree in science or engineering and be planning to practice patent law in the Chicago area. Along with their application, they must submit a 500-word personal statement on why they wish to prepare for a career in patent law, why they are interested in the sponsoring firm as a place to work, and how their background and/or life experiences would improve diversity in the field of intellectual property law. Selection is based on that statement, a resume (including their science or engineering educational credentials), a legal writing sample, undergraduate transcript, and at least 1 letter of recommendation.

Financial Data The stipend is $5,000.

Duration 1 year (the second year of law school).

Additional data This fellowship was first awarded in 2008. It includes a paid clerkship position at McAndrews, Held & Malloy during the summer after the first year of law school and possibly another clerkship during the summer after the second year.

Number awarded 1 each year.

Deadline January of each year.

[759]
MCDERMOTT MINORITY SCHOLARSHIP

McDermott Will & Emery
Attn: Recruiting Coordinator
227 West Monroe Street
Chicago, IL 60606
(312) 984-6470   Fax: (312) 984-7700
E-mail: mcdermottscholarship@mwe.com
Web: www.mwe.com

Summary To provide financial aid and work experience to Hispanic American and other minority law students.

Eligibility This program is open to second-year minority (African American, Asian, Hispanic, Middle Eastern, Native American, LGBT) law students at ABA-accredited U.S. law schools. Applicants must be able to demonstrate leadership, community involvement, and a commitment to improving diversity in the legal community. They must be interested in

participating in the sponsor's summer program and be able to meet its hiring criteria. Along with their application, they must submit an essay of 1 to 2 pages that provides ideas they have on how the number of minority students in law schools can be increased and how they have improved and intend to help improve diversity in the legal profession throughout their law school and legal career.

Financial Data The stipend is $15,000.

Duration 1 year.

Additional data Recipients also participate in a summer program at the sponsor's offices in Boston, Chicago, Houston, Los Angeles, Miami, New York, Orange County, San Diego, Silicon Valley, or Washington, D.C.

Number awarded 2 each year.

Deadline October of each year.

[760]
MCKNIGHT DOCTORAL FELLOWSHIP PROGRAM

Florida Education Fund
201 East Kennedy Boulevard, Suite 1525
Tampa, FL 33602
(813) 272-2772   Fax: (813) 272-2784
E-mail: mdf@fefonline.org
Web: www.fefonline.org/mdf.html

Summary To provide financial assistance to Hispanic and African American doctoral students from any state who are working on a degree in designated fields at selected universities in Florida and preparing for an academic career in that state.

Eligibility This program is open to African Americans and Hispanics from any state who are working on a Ph.D. degree at 1 of 9 universities in Florida. Fellowships may be given in any discipline in the arts and sciences, business, engineering, health sciences, nursing, or the visual and performing arts; preference is given to the following fields of study: agriculture, biology, business administration, chemistry, computer science, engineering, marine biology, mathematics, physics, or psychology. Academic programs that lead to professional degrees (such as the M.D., D.B.A., D.D.S., J.D., or D.V.M.) are not covered by the fellowship. Graduate study in education, whether leading to an Ed.D. or a Ph.D., is generally not supported. Because this program is intended to increase African American and Hispanic graduate enrollment at the 9 participating universities, currently-enrolled doctoral students at those universities are not eligible to apply. U.S. citizenship is required.

Financial Data Each award provides annual tuition up to $5,000 and an annual stipend of $12,000. Recipients are also eligible for the Fellows Travel Fund, which supports recipients who wish to attend and present papers at professional conferences.

Duration 3 years; an additional 2 years of support may be provided by the university if the recipient maintains satisfactory performance and normal progress toward the Ph.D. degree.

Additional data This program began in 1984. The participating universities are Florida Agricultural and Mechanical University, Florida Atlantic University, Florida Institute of Technology, Florida International University, Florida State

University, University of Central Florida, University of Florida, University of Miami, and University of South Florida.

Number awarded Up to 50 each year.

Deadline January of each year.

[761]
MEDICAL LIBRARY ASSOCIATION SCHOLARSHIP FOR MINORITY STUDENTS

Medical Library Association
Attn: Grants and Scholarships
65 East Wacker Place, Suite 1900
Chicago, IL 60601-7246
(312) 419-9094, ext. 15   Fax: (312) 419-8950
E-mail: grants@mlahq.org
Web: www.mlanet.org/awards/grants

Summary To assist Hispanic American and other minority students interested in preparing for a career in medical librarianship.

Eligibility This program is open to racial minority students (Asians, Blacks or African Americans, Hispanics or Latinos, Aboriginals, North American Indians or Alaskan Natives, or Native Hawaiians or other Pacific Islanders) who are entering an ALA-accredited graduate program in librarianship or who have completed less than half of their academic requirements for a master's degree in library science. They must be interested in preparing for a career in medical librarianship. Selection is based on academic record, letters of reference, professional potential, and the applicant's statement of career objectives. U.S. or Canadian citizenship or permanent resident status is required.

Financial Data The stipend is $5,000.

Duration 1 year.

Additional data This program began in 1973.

Number awarded 1 each year.

Deadline November of each year.

[762]
MENTAL HEALTH AND SUBSTANCE ABUSE FELLOWSHIP PROGRAM

Council on Social Work Education
Attn: Minority Fellowship Program
1701 Duke Street, Suite 200
Alexandria, VA 22314-3457
(703) 683-2050   Fax: (703) 683-8099
E-mail: cbrock@cswe.org
Web: www.cswe.org

Summary To provide financial assistance to Hispanic Americans and other minorities who are interested in preparing for a clinical career in the mental health fields.

Eligibility This program is open to U.S. citizens, noncitizen nationals, and permanent residents who have been underrepresented in the field of social work. These include but are not limited to the following groups: American Indians/Alaskan Natives, Asian/Pacific Islanders (e.g., Chinese, East Indians, South Asians, Filipinos, Hawaiians, Japanese, Koreans, and Samoans), Blacks, and Hispanics (e.g., Mexicans/Chicanos, Puerto Ricans, Cubans, Central or South Americans). Applicants must be interested in and committed to a career in mental health and/or substance abuse with specialization in the delivery of services of ethnic and racial minority groups. They must have a master's degree in social work and be

accepted to or enrolled in a full-time doctoral degree program. Selection is based on potential for assuming leadership roles; potential for success in doctoral studies; and commitment to a career providing mental health and substance abuse services to ethnic, racial, social, and cultural minority individuals and communities.

Financial Data Awards provide a stipend of $22,032 per year and tuition support to a maximum of $3,000.

Duration 1 academic year; renewable for 2 additional years if funds are available and the recipient makes satisfactory progress toward the degree objectives.

Additional data This program has been funded since 1978 by the Center for Mental Health Services (CMHS), the Center for Substance Abuse Prevention (CSAP), and the Center for Substance Abuse Treatment (CSAT) in the Substance Abuse and Mental Health Services Administration.

Number awarded Varies each year; recently, 9 new fellows and 16 returning fellows were appointed.

Deadline February of each year.

[763]
MENTAL HEALTH RESEARCH DISSERTATION GRANT TO INCREASE DIVERSITY

National Institute of Mental Health
Attn: Division of Extramural Activities
6001 Executive Boulevard, Room 6138
Bethesda, MD 20892-9609
(301) 443-3534   Fax: (301) 443-4720
TDD: (301) 451-0088   E-mail: armstrda@mail.nih.gov
Web: grants.nih.gov/grants/guide/pa-files/PAR-12-103.html

Summary To provide research funding to Hispanic American and other doctoral candidates from underrepresented groups planning to prepare for a research career in any area relevant to mental health and/or mental disorders.

Eligibility This program is open to doctoral candidates conducting dissertation research in a field related to mental health and/or mental disorders at a university, college, or professional school with an accredited doctoral degree granting program. Applicants must be 1) members of an ethnic or racial group that has been determined by the National Science Foundation to be underrepresented in health-related sciences (i.e., African Americans, Hispanic Americans, Alaska Natives, American Indians, Native Hawaiians, and other Pacific Islanders); 2) individuals with disabilities; or 3) individuals from socially, culturally, economically, or educationally disadvantaged backgrounds that have inhibited their ability to prepare for a career in health-related research. They must be U.S. citizens, nationals, or permanent residents.

Financial Data The stipend is $22,032. An additional grant up to $15,000 is provided for additional research expenses, fringe benefits (including health insurance), travel to scientific meetings, and research costs of the dissertation. Facilities and administrative costs are limited to 8% of modified total direct costs.

Duration Up to 2 years; nonrenewable.

Number awarded Varies each year.

Deadline April, August, or December of each year.

[764]
MEXICAN AMERICAN DREAM SCHOLARSHIPS

Council of Mexican Federations
125 Paseo de La Plaza, Suite 500
Los Angeles, CA 90012
(213) 417-8380   Toll Free: (866) 77-COFEM
Fax: (213) 625-0909   E-mail: scholarships@cofem.org
Web: www.cofem.org/programs/scholarships.html

Summary To provide financial assistance to undergraduate and graduate students who are either 1) members or family of members of a federation or club affiliated with the Council of Mexican Federations (COFEM) or 2) AB 540 students.

Eligibility This program is open to undergraduate and graduate students enrolled or planning to enroll full time at a 2- or 4-year college or university in any state. Applicants must be either 1) an AB 540 student; or 2) a member or relative of a member of a federation or club affiliated with COFEM. They must have a GPA of 3.0 or higher, be able to demonstrate financial need, and have a record of involvement in the community or work experience. AB 540 students must submit a 2-page essay on how they can help their community become stronger and more engaged on issues impacting their community. COFEM members must submit a 2-page essay on how they can help their club or federation become a stronger organization. All applicants must submit essays on 1) why they should receive this scholarship; and 2) how they believe this scholarship will help them contribute to the fulfillment of COFEM's mission through their intended career.

Financial Data Stipends are $500 for students at community colleges, $1,000 for students at 4-year colleges and universities, or $2,000 for graduate students.

Duration 1 year.

Number awarded Varies each year.

Deadline October of each year.

[765]
MEXICAN AMERICAN ENGINEERS AND SCIENTISTS SCHOLARSHIP PROGRAM

Society of Mexican American Engineers and Scientists
Attn: Scholarship Program
2437 Bay Area Boulevard, Suite 100
Houston, TX 77058
(281) 557-3677   Fax: (281) 715-5100
E-mail: questions@mymaes.org
Web: www.mymaes.org/program-item/maes-scholarships

Summary To provide financial assistance to undergraduate and graduate student members of the Society of Mexican American Engineers and Scientists (MAES).

Eligibility This program is open to MAES student members who are full-time undergraduate or graduate students at a college or university in the United States and have a GPA of 2.0 or higher. Community college students must be enrolled in majors that can transfer to a 4-year institution offering a baccalaureate degree. All applicants must be majoring in a field of science, technology, engineering, or mathematics. U.S. citizenship or permanent resident status is required. Along with their application, they must submit a personal statement that includes information on their family background, involvement in school and community activities, MAES involvement, and financial need.

Financial Data Stipends range from $1,000 to $4,000.

Duration 1 year.

Additional data This program includes Padrino/Madrina Scholarships at $4,000, graduate student scholarships at $3,000, the Founder's Scholarship at $2,500, the Presidential Scholarship at $2,500, the Pipeline Scholarships at $1,000, and general scholarships at $1,000 or $2,000. The Padrino/Madrina Scholarships are sponsored by Lockheed Martin; the Presidential and Pipeline Scholarships are sponsored by ExxonMobil; other scholarships are sponsored by various professional chapters of MAES. Recipients must attend the MAES International Symposium's Medalla de Oro Banquet in December.

Number awarded Varies each year; recently, available scholarships included 3 Padrino/Madrina Scholarships, 1 graduate scholarship, 1 Founder's Scholarship, 1 Presidential Scholarship, 2 Pipeline Scholarships, and up to 10 general scholarships.

Deadline September of each year.

[766]
MEXICAN FIESTA SCHOLARSHIPS

Wisconsin Hispanic Scholarship Foundation, Inc.
2997 South 20th Street
Milwaukee, WI 53215
(414) 383-7066   Fax: (414) 383-6677
E-mail: info@mexicanfiesta.org
Web: www.mexicanfiesta.org/scholarships.php

Summary To provide financial assistance to Hispanic American students in Wisconsin who are interested in attending college or graduate school in the state.

Eligibility This program is open to Wisconsin residents who are of at least 25% Hispanic descent and entering or enrolled at a 2- or 4-year college or university or graduate school in the state. Applicants must complete at least 20 hours of volunteer service during the Mexican Fiesta festival in Milwaukee during August of each year. Along with their application, they must submit an essay on how they plan to assist or help the Hispanic community after their receive their degree. U.S. citizenship or permanent resident status is required.

Financial Data Stipends range from $250 to $2,000.

Duration 1 year; recipients may reapply.

Additional data The sponsor is an affiliate of the League of United Latin American Citizens (LULAC) Wisconsin Councils 319 and 322.

Number awarded More than 100 each year.

Deadline March of each year.

[767]
MICHIGAN STEERING COMMITTEE MINORITY SCHOLARSHIPS

Michigan Association of Certified Public Accountants
Attn: Michigan Accountancy Foundation
5480 Corporate Drive, Suite 200
Troy, MI 48098-2642
(248) 267-3723   Toll Free: (888) 877-4CPE (within MI)
Fax: (248) 267-3737   E-mail: macpa@michcpa.org
Web: www.michcpa.org/Content/22461.aspx

Summary To provide financial assistance to Hispanic American and other students at Michigan colleges and universities who are working on a degree in accounting.

Eligibility This program is open to members of minority groups enrolled full time at accredited Michigan colleges and universities with a declared concentration in accounting. Applicants must be seniors planning to enter the fifth or graduate year of their school's program. They must intend to or have successfully passed the Michigan C.P.A. examination and intend to practice public accounting in the state. Along with their application, they must submit a 500-word statement about their educational and career aspirations, including internships and/or other employment, volunteer and community activities, professional affiliations, and full-time employment. Documentation of financial need may also be included. U.S. citizenship or eligibility for permanent employment in the United States is required.

Financial Data The stipend is $4,000; funds are disbursed directly to the recipient's college or university.

Duration 1 year.

Number awarded Varies each year; recently, 5 of these scholarships were awarded.

Deadline January of each year.

[768]
MIGRANT HEALTH SCHOLARSHIP

National Center for Farmworker Health, Inc.
Attn: Migrant Health Scholarship
1770 FM 967
Buda, TX 78610
(512) 312-2700   Toll Free: (800) 531-5120
Fax: (512) 312-2600   E-mail: info@ncfh.org
Web: www.ncfh.org/?pid=232

Summary To provide financial assistance to people working in the migrant health field, especially those with a farmworker background, who are interested in additional education.

Eligibility This program is open to staff in clinical, administrative, and support positions at community and migrant health centers who are interested in obtaining additional education at the undergraduate or graduate level. Applicants must submit a 1-page personal statement discussing such issues as why they are interested in migrant health, personal experiences and achievements, future career goals, and commitment to migrant health. Financial need is also considered in the selection process. Preference is given to applicants with a farmworker background.

Financial Data The stipend is $1,000.

Duration 1 year.

Additional data This program began in 1984.

Number awarded Varies each year; recently, 12 of these scholarships were awarded. Since the program was established, it has awarded 188 of these scholarships.

Deadline March of each year.

[769]
MILBANK DIVERSITY SCHOLARS PROGRAM

Milbank, Tweed, Hadley & McCloy LLP
Attn: Manager, Diversity and Inclusion
One Chase Manhattan Plaza
New York, NY 10005
(212) 530-5316   Fax: (212) 530-5219
E-mail: syohn@milbank.com
Web: www.milbank.com

Summary To provide financial aid and work experience to law students, especially those who are Hispanic Americans or members of other groups underrepresented at large law firms.

Eligibility This program is open to students who have completed their first year of a full-time J.D. program at an ABA-accredited law school. Joint degree candidates must have successfully completed 2 years of a J.D. program. Applications are particularly encouraged from members of groups traditionally underrepresented at large law firms. Applicants must submit a 500-word essay on 1) the challenges they have faced in pursuit of a legal career that have helped them understand the value of diversity and inclusion in the legal profession; and 2) the personal contributions they would make to furthering the diversity objectives of the sponsoring law firm. Selection is based on academic achievement, demonstrated leadership ability, writing and interpersonal skills, and interest in the firm's practice.

Financial Data The stipend is $25,000. A paid associate position during the summer after the second year of law school is also provided. If the student is offered and accepts a permanent position with the firm after graduation, an additional $25,000 scholarship stipend is also awarded.

Duration 1 year (the third year of law school).

Additional data Scholars may be offered a permanent position with the firm, but there is no guarantee of such an offer.

Number awarded At least 2 each year.

Deadline August of each year.

[770]
MILLER JOHNSON WEST MICHIGAN DIVERSITY LAW SCHOOL SCHOLARSHIP

Grand Rapids Community Foundation
Attn: Education Program Officer
185 Oakes Street S.W.
Grand Rapids, MI 49503-4008
(616) 454-1751, ext. 103   Fax: (616) 454-6455
E-mail: rbishop@grfoundation.org
Web: www.grfoundation.org/scholarshipslist

Summary To provide financial assistance to Hispanic Americans and other minorities from Michigan who are attending law school in any state.

Eligibility This program is open to U.S. citizens who are students of color (African American, Asian, Hispanic, Native American, Pacific Islander) and residents of Michigan. Applicants must be attending an accredited law school in any state. They must have a GPA of 3.0 or higher and be able to demonstrate financial need.

Financial Data The stipend is $5,000. Funds are paid directly to the recipient's institution.

Duration 1 year.

Number awarded 1 each year.

Deadline March of each year.

[771]
MILLER NASH LAW STUDENT DIVERSITY FELLOWSHIP PROGRAM

Miller Nash LLP
Attn: Director of Recruiting and Professional Development
3400 U.S. Bancorp Tower
111 S.W. Fifth Avenue
Portland, OR 97204-3699
(503) 224-5858   Fax: (503) 224-0155
E-mail: MNrecruiting@millernash.com
Web: www.millernash.com

Summary To provide financial aid and work experience to Hispanic American and other law students who contribute to diversity and are interested in living and working in the Pacific Northwest following graduation from law school.

Eligibility This program is open to first- and second-year students at ABA-accredited law schools in any state. Applicants must be able to demonstrate academic excellence, interpersonal skills, leadership qualities, contributions to diversity, and meaningful contributions to the community. They must intend to work, live, and practice law in the Pacific Northwest. Along with their application, they must submit a personal statement of 2 to 4 pages that includes a description of organizations or projects in which they currently participate or have participated that address diversity issues or support diversity in their legal, business, or local communities.

Financial Data Fellows receive a paid summer clerk position and a stipend of $7,500 for law school.

Duration 1 year (including 12 weeks for the summer clerk position); nonrenewable.

Additional data Summer clerk positions may be offered (depending on availability) at the sponsoring law firm's offices in Portland (Oregon), Seattle (Washington), or Vancouver (Washington).

Number awarded Up to 2 each year.

Deadline September of each year for second-year students; January of each year for first-year students.

[772]
MINORITIES IN GOVERNMENT FINANCE SCHOLARSHIP

Government Finance Officers Association
Attn: Scholarship Committee
203 North LaSalle Street, Suite 2700
Chicago, IL 60601-1210
(312) 977-9700   Fax: (312) 977-4806
Web: www.gfoa.org

Summary To provide financial assistance to Hispanic American and other minority upper-division and graduate students who are preparing for a career in state and local government finance.

Eligibility This program is open to upper-division and graduate students who are preparing for a career in public finance by working on a degree in public administration, accounting, finance, political science, economics, or business administration (with a specific focus on government or nonprofit management). Applicants must be members of a minority group, citizens or permanent residents of the United States or Canada, and able to provide a letter of recommendation from a representative of their school. Selection is based on career

plans, academic record, plan of study, letters of recommendation, and GPA. Financial need is not considered.

Financial Data The stipend is $5,000.

Duration 1 year.

Additional data This program defines minorities as Blacks or African Americans, American Indians or Alaskan Natives, Hispanics or Latinos, Native Hawaiians or other Pacific Islanders, or Asians.

Number awarded 1 or more each year.

Deadline February of each year.

[773]
MINORITY AND UNDERREPRESENTED ENVIRONMENTAL LITERACY PROGRAM

Missouri Department of Higher Education
Attn: Minority and Underrepresented Environmental
    Literacy Program
205 Jefferson Street
P.O. Box 1469
Jefferson City, MO 65102-1469
(573) 751-2361   Toll Free: (800) 473-6757
Fax: (573) 751-6635   E-mail: info@dhe.mo.gov
Web: dhe.mo.gov/ppc/grants/muelp_0310_final.php

Summary To provide financial assistance to Hispanic American and other underrepresented students from Missouri who are or will be working on a bachelor's or master's degree in an environmental field.

Eligibility This program is open to residents of Missouri who are high school seniors or current undergraduate or graduate students enrolled or planning to enroll full time at a college or university in the state. Priority is given to members of the following underrepresented minority ethnic groups: African Americans, Hispanic or Latino Americans, Native Americans and Alaska Natives, and Native Hawaiians and Pacific Islanders. Applicants must be working on or planning to work on a bachelor's or master's degree in 1) engineering (civil, chemical, environmental, mechanical, or agricultural); 2) environmental studies (geology, biology, wildlife management, natural resource planning, natural resources, or a closely-related course of study); 3) environmental chemistry; or 4) environmental law enforcement. They must be U.S. citizens or permanent residents or otherwise lawfully present in the United States. Graduating high school seniors must have a GPA of 3.0 or higher; students currently enrolled in college or graduate school must have a GPA of 2.5 or higher. Along with their application, they must submit a 1-page essay on their environmental education and career goals, 3 letters of recommendation, a resume of school and community activities, and transcripts that include SAT or ACT scores. Financial need is not considered in the selection process.

Financial Data Stipends vary each year; recently, they averaged approximately $3,996 per year.

Duration 1 year; may be renewed if the recipient maintains a GPA of 2.5 or higher and full-time enrollment.

Additional data This program was established by the Missouri Department of Natural Resources but transferred to the Department of Higher Education in 2009.

Number awarded Varies each year.

Deadline May of each year.

[774]
MINORITY FACULTY DEVELOPMENT SCHOLARSHIP AWARD IN PHYSICAL THERAPY

American Physical Therapy Association
Attn: Honors and Awards Program
1111 North Fairfax Street
Alexandria, VA 22314-1488
(703) 684-APTA   Toll Free: (800) 999-APTA
Fax: (703) 684-7343   TDD: (703) 683-6748
E-mail: honorsandawards@apta.org
Web: www.apta.org

Summary To provide financial assistance to Hispanic American and other minority faculty members in physical therapy who are interested in working on a post-professional doctoral degree.

Eligibility This program is open to U.S. citizens and permanent residents who are members of the following minority groups: African American or Black, Asian, Native Hawaiian or other Pacific Islander, American Indian or Alaska Native, or Hispanic/Latino. Applicants must be full-time faculty members, teaching in an accredited or developing professional physical therapist education program, who will have completed the equivalent of 2 full semesters of post-professional doctoral course work. They must possess a license to practice physical therapy in a U.S. jurisdiction and be enrolled as a student in an accredited post-professional doctoral program whose content has a demonstrated relationship to physical therapy. Along with their application, they must submit a personal essay on their professional goals, including their plans to contribute to the profession and minority services. Selection is based on 1) commitment to minority affairs and services; 2) commitment to further the physical therapy profession through teaching and research; and 3) scholastic achievement.

Financial Data A stipend is awarded (amount not specified).

Duration 1 year.

Additional data This program began in 1999.

Number awarded 1 or more each year.

Deadline November of each year.

[775]
MINORITY FELLOWSHIPS IN EDUCATION RESEARCH

American Educational Research Association
1430 K Street, N.W., Suite 1200
Washington, DC 20005
(202) 238-3200   Fax: (202) 238-3250
E-mail: fellowships@aera.net
Web: www.aera.net

Summary To provide funding to Hispanic American and other minority doctoral students writing their dissertation on educational research.

Eligibility This program is open to U.S. citizens and permanent residents who have advanced to candidacy and successfully defended their Ph.D./Ed.D. dissertation research proposal. Applicants must plan to work full time on their dissertation in educational research. This program is targeted for members of groups historically underrepresented in higher education (African Americans, American Indians, Alaskan Natives, Asian Americans, Native Hawaiian or Pacific Islanders, and Hispanics or Latinos). Selection is based on scholarly achievements and publications, letters of recommendation, quality and significance of the proposed research, and commitment of the applicant's faculty mentor to the goals of the program.

Financial Data The grant is $12,000. Up to $1,000 is provided to pay for travel to the sponsor's annual conference.

Duration 1 year; nonrenewable.

Additional data This program began in 1991.

Number awarded Up to 3 each year.

Deadline November of each year.

[776]
MINORITY LEAP SCHOLARSHIPS

Missouri Society of Certified Public Accountants
Attn: LEAP Program
540 Maryville Centre Drive, Suite 200
P.O. Box 419042
St. Louis, MO 63141-9042
(314) 997-7966, ext. 125
Toll Free: (800) 264-7966, ext. 125 (within MO)
Fax: (314) 997-2592   E-mail: lsimpson@mocpa.org
Web: www.mocpa.org/students/scholarships

Summary To provide financial assistance to Hispanic American and other minority residents of Missouri who are working on an undergraduate or graduate degree in accounting at a university in the state.

Eligibility This program is open to members of minority groups underrepresented in the accounting profession (Black/African American, Hispanic/Latino, Native American, Asian American) who are currently working full time on an undergraduate or graduate degree in accounting at a college or university in Missouri. Applicants must either be residents of Missouri or the children of members of the Missouri Society of Certified Public Accountants (MSCPA). They must be U.S. citizens, have completed at least 30 semester hours of college work, have a GPA of 3.3 or higher, and be student members of the MSCPA. Selection is based on the GPA, involvement in MSCPA, educator recommendations, and leadership potential. Financial need is not considered.

Financial Data The stipend is $1,250 per year.

Duration 1 year; may be renewed.

Additional data These scholarships are offered through the sponsor's Lead and Enhance the Accounting Profession (LEAP) program, established in 2001.

Number awarded Varies each year; recently, 2 of these scholarships were awarded.

Deadline February of each year.

[777]
MINORITY MEDICAL STUDENT AWARD PROGRAM OF THE AMERICAN SOCIETY OF HEMATOLOGY

American Society of Hematology
Attn: Awards Manager
2021 L Street, N.W., Suite 900
Washington, DC 20036
(202) 776-0544   Fax: (202) 776-0545
E-mail: awards@hematology.org
Web: www.hematology.org/Awards/MMSAP/2624.aspx

Summary To provide an opportunity for Hispanic American and other underrepresented minority medical students to conduct a research project in hematology.

Eligibility This program is open to medical students enrolled in D.O., M.D., or M.D./Ph.D. programs in the United States or Canada who are members of minority groups. For purposes of this program, minority is defined as a member of a racial or ethnic group that has been shown to be underrepresented in health-related sciences in the United States and Canada, including American Indians, Alaska Natives, Blacks or African Americans, Hispanics or Latinos, Native Hawaiians, other Pacific Islanders, African Canadians, Inuit, and First Nation Peoples. Applicants must be interested in conducting a research project in hematology at their home institution or at another institution that has agreed to host them. They must work with 2 mentors who are members of the American Society of Hematology (ASH): a research mentor who oversees the participant's work and progress and a career development mentor (who is from the same minority group as the student) who participates for the duration of the program. U.S. or Canadian citizenship or permanent resident status is required.

Financial Data The grant includes $5,000 for research support, an additional $1,000 to support travel to the annual meeting of the ASH, and another $1,000 for making a short presentation about the research experience at a special reception at the ASH annual meeting. Research mentors receive an allowance of $2,000 for supplies and $1,000 for attendance at the ASH annual meeting. Career development mentors receives $1,000 as a travel allowance each time they accompany the student to an ASH annual meeting during their remaining years of medical school and residency.

Duration 8 to 12 weeks.

Additional data This program is supported by Amgen, Celgene Corporation, Cephalon Oncology, and Genentech BioOncology.

Number awarded Up to 10 each year.

Deadline March of each year.

[778]
MINORITY MEDICAL STUDENT ELECTIVE IN HIV PSYCHIATRY

American Psychiatric Association
Attn: Office of HIV Psychiatry
1000 Wilson Boulevard, Suite 1825
Arlington, VA 22209-3901
(703) 907-8668   Toll Free: (888) 357-7849
Fax: (703) 907-1087   E-mail: dpennessi@psych.org
Web: www.psychiatry.org

Summary To provide an opportunity for Hispanic American and other minority medical students to spend an elective residency learning about HIV psychiatry.

Eligibility This program is open to medical students entering their fourth year at an accredited M.D. or D.O. degree-granting institution. Preference is given to minority candidates and those who have primary interests in services related to HIV/AIDS and substance abuse and its relationship to the mental health or the psychological well-being of ethnic minorities. Applicants should be interested in a psychiatry, internal medicine, pediatrics, or research career. They must be interested in participating in a program that includes intense training in HIV mental health (including neuropsychiatry), a clini-

cal and/or research experience working with a mentor, and participation in the Committee on AIDS of the American Psychiatric Association (APA). U.S. citizenship is required.

Financial Data A small stipend is provided (amount not specified).

Duration 1 year.

Additional data The heart of the program is in establishing a mentor relationship at 1 of 5 sites, becoming involved with a cohort of medical students interested in HIV medicine/psychiatry, participating in an interactive didactic/experimental learning program, and developing expertise in areas related to ethnic minority mental health research or psychiatric services. Students selected for the program who are not APA members automatically receive membership.

Number awarded Varies each year.

Deadline March of each year.

[779]
MINORITY MEDICAL STUDENT SUMMER EXTERNSHIP IN ADDICTION PSYCHIATRY

American Psychiatric Association
Attn: Department of Minority and National Affairs
1000 Wilson Boulevard, Suite 1825
Arlington, VA 22209-3901
(703) 907-8653   Toll Free: (888) 35-PSYCH
Fax: (703) 907-7852   E-mail: mking@psych.org
Web: www.psychiatry.org

Summary To provide funding to Hispanic American and other minority medical students who are interested in working on a research project during the summer with a mentor who specializes in addiction psychiatry.

Eligibility This program is open to minority medical students who have a specific interest in services related to substance abuse treatment and prevention. Minorities include American Indians, Alaska Natives, Native Hawaiians, Asian Americans, Hispanics/Latinos, and African Americans. Applicants must be interested in working with a mentor who specializes in addiction psychiatry. Work settings provide an emphasis on working clinically with or studying underserved minority populations and issues of co-occurring disorders, substance abuse treatment, and mental health disparity. Most of them are in inner-city or rural settings.

Financial Data Externships provide $1,500 for travel expenses to go to the work setting of the mentor and up to another $1,500 for out-of-pocket expenses directly related to the conduct of the externship.

Duration 1 month during the summer.

Additional data Funding for this program is provided by the Substance Abuse and Mental Health Services Administration (SAMHSA).

Number awarded 10 each year.

Deadline February of each year.

[780]
MINORITY MEDICAL STUDENT SUMMER MENTORING PROGRAM

American Psychiatric Association
Attn: Department of Minority and National Affairs
1000 Wilson Boulevard, Suite 1825
Arlington, VA 22209-3901
(703) 907-8653   Toll Free: (888) 35-PSYCH
Fax: (703) 907-7852   E-mail: mking@psych.org
Web: www.psychiatry.org

Summary   To provide an opportunity for Hispanic American and other minority medical students to spend an elective residency learning about HIV psychiatry.

Eligibility   This program is open to minority medical students who are interested in psychiatric issues. Minorities include American Indians, Alaska Natives, Native Hawaiians, Asian Americans, Hispanic/Latinos, and African Americans. Applicants must be interested in working with a psychiatrist mentor, primarily on clinical work with underserved minority populations and mental health care disparities. Work settings may be in a research, academic, or clinical environment. Most of them are inner-city or rural and deal with psychiatric subspecialties, particularly substance abuse and geriatrics. Selection is based on interest of the medical student and specialty of the mentor, practice setting, and geographic proximity of the mentor to the student. U.S. citizenship or permanent resident status is required.

Financial Data   Fellowships provide $1,500 for living and out-of-pocket expenses directly related to the conduct of the fellowship.

Duration   Summer months.

Additional data   This program is funded by the Substance Abuse and Mental Health Services Administration.

Number awarded   Varies each year.

Deadline   March of each year.

[781]
MINORITY NURSE MAGAZINE SCHOLARSHIP PROGRAM

Minority Nurse Magazine
c/o Alloy Education
2 LAN Drive, Suite 100
Westford, MA 01886
Toll Free: (877) ASK-ALLO
E-mail: editor@minoritynurse.com
Web: www.minoritynurse.com

Summary   To provide financial assistance to Hispanic Americans and members of other minority groups who are working on a bachelor's or master's degree in nursing.

Eligibility   This program is open to students currently enrolled in 1) the third or fourth year of an accredited B.S.N. program; 2) an accelerated program leading to a B.S.N. degree (e.g., R.N. to B.S.N., B.A. to B.S.N.); or 3) an accelerated master's entry nursing program (e.g., B.A. to M.S.N.) for students with bachelor's degrees in fields other than nursing. Graduate students who already have a bachelor's degree in nursing are not eligible. Along with their application, they must submit a 250-word essay on their academic and personal accomplishments, community service, and goals for their future nursing career. Selection is based on academic excellence (GPA of 3.0 or higher), demonstrated commitment

of service to the student's minority community, and financial need. U.S. citizenship of permanent resident status is required.

Financial Data   The stipends are $3,000 or $1,000.

Duration   1 year.

Additional data   This program began in 2000. Winners are announced in the summer issue of *Minority Nurse* magazine.

Number awarded   3 each year: 1 at $3,000 and 2 at $1,000.

Deadline   January of each year.

[782]
MINORITY PRE-DOCTORAL FELLOWSHIP IN CLINICAL PHARMACEUTICAL SCIENCE

American Foundation for Pharmaceutical Education
Attn: Grants Manager
2107 Wilson Boulevard, Suite 700
Arlington, VA 22201-3042
(703) 875-3095   Fax: (703) 875-3098
E-mail: info@afpenet.org
Web: www.afpenet.org/applicant.htm

Summary   To provide funding for dissertation research to Hispanic American and Hispanic graduate students working on a Ph.D. in clinical pharmaceutical science.

Eligibility   This program is open to African American/Black and Hispanic/Latino students who have completed at least 3 semesters of graduate study and have no more than 3 and a half years remaining to complete a Ph.D. in clinical pharmaceutical science at a U.S. school or college of pharmacy. Students enrolled in joint Pharm.D./Ph.D. programs are eligible if they have completed 3 full semesters of graduate credit toward the Ph.D. and if the Ph.D. degree will be awarded within 3 additional years. Applicants must be U.S. citizens or permanent residents. Along with their application, they must submit 1) a brief statement on their objective in pursuing graduate study; 2) a brief statement on their future career plans; and 3) a description of their dissertation research project that includes its nature and scope, area of research, hypothesis to be tested, plan of investigation, and methodologies to be employed. Students with the following majors are encouraged to apply: clinical pharmaceutical sciences, medicinal/pharmaceutical chemistry, pharmaceutics, pharmacology/toxicology, pharmacognosy, pharmacoeconomics and health outcomes, pharmacokinetics/metabolism, pharmacotherapy and experimental therapeutics, or social and administrative science.

Financial Data   The grant is $6,500 per year. Funds must be used to enable the students to make progress on their Ph.D. (e.g., student stipend, laboratory supplies, books, materials, travel) but not for indirect costs for the institution.

Duration   1 year; may be renewed 1 additional year.

Number awarded   Up to 5 each year.

Deadline   February of each year.

[783]
MINORITY PRE-DOCTORAL FELLOWSHIP IN PHARMACEUTICAL SCIENCE

American Foundation for Pharmaceutical Education
Attn: Grants Manager
2107 Wilson Boulevard, Suite 700
Arlington, VA 22201-3042
(703) 875-3095   Fax: (703) 875-3098
E-mail: info@afpenet.org
Web: www.afpenet.org/applicant.htm

Summary To provide funding for dissertation research to Hispanic and African American graduate students working on a Ph.D. in pharmaceutical science.

Eligibility This program is open to African American/Black and Hispanic/Latino students who have completed at least 3 semesters of graduate study and have no more than 3 and a half years remaining to complete a Ph.D. in pharmaceutical science at a U.S. school or college of pharmacy. Students enrolled in joint Pharm.D./Ph.D. programs are eligible if they have completed 3 full semesters of graduate credit toward the Ph.D. and if the Ph.D. degree will be awarded within 3 additional years. Applicants must be U.S. citizens or permanent residents. Along with their application, they must submit 1) a brief statement on their objective in pursuing graduate study; 2) a brief statement on their future career plans; and 3) a description of their dissertation research project that includes its nature and scope, area of research, hypothesis to be tested, plan of investigation, and methodologies to be employed. Students with the following majors are encouraged to apply: pharmaceutical sciences, medicinal/pharmaceutical chemistry, pharmaceutics, pharmacology/toxicology, pharmacognosy, pharmacoeconomics and health outcomes, pharmacokinetics/metabolism, pharmacotherapy and experimental therapeutics, or social and administrative science.

Financial Data The grant is $6,000 per year. Funds must be used to enable the students to make progress on their Ph.D. (e.g., student stipend, laboratory supplies, books, materials, travel) but not for indirect costs for the institution.

Duration 1 year; may be renewed 1 additional year.

Number awarded Up to 5 each year.

Deadline February of each year.

[784]
MINORITY TEACHERS OF ILLINOIS SCHOLARSHIP PROGRAM

Illinois Student Assistance Commission
Attn: Scholarship and Grant Services
1755 Lake Cook Road
Deerfield, IL 60015-5209
(847) 948-8550   Toll Free: (800) 899-ISAC
Fax: (847) 831-8549   TDD: (800) 526-0844
E-mail: isac.studentservices@isac.illinois.gov
Web: www.collegeillinois.org

Summary To provide funding to Hispanic American and other minority students in Illinois who plan to become teachers at the preschool, elementary, or secondary level.

Eligibility Applicants must be Illinois residents, U.S. citizens or eligible noncitizens, members of a minority group (African American/Black, Hispanic American, Asian American, or Native American), and high school graduates or holders of a General Educational Development (GED) certificate. They must be enrolled at least half time as an undergraduate or graduate student, have a GPA of 2.5 or higher, not be in default on any student loan, and be enrolled or accepted for enrollment in a teacher education program.

Financial Data Grants up to $5,000 per year are awarded. This is a scholarship/loan program. Recipients must agree to teach full time 1 year for each year of support received. The teaching agreement may be fulfilled at a public, private, or parochial preschool, elementary school, or secondary school in Illinois; at least 30% of the student body at those schools must be minority. It must be fulfilled within the 5-year period following the completion of the undergraduate program for which the scholarship was awarded. The time period may be extended if the recipient serves in the U.S. armed forces, enrolls full time in a graduate program related to teaching, becomes temporarily disabled, is unable to find employment as a teacher at a qualifying school, or takes additional courses on at least a half-time basis to obtain certification as a teacher in Illinois. Recipients who fail to honor this work obligation must repay the award with 5% interest.

Duration 1 year; may be renewed for a total of 8 semesters or 12 quarters.

Number awarded Varies each year.

Deadline Priority consideration is given to applications received by February of each year.

[785]
MIRIAM WEINSTEIN PEACE AND JUSTICE EDUCATION AWARD

Philanthrofund Foundation
Attn: Scholarship Committee
1409 Willow Street, Suite 109
Minneapolis, MN 55403-2241
(612) 870-1806   Toll Free: (800) 435-1402
Fax: (612) 871-6587   E-mail: info@PfundOnline.org
Web: www.pfundonline.org/scholarships.html

Summary To provide financial assistance to Hispanic American and other minority students from Minnesota who have supported gay, lesbian, bisexual, and transgender (GLBT) activities and are interested in working on a degree in education.

Eligibility This program is open to residents of Minnesota and students attending a Minnesota educational institution who are members of a religious, racial, or ethnic minority. Applicants must be self-identified as GLBT or from a GLBT family and have demonstrated a commitment to peace and justice issues. They may be attending or planning to attend trade school, technical college, college, or university (as an undergraduate or graduate student). Preference is given to students who have completed at least 2 years of college and are working on a degree in education. Selection is based on the applicant's 1) affirmation of GLBT or allied identity; 2) evidence of experience and skills in service and leadership; and 3) evidence of service, leading, and working for change in GLBT communities, including serving as a role model, mentor, and/or adviser.

Financial Data The stipend is $3,000. Funds must be used for tuition, books, fees, or dissertation expenses.

Duration 1 year.

Number awarded 1 each year.

Deadline January of each year.

[786]
MLA/NLM SPECTRUM SCHOLARSHIPS

Medical Library Association
Attn: Grants and Scholarships
65 East Wacker Place, Suite 1900
Chicago, IL 60601-7246
(312) 419-9094, ext. 15   Fax: (312) 419-8950
E-mail: grants@mlahq.org
Web: www.mlanet.org/awards/grants

Summary To provide financial assistance to Hispanic Americans and other minorities who are interested in preparing for a career as a medical librarian.

Eligibility This program is open to members of minority groups (African Americans, Hispanics, Asian, Native Americans, and Pacific Islanders) who are attending library schools accredited by the American Library Association (ALA). Applicants must be interested in preparing for a career as a health sciences information professional.

Financial Data The stipend is $3,250.

Duration 1 year.

Additional data This program, established in 2001, is jointly sponsored by the Medical Library Association (MLA) and the National Library of Medicine (NLM) of the U.S. National Institutes of Health (NIH). It operates as a component of the Spectrum Initiative Scholarship program of the ALA.

Number awarded 2 each year.

Deadline February of each year.

[787]
MORGAN STANLEY MBA FELLOWSHIP

Morgan Stanley
Attn: Diversity Recruiting
1585 Broadway
New York, NY 10036
(212) 762-0211   Toll Free: (888) 454-3965
Fax: (212) 507-4972
E-mail: mbafellowship@morganstanley.com
Web: www.morganstanley.com

Summary To provide financial aid and work experience to Hispanic Americans and members of other underrepresented groups who are working on an M.B.A. degree.

Eligibility This program is open to full-time M.B.A. students who are women, African Americans, Hispanics, Native Americans, or lesbian/gay/bisexual/transgender. Selection is based on assigned essays, academic achievement, recommendations, extracurricular activities, leadership qualities, and on-site interviews.

Financial Data The program provides full payment of tuition and fees and a paid summer internship.

Duration 1 year; may be renewed for a second year, providing the student remains enrolled full time in good academic standing and completes the summer internship following the first year.

Additional data The paid summer internship is offered within Morgan Stanley institutional securities (equity research, fixed income, institutional equity, investment banking), investment management, or private wealth management. This program was established in 1999.

Number awarded 1 or more each year.

Deadline December of each year.

[788]
MOSAIC SCHOLARSHIPS

Society of American Archivists
Attn: Chair, Awards Committee
17 North State Street, Suite 1425
Chicago, IL 60602-4061
(312) 606-0722   Toll Free: (866) 722-7858
Fax: (312) 606-0728   E-mail: info@archivists.org
Web: www.archivists.org/recognition

Summary To provide financial assistance to Hispanic American and other minority students who are working on a graduate degree in archival science.

Eligibility This program is open to minority graduate students, defined as those of American Indian/Alaska Native, Asian, Black/African American, Hispanic/Latino, or Native Hawaiian/other Pacific Islander descent. Applicants must be enrolled or planning to enroll full or part time in a graduate program or a multi-course program in archival administration. They may have completed no more than half of the credit requirements for a degree. Along with their application, they must submit a 500-word essay outlining their interests and future goals in the archives profession. U.S. or Canadian citizenship or permanent resident status is required.

Financial Data The stipend is $5,000.

Duration 1 year.

Additional data This program began in 2009.

Number awarded 2 each year.

Deadline February of each year.

[789]
MOSS ADAMS FOUNDATION SCHOLARSHIP

Educational Foundation for Women in Accounting
Attn: Foundation Administrator
136 South Keowee Street
Dayton, OH 45402
(937) 424-3391   Fax: (937) 222-5749
E-mail: info@efwa.org
Web: www.efwa.org/scholarships_MossAdams.php

Summary To provide financial support to women (preference given to Hispanic American and other minority women) who are working on an accounting degree.

Eligibility This program is open to women who are enrolled in an accounting degree program at an accredited college or university. Applicants must meet 1 of the following criteria: 1) women pursuing a fifth-year requirement either through general studies or within a graduate program; 2) women returning to school as current or reentry juniors or seniors; or 3) minority women. Selection is based on aptitude for accounting and business, commitment to the goal of working on a degree in accounting (including evidence of continued commitment after receiving this award), clear evidence that the candidate has established goals and a plan for achieving those goals (both personal and professional), financial need, and a demonstration of how the scholarship will impact her life. U.S. citizenship is required.

Financial Data The stipend is $1,000.

Duration 1 year.

Additional data This program was established by Rowling, Dold & Associates LLP, a woman-owned C.P.A. firm based in San Diego. It was renamed when that firm merged with Moss Adams LLP.

Number awarded 1 each year.

Deadline April of each year.

[790]
M&T BANK SCHOLARSHIP PROGRAM

Hispanic College Fund
Attn: Scholarship Processing
1300 L Street, N.W., Suite 975
Washington, DC 20005
(202) 296-5400   Toll Free: (800) 644-4223
Fax: (202) 296-3774   E-mail: hcf-info@hispanicfund.org
Web: scholarships.hispanicfund.org/applications

Summary To provide financial assistance to Hispanic American undergraduate and graduate students from designated areas who plan to work on a degree in a field related to banking at a school in the United States or Puerto Rico.

Eligibility This program is open to U.S. citizens and permanent residents of Hispanic background (at least 1 grandparent must be 100% Hispanic) who reside in the Washington, D.C. region, New York, or Pennsylvania. Applicants must be enrolled or planning to enroll full time at a college or university in the United States or Puerto Rico and work on an undergraduate or graduate degree in a field related to banking, including accounting, business, or finance. They must have a GPA of 3.0 or higher and be able to demonstrate financial need. Preference is given to applicants who have a strong record of community service.

Financial Data This stipend ranges from $2,000 to $3,000. Funds are paid directly to the recipient's college or university to help cover tuition and fees.

Duration 1 year.

Additional data This program is sponsored by M&T Bank. All applications must be submitted online; no paper applications are available.

Number awarded 1 or more each year.

Deadline February of each year.

[791]
NAHJ FORD MOTOR COMPANY SCHOLARSHIPS

National Association of Hispanic Journalists
Attn: Scholarship Committee
1050 Connecticut Avenue, N.W., Tenth Floor
Washington, DC 20036
(202) 662-7145   Toll Free: (888) 346-NAHJ
Fax: (202) 662-7144   E-mail: nahj@nahj.org
Web: www.nahj12.com/scholarships

Summary To provide financial assistance to undergraduate and graduate student members of the National Association of Hispanic Journalists (NAHJ) who are interested in preparing for careers in the media.

Eligibility This program is open to Hispanic American high school seniors, undergraduates, and graduate students who are interested in preparing for a career in print, broadcast (radio or television), online, or visual journalism. Applicants must be enrolled full time at a college or university in the United States or Puerto Rico. They must have a GPA of 2.0 or higher and be NAHJ members. Along with their application, they must submit transcripts, a 1-page resume, 2 letters of recommendation, work samples, and a 1,000-word autobiographical essay that includes why they are interested in a career in journalism, what inspired them to prepare for a

career in the field, what hardships or obstacles they have experienced while trying to realize their goal of becoming a journalist, and the role Latino journalists play in the news industry. Selection is based on commitment to the field of journalism, academic achievement, awareness of the Latino community, and financial need.

Financial Data Stipends range up to $2,500.

Duration 1 year; may be renewed until completion of a college degree.

Additional data This program is sponsored by Ford Motor Company.

Number awarded Varies each year; recently, 8 of these scholarships were awarded.

Deadline January of each year.

[792]
NASCAR/WENDELL SCOTT AWARD

Hispanic Association of Colleges and Universities
Attn: National Scholarship Program
8415 Datapoint Drive, Suite 400
San Antonio, TX 78229
(210) 692-3805   Fax: (210) 692-0823
TDD: (800) 855-2880   E-mail: scholarship@hacu.net
Web: www.hacu.net/hacu/Scholarships.asp

Summary To provide financial assistance to undergraduate and graduate students majoring in specified fields at member institutions of the Hispanic Association of Colleges and Universities (HACU) in designated states.

Eligibility This program is open to full-time undergraduate and graduate students at 4-year HACU member institutions in Florida, Georgia, or North Carolina. Applicants must be working on a degree in business, engineering, management, marketing, mass media, public relations, sports marketing, or technology. They must have a GPA of 3.0 or higher and be able to demonstrate financial need. Along with their application, they must submit an essay that focuses on their personal motivation for applying to this scholarship program, their academic and/or career goals, and the skills they could bring to an employer.

Financial Data The stipend is $2,200.

Duration 1 year.

Additional data This program is sponsored by NASCAR and administered by HACU.

Number awarded 1 or more each year.

Deadline June of each year.

[793]
NATIONAL ASSOCIATION OF HISPANIC JOURNALISTS BROADCAST SCHOLARSHIPS

National Association of Hispanic Journalists
Attn: Scholarship Committee
1050 Connecticut Avenue, N.W., Tenth Floor
Washington, DC 20036
(202) 662-7145   Toll Free: (888) 346-NAHJ
Fax: (202) 662-7144   E-mail: nahj@nahj.org
Web: www.nahj12.com/scholarships

Summary To provide financial assistance to undergraduate and graduate student members of the National Association of Hispanic Journalists (NAHJ) who are interested in preparing for a career in television broadcast journalism.

Eligibility This program is open to Hispanic American undergraduate and graduate students who are interested in preparing for a career in television broadcast journalism. Applicants must be enrolled full time at a college or university in the United States or Puerto Rico. They must be NAHJ members. Along with their application, they must submit transcripts, a 1-page resume, 2 letters of recommendation, work samples, and a 1,000-word autobiographical essay that includes why they are interested in a career in journalism, what inspired them to prepare for a career in the field, what hardships or obstacles they have experienced while trying to realize their goal of becoming a journalist, and the role Latino journalists play in the news industry. Selection is based on commitment to the field of journalism, academic achievement, awareness of the Latino community, and financial need.

Financial Data The stipend ranges up to $5,000.

Duration 1 year.

Additional data This program includes the Soledad O'Brien Scholarship and the Jane Velez-Mitchell Scholarship.

Number awarded 2 each year.

Deadline January of each year.

[794]
NATIONAL ASSOCIATION OF HISPANIC NURSES SCHOLARSHIPS

National Association of Hispanic Nurses
Attn: National Awards and Scholarship Committee Chair
1455 Pennsylvania Avenue, N.W., Suite 400
Washington, DC 20004
(202) 387-2477   Fax: (202) 483-7183
E-mail: info@thehispanicnurses.org
Web: www.nahnnet.org/NAHNScholarships.html

Summary To provide financial assistance for nursing education to members of the National Association of Hispanic Nurses (NAHN).

Eligibility Eligible are members of the association enrolled in associate, diploma, baccalaureate, graduate, or practical/vocational nursing programs at NLN-accredited schools of nursing. Applicants must have a GPA of 3.0 or higher. Along with their application, they must submit a letter of recommendation; a 300-word essay that reflects their qualifications and potential for leadership in nursing in the Hispanic community; a resume that includes earned certificates, awards, and special honors; information on their financial status; and an official transcript. U.S. citizenship or permanent resident status is required.

Financial Data The stipend is $2,500.

Duration 1 year.

Additional data Support for this program is provided by Lilly USA, LLC.

Number awarded Varies each year; recently, 4 of these scholarships were awarded.

Deadline June of each year.

[795]
NATIONAL ASSOCIATION OF SCHOOL PSYCHOLOGISTS MINORITY SCHOLARSHIP

National Association of School Psychologists
Attn: Education and Research Trust
4340 East-West Highway, Suite 402
Bethesda, MD 20814
(301) 657-0270   Toll Free: (866) 331-NASP
Fax: (301) 657-0275   TDD: (301) 657-4155
E-mail: kbritton@naspweb.org
Web: www.nasponline.org

Summary To provide financial assistance to Hispanic American and other minority graduate students who are members of the National Association of School Psychologists (NASP) and enrolled in a school psychology program.

Eligibility This program is open to minority students who are NASP members enrolled in a regionally-accredited school psychology program in the United States. Applicants must have a GPA of 3.0 or higher. Doctoral candidates are not eligible. Applications must be accompanied by 1) a resume that includes undergraduate and/or graduate schools attended, awards and honors, student and professional activities, work and volunteer experiences, research and publications, workshops or other presentations, and any special skills, training, or experience, such as bilingualism, teaching experience, or mental health experience; 2) a statement, up to 1,000 words, of professional goals; 3) at least 2 letters of recommendation, including at least 1 from a faculty member from their undergraduate or graduate studies (if a first-year student) or at least 1 from a faculty member of their school psychology program (if a second- or third-year student); 4) a completed financial statement; 5) an official transcript of all graduate course work (first-year students may submit an official undergraduate transcript); 6) other personal accomplishments that the applicant wishes to be considered; and 7) a letter of acceptance from a school psychology program for first-year applicants. U.S. citizenship is required.

Financial Data The stipend is $5,000 per year.

Duration 1 year; may be renewed up to 2 additional years.

Number awarded Varies each year; recently, 4 of these scholarships were awarded.

Deadline October of each year.

[796]
NATIONAL DEFENSE SCIENCE AND ENGINEERING GRADUATE FELLOWSHIP PROGRAM

American Society for Engineering Education
Attn: NDSEG Fellowship Program
1818 N Street, N.W., Suite 600
Washington, DC 20036-2479
(202) 649-3831   Fax: (202) 265-8504
E-mail: ndseg@asee.org
Web: ndseg.asee.org

Summary To provide financial assistance to students (particularly Hispanic Americans, other minorities, women, and students with disabilities) who are working on a doctoral degree in areas of science and engineering that are of potential military importance.

Eligibility This program is open to U.S. citizens and nationals entering or enrolled in the early stages of a doctoral program in aeronautical and astronautical engineering; biosciences, including toxicology; chemical engineering; chemistry; civil engineering; cognitive, neural, and behavioral sciences; computer and computational sciences; electrical engineering; geosciences, including terrain, water, and air; materials science and engineering; mathematics; mechanical engineering; naval architecture and ocean engineering; oceanography; or physics, including optics. Applicants must be enrolled or planning to enroll as full-time students. Applications are particularly encouraged from women, members of ethnic minority groups (American Indians, African Americans, Hispanics or Latinos, Native Hawaiians, Alaska Natives, Asians, and Pacific Islanders), and persons with disabilities. Selection is based on all available evidence of ability, including academic records, letters of recommendation, and GRE scores.

Financial Data The annual stipend is $30,500 for the first year, $31,000 for the second year; and $31,500 for the third year; the program also pays the recipient's institution full tuition and required fees (not to include room and board). Medical insurance is covered up to $1,000 per year.

Duration 3 years, as long as satisfactory academic progress is maintained.

Additional data This program is sponsored by the High Performance Computing Modernization Program within the Department of Defense, the Army Research Office, the Air Force Office of Scientific Research, and the Office of Naval Research. Recipients do not incur any military or other service obligation.

Number awarded Approximately 200 each year.

Deadline December of each year.

[797]
NATIONAL ESTUARINE RESEARCH RESERVE SYSTEM GRADUATE FELLOWSHIPS

National Oceanic and Atmospheric Administration
Attn: Estuarine Reserves Division
1305 East-West Highway
N/ORMS, SSMC4, Station 10503
Silver Spring, MD 20910
(301) 713-3155, ext. 105   Fax: (301) 713-4367
E-mail: Alison.Krepp@noaa.gov
Web: www.nerrs.noaa.gov/Fellowship.aspx

Summary To provide funding to graduate students (particularly Hispanic Americans and other minorities) who are interested in conducting research within the National Estuarine Research Reserve System (NERRS).

Eligibility This program is open to students admitted to or enrolled in a full-time master's or doctoral program at U.S. accredited universities. Applicants should have completed a majority of their course work at the beginning of their fellowship and have an approved thesis research program focused on improving coastal zone management while providing hands-on training in conducting ecological monitoring. Proposed research topics must address 1 of the following topics: 1) eutrophication, effects of non-point source pollution and/or nutrient dynamics; 2) habitat conservation and/or restoration; 3) biodiversity and/or the effects of invasive species; 4) mechanisms for sustaining resources within estuarine ecosystems; or 5) economic, sociological, and/or anthropological research applicable to estuarine ecosystem management. They must be willing to conduct their research within the NERRS. Minor-

ity students are specifically encouraged to apply. Selection is based on academic record and a statement of career goals and objectives (5%), quality of proposed research and its applicability to the NERRS research focus areas (70%), the research's applicability to specific reserve research and resource management goals (20%), and recommendations and endorsements (5%).

Financial Data The stipend is $28,5720 per year, of which the federal government provides $20,000 and the recipient's institution provides $8,572 as matching funds. Grants may be used for any combination of research support, salary, tuition, supplies, or other costs as needed, including overhead.

Duration 1 to 3 years.

Additional data This program began in 1997. For a list of the National Estuarine Research Reserves, with the name and address of a coordinator at each, contact NERRS. Fellows are required to work with the research coordinator or manager at the host reserve to develop a plan to participate in the reserve's research and/or monitoring program for up to 15 hours per week.

Number awarded Varies each year; recently, 9 of these fellowships were available.

Deadline October of each year.

[798]
NATIONAL HISPANIC BUSINESS WOMEN ASSOCIATION EDUCATIONAL SCHOLARSHIPS

National Hispanic Business Women Association
2024 North Broadway, Suite 100
Santa Ana, CA 92706
(714) 836-4042
Web: nationalhbwa.com/main/?page_id=367

Summary To provide financial assistance to women in California who are working on an undergraduate or graduate degree at a school in any state and submit an essay related to Latinas in education.

Eligibility This program is open to female residents of California who are currently enrolled as undergraduate or graduate students at a school in any state. Applicants must have a GPA of 3.0 or higher and be able to demonstrate financial need. They must also have a record of participation in some form of community service. Along with their application, they must submit 2 essays of 2 pages each on 1) their academic and professional goals; and 2) the importance or value of obtaining a higher education, the potential impacts or influences of a growing Latino population in relation to their field of interest, or the specific challenges faced by Latinas in pursuit of higher education.

Financial Data Stipends range from $500 to $1,000.

Duration 1 year.

Number awarded Varies each year; recently, 13 of these scholarships were awarded.

Deadline March of each year.

[799]
NATIONAL HISPANIC FOUNDATION FOR THE ARTS SCHOLARSHIP PROGRAM

National Hispanic Foundation for the Arts
Attn: Scholarship Selection Committee
1050 Connecticut Avenue, N.W., Tenth Floor
Washington, DC 20007
(202) 293-8330   Fax: (202) 722-3101
E-mail: info@hispanicarts.org
Web: www.hispanicarts.org

Summary   To provide financial assistance to Hispanic students working on a graduate degree in fields related to the performing arts at designated universities.

Eligibility   This program is open to U.S. citizens and permanent residents who are of Hispanic heritage (1 parent fully Hispanic or each parent half Hispanic). Applicants must be enrolled full time at a designated university and working on a graduate degree in drama/theater, set design/costume design, lighting design, film (writing/directing/producing), broadcast communications, entertainment law, or business administration with an emphasis on entertainment management. They must have a GPA of 3.0 or higher. Selection is based on academic record, academic plans and career goals, financial need, community service, an essay, a letter of recommendation, and a portfolio.

Financial Data   A stipend is awarded (amount not specified).

Duration   1 year.

Additional data   The designated universities are Columbia University, Harvard University, New York University, Northwestern, University of California at Los Angeles, University of Southern California, University of Texas at Austin, and Yale University.

Number awarded   Varies each year; since its founding in 1997, this foundation has awarded more than 350 scholarships worth more than $1 million.

Deadline   July of each year.

[800]
NATIONAL HISPANIC HEALTH PROFESSIONAL STUDENT SCHOLARSHIP

National Hispanic Medical Association
Attn: National Hispanic Health Foundation
1411 K Street, Suite 1100
Washington, DC 20005
(202) 628-5895   Fax: (202) 628-5898
E-mail: scholarship@nhmamd.org
Web: www.nhmafoundation.org/scholarshipprogram.html

Summary   To provide financial assistance to Hispanic students from California, Connecticut, New Jersey, and New York who are working on a health-related degree at a school in their home state.

Eligibility   This program is open to residents of California, Connecticut, New Jersey, and New York. Applicants must be currently enrolled full time at a dental, medical, nursing, public health, or health policy school in their home state. They are not required to be Hispanic, but they must be able to demonstrate an affinity for the health of Hispanic communities. Along with their application, they must submit a letter of recommendation, transcripts, a personal statement that includes their career goals, and a current curriculum vitae. Students in pre-health professional program are not eligible. Selection is based on academic performance, leadership, and commitment to their Hispanic community.

Financial Data   Stipends are $5,000 or $2,000.

Duration   1 year.

Additional data   This program began in 2005 in affiliation with the Robert F. Wagner Graduate School of Public Service at New York University.

Number awarded   20 each year: 16 at $5,000 and 4 at $2,000.

Deadline   September of each year for students from California; October of each year for students from Connecticut, New Jersey, and New York.

[801]
NATIONAL MEDICAL FELLOWSHIPS EMERGENCY SCHOLARSHIP FUND

National Medical Fellowships, Inc.
Attn: Scholarship Program
347 Fifth Avenue, Suite 510
New York, NY 10016
(212) 483-8880   Toll Free: (877) NMF-1DOC
Fax: (212) 483-8897   E-mail: info@nmfonline.org
Web: www.nmfonline.org

Summary   To provide financial assistance to Hispanic American and other minority medical students who are facing financial emergencies.

Eligibility   This program is open to U.S. citizens who are enrolled in the third or fourth year of an accredited M.D. or D.O. degree-granting program in the United States and are facing extreme financial difficulties because of unforeseen training-related expenses. Applicants must be African Americans, Latinos, Native Hawaiians, Alaska Natives, American Indians, Pacific Islanders, Vietnamese, or Cambodians who permanently reside in the United States. They must be interested in primary care practice in underserved communities.

Financial Data   Assistance ranges up to $10,000.

Duration   1 year; nonrenewable.

Additional data   This program began in 2008, with support from the W.K. Kellogg Foundation.

Number awarded   Varies each year; recently, 3 of these scholarships were awarded.

Deadline   August of each year.

[802]
NATIONAL OCEANIC AND ATMOSPHERIC ADMINISTRATION EDUCATIONAL PARTNERSHIP PROGRAM WITH MINORITY SERVING INSTITUTIONS GRADUATE SCIENCES PROGRAM

National Oceanic and Atmospheric Administration
Attn: Office of Education
1315 East-West Highway
SSMC3, Room 10703
Silver Spring, MD 20910
(301) 713-9437, ext. 150   Fax: (301) 713-9465
E-mail: gsp@noaa.gov
Web: www.epp.noaa.gov/ssp_grad_sciences_page.html

Summary   To provide financial aid and summer research experience to graduate students at Minority Serving Institutions who are majoring in scientific fields of interest to the National Oceanic and Atmospheric Administration (NOAA).

Eligibility This program is open to full-time graduate students working on master's or doctoral degrees at Minority Serving Institutions, including Alaska Native Serving Institutions (ANSIs), Hispanic Serving Institutions (HSIs), Historically Black Colleges and Universities (HBCUs), Native Hawaiian Serving Institutions (NHSIs), and Tribal Colleges and Universities (TCUs). Applicants must be working on a degree in biology, chemistry, computer science, economics, engineering, environmental law, geography, geology, mathematics, physical science, physics, or social science. They must have a GPA of 3.0 or higher. The program includes a training program during the summer at a NOAA research facility. Selection is based on academic records, a statement of career interests and goals, and compatibility of applicant's background with the interests of NOAA. U.S. citizenship is required.

Financial Data During the school year, the program provides payment of tuition, laboratory fees, books, travel expenses, and a housing allowance at selected universities. During the summer, students receive a salary and benefits from NOAA.

Duration 1 year; may be renewed 1 additional year for master's candidates or 3 additional years for doctoral students, provided the recipient maintains a GPA of 3.0 or higher.

Number awarded Varies each year; recently, 2 of these fellowships were awarded.

Deadline January of each year.

[803]
NATIONAL PHYSICAL SCIENCE CONSORTIUM GRADUATE FELLOWSHIPS

National Physical Science Consortium
c/o University of Southern California
3716 South Hope Street, Suite 348
Los Angeles, CA 90007-4344
(213) 821-2409   Toll Free: (800) 854-NPSC
Fax: (213) 821-2407   E-mail: npschq@npsc.org
Web: www.npsc.org

Summary To provide financial assistance and summer work experience to Hispanic Americans, other underrepresented minorities and women interested in working on a Ph.D. in designated science and engineering fields.

Eligibility This program is open to U.S. citizens who are seniors graduating from college with a GPA of 3.0 or higher, enrolled in the first year of a doctoral program, completing a terminal master's degree, or returning from the workforce and holding no more than a master's degree. Students currently in the third or subsequent year of a Ph.D. program or who already have a doctoral degree in any field (Ph.D., M.D., J.D., Ed.D.) are ineligible. Applicants must be interested in working on a Ph.D. in fields that vary but emphasize astronomy, chemistry, computer science, engineering (chemical, computer, electrical, environmental, or mechanical), geology, materials science, mathematical sciences, or physics. The program welcomes applications from all qualified students and continues to emphasize the recruitment of underrepresented minority (African American, Hispanic, Native American Indian, Eskimo, Aleut, and Pacific Islander) and women physical science and engineering students. Fellowships are provided to

students at more than 100 universities that are members of the consortium. Selection is based on academic standing (GPA), course work taken in preparation for graduate school, university and/or industry research experience, letters of recommendation, and GRE scores.

Financial Data The fellowship pays tuition and fees plus an annual stipend of $20,000. It also provides on-site paid summer employment to enhance technical experience. The exact value of the fellowship depends on academic standing, summer employment, and graduate school attended; the total amount generally exceeds $200,000.

Duration Support is initially provided for 2 or 3 years, depending on the employer-sponsor. If the fellow makes satisfactory progress and continues to meet the conditions of the award, support may continue for a total of up to 6 years or completion of the Ph.D., whichever comes first.

Additional data This program began in 1989. Tuition and fees are provided by the participating universities. Stipends and summer internships are provided by sponsoring organizations. Students must submit separate applications for internships, which may have additional eligibility requirements. Internships are currently available at Lawrence Livermore National Laboratory in Livermore, California (astronomy, chemistry, computer science, geology, materials science, mathematics, and physics); National Institute of Standards and Technology in Gaithersburg, Maryland (various fields of STEM); National Security Agency in Fort Meade, Maryland (astronomy, chemistry, computer science, geology, materials science, mathematics, and physics); Sandia National Laboratory in Livermore, California (biology, chemistry, computer science, environmental science, geology, materials science, mathematics, and physics); and Sandia National Laboratory in Albuquerque, New Mexico (chemical engineering, chemistry, computer science, materials science, mathematics, mechanical engineering, and physics). Fellows must submit a separate application for dissertation support in the year prior to the beginning of their dissertation research program, but not until they can describe their intended research in general terms.

Number awarded Varies each year; recently, 11 of these fellowships were awarded.

Deadline November of each year.

[804]
NATIONAL SOCIETY OF HISPANIC MBAS FOUNDATION SCHOLARSHIP PROGRAM

National Society of Hispanic MBAs
Attn: NSHMBA Foundation
450 East John Carpenter Freeway, Suite 200
Irving, TX 75062
(214) 596-9338   Toll Free: (877) 467-4622
Fax: (214) 596-9325   E-mail: scholarships@nshmba.org
Web: www.nshmba.org/scholarship

Summary To provide financial assistance to members of the National Society of Hispanic MBAs (NSHMBA) who are interested in working on a master's degree in business administration.

Eligibility This program is open to NSHMBA members who are interested in working full or part time on a master's degree in management or business at an AACSB-accredited college or university in the United States or Puerto Rico. Applicants must be U.S. citizens or permanent residents and of Hispanic background (1 parent must be fully Hispanic or both parents must be half Hispanic). They must have a GPA of 3.0 or higher. Selection is based on academic achievement, a personal statement of goals and aspirations, community service, and NSHMBA ambassadorship; financial need is considered for applicants who wish to be considered for the top awards.

Financial Data Stipends range from $2,500 to $10,000. All awards include a travel voucher for $250 to attend an NSHMBA conference.

Duration 1 year; may be renewed until completion of a master's degree, provided the recipient maintains a GPA of 3.0 or higher and participates in NSHMBA activities during the year.

Additional data This program is administered by Scholarship Management Services, a division of Scholarship America.

Number awarded Varies each year; recently, more than 100 of these scholarships were awarded, including 5 top awards at $10,000 each.

Deadline April of each year.

[805]
NATIONAL SPACE GRANT COLLEGE AND FELLOWSHIP PROGRAM

National Aeronautics and Space Administration
Attn: Office of Education
300 E Street, S.W.
Mail Suite 6M35
Washington, DC 20546-0001
(202) 358-1069   Fax: (202) 358-7097
E-mail: Diane.D.DeTroye@nasa.gov
Web: www.nasa.gov

Summary To provide financial assistance to undergraduate and graduate students (particularly Hispanic Americans, other underrepresented minorities, and women) who are interested in preparing for a career in a space-related field.

Eligibility This program is open to undergraduate and graduate students at colleges and universities that participate in the National Space Grant program of the U.S. National Aeronautics and Space Administration (NASA) through their state consortium. Applicants must be interested in a program of study and/or research in a field of science, technology, engineering, or mathematics (STEM) related to space. A specific goal of the program is to recruit and train U.S. citizens, especially underrepresented minorities, women, and persons with disabilities, for careers in aerospace science and technology. Financial need is not considered in the selection process.

Financial Data Each consortium establishes the terms of the fellowship program in its state.

Additional data NASA established the Space Grant program in 1989. It operates through 52 consortia in each state, the District of Columbia, and Puerto Rico. Each consortium includes selected colleges and universities in that state as well as other affiliates from industry, museums, science centers, and state and local agencies.

Number awarded Varies each year.

Deadline Each consortium sets its own deadlines.

[806]
NATIONAL URBAN FELLOWS PROGRAM

National Urban Fellows, Inc.
Attn: Program Director
989 Avenue of the Americas, Suite 400
New York, NY 10018
(212) 730-1700   Fax: (212) 730-1823
E-mail: info@nuf.org
Web: www.nuf.org/fellows-overview

Summary To offer financial assistance to mid-career public sector professionals (especially Hispanic Americans, other minorities, and women) who are interested in working on a master's degree program coupled with a mentorship.

Eligibility This program is open to U.S. citizens who have a bachelor's degree, have at least 3 years of administrative or managerial experience, have demonstrated exceptional ability and leadership potential, meet academic admission requirements, have a high standard of integrity and work ethic, and are committed to the solution of urban problems. Applicants must a 1,000-word autobiographical statement and a 1,000-word statement on their career goals. They may be of any racial or ethnic background, but the program's goal is to increase the number of competent administrators from underrepresented ethnic and cultural groups at all levels of public and private urban management organizations. Semifinalists are interviewed.

Financial Data The stipend is $25,000. The program also provides full payment of tuition, a relocation allowance of $500, a book allowance of $500, and reimbursement for program-related travel.

Duration 14 months.

Additional data The program begins with a summer semester of study at Bernard M. Baruch College of the City University of New York. Following this, fellows spend 9 months in mentorship assignments with a senior administrator in a government agency, a major nonprofit, or a foundation. The final summer is spent in another semester of study at Baruch College. Fellows who successfully complete all requirements are granted a master's of public administration from that college. A $75 processing fee must accompany each application.

Number awarded Varies; approximately 40 each year.

Deadline February of each year.

[807]
NCAA ETHNIC MINORITY ENHANCEMENT SCHOLARSHIP PROGRAM

National Collegiate Athletic Association
Attn: Office for Diversity and Inclusion
700 West Washington Street
P.O. Box 6222
Indianapolis, IN 46206-6222
(317) 917-6222   Fax: (317) 917-6888
E-mail: tstrum@ncaa.org
Web: www.ncaa.org

Summary To provide funding to Hispanic American and other ethnic minority graduate students who are interested in preparing for a career in intercollegiate athletics.

Eligibility This program is open to members of minority groups who have been accepted into a program at a National Collegiate Athletic Association (NCAA) member institution that will prepare them for a career in intercollegiate athletics (athletics administrator, coach, athletic trainer, or other career that provides a direct service to intercollegiate athletics). Applicants must be U.S. citizens, have performed with distinction as a student body member at their respective undergraduate institution, and be entering the first semester or term of full-time postgraduate study. Selection is based on the applicant's involvement in extracurricular activities, course work, commitment to preparing for a career in intercollegiate athletics, and promise for success in that career. Financial need is not considered.

Financial Data   The stipend is $6,000; funds are paid to the college or university of the recipient's choice.

Duration   1 year; nonrenewable.

Number awarded   13 each year.

Deadline   November of each year.

[808]
NELLIE STONE JOHNSON SCHOLARSHIP

Nellie Stone Johnson Scholarship Program
P.O. Box 40309
St. Paul, MN 55104
(651) 738-1404   Toll Free: (866) 738-5238
E-mail: info@nelliestone.org
Web: www.nelliestone.org

Summary   To provide financial assistance to Hispanic American and other minority union members or their families who are interested in working on an undergraduate or graduate degree in any field at a Minnesota state college or university.

Eligibility   This program is open to students in undergraduate and graduate programs at a 2- or 4-year institution that is a component of Minnesota State Colleges and Universities (MnSCU). Applicants must be a minority (Asian, American Indian, Alaska Native, Black/African American, Hispanic/Latino, Native Hawaiian, or Pacific Islander) union member or the child, grandchild, or spouse of a minority union member. They must submit a 2-page essay about their background, educational goals, career goals, and other activities that may impact the cause of human or civil rights. Undergraduates must have a GPA of 2.0 or higher; graduate students must have a GPA of 3.0 or higher. Preference is given to Minnesota residents. Selection is based on the essay, commitment to human or civil rights, extracurricular activities, volunteer activities, community involvement, academic standing, and financial need.

Financial Data   Stipends range from $500 to $2,000 per year.

Duration   1 year; may be renewed up to 3 additional years for students working on a bachelor's degree, 1 additional year for students working on a master's degree, or 1 additional year for students in a community or technical college program.

Number awarded   Varies each year; recently, 18 of these scholarships were awarded.

Deadline   April of each year.

[809]
NEW MEXICO ALLIANCE FOR HISPANIC EDUCATION SCHOLARSHIPS

New Mexico Alliance for Hispanic Education
Attn: Program Director
P.O. Box 25806
Albuquerque, NM 87125
(505) 342-3504
Web: www.nmalliance.org/scholarships.html

Summary   To provide financial assistance to Hispanic residents of New Mexico who are interested in attending college or graduate school in any state.

Eligibility   This program is open to residents of New Mexico who are of Hispanic heritage and interested enrolling full time at an accredited 2- or 4-year college or university in the United States, Puerto Rico, the U.S. Virgin Islands, or Guam. Applicants must have a GPA of 3.0 or higher and be working on or planning to work on an undergraduate or graduate degree. They must be U.S. citizens, permanent residents, or visitors with a passport stamped I-551. In addition to submitting the application, they must apply for federal financial aid by completing the Free Application for Federal Student Aid (FAFSA).

Financial Data   Stipends range from $1,000 to $2,500.

Duration   1 year.

Number awarded   Varies each year.

Deadline   February of each year.

[810]
NEW MEXICO MINORITY DOCTORAL LOAN-FOR-SERVICE PROGRAM

New Mexico Higher Education Department
Attn: Financial Aid Division
2048 Galisteo Street
Santa Fe, NM 87505-2100
(505) 476-8411   Toll Free: (800) 279-9777
Fax: (505) 476-8454   E-mail: feliz.romero1@state.nm.us
Web: hed.state.nm.us/MinDoc.aspx

Summary   To provide funding to Hispanic Americans, other underrepresented minorities, and women who reside in New Mexico and are interested in working on a doctoral degree in selected fields.

Eligibility   This program is open to ethnic minorities and women who are residents of New Mexico and have received a baccalaureate degree from a public 4-year college or university in the state in mathematics, engineering, the physical or life sciences, or any other academic discipline in which ethnic minorities and women are demonstrably underrepresented in New Mexico academic institutions. Applicants must have been admitted as a full-time doctoral student at an approved university in any state. They must be sponsored by a New Mexico institution of higher education which has agreed to employ them in a tenure-track faculty position after they obtain their degree. U.S. citizenship is required.

Financial Data   Loans average $15,000. This is a loan-for-service program; for every year of service as a college faculty member in New Mexico, a portion of the loan is forgiven. If the entire service agreement is fulfilled, 100% of the loan is eligible for forgiveness. Penalties may be assessed if the service agreement is not satisfied.

Duration   1 year; may be renewed up to 3 additional years.

Number awarded Up to 12 each year.

Deadline March of each year.

[811]
NEW YORK CITY DEPARTMENT OF EDUCATION GRADUATE SCHOLARSHIP PROGRAM

New York City Department of Education
Attn: Office of Scholarship and Incentive Programs
65 Court Street, Room 508
Brooklyn, NY 11201
(718) 935-2449
Web: www.teachnycprograms.net

Summary To provide funding to bilingual and other college graduates who are interested in working on a master's degree in a designated critical shortage area and subsequently working in that field in the New York City public schools.

Eligibility This program is open to college graduates who have a bachelor's degree from a college or university in any state. Applicants must be interested in working on a master's degree in 1 of the following areas: monolingual or bilingual speech language pathology, monolingual or bilingual visually impaired, bilingual special education, or bilingual school psychology. They must have a GPA of 3.0 or higher. For the bilingual programs, applicants must be proficient in both English and a language other than English. U.S. citizenship or permanent resident status is required. For each critical subject shortage area, specified colleges or universities in the New York City region are designated where the degree may be obtained.

Financial Data This is a scholarship/loan program. Recipients are reimbursed for the full cost of tuition for their approved master's degree. They must serve as New York State certified professionals for the New York City public schools in the area in which they earn a master's degree for 2 years per year of support.

Duration Until completion of a master's degree.

Additional data Applications must be filed in person. There is a non-refundable $30 application fee. Recipients must complete at least 12 credits per year with a grade of "C" or better.

Number awarded Varies each year.

Deadline May of each year.

[812]
NEXSEN PRUET DIVERSITY SCHOLARSHIPS

Nexsen Pruet
Attn: Diversity Scholarship
1230 Main Street, Suite 700
P.O. Drawer 2426
Columbia, SC 29202-2426
(803) 771-8900   Fax: (803) 727-1469
E-mail: diversity@nexsenpruet.com
Web: www.nexsenpruet.com/firm-diversity.html

Summary To provide financial assistance to Hispanic Americans and members of other minority groups attending designated law schools in North and South Carolina.

Eligibility This program is open to minority students currently enrolled in the first year at the University of North Carolina School of Law, University of South Carolina School of Law, Wake Forest University School of Law, North Carolina

Central University School of Law, Charleston School of Law, or Charlotte School of Law. Applicants must be interested in practicing law in North or South Carolina after graduation. Along with their application, they must submit information on their academic achievements; their contributions to promoting diversity in their community, school, or work environment; and their ability to overcome challenges in the pursuit of their goals. They must also submit essays of 250 words each on 1) their reasons for preparing for a legal career; 2) their interest in the private practice of law in North Carolina and/or South Carolina; 3) any obstacles, including but not limited to financial obstacles, that the scholarship will help them overcome; and 4) what they see as potential obstacles, issues, and opportunities facing new minority lawyers.

Financial Data The stipend is $3,000 per year.

Duration 1 year; recipients may reapply.

Additional data Recipients are considered for summer employment in an office of the firm after completion of their first year of law school.

Number awarded Varies each year; recently, 3 of these scholarships were awarded.

Deadline October of each year.

[813]
NLGJA/KAY LONGCOPE SCHOLARSHIP AWARD

National Lesbian & Gay Journalists Association
2120 L Street, N.W., Suite 850
Washington, DC 20037
(202) 588-9888   Fax: (202) 588-1818
E-mail: info@nlgfa.org
Web: www.nlgja.org/students/longcope

Summary To provide financial assistance to Hispanic American and other lesbian, gay, bisexual, and transgender (LGBT) undergraduate and graduate students of color who are interested in preparing for a career in journalism.

Eligibility This program is open to LGBT students of color who are 1) high school seniors accepted to a U.S. community college or 4-year university and planning to enroll full time; 2) full-time undergraduate students at U.S. community colleges and 4-year universities; or 3) undergraduate students who have been accepted for their first year at a U.S. graduate school. Applicants must be planning a career in journalism and be committed to furthering the sponsoring organization's mission of fair and accurate coverage of the LGBT community. They must demonstrate an awareness of the issues facing the LGBT community and the importance of fair and accurate news coverage. For undergraduates, a declared major in journalism and/or communications is desirable but not required; non-journalism majors may demonstrate their commitment to a journalism career through work samples, internships, and work on a school news publication, online news service, or broadcast affiliate. Graduate students must be enrolled in a journalism program. Along with their application, they must submit a 1-page resume, 5 work samples, official transcripts, 3 letters of recommendation, and a 750-word news story on a designated subject involving the LGBT community. U.S. citizenship or permanent resident status is required. Selection is based on journalistic and scholastic ability.

Financial Data The stipend is $3,000.

Duration 1 year.

Additional data This program began in 2008.

Number awarded 1 each year.

Deadline June of each year.

[814]
NORMAN'S ORCHIDS MASTERS SCHOLARSHIP

American Orchid Society
c/o Fairchild Tropical Botanic Garden
10901 Old Cutler Road
Coral Gables, FL 33156
(305) 740-2010   Fax: (305) 740-2011
E-mail: TheAOS@aos.org
Web: www.aos.org/Default.aspx?id=545

Summary To provide funding for research to students (particularly Hispanic Americans, other underrepresented minorities, women, and individuals with disabilities) who are working on a master's degree in a field related to orchids.

Eligibility This program is open to students working on a master's degree at an accredited institution. Applicants must have a thesis project that deals with an aspect of orchid education, applied science, or orchid biology in the disciplines of physiology, molecular biology, structure, systematics, cytology, ecology, or evolution. They must submit a current curriculum vitae, transcripts of all college course work, a synopsis of the proposed project or research, a 1-page statement of the value of their project and importance to the future of orchid education or orchidology, and a letter of recommendation from their chairperson. Women, minorities, and persons with disabilities are especially encouraged to apply.

Financial Data The grant is $5,000 per year. Funds are paid through the recipient's college or university, but institutional overhead is not allowed.

Duration 2 years.

Additional data This program, established in 2005, is supported by Norman's Orchids of Montclair, California.

Number awarded 1 each year.

Deadline March of each year.

[815]
NORTH CAROLINA CPA FOUNDATION OUTSTANDING MINORITY ACCOUNTING STUDENT SCHOLARSHIPS

North Carolina Association of Certified Public
  Accountants
Attn: North Carolina CPA Foundation, Inc.
3100 Gateway Centre Boulevard
P.O. Box 80188
Raleigh, NC 27623-0188
(919) 469-1040, ext. 130   Toll Free: (800) 722-2836
Fax: (919) 378-2000   E-mail: jtahler@ncacpa.org
Web: ncacpa.org

Summary To provide financial assistance to Hispanic American and other minority undergraduate and graduate students working on a degree in accounting at colleges and universities in North Carolina.

Eligibility This program is open to North Carolina residents who have completed at least 36 semester hours, including at least 4 accounting courses, at a college or university in the state. Applicants must be members of a minority group, defined as Black, Native American/Alaskan Native, Middle-Eastern, Asian or Pacific Islander, or Hispanic. They must be enrolled full time in an academic program leading to a degree in accounting or its equivalent and have a GPA of 3.0 or higher. Along with their application, they must submit a 500-word essay on 1 of the following questions: 1) what the profession can do to educate minorities about understanding the impact of and ways to survive the national financial crisis; 2) how they will impact minority communities by becoming a C.P.A.; or 3) the challenges that minority C.P.A.s face in the profession. Selection is based on GPA (30%), extracurricular activities (20%), essay content (25%), and essay grammar (25%).

Financial Data Stipends are $2,000 or $1,000.

Duration 1 year; may be renewed up to 2 additional years.

Number awarded 2 each year: 1 at $2,000 and 1 at $1,000.

Deadline March of each year.

[816]
NOTRE DAME INSTITUTE FOR ADVANCED STUDY GRADUATE STUDENT FELLOWSHIPS

University of Notre Dame
Institute for Advanced Study
Attn: Programs Administrator
1124 Flanner Hall
Notre Dame, IN 46556
(574) 631-6240   E-mail: csherman@nd.edu
Web: ndias.nd.edu/fellowships/graduate-student

Summary To provide funding to graduate students (particularly Hispanic Americans and members of other traditionally underrepresented groups) who are interested in conducting research on topics of interest to the Notre Dame Institute for Advanced Study (NDIAS) while in residence at the institute.

Eligibility This program is open to graduate students in all disciplines, including the arts, engineering, the humanities, law, and the natural, social, and physical sciences. Applicants must be interested in conducting research that furthers the work of the NDIAS, defined as cultivating "the contemplative ideal that is an essential factor in the Catholic intellectual tradition and vital for the progression of scholarship." They must be able to demonstrate excellent records of scholarly, artistic, or research accomplishment in their field; ability to interact with other fellows and to engage in collegial discussions of research presentations; a willingness to contribute to a cooperative community of scholars; and projects that touch on normative, integrative, or ultimate questions, especially as the involve the Catholic intellectual tradition. Applications are especially encouraged from traditionally underrepresented groups. There are no citizenship requirements; non-U.S. nationals are welcome to apply.

Financial Data The grant is $25,000, including a $1,000 research account, office facilities, a computer and printer, access to libraries and other facilities, and weekly institute seminars and events.

Duration 1 academic year.

Number awarded 1 or more each year.

Deadline October of each year.

[817]
NSCA MINORITY SCHOLARSHIPS

National Strength and Conditioning Association
Attn: Grants and Scholarships Program
1885 Bob Johnson Drive
Colorado Springs, CO 80906-4000
(719) 632-6722, ext. 152   Toll Free: (800) 815-6826
Fax: (719) 632-6367   E-mail: foundation@nsca-lift.org
Web: www.nsca-lift.org/Foundation/grants-and-scholarships

Summary To provide financial assistance to Hispanic Americans and other minorities who are interested in working on an undergraduate or graduate degree in strength training and conditioning.

Eligibility This program is open to Blacks, Hispanics, Asian Americans, and Native Americans who are 17 years of age and older. Applicants must have been accepted into an accredited postsecondary institution to work on an undergraduate or graduate degree in the strength and conditioning field. Along with their application, they must submit a 500-word essay on their personal and professional goals and how receiving this scholarship will assist them in achieving those goals. Selection is based on that essay, academic achievement, strength and conditioning experience, honors and awards, community involvement, letters of recommendation, and involvement in the National Strength and Conditioning Association (NSCA).

Financial Data The stipend is $1,500.

Duration 1 year.

Additional data The NSCA is a nonprofit organization of strength and conditioning professionals, including coaches, athletic trainers, physical therapists, educators, researchers, and physicians. This program was first offered in 2003.

Number awarded Varies each year; recently, 9 of these scholarships were awarded.

Deadline March of each year.

[818]
NSF GRADUATE RESEARCH FELLOWSHIP PROGRAM

National Science Foundation
Directorate for Education and Human Resources
Attn: Division of Graduate Education
4201 Wilson Boulevard, Room 875S
Arlington, VA 22230
(703) 292-8694   Toll Free: (866) NSF-GRFP
Fax: (703) 292-9048   E-mail: info@nsfgrfp.org
Web: www.nsf.gov/funding/pgm_summ.jsp?pims_id=6201

Summary To provide financial assistance to graduate students (particularly Hispanic Americans, other minorities, women, veterans, and students with disabilities) who are interested in working on a master's or doctoral degree in fields supported by the National Science Foundation (NSF).

Eligibility This program is open to U.S. citizens, nationals, and permanent residents who wish to work on research-based master's or doctoral degrees in a field of science, technology, engineering, or mathematics (STEM) supported by NSF (including astronomy, chemistry, computer and information sciences and engineering, geosciences, engineering, life sciences, materials research, mathematical sciences, physics, psychology, social sciences, or STEM education and learning). Other work in medical, dental, law, public health, or practice-oriented professional degree programs, or in joint science-professional degree programs, such as M.D./Ph.D. and J.D./Ph.D. programs, is not eligible. Applications normally should be submitted during the senior year in college or in the first year of graduate study; eligibility is limited to those who have completed no more than 12 months of graduate study since completion of a baccalaureate degree. Applicants who have already earned an advanced degree in science, engineering, or medicine (including an M.D., D.D.S., or D.V.M.) are ineligible. Selection is based on 1) intellectual merit of the proposed activity: strength of the academic record, proposed plan of research, previous research experience, references, appropriateness of the choice of institution; and 2) broader impacts of the proposed activity: how well does the activity advance discovery and understanding, how well does it broaden the participation of underrepresented groups (e.g., women, minorities, persons with disabilities, veterans), to what extent will it enhance the infrastructure for research and education, will the results be disseminated broadly to enhance scientific and technological understanding, what may be the benefits of the proposed activity to society).

Financial Data The stipend is $30,000 per year; an additional $12,000 cost-of-education allowance is provided to the recipient's institution.

Duration Up to 3 years, usable over a 5-year period.

Number awarded Approximately 2,000 each year.

Deadline November of each year.

[819]
NSNA/BREAKTHROUGH TO NURSING SCHOLARSHIPS

National Student Nurses' Association
Attn: Foundation
45 Main Street, Suite 606
Brooklyn, NY 11201
(718) 210-0705   Fax: (718) 797-1186
E-mail: nsna@nsna.org
Web: www.nsna.org

Summary To provide financial assistance to Hispanic American and other minority undergraduate and graduate students who wish to prepare for careers in nursing.

Eligibility This program is open to students currently enrolled in state-approved schools of nursing or pre-nursing associate degree, baccalaureate, diploma, generic master's, generic doctoral, R.N. to B.S.N., R.N. to M.S.N., or L.P.N./L.V.N. to R.N. programs. Graduating high school seniors are not eligible. Support for graduate education is provided only for a first degree in nursing. Applicants must be members of a racial or ethnic minority underrepresented among registered nurses (American Indian or Alaska Native, Hispanic or Latino, Native Hawaiian or other Pacific Islander, Black or African American, or Asian). They must be committed to providing quality health care services to underserved populations. Along with their application, they must submit a 200-word description of their professional and educational goals and how this scholarship will help them achieve those goals. Selection is based on academic achievement, financial need, and involvement in student nursing organizations and community health activities. U.S. citizenship or permanent resident status is required.

Financial Data Stipends range from $1,000 to $2,500.

Duration 1 year.

Additional data　Applications must be accompanied by a $10 processing fee.

Number awarded　Varies each year; recently, 13 of these scholarships were awarded: 10 sponsored by the American Association of Critical-Care Nurses and 3 sponsored by the Mayo Clinic.

Deadline　January of each year.

[820]
NWA/DAVID SANKEY MINORITY SCHOLARSHIP IN METEOROLOGY

National Weather Association
Attn: Executive Director
228 West Millbrook Road
Raleigh, NC 27609-4304
(919) 845-1546　　　　　Fax: (919) 845-2956
E-mail: exdir@nwas.org
Web: www.nwas.org

Summary　To provide financial assistance to Hispanic Americans and other members of minority groups who are working on an undergraduate or graduate degree in meteorology.

Eligibility　This program is open to members of minority ethnic groups who are either entering their sophomore or higher year of undergraduate study or enrolled as graduate students. Applicants must be working on a degree in meteorology. Along with their application, they must submit a 1-page statement explaining why they are applying for this scholarship. Selection is based on that statement, academic achievement, and 2 letters of recommendation.

Financial Data　The stipend is $1,000.

Duration　1 year.

Additional data　This program began in 2002.

Number awarded　1 each year.

Deadline　April of each year.

[821]
OLIVER GOLDSMITH, M.D. SCHOLARSHIP

Kaiser Permanente Southern California
Attn: Residency Administration and Recruitment
393 East Walnut Street, Fifth Floor
Pasadena, CA 91188
Toll Free: (877) 574-0002　　　　Fax: (626) 405-6581
E-mail: socal.residency@kp.org
Web: residency.kp.org

Summary　To provide financial assistance to Hispanic American and other medical students who will help bring diversity to the profession.

Eligibility　This program is open to students entering their third or fourth year of allopathic or osteopathic medical school. Members of all ethnic and racial groups are encouraged to apply, but applicants must have demonstrated their commitment to diversity through community service, clinical volunteering, or research. They may be attending medical school in any state, but they must intend to practice in southern California and they must be available to participate in a mentoring program and a clerkship at a Kaiser Permanente facility in that region.

Financial Data　The stipend is $5,000.

Duration　1 year.

Additional data　This program began in 2004.

Number awarded　14 each year.

Deadline　February of each year.

[822]
OLIVER W. HILL SCHOLARSHIP

LeClairRyan
Attn: Recruiting Manager
Riverfront Plaza, East Tower
951 East Byrd Street, Eighth Floor
Richmond, VA 23219
(804) 783-7597　　　　　Fax: (804) 783-2294
E-mail: droberts@leclairryan.com
Web: www.leclairryan.com

Summary　To provide financial assistance to Hispanic Americans and other students of color at law schools in designated states.

Eligibility　This program is open to students who have completed at least 1 semester at a law school in a state in which the sponsoring firm has an office (currently, California, Connecticut, Massachusetts, Michigan, New Jersey, New York, Pennsylvania, Virginia, and Washington, D.C.). Applicants must identify as a member of a minority racial ethnic group or as LGBT. They must have a GPA of 3.0 or higher. Along with their application, they must submit a 2,000-word essay presenting their ideas of pursuing social justice through the law.

Financial Data　The stipend is $5,000.

Duration　1 year.

Additional data　This program began in 2009.

Number awarded　1 each year.

Deadline　April of each year.

[823]
OLYMPIA BROWN AND MAX KAPP AWARD

Unitarian Universalist Association
Attn: Ministerial Credentialing Office
25 Beacon Street
Boston, MA 02108-2800
(617) 948-6403　　　　　Fax: (617) 742-2875
E-mail: mcoadministrator@uua.org
Web: www.uua.org

Summary　To provide financial assistance to Unitarian Universalist (UU) candidates for the ministry (especially Hispanic Americans and other students of color) who submit a project on an aspect of Universalism.

Eligibility　This program is open to students currently enrolled full or at least half time in a UU ministerial training program with candidate status. Applicants are primarily citizens of the United States or Canada. Along with their application, they may submit a paper, sermon, or a special project on an aspect of Unitarian Universalism. Priority is given first to those who have demonstrated outstanding ministerial ability and secondarily to students with the greatest financial need (especially persons of color).

Financial Data　The stipend is $2,500.

Duration　1 year.

Number awarded　1 each year.

Deadline　April of each year.

[824]
OPERATION JUMP START III SCHOLARSHIPS

American Association of Advertising Agencies
Attn: AAAA Foundation
1065 Avenue of the Americas, 16th Floor
New York, NY 10018
(212) 262-2500   E-mail: ameadows@aaaa.org
Web: www.aaaa.org

Summary   To provide financial assistance to Hispanic American and other multicultural art directors and copywriters interested in working on an undergraduate or graduate degree in advertising.

Eligibility   This program is open to African Americans, Asian Americans, Hispanic Americans, and Native Americans who are U.S. citizens or permanent residents. Applicants must be incoming graduate students at 1 of 6 designated portfolio schools or full-time juniors at 1 of 2 designated colleges. They must be able to demonstrate extreme financial need, creative talent, and promise. Along with their application, they must submit 10 samples of creative work in their respective field of expertise.

Financial Data   The stipend is $5,000 per year.

Duration   Most awards are for 2 years.

Additional data   Operation Jump Start began in 1997 and was followed by Operation Jump Start II in 2002. The current program began in 2006. The 6 designated portfolio schools are the AdCenter at Virginia Commonwealth University, the Creative Circus in Atlanta, the Portfolio Center in Atlanta, the Miami Ad School, the University of Texas at Austin, and Pratt Institute. The 2 designated colleges are the Minneapolis College of Art and Design and the Art Center College of Design at Pasadena, California.

Number awarded   20 each year.

Deadline   Deadline not specified.

[825]
OREGON STATE BAR SCHOLARSHIPS

Oregon State Bar
Attn: Diversity and Inclusion Department
16037 S.W. Upper Boones Ferry Road
P.O. Box 231935
Tigard, OR 97281-1935
(503) 431-6338
Toll Free: (800) 452-8260, ext. 338 (within OR)
Fax: (503) 598-6938   E-mail: tkelich@osbar.org
Web: www.osbar.org/diversity

Summary   To provide financial assistance to entering and continuing students from any state enrolled at law schools in Oregon, especially those who will help the Oregon State Bar achieve its diversity objectives.

Eligibility   This program is open to students entering or continuing at 1 of the law schools in Oregon (Willamette, University of Oregon, and Lewis and Clark). Preference is given to students who will contribute to the Oregon State Bar's diversity program to "increase the diversity of the Oregon bench and bar to reflect the diversity of the people of Oregon." Applicants must submit 1) a personal statement on their history of disadvantage or barriers to educational advancement, personal experiences of discrimination, extraordinary financial obligations, composition of immediate family, extraordinary health or medical needs, and languages in which they are fluent as well as barriers they have experienced because English is a second language; and 2) a state bar statement on why they chose to attend an Oregon law school; if they are not committed but are considering practicing in Oregon, what would help them to decide to practice in the state; and how they will improve the quality of legal service or increase access to justice in Oregon. Selection is based on financial need (30%), the personal statement (25%), the state bar statement (25%), community activities (10%), and employment history (10%).

Financial Data   The stipend is $2,000 per year. Funds are credited to the recipient's law school tuition account.

Duration   1 year; recipients may reapply.

Number awarded   8 each year.

Deadline   March of each year.

[826]
PATRICIA G. ARCHBOLD PREDOCTORAL SCHOLAR AWARD

Gerontological Society of America
Attn: National Hartford Centers of Gerontological Nursing Excellence
1220 L Street, N.W., Suite 901
Washington, DC 20005-4001
(202) 842-1275   Fax: (202) 842-1150
E-mail: nhcgne@geron.org
Web: www.geriatricnursing.org

Summary   To provide funding to Hispanic American and other nurses from underrepresented minority groups who are interested in working on a doctoral degree in gerontological nursing.

Eligibility   This program is open to registered nurses who are members of underrepresented minority groups (American Indians, Alaska Natives, Asians, Blacks or African Americans, Hispanics or Latinos/Latinas, Native Hawaiians or other Pacific Islanders) and have been admitted to a doctoral program as a full-time student. Applicants must plan an academic research career in geriatric nursing. They must identify a mentor/adviser with whom they will work and whose program of research in geriatric nursing is a good match with their own research interest area. Selection is based on potential for substantial long-term contributions to the knowledge base in geriatric nursing; leadership potential; evidence of commitment to a career in academic geriatric nursing; and evidence of involvement in educational, research, and professional activities. U.S. citizenship or permanent resident status is required.

Financial Data   The stipend is $50,000 per year. An additional stipend of $5,000 is available to fellows whose research includes the study of pain in the elderly.

Duration   2 years.

Additional data   This program began in 2001 with funding from the John A. Hartford Foundation. In 2004, the Mayday Fund added support to scholars who focus on the study of pain in the elderly. Until 2013 it was known as the Building Academic Geriatric Nursing Capacity Program.

Number awarded   Varies each year; recently, 12 of these scholarships were awarded.

Deadline   January of each year.

[827]
PATRICK D. MCJULIEN MINORITY GRADUATE SCHOLARSHIP

Association for Educational Communications and
  Technology
Attn: ECT Foundation
1800 North Stonelake Drive, Suite 2
P.O. Box 2447
Bloomington, IN 47402-2447
(812) 335-7675   Toll Free: (877) 677-AECT
Fax: (812) 335-7678   E-mail: aect@aect.org
Web: www.aect.org/newsite

Summary To provide financial assistance to Hispanic American and other minority members of the Association for Educational Communications and Technology (AECT) who are working on a graduate degree in the field of educational communications and technology.

Eligibility This program is open to AECT members who are members of minority groups. Applicants must be full-time graduate students enrolled in a degree-granting program in educational technology at the master's (M.S.), specialist (Ed.S.), or doctoral (Ph.D., Ed.D.) levels. They must have a GPA of 3.0 or higher.

Financial Data A stipend is awarded (amount not specified).

Duration 1 year.

Number awarded 1 each year.

Deadline July of each year.

[828]
PAUL D. WHITE SCHOLARSHIP

BakerHostetler LLP
Attn: Attorney Recruitment and Development Manager
PNC Center
1900 East Ninth Street, Suite 3200
Cleveland, OH 44114-3482
(216) 621-0200   Fax: (216) 696-0740
E-mail: ddriscole@bakerlaw.com
Web: www.bakerlaw.com/firmdiversity/scholarship

Summary To provide financial aid and summer work experience to Hispanic American and other minority law school students.

Eligibility This program is open to first- and second-year law students of Black/African American, Hispanic/Latino, Asian, Native Hawaiian/Pacific Islander or American Indian/Alaska Native descent. Selection is based on law school performance, demonstrated leadership abilities (as evidenced by community and collegiate involvement), collegiate academic record, extracurricular activities, work experience, and a written personal statement.

Financial Data The program provides a stipend of $7,500 for the scholarship and a paid summer clerkship with the sponsoring firm. To date, the firm has expended more than $2.0 million in scholarships and clerkships.

Duration 1 year, including the following summer.

Additional data This program began in 1997. Clerkships may be performed at any of the firm's offices in Cincinnati, Cleveland, or Orlando.

Number awarded 1 or more each year.

Deadline January of each year.

[829]
PEERMUSIC LATIN SCHOLARSHIP

Broadcast Music Inc.
Attn: BMI Foundation, Inc.
7 World Trade Center
250 Greenwich Street
New York, NY 10007-0030
(212) 220-3000
E-mail: latinscholarship@bmifoundation.org
Web: www.bmifoundation.org

Summary To recognize and reward students at colleges and universities who submit outstanding songs or instrumental works in a Latin genre.

Eligibility This competition is open to students between 16 and 24 years of age enrolled at colleges and universities in the United States and Puerto Rico. Applicants may not have had any musical work commercially recorded or distributed. They must submit an original song or instrumental work in a Latin genre. The entry must be submitted on CD or MP3, accompanied by 3 typed copies of the lyric.

Financial Data The award is $5,000.

Duration The award is presented annually.

Additional data This award, first presented in 2003, is sponsored by peermusic Companies.

Number awarded 1 each year.

Deadline February of each year.

[830]
PEPSICO SCHOLARSHIPS OF THE NATIONAL ASSOCIATION OF HISPANIC JOURNALISTS

National Association of Hispanic Journalists
Attn: Scholarship Committee
1050 Connecticut Avenue, N.W., Tenth Floor
Washington, DC 20036
(202) 662-7145   Toll Free: (888) 346-NAHJ
Fax: (202) 662-7144   E-mail: nahj@nahj.org
Web: www.nahj12.com/scholarships

Summary To provide financial assistance to undergraduate and graduate student members of the National Association of Hispanic Journalists (NAHJ) who are interested in preparing for careers in the media.

Eligibility This program is open to Hispanic American high school seniors, undergraduates, and graduate students who are interested in preparing for a career in print, broadcast (radio or television), online, or visual journalism. Applicants must be enrolled full time at a college or university in the United States or Puerto Rico. They must have a GPA of 2.0 or higher and be NAHJ members. Along with their application, they must submit transcripts, a 1-page resume, 2 letters of recommendation, work samples, and a 1,000-word autobiographical essay that includes why they are interested in a career in journalism, what inspired them to prepare for a career in the field, what hardships or obstacles they have experienced while trying to realize their goal of becoming a journalist, and the role Latino journalists play in the news industry. Selection is based on commitment to the field of journalism, academic achievement, awareness of the Latino community, and financial need.

Financial Data Stipends range up to $2,500.

Duration 1 year; may be renewed until completion of a college degree.

Additional data This program is sponsored by PepsiCo.

Number awarded Varies each year.

Deadline January of each year.

[831]
PERKINS COIE DIVERSITY STUDENT FELLOWSHIPS

Perkins Coie LLP
Attn: Chief Diversity Officer
131 South Dearborn Street, Suite 1700
Chicago, IL 60603-5559
(312) 324-8593   Fax: (312) 324-9400
E-mail: diversity@perkinscoie.com
Web: www.perkinscoie.com/diversity/Diversity.aspx

Summary To provide financial assistance to Hispanic American and other law students who reflect the diversity of communities in the country.

Eligibility This program is open to students enrolled in the first year of a J.D. program at an ABA-accredited law school. Applicants must contribute meaningfully to the diversity of the law school student body and the legal profession. Diversity is defined broadly to include members of racial, ethnic, disabled, and sexual orientation minority groups, as well as those who may be the first person in their family to pursue higher education. Applicants must submit a 1-page personal statement that describes their unique personal history, a legal writing sample, a current resume, and undergraduate and law school transcripts. They are not required to disclose their financial circumstances, but a demonstrated need for financial assistance may be taken into consideration.

Financial Data The stipend is $7,500.

Duration 1 year.

Additional data Fellows are also offered a summer associateship at their choice of the firm's offices in Anchorage, Bellevue, Boise, Chicago, Dallas, Los Angeles, Madison, Palo Alto, Phoenix, Portland, San Diego, San Francisco, Seattle, or Washington, D.C.

Number awarded Varies each year; recently, 7 of these fellowships were awarded.

Deadline January of each year.

[832]
PFATS-NFL CHARITIES MINORITY SCHOLARSHIPS

Professional Football Athletic Trainers Society
c/o Britt Brown, ATC, Associate Athletic Trainer
Dallas Cowboys
One Cowboys Parkway
Irving, TX 75063
(972) 497-4992   E-mail: bbrown@dallascowboys.net
Web: www.pfats.com/about/scholarships

Summary To provide financial assistance to Hispanic American and other minority undergraduate and graduate students working on a degree in athletic training.

Eligibility This program is open to ethnic minority students who are working on an undergraduate or graduate degree in athletic training. Applicants must have a GPA of 2.5 or higher. Along with their application, they must submit a cover letter, a curriculum vitae, and a letter of recommendation from their supervising athletic trainer.

Financial Data A stipend is awarded (amount not specified).

Duration 1 year.

Additional data Recipients also have an opportunity to work at summer training camp of a National Football League (NFL) team. Support for this program, which began in 1993, is provided by NFL Charities.

Number awarded 1 or more each year.

Deadline March of each year.

[833]
PHYSICAL AND LIFE SCIENCES DIRECTORATE INTERNSHIPS

Lawrence Livermore National Laboratory
Physical and Life Sciences Directorate
Attn: Education Coordinator
7000 East Avenue, L-418
Livermore, CA 94550
(925) 422-0455   E-mail: hutcheon3@llnl.gov
Web: www-pls.llnl.gov

Summary To provide an opportunity for undergraduate and graduate students (particularly Hispanic Americans, other minorities, and women) to work on summer research projects within the Physical and Life Sciences Directorate (PLS) of Lawrence Livermore National Laboratory (LLNL).

Eligibility This program is open to full-time undergraduate and graduate students who are interested in working on research projects within the PLS Directorate of LLNL. Openings are currently available in chemistry (organic, inorganic, synthetic, analytical, computational, nuclear, and environmental) and materials science (theory, simulation and modeling, synthesis and processing, materials under extreme conditions, dynamic materials science, metallurgy, nuclear fuels, optical materials, and surface science). Applicants must have a GPA of 3.0 or higher. Selection is based on academic record, aptitude, research interests, and recommendations of instructors. Women and minorities are encouraged to apply.

Financial Data The stipend is $14 to $20 per hour for undergraduates or $4,100 to $4,900 per month for graduate students. Living accommodations and arrangements are the responsibility of the intern.

Duration 2 or 3 months, during the summer.

Number awarded Varies each year.

Deadline February of each year.

[834]
PORTER PHYSIOLOGY DEVELOPMENT AWARDS

American Physiological Society
Attn: Education Office
9650 Rockville Pike, Room 3111
Bethesda, MD 20814-3991
(301) 634-7132   Fax: (301) 634-7098
E-mail: education@the-aps.org
Web: www.the-aps.org

Summary To provide financial assistance to Hispanic Americans and other minorities who are members of the American Physiological Society (APS) and interested in working on a doctoral degree in physiology.

Eligibility This program is open to U.S. citizens and permanent residents who are members of racial or ethnic minority groups (Hispanic or Latino, American Indian or Alaska

Native, Asian, Black or African American, or Native Hawaiian or other Pacific Islander). Applicants must be currently enrolled in or accepted to a doctoral program in physiology at a university as full-time students. They must be APS members and have actively participated in its work. Selection is based on the applicant's potential for success (academic record, statement of interest, previous awards and experiences, letters of recommendation); applicant's proposed training environment (including quality of preceptor); and applicant's research and training plan (clarity and quality).

Financial Data The stipend is $23,500 per year. No provision is made for a dependency allowance or tuition and fees.

Duration 1 year; may be renewed for 1 additional year and, in exceptional cases, for a third year.

Additional data This program is supported by the William Townsend Porter Foundation (formerly the Harvard Apparatus Foundation). The first Porter Fellowship was awarded in 1920. In 1966 and 1967, the American Physiological Society established the Porter Physiology Development Committee to award fellowships to minority students engaged in graduate study in physiology. The highest ranked applicant for these fellowships is designated the Eleanor Ison Franklin Fellow.

Number awarded Varies each year; recently, 8 of these fellowships were awarded.

Deadline January of each year.

[835]
PREDOCTORAL FELLOWSHIPS IN BEHAVIORAL NEUROSCIENCE

Texas Consortium in Behavioral Neuroscience
c/o University of Texas at Austin
Department of Psychology
1 University Station A8000
Austin, TX 78712
(512) 471-1068   Fax: (512) 471-1073
E-mail: lima@mail.utexas.edu
Web: homepage.psy.utexas.edu

Summary To provide an opportunity for Hispanic American and other doctoral candidates from underrepresented groups to obtain research training in neuroscience at selected universities in Texas.

Eligibility This program is open to members of populations underrepresented in health-related sciences, including specified racial and ethnic groups (Blacks, Hispanics, and Native Americans), individuals with disabilities, and individuals from disadvantaged backgrounds. Applicants must have a bachelor's degree and plan to work on a doctoral degree in neuroscience. They must be interested in a program of research training at the University of Texas at Austin, the University of Texas at San Antonio, the University of Texas Health Science Center at San Antonio, Texas A&M University, or Texas A&M University System Health Science Center. U.S. citizenship or permanent resident status is required.

Financial Data The stipend is $22,032 per year.

Duration 3 years.

Additional data This program is sponsored by 3 components of the NIH: the National Institute of Mental Health, the National Institute on Drug Abuse, and the National Institute of Neurological Disorders and Stroke. The training program covers brain metabolic mapping of behavioral functions, neuropharmacology, neuroimaging, and electrophysiology. Trainees are required to complete courses covering the brain and behavior, scientific ethics, experimental design, and statistical analysis.

Number awarded 10 each year.

Deadline Applications may be submitted at any time.

[836]
PREDOCTORAL FELLOWSHIPS OF THE FORD FOUNDATION DIVERSITY FELLOWSHIP PROGRAM

National Research Council
Attn: Fellowships Office, Keck 576
500 Fifth Street, N.W.
Washington, DC 20001
(202) 334-2872   Fax: (202) 334-3419
E-mail: infofell@nas.edu
Web: sites.nationalacademies.org

Summary To provide financial assistance for graduate school to Hispanic Americans and other students whose success will increase the racial and ethnic diversity of U.S. colleges and universities.

Eligibility This program is open to citizens, permanent residents, and nationals of the United States who are enrolled or planning to enroll full time in a Ph.D. or Sc.D. degree program and are committed to a career in teaching and research at the college or university level. Applicants may be undergraduates in their senior year, individuals who have completed undergraduate study or some graduate study, or current Ph.D. or Sc.D. students who can demonstrate that they can fully utilize a 3-year fellowship award. They must be working on or planning to work on a degree in most areas of the arts, sciences, humanities, and social sciences or in interdisciplinary ethnic or area studies. Support is not provided to students working on a degree in most practice-oriented areas, terminal master's degrees, other doctoral degrees (e.g., Ed.D., D.F.A., Psy.D.), professional degrees (e.g., medicine, law, public health), or joint degrees (e.g., M.D./Ph.D., J.D./Ph.D., M.F.A./Ph.D.). The following are considered as positive factors in the selection process: evidence of superior academic achievement; promise of continuing achievement as scholars and teachers; membership in a group whose underrepresentation in the American professoriate has been severe and long-standing, including Black/African Americans, Puerto Ricans, Mexican Americans/Chicanos/Chicanas, Native American Indians, Alaska Natives (Eskimos, Aleuts, and other indigenous people of Alaska), and Native Pacific Islanders (Hawaiians, Micronesians, or Polynesians); capacity to respond in pedagogically productive ways to the learning needs of students from diverse backgrounds; sustained personal engagement with communities that are underrepresented in the academy and an ability to bring this asset to learning, teaching, and scholarship at the college and university level; and likelihood of using the diversity of human experience as an educational resource in teaching and scholarship.

Financial Data The program provides a stipend to the student of $20,000 per year and an award to the host institution of $2,000 per year in lieu of tuition and fees.

Duration 3 years of support is provided, to be used within a 5-year period.

Additional data The competition for this program is conducted by the National Research Council on behalf of the Ford Foundation. Applicants who merit receiving the fellowship but to whom awards cannot be made because of insufficient funds are given Honorable Mentions; this recognition does not carry with it a monetary award but honors applicants who have demonstrated substantial academic achievement. The National Research Council publishes a list of those Honorable Mentions who wish their names publicized. Fellows may not accept remuneration from another fellowship or similar external award while on this program; however, supplementation from institutional funds, educational benefits from the Department of Veterans Affairs, or educational incentive funds may be received concurrently with Ford Foundation support. Predoctoral fellows are required to submit an interim progress report 6 months after the start of the fellowship and a final report at the end of the 12 month tenure.

Number awarded   Approximately 60 each year.

Deadline   November of each year.

[837]
PREDOCTORAL RESEARCH TRAINING FELLOWSHIPS IN EPILEPSY

Epilepsy Foundation
Attn: Research Department
8301 Professional Place
Landover, MD 20785-2353
(301) 459-3700   Toll Free: (800) EFA-1000
Fax: (301) 577-2684   TDD: (800) 332-2070
E-mail: grants@efa.org
Web: www.epilepsyfoundation.org

Summary   To provide funding to doctoral candidates (particularly Hispanic Americans, other minorities, women, and individuals with disabilities) who are enrolled in designated fields and interested in conducting dissertation research on a topic related to epilepsy.

Eligibility   This program is open to full-time graduate students working on a Ph.D. in biochemistry, genetics, neuroscience, nursing, pharmacology, pharmacy, physiology, or psychology. Applicants must be conducting dissertation research on a topic relevant to epilepsy under the guidance of a mentor with expertise in the area of epilepsy investigation. Applications from women, members of minority groups, and people with disabilities are especially encouraged. U.S. citizenship is not required, but the project must be conducted in the United States. Selection is based on the relevance of the proposed work to epilepsy, the applicant's qualifications, the mentor's qualifications, the scientific quality of the proposed dissertation research, the quality of the training environment for research related to epilepsy, and the adequacy of the facility.

Financial Data   The grant is $20,000, consisting of $19,000 for a stipend and $1,000 to support travel to attend the annual meeting of the American Epilepsy Society.

Duration   1 year.

Additional data   Support for this program, which began in 1998, is provided by many individuals, families, and corporations, especially the American Epilepsy Society, Abbott Laboratories, Ortho-McNeil Pharmaceutical, and Pfizer Inc.

Number awarded   Varies each year.

Deadline   August of each year.

[838]
PROCTER & GAMBLE PROFESSIONAL ORAL CARE–HDA FOUNDATION SCHOLARSHIPS

Hispanic Dental Association
Attn: HDA Foundation
1111 14th Street, N.W., Suite 1100
Washington, DC 20005
(202) 629-3628   Fax: (202) 629-3802
E-mail: scholarships@hdassoc.org
Web: www.hdassoc.org

Summary   To provide financial assistance to members of the Hispanic Dental Association (HDA) interested in preparing for a career in a dental profession.

Eligibility   This program is open to HDA members who are entering as first- or second-year full-time students at an accredited dental, dental hygiene, dental assisting, or dental technician program. Applicants must be permanent U.S. residents. They must have a GPA of 3.0 or higher. Along with their application, they must submit an essay on why they want to be a dental professional and how they will help to improve their community when they have reached their goal. Selection is based on scholastic achievement, community service, leadership skills, and commitment to improving the oral health of the Hispanic community.

Financial Data   The stipend is $1,000.

Duration   1 year.

Additional data   This program, which began in 1994, is sponsored by Procter & Gamble Company.

Number awarded   Varies each year; recently, 6 of these scholarships were awarded.

Deadline   June of each year.

[839]
PUBLIC INTEREST FELLOWSHIPS FOR LAW STUDENTS OF COLOR

Goodwin Procter LLP
Attn: Recruiting Manager
53 State Street
Boston, MA 02109
(617) 570-8156   Fax: (617) 523-1231
E-mail: fellowships@goodwinprocter.com
Web: www.goodwinprocter.com

Summary   To provide financial aid and work experience to Hispanic American and other minority students who are interested in public interest law.

Eligibility   This program is open to students of color entering their second year at a law school in any state. Applicants must actively express an interest in working in the sponsoring firm's summer program in public interest law. If they are applying for the Goodwin MassMutual Diversity Fellowship, they must express an interest in working with MassMutual's legal department in Springfield, Massachusetts for 2 weeks as part of the summer program and specializing in the investment or insurance business or in a legal focus to advance business objectives. Selection is based on academic performance, leadership abilities, involvement in minority student organizations, commitment to community service, interpersonal skills, other special achievements and honors, and interest in working with the firm during the summer.

Financial Data   The stipend is $7,500.

Duration   1 year; nonrenewable.

Additional data This program began in 2005. In 2007, it added the Goodwin MassMutual Diversity Fellowship, created in conjunction with its long-standing client, Massachusetts Mutual Life Insurance Company (MassMutual). Summer positions are available at the firm's offices in Boston, Los Angeles, New York, Palo Alto, San Diego, San Francisco, and Washington, D.C.

Number awarded 4 each year, including 1 Goodwin MassMutual Diversity Fellowship.

Deadline October of each year.

[840]
PUERTO RICAN BAR ASSOCIATION SCHOLARSHIP PROGRAM

Puerto Rican Bar Association
Attn: PRBA Scholarship Fund
303 Park Avenue South, Suite 1405
New York, NY 10010
E-mail: scholarship@prba.net
Web: www.prba.net

Summary To provide financial assistance to Latino law students who are residents of New York or attending law school in the state.

Eligibility This program is open to Latino law students who are enrolled at law schools in New York or are permanent residents of that state. Applicants may be first- or second-year students or third-year evening students. Along with their application, they must submit a 2-page personal statement discussing their career goals, school and community activities, and any activities demonstrating their commitment to serve the Latino community. Candidates for an LL.M. degree are not eligible. Selection is based on academic achievement, community involvement, and financial need.

Financial Data Stipends range from $2,500 to $5,000.

Duration 1 year.

Number awarded Varies each year; recently, 10 of these scholarships were awarded.

Deadline April of each year.

[841]
PUERTO RICAN BAR FOUNDATION SCHOLARSHIP

Puerto Rican Bar Association of Illinois
c/o Evans, Loewenstein, Shimanovsky & Moscardini, LTD
130 South Jefferson, Suite 350
Chicago, IL 60661
(312) 782-1850　　　　　　　　Fax: (312) 466-0819
E-mail: prbalawscholarship@gmail.com
Web: www.prbalawil.com/foundation

Summary To provide financial assistance to law students from any state who have demonstrated a commitment to the Hispanic community.

Eligibility This program is open to students who have completed 1 year of law school. Applicants must have distinguished themselves academically, have demonstrated a commitment to the advancement of the Hispanic community, and have financial need. Special consideration is given to students who plan to practice law in Illinois after graduation from law school.

Financial Data A stipend is awarded (amount not specified).

Duration 1 year; nonrenewable.

Additional data This program began in 2004.

Number awarded 3 each year.

Deadline September of each year.

[842]
RACIAL ETHNIC PASTORAL LEADERSHIP PROGRAM

Synod of Southern California and Hawaii
Attn: Racial Ethnic Pastoral Leadership Work Group
3325 Wilshire Boulevard, Suite 850
Los Angeles, CA 90010-1761
(213) 483-3840, ext. 103　　　　　Fax: (213) 483-4275
E-mail: LeonFanniel@synod.org
Web: www.synod.org/repl/index.html

Summary To provide financial assistance to Hispanic Americans and members of other racial minority groups in the Presbyterian Church (USA) Synod of Southern California and Hawaii who are preparing for a career as a pastor or other church vocation.

Eligibility Applicants must be under care of their church's Session and enrolled with a Presbytery within the Synod of Southern California and Hawaii. They must be members of racial ethnic groups interested in becoming a Presbyterian pastor or other church worker (e.g., commissioned ruling elder, certified Christian educator) and serving in a racial ethnic ministry within the PCUSA. Racial ethnic persons who already have an M.Div. degree, are from another denomination in correspondence with the PCUSA, and are seeking to meet PCUSA requirements for ordination or transfer may also be eligible if they plan to serve in a racial ethnic congregation or an approved specialized ministry. Applicants must submit documentation of financial need, recommendations from the appropriate presbytery committee or session, a current transcript, and essays on their goals and objectives. They must be enrolled full or part time in a PCUSA seminary or other seminary approved by the Committee on Preparation for Ministry of their Presbytery.

Financial Data The stipend is $2,000 per year.

Duration 1 year; may be renewed.

Additional data This program began in 1984.

Number awarded Varies each year.

Deadline April of each year.

[843]
RACIAL ETHNIC SUPPLEMENTAL GRANTS

Presbyterian Church (USA)
Attn: Office of Financial Aid for Studies
100 Witherspoon Street, Room M-052
Louisville, KY 40202-1396
(502) 569-5224　　　　Toll Free: (800) 728-7228, ext. 5224
Fax: (502) 569-8766　　　　TDD: (800) 833-5955
E-mail: finaid@pcusa.org
Web: gamc.pcusa.org

Summary To provide financial assistance to Hispanic American and other minority graduate students who are Presbyterian Church (USA) members interested in preparing for church occupations.

Eligibility This program is open to racial/ethnic graduate students (Asian American, African American, Hispanic American, Native American, or Alaska Native) who are enrolled full time at a PCUSA seminary or accredited theological institution approved by their Committee on Preparation for Ministry. Applicants must be working on 1) an M.Div. degree and enrolled as an inquirer or candidate by a PCUSA presbytery; or 2) an M.A.C.E. degree and preparing for a church occupation. They must be PCUSA members, U.S. citizens or permanent residents, able to demonstrate financial need, and recommended by the financial aid officer at their theological institution. Along with their application, they must submit a 1,000-word essay on what they believe God is calling them to do in ministry.

Financial Data Stipends range from $500 to $1,000 per year. Funds are intended as supplements to students who have been awarded a Presbyterian Study Grant but still demonstrate remaining financial need.

Duration 1 year; may be renewed up to 2 additional years.

Number awarded Varies each year.

Deadline June of each year.

[844]
RALPH W. SHRADER DIVERSITY SCHOLARSHIPS

Armed Forces Communications and Electronics
  Association
Attn: AFCEA Educational Foundation
4400 Fair Lakes Court
Fairfax, VA 22033-3899
(703) 631-6138   Toll Free: (800) 336-4583, ext. 6138
Fax: (703) 631-4693   E-mail: scholarshipsinfo@afcea.org
Web: www.afcea.org

Summary To provide financial assistance to Hispanic American and other master's degree students in fields related to communications and electronics.

Eligibility This program is open to U.S. citizens working on a master's degree at an accredited college or university in the United States. Applicants must be enrolled full time and studying computer science, computer technology, engineering (chemical, electrical, electronic, communications, or systems), mathematics, physics, management information systems, or a field directly related to the support of U.S. national security or intelligence enterprises. At least 1 of these scholarships is set aside for a woman or a minority. Selection is based primarily on academic excellence.

Financial Data The stipend is $3,000. Funds are paid directly to the recipient.

Duration 1 year.

Additional data This program is sponsored by Booz Allen Hamilton.

Number awarded Up to 5 each year, at least 1 of which is for a woman or minority candidate.

Deadline February of each year.

[845]
RANDY GERSON MEMORIAL GRANT

American Psychological Foundation
750 First Street, N.E.
Washington, DC 20002-4242
(202) 336-5843   Fax: (202) 336-5812
E-mail: foundation@apa.org
Web: www.apa.org/apf/funding/gerson.aspx

Summary To provide funding to graduate students (particularly Hispanic Americans, other minorities, women, and students with disabilities) who are interested in conducting research in the psychology of couple and/or family dynamics and/or multi-generational processes.

Eligibility This program is open to full-time graduate students in psychology. Applicants must be proposing a project that advances the systemic understanding of couple and/or family dynamics and/or multi-generational processes. Work that advances theory, assessment, or clinical practice in those areas is eligible. Preference is given to projects that use or contribute to the development of Bowen family systems. Selection is based on conformance with stated program goals, magnitude of incremental contribution, quality of proposed work, and applicant's demonstrated scholarship and research competence. The sponsor encourages applications from individuals who represent diversity in race, ethnicity, gender, age, disability, and sexual orientation.

Financial Data The grant is $6,000.

Duration The grant is presented annually.

Additional data This grant was first awarded in 1998.

Number awarded 1 each year.

Deadline January of each year.

[846]
RAY AND CARMELLA MELLADO SCHOLARSHIP

Great Minds in STEM
Attn: HENAAC Scholars Program
602 Monterey Pass Road
Monterey Park, CA 91754
(323) 262-0997   Fax: (323) 262-0946
E-mail: gcruz@greatmindsinstem.org
Web: www.greatmindsinstem.org

Summary To provide financial assistance to Hispanic undergraduate and graduate students who are enrolled at a university in any state and working on a degree in a field of science, technology, engineering, or mathematics (STEM).

Eligibility This program is open to Hispanic undergraduate and graduate students who are working on a degree in a field of STEM at colleges and universities in any state. Applicants must be of Hispanic origin and/or must significantly participate in and promote organizations and activities in the Hispanic community. They must have a GPA of 3.0 or higher. There is no citizenship requirement. Along with their application, they must submit a 700-word essay on a topic that changes annually. Selection is based on leadership, academic achievements, and campus and community activities; financial need is not considered.

Financial Data Stipends range from $500 to $10,000.

Duration 1 year; recipients may reapply.

Additional data The Hispanic Engineer National Achievement Awards Conference (HENAAC) was established in 1989 and initiated a scholarship program in 2000. In 2010, the sponsoring organization officially adopted its current name, but it continues to hold the annual HENAAC conference, at which the scholarships are presented. Recipients must attend the conference to accept their scholarship.

Number awarded 1 or more each year.

Deadline April of each year.

[847]
RDW GROUP, INC. MINORITY SCHOLARSHIP FOR COMMUNICATIONS

Rhode Island Foundation
Attn: Funds Administrator
One Union Station
Providence, RI 02903
(401) 427-4017   Fax: (401) 331-8085
E-mail: lmonahan@rifoundation.org
Web: www.rifoundation.org

Summary To provide financial assistance to Hispanic Americans and other residents of color from Rhode Island who are working on a undergraduate or graduate degree in communications in any state.

Eligibility This program is open to undergraduate and graduate students at colleges and universities in any state who are Rhode Island residents of color. Applicants must intend to work on a degree in communications (including computer graphics, art, cinematography, or other fields that would prepare them for a career in advertising). They must be able to demonstrate financial need and a commitment to a career in communications. Along with their application, they must submit an essay (up to 300 words) on the impact they would like to have on the communications field.

Financial Data The stipend is approximately $2,000 per year.

Duration 1 year; recipients may reapply.

Additional data This program is sponsored by the RDW Group, Inc.

Number awarded 1 each year.

Deadline April of each year.

[848]
REED SMITH DIVERSE SCHOLARS PROGRAM

Reed Smith LLP
Attn: U.S. Director of Legal Recruiting
2500 One Liberty Place
1650 Market Street
Philadelphia, PA 19103
(215) 851-8100   E-mail: dlevin@reedsmith.com
Web: www.reedsmith.com/Diverse_Scholars_Program

Summary To provide financial aid and summer work experience to Hispanic American and other law students who are will contribute to diversity in the field.

Eligibility This program is open to students completing their first year of law school. Applicants must be able to demonstrate a record of academic excellence and a commitment to diversity, inclusion, and community. Along with their application, they must submit a 750-word personal statement on how they believe they can contribute to the sponsoring law firm's goals of diversity and inclusion, including 1) how their life experiences have impacted their commitment to diversity; 2) their community involvement; and 3) their academic or leadership achievements.

Financial Data The stipend is $15,000. Recipients are also offered a summer associate position at their choice of the firm's 9 U.S. offices after completion of their second year of law school (in Chicago, Houston, Los Angeles, New York, Philadelphia, Pittsburgh, Richmond, San Francisco, or Washington, D.C.).

Duration 1 year (the second year of law school).

Additional data The firm established this program in 2008 as part of its commitment to promote diversity in the legal profession.

Number awarded 2 each year.

Deadline August of each year.

[849]
REFORMA SCHOLARSHIP

REFORMA (National Association to Promote Library and Information Services to Latinos and the Spanish Speaking)
c/o Salvador Avila, Scholarship Committee
Enterprise Library
25 East Shelbourne Avenue
Las Vegas, NV 89123
(702) 507-3760   E-mail: avilas@lvccld.org
Web: www.reforma.org

Summary To provide financial assistance to Spanish-speaking students interested in preparing for a career in library or information science.

Eligibility The program is open to citizens and permanent residents of the United States who are Spanish-speaking college seniors. While eligibility is not restricted by age, sex, creed, national origin, or minority group/association membership, it is required that those who apply have a definite interest in service to the Spanish-speaking community. Applicants must show evidence of commitment to a career in librarianship and the potential for high academic achievement. Along with their application, they must submit a personal statements on how they plan to serve Latinos and Spanish-speakers if they are awarded this scholarship. Selection is based on that statement (50 points), language proficiency (10 points), employment history (20 points), and recommendations (20 points).

Financial Data The stipend is $1,500.

Duration 1 year.

Number awarded Varies each year; recently, 5 of these scholarships were awarded.

Deadline March of each year.

[850]
RICHARD AND HELEN BROWN COREM SCHOLARSHIPS

United Church of Christ
Parish Life and Leadership Ministry Team
Attn: COREM Administrator
700 Prospect Avenue East
Cleveland, OH 44115-1100
(216) 736-2113   Toll Free: (866) 822-8224, ext. 2113
Fax: (216) 736-3783
Web: www.ucc.org/seminarians/ucc-scholarships-for.html

Summary To provide financial assistance to Hispanic American and other minority seminary students who are interested in becoming a pastor in the United Church of Christ (UCC).

Eligibility This program is open to students at accredited seminaries who have been members of a UCC congregation for at least 1 year. Applicants must work through 1 of the member bodies of the Council for Racial and Ethnic Ministries (COREM): United Black Christians (UBC), Ministers for Racial, Social and Economic Justice (MRSEJ), Council for

Hispanic Ministries (CHM), Pacific Islander and Asian American Ministries (PAAM), or Council for American Indian Ministries (CAIM). They must 1) have a GPA of 3.0 or higher; 2) be enrolled in a course of study leading to ordained ministry; 3) be in care of an association or conference at the time of application; and 4) demonstrate leadership ability through participation in their local church, association, conference, or academic environment.

Financial Data Stipends are approximately $10,000 per year.

Duration 1 year.

Number awarded Varies each year; recently, 7 scholarships were awarded by UBC, 2 by MRSEJ, 1 by PAAM, and 2 by CHM.

Deadline Deadline not specified.

[851]
RICHARD D. HAILEY AAJ LAW STUDENT SCHOLARSHIPS

American Association for Justice
Attn: Scholarships
777 Sixth Street, N.W., Suite 200
Washington, DC 20001
(202) 965-3500, ext. 2834
Toll Free: (800) 424-2725, ext. 2834
Fax: (202) 965-0355
E-mail: catherine.rodman@justice.org
Web: www.justice.org/cps/rde/xchg/justice/hs.xsl/648.htm

Summary To provide financial assistance for law school to Hispanic American and other minority student members of the American Association for Justice (AAJ).

Eligibility This program is open to African American, Hispanic, Asian American, Native American, and biracial members of the association who are entering the first, second, or third year of law school. Applicants must submit a 500-word essay on how they meet the selection criteria: commitment to the association, involvement in student chapter and minority caucus activities, desire to represent victims, interest and proficiency of skills in trial advocacy, and financial need.

Financial Data The stipend is $1,000.

Duration 1 year.

Additional data The American Association for Justice was formerly the Association of Trial Lawyers of America.

Number awarded Up to 6 each year.

Deadline May of each year.

[852]
RISING FARMWORKER DREAM FUND PRE-MBA FELLOWSHIP

Rising Farmworker Dream Fund
c/o Martin Curiel
9512 Rachel Street
Live Oak, CA 95953
E-mail: info@risingfarmworkers.org
Web: www.risingfarmworkers.org/fellowships

Summary To provide financial assistance to children of farmworkers who plan to earn an M.B.A. degree at a highly-ranked business school.

Eligibility Applicants to this program must either 1) be a child of a farm worker, and/or 2) have worked in the agricultural sector as a farm laborer for at least 5 years. They must be in the process of applying to a business school identified by the sponsor as 1 of the top M.B.A. programs in the country (for a list of the eligible schools, contact the sponsor). There is no formal application; students enter the sponsor's online "Stock Exchange" through which they raise funds from benefactors. Selection is based on quality of application, demonstrated willingness to help improve the lives of farmworkers and migrant students, and demonstrated leadership skills in the community, business, or other areas.

Financial Data The stipend is $10,000, of which half is paid after acceptance at a qualifying business school, and half is paid during the second year of study after the recipients have completed community service projects by agreement with their benefactors.

Duration The award is disbursed over a 2-year period.

Additional data This fellowship was first awarded in 2007.

Number awarded 1 or more each year.

Deadline May of each year.

[853]
RIXIO MEDINA & ASSOCIATES SCHOLARSHIP FOR HISPANICS IN SAFETY

American Society of Safety Engineers
Attn: ASSE Foundation
Scholarship Award Program
1800 East Oakton Street
Des Plaines, IL 60018
(847) 699-2929   Fax: (847) 768-3434
E-mail: bzylstra@asse.org
Web: www.asse.org

Summary To provide financial assistance to Hispanic upper-division and graduate students working on a degree related to occupational safety.

Eligibility This program is open to ASSE student members who are working on an undergraduate or graduate degree in occupational safety, health, environment, industrial hygiene, occupational health nursing, or a closely-related field (e.g., industrial or environmental engineering). Applicants must be bilingual (Spanish-English); Hispanic ethnicity is preferred. Students enrolled in an ASAC/ABET-accredited safety program also receive preference. They must be full-time students who have completed at least 60 semester hours with a GPA of 3.0 or higher as undergraduates or at least 9 semester hours as graduate students. U.S. citizenship is not required. Membership in the American Society of Safety Engineers (ASSE) is not required, but preference is given to members.

Financial Data The stipend is $4,000 per year.

Duration 1 year; recipients may reapply.

Additional data This program began in 2005.

Number awarded 1 each year.

Deadline November of each year.

[854]
ROBERT D. WATKINS GRADUATE RESEARCH FELLOWSHIP

American Society for Microbiology
Attn: Education Board
1752 N Street, N.W.
Washington, DC 20036-2904
(202) 942-9283   Fax: (202) 942-9329
E-mail: fellowships@asmusa.org
Web: www.asm.org/index.php/fellowships-2

Summary   To provide funding for research in microbiology to Hispanic American and other underrepresented minority doctoral students who are members of the American Society for Microbiology (ASM).

Eligibility   This program is open to African Americans, Hispanics, Native Americans, Alaskan Natives, and Pacific Islanders enrolled as full-time graduate students who have completed their first year of doctoral study and who are members of the society. Applicants must propose a joint research plan in collaboration with a society member scientist. They must have completed all graduate course work requirements for the doctoral degree by the date of the activation of the fellowship. U.S. citizenship or permanent resident status is required. Selection is based on academic achievement, evidence of a successful research plan developed in collaboration with a research adviser/mentor, relevant career goals in the microbiological sciences, and involvement in activities that serve the needs of underrepresented groups.

Financial Data   Students receive $21,000 per year as a stipend; funds may not be used for tuition or fees.

Duration   3 years.

Number awarded   Varies each year.

Deadline   April of each year.

[855]
ROBERT TOIGO FOUNDATION FELLOWSHIPS

Robert Toigo Foundation
Attn: Fellowship Program Administrator
180 Grand Avenue, Suite 900
Oakland, CA 94612
(510) 763-5771   Fax: (510) 763-5778
E-mail: info@toigofoundation.org
Web: www.toigofoundation.org

Summary   To provide financial assistance to Hispanic American and other minority students working on a master's degree in business administration or a related field.

Eligibility   This program is open to members of minority groups (African American, Hispanic/Latino, Native American/ Alaskan Native, South Asian American, or Asian American/ Pacific Islander) who are entering or enrolled in a program for an M.B.A., J.D./M.B.A., master's in real estate, or master's in finance. Applicants must be preparing for a career in finance, including (but not limited to) investment management, investment banking, corporate finance, real estate, private equity, venture capital, business development, pension fund investment, or financial services consulting. U.S. citizenship or permanent resident status is required.

Financial Data   The stipend is $2,500 per year.

Duration   Up to 2 years.

Additional data   The application fee is $40.

Number awarded   Approximately 50 to 60 each year.

Deadline   March of each year.

[856]
RONALD M. DAVIS SCHOLARSHIP

American Medical Association
Attn: AMA Foundation
515 North State Street
Chicago, IL 60610
(312) 464-4193   Fax: (312) 464-4142
E-mail: amafoundation@ama-assn.org
Web: www.ama-assn.org

Summary   To provide financial assistance to medical school students who are Hispanic Americans or members of other underrepresented minority groups and planning to become a primary care physician.

Eligibility   This program is open to first- and second-year medical students who are members of the following minority groups: African American/Black, American Indian, Native Hawaiian, Alaska Native, or Hispanic/Latino. Candidates must have an interest in becoming a primary care physician. Only nominations are accepted. Each medical school is invited to submit 2 nominees. U.S. citizenship or permanent resident status is required.

Financial Data   The stipend is $10,000.

Duration   1 year.

Additional data   This program is offered by the AMA Foundation of the American Medical Association in collaboration with the National Business Group on Health.

Number awarded   1 each year.

Deadline   April of each year.

[857]
ROSA L. PARKS SCHOLARSHIPS

Conference of Minority Transportation Officials
Attn: National Scholarship Program
1875 I Street, N.W., Suite 500
Washington, DC 20006
(703) 234-4072   Fax: (202) 318-0364
Web: www.comto.org/?page=Scholarships

Summary   To provide financial assistance for college to children of members of the Conference of Minority Transportation Officials (COMTO) and to other students interested in working on a bachelor's or master's degree in transportation.

Eligibility   This program is open to 1) college-bound high school seniors whose parent has been a COMTO member for at least 1 year; 2) undergraduates who have completed at least 60 semester credit hours in a transportation discipline; and 3) students working on a master's degree in transportation who have completed at least 15 credits. Applicants must have a GPA of 3.0 or higher. Along with their application, they must submit a cover letter with a 500-word statement of career goals. Financial need is not considered in the selection process. U.S. citizenship or legal resident status is required.

Financial Data   The stipend is $4,500. Funds are paid directly to the recipient's college or university.

Duration   1 year.

Additional data   COMTO was established in 1971 to promote, strengthen, and expand the roles of minorities in all aspects of transportation. Recipients are expected to attend the COMTO National Scholarship Luncheon.

Number awarded 1 each year.

Deadline May of each year.

[858]
ROY H. POLLACK SCHOLARSHIP

Unitarian Universalist Association
Attn: Ministerial Credentialing Office
25 Beacon Street
Boston, MA 02108-2800
(617) 948-6403　　　　　　　Fax: (617) 742-2875
E-mail: mcoadministrator@uua.org
Web: www.uua.org

Summary To provide financial assistance to seminary students (especially Hispanic Americans and other students of color) preparing for the Unitarian Universalist (UU) ministry.

Eligibility This program is open to seminary students who are enrolled full or at least half time in their second or third year in a UU ministerial training program with candidate status. Applicants must be citizens of the United States or Canada. Priority is given first to those who have demonstrated outstanding ministerial ability and secondarily to students with the greatest financial need (especially persons of color).

Financial Data The stipend ranges from $1,000 to $15,000 per year.

Duration 1 year.

Number awarded Varies each year; recently, 2 of these scholarships were awarded.

Deadline April of each year.

[859]
ROY SCRIVNER MEMORIAL RESEARCH GRANTS

American Psychological Foundation
750 First Street, N.E.
Washington, DC 20002-4242
(202) 336-5843　　　　　　　Fax: (202) 336-5812
E-mail: foundation@apa.org
Web: www.apa.org/apf/funding/scrivner.aspx

Summary To provide funding to graduate students (particularly Hispanic Americans and other students from diverse backgrounds) who are interested in conducting dissertation research on lesbian, gay, bisexual, and transgender (LGBT) family psychology and therapy.

Eligibility This program is open to doctoral candidates who are interested in conducting empirical research in all fields of the behavioral and social sciences that focus on LGBT family psychology and LGBT family therapy. Proposals are especially encouraged for empirical studies that address the following: problems faced by LGBT families such as those associated with cultural, racial, socioeconomic, and family structure diversity; successful coping mechanisms such as sources of support and resilience for family members; and clinical issues and interventions in the domain of LGBT. Selection is based on conformance with stated program goals, magnitude of incremental contribution, quality of proposed work, and applicant's demonstrated scholarship and research competence. The sponsor encourages applications from individuals who represent diversity in race, ethnicity, gender, age, disability, and sexual orientation.

Financial Data The grant is $12,000.

Duration 1 year.

Number awarded 1 each year.

Deadline October of each year.

[860]
RUBEN SALAZAR SCHOLARSHIPS

National Association of Hispanic Journalists
Attn: Scholarship Committee
1050 Connecticut Avenue, N.W., Tenth Floor
Washington, DC 20036
(202) 662-7145　　　　　　　Toll Free: (888) 346-NAHJ
Fax: (202) 662-7144　　　　　　E-mail: nahj@nahj.org
Web: www.nahj12.com/scholarships

Summary To provide financial assistance to undergraduate and graduate student members of the National Association of Hispanic Journalists (NAHJ) who are interested in preparing for careers in the media.

Eligibility This program is open to Hispanic American high school seniors, undergraduates, and graduate students who are interested in preparing for a career in English- or Spanish-language print, broadcast (radio or television), online, or photojournalism; students majoring in other fields must be able to demonstrate a strong interest in preparing for a career in journalism. Applicants must be enrolled full time at a college or university in the United States or Puerto Rico. They must be NAHJ members. Along with their application, they must submit transcripts, a 1-page resume, 2 letters of recommendation, work samples, and a 1,000-word autobiographical essay that includes why they are interested in a career in journalism, what inspired them to prepare for a career in the field, what hardships or obstacles they have experienced while trying to realize their goal of becoming a journalist, and the role Latino journalists play in the news industry. Selection is based on commitment to the field of journalism, academic achievement, awareness of the Latino community, and financial need.

Financial Data Stipends are $2,000 or $1,000.

Duration 1 year.

Number awarded Varies each year; recently, 10 of these scholarships were awarded: 5 at $2,000 and 5 at $1,000.

Deadline January of each year.

[861]
RUBINOS-MESIA SCHOLARSHIP

Structural Engineers Association of Illinois
Attn: Structural Engineers Foundation
134 North LaSalle Street, Suite 1910
Chicago, IL 60602
(312) 726-4165　　　　　　　Fax: (312) 277-1991
E-mail: office@seaol.org
Web: www.seaoi.org/sef.htm

Summary To provide financial assistance to upper-division and graduate students of Hispanic descent interested in a career in structural engineering.

Eligibility This program is open to students of Hispanic descent who are 1) entering their third or higher year of an undergraduate program; or 2) entering or continuing a graduate program. Applicants must be enrolled in a civil or architectural engineering program and planning to continue with a structural engineering specialization. Students enrolled in structural engineering technology programs are also eligible if they are qualified to take the Fundamentals of Engineering and Principles and Practice licensure examinations in their home state upon graduation. U.S. citizenship or permanent resident status is required. Students enrolled in military academies or ROTC programs are not eligible. Selection is based on a statement giving reasons why the applicant should receive the award (including plans for continued formal education), academic performance, and potential for development and leadership. Financial need is not considered.

Financial Data The stipend is $2,000.

Duration 1 year; nonrenewable.

Number awarded 1 or more each year.

Deadline April of each year.

[862]
RUTH L. KIRSCHSTEIN NATIONAL RESEARCH SERVICE AWARDS FOR INDIVIDUAL PREDOCTORAL FELLOWSHIPS TO PROMOTE DIVERSITY IN HEALTH-RELATED RESEARCH

National Institutes of Health
Office of Extramural Research
Attn: Grants Information
6705 Rockledge Drive, Suite 4090
Bethesda, MD 20892-7983
(301) 435-0714   Fax: (301) 480-0525
TDD: (301) 451-5936   E-mail: grantsinfo@od.nih.gov
Web: grants.nih.gov/grants/guide/pa-files/PA-11-112.html

Summary To provide financial assistance to Hispanic Americans and other students from underrepresented groups who are interested in working on a doctoral degree and preparing for a career in biomedical and behavioral research.

Eligibility This program is open to students enrolled or accepted for enrollment in a Ph.D. or equivalent research degree program; a formally combined M.D./Ph.D. program; or other combined professional doctoral/research Ph.D. program in the biomedical, behavioral, health, or clinical sciences. Students in health professional degree programs (e.g., M.D., D.O., D.D.S., D.V.M.) are not eligible. Applicants must be 1) members of an ethnic or racial group underrepresented in biomedical or behavioral research; 2) individuals with disabilities; or 3) individuals from socially, culturally, economically, or educationally disadvantaged backgrounds that have inhibited their ability to prepare for a career in health-related research. They must be U.S. citizens, nationals, or permanent residents.

Financial Data The fellowship provides an annual stipend of $22,032, a tuition and fee allowance (60% of costs up to $16,000 or 60% of costs up to $21,000 for dual degrees), and an institutional allowance of $4,200 ($3,100 at for-profit and federal institutions) for travel to scientific meetings, health insurance, and laboratory and other training expenses.

Duration Up to 5 years.

Additional data These fellowships are offered by most components of the National Institutes of Health (NIH). Contact the NIH for a list of names and telephone numbers of responsible officers at each component.

Number awarded Varies each year.

Deadline April, August, or December of each year.

[863]
SBE DOCTORAL DISSERTATION RESEARCH IMPROVEMENT GRANTS

National Science Foundation
Attn: Directorate for Social, Behavioral, and Economic
  Sciences
4201 Wilson Boulevard, Room 905N
Arlington, VA 22230
(703) 292-8700   Fax: (703) 292-9083
TDD: (800) 281-8749
Web: www.nsf.gov/funding/pgm_summ.jsp?pims_id=13453

Summary To provide partial support to doctoral candidates (particularly Hispanic Americans, other minorities, women, and students with disabilities) who are conducting dissertation research in areas of interest to the Directorate for Social, Behavioral, and Economic Sciences (SBE) of the National Science Foundation (NSF).

Eligibility Applications may be submitted through regular university channels by dissertation advisers on behalf of graduate students who have advanced to candidacy and have begun or are about to begin dissertation research. Students must be enrolled at U.S. institutions, but they need not be U.S. citizens. The proposed research must relate to SBE's Division of Behavioral and Cognitive Sciences (archaeology, cultural anthropology, documenting endangered languages, geography and spatial sciences, linguistics, or biological anthropology); Division of Social and Economic Sciences (decision, risk, and management science; economics; law and social science; methodology, measurement, and statistics; political science; sociology; or science, technology, and society); National Center for Science and Engineering Statistics (science and technology surveys and statistics); or Office of Multidisciplinary Activities (science and innovation policy). Women, minorities, and persons with disabilities are strongly encouraged to apply.

Financial Data Grants have the limited purpose of providing funds to enhance the quality of dissertation research. They are to be used exclusively for necessary expenses incurred in the actual conduct of the dissertation research, including (but not limited to) conducting field research in settings away from campus that would not otherwise be possible, data collection and sample survey costs, payments to subjects or informants, specialized research equipment, analysis and services not otherwise available, supplies, travel to archives, travel to specialized facilities or field research locations, and partial living expenses for conducting necessary research away from the student's U.S. academic institution. Funding is not provided for stipends, tuition, textbooks, journals, allowances for dependents, travel to scientific meetings, publication costs, dissertation preparation or reproduction, or indirect costs.

Duration Up to 2 years.

Number awarded 200 to 300 each year. Approximately $2.5 million is available for this program annually.

Deadline Deadline dates for the submission of dissertation improvement grant proposals differ by program within the divisions of the SBE Directorate; applicants should obtain information regarding target dates for proposals from the relevant program.

[864]
SCHOLARSHIPS FOR MINORITY ACCOUNTING STUDENTS

American Institute of Certified Public Accountants
Attn: Academic and Career Development Division
220 Leigh Farm Road
Durham, NC 27707-8110
(919) 402-4931   Fax: (919) 419-4705
E-mail: scholarships@aicpa.org
Web: www.aicpa.org

Summary To provide financial assistance to Hispanic Americans and other minorities interested in studying accounting at the undergraduate or graduate school level.

Eligibility This program is open to minority undergraduate and graduate students, enrolled full time, who have a GPA of 3.3 or higher (both cumulatively and in their major) and intend to pursue a C.P.A. credential. The program defines minority students as those whose heritage is Black or African American, Hispanic or Latino, Native American, or Asian American. Undergraduates must have completed at least 30 semester hours, including at least 6 semester hours of a major in accounting. Graduate students must be working on a master's degree in accounting, finance, taxation, or a related program. Applicants must be U.S. citizens or permanent residents and student affiliate members of the American Institute of Certified Public Accountants (AICPA). Along with their application, they must submit 500-word essays on 1) why they want to become a C.P.A. and how attaining that licensure will contribute to their goals; and 2) how they would spread the message about accounting and the C.P.A. profession in their community and school. In the selection process, some consideration is given to financial need.

Financial Data Stipends range from $1,500 to $3,000 per year. Funds are disbursed directly to the recipient's school.

Duration 1 year; may be renewed up to 3 additional years or until completion of a bachelor's or master's degree, whichever is earlier.

Additional data This program began in 1969.

Number awarded Varies each year; recently, 78 students received funding through this program.

Deadline March of each year.

[865]
SCHOLARSHIPS SUPPORTING POST-SECONDARY EDUCATION FOR A CAREER IN THE AUDIOVISUAL INDUSTRY

InfoComm International
International Communications Industries Foundation
11242 Waples Mill Road, Suite 200
Fairfax, VA 22030
(703) 273-7200   Toll Free: (800) 659-7469
Fax: (703) 278-8082   E-mail: jhardwick@infocomm.org
Web: www.infocomm.org

Summary To provide financial assistance to undergraduate and graduate students (particularly Hispanic Americans, other minorities, and women) who are interested in preparing for a career in the audiovisual (AV) industry.

Eligibility This program is open to second-year students at 2-year colleges, juniors and seniors at 4-year institutions, and graduate students. Applicants must have a GPA of 2.75 or higher and be majoring or planning to major in audiovisual subjects or related fields, including audio, video, audiovisual, radio/television/film, or other field related to a career in the audiovisual industry. Students in other programs, such as journalism, may be eligible if they can demonstrate a relationship to career goals in the AV industry. Along with their application, they must submit 1) an essay of 150 to 200 words on the career path they plan to pursue in the audiovisual industry in the next 5 years; and 2) an essay of 250 to 300 words on the experience or person influencing them the most in selecting the audiovisual industry as their career of choice. Minority and women candidates are especially encouraged to apply. Selection is based on the essays, presentation of the application, GPA, AV-related experience, work experience, and letters of recommendation.

Financial Data The stipend is $4,000. Funds are sent directly to the school.

Duration 1 year.

Additional data InfoComm International, formerly the International Communications Industries Association, established the International Communications Industries Foundation (ICIF) to manage its charitable and educational activities.

Number awarded Varies each year.

Deadline April of each year.

[866]
SCHWABE, WILLIAMSON & WYATT SUMMER ASSOCIATE DIVERSITY SCHOLARSHIP

Schwabe, Williamson & Wyatt, Attorneys at Law
Attn: Attorney Recruiting Administrator
1211 S.W. Fifth Avenue, Suite 1500-2000
Portland, OR 97204
(503) 796-2889   Fax: (503) 796-2900
E-mail: dcphillips@schwabe.com
Web: www.schwabe.com/recruitdiversity.aspx

Summary To provide financial aid and summer work experience in Portland, Oregon or Seattle, Washington to Hispanic American and other law students who will contribute to the diversity of the legal profession.

Eligibility This program is open to first-year students working on a J.D. degree at an ABA-accredited law school. Applicants must 1) contribute to the diversity of the law school student body and the legal community; 2) possess a record of academic achievement, capacity, and leadership as an undergraduate and in law school that indicates promise for a successful career in the legal profession; and 3) demonstrate a commitment to practice law in the Pacific Northwest upon completion of law school. They must be interested in a paid summer associateship at the sponsoring law firm's office in Portland, Oregon or Seattle, Washington. Along with their application, they must submit a resume, undergraduate and law school transcripts, a legal writing sample, and a 1- to 2-page personal statement explaining their interest in the scholarship and how they will contribute to diversity in the legal community.

Financial Data The program provides a paid summer associateship during the summer following completion of the first year of law school and an academic scholarship of $7,500 to help pay tuition and other expenses during the recipient's second year of law school.

Duration 1 year.

Number awarded 1 each year.
Deadline January of each year.

[867]
SCOTT AND PAUL PEARSALL SCHOLARSHIP

American Psychological Foundation
750 First Street, N.E.
Washington, DC 20002-4242
(202) 336-5843   Fax: (202) 336-5812
E-mail: foundation@apa.org
Web: www.apa.org/apf/funding/pearsall.aspx

Summary To provide funding to graduate students (particularly Hispanic Americans, other minorities, and students with disabilities) who are interested in conducting research on the psychological effect of stigma on people with disabilities.

Eligibility This program is open to full-time graduate students at accredited universities in the United States and Canada. Applicants must be interested in conducting research that seeks to increase the public's understanding of the psychological pain and stigma experiences by adults living with physical disabilities, such as cerebral palsy. Selection is based on conformance with stated program goals and the quality of proposed work. The sponsor encourages applications from individuals who represent diversity in race, ethnicity, gender, age, disability, and sexual orientation.

Financial Data The grant is $10,000.
Duration 1 year.
Additional data This program began in 2013.
Number awarded 1 each year.
Deadline September of each year.

[868]
SELECTED PROFESSIONS FELLOWSHIPS FOR WOMEN OF COLOR

American Association of University Women
Attn: AAUW Educational Foundation
301 ACT Drive, Department 60
P.O. Box 4030
Iowa City, IA 52243-4030
(319) 337-1716, ext. 60   Fax: (319) 337-1204
E-mail: aauw@act.org
Web: www.aauw.org

Summary To provide financial assistance to Hispanic American and other women of color who are in their final year of graduate training in the fields of business administration, law, or medicine.

Eligibility This program is open to women who are working full time on a degree in fields in which women of color have been historically underrepresented: business administration (M.B.A.), law (J.D.), or medicine (M.D., D.O.). They must be African Americans, Mexican Americans, Puerto Ricans and other Hispanics, Native Americans, Alaska Natives, Asian Americans, or Pacific Islanders. U.S. citizenship or permanent resident status is required. Applicants in business administration must be entering their second year of study; applicants in law must be entering their third year of study; applicants in medicine may be entering their third or fourth year of study. Special consideration is given to applicants who 1) demonstrate their intent to enter professional practice in disciplines in which women are underrepresented, to serve underserved populations and communities, or to pursue pub-

lic interest areas; and 2) are nontraditional students. Selection is based on professional promise and personal attributes (50%), academic excellence and related academic success indicators (40%), and financial need (10%).

Financial Data Stipends range from $5,000 to $18,000.
Duration 1 academic year, beginning in September.
Additional data The filing fee is $35.
Number awarded Varies each year; recently, a total of 25 Selected Professions Fellowships were awarded.
Deadline January of each year.

[869]
SEMICONDUCTOR RESEARCH CORPORATION MASTER'S SCHOLARSHIP PROGRAM

Semiconductor Research Corporation
Attn: Global Research Collaboration
1101 Slater Road, Suite 120
P.O. Box 12053
Research Triangle Park, NC 27709-2053
(919) 941-9400   Fax: (919) 941-9450
E-mail: students@src.org
Web: www.src.org/student-center/fellowship

Summary To provide financial assistance to Hispanic Americans, other minorities, and women who are interested in working on a master's degree in a field of microelectronics relevant to the interests of the Semiconductor Research Corporation (SRC).

Eligibility This program is open to women and members of underrepresented minority groups (African Americans, Hispanics, and Native Americans). Applicants must be U.S. citizens or have permanent resident, refugee, or political asylum status in the United States. They must be admitted to an SRC participating university to work on a master's degree in a field relevant to microelectronics under the guidance of an SRC-sponsored faculty member and under an SRC-funded contract. Selection is based on academic achievement.

Financial Data The fellowship provides full tuition and fee support, a competitive stipend (recently, $2,186 per month), an annual grant of $2,000 to the university department with which the student recipient is associated, and travel expenses to the Graduate Fellowship Program Annual Conference.

Duration Up to 2 years.
Additional data This program began in 1997 for underrepresented minorities and expanded to include women in 1999.
Number awarded Approximately 12 each year.
Deadline February of each year.

[870]
SHERRY R. ARNSTEIN MINORITY STUDENT SCHOLARSHIP

American Association of Colleges of Osteopathic Medicine
Attn: Scholarships
5550 Friendship Boulevard, Suite 310
Chevy Chase, MD 20815-7231
(301) 968-4142   Fax: (301) 968-4101
Web: www.aacom.org

Summary To provide financial assistance to Hispanic American and other underrepresented minority students already enrolled in osteopathic medical school.

Eligibility This program is open to African American, mainland Puerto Rican, Hispanic, Native American, Native Hawaiian, and Alaska Native students currently enrolled in good standing in their first, second, or third year of osteopathic medical school. Applicants must submit a 750-word essay on what osteopathic medical schools can do to recruit and retain more underrepresented minority students, what they personally plan to do as a student and as a future D.O. to help increase minority student enrollment at a college of osteopathic medicine, and how and why they were drawn to osteopathic medicine.

Financial Data The stipend is $2,500.

Duration 1 year; nonrenewable.

Number awarded 1 each year.

Deadline March of each year.

[871]
SHERRY R. ARNSTEIN NEW STUDENT MINORITY STUDENT SCHOLARSHIP

American Association of Colleges of Osteopathic
  Medicine
Attn: Scholarships
5550 Friendship Boulevard, Suite 310
Chevy Chase, MD 20815-7231
(301) 968-4142   Fax: (301) 968-4101
Web: www.aacom.org

Summary To provide financial assistance to Hispanic American and other underrepresented minority students planning to enroll at an osteopathic medical school.

Eligibility This program is open to African American, mainland Puerto Rican, Hispanic, Native American, Native Hawaiian, and Alaska Native students who have been accepted and are planning to enroll as a first-time student at any of the colleges of osteopathic medicine that are members of the American Association of Colleges of Osteopathic Medicine (AACOM). Applicants must submit a 750-word essay on what osteopathic medical schools can do to recruit and retain more underrepresented minority students, what they personally plan to do as a student and as a future D.O. to help increase minority student enrollment at a college of osteopathic medicine, and how and why they were drawn to osteopathic medicine.

Financial Data The stipend is $2,500.

Duration 1 year; nonrenewable.

Number awarded 1 each year.

Deadline March of each year.

[872]
SHPE/CDM SMITH SCHOLARSHIP AND INTERNSHIP

Society of Hispanic Professional Engineers Foundation,
  Inc.
Attn: Advancing Hispanic Excellence in Technology,
  Engineering, Math and Science
13181 Crossroads Parkway North, Suite 450
P.O. Box 93577
City of Industry, CA 91715
(323) 725-3970, ext. 118   Fax: (323) 622-1046
E-mail: shpefoundation@shpe.org
Web: www.shpefoundation.org

Summary To provide financial assistance and work experience to members of the Society of Hispanic Professional Engineers (SHPE) who will be working on a master's degree in a field related to construction engineering.

Eligibility This program is open to SHPE members graduating from accredited colleges and universities in the United States or Puerto Rico who have a GPA of 3.0 or higher. Applicants must be majoring in an engineering, science, or construction discipline (such as chemical, civil, electrical, environmental, geotechnical, mechanical, or structural engineering) and planning to continue on to a master's degree program in those fields. They must be interested in a summer internship at an office of CDM (Camp Dresser and McKee, Inc.) or its subsidiaries: CDM Federal Programs Corporation or CDM Constructors Inc. Along with their application, they must submit a 500-word personal statement on why they are interested in working with CDM, challenges they have overcome, family background, community involvement, leadership, academic achievements, research internship or co-op experiences, and short- and long-term goals and aspirations.

Financial Data The internship stipend is $2,000. After the successful completion of the internship, participants receive a $6,000 scholarship for the next academic year.

Duration 1 year.

Additional data Advancing Hispanic Excellence in Technology, Engineering, Math and Science (AHETEMS) was established in 2004 by SHPE as an independent nonprofit foundation. CDM selects the recipients and provides mentors to work with the interns during the summer and throughout their college career.

Number awarded 1 or more each year.

Deadline December of each year.

[873]
SIDLEY DIVERSITY AND INCLUSION SCHOLARSHIP

Sidley Austin LLP
Attn: Scholarships
One South Dearborn Street
Chicago, IL 60603
(312) 853-7000   Fax: (312) 853-7036
E-mail: scholarship@sidley.com
Web: www.sidley.com

Summary To provide financial aid and work experience to Hispanic American and other law students who come from a diverse background.

Eligibility The program is open to students entering their second year of law school; preference is given to students at schools where the sponsor conducts on-campus interviews or participates in a resume collection. Applicants must have a demonstrated ability to contribute meaningfully to the diversity of the law school and/or legal profession. Along with their application, they must submit a 500-word essay that includes their thoughts on and efforts to improve diversity, how they might contribute to the sponsor's commitment to improving diversity, and their interest in practicing law at a global firm (specifically the sponsor). Selection is based on academic achievement and leadership qualities.

Financial Data The stipend is $15,000.

Duration 1 year.

Additional data These scholarships were first offered in 2011. Recipients are expected to participate in the sponsor's summer associate program following their second year of law school. They must apply separately for the associate position. The firm has offices in Chicago, Dallas, Los Angeles, New York, Palo Alto, San Francisco, and Washington, D.C.

Number awarded A limited number are awarded each year.

Deadline August of each year.

[874]
SIDNEY B. WILLIAMS, JR. INTELLECTUAL PROPERTY LAW SCHOOL SCHOLARSHIPS

Thurgood Marshall College Fund
4801 Woodway, Suite 300 E
Houston, TX 77056
(713) 574-4923   Fax: (480) 287-9632
E-mail: misha.lesley@tmcfund.org
Web: www.thurgoodmarshallcollegefund.org

Summary To provide financial assistance to Hispanic American and other underrepresented minority law school students who are interested in preparing for a career in intellectual property law.

Eligibility This program is open to members of underrepresented minority groups currently enrolled in or accepted to an ABA-accredited law school. Applicants must be U.S. citizens with a demonstrated intent to engage in the full-time practice of intellectual property law. Along with their application, they must submit a 250-word essay on how this scholarship will make a difference to them in meeting their goal of engaging in the full-time practice of intellectual property law and why they intend to do so. Selection is based on 1) demonstrated commitment to developing a career in intellectual property law; 2) academic performance at the undergraduate, graduate, and law school levels (as applicable); 3) general factors, such as leadership skills, community activities, or special accomplishments; and 4) financial need.

Financial Data The stipend is $10,000 per year. Funds may be used for tuition, fees, books, supplies, room, board, and a patent bar review course.

Duration 1 year; may be renewed if the recipient maintains a GPA of 2.0 or higher.

Additional data This program, which began in 2002, is administered by the Thurgood Marshall College Fund with support from the American Intellectual Property Law Education Foundation.

Number awarded Varies each year; recently, 12 of these scholarships were awarded.

Deadline March of each year.

[875]
SMITHSONIAN MINORITY AWARDS PROGRAM

Smithsonian Institution
Attn: Office of Fellowships and Internships
470 L'Enfant Plaza, Suite 7102
P.O. Box 37012, MRC 902
Washington, DC 20013-7012
(202) 633-7070   Fax: (202) 633-7069
E-mail: siofi@si.edu
Web: www.smithsonianofi.com

Summary To provide funding to Hispanic American and other minority undergraduate and graduate students who are interested in conducting research at the Smithsonian Institution.

Eligibility This program is open to members of U.S. minority groups underrepresented in the Smithsonian's scholarly programs. Applicants must be undergraduates or beginning graduate students interested in conducting research in the Institution's disciplines and in the museum field. They must be U.S. citizens or permanent residents and have a GPA of 3.0 or higher.

Financial Data Students receive a grant of $600 per week.

Duration Up to 10 weeks.

Additional data Recipients must carry out independent research projects in association with the Smithsonian's research staff. Eligible fields of study currently include animal behavior, ecology, and environmental science (including an emphasis on the tropics); anthropology (including archaeology); astrophysics and astronomy; earth sciences and paleobiology; evolutionary and systematic biology; history of science and technology; history of art (especially American, contemporary, African, Asian, and 20th-century art); American crafts and decorative arts; social and cultural history of the United States; and folk life. Students are required to be in residence at the Smithsonian for the duration of the fellowship.

Number awarded Varies each year; recently, 25 of these awards were granted: 2 for fall, 19 for summer, and 4 for spring.

Deadline January of each year for summer and fall residency; September of each year for spring residency.

[876]
SOCIETY OF PEDIATRIC PSYCHOLOGY DIVERSITY RESEARCH GRANT

American Psychological Association
Attn: Division 54 (Society of Pediatric Psychology)
c/o Anna Maria Patino-Fernandez
University of Miami School of Medicine
Mailman Center for Child Development
Division of Clinical Psychology
1601 N.W. 12th Avenue, 4018B
Miami, FL 33136-1005
(305) 243-6837   Fax: (305) 243-8470
E-mail: Apatino-fernandez@med.miami.edu
Web: www.apadivisions.org

Summary To provide funding to graduate student and postdoctoral members of the Society of Pediatric Psychology (particularly Hispanic Americans and others who come from diverse backgrounds) who are interested in conducting research on diversity aspects of pediatric psychology.

Eligibility This program is open to current members of the society who are graduate students, fellows, or early-career (within 3 years of appointment) faculty. Applicants must be interested in conducting pediatric psychology research that features diversity-related variables, such as race or ethnicity, gender, culture, sexual orientation, language differences, socioeconomic status, and/or religiosity. Along with their application, they must submit a 2,000-word description of the project, including its purpose, methodology, predictions, and implications; a detailed budget; a current curriculum vitae, and (for students) a curriculum vitae of the faculty research mentor and a letter of support from that mentor. Selection is based on relevance to diversity in child health (5 points), significance of the study (5 points), study methods and procedures (10 points), and investigator qualifications (10 points).

Financial Data Grants up to $1,000 are available. Funds may not be used for convention or meeting travel, indirect costs, stipends of principal investigators, or costs associated with manuscript preparation.

Duration The grant is presented annually.

Additional data The Society of Pediatric Psychology is Division 54 of the American Psychological Association (APA). This grant was first presented in 2008.

Number awarded 1 each year.

Deadline September of each year.

[877]
SOUTHERN REGIONAL EDUCATION BOARD DISSERTATION AWARDS

Southern Regional Education Board
Attn: Coordinator, Program and Scholar Services
592 Tenth Street N.W.
Atlanta, GA 30318-5776
(404) 879-5569   Fax: (404) 872-1477
E-mail: doctoral.scholars@sreb.org
Web: www.sreb.org/page/1113/types_of_awards.html

Summary To provide funding to Hispanic American and other minority students who wish to complete a Ph.D. dissertation, especially in the fields of science, technology, engineering, or mathematics (STEM), while in residence at a university in the southern states.

Eligibility This program is open to U.S. citizens and permanent residents who are members of racial/ethnic minority groups (Native Americans, Hispanic Americans, Asian Americans, and African Americans) and have completed all requirements for a Ph.D. except the dissertation. Applicants must be enrolled at a designated college or university in the following 10 states: Alabama, Arkansas, Georgia, Kentucky, Louisiana, Mississippi, South Carolina, Tennessee, Virginia, West Virginia. Enrollment at a graduate school in 5 of those states (Georgia, Mississippi, South Carolina, Tennessee, and Virginia) is available only to residents of those states. Residents of any state in the country may attend a university in the other 5 states. Preference is given to students in STEM disciplines with particularly low minority representation, although all academic fields are eligible. Applicants must be in a position to write full time and must expect to complete their dissertation within the year of the fellowship. Eligibility is limited to individuals who plan to become full-time faculty members at a college or university upon completion of their doctoral degree. The program is not open to students working on other doctoral degrees (e.g., M.D., D.B.A., D.D.S., J.D., D.V.M., Ed.D., Pharm.D., D.N.P., D.P.T.).

Financial Data Fellows receive waiver of tuition and fees (in or out of state), a stipend of $20,000, a $500 research allowance, and reimbursement of expenses for attending the Compact for Faculty Diversity's annual Institute on Teaching and Mentoring.

Duration 1 year; nonrenewable.

Additional data This program began in 1993 as part of the Compact for Faculty Diversity, supported by the Pew Charitable Trusts and the Ford Foundation. It currently operates at universities in 10 of the member states of the Southern Regional Education Board (SREB): Alabama, Arkansas, Georgia, Kentucky, Louisiana, Mississippi, South Carolina, Tennessee, Virginia, and West Virginia; the other 6 member states (Delaware, Florida, Maryland, North Carolina, Oklahoma, and Texas) do not participate.

Number awarded Varies each year.

Deadline March of each year.

[878]
SPANISH BAPTIST CONVENTION OF NEW MEXICO SCHOLARSHIP

Baptist Convention of New Mexico
Attn: Missions Mobilization Team
5325 Wyoming Boulevard, N.E.
P.O. Box 94485
Albuquerque, NM 87199-4485
(505) 924-2315   Toll Free: (800) 898-8544
Fax: (505) 924-2320   E-mail: cpairett@bcnm.com
Web: www.bcnm.com

Summary To provide financial assistance to Hispanic Baptist students from New Mexico interested in attending college or seminary in any state.

Eligibility This program is open to college and seminary students who are active members of churches affiliated with the Baptist Convention of New Mexico. Applicants must be of Hispanic background and committed to full-time Christian service. They must be attending college or seminary in any state.

Financial Data A stipend is awarded (amount not specified).

Duration 1 year; may be renewed.

Number awarded 1 or more each year.

Deadline April of each year.

[879]
SPIE SCHOLARSHIP PROGRAM

SPIE-The International Society for Optical Engineering
Attn: Scholarship Committee
1000 20th Street
P.O. Box 10
Bellingham, WA 98227-0010
(360) 676-3290   Toll Free: (888) 504-8171
Fax: (360) 647-1445   E-mail: scholarships@spie.org
Web: spie.org/x7236.xml

Summary To provide financial assistance to entering or continuing undergraduate and graduate student members of SPIE-The International Society for Optical Engineering (particularly Hispanic Americans, other minorities, women, and veterans) who are preparing for a career in optical science or engineering.

Eligibility This program is open to high school seniors planning to attend college, current undergraduate students, and current graduate students. Applicants must be society members majoring or planning to enroll full or part time and major in optics, optoelectronics, photonics, imaging, or a related discipline (e.g., physics, electrical engineering) at a college or university anywhere in the world. Along with their application, they must submit a 500-word essay on their academic work, career objectives, how this scholarship would help them attain their goals, and what they have achieved and learned through their studies and activities. Financial need is not considered in the selection process. Women, minorities, and veterans are encouraged to apply.

Financial Data Stipends range from $2,000 to $11,000. Special awards include the D.J. Lovell Scholarship at $11,000; the John Kiel Scholarship at $10,000; the Laser Technology, Engineering, and Applications Scholarship at $5,000; the Optical Design and Engineering Scholarship at $5,000, and the BACUS Scholarship at $5,000.

Duration 1 year.

Additional data The International Society for Optical Engineering was founded in 1955 as the Society of Photo-Optical Instrumentation Engineers (SPIE). This program includes the following special named scholarships: the D.J. Lovell Scholarship, sponsored by SPIE (the most prestigious of the scholarships); the John Kiel Scholarship, awarded for a student's potential for long-term contribution to the field of optics and optical engineering; the Optical Design and Engineering Scholarship in Optical Engineering, established to honor Bill Price and Warren Smith and awarded to a full-time graduate or undergraduate student in the field of optical design and engineering; the Laser Technology, Engineering, and Applications Scholarship (formerly the F-MADE Scholarship), sponsored by the Forum for Military Applications of Directed Energy (F-MADE) in recognition of a student's scholarly achievement in laser technology, engineering, or applications; and the BACUS Scholarship, awarded to a full-time undergraduate or graduate student in the field of microlithography with an emphasis on optical tooling and/or semiconductor manufacturing technologies, sponsored by BACUS (SPIE's photomask international technical group).

Number awarded Varies each year; recently, this program awarded 140 scholarships with a value of $353,000. Since the program was established, it has awarded more than $3.8 million to nearly 2,000 students in 86 countries.

Deadline February of each year.

[880]
SREB DOCTORAL AWARDS

Southern Regional Education Board
Attn: Coordinator, Program and Scholar Services
592 Tenth Street N.W.
Atlanta, GA 30318-5776
(404) 879-5569   Fax: (404) 872-1477
E-mail: doctoral.scholars@sreb.org
Web: www.sreb.org/page/1113/types_of_awards.html

Summary To provide financial assistance to Hispanic American and other minority students who wish to work on a doctoral degree, especially in fields of science, technology, engineering, or mathematics (STEM), at designated universities in the southern states.

Eligibility This program is open to U.S. citizens and permanent residents who are members of racial/ethnic minority groups (Native Americans, Hispanic Americans, Asian Americans, and African Americans) and have or will receive a bachelor's or master's degree. Applicants must be entering or enrolled in the first year of a Ph.D. program at a designated college or university in the following 10 states: Alabama, Arkansas, Georgia, Kentucky, Louisiana, Mississippi, South Carolina, Tennessee, Virginia, West Virginia. Enrollment at a graduate school in 5 of those states (Georgia, Mississippi, South Carolina, Tennessee, and Virginia) is available only to

residents of those states. Residents of any state in the country may attend a university in the other 5 states. Applicants must indicate an interest in becoming a full-time college or university professor. The program does not support students working on other doctoral degrees (e.g., M.D., D.B.A., D.D.S., J.D., D.V.M., Ed.D., Pharm.D., D.N.P., D.P.T.). Preference is given to applicants in STEM disciplines with particularly low minority representation, although all academic fields are eligible.

Financial Data Scholars receive a waiver of tuition and fees (in or out of state) for up to 5 years, an annual stipend of $20,000 for 3 years, an annual allowance of $500 for research and professional development activities, and reimbursement of travel expenses to attend the Compact for Faculty Diversity's annual Institute on Teaching and Mentoring.

Duration Up to 5 years.

Additional data This program began in 1993 as part of the Compact for Faculty Diversity, supported by the Pew Charitable Trusts and the Ford Foundation.

Number awarded Varies each year; recently, the program was supporting more than 300 scholars.

Deadline March year.

[881]
SSSP RACIAL/ETHNIC MINORITY GRADUATE SCHOLARSHIP

Society for the Study of Social Problems
Attn: Executive Officer
University of Tennessee
901 McClung Tower
Knoxville, TN 37996-0490
(865) 689-1531   Fax: (865) 689-1534
E-mail: sssp@utk.edu
Web: www.sssp1.org

Summary To provide funding to Hispanic American and other minority members of the Society for the Study of Social Problems (SSSP) who are interested in conducting research for their doctoral dissertation.

Eligibility This program is open to SSSP members who are Black or African American, Hispanic or Latino, Asian or Asian American, Native Hawaiian or other Pacific Islander, or American Indian or Alaska Native. Applicants must have completed all requirements for a Ph.D. (course work, examinations, and approval of a dissertation prospectus) except the dissertation. They must have a GPA of 3.25 or higher and be able to demonstrate financial need. Their field of study may be any of the social and/or behavioral sciences that will enable them to expand their perspectives in the investigation into social problems. U.S. citizenship or permanent resident status is required.

Financial Data The stipend is $12,000. Additional grants provide $500 for the recipient to 1) attend the SSSP annual meeting prior to the year of the work to receive the award; and 2) attend the meeting after the year of the award to present a report on the work completed.

Duration 1 year.

Number awarded 1 each year.

Deadline January of each year.

[882]
STAN BECK FELLOWSHIP

Entomological Society of America
Attn: Entomological Foundation
9332 Annapolis Road, Suite 210
Lanham, MD 20706-3150
(301) 459-9082   Fax: (301) 459-9084
E-mail: melodie@entfdn.org
Web: www.entfdn.org/awards_education.php

Summary To assist "needy" students working on an undergraduate or graduate degree in entomology who are nominated by members of the Entomological Society of America (ESA).

Eligibility This program is open to students working on an undergraduate or graduate degree in entomology at a college or university in Canada, Mexico, or the United States. Candidates must be nominated by members of the society. They must be "needy" students; for the purposes of this program, need may be based on physical limitations, or economic, minority, or environmental conditions.

Financial Data The stipend is $2,000 per year.

Duration 1 year; may be renewed up to 3 additional years.

Additional data This fellowship was first awarded in 1996. Recipients are expected to be present at the society's annual meeting, where the award will be presented.

Number awarded 1 each year.

Deadline June of each year.

[883]
STAR FELLOWSHIPS FOR GRADUATE ENVIRONMENTAL STUDY

Environmental Protection Agency
Attn: National Center for Environmental Research
Ariel Rios Building
1200 Pennsylvania Avenue, N.W.
Washington, DC 20460
(202) 343-9850   Toll Free: (800) 490-9194
E-mail: jones.brandon@epa.gov
Web: www.epa.gov/careers/fellowships

Summary To provide financial support to graduate students (particularly Hispanic Americans, other minorities, women, and students with disabilities) who are planning to obtain advanced degrees and prepare for a career in environmentally-related fields.

Eligibility Applicants must be U.S. citizens or permanent residents enrolled or accepted for enrollment at an accredited U.S. college or university. They must be interested in working on a master's or doctoral degree, in the United States or abroad, in an environmentally-related field of specialization. Relevant fields of study include ecology, economics, engineering, modeling, the health sciences, physical sciences, earth sciences, exposure sciences, social sciences, informational sciences, mathematical and computer sciences, and environmental sciences; applications are also welcome from students who have not participated in traditional environmental conversations or research, especially those that attend Minority Academic Institutions. Selection is based on demonstrated commitment to an environmental career, potential for success in the proposed area of inquiry, and potential for their proposal to have broader societal impacts. The program strongly encourages women, minorities, and persons with disabilities to apply. At least 10% of the awards are reserved for students at Minority Academic Institutions, defined as Historically Black Colleges and Universities, Tribal Colleges and Universities, Hispanic Serving Institutions, and Asian American and Native Pacific Islander-Serving Institutions.

Financial Data The total award is $42,000 per year, including a student stipend of $25,000 (paid at the rate of $2,083 per month for 12 months), an expense allowance of $5,000, and an allowance of up to $12,000 for tuition and fees paid directly to the institution.

Duration Up to 2 years for master's students; up to 3 years for doctoral students, usable over a period of 5 years.

Additional data This program, which began in 1995, is the graduate student component of the Science to Achieve Results (STAR) program of the Environmental Protection Agency. Fellows may conduct research outside the United States, but no additional funding is provided for foreign travel or other expenses.

Number awarded Approximately 80 each year, of which 8 are reserved for students at Minority Academic Institutions.

Deadline November of each year.

[884]
STATE REPRESENTATIVE IRMA RANGEL MEMORIAL SCHOLARSHIPS

Hispanic Scholarship Consortium
Attn: Scholarship Selection Committee
1107 South Eighth Street
Austin, TX 78704
(512) 368-2956   Fax: (512) 692-1831
E-mail: scholarships@hispanicscholar.org
Web: www.hispanicscholar.org

Summary To provide financial assistance to Hispanic residents of Texas who are pre-law students at designated universities in the state or law students in any state.

Eligibility This program is open to residents of Texas who are of Hispanic heritage and are either 1) rising juniors or seniors at Concordia University, St. Edward's University, Southwestern University, Texas State University, or the University of Texas at Austin; or 2) students enrolled at a law school in any state. Rising seniors must be planning to take the LSAT examination in the current academic year and rising juniors must be planning to take that examination in the following academic year. Applicants must submit a 500-word essay on why they would like to become an attorney. They must have a GPA of 3.0 or higher. Selection is based on academic record, community service, financial need, and a personal interview. U.S. citizenship or permanent resident status is required.

Financial Data The stipend is $2,000.

Duration 1 year.

Additional data This program is sponsored by the Hispanic Bar Association of Austin College Fund.

Number awarded 1 or more each year.

Deadline August of each year.

[885]
STOEL RIVES FIRST-YEAR DIVERSITY FELLOWSHIPS

Stoel Rives LLP
Attn: Lawyer Recruiting Manager
900 S.W. Fifth Avenue, Suite 2600
Portland, OR 97204
(503) 224-3380   Fax: (503) 220-2480
E-mail: portlandfellowship@stoel.com
Web: www.stoel.com/diversity.aspx?Show=2805

Summary   To provide financial aid for law school and work experience to law students who bring diversity to the profession and are interested in a summer associate position with Stoel Rives.

Eligibility   This program is open to first-year law students who contribute to the diversity of the student body at their law school and who will contribute to the diversity of the legal community. Diverse students include those who are American Indian or Alaskan Native, Asian, Black or African American, Hispanic or Latino, Native Hawaiian or other Pacific Islander, disabled, or LGBT. Applicants must be willing to accept a summer associate position at Stoel Rives offices in designated communities. Selection is based on academic excellence, leadership, community service, interest in practicing in the Pacific Northwest, and financial need.

Financial Data   The program provides a stipend of $7,500 to help defray expenses of law school and a salaried summer associate position.

Duration   1 year.

Additional data   This program began in 2004. The firm has offices in Anchorage, Boise, Lake Tahoe, Minneapolis, Portland, Sacramento, Salt Lake City, San Diego, San Francisco, Seattle, and Vancouver.

Number awarded   At least 2 each year.

Deadline   January of each year.

[886]
STUDENT AFFILIATES IN SCHOOL PSYCHOLOGY DIVERSITY SCHOLARSHIPS

American Psychological Association
Attn: Division 16 (School Psychology)
750 First Street, N.E.
Washington, DC 20002-4242
(202) 336-6165   Fax: (202) 218-3599
TDD: (202) 336-6123   E-mail: cchambers@apa.org
Web: www.apadivisions.org/division-16/awards/index.aspx

Summary   To provide financial assistance to graduate student members of the Student Affiliates in School Psychology (SASP) of Division 16 (School Psychology) of the American Psychological Association (APA) who are Hispanic Americans or from other underrepresented cultural backgrounds.

Eligibility   This program is open to SASP members who come from underrepresented cultural backgrounds. Applicants must be working on a graduate degree to prepare for a career as a school psychologist. Awards are available to both incoming students (entering their first or second year of graduate study) and advanced students (entering their third, fourth, or fifth year of graduate study).

Financial Data   The stipend is $1,000.

Duration   1 year; nonrenewable.

Number awarded   2 each year: 1 to an incoming student and 1 to an advanced student.

Deadline   Deadline not specified.

[887]
SUMMER RESEARCH OPPORTUNITY PROGRAM IN PATHOLOGY

American Society for Investigative Pathology
Attn: Executive Officer
9650 Rockville Pike, Suite E133
Bethesda, MD 20814-3993
(301) 634-7130   Fax: (301) 634-7990
E-mail: asip@asip.org
Web: www.asip.org/awards/sropp.cfm

Summary   To provide an opportunity for Hispanic Americans and members of other underrepresented minority groups to participate in a summer research program in pathology.

Eligibility   This program is open to students who are members of underrepresented minority groups. Applicants must be interested in visiting prominent research laboratories and institutions during the summer to learn and participate in new research in the mechanisms of disease. To qualify for additional funding, they must select a pathology mentor.

Financial Data   The program provides 1) a travel and living allowance to cover airfare, ground transportation, meals, housing, and related expenses incurred during the summer research program; 2) a grant up to $1,650 to provide travel support to submit and present an abstract at the Experimental Biology meeting; and 3) for students who select a pathology mentor, a supplemental grant of $2,500 to cover travel and subsistence.

Additional data   This program operates as a component of the Minority Access to Research Careers (MARC) program of the Federation of American Societies for Experimental Biology (FASEB), funded by the National Institute of General Medical Sciences of the National Institutes of Health. Additional support is provided by the Intersociety Council for Pathology Information, Inc.

Number awarded   Varies each year; recently, 6 of these grants were awarded.

Deadline   Deadline not specified.

[888]
SUNY GRADUATE DIVERSITY FELLOWSHIP PROGRAM

State University of New York
Attn: Office of Diversity, Equity and Inclusion
State University Plaza
353 Broadway
Albany, NY 12246
(518) 320-1189
Web: www.suny.edu/provost/odee/programs.cfm

Summary   To provide financial assistance to Hispanic Americans and other graduate students at campuses of the State University of New York (SUNY) who will contribute to the diversity of the student body.

Eligibility   This program is open to U.S. citizens and permanent residents who are entering or enrolled full-time graduate or professional students at any of the participating SUNY colleges. Applicants must be able to demonstrate how they will contribute to the diversity of the student body for the program for which they are applying, including having overcome a disadvantage or other impediment to success in higher education. Economic disadvantage, although not a requirement, may be the basis for eligibility. Membership in a racial or ethnic group that is underrepresented in the graduate or professional program involved may serve as a plus factor in making awards, but may not form the sole basis of selection. Awards are granted in the following priority order: 1) new graduate students who are being recruited but have not yet accepted admission to a graduate program; 2) Graduate Opportunity Waiver Program students who can be awarded a stipend to supplement their waiver to tuition; 3) currently-enrolled doctoral candidates who have completed all degree requirements except the dissertation; and 4) graduate assistants and teaching assistants who can receive a supplement to their current stipends to enhance their retention in graduate studies.

Financial Data Stipends range from $7,500 to $10,000.

Duration 1 year; renewable.

Number awarded Varies each year; recently, this program awarded nearly $6 million in fellowships to 551 graduate students on 24 SUNY campuses. Of the recipients 38% were Latinos, 35% African Americans, 12% Whites, 6% Asians, and 6% Native Americans.

Deadline Deadline not specified.

[889]
SUSAN M. JACKSON MINISTERIAL SCHOLARS FUND

Unitarian Universalist Association
Attn: Ministerial Credentialing Office
25 Beacon Street
Boston, MA 02108-2800
(617) 948-6403　　　　　　　　Fax: (617) 742-2875
E-mail: mcoadministrator@uua.org
Web: www.uua.org

Summary To provide financial assistance to seminary students (particularly Hispanic Americans and other students of color) who are preparing for the Unitarian Universalist (UU) ministry and demonstrate enthusiasm about their faith.

Eligibility This program is open to seminary students who are enrolled full or at least half time in a UU ministerial training program with candidate status. Applicants must be citizens of the United States or Canada. They must be able to demonstrate their enthusiasm about Unitarian Universalist ideas and conclusions, drawn from their faith, that influence their lives. Priority is given first to those who have demonstrated outstanding ministerial ability and secondarily to students with the greatest financial need (especially persons of color).

Financial Data The stipend ranges from $1,000 to $15,000 per year.

Duration 1 year.

Number awarded 1 each year.

Deadline April of each year.

[890]
SYNOD OF LAKES AND PRAIRIES RACIAL ETHNIC SCHOLARSHIPS

Synod of Lakes and Prairies
Attn: Committee on Racial Ethnic Ministry
2115 Cliff Drive
Eagen, MN 55122-3327
(651) 357-1140　　　　　Toll Free: (800) 328-1880, ext. 202
Fax: (651) 357-1141　E-mail: mkes@lakesandprairies.org
Web: www.lakesandprairies.org

Summary To provide financial assistance to Hispanic American and other minority residents of the Presbyterian Church (USA) Synod of Lakes and Prairies who are working on an undergraduate or graduate degree at a college or seminary in any state in preparation for service to the church.

Eligibility This program is open to members of Presbyterian churches who reside within the Synod of Lakes and Prairies (Iowa, Minnesota, Nebraska, North Dakota, South Dakota, and Wisconsin). Applicants must be members of ethnic minority groups studying at least half time for service in the Presbyterian Church (USA) as a teaching elder, ordained minister, commissioned ruling elder, lay professional, or volunteer. They must be in good academic standing, making progress toward an undergraduate or graduate degree, and able to demonstrate financial need. Along with their application, they must submit essays of 200 to 500 words on 1) what the church needs to do to be faithful to its mission in the world today; and 2) the people, practices, or events that influence their commitment to Christ in ways that renew their fair and strengthen their service.

Financial Data Stipends range from $850 to $3,500.

Duration 1 year.

Number awarded Varies each year; recently, 9 of these scholarships were awarded.

Deadline September of each year.

[891]
SYNOD OF THE COVENANT ETHNIC THEOLOGICAL SCHOLARSHIPS

Synod of the Covenant
Attn: Ministries in Higher Education
1911 Indianwood Circle, Suite B
Maumee, OH 43537-4063
(419) 754-4050
Toll Free: (800) 848-1030 (within MI and OH)
Fax: (419) 754-4051
E-mail: SOC@synodofthecovenant.org
Web: www.synodofthecovenant.org

Summary To provide financial assistance to Hispanic American and other ethnic students working on a master's degree at an approved Presbyterian theological institution (with priority given to Presbyterian applicants from Ohio and Michigan).

Eligibility This program is open to ethnic individuals enrolled full time in church vocations programs at approved Presbyterian theological institutions. Priority is given to Presbyterian applicants from the states of Michigan and Ohio. Financial need is considered in the selection process.

Financial Data Students may be awarded a maximum of $1,500 on initial application. They may receive up to $2,000 on subsequent applications, with evidence of continuing progress. Funds are made payable to the session for distribution.

Duration Students are eligible to receive scholarships 1 time per year, up to a maximum of 5 years.

Number awarded Varies each year.

Deadline August of each year.

[892]
TEXAS ASSOCIATION OF CHICANOS IN HIGHER EDUCATION GRADUATE FELLOWSHIP AWARDS

Texas Association of Chicanos in Higher Education
Attn: Awards Committee
P.O. Box 396
Canyon, TX 79015
E-mail: maria.aguirre@tstc.edu
Web: www.tache.org/Awards.aspx

Summary To provide financial assistance to Hispanic residents of Texas who are enrolled in a graduate program in any state to prepare for a career in higher education.

Eligibility This program is open to residents of Texas who are of Chicano/Latino heritage (1 parent fully Hispanic or both parents half Hispanic). Applicants must be enrolled full time in a U.S. graduate or professional school in a degree program to prepare for a career in higher education or administration. They must have a cumulative GPA of 3.0 or higher. Along with their application, they must submit a 2-page personal statement that describes their socioeconomic background, family and financial responsibilities, other factors that can be considered obstacles in attaining graduate studies, and how this award will be used to support educational career goals and plans for future contributions to the educational advancement of Latinos in Texas. They must also submit a resume that includes their contributions, achievements, awards, honors, and service activities related to the Chicano/Latino culture and community in Texas.

Financial Data The stipend is $2,000 per year.

Duration 1 year.

Additional data Recipients are required to become members of the Texas Association of Chicanos in Higher Education.

Number awarded 4 each year: 2 to students whose career emphasis is in community college education and 2 to students whose study emphasis is in university or postgraduate education.

Deadline December of each year.

[893]
TEXAS MEDICAL ASSOCIATION MINORITY SCHOLARSHIP PROGRAM

Texas Medical Association
Attn: Educational Loans Department
401 West 15th Street
Austin, TX 78701-1680
(512) 370-1300   Toll Free: (800) 880-2828
Fax: (512) 370-1693   E-mail: info@tmaloanfunds.com
Web: www.tmaloanfunds.com/Content/Template.aspx?id=9

Summary To provide financial assistance to Hispanic Americans and members of other underrepresented minority groups from any state who are entering medical school in Texas.

Eligibility This program is open to members of minority groups that are underrepresented in the medical profession (African American, Mexican American, Native American). Applicants must have been accepted at a medical school in Texas; students currently enrolled are not eligible. Along with their application, they must submit a 750-word essay on how they, as a physician, would improve the health of all Texans.

Financial Data The stipend is $5,000.

Duration 1 year; renewable.

Additional data This program began in 1999.

Number awarded 1 to 8 each year.

Deadline February of each year.

[894]
TEXAS YOUNG LAWYERS ASSOCIATION MINORITY SCHOLARSHIP PROGRAM

Texas Young Lawyers Association
Attn: Minority Involvement Committee
1414 Colorado, Suite 502
P.O. Box 12487
Austin, TX 78711-2487
(512) 427-1529   Toll Free: (800) 204-2222, ext. 1529
Fax: (512) 427-4117   E-mail: btrevino@texasbar.com
Web: www.tyla.org

Summary To provide financial assistance to Hispanic Americans, other minorities, and women from any state who are attending law school in Texas.

Eligibility This program is open to members of recognized minority groups, including students of varying gender, national origin, racial and ethnic backgrounds, sexual orientation and gender identity, and of disability status. Applicants must be attending an ABA-accredited law school in Texas. Along with their application, they must submit a 2-page essay on either 1) the role the minority attorney should play in the community and profession; or 2) how attorneys, specifically minority attorneys, can improve the image of the legal profession. Selection is based on academic performance, merit, participation in extracurricular activities inside and outside law school, and financial need.

Financial Data The stipend is $1,000.

Duration 1 year.

Number awarded 9 each year: 1 at each accredited law school in Texas.

Deadline October of each year.

[895]
THE REV. DR. HECTOR E. LOPEZ SCHOLARSHIP

United Church of Christ
Parish Life and Leadership Ministry Team
Attn: Grants, Scholarships, and Resources
700 Prospect Avenue East
Cleveland, OH 44115-1100
(216) 736-3839   Toll Free: (866) 822-8224, ext. 3839
Fax: (216) 736-3783   E-mail: jeffersv@ucc.org
Web: www.ucc.org

Summary To provide financial assistance to Latino/a students at seminaries of the United Church of Christ (UCC).

Eligibility This program is open to Latino/a students working on a master's degree at any of the 7 seminaries of the UCC. Applicants must 1) have a GPA of 3.0 or higher; 2) be a member in discernment of a UCC congregation; and 3) be planning to return from seminary to lead vital congregations and minister to Latino constituencies, multi-cultural communities, and the whole church.

Financial Data Stipends range from $1,500 to $2,500 per year. Funds are paid directly to the seminary, to be applied toward tuition.

Duration 1 year.

Additional data The UCC seminaries are Andover Newton Theological School (Newton Centre, Massachusetts), Bangor Theological Seminary (Bangor, Maine), Chicago Theological Seminary (Chicago, Illinois), Eden Theological Seminary (St. Louis, Missouri), Lancaster Theological Seminary (Lancaster, Pennsylvania), Pacific School of Religion (Berkeley, California), and United Theological Seminary of the Twin Cities (New Brighton, Minnesota).

Number awarded 1 or more each year.

Deadline February of each year.

[896]
THOMAS G. NEUSOM SCHOLARSHIPS

Conference of Minority Transportation Officials
Attn: National Scholarship Program
1875 I Street, N.W., Suite 500
Washington, DC 20006
(703) 234-4072   Fax: (202) 318-0364
Web: www.comto.org/?page=Scholarships

Summary To provide financial assistance for college or graduate school to Hispanic American and other members of the Conference of Minority Transportation Officials (COMTO).

Eligibility This program is open to undergraduate and graduate students who have been members of COMTO for at least 1 year. Applicants must be working (either full or part time) on a degree in a field related to transportation and have a GPA of 2.5 or higher. Along with their application, they must submit a cover letter with a 500-word statement of career goals. Financial need is not considered in the selection process. U.S. citizenship or legal resident status is required.

Financial Data The stipend is $5,500. Funds are paid directly to the recipient's college or university.

Duration 1 year.

Additional data COMTO was established in 1971 to promote, strengthen, and expand the roles of minorities in all aspects of transportation. Recipients are expected to attend the COMTO National Scholarship Luncheon.

Number awarded 1 each year.

Deadline May of each year.

[897]
TRAILBLAZER SCHOLARSHIP

Conference of Minority Transportation Officials
Attn: National Scholarship Program
1875 I Street, N.W., Suite 500
Washington, DC 20006
(703) 234-4072   Fax: (202) 318-0364
Web: www.comto.org/?page=Scholarships

Summary To provide financial assistance to Hispanic American and other minority undergraduate and graduate students working on a degree in a field related to transportation.

Eligibility This program is open to minority undergraduate and graduate students who are working (either full or part time) on a degree in a field related to transportation and have a GPA of 2.5 or higher. Along with their application, they must submit a cover letter with a 500-word statement of career goals. Financial need is not considered in the selection process. U.S. citizenship or legal resident status is required.

Financial Data The stipend is $2,500. Funds are paid directly to the recipient's college or university.

Duration 1 year.

Additional data The Conference of Minority Transportation Officials (COMTO) was established in 1971 to promote, strengthen, and expand the roles of minorities in all aspects of transportation. Recipients are expected to attend the COMTO National Scholarship Luncheon.

Number awarded 1 each year.

Deadline May of each year.

[898]
UNDERREPRESENTED MINORITY DENTAL STUDENT SCHOLARSHIP

American Dental Association
Attn: ADA Foundation
211 East Chicago Avenue
Chicago, IL 60611
(312) 440-2547   Fax: (312) 440-3526
E-mail: adaf@ada.org

Summary To provide financial assistance to Hispanic American and other underrepresented minorities who wish to enter the field of dentistry.

Eligibility This program is open to U.S. citizens from a minority group that is currently underrepresented in the dental profession: Native American, African American, or Hispanic. Applicants must have a GPA of 3.0 or higher and be entering their second year of study at a dental school in the United States accredited by the Commission on Dental Accreditation. Selection is based upon academic achievement, a written summary of personal and professional goals, letters of reference, and demonstrated financial need.

Financial Data The maximum stipend is $2,500. Funds are sent directly to the student's financial aid office to be used to cover tuition, fees, books, supplies, and living expenses.

Duration 1 year.

Additional data This program, established in 1991, is supported by the Harry J. Bosworth Company, Colgate-Palmolive, Sunstar Americas, and Procter & Gamble Company. Students receiving a full scholarship from any other source are ineligible to receive this scholarship.

Number awarded Approximately 25 each year.

Deadline October of each year.

[899]
UNITED HEALTH FOUNDATION/NMF DIVERSE MEDICAL SCHOLARS PROGRAM

National Medical Fellowships, Inc.
Attn: Scholarship Program
347 Fifth Avenue, Suite 510
New York, NY 10016
(212) 483-8880   Toll Free: (877) NMF-1DOC
Fax: (212) 483-8897 E-mail: scholarships@nmfonline.org
Web: www.nmfonline.org/uhf

Summary To provide financial assistance to Hispanic American and other underrepresented minority students at medical schools in designated areas who are interested in conducting a community health project.

Eligibility This program is open to African Americans, Hispanics/Latinos, Native Americans, Vietnamese, Cambodians, and Pacific Islanders who are currently enrolled at an accredited medical school in the greater New York City metropolitan area (including Connecticut, New Jersey, New York, and Pennsylvania), Florida (greater Miami area), Louisiana (Baton Rouge, New Orleans, or Shreveport), or Georgia (Atlanta). Applicants must have demonstrated leadership and a commitment to serving medically underserved communities. They must be interested in conducting a self-directed health project of 200 hours at a site of choice in an underserved community in the same area as their medical school. U.S. citizenship is required.

Financial Data The grant is $7,000.

Duration 1 year; recipients may apply for a second year of funding.

Additional data This program, sponsored by United Health Foundation, began in 2007.

Number awarded 22 each year.

Deadline October of each year.

[900]
UNITED METHODIST WOMEN OF COLOR SCHOLARS PROGRAM

United Methodist Church
Attn: General Board of Higher Education and Ministry
Office of Loans and Scholarships
1001 19th Avenue South
P.O. Box 340007
Nashville, TN 37203-0007
(615) 340-7344   Fax: (615) 340-7367
E-mail: umscholar@gbhem.org
Web: www.gbhem.org

Summary To provide financial assistance to Hispanic American and other Methodist women of color who are working on a doctoral degree to prepare for a career as an educator at a United Methodist seminary.

Eligibility This program is open to women of color (have at least 1 parent who is African American, African, Hispanic, Asian, Native American, Alaska Native, or Pacific Islander) who have an M.Div. degree. Applicants must have been active, full members of a United Methodist Church for at least 3 years prior to applying. They must be enrolled full time in a degree program at the Ph.D. or Th.D. level to prepare for a career teaching at a United Methodist seminary.

Financial Data The maximum stipend is $10,000 per year.

Duration 1 year; may be renewed up to 3 additional years.

Number awarded Varies each year; recently, 10 of these scholarships were awarded.

Deadline January of each year.

[901]
USHCC-WELLS FARGO SCHOLARSHIPS

Hispanic Scholarship Fund
Attn: Selection Committee
1411 West 190th Street, Suite 325
Gardena, CA 90248
Toll Free: (877) HSF-INFO   E-mail: scholar1@hsf.net
Web: www.hsf.net

Summary To provide financial assistance for college or graduate school to dependents and relatives of members of the U.S. Hispanic Chamber of Commerce (USHCC).

Eligibility This program is open to U.S. citizens and permanent residents (must have a permanent resident card or a passport stamped I-551) who are of Hispanic heritage. Applicants must be enrolling as a full-time undergraduate or graduate student at a 4-year college or university in the United States and have a GPA of 3.0 or higher. They must be a dependent or relative of a USHCC member or employee or a former USHCC BizFest participant. Selection is based on academic achievement, personal strengths, leadership, and financial need.

Financial Data The stipend is $2,500.

Duration 1 year.

Additional data This program is funded by Wells Fargo Bank.

Number awarded 57 each year.

Deadline January of each year.

[902]
VARNUM DIVERSITY AND INCLUSION FELLOWSHIPS

Varnum LLP
Attn: Human Resources
333 Bridge Street N.W.
P.O. Box 352
Grand Rapids, MI 49501-0352
(616) 336-6620   Fax: (616) 336-7000
E-mail: 2Lfellowship@varnumlaw.com
Web: www.varnumlaw.com

Summary To provide financial assistance to Hispanic Americans and other law students who will contribute to diversity in the legal profession and are interested in a summer associateship in Grand Rapids, Michigan.

Eligibility This program is open to students currently enrolled at an accredited law school in any state who have a GPA of 3.3 or higher. Applicants must be members of an ethnic or racial minority or demonstrate a significant commitment to issues of diversity and inclusion. They must have a GPA of 3.0 or higher and have accepted an offer to participate in the sponsoring firm's summer associate program. Along with their application, they must submit a 750-word statement on their efforts to promote greater ethnic or racial diversity and inclusion within the legal profession and/or their community.

Financial Data The stipend is $7,500.

Duration 1 year.

Number awarded 2 each year.

Deadline October of each year.

[903]
VINSON & ELKINS DIVERSITY FELLOWSHIPS

Vinson & Elkins L.L.P.
Attn: Talent Management
1001 Fannin Street, Suite 2500
Houston, TX 77002-6760
(713) 758-2222   Fax: (713) 758-2346
Web: www.velaw.com/careers/law_students.aspx?id=602

Summary To provide financial assistance to Hispanic American and other minority law students who are interested in working in a law firm setting.

Eligibility This program is open to students who are entering the second year at an ABA-accredited law school and are members of a racial or ethnic group that has been historically underrepresented in the legal profession (Asian, American Indian/Alaskan Native, Black/African American, Hispanic/Latino, multiracial, or Native Hawaiian or other Pacific Islander). Applicants must be able to demonstrate a strong undergraduate and law school record, excellent writing skills, and an interest in working in a law firm setting.

Financial Data The stipend is $3,500 per year.

Duration 2 years (the second and third year of law school).

Additional data Fellows are also considered for summer associate positions at the sponsor's offices in Austin, Dallas, or Houston following their first year of law school.

Number awarded 4 each year.

Deadline January of each year.

[904]
VIOLET AND CYRIL FRANKS SCHOLARSHIP

American Psychological Foundation
750 First Street, N.E.
Washington, DC 20002-4242
(202) 336-5843   Fax: (202) 336-5812
E-mail: foundation@apa.org
Web: www.apa.org/apf/funding/franks.aspx

Summary To provide funding to doctoral students (particularly Hispanic Americans and others from diverse backgrounds) who are interested in conducting research related to mental illness.

Eligibility This program is open to full-time graduate students who are interested in conducting a research project that uses a psychological perspective to help understand and reduce stigma associated with mental illness. Applicants must identify the project's goal, the prior research that has been conducted in the area, whom the project will serve, the in intended outcomes and how the project will achieve those, and the total cost of the project. Selection is based on conformance with stated program goals and quality of proposed work. The sponsor encourages applications from individuals who represent diversity in race, ethnicity, gender, age, disability, and sexual orientation.

Financial Data The grant is $5,000.

Duration 1 year.

Additional data This grant was first awarded in 2007.

Number awarded 1 each year.

Deadline May of each year.

[905]
VIRGINIA NURSE PRACTITIONER/NURSE MIDWIFE SCHOLARSHIP PROGRAM

Virginia Department of Health
Attn: Office of Minority Health and Public Health Policy
109 Governor Street, Suite 1016 East
Richmond, VA 23219
(804) 864-7435   Fax: (804) 864-7440
E-mail: IncentivePrograms@vdh.virginia.gov
Web: www.vdh.virginia.gov

Summary To provide funding to nursing students in Virginia (particularly Hispanic Americans and other minorities) who are willing to work as nurse practitioners and/or midwives in the state following graduation.

Eligibility This program is open to residents of Virginia who are enrolled or accepted for enrollment full or part time at a nurse practitioner program in the state or a nurse midwifery program in Virginia or a nearby state. Applicants must have a cumulative GPA of at least 3.0 in undergraduate and/or graduate courses. Preference is given to 1) residents of designated medically underserved areas of Virginia; 2) students enrolled in family practice, obstetrics and gynecology, pediatric, adult health, and geriatric nurse practitioner programs; and 3) minority students. Selection is based on scholastic achievement, character, and stated commitment to postgraduate employment in a medically underserved area of Virginia.

Financial Data The stipend is $5,000 per year. Recipients must agree to serve in a designated medically underserved area of Virginia for a period of years equal to the number of years of scholarship support received. The required service must begin within 2 years of the recipient's graduation and must be in a facility that provides services to persons who are unable to pay for the service and that participates in all government-sponsored insurance programs designed to assure full access to medical care service for covered persons. If the recipient fails to complete the course of study, or pass the licensing examination, or provide the required service, all scholarship funds received must be repaid with interest and a penalty.

Duration 1 year; may be renewed for 1 additional year.

Number awarded Up to 5 each year.

Deadline June of each year.

[906]
VISITING RESEARCH INTERNSHIP PROGRAM

Harvard Medical School
Office for Diversity Inclusion and Community Partnership
Attn: Minority Faculty Development Program
164 Longwood Avenue, Second Floor
Boston, MA 02115-5818
(617) 432-1892   Fax: (617) 432-3834
E-mail: rachel_milliron@hms.harvard.edu
Web: www.mfdp.med.harvard.edu

Summary To provide an opportunity for medical students, especially Hispanic Americans and other underrepresented minorities, to conduct a mentored research project at Harvard Medical School during the summer.

Eligibility This program is open to first- and second-year medical students, particularly underrepresented minority and/or disadvantaged individuals, in good standing at accredited U.S. medical schools. Applicants must be interested in conducting a summer research project at Harvard Medical School under the mentorship of a faculty advisor. They must be interested in a research and health-related career, especially in clinical or translational research or research that transforms scientific discoveries arising from laboratory, clinical, or population studies into clinical or population-based applications to improve health. U.S. citizenship, nationality, or permanent resident status is required.

Financial Data Participants receive a stipend (amount not specified), housing, and limited reimbursement of transportation costs to Boston.

Duration 8 weeks during the summer.

Additional data This program, established in 2008, is funded by the National Center for Research Resources of the National Institutes of Health NIH). It is a joint enterprise of

Harvard University, its 10 schools, its 17 Academic Health-care Centers, Boston College School of Nursing, MIT, the Cambridge Health Alliance, and other community partners. Interns attend weekly seminars with Harvard faculty focusing on such topics as research methodology, health disparities, ethics, and career paths. They also have the opportunity to participate in offerings of other Harvard Medical School programs, such a career development seminars and networking dinners.

Number awarded Varies each year; recently, 6 medical students were admitted to this program.

Deadline February of each year.

[907]
WAKE FOREST UNIVERSITY SCHOOL OF MEDICINE EXCELLENCE IN CARDIOVASCULAR SCIENCES SUMMER RESEARCH PROGRAM

Wake Forest University School of Medicine
Attn: Hypertension and Vascular Research Center
Medical Center Boulevard
Winston-Salem, NC 27157-1032
(336) 716-1080   Fax: (336) 716-2456
E-mail: nsarver@wakehealth.edu
Web: www.wakehealth.edu

Summary To provide Hispanic American and other under-represented or disadvantaged students with an opportunity to engage in a summer research project in cardiovascular science at Wake Forest University in Winston-Salem, North Carolina.

Eligibility This program is open to undergraduates and master's degree students who are members of underrepresented minority groups (African Americans, Alaskan Natives, Asian Americans, Native Americans, Pacific Islanders, and Hispanics) or who come from disadvantaged backgrounds (e.g., rural areas, first-generation college students). Applicants must be interested in participating in a program of summer research in the cardiovascular sciences that includes "hands-on" laboratory research, a lecture series by faculty and guest speakers, and a research symposium at which students present their research findings. U.S. citizenship or permanent resident status is required.

Financial Data The stipend is $1,731 per month, housing in a university dormitory, and round-trip transportation expense.

Duration 2 months during the summer.

Additional data This program is sponsored by the National Heart, Lung, and Blood Institute (NHLBI) of the National Institutes of Health (NIH).

Number awarded Approximately 12 each year.

Deadline February of each year.

[908]
WARNER NORCROSS & JUDD LAW SCHOOL SCHOLARSHIP

Grand Rapids Community Foundation
Attn: Education Program Officer
185 Oakes Street S.W.
Grand Rapids, MI 49503-4008
(616) 454-1751, ext. 103   Fax: (616) 454-6455
E-mail: rbishop@grfoundation.org
Web: www.grfoundation.org/scholarshipslist

Summary To provide financial assistance to Hispanic Americans and other minorities from Michigan who are attending law school.

Eligibility This program is open to students of color who are attending or planning to attend an accredited law school. Applicants must be residents of Michigan or attending law school in the state. They must be U.S. citizens or permanent residents and have a GPA of 2.5 or higher. Financial need is considered in the selection process.

Financial Data The stipend is $5,000. Funds are paid directly to the recipient's institution.

Duration 1 year.

Additional data Funding for this program is provided by the law firm Warner Norcross & Judd LLP.

Number awarded 1 each year.

Deadline March of each year.

[909]
WATSON MIDWIVES OF COLOR SCHOLARSHIP

American College of Nurse-Midwives
Attn: ACNM Foundation, Inc.
8403 Colesville Road, Suite 1550
Silver Spring, MD 20910-6374
(240) 485-1850   Fax: (240) 485-1818
E-mail: fdn@acnm.org
Web: www.midwife.org

Summary To provide financial assistance for midwifery education to Hispanic Americans and other students of color who belong to the American College of Nurse-Midwives (ACNM).

Eligibility This program is open to ACNM members of color (African Americans, Asian Americans, Hispanic Americans, and Native Americans). They must be interested in preparing for a career as a midwife and working on an undergraduate or graduate degree.

Financial Data The stipend is $3,000.

Duration 1 year.

Number awarded Varies each year; recently, 3 of these scholarships were awarded.

Deadline March of each year.

[910]
WAYNE F. PLACEK GRANTS

American Psychological Foundation
750 First Street, N.E.
Washington, DC 20002-4242
(202) 336-5843   Fax: (202) 336-5812
E-mail: foundation@apa.org
Web: www.apa.org/apf/funding/placek.aspx

Summary To provide funding to pre- and postdoctoral scholars (particularly Hispanic Americans, other minorities, women, and individuals with disabilities) who are interested in conducting research that will increase the general public's understanding of homosexuality and alleviate the stress experienced by gay men and lesbians.

Eligibility This program is open to scholars who have a doctoral degree (e.g., Ph.D., Psy.D., M.D.) and to graduate students in all fields of the behavioral and social sciences. Applicants must be interested in conducting empirical studies that address the following topics: prejudice, discrimination, and violence based on sexual orientation, including heterosexuals' attitudes and behaviors toward lesbian, gay, bisexual, and transgender (LGBT) people; family and workplace issues relevant to LGBT people; and subgroups of the LGBT population that have been historically underrepresented in scientific research. Selection is based on conformance with stated program goals, magnitude of incremental contribution, quality of proposed work, and applicant's demonstrated scholarship and research competence. The sponsor encourages applications from individuals who represent diversity in race, ethnicity, gender, age, disability, and sexual orientation.

Financial Data The grant is $15,000.

Duration 1 year.

Additional data This program began in 1995.

Number awarded 1 or 2 each year.

Deadline February of each year.

[911]
WILLIAM G. ANDERSON, D.O. MINORITY SCHOLARSHIP

American Osteopathic Foundation
Attn: Director of Programs
142 East Ontario Street
Chicago, IL 60611-2864
(312) 202-8232   Toll Free: (866) 455-9383
Fax: (312) 202-8216   E-mail: vheck@aof-foundation.org
Web: www.aof-foundation.org

Summary To provide financial assistance to Hispanic American and other minority students enrolled in colleges of osteopathic medicine.

Eligibility This program is open to minority (African American, Native American, Asian American, Pacific Islander, or Hispanic) students entering their second, third, or fourth year at an accredited college of osteopathic medicine. Applicants must demonstrate 1) interest in osteopathic medicine, its philosophy, and its principles; 2) academic achievement; 3) leadership efforts in addressing the educational, societal, and health needs of minorities; 4) leadership efforts in addressing inequities in medical education and health care; 5) accomplishments, awards and honors, clerkships or special projects; and extracurricular activities in which the student has shown leadership abilities; and 6) financial need.

Financial Data The stipend is $5,000.

Duration 1 year.

Additional data This program began in 1998.

Number awarded 1 each year.

Deadline April of each year.

[912]
WILLIAM K. SCHUBERT M.D. MINORITY NURSING SCHOLARSHIP PROGRAM

Cincinnati Children's Hospital Medical Center
Attn: Office of Diversity and Inclusion, MLC 9008
3333 Burnet Avenue
Cincinnati, OH 45229-3039
(513) 803-6416   Toll Free: (800) 344-2462
Fax: (513) 636-5643   TDD: (513) 636-4900
E-mail: diversity@cchmc.org
Web: www.cincinnatichildrens.org

Summary To provide financial assistance to Hispanic Americans and members of other underrepresented groups who are interested in working on a bachelor's or master's degree in nursing to prepare for licensure in Ohio.

Eligibility This program is open to members of groups underrepresented in the nursing profession (males, American Indians or Alaska Natives, Blacks or African Americans, Hawaiian Natives or other Pacific Islanders, Hispanics or Latinos, or Asians). Applicants must be enrolled or accepted in a professional bachelor's or master's registered nurse program at an accredited school of nursing to prepare for initial licensure in Ohio. They must have a GPA of 2.75 or higher. Along with their application, they must submit a 750-word essay that covers 1) their long-range personal, educational, and professional goals; 2) why they chose nursing as a profession; 3) how their experience as a member of an underrepresented group has influenced a major professional and/or personal decision in their life; 4) any unique qualifications, experiences, or special talents that demonstrate their creativity; and 5) how their work experience has contributed to their personal development.

Financial Data The stipend is $2,750 per year.

Duration 1 year. May be renewed up to 3 additional years for students working on a bachelor's degree or 1 additional year for students working on a master's degree; renewal requires that students maintain a GPA of 2.75 or higher.

Number awarded 1 or more each year.

Deadline April of each year.

[913]
WILLIAM TOWNSEND PORTER FELLOWSHIP FOR MINORITY INVESTIGATORS

Marine Biological Laboratory
Attn: Chief Academic and Scientific Officer
7 MBL Street
Woods Hole, MA 02543-1015
(508) 289-7173   Fax: (508) 457-1924
E-mail: casoofice@mbl.edu
Web: hermes.mbl.edu

Summary To support Hispanic Americans and other underrepresented minorities who wish to conduct research during the summer at the Marine Biological Laboratory (MBL) in Woods Hole, Massachusetts.

Eligibility This program is open to young scientists (undergraduates, senior graduate students, and postdoctoral trainees) who are from an underrepresented minority group (African American, Hispanic American, or Native American), are U.S. citizens or permanent residents, and are interested in conducting research with senior investigators at MBL. Applicants must submit a statement of the potential impact of this award on their career development. Fields of study include, but are not limited to, cell biology, developmental biology, ecology, evolution, microbiology, neurobiology, physiology, regenerative biology, and tissue engineering.

Financial Data Grants range from $5,000 to $25,000, typically to cover laboratory rental and/or housing costs. Awardees are responsible for other costs, such as supplies, shared resource usage, affiliated staff who accompany them, or travel.

Duration 8 to 10 weeks during the summer.

Additional data This fellowship was first awarded in 1921. Funding is provided by the Harvard Apparatus Foundation.

Number awarded 1 or more each year.

Deadline December of each year.

[914]
WINSTON & STRAWN DIVERSITY SCHOLARSHIP PROGRAM

Winston & Strawn LLP
Attn: Amanda Sommerfeld
333 South Grand Avenue
Los Angeles, CA 90071-1543
(213) 615-1724   Fax: (213) 615-1750
E-mail: asommerfeld@winston.com
Web: www.winston.com

Summary To provide financial assistance to Hispanic American and other diverse law students who are interested in practicing in a city in which Winston & Strawn LLP has an office.

Eligibility This program is open to second-year law students who self-identify as a member of 1 of the following groups: American Indian or Alaska Native, Asian or Pacific Islander, Black or African American, or Hispanic or Latino. Applicants must submit a resume, law school transcript, and 500-word personal statement. Selection is based on 1) interest in practicing law after graduation in a large law firm in a city in which Winston & Strawn has an office (currently, Charlotte, Chicago, Houston, Los Angeles, New York, San Francisco, and Washington, D.C.); 2) law school and undergraduate record, including academic achievements and involvement in extracurricular activities; 3) demonstrated leadership skills; 4) and interpersonal skills.

Financial Data The stipend is $10,000.

Duration 1 year (the third year of law school).

Additional data This program began in 2004.

Number awarded 3 each year.

Deadline September of each year.

[915]
WISCONSIN MINORITY TEACHER LOANS

Wisconsin Higher Educational Aids Board
131 West Wilson Street, Suite 902
P.O. Box 7885
Madison, WI 53707-7885
(608) 267-2212   Fax: (608) 267-2808
E-mail: deanna.schulz@wisconsin.gov
Web: heab.state.wi.us/programs.html

Summary To provide funding to Hispanic Americans and other minorities in Wisconsin who are interested in teaching in Wisconsin school districts with large minority enrollments.

Eligibility This program is open to residents of Wisconsin who are African Americans, Hispanic Americans, American Indians, or southeast Asians (students who were admitted to the United States after December 31, 1975 and who are a former citizen of Laos, Vietnam, or Cambodia or whose ancestor was a citizen of 1 of those countries). Applicants must be enrolled at least half time as juniors, seniors, or graduate students at an independent or public institution in the state in a program leading to teaching licensure and have a GPA of 2.5 or higher. They must agree to teach in a Wisconsin school district in which minority students constitute at least 29% of total enrollment or in a school district participating in the inter-district pupil transfer program. Financial need is not considered in the selection process.

Financial Data Loans are provided up to $2,500 per year. For each year the student teaches in an eligible school district, 25% of the loan is forgiven; if the student does not teach in an eligible district, the loan must be repaid at an interest rate of 5%.

Duration 1 year; may be renewed 1 additional year.

Additional data Eligible students should apply through their school's financial aid office.

Number awarded Varies each year.

Deadline Deadline dates vary by institution; check with your school's financial aid office.

[916]
WOMBLE CARLYLE SCHOLARS PROGRAM

Womble Carlyle Sandridge & Rice, PLLC
Attn: Director of Entry-Level Recruiting and Development
301 South College Street, Suite 3500
Charlotte, NC 28202-6037
(704) 331-4900   Fax: (704) 331-4955
E-mail: wcsrscholars@wcsr.com
Web: www.wcsr.com

Summary To provide financial aid and summer work experience to Hispanic Americans and other diverse students at designated law schools.

Eligibility This program is open to students at designated law schools who are members of underrepresented groups. Applicants must be able to demonstrate solid academic credentials, personal or professional achievement outside the classroom, and significant participation in community service. Along with their application, they must submit a 300-word essay on their choice of 2 topics that change annually but relate to the legal profession. They must also submit a brief statement explaining how they would contribute to the goal of creating a more diverse legal community.

Financial Data The stipend is $4,000 per year. Recipients are also offered summer employment at 1 of the 14 offices of the sponsoring law firm. Salaries are the same as the firm's other summer associates in each office.

Duration 1 year (the second year of law school); may be renewed 1 additional year.

Additional data This program began in 2004. The eligible law schools are North Carolina Central University School of Law (Durham, North Carolina), University of North Carolina at Chapel Hill School of Law (Chapel Hill, North Carolina), Duke University School of Law (Durham, North Carolina), Wake Forest University School of Law (Winston-Salem, North Carolina), University of South Carolina School of Law (Columbia, South Carolina), Howard University School of Law (Washington, D.C.), University of Virginia School of Law (Charlottesville, Virginia), University of Georgia School of Law (Athens, Georgia), Georgia Washington University Law School (Washington, D.C.), Emory University School of Law (Atlanta, Georgia), and University of Maryland School of Law (Baltimore, Maryland). The sponsoring law firm has offices in Atlanta (Georgia), Baltimore (Maryland), Charleston (South Carolina), Charlotte (North Carolina), Columbia (South Carolina), Greensboro (North Carolina), Greenville (South Carolina), Raleigh (North Carolina), Research Triangle Park (North Carolina), Silicon Valley (Cupertino, California),

Tysons Corner (Virginia), Washington (D.C.), Wilmington (Delaware), and Winston-Salem (North Carolina).

Number awarded Varies each year; recently, 9 of these scholarships were awarded.

Deadline May of each year.

[917]
WOMEN OF ALPFA DELOITTE STUDENT ESSAY COMPETITION

Association of Latino Professionals in Finance and Accounting
Attn: Student Essay Contest
801 South Grand Avenue, Suite 650
Los Angeles, CA 90017
(213) 243-0004 Fax: (213) 243-0006
Web: www.alpfa.org

Summary To recognize and reward, with scholarships for further study, female members of the Association of Latino Professionals in Finance and Accounting (ALPFA) who submit outstanding essays on topics related to business.

Eligibility This competition is open to women who are members of ALPFA and working full time on an undergraduate or master's degree in accounting, business, finance, or a related field at a college or university in the United States or Puerto Rico. Applicants must have a GPA of 3.0 or higher. They must submit an essay, approximately 800 words in length, in response to an assigned problem related to professional development in business-related fields. Their essay should include descriptions and explanations of their ability to demonstrate leadership, strategize and problem solve effectively, overcome team doubt, and show strength derived from their culture. U.S. citizenship or permanent resident status is required.

Financial Data The award is a $1,200 scholarship. The winner also receives complimentary registration, airfare, and accommodations for the ALPFA annual convention.

Duration The competition is held annually.

Additional data This competition is sponsored by Deloitte LLP.

Number awarded 1 each year.

Deadline May of each year.

[918]
WORLD COMMUNION NATIONAL SCHOLARSHIPS

United Methodist Church
General Board of Global Ministries
Attn: Scholarship/Leadership Development Office
475 Riverside Drive, Room 333
New York, NY 10115
(212) 870-3787 Toll Free: (800) UMC-GBGM
E-mail: scholars@umcmission.org
Web: www.umcmission.org/Explore-Our-Work/Scholarships

Summary To provide financial assistance to Hispanic Americans and other students of color who are interested in attending graduate school to prepare for leadership in promoting the mission goals of the United Methodist Church.

Eligibility This program is open to U.S. citizens and permanent residents who are members of a community of color. Applicants must have applied to or been admitted to a master's, doctoral, or professional program at an institution of higher education in the United States. They must indicate a willingness to provide 5 years of Christian service after graduation in the areas of elimination of poverty, expansion of global health, leadership development, or congregational development. High priority is given to members of the United Methodist Church. Financial need is considered in the selection process.

Financial Data The stipend ranges from $1,000 to $12,500, depending on the recipient's related needs and school expenses.

Duration 1 year.

Additional data These awards are funded by the World Communion Offering received in United Methodist Churches on the first Sunday in October.

Number awarded 5 to 10 each year.

Deadline November of each year.

[919]
XEROX TECHNICAL MINORITY SCHOLARSHIP PROGRAM

Xerox Corporation
Attn: Technical Minority Scholarship Program
150 State Street, Fourth Floor
Rochester, NY 14614
(585) 422-7689 E-mail: GlobalCareers@xerox.com
Web: www.xerox.com/jobs/minority-scholarships/enus.html

Summary To provide financial assistance to Hispanic Americans and other minorities interested in undergraduate or graduate education in the sciences and/or engineering.

Eligibility This program is open to minorities (people of African American, Asian, Pacific Islander, Native American, Native Alaskan, or Hispanic descent) working full time on a bachelor's, master's, or doctoral degree in chemistry, computing and software systems, engineering (chemical, computer, electrical, imaging, manufacturing, mechanical, optical, or software), information management, laser optics, materials science, physics, or printing management science. Applicants must be U.S. citizens or permanent residents with a GPA of 3.0 or higher and attending a 4-year college or university.

Financial Data Stipends range from $1,000 to $10,000.

Duration 1 year.

Number awarded Varies each year, recently, 130 of these scholarships were awarded.

Deadline September of each year.

[920]
YEAR-LONG MEDICAL RESEARCH FELLOWS PROGRAM AT AN ACADEMIC OR NONPROFIT RESEARCH INSTITUTION

Howard Hughes Medical Institute
Attn: Department of Science Education
4000 Jones Bridge Road
Chevy Chase, MD 20815-6789
(301) 951-6708 Toll Free: (800) 448-4882, ext. 8889
Fax: (301) 215-8888 E-mail: medfellows@hhmi.org
Web: www.hhmi.org

Summary To provide financial assistance to medical, dental, and veterinary students (particularly Hispanic Americans, other underrepresented minorities, and women) who are interested in pursuing research training.

Eligibility Applicants must be enrolled in a medical, dental, or veterinary school in the United States, although they may be citizens of any country with a visa authorizing them to work in this country. They must describe a proposed research project to be conducted at an academic or nonprofit research institution in the United States (other than a facility of the National Institutes of Health in Bethesda, Maryland) or abroad. Research proposals should reflect the interests of the Howard Hughes Medical Institute (HHMI), especially in biochemistry, bioinformatics, biomedical engineering, biophysics, biostatistics, cell biology, developmental biology, epidemiology, genetics, immunology, mathematical and computational biology, microbiology, molecular biology, neuroscience, pharmacology, physiology, structural biology, or virology. Applications from women and minorities underrepresented in the sciences (Blacks or African Americans, Hispanics, American Indians, Native Alaskans, and Native Pacific Islanders) are especially encouraged. Students enrolled in M.D./Ph.D., Ph.D., or Sc.D. programs and those who have completed a Ph.D. or Sc.D. in a laboratory-based science are not eligible. Selection is based on the applicant's ability and promise for a research career as a physician-scientist and the quality of training that will be provided.

Financial Data Fellows receive a stipend of $29,000 per year. Indirect costs are not covered, but the institution receives an institutional allowance of $5,500 and a research allowance of $5,500. If fellows are conducting research at an institution other than their own, a travel and moving allowance of $1,500 is provided.

Duration 12 months, beginning any time between June and August.

Additional data This program complements the HHMI-NIH Research Scholars Program; students may not apply to both programs in the same year. HHMI has entered into partnership agreements with designated sponsors to support fellows in certain areas; those include the Burroughs Wellcome Fund for veterinary students, the Foundation Fighting Blindness for ophthalmology research (particularly in the area of inherited retinal degenerative diseases), the GM Trust for research in a field related to Duchenne Muscular Dystrophy, and the Society of Interventional Radiology Foundation for preclinical research in interventional radiology.

Number awarded Up to 66 each year.

Deadline January of each year.

Professionals/ Postdoctorates

Listed alphabetically by program title and described in detail here are 253 grants, awards, educational support programs, residencies, and other sources of "free money" available to Hispanic American professionals and postdoctorates. This funding is available to support research, creative activities, professional projects, training courses, and/or residencies in the United States.

[921]
AAOGF FOUNDATION SCHOLARSHIPS

American Association of Obstetricians and Gynecologists
  Foundation
2105 Laurel Bush Road, Suite 201
Bel Air, MD 21015
(443) 640-1051   Fax: (443) 640-1031
E-mail: info@aaogf.org
Web: www.aaogf.org/scholarship.asp

Summary To provide funding to physicians (particularly Hispanic Americans, other minorities, and women) who are interested in a program of research training in obstetrics and gynecology.

Eligibility Applicants must have an M.D. degree and be eligible for the certification process of the American Board of Obstetrics and Gynecology (ABOG). They must be interested in participating in research training conducted by 1 or more faculty mentors at an academic department of obstetrics and gynecology in the United States or Canada. The research training may be either laboratory-based or clinical, and should focus on fundamental biology, disease mechanisms, interventions or diagnostics, epidemiology, or translational research. Applicants for the scholarship co-sponsored by the Society for Maternal-Fetal Medicine (SMFM) must also be members or associate members of the SMFM. Women and minority candidates are strongly encouraged to apply. Selection is based on the scholarly, clinical, and research qualifications of the candidate; evidence of the candidate's commitment to an investigative career in academic obstetrics and gynecology in the United States or Canada; qualifications of the sponsoring department and mentor; overall quality of the mentoring plan; and quality of the research project.

Financial Data The grant is $120,000 per year. Sufficient funds to support travel to the annual fellows' retreat must be set aside. The balance of the funds may be used for salary, technical support, and supplies.

Duration 1 year; may be renewed for 2 additional years, based on satisfactory progress of the scholar.

Additional data Scholars must devote at least 75% of their effort to the program of research training.

Number awarded 2 each year: 1 co-sponsored by ABOG and 1 co-sponsored by SMFM.

Deadline June of each year.

[922]
ACADEMY OF NUTRITION AND DIETETICS GRADUATE SCHOLARSHIPS

Academy of Nutrition and Dietetics
Attn: Foundation
120 South Riverside Plaza, Suite 2000
Chicago, IL 60606-6995
(312) 899-0040   Toll Free: (800) 877-1600, ext. 1133
Fax: (312) 899-4817   E-mail: scholarships@eatright.org
Web: www.eatright.org/Foundation/scholarships

Summary To provide financial assistance to Hispanic American and other graduate student members of the Academy of Nutrition and Dietetics.

Eligibility This program is open to members of the academy who are enrolled in the second year of a master's or doctoral degree program in dietetics. Applicants who are currently completing a dietetic internship or preprofessional practice program that is combined with a graduate program may also apply. The graduate scholarships are available only to U.S. citizens and permanent residents. Applicants should intend to practice in the field of dietetics. Some scholarships require specific areas of study (e.g., public health nutrition, food service administration) and status as a registered dietitian. Others may require membership in a specific dietetic practice group, residency in a specific state, or underrepresented minority group status. The same application form can be used for all categories.

Financial Data Stipends normally range from $500 to $3,000; recently, they averaged approximately $1,870.

Duration 1 year.

Additional data The Academy of Nutrition and Dietetics was formerly the American Dietetic Association.

Number awarded Approximately 60 each year.

Deadline February of each year.

[923]
ADVANCED POSTDOCTORAL CAREER TRANSITION AWARD TO PROMOTE DIVERSITY IN NEUROSCIENCE RESEARCH

National Institute of Neurological Disorders and Stroke
Attn: Office of Training, Career Development and
  Workforce Diversity
6001 Executive Boulevard, Suite 2149
Bethesda, MD 20892-9535
(301) 451-7966   Fax: (301) 594-5929
TDD: (301) 451-0088   E-mail: jonesmiche@ninds.nih.gov
Web: grants.nih.gov/grants/guide/pa-files/PAR-12-163.html

Summary To provide funding to postdoctoral fellows who are Hispanic Americans or members of other underrepresented groups and are interested in preparing for a career as an independent investigator in neuroscience.

Eligibility This program is open to U.S. citizens, nationals, and permanent residents who have a doctoral degree in a field of neuroscience and have completed 2 to 5 years of postdoctoral research training. Applicants must be interested in participating in a program of training that will help them transition to a stable and productive independent research position. They must qualify as 1) a member of an ethnic or racial group shown to be underrepresented in health-related sciences on a national basis; or 2) an individual with a disability. Selection is based on scientific merit and programmatic considerations. The program expects fellows to devote the first phase to advanced postdoctoral training, after which they should obtain a faculty position.

Financial Data During the first phase of advanced postdoctoral training, grants range from $44,340 for fellows with 2 years of postdoctoral training to $49,884 for those with 5 years of training. During a subsequent phase as a faculty member, grants provide an annual award of up to $85,000 for salary and fringe benefits. The program also provides an annual research allowance of up to $25,000 during the first phase and up to $100,000 per year during the second phase for direct research and career development costs. The institution may apply for up to 8% of direct costs for facilities and administrative costs.

Duration Up to 5 years, including the first phase of up to 3 years of support for the advanced postdoctoral training period and a second phase of up to 3 years for a subsequent first faculty position.

Additional data Recipients must devote 75% of full-time professional effort to conducting health-related research.

Number awarded Varies each year.

Deadline February, June, or October of each year.

[924]
ADVANCED POSTDOCTORAL FELLOWSHIPS IN DIABETES RESEARCH

Juvenile Diabetes Research Foundation International
Attn: Grant Administrator
26 Broadway, 14th Floor
New York, NY 10004
(212) 479-7572   Toll Free: (800) 533-CURE
Fax: (212) 785-9595   E-mail: info@jdrf.org
Web: jdrf.org

Summary To provide advanced research training to scientists (particularly Hispanic Americans, other underrepresented minorities, women, and individuals with disabilities) who are beginning their professional careers and are interested in conducting research on the causes, treatment, prevention, or cure of diabetes or its complications.

Eligibility This program is open to postdoctorates who show extraordinary promise for a career in diabetes research. Applicants must have received their first doctoral degree (M.D., Ph.D., D.M.D., or D.V.M.) within the past 5 years and should have completed 1 to 3 years of postdoctoral training. They may not have a faculty appointment. There are no citizenship requirements. Applications are encouraged from women, members of minority groups underrepresented in the sciences, and people with disabilities. The proposed research training may be conducted at foreign or domestic, for-profit or nonprofit, or public or private institutions, including universities, colleges, hospitals, laboratories, units of state or local government, or eligible agencies of the federal government. Selection is based on the applicant's previous experience and academic record; the caliber of the proposed research; the quality of the mentor, training program, and environment; and the applicant's potential to obtain an independent research position in the future. Fellows who obtain a faculty position at any time during the term of the fellowship may apply for a transition award for support during their first year as a faculty member.

Financial Data The total grant is $90,000 per year, including salary that depends on number of years of experience, ranging from $39,264 for zero up to $54,180 for 7 or more years of experience. In the first year only, funds in excess of the grant may be used for travel to scientific meetings (up to $2,000), journal subscriptions, books, training courses, laboratory supplies, equipment, or purchase of a personal computer (up to $2,000). Indirect costs are not allowed. Fellows who receive a faculty position are granted a transition award of up to $110,000 for 1 year, including up to 10% in indirect costs.

Duration Up to 3 years.

Number awarded Varies each year.

Deadline August of each year.

[925]
ADVANCING HISPANIC EXCELLENCE IN TECHNOLOGY, ENGINEERING, MATH AND SCIENCE (AHETEMS) PROFESSIONAL SCHOLARSHIPS

Society of Hispanic Professional Engineers Foundation, Inc.
Attn: Advancing Hispanic Excellence in Technology, Engineering, Math and Science
13181 Crossroads Parkway North, Suite 450
P.O. Box 93577
City of Industry, CA 91715
(323) 725-3970, ext. 118   Fax: (323) 622-1046
E-mail: shpefoundation@shpe.org
Web: www.shpefoundation.org

Summary To provide financial assistance to Hispanic professionals working on a graduate degree in science, technology, engineering, or mathematics.

Eligibility This program is open to members of the Society of Hispanic Professional Engineers (SHPE) who are employed full time in the United States or Puerto Rico in a technical career field. Applicants must be enrolled at least half time in a science, technology, engineering, or mathematics (STEM) degree program in the United States or Puerto Rico. They must have a GPA of 3.25 or higher. Along with their application, they must submit a 500-word personal statement covering their community involvement, leadership, academic achievements, research internship and co-op experiences, and short-term and long-term goals and aspirations. Selection is based on merit. U.S. citizenship or permanent resident status is not required.

Financial Data The stipend is $2,000.

Duration 1 year.

Additional data Advancing Hispanic Excellence in Technology, Engineering, Math and Science (AHETEMS) was established in 2004 by SHPE as an independent nonprofit foundation.

Number awarded 1 or more each year.

Deadline April of each year.

[926]
AERA-AIR FELLOWS PROGRAM

American Educational Research Association
1430 K Street, N.W., Suite 1200
Washington, DC 20005
(202) 238-3200   Fax: (202) 238-3250
E-mail: fellowships@aera.net
Web: www.aera.net

Summary To provide an opportunity for junior scholars in the field of education (particularly Hispanic Americans and other underrepresented minorities) to engage in a program of research and advanced training while in residence in Washington, D.C.

Eligibility This program is open to early scholars who received a Ph.D. or Ed.D. degree within the past 3 years in a field related to education and educational processes. Applicants must be proposing a program of intensive research and training in Washington, D.C. Selection is based on past academic record, writing sample, goal statement, range and quality of research experiences, other relevant work or professional experiences, potential contributions to education research, and references. A particular goal of the program is to increase the number of underrepresented minority professionals conducting advanced research or providing technical assistance. U.S. citizenship or permanent resident status is required.

Financial Data Stipends range from $55,000 to $65,000 per year.

Duration Up to 2 years.

Additional data This program, jointly sponsored by the American Educational Research Association (AERA) and the American Institutes for Research (AIR), was first offered for 2006. Fellows rotate between the 2 organizations and receive mentoring from recognized researchers and practitioners in a variety of substantive areas in education.

Number awarded Up to 3 each year.

Deadline November of each year.

[927]
AFRL/DAGSI OHIO STUDENT-FACULTY RESEARCH FELLOWSHIP PROGRAM

Dayton Area Graduate Studies Institute
3155 Research Boulevard, Suite 205
Kettering, OH 45420
(937) 781-4001   Fax: (937) 781-4005
E-mail: kelam@dagsi.org
Web: www.dagsi.org/pages/osrfp_proinforeq.html

Summary To provide funding to faculty and graduate students (particularly Hispanic Americans and other minorities, women, and individuals with disabilities) at designated universities in Ohio who are from any state and interested in conducting research in aerospace technologies of interest to the U.S. Air Force.

Eligibility This program is open to research teams of full-time graduate students and faculty at 18 designated Ohio universities. Applicants must be interested in conducting research that will utilize the facilities of the Air Force Research Laboratory (AFRL) at Wright-Patterson Air Force Base. All 6 directorates at the AFRL (air vehicles, propulsion, sensors, materials and manufacturing, human effectiveness, and information) participate in this program. Applications from Ph.D. candidates must be developed and written largely by the student, with support, guidance, and input as necessary from the faculty partner. For master's projects, the proposal can be developed and written jointly by the faculty member and the student. All participants (faculty and student) must be U.S. citizens. Underrepresented minorities, women, and persons with disabilities are strongly urged to apply.

Financial Data Grants provide stipends of $23,500 for students who have a master's degree and are working on a Ph.D. or $18,500 for students who have a bachelor's degree and are working on a master's; student's tuition for 1 academic year; a faculty stipend of $11,000; student and faculty allowances of $3,000 each for program-related travel or other approved expenses; and overhead at a maximum off-campus rate of 26% of student and faculty stipends and miscellaneous allowances.

Duration 1 year; may be renewed for 1 additional year by master's students and for 2 additional years by Ph.D. candidates. Students are expected to spend 8 consecutive weeks conducting research at AFRL and faculty members are expected to spend at least 1 month conducting research at AFRL.

Additional data DAGSI was established in 1994 as a consortium of graduate engineering schools at the University of Dayton, Wright State University, and the Air Force Institute of Technology. The Ohio State University and the University of Cincinnati joined as affiliated members in 1996 and Miami University and Ohio University joined as associate members in 2001. Students from the following universities are also eligible to participate in this program: University of Akron, Bowling Green State University, Central State University, Cleveland State University, Kent State University, Shawnee State University, University of Toledo, Youngstown State University, Medical College of Ohio, Northeastern Ohio Universities College of Medicine, and Case Western Reserve University.

Number awarded At least 20 each year.

Deadline January of each year.

[928]
AGA RESEARCH SCHOLAR AWARDS

American Gastroenterological Association
Attn: AGA Research Foundation
Research Awards Manager
4930 Del Ray Avenue
Bethesda, MD 20814-2512
(301) 222-4012   Fax: (301) 654-5920
E-mail: awards@gastro.org
Web: www.gastro.org/aga-foundation/grants

Summary To provide research funding to young investigators (particularly Hispanic Americans, other minorities, and women) who are developing an independent career in an area of gastroenterology, hepatology, or related fields.

Eligibility Applicants must hold full-time faculty positions at North American universities or professional institutes at the time of application. They should be early in their careers (fellows and established investigators are not appropriate candidates). Candidates with an M.D. degree must have completed clinical training within the past 5 years and those with a Ph.D. must have completed their degree within the past 5 years. Membership in the American Gastroenterological Association (AGA) is required. Selection is based on significance, investigator, innovation, approach, environment, relevance to AGA mission, and evidence of institutional commitment. Women, minorities, and physician/scientist investigators are strongly encouraged to apply.

Financial Data The grant is $90,000 per year. Funds are to be used for project costs, including salary, supplies, and equipment but excluding travel. Indirect costs are not allowed.

Duration 2 years.

Additional data At least 70% of the recipient's research effort should relate to the gastrointestinal tract or liver.

Number awarded 4 each year.

Deadline October of each year.

[929]
AHRQ INDIVIDUAL AWARDS FOR POSTDOCTORAL FELLOWS

Agency for Healthcare Research and Quality
Attn: Office of Extramural Research, Education, and
  Priority Populations
540 Gaither Road
Rockville, MD 20850
(301) 427-1528   Fax: (301) 427-1562
TDD: (301) 451-0088
E-mail: Shelley.Benjamin@ahrq.hhs.gov
Web: grants.nih.gov/grants/guide/pa-files/PA-12-261.html

Summary To provide funding to postdoctoral scholars (particularly Hispanic Americans, other underrepresented minorities, and individuals with disabilities) who are interested in academic training and supervised experience in applying quantitative research methods to the systematic analysis and evaluation of health services.

Eligibility Applicants must be U.S. citizens, nationals, or permanent residents who have received a Ph.D., M.D., D.O., D.C., D.D.S., D.V.M., O.D., Sc.D., Eng.D., D.P.M., D.N.Sc., N.D., Dr.P.H., Pharm.D., D.S.W., Psych.D., or equivalent doctoral degree from an accredited domestic or foreign institution. They must be proposing to pursue postdoctoral training at an appropriate institution under the guidance of a sponsor who is an established investigator active in health services research. The proposed training should help promote the sponsoring agency's strategic research goals of 1) reducing the risk of harm from health care services by promoting the delivery of appropriate care that achieves the best quality outcomes; 2) achieving wider access to effective health care services and reducing health care costs; and 3) assuring that providers and consumers/patients use beneficial and timely health care information to make informed decisions. Preference is given to proposals that address health services research issues critical to such priority populations as individuals living in inner city and rural (including frontier) areas; low-income and minority groups; women, children, and the elderly; and individuals with special health care needs, including those with disabilities and those who need chronic or end-of-life health care. Members of underrepresented ethnic and racial groups, individuals from disadvantaged backgrounds, and individuals with disabilities are especially encouraged to apply.

Financial Data The award provides an annual stipend based on the number of years of postdoctoral experience, ranging from $41,364 for less than 1 year to $54,180 for 7 or more years. For fellows sponsored by domestic non-federal institutions, the stipend is paid through the sponsoring institution; for fellows sponsored by federal or foreign institutions, the monthly stipend is paid directly to the fellow. Institutions also receive an allowance to help defray such awardee expenses as self-only health insurance, research supplies, equipment, travel to scientific meetings, and related items; the allowance is $7,850 per 12-month period for fellows at non-federal, nonprofit, and foreign institutions and $6,750 per 12-month period at federal laboratories and for-profit institutions. In addition, tuition and fees are reimbursed at a rate of 60%, up to $16,000 for an additional degree.

Duration 1 to 3 years.

Number awarded Varies each year.

Deadline April, August, or December of each year.

[930]
AHRQ SMALL RESEARCH GRANT PROGRAM

Agency for Healthcare Research and Quality
Attn: Office of Extramural Research, Education, and
  Priority Populations
540 Gaither Road
Rockville, MD 20850
(301) 427-1556   Fax: (301) 427-1562
TDD: (301) 451-0088
E-mail: Kishena.Wadhwani@ahrq.hhs.gov
Web: grants.nih.gov/grants/guide/pa-files/PA-10-168.html

Summary To provide funding (especially to Hispanic Americans, other minorities, individuals with disabilities, and new investigators) for small research projects designed to improve the quality, appropriateness, and effectiveness of health care services and access to those services.

Eligibility This program is open to investigators at domestic, nonprofit, public and private organizations, including universities, clinics, units of state and local governments, nonprofit firms, and nonprofit foundations. Applicants must be proposing projects in 1 of the research portfolio areas of the Agency for Healthcare Research and Quality (AHRQ): 1) the value portfolio, for research that can be used to reduce unnecessary health care costs (waste) while maintaining or improving health care quality; 2) the health information technology portfolio, for the use of information and communication technology in health care to support the delivery of patient or population care; 3) the comparative effectiveness portfolio, for research focusing on comparative effectiveness of different clinical treatments and services; 4) the prevention/care management portfolio, to improve the quality, safety, efficiency, and effectiveness of preventive services and chronic care management in ambulatory care settings; 5) the patient safety portfolio, for research projects to identify the risks and hazards encountered by patients as a result of health care; or 6) the innovations and emerging areas portfolio, for research on ideas that have the potential for high impact. Members of underrepresented ethnic and racial groups, individuals with disabilities, and new investigators are especially encouraged to apply. U.S. citizenship or permanent resident status is required.

Financial Data Total costs (including direct costs and facilities and administrative costs) may not exceed $100,000.

Duration Up to 2 years.

Additional data Funding from this program may not be used for dissertation research.

Number awarded Varies each year.

Deadline February, June, or October of each year.

[931]
AIR FORCE SUMMER FACULTY FELLOWSHIP PROGRAM

American Society for Engineering Education
Attn: AFSFF Program
1818 N Street, N.W., Suite 600
Washington, DC 20036-2479
(202) 649-3834   Fax: (202) 265-8504
E-mail: sffp@asee.org
Web: sffp.asee.org

Summary To provide funding to science and engineering faculty and graduate students (particularly Hispanic Americans and other underrepresented minorities) who are interested in conducting research during the summer at Air Force facilities.

Eligibility This program is open to U.S. citizens and permanent residents who have a full-time faculty appointment at a U.S. college or university in a field of engineering or science of interest to the Air Force. Applicants must be interested in conducting a research project, under the direction of an Air Force research adviser, at an Air Force Research Laboratory, the U.S. Air Force Academy, or the Air Force Institute of Technology. A graduate student may accompany the faculty member. Faculty and students at Historically Black Colleges and Universities ((HBCUs), Minority Institutions (MIs), American Indian Tribal Colleges and Universities (TCUs), and Hispanic Serving Institutions (HSIs) are especially encouraged to apply.

Financial Data Stipends are $1,700 per week for full professors, $1,500 per week for associate professors, $1,300 per week for assistant professors, $884 per week for graduate students working on a master's degree, or $1,037 per week for graduate students working on a doctoral degree. Relocation reimbursement and a daily expense allowance of $50 (for fellows with a commute distance greater than 50 miles) are also available.

Duration 8 to 12 weeks during the summer. May be renewed for a second and third summer, but recipients may not reapply for 2 years after completing a third summer.

Additional data This program first operated in 2005. Research must be conducted in residence at an Air Force facility.

Number awarded Approximately 100 each year.

Deadline December of each year.

[932]
ALEXANDER GRALNICK RESEARCH INVESTIGATOR PRIZE

American Psychological Foundation
750 First Street, N.E.
Washington, DC 20002-4242
(202) 336-5843　　　　　　　　Fax: (202) 336-5812
E-mail: foundation@apa.org
Web: www.apa.org/apf/funding/gralnick.aspx

Summary To recognize and reward psychologists (particularly Hispanic Americans and members of other groups representing diversity) who have conducted exceptional research on serious mental illness.

Eligibility This program is open to psychologists who have a doctoral degree, have a record of significant research productivity, and are able to demonstrate evidence on continuing creativity in the area of research on serious mental illness (including, but not limited to, schizophrenia, bipolar disorder, and paranoia). Nominees must also have significant involvement in training and development of younger investigators. They must have an affiliation with an accredited college, university, or other treatment or research institution. The sponsor encourages nominations of individuals who represent diversity in race, ethnicity, gender, age, disability, and sexual orientation.

Financial Data The award is $20,000.

Duration The award is presented biennially, in even-numbered years.

Additional data This award was first presented in 2002.

Number awarded 1 each even-numbered year.

Deadline April of each even-numbered year.

[933]
ALFRED P. SLOAN FOUNDATION RESEARCH FELLOWSHIPS

Alfred P. Sloan Foundation
630 Fifth Avenue, Suite 2550
New York, NY 10111-0242
(212) 649-1649　　　　　　　　Fax: (212) 757-5117
E-mail: researchfellows@sloan.org
Web: www.sloan.org/sloan-research-fellowships

Summary To provide funding for research in selected fields of science to recent doctorates (particularly Hispanic Americans, other underrepresented minorities, and women).

Eligibility This program is open to scholars who are no more than 6 years from completion of the most recent Ph.D. or equivalent in computational and evolutionary molecular biology, chemistry, computer science, economics, mathematics, ocean sciences (including marine biology), neuroscience, physics, or a related interdisciplinary field. Applicants must have a tenure track position at a college or university in the United States or Canada. Direct applications are not accepted; candidates must be nominated by department heads or other senior scholars. Although fellows must be at an early stage of their research careers, they should give strong evidence of independent research accomplishments and creativity. The sponsor strongly encourages the participation of women and members of underrepresented minority groups.

Financial Data The stipend is $25,000 per year. Funds are paid directly to the fellow's institution to be used by the fellow for equipment, technical assistance, professional travel, trainee support, or any other research-related expense; they may not be used to augment an existing full-time salary.

Duration 2 years; may be extended if unexpended funds still remain.

Additional data This program began in 1955, when it awarded $235,000 to 22 chemists, physicists, and pure mathematicians. Neuroscience was added in 1972, economics and applied mathematics in 1980, computer science in 1993, computational and evolutionary molecular biology in 2002, and ocean sciences in 2012. Currently, the program awards more than $5.5 million in grants annually.

Number awarded 126 each year: 23 in chemistry, 12 in computational and evolutionary molecular biology, 16 in computer science, 8 in economics, 20 in mathematics, 16 in neuroscience, 8 in ocean sciences, and 23 in physics.

Deadline September of each year.

[934]
ALONZO DAVIS FELLOWSHIP

Virginia Center for the Creative Arts
Attn: Admissions Committee
154 San Angelo Drive
Amherst, VA 24521
(434) 946-7236　　　　　　　　Fax: (434) 946-7239
E-mail: vcca@vcca.com
Web: www.vcca.com

Summary To provide support to writers, visual artists, and composers who are of Latino or African descent and interested in a residency at the Virginia Center for the Creative Arts in Sweet Briar, Virginia.

Eligibility This program is open to writers, visual artists, and composers who are interested in a residency at the center so they can concentrate solely on their creative work. Applicants must be U.S citizens of African or Latino descent. They must submit samples of their work completed within the past 4 years.

Financial Data The fellowship provides payment of all residency costs, including a private bedroom, separate studio, and 3 prepared meals a day.

Duration Up to 1 month.

Additional data This fellowship was established in 2004. The application fee is $30.

Number awarded 1 each year.

Deadline January of each year for June to September residencies; May of each year for October to January residencies; September of each year for February to May residencies.

[935]
ALZHEIMER'S ASSOCIATION INVESTIGATOR-INITIATED RESEARCH GRANTS

Alzheimer's Association
Attn: Medical and Scientific Affairs
225 North Michigan Avenue, 17th Floor
Chicago, IL 60601-7633
(312) 335-5747   Toll Free: (800) 272-3900
Fax: (866) 699-1246   TDD: (312) 335-5886
E-mail: grantsapp@alz.org
Web: www.alz.org

Summary To provide funding to scientists (particularly Hispanic Americans and members of other underrepresented groups) who are interested in conducting research on Alzheimer's Disease.

Eligibility This program is open to postdoctoral investigators at public, private, domestic, and foreign research laboratories, medical centers, hospitals, and universities. Applicants must be proposing to conduct research with focus areas that change annually but are related to Alzheimer's Disease. They must have a full-time staff or faculty appointment. Scientists from underrepresented groups are especially encouraged to apply.

Financial Data Grants up to $100,000 per year, including direct expenses and up to 10% for overhead costs, are available. The total award for the life of the grant may not exceed $240,000.

Duration Up to 3 years.

Number awarded Up to 20 each year.

Deadline Letters of intent must be submitted by the end of January of each year. Final applications are due in March.

[936]
ALZHEIMER'S ASSOCIATION NEW INVESTIGATOR RESEARCH GRANTS

Alzheimer's Association
Attn: Medical and Scientific Affairs
225 North Michigan Avenue, 17th Floor
Chicago, IL 60601-7633
(312) 335-5747   Toll Free: (800) 272-3900
Fax: (866) 699-1246   TDD: (312) 335-5886
E-mail: grantsapp@alz.org
Web: www.alz.org

Summary To provide funding for research on Alzheimer's Disease to junior and postdoctoral investigators (particularly Hispanic Americans and members of other underrepresented groups).

Eligibility This program is open to investigators, including postdoctoral fellows, at public, private, domestic, and foreign research laboratories, medical centers, hospitals, and universities. Applicants must be proposing to conduct research with focus areas that change annually but are related to Alzheimer's Disease. Eligibility is restricted to investigators who have less than 10 years of research experience, including postdoctoral fellowships or residencies. Scientists from underrepresented groups are especially encouraged to apply.

Financial Data Grants up to $60,000 per year, including direct expenses and up to 10% for overhead costs, are available. The total award for the life of the grant may not exceed $100,000.

Duration Up to 2 years.

Number awarded Up to 25 each year.

Deadline Letters of intent must be submitted by the end of January or September of each year. Final applications are due in March or October.

[937]
AMERICAN ASSOCIATION FOR THE ADVANCEMENT OF SCIENCE CONGRESSIONAL FELLOWSHIPS

American Association for the Advancement of Science
Attn: Science and Technology Policy Fellowships
1200 New York Avenue, N.W.
Washington, DC 20005-3920
(202) 326-6700   Fax: (202) 289-4950
E-mail: fellowships@aaas.org
Web: www.fellowships.aaas.org

Summary To provide a fellowship to postdoctoral scientists and engineers (particularly Hispanic Americans, other minorities, and individuals with disabilities) so they can work as special legislative assistants on the staffs of members of Congress or Congressional committees.

Eligibility This program is open to doctoral-level scientists (Ph.D., M.D., D.V.M., D.Sc., and other terminal degrees) in any field of science (behavioral, biological, computational, earth, health, medical, physical, or social), engineering, or mathematics. Engineers with a master's degree and at least 3 years of professional experience are also eligible. Applicants must demonstrate solid scientific and technical credentials; a commitment to serve society; good communication skills; the ability to engage with non-scientific audiences; and an interest in working as special legislative assistants for Congress. U.S. citizenship is required; federal employees are not eligible. The sponsor seeks candidates from a broad array of backgrounds and a diversity of geographic, disciplinary, gender, and ethnic perspectives, as well as disability status.

Financial Data The stipend is $74,872. Also provided are a $4,000 relocation allowance for fellows from outside the Washington, D.C. area, reimbursement for health insurance, and a $4,000 travel allowance.

Duration 1 year, beginning in September.

Additional data The program includes an orientation on Congressional and executive branch operations and a year-long seminar program on issues involving science and public policy. Approximately 30 other national science and engineering societies sponsor fellows in collaboration with this program; for a list of all of those, contact the sponsor.

Number awarded 2 each year.

Deadline October of each year.

[938]
AMERICAN ASSOCIATION OF HISPANICS IN HIGHER EDUCATION AND EDUCATIONAL TESTING SERVICE OUTSTANDING DISSERTATIONS COMPETITION

American Association of Hispanics in Higher Education
c/o Azara Santiago-Rivera, Dissertations Competition Chair
The Chicago School of Professional Psychology
Washington DC Campus
Department of Counseling Psychology
901 15th Street, N.W.
Washington, DC 20005
(202) 706-5059
E-mail: azararivera@thechicagoschool.edu
Web: www.aahhe.org

Summary To recognize and reward authors of outstanding doctoral dissertations who either are Hispanics in the social sciences or wrote about Hispanics in higher education in their dissertation.

Eligibility This competition is open to anyone who has completed a doctoral dissertation during the preceding period of approximately 30 months. The author of the dissertation must be an Hispanic working in the social sciences (broadly defined) or an individual who wrote about Hispanics in higher education. Eligible fields are those that relate to the corporate mission of the Educational Testing Service (ETS), including education, linguistics, psychology, statistics, and testing; dissertations in the humanities, basic sciences, technology, engineering, and mathematics are not eligible. Dissertations may use any research approach (e.g., historical, experimental, qualitative, survey). Applicants must submit an abstract, up to 25 pages in length, of their dissertation. Judging is based on the appropriateness of the research approach used, the impact the dissertation will have on the field, the creativity and innovation of the study, the scholarly quality of the dissertation, and significance of contribution to knowledge in the field. Based on the abstracts, 5 to 7 semifinalists are selected and asked to submit their complete dissertation. From among those, 3 finalists are invited to present their dissertations at the national conference of the American Association of Hispanics in Higher Education (AAHHE), where winners are selected.

Financial Data Awards are $5,000 for first place, $2,000 for second, and $1,000 for third. All travel expenses of finalists to attend the AAHHE national conference are paid.

Duration The awards are presented annually.

Additional data This program began in 2010 as a joint undertaking of AAHHE and ETS.

Number awarded 3 cash awards are presented each year.

Deadline August of each year.

[939]
AMERICAN ASSOCIATION OF UNIVERSITY WOMEN CAREER DEVELOPMENT GRANTS

American Association of University Women
Attn: AAUW Educational Foundation
301 ACT Drive, Department 60
P.O. Box 4030
Iowa City, IA 52243-4030
(319) 337-1716, ext. 60   Fax: (319) 337-1204
E-mail: aauw@act.org
Web: www.aauw.org

Summary To provide financial assistance to Hispanic American and other women who are seeking career advancement, career change, or reentry into the workforce.

Eligibility This program is open to women who are U.S. citizens or permanent residents, have earned a bachelor's degree, received their most recent degree more than 4 years ago, and are making career changes, seeking to advance in current careers, or reentering the workforce. Applicants must be interested in working toward a master's degree, second bachelor's or associate degree, professional degree (e.g., M.D., J.D.), certification program, or technical school certificate. They must be planning to undertake course work at an accredited 2- or 4-year college or university (or a technical school that is licensed, accredited, or approved by the U.S. Department of Education). Primary consideration is given to women of color and women pursuing their first advanced degree or credentials in nontraditional fields. Support is not provided for prerequisite course work or for Ph.D. course work or dissertations. Selection is based on demonstrated commitment to education and equity for women and girls, reason for seeking higher education or technical training, degree to which study plan is consistent with career objectives, potential for success in chosen field, documentation of opportunities in chosen field, feasibility of study plans and proposed time schedule, validity of proposed budget and budget narrative (including sufficient outside support), and quality of written proposal.

Financial Data Grants range from $2,000 to $12,000. Funds may be used for tuition, fees, books, supplies, local transportation, dependent child care, or purchase of a computer required for the study program.

Duration 1 year, beginning in July; nonrenewable.

Additional data The filing fee is $35.

Number awarded Varies each year; recently, 63 of these grants, with a value of $670,000, were awarded.

Deadline December of each year.

[940]
AMERICAN EDUCATIONAL RESEARCH ASSOCIATION RESEARCH GRANTS PROGRAM

American Educational Research Association
1430 K Street, N.W., Suite 1200
Washington, DC 20005
(202) 238-3200   Fax: (202) 238-3250
E-mail: fellowships@aera.net
Web: www.aera.net

Summary To provide funding to faculty members and other postdoctorates (particularly Hispanic Americans and other underrepresented minorities) who are interested in conducting research on educational policy.

Eligibility This program is open to scholars who have completed a doctoral degree in such disciplines as (but not limited to) education, sociology, economics, psychology, demography, statistics, or psychometrics. Applicants may be U.S. citizens, U.S. permanent residents, or non-U.S. citizens working at a U.S. institution. Underrepresented minority researchers are strongly encouraged to apply. Research topics may cover a wide range of policy-related issues, but priority is given to proposals that 1) develop or benefit from new quantitative measures or methodological approaches for addressing education issues; 2) include interdisciplinary teams with subject matter expertise, especially when studying science, technology, engineering, or mathematics (STEM) learning; 3) analyze TIMSS, PISA, or other international data resources; or 4) include the integration and analysis of more than 1 data set. Research projects must include the analysis of data from at least 1 of the large-scale, nationally or internationally representative data sets, such as those of the National Science Foundation (NSF), National Center for Education Statistics (NCES), or National Institutes of Health (NIH). Selection is based on the importance of the proposed policy issue, the strength of the methodological model and proposed statistical analysis of the study, and relevant experience or research record.

Financial Data Grants up to $20,000 for 1 year or $35,000 for 2 years are available. Funding is linked to the approval of the recipient's progress report and final report. Grantees receive one-third of the total award at the beginning of the grant period, one-third upon acceptance of the progress report, and one-third upon acceptance of the final report.

Duration 1 or 2 years.

Additional data Funding for this program is provided by the NSF and the NCES. Grantees must submit a brief (3 to 6 pages) progress report midway through the grant period. A final report must be submitted at the end of the grant period.

Number awarded Approximately 15 each year.

Deadline January, March, or August of each year.

[941]
AMERICAN SOCIETY OF TRANSPLANTATION BASIC SCIENCE FELLOWSHIP GRANT

American Society of Transplantation
Attn: Chair, Awards and Grants Committee
15000 Commerce Parkway, Suite C
Mt. Laurel, NJ 08054
(856) 439-9986   Fax: (856) 439-9982
E-mail: info@a-s-t.org
Web: www.a-s-t.org/research-funding/research-funding

Summary To provide funding to recent postdoctorates (particularly Hispanic Americans, other minorities, and women) who are interested in a program of research training related to the basic science of transplantation under the mentorship of a member of the American Society of Transplantation (AST).

Eligibility This program is open to scientists who have an M.D., D.O., Ph.D., D.V.M. or equivalent graduate degree and have spent 2 years or less performing research in basic transplantation science since obtaining their last degree. Applicants must be sponsored by an AST member at a North American institution who will serve as their mentor. They must be citizens, permanent residents, or lawfully-admitted foreign nationals with appropriate visas in Canada, Mexico, or the United States. Their proposed research training must involve support work in transplantation biology, ranging from pertinent basic immunology to animal studies; all types of organ, tissue, and cell transplants are considered. Research topics that involve underrepresented areas (minorities, women, and pediatrics) are strongly encouraged. The AST also encourages applications from women and underrepresented minority investigators. Selection is based on the quality of the applicant, scientific project, sponsor, and institution, with an emphasis on preparing the applicant for a career as an independent investigator.

Financial Data The grant is $40,000 per year. Funds are to support the fellow's salary and cannot be used for indirect costs.

Duration 2 years.

Additional data The American Society of Transplantation also sponsors a number of other similar grants, including the American Society of Transplantation Basic Science Faculty Development Grant, American Society of Transplantation Branch-Out Grants, American Society of Transplantation Clinical Science Faculty Development Grant, and American Society of Transplantation Clinical Science (applicants can receive only 1 of these awards at a time). Fellowship Grants.

Number awarded 1 or more each year.

Deadline December of each year.

[942]
ANDRES MONTOYA POETRY PRIZE

University of Notre Dame
Attn: Institute for Latino Studies
230 McKenna Hall
Notre Dame, IN 46556
(574) 631-4440   Toll Free: (866) 460-5586
Fax: (574) 631-3522
Web: latinostudies.ne.edu/poetry_prize/guidelines.htm

Summary To recognize and reward Latino/a poets who submit examples of their work.

Eligibility This competition is open to Latino/a poets who have not had a book professionally published and are U.S. citizens or permanent residents. Applicants must submit manuscripts of 50 to 100 pages of poetry, in English, in any style or on any subject. Authors of chapbooks and self-published works are eligible, but the manuscript submitted may not have been published as a whole in any form.

Financial Data The prize is $1,000 and publication by the University of Notre Dame Press.

Duration The prize is awarded biennially, in even-numbered years.

Additional data This prize was first awarded in 2004.

Number awarded 1 each even-numbered year.

Deadline January of each even-numbered year.

[943]
ANISFIELD-WOLF BOOK AWARDS

Cleveland Foundation
1422 Euclid Avenue, Suite 1300
Cleveland, OH 44115-2001
(216) 861-3810　　　　　Fax: (216) 861-1729
E-mail: Hello@anisfield-wolf.org
Web: www.anisfield-wolf.org

Summary To recognize and reward recent books that have contributed to an understanding of racism or appreciation of the rich diversity of human cultures.

Eligibility Works published in English during the preceding year that "contribute to our understanding of racism or our appreciation of the rich diversity of human cultures" are eligible to be considered. Entries may be either scholarly or imaginative (fiction, poetry, memoir). Plays and screenplays are not eligible, nor are works in progress. Manuscripts and self-published works are not eligible, and no grants are made for completing or publishing manuscripts.

Financial Data The prize is $10,000. If more than 1 author is chosen in a given year, the prize is divided equally among the winning books.

Duration The award is presented annually.

Additional data This program began in 1936.

Number awarded 5 each year: 2 for fiction, 1 for poetry, 1 for nonfiction, and 1 for lifetime achievement.

Deadline December of each year.

[944]
APA/SAMHSA MINORITY FELLOWSHIP PROGRAM

American Psychiatric Association
Attn: Department of Minority and National Affairs
1000 Wilson Boulevard, Suite 1825
Arlington, VA 22209-3901
(703) 907-8653　　　　　Toll Free: (888) 35-PSYCH
Fax: (703) 907-7852　　　　E-mail: mking@psych.org
Web: www.psychiatry.org

Summary To provide educational enrichment to psychiatrists-in-training (particularly Hispanic Americans and other minorities) who are interested in providing quality and effective services to minorities and the underserved.

Eligibility This program is open to residents who are in at least their second year of psychiatric training, members of the American Psychiatric Association (APA), and U.S. citizens or permanent residents. A goal of the program is to develop leadership to improve the quality of mental health care for members of ethnic minority groups (American Indians, Native Alaskans, Asian Americans, Native Hawaiians, Native Pacific Islanders, African Americans, and Hispanics/Latinos). Applicants must be interested in working with a component of the APA that is of interest to them and relevant to their career goals. Along with their application, they must submit a 2-page essay on how the fellowship would be utilized to alter their present training and ultimately assist them in achieving their career goals. Selection is based on commitment to serve ethnic minority populations, demonstrated leadership abilities,

awareness of the importance of culture in mental health, and interest in the interrelationship between mental health/illness and transcultural factors.

Financial Data Fellows receive a monthly stipend (amount not specified) and reimbursement of transportation, lodging, meals, and incidentals in connection with attendance at program-related activities. They are expected to use the funds to enhance their own professional development, improve training in cultural competence at their training institution, improve awareness of culturally relevant issues in psychiatry at their institution, expand research in areas relevant to minorities and underserved populations, enhance the current treatment modalities for minority patients and underserved individuals at their institution, and improve awareness in the surrounding community about mental health issues (particularly with regard to minority populations).

Duration 1 year; may be renewed 1 additional year.

Additional data Funding for this program is provided by the Substance Abuse and Mental Health Services Administration (SAMHSA). As part of their assignment to an APA component, fellows must attend the fall component meetings in September and the APA annual meeting in May. At those meeting, they can share their experiences as residents and minorities and discuss issues that impact on minority populations. This program is an outgrowth of the fellowships that were established in 1974 under a grant from the National Institute of Mental Health in answer to concerns about the underrepresentation of minorities in psychiatry.

Number awarded Varies each year; recently, 21 of these fellowships were awarded.

Deadline January of each year.

[945]
APA SUBSTANCE ABUSE FELLOWSHIP PROGRAM

American Psychiatric Association
Attn: Department of Minority and National Affairs
1000 Wilson Boulevard, Suite 1825
Arlington, VA 22209-3901
(703) 907-8653　　　　　Toll Free: (888) 35-PSYCH
Fax: (703) 907-7852　　　　E-mail: mking@psych.org
Web: www.psychiatry.org

Summary To provide educational enrichment to Hispanic American and other minority psychiatrists-in-training and stimulate their interest in providing quality and effective services related to substance abuse to minorities and the underserved.

Eligibility This program is open to psychiatric residents who are members of the American Psychiatric Association (APA) and U.S. citizens or permanent residents. A goal of the program is to develop leadership to improve the quality of mental health care for members of ethnic minority groups (American Indians, Native Alaskans, Asian Americans, Native Hawaiians, Native Pacific Islanders, African Americans, and Hispanics/Latinos). Applicants must be in at least their fifth year of a substance abuse training program approved by an affiliated medical school or agency where a significant number of substance abuse patients are from minority and underserved groups. They must also be interested in working with a component of the APA that is of interest to them and relevant to their career goals. Along with their application, they must submit a 2-page essay on how the fellowship would be utilized to alter their present training and ultimately assist them in achieving their career goals. Selection is based on commitment to serve ethnic minority populations, demonstrated leadership abilities, awareness of the importance of culture in mental health, and interest in the interrelationship between mental health/illness and transcultural factors.

Financial Data　Fellows receive a monthly stipend (amount not specified) and reimbursement of transportation, lodging, meals, and incidentals in connection with attendance at program-related activities. They are expected to use the funds to enhance their own professional development, improve training in cultural competence at their training institution, improve awareness of culturally relevant issues in psychiatry at their institution, expand research in areas relevant to minorities and underserved populations, enhance the current treatment modalities for minority patients and underserved individuals at their institution, and improve awareness in the surrounding community about mental health issues (particularly with regard to minority populations).

Duration　1 year; may be renewed 1 additional year.

Additional data　Funding for this program is provided by the Substance Abuse and Mental Health Services Administration (SAMHSA). As part of their assignment to an APA component, fellows must attend the fall component meetings in September and the APA annual meeting in May. At those meeting, they can share their experiences as residents and minorities and discuss issues that impact minority populations. This program is an outgrowth of the fellowships that were established in 1974 under a grant from the National Institute of Mental Health in answer to concerns about the underrepresentation of minorities in psychiatry.

Number awarded　Varies each year; recently, 3 of these fellowships were awarded.

Deadline　January of each year.

[946]
ARL BROAD AGENCY ANNOUNCEMENT

　　Army Research Office
　　Attn: Army Contracting Command-Aberdeen Proving
　　　Ground
　　4300 South Miami Boulevard
　　P.O. Box 12211
　　Research Triangle Park, NC 27709-2211
　　(919) 549-4375　　　　　　　　Fax: (919) 549-4388
　　Web: www.arl.army.mil/www/default.cfm?Page=8

Summary　To provide funding to investigators (particularly those at Hispanic Serving Institutions) who are interested in conducting scientific research of interest to the U.S. Army.

Eligibility　This program is open to investigators qualified to perform research in designated scientific and technical areas of interest to the Army Research Laboratory (ARL) and the Army Research Office (ARO). Those areas include ballistics and aeromechanics sciences, chemistry, computing and network sciences, electronics, environmental sciences, human sciences, information sciences, life sciences, materials sciences, mathematics, mechanical sciences, physics and survivability, lethality, and vulnerability analysis and assessment. Applications are especially encouraged from Historically Black Colleges and Universities (HBCUs) and Minority Institutions (MIs).

Financial Data　The amounts of the awards depend on the nature of the proposal and the availability of funds.

Duration　3 years.

Additional data　Although the Army Research Office intends to award a fair proportion of its acquisitions to HBCUs and MIs, it does not set aside a specified percentage.

Number awarded　Varies each year.

Deadline　Applications may be submitted at any time.

[947]
ARNULFO D. TREJO LIBRARIAN OF THE YEAR AWARD

　　REFORMA (National Association to Promote Library and
　　　Information Services to Latinos and the Spanish
　　　Speaking)
　　c/o Susan Luevano, Librarian of the Year Award
　　　Committee
　　California State University at Long Beach
　　University Library
　　1250 Bellflower Boulevard
　　Long Beach, CA 90840-1901
　　(562) 985-5891　　　　　　　E-mail: sluevano@csulb.edu
　　Web: www.reforma.org

Summary　To recognize and reward members of REFORMA, the National Association to Promote Library Services to the Spanish Speaking, who have made significant contributions to Latino librarianship.

Eligibility　This award is available to members of the association in good standing. Letters of nomination should describe 1) the degree to which the nominee's work filled any unmet library or other needs in the Latino and Spanish-speaking community, including work in administration, instruction, technical services, or computer-oriented activities; and 2) the contributions the nominee has made to REFORMA. Nominations may be submitted by individual members or chapters of the association. Priority is given to early and mid-career candidates who have promoted and advocated services to the Latino and Spanish-speaking community during the previous year.

Financial Data　The award is $1,000.

Duration　The award is presented annually.

Additional data　This program began in 1992.

Number awarded　1 each year.

Deadline　May of each year.

[948]
ASH-AMFDP AWARDS

　　American Society of Hematology
　　Attn: Awards Manager
　　2021 L Street, N.W., Suite 900
　　Washington, DC 20036
　　(202) 776-0544　　　　　　　　Fax: (202) 776-0545
　　E-mail: awards@hematology.org
　　Web: www.hematology.org

Summary　To provide an opportunity for Hispanic Americans and other historically disadvantaged postdoctoral physicians to conduct a research project in hematology.

Eligibility　This program is open to postdoctoral physicians who are members of historically disadvantaged groups, defined as individuals who face challenges because of their race, ethnicity, socioeconomic status, or other similar factors.

Applicants must be committed to a career in academic medicine in hematology and to serving as a role model for students and faculty of similar backgrounds. They must identify a mentor at their institution to work with them and give them research and career guidance. Selection is based on excellence in educational career; willingness to devote 4 consecutive years to research; and commitment to an academic career, improving the health status of the underserved, and decreasing health disparities. U.S. citizenship or permanent resident status is required.

Financial Data The grant includes a stipend of up to $75,000 per year, a grant of $30,000 per year for support of research activities, complimentary membership in the American Society of Hematology (ASH), and travel support to attend the ASH annual meeting.

Duration 4 years.

Additional data This program, first offered in 2006, is a partnership between the ASH and the Robert Wood Johnson Foundation, whose Minority Medical Faculty Development Program (MMFDP) was renamed the Harold Amos Medical Faculty Development Program (AMFDP) in honor of the first African American to chair a department at the Harvard Medical School. Scholars must spend at least 70% of their time in research activities.

Number awarded At least 1 each year.

Deadline March of each year.

[949]
ASTRONOMY AND ASTROPHYSICS POSTDOCTORAL FELLOWSHIPS

National Science Foundation
Directorate for Mathematical and Physical Sciences
Attn: Division of Astronomical Sciences
4201 Wilson Boulevard, Room 1030S
Arlington, VA 22230
(703) 292-5039　　　　　Fax: (703) 292-9034
TDD: (800) 281-8749　　　E-mail: eajhar@nsf.gov
Web: www.nsf.gov/funding/pgm_summ.jsp?pims_id=5291

Summary To provide funding to recent doctoral recipients in astronomy or astrophysics (particularly Hispanic Americans, other underrepresented minorities, women, and individuals with disabilities) who are interested in pursuing a program of research and education.

Eligibility This program is open to U.S. citizens, nationals, and permanent residents who completed a Ph.D. in astronomy or astrophysics during the previous 5 years. Applicants must be interested in a program of research of an observational, instrumental, or theoretical nature, especially research that is facilitated or enabled by new ground-based capability in radio, optical/IR, or solar astrophysics. Research may be conducted at a U.S. institution of higher education; a national center, facility, or institute funded by the National Science Foundation (NSF), such as the Kavli Institute for Theoretical Physics; a U.S. nonprofit organization with research and educational missions; and/or an international site operated by a U.S. organization eligible for NSF funding, such as Cerro Tololo InterAmerican Observatory. The proposal must include a coherent program of educational activities, such as teaching a course each year at the host institution or an academic institution with ties to the host institution, developing educational materials, or engaging in a significant program of outreach or general education. In the selection process, consid-

eration is given to the achievement of societally relevant outcomes, including full participation of women, persons with disabilities, and underrepresented minorities.

Financial Data Grants up to $89,000 per year are available, including a stipend of $62,000 per year paid directly to the fellow and an allowance of $27,000 per year to cover expenses directly related to the research, facilities and other institutional resources, and fringe benefits.

Duration Up to 3 years.

Number awarded 8 to 9 each year.

Deadline October of each year.

[950]
ATMOSPHERIC AND GEOSPACE SCIENCES POSTDOCTORAL RESEARCH FELLOWSHIPS

National Science Foundation
Directorate for Geosciences
Attn: Division of Atmospheric and Geospace Sciences
4201 Wilson Boulevard, Room 775S
Arlington, VA 22230
(703) 292-4708　　　　　Fax: (703) 292-9022
TDD: (800) 281-8749　　　E-mail: lgeorge@nsf.gov
Web: www.nsf.gov/funding/pgm_summ.jsp?pims_id=12779

Summary To provide funding to postdoctoral scientists (particularly Hispanic Americans, other underrepresented minorities, women, and individuals with disabilities) who are interested in conducting research related to activities of the National Science Foundation (NSF) Division of Atmospheric and Geospace Sciences.

Eligibility This program is open to U.S. citizens, nationals, and permanent residents who received a Ph.D. within the past 3 years. Applicants must be interested in conducting a research project that is relevant to the activities of NSF Division of Atmospheric and Geospace Sciences: studies of the physics, chemistry, and dynamics of Earth's upper and lower atmosphere and its space environment; research on climate processes and variations; or studies to understand the natural global cycles of gases and particles in Earth's atmosphere. The project should be conducted at an institution (college or university, private nonprofit institute or museum, government installation, or laboratory) in the United States or abroad other than the applicant's Ph.D.-granting institution. In the selection process, consideration is given to the achievement of societally relevant outcomes, including full participation of women, persons with disabilities, and underrepresented minorities.

Financial Data Grants are $86,000 per year, including a stipend of $58,000 per year, a research allowance of $19,000 per year, and a fringe benefit allowance of $9,000 per year.

Duration 2 years.

Number awarded 10 each year.

Deadline January of each year.

[951]
AWARDS FOR FACULTY AT HISPANIC-SERVING INSTITUTIONS

National Endowment for the Humanities
Attn: Division of Research Programs
1100 Pennsylvania Avenue, N.W., Room 318
Washington, DC 20506
(202) 606-8200   Toll Free: (800) NEH-1121
Fax: (202) 606-8204   TDD: (866) 372-2930
E-mail: FacultyAwards@neh.gov
Web: www.neh.gov

Summary To provide funding for research to faculty at colleges and universities designated as Hispanic Serving Institutions (HSIs).

Eligibility This program is open to faculty members at HSIs who are interested in conducting research of value to humanities scholars, students, or general audiences. Eligible projects include conducting research in primary and secondary sources; producing articles, monographs, books, digital materials, archaeological site reports, translations, editions, or other scholarly resources; or conducting basic research leading to the improvement of an existing undergraduate course or the achievement or institutional or community research goals. Applicants must be U.S. citizens or foreign nationals who have lived in the United States for at least 3 years. They are not required to have advanced degrees, but individuals enrolled in a degree-granting program are ineligible.

Financial Data The grant is $4,200 per month, to a maximum of $50,400 for 12 months.

Duration 2 to 12 months.

Number awarded Approximately 2 each year.

Deadline April of each year.

[952]
BEHAVIORAL SCIENCES POSTDOCTORAL FELLOWSHIPS IN EPILEPSY

Epilepsy Foundation
Attn: Research Department
8301 Professional Place
Landover, MD 20785-2353
(301) 459-3700   Toll Free: (800) EFA-1000
Fax: (301) 577-2684   TDD: (800) 332-2070
E-mail: grants@efa.org
Web: www.epilepsyfoundation.org

Summary To provide funding to postdoctorates in the behavioral sciences (particularly Hispanic Americans, other minorities, women, and individuals with disabilities) who wish to pursue research training in an area related to epilepsy.

Eligibility Applicants must have received a Ph.D. or equivalent degree in a field of social science, including (but not limited to) sociology, social work, anthropology, nursing, or economics. They must be interested in receiving additional research training to prepare for a career in clinical behavioral aspects of epilepsy. Academic faculty holding the rank of instructor or above are not eligible, nor are graduate or medical students, medical residents, permanent government employees, or employees in private industry. Because these fellowships are designed as training opportunities, the quality of the training plans and environment are considered in the selection process. Other selection criteria include the scientific quality of the proposed research, a statement regarding the relevance of the research to epilepsy, the applicant's qualifications, the preceptor's qualifications, adequacy of the facility, and related epilepsy programs at the institution. Applications from women, members of minority groups, and people with disabilities are especially encouraged. U.S. citizenship is not required, but the research must be conducted in the United States.

Financial Data Grants up to $40,000 are available.

Duration 1 year.

Number awarded Varies each year.

Deadline March of each year.

[953]
BELFER CENTER FOR SCIENCE AND INTERNATIONAL AFFAIRS FELLOWSHIPS

Harvard University
John F. Kennedy School of Government
Belfer Center for Science and International Affairs
Attn: Fellowship Coordinator
79 John F. Kennedy Street, Mailbox 53
Cambridge, MA 02138
(617) 495-8806   Fax: (617) 495-8963
E-mail: bcsia_fellowships@hks.harvard.edu
Web: belfercenter.ksg.harvard.edu/fellowships

Summary To provide funding to professionals, postdoctorates, and doctoral students (particularly Hispanic Americans, other minorities, and women) who are interested in conducting research in areas of concern to the Belfer Center for Science and International Affairs at Harvard University in Cambridge, Massachusetts.

Eligibility The postdoctoral fellowship is open to recent recipients of the Ph.D. or equivalent degree, university faculty members, and employees of government, military, international, humanitarian, and private research institutions who have appropriate professional experience. Applicants for predoctoral fellowships must have passed their general examinations. Lawyers, economists, political scientists, those in the natural sciences, and others of diverse disciplinary backgrounds are also welcome to apply. The program especially encourages applications from women, minorities, and citizens of all countries. All applicants must be interested in conducting research in 1 of the 2 major program areas of the center: 1) the International Security Program (ISP), which addresses U.S. defense and foreign policy, security policy, nuclear proliferation, terrorism, internal and ethnic conflict, and related topics; and 2) the Science, Technology, and Public Policy Program (STPP), including technology and innovation, information and communications technology, water-energy nexus, managing the atom, energy technology innovation policy, China and environmental sustainability, geoengineering and climate policy, geopolitics of energy, and geospatial policy and management.

Financial Data The stipend is $34,000 for postdoctoral research fellows or $20,000 for predoctoral research fellows. Health insurance is also provided.

Duration 10 months.

Number awarded A limited number each year.

Deadline January of each year.

[954]
BIG DATA AND ANALYTICS FELLOWSHIPS OF THE AMERICAN ASSOCIATION FOR THE ADVANCEMENT OF SCIENCE

American Association for the Advancement of Science
Attn: Science and Technology Policy Fellowships
1200 New York Avenue, N.W.
Washington, DC 20005-3920
(202) 326-6700   Fax: (202) 289-4950
E-mail: fellowships@aaas.org
Web: www.fellowships.aaas.org

Summary   To provide postdoctoral scientists and engineers (particularly Hispanic Americans, other minorities, women, and individuals with disabilities) at all career stages with an opportunity to work at a federal agency on data and trend analysis issues.

Eligibility   This program is open to doctoral-level scientists (Ph.D., M.D., D.V.M., D.Sc., and other terminal degrees) in any field of science (behavioral, biological, computational, earth, health, medical, physical, or social), engineering, or mathematics. Engineers with a master's degree and at least 3 years of professional experience are also eligible. Applicants should be able to apply their analytical skills to data and trend analysis issues from infrastructure, technology, quality control, and presentation to security, integrity, and ethics. They must demonstrate solid scientific and technical credentials; a commitment to serve society; good communication skills; the ability to engage with non-scientific audiences; and an interest in working as special assistants for any federal agency in Washington, D.C. that partners with the sponsoring organization. U.S. citizenship is required; federal employees are not eligible. The sponsor seeks candidates from a broad array of backgrounds and a diversity of geographic, disciplinary, gender, and ethnic perspectives, as well as disability status.

Financial Data   The stipend for fellows with 0 to 7 years of postdoctoral experience is $74,872 in the first year and $77,368 in the second year. For fellows with 7 to 15 years of experience, the stipend is $84,855 in the first year and $87,350 in the second year. Fellows who have 15 or more years of postdoctoral experience receive $97,333 in the first year and $99,829 in the second year. Also provided are a $4,000 relocation allowance for fellows from outside the Washington, D.C. area, reimbursement for health insurance, and a $4,000 travel allowance.

Duration   1 year, beginning in September; may be renewed for 1 additional year.

Additional data   This program began in 2014.

Number awarded   5 to 15 each year.

Deadline   October of each year.

[955]
BIOMEDICAL RESEARCH TRAINING PROGRAM FOR UNDERREPRESENTED GROUPS

National Heart, Lung, and Blood Institute
Attn: Office of Training and Minority Health
6701 Rockledge Drive, Suite 9180
Bethesda, MD 20892-7913
(301) 451-5081   Toll Free: (301) 451-0088
Fax: (301) 480-0862   E-mail: mishoeh@nhlbi.nih.gov
Web: www.nhlbi.nih.gov

Summary   To provide training in fundamental biomedical sciences and clinical research disciplines to postbaccalaureate students from underrepresented groups (particularly Hispanic Americans, other underrepresented minorities, and individuals with disabilities).

Eligibility   This program is open to members of underrepresented groups who are interested in receiving training in fundamental biomedical sciences and clinical research disciplines of interest to the National Heart, Lung, and Blood Institute (NHLBI) of the National Institutes of Health (NIH). Underrepresented individuals include African Americans, Hispanic Americans, American Indians, Alaskan Natives, Native Hawaiians and Pacific Islanders, individuals with disabilities, and individuals from disadvantaged backgrounds. Applicants must be U.S. citizens or permanent residents who have recently completed or will complete a bachelor's degree by the summer of selection with course work relevant to biomedical, behavioral, or statistical research. They must have a GPA of 3.3 or higher. Research experiences are available in the NHLBI Division of Intramural Research and its Division of Cardiovascular Sciences.

Financial Data   Stipends in the first year of work are $27,200 for participants with 0 to 1 year of experience or $29,100 for those with 1 to 2 years of experience. In the second year of work, stipends are $29,100 for those who begin with 0 to 1 year of experience or $30,400 for those with 1 to 2 years of experience.

Duration   1 to 2 years, beginning from June to September of the selection year.

Additional data   Training is conducted in the laboratories of the NHLBI in Bethesda, Maryland. Activities in the Division of Intramural Research include clinical research training in the hematology branch and the cardio-pulmonary branch; basic science research training is provided by its centers for genetics and developmental biology, immunology, molecular medicine, systems biology, cell biology and physiology, and biochemistry and biophysics. The Division of Cardiovascular Sciences provides training in the basic principles of design, implementation, and analysis of epidemiology studies and clinical trials. Upon completion of this training, participants are expected to apply to graduate or professional school.

Number awarded   Varies each year.

Deadline   January of each year.

[956]
BRANDON FRADD FELLOWSHIP IN MUSIC COMPOSITION

Cintas Foundation, Inc.
c/o Jessica Brodsky, Cintas Fellows Collection
Miami Dade College
300 N.E. Second Avenue
Miami, FL 33132-2204
(305) 237-7722   Fax: (305) 237-7711
E-mail: jbrodsky@mdc.edu
Web: www.cintasfoundation.org/fellowships_music.htm

Summary   To provide funding for creative activities in composing to Cubans who are living outside of Cuba.

Eligibility   This program is open to composers of Cuban citizenship or lineage (having a Cuban parent or grandparent) but living in the United States or any other country except Cuba. Applicants must be interested in completing a project in the field of musical composition. Submissions should include from 3 to 5 recordings, of which 2 should be of recent works. Scores must accompany the recordings. They must include 2 narrative statements in English or Spanish: 1) a record of their personal history, their development as an artist, and their plans for the future; and 2) a description of the project or activity that they would undertake if awarded a fellowship. Fellowships are not awarded for academic study, research, or writing; performing artists are not eligible.

Financial Data   Grants are $10,000.

Duration   1 year.

Number awarded   1 each year.

Deadline   July of each year.

[957]
BROADENING PARTICIPATION RESEARCH INITIATION GRANTS IN ENGINEERING (BRIGE)

National Science Foundation
Directorate for Engineering
Attn: Engineering Education and Centers
4201 Wilson Boulevard, Room 585N
Arlington, VA 22230
(703) 292-8071   Fax: (703) 292-9085
TDD: (800) 281-8749   E-mail: rnsmith@nsf.gov
Web: www.nsf.gov

Summary   To provide funding to Hispanic Americans and members of other underrepresented groups who are junior faculty members interested in conducting research in engineering.

Eligibility   This program is open to U.S. citizens or permanent residents who are members of groups underrepresented in engineering: women, persons with disabilities, African Americans, Hispanics, Native Americans, Alaska Natives, and Pacific Islanders. Applicants must have held a full-time tenure-track faculty position for no more than 3 years. They must be interested in conducting engineering research that is innovative and potentially transformative. Faculty at Minority Serving Institutions (Historically Black Colleges and Universities, Hispanic Serving Institutions, Tribal Colleges and Universities, and Predominantly Black Institutions) are also encouraged to apply.

Financial Data   The maximum grant is $175,000 in direct and indirect costs for up to 24 months.

Duration   Up to 2 years.

Number awarded   25 to 30 each year.

Deadline   April of each year.

[958]
BURROUGHS WELLCOME FUND CAREER AWARDS FOR MEDICAL SCIENTISTS

Burroughs Wellcome Fund
21 T.W. Alexander Drive, Suite 100
P.O. Box 13901
Research Triangle Park, NC 27709-3901
(919) 991-5100   Fax: (919) 991-5160
E-mail: info@bwfund.org
Web: www.bwfund.org

Summary   To provide funding to biomedical scientists in the United States and Canada (particularly Hispanic Americans, other underrepresented minorities, and women) who require assistance to make the transition from postdoctoral training to faculty appointment.

Eligibility   This program is open to citizens and permanent residents of the United States and Canada who have an M.D., D.D.S., or D.V.M. degree and from 2 to 10 years of postdoctoral research experience. Candidates who work in reproductive science are encouraged to apply. Applicants must be interested in a program of research training in the area of basic biomedical, disease-oriented, or translational research. Training must take place at a degree-granting medical school, graduate school, hospital, or research institute in the United States or Canada. Each U.S. and Canadian institution may nominate up to 5 candidates. The sponsor encourages institutions to nominate women and underrepresented minorities (African Americans, Hispanics, or Native Americans); if a woman or underrepresented minority is among the initial 5 candidates, the institution may nominate a sixth candidate who is a woman or underrepresented minority.

Financial Data   The stipend is $140,000 per year.

Duration   5 years.

Additional data   This program began in 1995 as Career Awards in the Biomedical Sciences (CABS). It was revised to its current format in 2006 as a result of the NIH K99/R00 Pathway to Independence program. As the CABS, the program provided more than $100 million in support to 241 U.S. and Canadian scientists. Awardees are required to devote at least 75% of their time to research-related activities.

Number awarded   Varies each year: recently, 10 of these awards were granted.

Deadline   September of each year.

[959]
BYRD FELLOWSHIP PROGRAM

Ohio State University
Byrd Polar Research Center
Attn: Fellowship Committee
Scott Hall Room 108
1090 Carmack Road
Columbus, OH 43210-1002
(614) 292-6531   Fax: (614) 292-4697
Web: bprc.osu.edu/byrdfellow

Summary   To provide funding to postdoctorates (particularly Hispanic Americans, other minorities, women, individuals with disabilities, and those with ties to the military) who are interested in conducting research on the Arctic or Antarctic areas at Ohio State University.

Eligibility   This program is open to postdoctorates of superior academic background who are interested in conducting advanced research on either Arctic or Antarctic problems at the Byrd Polar Research Center at Ohio State University. Applicants must have received their doctorates within the past 5 years. Along with their application, they must submit a description of the specific research to be conducted during the fellowship and a curriculum vitae. Women, minorities, Vietnam-era veterans, disabled veterans, and individuals with disabilities are particularly encouraged to apply.

Financial Data   The stipend is $42,000 per year; an allowance of $5,000 for research and travel is also provided.

Duration   18 months.

Additional data   This program was established by a major gift from the Byrd Foundation in memory of Rear Admiral Richard Evelyn Byrd and Marie Ames Byrd, his wife. Except for field work or other research activities requiring absence from campus, fellows are expected to be in residence at the university for the duration of the program.

Deadline March of each year.

[960]
CAREER DEVELOPMENT AWARDS IN DIABETES RESEARCH

Juvenile Diabetes Research Foundation International
Attn: Grant Administrator
26 Broadway, 14th Floor
New York, NY 10004
(212) 479-7572   Toll Free: (800) 533-CURE
Fax: (212) 785-9595   E-mail: info@jdrf.org
Web: jdrf.org

Summary To assist young scientists (particularly Hispanic Americans, other underrepresented minorities, individuals with disabilities, and women) to develop into independent investigators in diabetes-related research.

Eligibility This program is open to postdoctorates early in their faculty careers who show promise as diabetes researchers. Applicants must have received their first doctoral (M.D., Ph.D., D.M.D., D.V.M., or equivalent) degree at least 3 but not more than 7 years previously. They may not have an academic position at the associate professor, professor, or equivalent level, but they must be a faculty member (instructor or assistant professor) at a university, health science center, or comparable institution with strong, well-established research and training programs. The proposed research must relate to Type 1 diabetes, but it may be basic or clinical. There are no citizenship requirements. Applications are encouraged from women, members of minority groups underrepresented in the sciences, and people with disabilities. The proposed research may be conducted at foreign or domestic, for-profit or non-profit, or public or private institutions, including universities, colleges, hospitals, laboratories, units of state or local government, or eligible agencies of the federal government. Selection is based on the applicant's perceived ability and potential for a career in Type 1 diabetes research, the caliber of the proposed research, and the quality and commitment of the host institution.

Financial Data The total award may be up to $150,000 each year. Indirect costs cannot exceed 10%.

Duration Up to 5 years.

Additional data Fellows must spend up to 75% of their time in research.

Number awarded Varies each year.

Deadline August of each year.

[961]
CARLOS M. CASTANEDA JOURNALISM SCHOLARSHIP

Carlos M. Castañeda Educational Foundation
Attn: FECMC Journalism Scholarship
1925 Brickell Avenue, Suite D-1108
Miami, FL 33129
(305) 859-9617
E-mail: fundacion_educativa_cmc@yahoo.com
Web: fecmc.tripod.com

Summary To provide financial assistance to Spanish-speaking graduate students and journalists working on a master's degree in journalism.

Eligibility This program is open to Spanish-speaking students and journalists from any country (including the United States) who have been accepted into a graduate program in journalism at a university in the United States. Applicants must have completed a 4-year undergraduate degree with a GPA of 3.0 or higher. They are not required to have majored in journalism as an undergraduate, but their curriculum must have included courses in history and liberal arts. A knowledge of and interest in Hispanic culture and an awareness of current events in Latin America are also required. Along with their application, they must submit a curriculum vitae, a cover letter, 3 reference letters, a portfolio with 3 stories published by professional or school publications in Spanish, and a 2,000-word essay (in Spanish) on the work of Carlos M. Castañeda as a champion of freedom of the press and human rights. Financial need is considered in the selection process.

Financial Data The stipend is $7,000.

Duration 1 year; may be renewed 1 additional year if the recipient maintains a GPA of 3.0 or higher.

Additional data This program began in 2005.

Number awarded 1 or more each year.

Deadline April of each year.

[962]
CAROLINE CRAIG AUGUSTYN AND DAMIAN AUGUSTYN AWARD IN DIGESTIVE CANCER

American Gastroenterological Association
Attn: AGA Research Foundation
Research Awards Manager
4930 Del Ray Avenue
Bethesda, MD 20814-2512
(301) 222-4012   Fax: (301) 654-5920
E-mail: awards@gastro.org
Web: www.gastro.org/aga-foundation/grants

Summary To provide funding to junior investigators (particularly Hispanic Americans, other minorities, and individuals with disabilities) who are interested in conducting research related to digestive cancer.

Eligibility Applicants must have an M.D., Ph.D., or equivalent degree and a full-time faculty position at an accredited North American institution. They must have received an NIH K series or other federal or non-federal career development award of at least 4 years duration, but may not have received an R01 or equivalent award. For M.D. applicants, no more than 7 years may have elapsed following the completion of clinical training, and for Ph.D. applicants no more than 7 years may have elapsed since the completion of their degree. Individual membership in the American Gastroenterology Association (AGA) is required. The proposal must relate to the pathogenesis, prevention, diagnosis, or treatment of digestive cancer. Women and minority investigators are strongly encouraged to apply. Selection is based on the qualifications of the candidate and the novelty, feasibility, and significance of their research.

Financial Data The grant is $40,000. Funds may be used for salary, supplies, or equipment. Indirect costs are not allowed.

Duration 1 year.

Number awarded 1 each year.

Deadline January of each year.

[963]
CENTER FOR ADVANCED STUDY IN THE BEHAVIORAL SCIENCES RESIDENTIAL POSTDOCTORAL FELLOWSHIPS

Center for Advanced Study in the Behavioral Sciences
Attn: Secretary and Program Coordinator
75 Alta Road
Stanford, CA 94305-8090
(650) 736-0100   Fax: (650) 736-0221
E-mail: casbs-secretary@casbs.org
Web: www.casbs.org

Summary   To provide funding to behavioral scientists (particularly Hispanic Americans, other minorities, women, and younger scholars) who are interested in conducting research at the Center for Advanced Study in the Behavioral Sciences in Stanford, California.

Eligibility   Eligible to be nominated for this fellowship are scientists and scholars from this country or abroad who show exceptional accomplishment or promise in the core social and behavioral disciplines: anthropology, economics, political science, psychology, or sociology; applications are also accepted from scholars in a wide range of humanistic disciplines, education, linguistics, and the biological sciences. Selection is based on standing in the field rather than on the merit of a particular project under way at a given time. A special effort is made to promote diversity among the scholars by encouraging participation from groups that often have been overlooked in academia: younger scholars, women, minorities, international scholars, and scholars whose home universities are not research-oriented.

Financial Data   The stipend is based on the fellow's regular salary for the preceding year, with a cap of $65,000. In most cases, the fellow contributes to the cost of the stipend with support from sabbatical or other funding source.

Duration   From 9 to 11 months.

Additional data   Fellows must be in residence in a community within 10 miles of the center for the duration of the program (that requirement excludes San Francisco, Berkeley, and San Jose, for example).

Number awarded   Approximately 45 each year.

Deadline   September of each year.

[964]
CHARLES L. BREWER DISTINGUISHED TEACHING OF PSYCHOLOGY AWARD

American Psychological Foundation
750 First Street, N.E.
Washington, DC 20002-4242
(202) 336-5843   Fax: (202) 336-5812
E-mail: foundation@apa.org
Web: www.apa.org/apf/funding/brewer.aspx

Summary   To recognize and reward the distinguished career contributions of outstanding psychology professors, particularly those who are Hispanic Americans, other minorities, women, or individuals with disabilities.

Eligibility   This award is available to psychologists who demonstrate outstanding teaching. Selection is based on evidence of influence as a teacher of students who become psychologists, research on teaching, development of effective teaching methods and/or materials, development of innovation curricula and courses, performance as a classroom teacher, demonstrated training of teachers of psychology, teaching of advanced research methods and practice in psychology, and/or administrative facilitation of teaching. Nominators must complete an application form, write a letter of support, and submit the nominee's current vitae and bibliography. The sponsor encourages nominations of individuals who represent diversity in race, ethnicity, gender, age, disability, and sexual orientation.

Financial Data   Awardees receive a plaque, a $2,000 honorarium, and an all-expense paid trip to the annual convention where the award is presented.

Duration   The award is presented annually.

Additional data   This award, originally named the Distinguished Teaching in Psychology Award, was first presented in 1970.

Number awarded   1 each year.

Deadline   Nominations must be submitted by November of each year.

[965]
CHICANO STUDIES VISITING SCHOLAR AND VISITING RESEARCHER PROGRAM

University of California at Los Angeles
Institute of American Cultures
Attn: Chicano Studies Research Center
193 Haines Hall
P.O. Box 951544
Los Angeles, CA 90095-1544
(310) 825-2363   E-mail: jiribarren@chicano.ucla.edu
Web: www.iac.ucla.edu/fellowships_visitingscholar.html

Summary   To provide funding to scholars interested in conducting research in Chicano studies at UCLA's Chicano Studies Research Center.

Eligibility   Applicants must have completed a doctoral degree in Chicano or related studies. They must be interested in teaching or conducting research at UCLA's Chicano Studies Research Center. Visiting Scholar appointments are available to people who currently hold permanent academic appointments; Visiting Researcher appointments are available to postdoctorates who recently received their degree. UCLA faculty, students, and staff are not eligible. U.S. citizenship or permanent resident status is required.

Financial Data   Fellows receive a stipend of $32,000 to $35,000 (depending on rank, experience, and date of completion of the Ph.D.), health benefits, and up to $4,000 in research support. Visiting Scholars are paid through their home institution; Visiting Researchers receive their funds directly from UCLA.

Duration   9 months, beginning in October.

Additional data   Fellows must teach or do research in the programs of the center. The award is offered in conjunction with UCLA's Institute of American Cultures (IAC).

Number awarded   1 each year.

Deadline   February of each year.

[966]
CLINICAL RESEARCH POST-DOCTORAL FELLOWSHIP PROGRAM

American Nurses Association
Attn: SAMHSA Minority Fellowship Programs
8515 Georgia Avenue, Suite 400
Silver Spring, MD 20910-3492
(301) 628-5247   Toll Free: (800) 274-4ANA
Fax: (301) 628-5339   E-mail: janet.jackson@ana.org
Web: www.emfp.org

Summary To provide funding to Hispanic American and other minority postdoctoral nurses who are interested in a program of research and study on psychiatric, mental health, and substance abuse issues that impact the lives of ethnic minority people.

Eligibility This program is open to doctoral-prepared nurses who are members of an ethnic or racial minority group, including but not limited to Blacks or African Americans, Hispanics or Latinos, American Indians and Alaska Natives, Asian Americans, and Native Hawaiians and other Pacific Islanders. Applicants must be able to demonstrate a commitment to a research career in nursing and psychiatric/ mental health issues affecting ethnic minority populations. They must be interested in a program of full-time postdoctoral study, with a research focus on such issues of concern to minority populations as substance abuse treatment capacity, mental health system transformation, prevention, co-occurring disorders, seclusion and restraint, children and families, disaster readiness and response, homelessness, older adults, HIV/AIDS and hepatitis, and criminal and juvenile justice. U.S. citizenship or permanent resident status and membership in the American Nurses Association are required.

Financial Data The stipend depends on the number of years of postdoctoral experience, ranging from $39,264 for less than 1 year to $54,180 for 7 or more years.

Duration 1 to 2 years.

Additional data Funds for this program are provided by the Substance Abuse and Mental Health Services Administration (SAMHSA).

Number awarded 1 or more each year.

Deadline February of each year.

[967]
CLINICAL RESEARCH PRE-DOCTORAL FELLOWSHIP PROGRAM

American Nurses Association
Attn: SAMHSA Minority Fellowship Programs
8515 Georgia Avenue, Suite 400
Silver Spring, MD 20910-3492
(301) 628-5247   Toll Free: (800) 274-4ANA
Fax: (301) 628-5339   E-mail: janet.jackson@ana.org
Web: www.emfp.org

Summary To provide financial assistance to Hispanic American and other minority nurses who are doctoral candidates interested in psychiatric, mental health, and substance abuse issues that impact the lives of ethnic minority people.

Eligibility This program is open to nurses who have a master's degree and are members of an ethnic or racial minority group, including but not limited to Blacks or African Americans, Hispanics or Latinos, American Indians and Alaska Natives, Asian Americans, and Native Hawaiians and other Pacific Islanders. Applicants must be able to demonstrate a commitment to a research career in nursing and psychiatric/ mental health issues affecting ethnic minority populations. They must be interested in a program of full-time doctoral study, with a research focus on such issues of concern to minority populations as child abuse, violence in intimate relationships, mental health disorders, substance abuse, mental health service utilization, and stigma as a barrier to mental health care and personal resilience. U.S. citizenship or permanent resident status and membership in the American Nurses Association are required. Selection is based on research potential, scholarship, writing ability, knowledge of broad issues in mental health nursing, and professional commitment to ethnic minority concerns.

Financial Data The program provides an annual stipend of $22,032 and tuition assistance.

Duration 3 to 5 years.

Additional data Funds for this program are provided by the Substance Abuse and Mental Health Services Administration (SAMHSA).

Number awarded 1 or more each year.

Deadline February of each year.

[968]
CMS HISPANIC HEALTH SERVICES RESEARCH GRANT PROGRAM

Centers for Medicare & Medicaid Services
Attn: Center for Medicare and Medicaid Innovation
Mail Stop WB-06-05
7500 Security Boulevard
Baltimore, MD 21244-1850
(410) 786-7250   Toll Free: (877) 267-2323
TDD: (877) 486-2048   E-mail: Richard.bragg@cms.hhs. gov
Web: www.cms.gov

Summary To provide funding to scholars at Hispanic Serving Institutions (HSIs) who are interested in carrying out health services research activities.

Eligibility This program is open to scholars at an HSI that meets 1 of the following requirements: 1) offers a Ph.D. or master's degree in 1 or more of the following disciplines: allied health, gerontology, health care administration, nursing, pharmacology, public health, or social work; 2) is a member of a community-based health association with a Hispanic health services research component; or 3) is a member of a professional association focusing on Hispanic health services and health disparities issues. Applicants must be interested in conducting small research projects that address health care issues such as financing, delivery, access, quality, and barriers affecting the Hispanic community.

Financial Data Grants range up to $100,000 per year.

Duration Up to 2 years.

Additional data This program began in 1999. Until 2001, the Centers for Medicare & Medicaid Services was known as the Health Care Financing Administration.

Number awarded Varies each year; recently, 1 of these grants was available.

Deadline Letters of intent must be submitted by June of each year. Final applications are due in July.

[969]
CONGRESSIONAL HISPANIC CAUCUS INSTITUTE GRADUATE FELLOWSHIPS

Congressional Hispanic Caucus Institute, Inc.
911 Second Street, N.E.
Washington, DC 20002
(202) 543-1771   Toll Free: (800) EXCEL-DC
Fax: (202) 546-2143   E-mail: chci@chci.org
Web: www.chci.org/fellowships

Summary   To provide a fellowship to Latinos who recently completed a graduate degree in specified fields and are interested in applying their academic expertise in Washington, D.C.

Eligibility   This program is open to U.S. citizens and permanent residents of Latino background who completed a master's degree or higher within the past 3 years. Applicants must be interested in gaining experience in the following areas: higher education, secondary education, health, housing, law, or STEM (science, technology, engineering, and mathematics). They must be able to demonstrate high academic achievement (GPA of 3.0 or higher), evidence of leadership skills, potential for leadership growth, commitment to public service-oriented activities, and superior analytical and communication skills (oral and written).

Financial Data   This program provides transportation to and from Washington, D.C., a monthly stipend of $2,900, and health insurance.

Duration   9 months, beginning in late August.

Additional data   Placements are available in Congressional offices or committees and federal agencies. Fellows select the placement that best matches their interests.

Number awarded   6 each year: 1 in each of the program's areas.

Deadline   February of each year.

[970]
CONGRESSIONAL HISPANIC CAUCUS INSTITUTE PUBLIC POLICY FELLOWSHIP

Congressional Hispanic Caucus Institute, Inc.
911 Second Street, N.E.
Washington, DC 20002
(202) 543-1771   Toll Free: (800) EXCEL-DC
Fax: (202) 546-2143   E-mail: chci@chci.org
Web: www.chci.org/fellowships

Summary   To provide Latino recent college graduates with a fellowship that will allow them to apply their academic expertise in the area of public policy in Washington, D.C.

Eligibility   This program is open to U.S. citizens and permanent residents of Latino background who earned a bachelor's degree within the past 2 years and have not received credit towards an advanced degree. Applicants must be interested in gaining experience in the area of public policy. They must be able to demonstrate high academic achievement (preference is given to those with a GPA of 3.0 or higher), evidence of leadership skills, potential for leadership growth, and superior analytical and communication skills (oral and written).

Financial Data   This fellowship provides transportation to and from Washington, D.C., a monthly stipend of $2,400, and health insurance.

Duration   9 months, beginning in late August.

Additional data   Placements are available in Congressional offices and federal agencies, advocacy groups, media groups, and a broad range of policy-related organizations. Fellows select the placement that best matches their interests.

Number awarded   Up to 20 each year.

Deadline   February of each year.

[971]
CTA/MARTIN LUTHER KING, JR. MEMORIAL SCHOLARSHIP FUND

California Teachers Association
Attn: CTA Foundation for Teaching and Learning
1705 Murchison Drive
P.O. Box 921
Burlingame, CA 94011-0921
(650) 697-1400   E-mail: scholarships@cta.org
Web: www.cta.org

Summary   To provide financial assistance for college or graduate school to Hispanic Americans and other racial and ethnic minorities who are members of the California Teachers Association (CTA), children of members, or members of the Student CTA.

Eligibility   This program is open to members of racial or ethnic minority groups (African Americans, American Indians/Alaska Natives, Asians/Pacific Islanders, and Hispanics) who are 1) active CTA members; 2) dependent children of active, retired, or deceased CTA members; or 3) members of Student CTA. Applicants must be interested in preparing for a teaching career in public education or already engaged in such a career.

Financial Data   Stipends vary each year; recently, they ranged from $1,000 to $4,000.

Duration   1 year.

Number awarded   Varies each year; recently, 25 of these scholarships were awarded: 5 to CTA members, 10 to children of CTA members, and 10 to Student CTA members.

Deadline   February of each year.

[972]
DANIEL H. EFRON RESEARCH AWARD

American College of Neuropsychopharmacology
Attn: Executive Office
5034-A Thoroughbred Lane
Brentwood, TN 37027
(615) 324-2360   Fax: (615) 523-1715
E-mail: acnp@acnp.org
Web: www.acnp.org/programs/awards.aspx

Summary   To recognize and reward young scientists (particularly Hispanic Americans, other minorities, and women) who have completed outstanding basic or translational research to neuropsychopharmacology.

Eligibility   This award is available to scientists who are younger than 50 years of age. Nominees must have made an outstanding basic or translational contribution to neuropsychopharmacology. The contribution may be preclinical or work that emphasizes the relationship between basic and clinical research. Selection is based on the quality of the contribution and its impact on advancing neuropsychopharmacology. Membership in the American College of Neuropsychopharmacology (ACNP) is not required. Nomination of women and minorities is highly encouraged.

Financial Data The award consists of an expense-paid trip to the ACNP annual meeting, a monetary honorarium, and a plaque.

Duration The award is presented annually.

Additional data This award was first presented in 1974.

Number awarded 1 each year.

Deadline Nominations must be submitted by June of each year.

[973]
DEPARTMENT OF DEFENSE SMALL BUSINESS INNOVATION RESEARCH GRANTS

Department of Defense
Attn: Office of Small Business Programs
4800 Mark Center Drive, Suite 15G13
Alexandria, VA 22530
Toll Free: (866) SBIR-HLP
E-mail: administrator.dodsbir@osd.mil
Web: www.acq.osd.mil/osbp/sbir

Summary To support small businesses (especially those owned by Hispanic Americans, other minorities, or women) that have the technological expertise to contribute to the research and development mission of various agencies within the Department of Defense.

Eligibility For the purposes of this program, a "small business" is defined as a firm that is organized for profit with a location in the United States; is in the legal form of an individual proprietorship, partnership, limited liability company, corporation, joint venture, association, trust, or cooperative; is at least 51% owned and controlled by 1 or more individuals who are citizens or permanent residents of the United States; and has (including its affiliates) fewer than 500 employees. The primary employment of the principal investigator must be with the firm at the time of award and during the conduct of the proposed project. Applications are encouraged from 1) women-owned small business concerns, defined as those that are at least 51% owned by a woman or women who also control and operate them; and 2) socially and economically disadvantaged small business concerns that are at least 51% owned by an Indian tribe, a Native Hawaiian organization, or 1 or more socially and economically disadvantaged individuals (African Americans, Hispanic Americans, Native Americans, Asian Pacific Americans, or subcontinent Asian Americans). Agencies that offer Department of Defense Small Business Innovation Research (SBIR) programs are the Department of the Army, Department of the Navy, Department of the Air Force, Defense Advanced Research Projects Agency (DARPA), Defense Threat Reduction Agency (DTRA), Chemical and Biological Defense (CBD), Defense Health Program (DHP), Defense Logistics Agency (DLA), Special Operations Command (SOCOM), Missile Defense Agency (MDA), National Geospatial-Intelligence Agency (NGA), Defense Microelectronics Activity (DMEA), and Office of Secretary of Defense (OSD). Selection is based on the soundness, technical merit, and innovation of the proposed approach and its incremental progress toward topic or sub-topic solution; the qualifications of the principal investigator, supporting staff, and consultants; and the potential for commercial application and the benefits expected to accrue from this commercialization.

Financial Data Grants are offered in 2 phases. In phase 1, awards normally range from $70,000 to $150,000 (for both direct and indirect costs); in phase 2, awards normally range from $500,000 to $1,000,000 (including both direct and indirect costs).

Duration Phase 1 awards may extend up to 6 months; phase 2 awards may extend up to 2 years.

Number awarded Varies each year; recently, 1,816 Phase 1 awards were granted: 582 for Department of the Navy, 295 for Department of the Army, 480 for Department of the Air Force, 68 for DARPA, 17 for DTRA, 16 for CBD, 16 for SOCOM, 122 for MDA, 7 for DLA, 40 for DHP, 4 for NGA, and 160 for OSD. The number of Phase 2 awards was 938, including 321 for Department of the Navy, 190 for Department of the Army, 207 for Department of the Air Force, 60 for DARPA, 4 for DTRA, 12 for CBD, 8 for SOCOM, 67 for MDA, 2 for DLA, 1 for DMEA, 27 for DHP, and 39 for OSD. Total funding was approximately $1.04 billion.

Deadline September of each year.

[974]
DEPARTMENT OF DEFENSE SMALL BUSINESS TECHNOLOGY TRANSFER GRANTS

Department of Defense
Attn: Office of Small Business Programs
4800 Mark Center Drive, Suite 15G13
Alexandria, VA 22530
Toll Free: (866) SBIR-HLP
E-mail: administrator.dodsbir@osd.mil
Web: www.acq.osd.mil/osbp/sblr

Summary To provide financial support to cooperative research and development projects carried out between small business concerns (particularly those owned by Hispanic Americans, other minorities, or women) and research institutions in areas of interest to various agencies within the Department of Defense.

Eligibility For the purposes of this program, a "small business" is defined as a firm that is organized for profit with a location in the United States; is in the legal form of an individual proprietorship, partnership, limited liability company, corporation, joint venture, association, trust, or cooperative; is at least 51% owned and controlled by 1 or more individuals who are citizens or permanent residents of the United States; and has (including its affiliates) fewer than 500 employees. Unlike the Department of Defense Small Business Innovation Research Grants, the primary employment of the principal investigator does not need to be with the business concern. This program, however, requires that the small business apply in collaboration with a nonprofit research institution for conduct of a project that has potential for commercialization. At least 40% of the work must be performed by the small business and at least 30% of the work must be performed by the research institution. Principal investigators from the nonprofit research institution must commit at least 10% of their effort to the project. Applications are encouraged from 1) women-owned small business concerns, defined as those that are at least 51% owned by a woman or women who also control and operate them; and 2) socially and economically disadvantaged small business concerns that are at least 51% owned by an Indian tribe, a Native Hawaiian organization, or 1 or more socially and economically disadvantaged individuals (African Americans, Hispanic Americans, Native Americans,

Asian Pacific Americans, or subcontinent Asian Americans). Partnerships between small businesses and Historically Black Colleges and Universities (HBCUs) and Minority Institutions (MIs) are especially encouraged. Agencies of the Department of Defense currently participating in this program are the Department of the Army, Department of the Navy, Department of the Air Force, Defense Advanced Research Projects Agency (DARPA), Missile Defense Agency (MDA), and Office of Secretary of Defense (OSD). Selection is based on the soundness, technical merit, and innovation of the proposed approach and its incremental progress toward topic or subtopic solution; the qualifications of the proposed principal investigators, supporting staff, and consultants; and the potential for commercial application and the benefits expected to accrue from this commercialization.

Financial Data   In the first phase, annual awards range from $70,000 to $150,000 for direct costs, indirect costs, and negotiated fixed fees. In the second phase, awards from $500,000 to $1,000,000 for the full period are available.

Duration   Generally 1 year for the first phase and 2 years for the second phase.

Additional data   Grants in the first phase are to determine the scientific, technical, and commercial merit and feasibility of the proposed cooperative effort and the quality of performance of the small business concern. In the second phase, the research and development efforts continue, depending on the results of the first phase.

Number awarded   Varies each year; recently, 309 Phase 1 awards were granted: 63 for Department of the Army, 117 for Department of the Navy, 87 for Department of the Air Force, 23 for OSD, and 19 for MDA. The number of Phase 2 awards was 127, including 31 for Department of the Army, 54 for Department of the Navy, 28 for Department of the Air Force, 5 for DARPA, 3 for OSD, and 6 for MDA. Total funding was approximately $117 million.

Deadline   April of each year.

[975]
DEPARTMENT OF EDUCATION SMALL BUSINESS INNOVATION RESEARCH GRANTS

Department of Education
Attn: Institute of Education Sciences
555 New Jersey Avenue, N.W., Room 608D
Washington, DC 20208-5544
(202) 208-1983   Fax: (202) 219-2030
E-mail: Edward.metz@ed.gov
Web: www2.ed.gov/programs/sbir/index.html

Summary   To support small businesses (especially those owned by Hispanic Americans, other minorities, or women) that have the technological expertise to contribute to the research and development mission of the Department of Education.

Eligibility   For the purposes of this program, a "small business" is defined as a firm that is organized for profit with a location in the United States; is in the legal form of an individual proprietorship, partnership, limited liability company, corporation, joint venture, association, trust, or cooperative; is at least 51% owned and controlled by 1 or more individuals who are citizens or permanent residents of the United States; and has (including its affiliates) fewer than 500 employees. The primary employment of the principal investigator must be with the firm at the time of award and during the conduct of the

proposed project. Applications are encouraged from 1) women-owned small business concerns, defined as those that are at least 51% owned by a woman or women who also control and operate them; and 2) socially and economically disadvantaged small business concerns that are at least 51% owned by an Indian tribe, a Native Hawaiian organization, or 1 or more socially and economically disadvantaged individuals (African Americans, Hispanic Americans, Native Americans, Asian Pacific Americans, or subcontinent Asian Americans). Firms with strong research capabilities in science, engineering, or educational technology in any of the topic areas are encouraged to participate. Recently, the program operated in 2 branches of the Department of Education: 1) the National Institute on Disability and Rehabilitations Research (NIDRR) within the Office of Special Education and Rehabilitative Services (OSERS); and 2) the Institute of Education Sciences (IES), formerly the Office of Educational Research and Improvement (OERI). Selection is based on quality of project design (45 points), significance (25 points), quality of project personnel (20 points), and adequacy of resources (10 points).

Financial Data   Grants are offered in 2 phases. Phase 1 awards normally do not exceed $150,000; phase 2 awards normally do not exceed $750,000 for IES programs or $500,000 for OSERS/NIDRR programs.

Duration   Phase 1 awards may extend up to 6 months; phase 2 awards may extend up to 2 years.

Additional data   Information on the NIDRR program is available from the Office of Special Education and Rehabilitative Services, Potomac Center Plaza, 550 12th Street, Room 5140, Washington, DC 20202-2700, (202) 245-7338, E-mail: Lynn.Medley@ed.gov.

Number awarded   Varies each year; recently, 25 Phase 1 awards (9 for IES and 16 for NIDRR) and 21 Phase 1 awards (16 for IES and 5 for NIDRR) were granted.

Deadline   February of each year for IES proposals; June of each year for NIDRR proposals.

[976]
DEPARTMENT OF HOMELAND SECURITY SMALL BUSINESS INNOVATION RESEARCH GRANTS

Department of Homeland Security
Homeland Security Advanced Research Projects Agency
Attn: SBIR Program Manager
Washington, DC 20528
(202) 254-6768   Toll Free: (800) 754-3043
Fax: (202) 254-7170   E-mail: elissa.sobolewski@dhs.gov
Web: www.dhs.gov/files/grants/gc_1247254058883.shtm

Summary   To support small businesses (especially those owned by Hispanic Americans, other minorities, disabled veterans, or women) that have the technological expertise to contribute to the research and development mission of the Department of Homeland Security (DHS).

Eligibility   For the purposes of this program, a "small business" is defined as a firm that is organized for profit with a location in the United States; is in the legal form of an individual proprietorship, partnership, limited liability company, corporation, joint venture, association, trust, or cooperative; is at least 51% owned and controlled by 1 or more individuals who are citizens or permanent residents of the United States; and has (including its affiliates) fewer than 500 employees. The primary employment of the principal investigator must be with the firm at the time of award and during the conduct of the proposed project. Applications are encouraged from 1) women-owned small business concerns, defined as those that are at least 51% owned by a woman or women who also control and operate them; 2) socially and economically disadvantaged small business concerns that are at least 51% owned by an Indian tribe, a Native Hawaiian organization, or 1 or more socially and economically disadvantaged individuals (African Americans, Hispanic Americans, Native Americans, Asian Pacific Americans, or subcontinent Asian Americans); and 3) service-disabled veteran small business concerns that are at least 51% owned by a service-disabled veteran and controlled by such a veteran or (for veterans with permanent and severe disability) the spouse or permanent caregiver of such a veteran. Each year, DHS identifies specialized topics for investigation. Selection is based on the soundness, technical merit, and innovation of the proposed approach and its incremental progress toward topic or subtopic solution; the qualifications of the proposed principal investigators, supporting staff, and consultants; the potential for commercial application and the benefits expected to accrue from this commercialization; and the realism and reasonableness of the cost proposal.

Financial Data Grants are offered in 2 phases. In phase 1, awards normally range up to $100,000; in phase 2, awards normally range up to $750,000.

Duration Phase 1 awards may extend up to 6 months; phase 2 awards may extend up to 2 years.

Number awarded Varies each year; recently, 61 Phase 1 awards were granted.

Deadline January and July of each year.

[977]
DEPARTMENT OF HOMELAND SECURITY SUMMER FACULTY AND STUDENT RESEARCH TEAM PROGRAM

Oak Ridge Institute for Science and Education
Attn: Science and Engineering Education
P.O. Box 117
Oak Ridge, TN 37831-0117
(865) 574-1447   Fax: (865) 241-5219
E-mail: Patti.Obenour@orau.gov
Web: see.orau.org

Summary To provide an opportunity for teams of students and faculty from minority-serving educational institutions to conduct research during the summer in areas of interest to the Department of Homeland Security (DHS).

Eligibility This program is open to teams of up to 2 students (undergraduate and/or graduate) and 1 faculty from Historically Black Colleges and Universities (HBCUs), Hispanic Serving Institutions (HSIs), Tribal Colleges and Universities (TCUs), Alaska Native Serving Institutions (ANSIs), and Native Hawaiian Serving Institutions (NHSIs). Applicants must be interested in conducting research at designated DHS Centers of Excellence in science, technology, engineering, or mathematics related to homeland security (HS-STEM), including explosives detection, mitigation, and response; social and behavioral sciences; risk, economics, and decision sciences; human factors; chemical threats and countermeasures; biological threats and countermeasures; community, commerce, and infrastructure resilience; food and agricultural

security; transportation security; border security; immigration studies; maritime and port security; infrastructure protection; natural disasters and related geophysical studies; emergency preparedness and response; communications and interoperability; or advanced data analysis and visualization. Faculty must have a full-time appointment at an eligible institution and have received a Ph.D. in an HS-STEM discipline no more than 7 years previously; at least 2 years of full-time research and/or teaching experience is preferred. Students must have a GPA of 3.0 or higher and be enrolled full time. Undergraduates must be entering their junior or senior year. U.S. citizenship is required. Selection is based on relevance and intrinsic merit of the research (40%), faculty applicant qualifications (30%), academic benefit to the faculty applicant and his/her institution (10%), and student applicant qualifications (20%).

Financial Data Stipends are $1,200 per week for faculty, $600 per week for graduate students, and $500 per week for undergraduates. Faculty members who live more than 50 miles from their assigned site may receive a housing allowance of $1,500 and travel expenses up to an additional $500. Limited travel expenses for 1 round trip are reimbursed for undergraduate and graduate students living more than 50 miles from their assigned site.

Duration 12 weeks during the summer.

Additional data This program is funded by DHS and administered by Oak Ridge Institute for Science and Education (ORISE). Recently, the available DHS Centers of Excellence were the Center for Advancing Microbial Risk Assessment (led by Michigan State University and Drexel University); the National Center for Risk and Economic Analysis of Terrorism Events (led by University of Southern California); the National Center for Food Protection and Defense (led by University of Minnesota); the Center of Excellence for Zoonotic and Animal Disease Defense (led by Texas A&M University and Kansas State University); the National Consortium for the Study of Terrorism and Responses to Terrorism (led by University of Maryland); the Center of Excellence for Awareness and Localization of Explosives-Related Threats (led by Northeastern University and University of Rhode Island); the National Center for Border Security and Immigration (led by the University of Arizona and the University of Texas at El Paso); the Center for Maritime, Island and Remote and Extreme Environment Security (led by the University of Hawaii and Stevens Institute of Technology); the Coastal Hazards Center of Excellence (led by the University of North Carolina at Chapel Hill and Jackson State University); the National Transportation Security Center of Excellence (consisting of 7 institutions); and the Center of Excellence in Command, Control, and Interoperability (led by Purdue University and Rutgers University).

Number awarded Approximately 12 teams are selected each year.

Deadline January of each year.

[978]
DIANE J. WILLIS EARLY CAREER AWARD

American Psychological Foundation
750 First Street, N.E.
Washington, DC 20002-4242
(202) 336-5843   Fax: (202) 336-5812
E-mail: foundation@apa.org
Web: www.apa.org/apf/funding/div-37-willis.aspx

Summary To provide funding to young psychologists (particularly Hispanic Americans, other underrepresented minorities, women, and individuals with disabilities) who are interested in conducting research or other projects related to children and families.

Eligibility This program is open to young psychologists who completed a doctoral degree (Ed.D., Psy.D., Ph.D.) within the past 7 years. Applicants must be interested in conducting research or other projects that inform, advocate for, and improve the mental health and well-being of children and families, particularly through public policy. The sponsor encourages applications from individuals who represent diversity in race, ethnicity, gender, age, disability, and sexual orientation.

Financial Data The grant is $2,000.

Duration 1 year.

Additional data This program, sponsored by Division 37 (Child and Family Policy and Practice) of the American Psychological Association (APA), began in 2013.

Number awarded 1 each year.

Deadline January of each year.

[979]
DIPLOMACY, SECURITY, AND DEVELOPMENT FELLOWSHIPS OF THE AMERICAN ASSOCIATION FOR THE ADVANCEMENT OF SCIENCE

American Association for the Advancement of Science
Attn: Science and Technology Policy Fellowships
1200 New York Avenue, N.W.
Washington, DC 20005-3920
(202) 326-6700   Fax: (202) 289-4950
E-mail: fellowships@aaas.org
Web: www.fellowships.aaas.org

Summary To provide postdoctoral scientists and engineers (particularly Hispanic Americans, other minorities, women, and individuals with disabilities) with an opportunity to work at designated federal agencies on scientific and engineering issues related to diplomacy, security, and development.

Eligibility This program is open to doctoral-level scientists (Ph.D., M.D., D.V.M., D.Sc., and other terminal degrees) in any field of science (behavioral, biological, computational, earth, health, medical, physical, or social), engineering, or mathematics. Engineers with a master's degree and at least 3 years of professional experience are also eligible. Applicants should be able to contribute scientific and technical expertise into policy development, program planning, implementation, and evaluation in the areas of 1) foreign policy, international trade, treaty engagement, and multilateral cooperation; 2) disaster preparedness and response; 3) infrastructure, environmental, cyber and health security; terrorism and warfare prevention; and non-proliferation; or 4) international aid, capacity building, and development assistance. They must demonstrate solid scientific and technical credentials; a commitment to serve society; good communication skills; the ability to engage with non-scientific audiences; and an interest in working as special assistants for designated federal agencies (Department of Homeland Security (DHS), Agency for International Development (AID), Fogarty International Center of the National Institutes of Health (NIH), Foreign Agriculture Service of the U.S. Department of Agriculture (USDA), Department of Defense, or Department of State). U.S. citizen-

ship is required; federal employees are not eligible. The sponsor seeks candidates from a broad array of backgrounds and a diversity of geographic, disciplinary, gender, and ethnic perspectives, as well as disability status.

Financial Data The stipend for fellows with 0 to 7 years of postdoctoral experience is $74,872 in the first year and $77,368 in the second year. For fellows with 7 to 15 years of experience, the stipend is $84,855 in the first year and $87,350 in the second year. Fellows who have 15 or more years of postdoctoral experience receive $97,333 in the first year and $99,829 in the second year. Also provided are a $4,000 relocation allowance for fellows from outside the Washington, D.C. area, reimbursement for health insurance, and a $4,000 travel allowance.

Duration 1 year, beginning in September; may be renewed for 1 additional year.

Number awarded 35 to 45 each year.

Deadline October of each year.

[980]
DIRECTOR'S AWARD FOR DISTINGUISHED TEACHING SCHOLARS

National Science Foundation
Directorate for Education and Human Resources
Attn: Division of Undergraduate Education
4201 Wilson Boulevard, Room 835N
Arlington, VA 22230
(703) 292-4627   Fax: (703) 292-9015
TDD: (800) 281-8749   E-mail: npruitt@nsf.gov
Web: www.nsf.gov/funding/pgm_summ.jsp?pims_id=8170

Summary To recognize and reward Hispanic American and other scholars affiliated with institutions of higher education who have contributed to the teaching of science, technology, engineering, or mathematics (STEM) at the K-12 and undergraduate level.

Eligibility This program is open to teaching-scholars affiliated with institutions of higher education who are nominated by their president, chief academic officer, or other independent researcher. Nominees should have integrated research and education and approached both education and research in a scholarly manner. They should have demonstrated leadership in their respective fields as well as innovativeness and effectiveness in facilitating K-12 and undergraduate student learning in STEM disciplines. Consideration is given to faculty who have a history of substantial impact on 1) research in a STEM discipline or on STEM educational research; or 2) the STEM education of K-16 students who have diverse interests and aspirations, including future K-12 teachers of science and mathematics, students who plan to pursue STEM careers, and those who need to understand science and mathematics in a society increasingly dependent on science and technology. Based on letters of nomination, selected scholars are invited to submit applications for support of their continuing efforts to integrate education and research. Nominations of all citizens, including women and men, underrepresented minorities, and persons with disabilities are especially encouraged.

Financial Data The maximum grant is $300,000 for the life of the project.

Duration 4 years.

Number awarded Approximately 6 each year.

Deadline Letters of intent are due in September of each year; full applications must be submitted in October.

[981]
DIVISION 17 COUNSELING PSYCHOLOGY GRANTS

American Psychological Foundation
750 First Street, N.E.
Washington, DC 20002-4242
(202) 336-5843   Fax: (202) 336-5812
E-mail: foundation@apa.org
Web: www.apa.org/apf/funding/counseling.aspx

Summary To provide funding to psychologists (particularly Hispanic Americans, other underrepresented minorities, women, and individuals with disabilities) who wish to conduct a project related to counseling psychology.

Eligibility This program is open to psychologists who wish to conduct a project to enhance the science and practice of counseling psychology, including basic and applied research, literary, and educational activities. Applicants must be members of Division 17 (Society of Counseling Psychotherapy) of the American Psychological Association, members of an educational institution or nonprofit organization, or affiliate of an educational institution or nonprofit organization. Selection is based on conformance with stated program goals, magnitude of incremental contribution in specified activity area, quality of proposed work, and applicant's demonstrated competence and capability to execute the proposed work. The sponsor encourages applications from individuals who represent diversity in race, ethnicity, gender, age, disability, and sexual orientation.

Financial Data Grants range up to $5,000.

Duration 1 year.

Additional data These grants were first awarded in 2007.

Number awarded Varies each year; recently, 2 of these grants were awarded.

Deadline March of each year.

[982]
DIVISION 29 EARLY CAREER AWARD

American Psychological Foundation
750 First Street, N.E.
Washington, DC 20002-4242
(202) 336-5843   Fax: (202) 336-5812
E-mail: foundation@apa.org
Web: www.apa.org/apf/funding/div-29.aspx

Summary To recognize and reward young psychologists (particularly Hispanic Americans, other underrepresented minorities, women, and individuals with disabilities) who have made outstanding contributions to psychotherapy.

Eligibility This award is available to psychologists who are no more than 7 years past completion of their doctoral degree. Nominees must have demonstrated promising professional achievement related to psychotherapy theory, practice, research, or training. They must be members of Division 29 (Psychotherapy) of the American Psychological Association. Self-nominations are not accepted. Selection is based on conformance with stated program goals and qualifications and applicant's demonstrated accomplishments and promise. The sponsor encourages nominations of individuals who rep-

resent diversity in race, ethnicity, gender, age, disability, and sexual orientation.

Financial Data The award is $2,500.

Duration The award is presented annually.

Additional data This award was established in 1981 and named the Jack D. Krasner Memorial Award. It was renamed in 2007.

Number awarded 1 each year.

Deadline Nominations must be submitted by December of each year.

[983]
DOCTORAL/POST-DOCTORAL FELLOWSHIP PROGRAM IN LAW AND SOCIAL SCIENCE

American Bar Foundation
Attn: Administrative Assistant for Academic Affairs and
   Research Administration
750 North Lake Shore Drive
Chicago, IL 60611-4403
(312) 988-6517   Fax: (312) 988-6579
E-mail: aehrhardt@abfn.org
Web: www.americanbarfoundation.org

Summary To provide research funding to scholars (particularly Hispanic Americans and other minorities) who are completing or have completed doctoral degrees in fields related to law, the legal profession, and legal institutions.

Eligibility This program is open to Ph.D. candidates in the social sciences who have completed all doctoral requirements except the dissertation. Applicants who have completed the dissertation are also eligible. Doctoral and proposed research must be in the general area of sociolegal studies or in social scientific approaches to law, the legal profession, or legal institutions and legal processes. Applications must include 1) a dissertation abstract or proposal with an outline of the substance and methods of the research; 2) 2 letters of recommendation; and 3) a curriculum vitae. Minority candidates are especially encouraged to apply.

Financial Data The stipend is $30,000. Fellows may request up to $1,500 to reimburse expenses associated with research, travel to meet with advisers, or travel to conferences at which papers are presented. Relocation expenses of up to $2,500 may be reimbursed on application.

Duration 12 months, beginning in September.

Additional data Fellows are offered access to the computing and word processing facilities of the American Bar Foundation and the libraries of Northwestern University and the University of Chicago. This program was established in 1996. Fellowships must be held in residence at the American Bar Foundation. Appointments to the fellowship are full time; fellows are not permitted to undertake other work.

Number awarded 1 or more each year.

Deadline December of each year.

[984]
DOE SMALL BUSINESS INNOVATION RESEARCH GRANTS

Department of Energy
Attn: SBIR/STTR Program, SC-29
Germantown Building
1000 Independence Avenue, S.W.
Washington, DC 20585-1290
(301) 903-5707   Fax: (301) 903-5488
E-mail: sbir-sttr@science.doe.gov
Web: science.energy.gov/sbir

Summary To support small businesses (especially those owned by Hispanic Americans, other minorities, or women) that have the technological expertise to contribute to the research and development mission of the Department of Energy (DOE).

Eligibility For the purposes of this program, a "small business" is defined as a firm that is organized for profit with a location in the United States; is in the legal form of an individual proprietorship, partnership, limited liability company, corporation, joint venture, association, trust, or cooperative; is at least 51% owned and controlled by 1 or more individuals who are citizens or permanent residents of the United States; and has (including its affiliates) fewer than 500 employees. The primary employment of the principal investigator must be with the firm at the time of award and during the conduct of the proposed project. Applications are encouraged from 1) women-owned small business concerns, defined as those that are at least 51% owned by a woman or women who also control and operate them; and 2) socially and economically disadvantaged small business concerns that are at least 51% owned by an Indian tribe, a Native Hawaiian organization, or 1 or more socially and economically disadvantaged individuals (African Americans, Hispanic Americans, Native Americans, Asian Pacific Americans, or subcontinent Asian Americans). Each office within DOE defines technical topics eligible for research.

Financial Data Support is offered in 2 phases: in phase 1, awards normally do not exceed $150,000 (for both direct and indirect costs); in phase 2, awards normally do not exceed $1,000,000 (including both direct and indirect costs).

Duration Phase 1: up to 9 months; phase 2: up to 2 years.

Additional data The objectives of this program include increasing private sector commercialization of technology developed through research and development supported by the Department of Energy, stimulating technological innovation in the private sector, strengthening the role of small business in meeting federal research and development needs, and improving the return on investment from federally-funded research for economic and social benefits to the nation.

Number awarded Varies each year; recently 279 Phase 1 and 113 Phase 2 grants were awarded.

Deadline November of each year.

[985]
DOE SMALL BUSINESS TECHNOLOGY TRANSFER GRANTS

Department of Energy
Attn: SBIR/STTR Program, SC-29
Germantown Building
1000 Independence Avenue, S.W.
Washington, DC 20585-1290
(301) 903-5707   Fax: (301) 903-5488
E-mail: sbir-sttr@science.doe.gov
Web: science.energy.gov/sbir

Summary To provide financial support to cooperative research and development projects carried out between small business concerns (particularly those owned by Hispanic Americans, other minorities, or women) and research institutions in areas of interest to the Department of Energy (DOE).

Eligibility For the purposes of this program, a "small business" is defined as a firm that is organized for profit with a location in the United States; is in the legal form of an individual proprietorship, partnership, limited liability company, corporation, joint venture, association, trust, or cooperative; is at least 51% owned and controlled by 1 or more individuals who are citizens or permanent residents of the United States; and has (including its affiliates) fewer than 500 employees. Unlike the Department of Energy Small Business Innovation Research Grants, the primary employment of the principal investigator does not need to be with the business concern. This program, however, requires that the small business apply in collaboration with a nonprofit research institution for conduct of a project that has potential for commercialization. At least 40% of the work must be performed by the small business and at least 30% of the work must be performed by the research institution. Principal investigators from the nonprofit research institution must commit at least 10% of their effort to the project. Applications are encouraged from 1) women-owned small business concerns, defined as those that are at least 51% owned by a woman or women who also control and operate them; and 2) socially and economically disadvantaged small business concerns that are at least 51% owned by an Indian tribe, a Native Hawaiian organization, or 1 or more socially and economically disadvantaged individuals (African Americans, Hispanic Americans, Native Americans, Asian Pacific Americans, or subcontinent Asian Americans). Each office within DOE defines technical topics eligible for research.

Financial Data In the first phase, annual awards do not exceed $150,000 for direct costs, indirect costs, and negotiated fixed fees. In the second phase, awards up to $1,000,000 are available.

Duration Generally 9 months for the first phase and 2 years for the second phase.

Additional data Grants in the first phase are to determine the scientific, technical, and commercial merit and feasibility of the proposed cooperative effort and the quality of performance of the small business concern. In the second phase, the research and development efforts continue, depending on the results of the first phase.

Number awarded Varies each year; recently 39 Phase 1 and 15 Phase 2 grants were awarded.

Deadline January of each year.

[986]
DOLORES NYHUS GRADUATE FELLOWSHIP

California Dietetic Association
Attn: CDA Foundation
7740 Manchester Avenue, Suite 102
Playa del Rey, CA 90293-8499
(310) 822-0177   Fax: (310) 823-0264
E-mail: patsmith@dietitian.org
Web: www.dietitian.org/d_cdaf/cdaf_outreach.html

Summary To provide financial assistance to members (particularly Hispanic Americans or other minorities, men, and members with disabilities) of the Academy of Nutrition and Dietetics (AND) who live in California and are interested in working on a graduate degree in dietetics or a related field at a school in any state.

Eligibility This program is open to California residents who are AND members and have a bachelor's degree and 3 to 5 years of professional experience. Applicants must be a registered dietitian (R.D.), be a registered dietetic technician (D.T.R.), or have a credential earned at least 6 months previously. They must be enrolled in or admitted to a graduate school in any state in the areas of public health, gerontology, or a community-related program with the intention of practicing in the field of dietetics. Along with their application, they must submit a letter of application that includes a discussion of their career goals. Selection is based on that letter (15%), academic ability (25%), work or volunteer experience (15%), letters of recommendation (15%), extracurricular activities (5%), and financial need (25%). Applications are especially encouraged from ethnic minorities, men, and people with physical disabilities.

Financial Data The stipend is normally $1,000.

Duration 1 year.

Additional data The California Dietetic Association is the California affiliate of the AND.

Number awarded 1 each year.

Deadline April of each year.

[987]
DRS. ROSALEE G. AND RAYMOND A. WEISS RESEARCH AND PROGRAM INNOVATION GRANT

American Psychological Foundation
750 First Street, N.E.
Washington, DC 20002-4242
(202) 336-5843   Fax: (202) 336-5812
E-mail: foundation@apa.org
Web: www.apa.org/apf/funding/vision-weiss.aspx

Summary To provide funding to professionals (particularly Hispanic Americans, other minorities, women, and individuals with disabilities) who are interested in conducting projects that use psychology to solve social problems related to the priorities of the American Psychological Foundation (APF).

Eligibility This program is open to professionals at non-profit organizations engaged in research, education, and intervention projects and programs. Applicants must be interested in conducting an activity that uses psychology to solve social problems in the following priority areas: understanding and fostering the connection between mental and physical health; reducing stigma and prejudice; understanding and preventing violence to create a safer, more humane world; or

addressing the long-term psychological needs of individuals and communities in the aftermath of disaster. Selection is based on the criticality of the proposed funding for the proposed work; conformance with stated program goals and requirements; innovative and potential impact qualities; quality, viability, and promise of proposed work, and competence and capability of project leaders. The sponsor encourages applications from individuals who represent diversity in race, ethnicity, gender, age, disability, and sexual orientation.

Financial Data The grant is $2,500.

Duration 1 year; nonrenewable.

Additional data This program began in 2003.

Number awarded 1 each year.

Deadline March of each year.

[988]
DUPONT MINORITIES IN ENGINEERING AWARD

American Society for Engineering Education
Attn: Awards Administration
1818 N Street, N.W., Suite 600
Washington, DC 20036-2479
(202) 331-3550   Fax: (202) 265 8504
E-mail: board@asee.org
Web: www.asee.org/member-resources/awards

Summary To recognize and reward outstanding achievements by Hispanic American and other engineering educators who have worked to increase diversity by ethnicity and gender in science, engineering, and technology.

Eligibility Eligible for nomination are engineering or engineering technology educators who, as part of their educational activity, either assume or are charged with the responsibility of motivating underrepresented students to enter and continue in engineering or engineering technology curricula at the college or university level, graduate or undergraduate. Nominees must demonstrate leadership in the conception, organization, and operation of pre-college and college activities designed to increase participation by underrepresented students in engineering and engineering technology.

Financial Data The award consists of $1,500, a certificate, and a grant of $500 for travel expenses to the ASEE annual conference.

Duration The award is granted annually.

Additional data Funding for this award is provided by DuPont. It was originally established in 1956 as the Vincent Bendix Minorities in Engineering Award.

Number awarded 1 each year.

Deadline January of each year.

[989]
EARLY CAREER PATIENT-ORIENTED DIABETES RESEARCH AWARD

Juvenile Diabetes Research Foundation International
Attn: Grant Administrator
26 Broadway, 14th Floor
New York, NY 10004
(212) 479-7572   Toll Free: (800) 533-CURE
Fax: (212) 785-9595   E-mail: info@jdrf.org
Web: jdrf.org

Summary To provide funding to physician scientists (particularly Hispanic Americans, other minorities, women, and persons with disabilities) who are interested in pursuing a program of clinical diabetes-related research training.

Eligibility This program is open to investigators in diabetes-related research who have an M.D. or M.D./Ph.D. degree and a faculty appointment at the late training or assistant professor level. Applicants must be sponsored by an investigator who is affiliated full time with an accredited institution, who pursues patient-oriented clinical research, and who agrees to supervise the applicant's training. There are no citizenship requirements. Applications are encouraged from women, members of minority groups underrepresented in the sciences, and people with disabilities. Areas of relevant research can include: mechanisms of human disease, therapeutic interventions, clinical trials, and the development of new technologies. The proposed research may be conducted at foreign or domestic, for-profit or nonprofit, or public or private institutions, including universities, colleges, hospitals, laboratories, units of state or local government, or eligible agencies of the federal government.

Financial Data The total award may be up to $150,000 each year, up to $75,000 of which may be requested for research (including a technician, supplies, equipment, and travel). The salary request must be consistent with the established salary structure of the applicant's institution. Equipment purchases in years other than the first must be strongly justified. Indirect costs may not exceed 10%.

Duration The award is for 5 years and is generally nonrenewable.

Number awarded Varies each year.

Deadline August of each year.

[990]
EARTH SCIENCES POSTDOCTORAL FELLOWSHIPS

National Science Foundation
Directorate for Geosciences
Attn: Division of Earth Sciences
4201 Wilson Boulevard, Room 785S
Arlington, VA 22230
(703) 292-5047   Fax: (703) 292-9025
TDD: (800) 281-8749   E-mail: lpatino@nsf.gov
Web: www.nsf.gov

Summary To provide funding to postdoctoral scientists (particularly Hispanic Americans, other underrepresented minorities, women, and individuals with disabilities) who are interested in participating in a program of research training and education, in the United States or abroad, in a field relevant to the work of the Division of Earth Sciences of the National Science Foundation (NSF).

Eligibility This program is open to U.S. citizens, nationals, and permanent residents who received a Ph.D. within the past 18 months. Applicants must be interested in a program of research training in any of the disciplines supported by the NSF Division of Earth Sciences: geobiology and low temperature geochemistry, geomorphology and land use dynamics, geophysics, hydrologic sciences, petrology and geochemistry, sedimentary geology and paleobiology, and tectonics. The project should be conducted at an institution in the United States or abroad other than the applicant's Ph.D.-granting institution. The application must include a plan to broaden the participation of groups underrepresented in earth sciences (women, persons with disabilities, African

Americans, Hispanics, Native Americans, Alaska Natives, and Pacific Islanders).

Financial Data Grants are $87,000 per year, including a stipend of $62,000 per year and an annual fellowship allowance of $25,000 that is intended to cover direct research expenses, facilities and other institutional resources, and fringe benefits.

Duration 2 years.

Number awarded 10 each year.

Deadline July of each year.

[991]
ECOLOGY OF INFECTIOUS DISEASES INITIATIVE

Fogarty International Center
Attn: Division of International Training and Research
31 Center Drive, Room B2C39
Bethesda, MD 20892-2220
(301) 496-1653   Fax: (301) 402-0779
TDD: (301) 451-0088   E-mail: Christine.Jessup@nih.gov
Web: www.fic.nih.gov

Summary To provide funding to U.S. scientists (particularly Hispanic Americans, other underrepresented minorities, and individuals with disabilities) who are interested in conducting research on the underlying ecological and biological mechanisms that govern relationships between human-induced environmental changes and the emergence and transmission of infectious diseases.

Eligibility This program is open to investigators at domestic and foreign for-profit and nonprofit organizations, both public and private, such as universities, colleges, hospitals, laboratories, units of state and local governments, and eligible agencies of the federal government. Applicants should be proposing to conduct research on the ecological and socio-ecological determinants of transmission by vectors or abiotic agents, the population dynamics of reservoir species, the transmission to humans or other hosts, or the cultural, social, behavioral, and economic dimensions of disease communication. Proposals for research on disease systems of public health concern to developing countries are strongly encouraged. Applicants are also encouraged to include links to the public health research community in the United States and developing countries, including participation by epidemiologists, physicians, veterinarians, medical social scientists, medical entomologists, virologists, or parasitologists. The program encourages applications from all citizens, including women and men, underrepresented minorities, and persons with disabilities.

Financial Data Grants provide up to $500,000 per year.

Duration Up to 5 years.

Additional data This program, established in 2000, is jointly funded by 3 components of the National Science Foundation (NSF): the Directorate for Biological Sciences, the Directorate for Geosciences, and the Directorate for Social, Behavioral, and Economic Sciences, and 3 components of the National Institutes of Health (NIH): the Fogarty International Center, the National Institute of Allergy and Infectious Diseases, and the National Institute of General Medical Sciences.

Number awarded Approximately 8 each year.

Deadline December of each year.

[992]
EDWARD A. BOUCHET AWARD

American Physical Society
Attn: Honors Program
One Physics Ellipse
College Park, MD 20740-3844
(301) 209-3268   Fax: (301) 209-0865
E-mail: honors@aps.org
Web: www.aps.org/programs/honors/awards/bouchet.cfm

Summary To recognize and reward outstanding research in physics by Hispanic Americans and members of other underrepresented minority groups.

Eligibility Nominees for this award must be African Americans, Hispanic Americans, or Native Americans who have made significant contributions to physics research and are effective communicators.

Financial Data The award consists of a grant of $3,500 to the recipient, a travel allowance for the recipient to visit 3 academic institutions to deliver lectures, and an allowance for travel expenses to the meeting of the American Physical Society (APS) at which the prize is presented.

Duration The award is presented annually.

Additional data This award was established in 1994 and is currently funded by a grant from the Research Corporation. As part of the award, the recipient visits 3 academic institutions where the impact of the visit on minority students will be significant. The purpose of those visits is to deliver technical lectures on the recipient's field of specialization, to visit classrooms where appropriate, to assist the institution with precollege outreach efforts where appropriate, and to talk informally with faculty and students about research and teaching careers in physics.

Number awarded 1 each year.

Deadline June of each year.

[993]
E.E. JUST ENDOWED RESEARCH FELLOWSHIP FUND

Marine Biological Laboratory
Attn: Chief Academic and Scientific Officer
7 MBL Street
Woods Hole, MA 02543-1015
(508) 289-7173   Fax: (508) 457-1924
E-mail: casoofice@mbl.edu
Web: hermes.mbl.edu

Summary To provide funding to Hispanic American and other minority scientists who wish to conduct research during the summer at the Marine Biological Laboratory (MBL) in Woods Hole, Massachusetts.

Eligibility This program is open to minority faculty members who are interested in conducting summer research at the MBL. Applicants must submit a statement of the potential impact of this award on their career development. Fields of study include, but are not limited to, cell biology, developmental biology, ecology, evolution, microbiology, neurobiology, physiology, regenerative biology, and tissue engineering.

Financial Data Grants range from $5,000 to $25,000, typically to cover laboratory rental and/or housing costs. Awardees are responsible for other costs, such as supplies, shared resource usage, affiliated staff who accompany them, or travel.

Duration 8 to 10 weeks during the summer.

Number awarded 1 each year.

Deadline December of each year.

[994]
EINSTEIN POSTDOCTORAL FELLOWSHIP PROGRAM

Smithsonian Astrophysical Observatory
Attn: Chandra X-Ray Center
Einstein Fellowship Program Office
60 Garden Street, MS4
Cambridge, MA 02138
(617) 496-7941   Fax: (617) 495-7356
E-mail: fellows@head.cfa.harvard.edu
Web: cxc.harvard.edu/fellows

Summary To provide funding to recent postdoctoral scientists (particularly Hispanic Americans, other minorities, and women) who are interested in conducting research related to high energy astrophysics missions of the National Aeronautics and Space Administration (NASA).

Eligibility This program is open to postdoctoral scientists who completed their Ph.D., Sc.D., or equivalent doctoral degree within the past 3 years in astronomy, physics, or related disciplines. Applicants must be interested in conducting research related to NASA Physics of the Cosmos program missions: Chandra, Fermi, XMM-Newton and International X-Ray Observatory, cosmological investigations relevant to the Planck and JDEM missions, and gravitational astrophysics relevant to the LISA mission. They must be citizens of the United States or English-speaking citizens of other countries who have valid visas. Women and minorities are strongly encouraged to apply.

Financial Data Stipends are approximately $66,500 per year. Fellows may also receive health insurance, relocation costs, and moderate support (up to $16,000 per year) for research-related travel, computing services, publications, and other direct costs.

Duration 3 years (depending on a review of scientific activity).

Additional data This program, which began in 2009 with funding from NASA, incorporates the former Chandra and GLAST Fellowship programs.

Number awarded Up to 10 each year.

Deadline November of each year.

[995]
ELSEVIER PILOT RESEARCH AWARDS

American Gastroenterological Association
Attn: AGA Research Foundation
Research Awards Manager
4930 Del Ray Avenue
Bethesda, MD 20814-2512
(301) 222-4012   Fax: (301) 654-5920
E-mail: awards@gastro.org
Web: www.gastro.org/aga-foundation/grants

Summary To provide funding to new or established investigators (particularly Hispanic Americans, other minorities, and women) for pilot research projects in areas related to gastroenterology or hepatology.

Eligibility Applicants must have an M.D., Ph.D., or equivalent degree and a full-time faculty position at an accredited

North American institution. They may not hold grants for projects on a similar topic from other agencies. Individual membership in the American Gastroenterology Association (AGA) is required. The proposal must involve obtaining new data that can ultimately provide the basis for subsequent grant applications for more substantial funding and duration in gastroenterology- or hepatology-related areas. Women and minority investigators are strongly encouraged to apply. Selection is based on novelty, importance, feasibility, environment, commitment of the institution, and overall likelihood that the project will lead to more substantial grant applications.

Financial Data The grant is $25,000. Funds may be used for salary, supplies, or equipment. Indirect costs are not allowed.

Duration 1 year.

Additional data This award is sponsored by Elsevier Science.

Number awarded 3 each year.

Deadline January of each year.

[996]
ENERGY, ENVIRONMENT, AND AGRICULTURE FELLOWSHIPS OF THE AMERICAN ASSOCIATION FOR THE ADVANCEMENT OF SCIENCE

American Association for the Advancement of Science
Attn: Science and Technology Policy Fellowships
1200 New York Avenue, N.W.
Washington, DC 20005-3920
(202) 326-6700   Fax: (202) 289-4950
E-mail: fellowships@aaas.org
Web: www.fellowships.aaas.org

Summary To provide a fellowship to postdoctoral scientists and engineers (particularly Hispanic Americans, other minorities, women, and individuals with disabilities) who are interested in participating on projects relating to energy, environment, or agriculture at specified federal agencies.

Eligibility This program is open to doctoral-level scientists (Ph.D., M.D., D.V.M., D.Sc., and other terminal degrees) in any field of science (behavioral, biological, computational, earth, health, medical, physical, or social), engineering, or mathematics. Engineers with a master's degree and at least 3 years of professional experience are also eligible. Applicants should be able to engage in projects, policies, risk assessment, evaluation, and outreach initiatives to 1) protect animal, plant, and environmental health; 2) address ecosystem degradation, pollution, and biological threats; 3) tackle challenges and opportunities in agriculture, fisheries, climate change, and energy; or 4) safeguard air, water, land, wildlife, and natural resources. They must demonstrate solid scientific and technical credentials; a commitment to serve society; good communication skills; the ability to engage with non-scientific audiences; and an interest in working as special assistants for designated federal agencies (the U.S. Department of Agriculture (USDA), the Department of Energy (DOE), the National Oceanic and Atmospheric Administration (NOAA), the National Science Foundation (NSF), the Environmental Protection Agency (EPA), the National Aeronautics and Space Administration (NASA), the U.S. Geological Survey (USGS), or the Forest Service). U.S. citizenship is required; federal employees are not eligible. The sponsor seeks candidates from a broad array of backgrounds and a diversity of geographic, disciplinary, gender, and ethnic perspectives, as well as disability status.

Financial Data The stipend for fellows with 0 to 7 years of postdoctoral experience is $74,872 in the first year and $77,368 in the second year. For fellows with 7 to 15 years of experience, the stipend is $84,855 in the first year and $87,350 in the second year. Fellows who have 15 or more years of postdoctoral experience receive $97,333 in the first year and $99,420 in the second year. Also provided are a $4,000 relocation allowance for fellows from outside the Washington, D.C. area, reimbursement for health insurance, and a $4,000 travel allowance.

Duration 1 year, beginning in September; may be renewed 1 additional year.

Number awarded 35 to 45 each year.

Deadline October of each year.

[997]
EPILEPSY FOUNDATION RESEARCH GRANTS PROGRAM

Epilepsy Foundation
Attn: Research Department
8301 Professional Place
Landover, MD 20785-2353
(301) 459-3700   Toll Free: (800) EFA-1000
Fax: (301) 577-2684   TDD: (800) 332-2070
E-mail: grants@efa.org
Web: www.epilepsyfoundation.org

Summary To provide funding to junior investigators (particularly Hispanic Americans, other minorities, women, and individuals with disabilities) who are interested in conducting research that will advance the understanding, treatment, and prevention of epilepsy.

Eligibility Applicants must have a doctoral degree and an academic appointment at the level of assistant professor in a university or medical school (or equivalent standing at a research institution or medical center). They must be interested in conducting basic or clinical research to advance understanding of the behavioral and psychosocial aspects of having epilepsy. Faculty with appointments at the level of associate professor or higher are not eligible. Applications from women, members of minority groups, and people with disabilities are especially encouraged. U.S. citizenship is not required, but the research must be conducted in the United States. Selection is based on the scientific quality of the research plan, the relevance of the proposed research to epilepsy, the applicant's qualifications, and the adequacy of the institution and facility where research will be conducted.

Financial Data The grant is $50,000 per year.

Duration 1 year; recipients may reapply for 1 additional year of funding.

Additional data Support for this program is provided by many individuals, families, and corporations, especially the American Epilepsy Society, Abbott Laboratories, Ortho-McNeil Pharmaceutical, and Pfizer Inc.

Number awarded Varies each year.

Deadline August of each year.

[998]
EPILEPSY RESEARCH RECOGNITION AWARDS PROGRAM

American Epilepsy Society
342 North Main Street
West Hartford, CT 06117-2507
(860) 586-7505   Fax: (860) 586-7550
E-mail: ctubby@aesnet.org
Web: www.aesnet.org/research/research-awards

Summary To provide funding to investigators (particularly Hispanic Americans, other minorities, and women) who are interested in conducting research related to epilepsy.

Eligibility This program is open to active scientists and clinicians working in any aspect of epilepsy. Candidates must be nominated by their home institution and be at the level of associate professor or professor. There are no geographic restrictions; nominations from outside the United States and North America are welcome. Nominations of women and members of minority groups are especially encouraged. Selection is based on pioneering research, originality of research, quality of publications, research productivity, relationship of the candidate's work to problems in epilepsy, training activities, other contributions in epilepsy, and productivity over the next decade; all criteria are weighted equally.

Financial Data The grant is $10,000. No institutional overhead is allowed.

Additional data This program began in 1991.

Number awarded 2 each year.

Deadline August of each year.

[999]
ETAC GRANTS

Alzheimer's Association
Attn: Medical and Scientific Affairs
225 North Michigan Avenue, 17th Floor
Chicago, IL 60601-7633
(312) 335-5747   Toll Free: (800) 272-3900
Fax: (866) 699-1246   TDD: (312) 335-5886
E-mail: grantsapp@alz.org
Web: www.alz.org

Summary To provide funding to investigators (particularly Hispanic Americans and members of other underrepresented groups) who are interested in developing technology for uses related to Alzheimer's Disease.

Eligibility This program is open to investigators who are full-time staff or faculty at public, private, domestic, and foreign research laboratories, medical centers, hospitals, and universities. Applicants must be interested in conducting research on personalized diagnostics, preventive tools, and interventions for adults coping with the spectrum of cognitive aging and neurodegenerative disease, particularly Alzheimer's Disease. Priority is given to groundbreaking studies on emerging information and communication technologies as well as their clinical and social implications. Research topics may include, but are not limited to, behavioral assessment for early detection, prevention, safety monitoring and support for caregivers, supporting independent function in daily life, social support through face or audio recognition, detecting moments and patterns of lucidity, and privacy and security concerns of Alzheimer's families. Scientists from underrepresented groups are especially encouraged to apply.

Financial Data Grants up to $90,000 per year, including direct expenses and up to 10% for overhead costs, are available. The total award for the life of the grant may not exceed $200,000.

Duration Up to 3 years.

Additional data This program is jointly supported by the Alzheimer's Association and Intel Corporation.

Number awarded Up to 2 each year.

Deadline Letters of intent must be submitted by the end of January of each year. Final applications are due in March.

[1000]
ETS POSTDOCTORAL FELLOWSHIP AWARD PROGRAM

Educational Testing Service
Attn: Fellowships
660 Rosedale Road
MS 19-T
Princeton, NJ 08541-0001
(609) 734-5543   Fax: (609) 734-5410
E-mail: internfellowships@ets.org
Web: www.ets.org/research/fellowships

Summary To provide funding to postdoctorates (particularly Hispanic Americans and members of other underrepresented groups) who wish to conduct independent research at the Educational Testing Service (ETS).

Eligibility Applicants must have a doctorate in a relevant discipline and be able to provide evidence of prior research. They must be interested in conducting research at ETS in 1 of the following areas: measurement theory, validity, natural language processing and computational linguistics, cognitive psychology, learning theory, linguistics, speech recognition and processing, teaching and classroom research, or statistics. Selection is based on the scholarly and technical strength of the proposed research, the relationship between the objective of the research and ETS goals and priorities, and the ETS affirmative action objectives. An explicit goal of the program is to increase the number of scholars and students from diverse backgrounds, especially such traditionally underrepresented groups as African Americans, Hispanic/Latino Americans, and American Indians, who are conducting research in educational measurement and related fields.

Financial Data The stipend is $55,000 per year; fellows and their families also receive limited reimbursement for relocation expenses.

Duration Up to 2 years.

Additional data Fellows work with senior staff at ETS in Princeton, New Jersey.

Number awarded Up to 3 each year.

Deadline Preliminary application materials must be submitted by December of each year; final application materials are due by the end of February.

[1001]
EVA KING KILLAM RESEARCH AWARD

American College of Neuropsychopharmacology
Attn: Executive Office
5034-A Thoroughbred Lane
Brentwood, TN 37027
(615) 324-2360   Fax: (615) 523-1715
E-mail: acnp@acnp.org
Web: www.acnp.org/programs/awards.aspx

Summary To recognize and reward young scientists (particularly Hispanic Americans, other minorities, and individuals with disabilities) who have made outstanding translational research contributions to neuropsychopharmacology.

Eligibility This award is available to scientists who are younger than 50 years of age. Nominees must have made an outstanding translational research contribution to neuropsychopharmacology. The contributions should focus on translating advances from basic science to human investigations. Selection is based on the quality of the contribution and its impact in advancing neuropsychopharmacology. Neither membership in the American College of Neuropsychopharmacology (ACNP) nor U.S. citizenship are required. Nomination of women and minorities is highly encouraged.

Financial Data The award consists of an expense-paid trip to the ACNP annual meeting, a monetary honorarium, and a plaque.

Duration The award is presented annually.

Additional data This award was first presented in 2011.

Number awarded 1 each year.

Deadline Nominations must be submitted by June of each year.

[1002]
FACULTY AT FDA GRANTS

National Science Foundation
Directorate for Engineering
Attn: Division of Chemical, Bioengineering,
   Environmental, and Transport Systems
4201 Wilson Boulevard, Room 565S
Arlington, VA 22230
(703) 292-7942   Fax: (703) 292-9098
TDD: (800) 281-8749   E-mail: lesterow@nsf.gov
Web: www.nsf.gov/funding/pgm_summ.jsp?pims_id=5605

Summary To provide an opportunity for faculty members (particularly Hispanic Americans, other minorities, and individuals with disabilities) to conduct research at an intramural laboratory of the U.S. Food and Drug Administration (FDA).

Eligibility This program is open to full-time faculty members at U.S. colleges and universities in science, engineering, and mathematics fields of interest to the National Science Foundation (NSF). Applicants must be U.S. citizens, nationals, or permanent residents. They must present a plan for collaboration between their institution and the FDA, with a description of the facilities and resources that will be available at an FDA laboratory to support the proposed research. The program encourages applications from all citizens, including women and men, underrepresented minorities, and persons with disabilities.

Financial Data Grants range from $25,000 to $150,000, including 85% of the faculty member's salary and fringe benefits during the industrial residency period. Up to 20% of the total requested amount may be used for travel and research expenses for the faculty and his/her students, including materials but excluding equipment. In lieu of indirect costs, up to 15% of the total cost may be allocated for administrative expenses. The fellow's home institution must commit to support the other 15% of the faculty salary and fringe benefits. FDA provides office space, research facilities, research costs in the form of expendable and minor equipment purchases in the host laboratory, and the time of its research staff.

Duration 3 to 12 months.

Additional data This program is also offered by the NSF Directorate for Computer and Information Science and Engineering.

Number awarded A total of 3 to 10 grants for all FDA programs is awarded each year; total funding is approximately $500,000.

Deadline March of each year.

[1003]
FACULTY DEVELOPMENT AWARD TO PROMOTE DIVERSITY IN NEUROSCIENCE RESEARCH

National Institute of Neurological Disorders and Stroke
Attn: Office of Training, Career Development and
   Workforce Diversity
6001 Executive Boulevard, Suite 2149
Bethesda, MD 20892-9535
(301) 451-7966   Fax: (301) 594-5929
TDD: (301) 451-0088 E-mail: jonesmiche@ninds.nih.gov
Web: grants.nih.gov/grants/guide/pa-files/PAR-12-152.html

Summary To provide funding to neurological research scientists who are Hispanic Americans or members of other underrepresented groups and interested in preparing for a career as an independent investigator.

Eligibility This program is open to U.S. citizens, nationals, and permanent residents who have a doctoral degree in a field of neuroscience and are in the first 3 years of a faculty appointment. Applicants must be interested in participating in an intensive, supervised career development experience in neuroscience research. They must qualify as 1) a member of an ethnic or racial group shown to be underrepresented in health-related sciences on a national basis; 2) an individual with a disability; or 3) an individual from a disadvantaged background. Selection is based on scientific merit and programmatic considerations.

Financial Data Grants provide an annual award of up to $85,000 for salary and fringe benefits and an annual research allowance of up to $100,000 per year for direct research costs. The institution may apply for up to 8% of direct costs for facilities and administrative costs.

Duration Up to 3 years; nonrenewable.

Additional data Recipients must devote 75% of full-time professional effort to conducting health-related research.

Number awarded Varies each year.

Deadline February, June, or October of each year.

[1004]
FACULTY EARLY CAREER DEVELOPMENT PROGRAM

National Science Foundation
Directorate for Education and Human Resources
Senior Staff Associate for Cross Directorate Programs
4201 Wilson Boulevard, Room 805
Arlington, VA 22230
(703) 292-8600   TDD: (800) 281-8749
E-mail: info@nsf.gov
Web: www.nsf.gov

Summary To provide funding to outstanding new faculty (particularly Hispanic Americans, other underrepresented minorities, and individuals with disabilities) who are working in science and engineering fields of interest to the National Science Foundation (NSF) and intend to develop academic careers involving both research and education.

Eligibility This program, identified as the CAREER program, is open to faculty members who meet all of the following requirements: 1) be employed in a tenure-track (or equivalent) position at an institution in the United States, its territories or possessions, or the Commonwealth of Puerto Rico that awards degrees in a field supported by NSF or that is a nonprofit, non-degree granting organization, such as a museum, observatory, or research laboratory; 2) have a doctoral degree in a field of science or engineering supported by NSF: 3) not have competed more than 3 times in this program; 4) be untenured; and 5) not be a current or former recipient of a Presidential Early Career Award for Scientists and Engineers (PECASE) or CAREER award. Applicants are not required to be U.S. citizens or permanent residents. They must submit a career development plan that indicates a description of the proposed research project, including preliminary supporting data (if appropriate), specific objectives, methods, procedures to be used, and expected significance of the results; a description of the proposed educational activities, including plans to evaluate their impact; a description of how the research and educational activities are integrated with each other; and results of prior NSF support (if applicable). Proposals from women, underrepresented minorities, and persons with disabilities are especially encouraged.

Financial Data The grant is at least $80,000 per year (or $100,000 per year for the Directorate of Biological Sciences or the Office of Polar Programs), including indirect costs or overhead.

Duration 5 years.

Additional data This program is operated by various disciplinary divisions within the NSF; for a list of the participating divisions and their telephone numbers, contact the sponsor. Outstanding recipients of these grants are nominated for the NSF component of the PECASE awards, which are awarded to 20 recipients of these grants as an honorary award.

Number awarded Approximately 600 each year.

Deadline July of each year.

[1005]
FELLOWSHIP IN ARCHITECTURE

Cintas Foundation, Inc.
c/o Jessica Brodsky, Cintas Fellows Collection
Miami Dade College
300 N.E. Second Avenue
Miami, FL 33132-2204
(305) 237-7722   Fax: (305) 237-7711
E-mail: jbrodsky@mdc.edu
Web: www.cintasfoundation.org

Summary To provide funding for creative activities in architecture to Cubans who are living outside of Cuba.

Eligibility This program is open to architects of Cuban citizenship or lineage (having a Cuban parent or grandparent) but living in the United States or any other country except Cuba. Applicants must be interested in completing a project in the field of architectural design. They must include 2 narrative statements in English or Spanish: 1) a record of their personal history, their development as an artist, and their plans for the future; and 2) a description of the project or activity that they would undertake if awarded a fellowship. Fellowships are not awarded for academic study, research, or writing.

Financial Data Grants are $10,000.

Duration 1 year.

Number awarded 1 each odd-numbered year.

Deadline July of odd-numbered years.

[1006]
FELLOWSHIP IN CREATIVE WRITING

Cintas Foundation, Inc.
c/o Jessica Brodsky, Cintas Fellows Collection
Miami Dade College
300 N.E. Second Avenue
Miami, FL 33132-2204
(305) 237-7722   Fax: (305) 237-7711
E-mail: jbrodsky@mdc.edu
Web: www.cintasfoundation.org/fellowships_writing.htm

Summary To provide funding for creative activities in writing to Cubans who are living outside of Cuba.

Eligibility This program is open to writers of Cuban citizenship or lineage (having a Cuban parent or grandparent) but living in the United States or any other country except Cuba. Applicants must be interested in completing a project in the field of creative writing. Submissions must be original manuscripts up to 25 pages in length. They must include 2 narrative statements in English or Spanish: 1) a record of their personal history, their development as an artist, and their plans for the future; and 2) a description of the project or activity that they would undertake if awarded a fellowship. Fellowships are not awarded for academic study, research, or writing.

Financial Data Grants are $10,000.

Duration 1 year.

Number awarded 1 each even-numbered year.

Deadline July of even-numbered years.

[1007]
FELLOWSHIP IN VISUAL ARTS

Cintas Foundation, Inc.
c/o Jessica Brodsky, Cintas Fellows Collection
Miami Dade College
300 N.E. Second Avenue
Miami, FL 33132-2204
(305) 237-7722   Fax: (305) 237-7711
E-mail: jbrodsky@mdc.edu
Web: www.cintasfoundation.org/fellowships_arts.htm

Summary To provide funding for creative activities in visual arts to Cubans who are living outside of Cuba.

Eligibility This program is open to artists of Cuban citizenship or lineage (having a Cuban parent or grandparent) but living in the United States or any other country except Cuba. Applicants must be interested in completing a project in the field of visual arts, including painting, sculpture, installation art, photography, film, and the media arts. Submissions may consist of up to 10 digital images. They must include 2 narrative statements in English or Spanish: 1) a record of their personal history, their development as an artist, and their plans for the future; and 2) a description of the project or activity that they would undertake if awarded a fellowship. Fellowships are not awarded for academic study, research, or writing.

Financial Data Grants are $10,000.

Duration 1 year.

Number awarded 1 each year.

Deadline July of each year.

[1008]
FELLOWSHIP PROGRAM IN MEASUREMENT

American Educational Research Association
1430 K Street, N.W., Suite 1200
Washington, DC 20005
(202) 238-3200   Fax: (202) 238-3250
E-mail: fellowships@aera.net
Web: www.aera.net

Summary To provide an opportunity for junior scholars in the field of education (particularly Hispanic Americans, other underrepresented minorities, and women) to engage in a program of research and advanced training while in residence at Educational Testing Service (ETS) in Princeton, New Jersey.

Eligibility This program is open to junior scholars and early career research scientists in fields and disciplines related to education research. Applicants must have completed their Ph.D. or Ed.D. degree within the past 3 years. They must be proposing a program of intensive research and training at the ETS campus in Princeton, New Jersey in such areas as educational measurement, assessment design, psychometrics, statistical analyses, large-scale evaluations, and other studies directed to explaining student progress and achievement. A particular goal of the program is to increase the involvement of women and underrepresented minority professionals in measurement, psychometrics, assessment, and related fields. U.S. citizenship or permanent resident status is required.

Financial Data The stipend is $55,000 per year. Fellows also receive relocation expenses and ETS employee benefits.

Duration Up to 2 years.

Additional data This program is jointly sponsored by the American Educational Research Association (AERA) and ETS.

Number awarded Up to 2 each year.

Deadline November of each year.

[1009]
FELLOWSHIPS FOR TRANSFORMATIVE COMPUTATIONAL SCIENCE USING CYBERINFRASTRUCTURE

National Science Foundation
Attn: Office of Cyberinfrastructure
4201 Wilson Boulevard, Room 1145S
Arlington, VA 22230
(703) 292-8061   Fax: (703) 292-9060
TDD: (800) 281-8749   E-mail: citracs@nsf.gov
Web: www.nsf.gov

Summary To provide funding for research training to postdoctoral scientists (particularly Hispanic Americans, other underrepresented minorities, and individuals with disabilities) who plan to work in areas of interest to the Office of Cyberinfrastructure of the National Science Foundation (NSF).

Eligibility This program is open to citizens, nationals, and permanent residents of the United States who are graduate students completing a Ph.D. or have earned the degree no earlier than 2 years preceding the deadline date. Applicants must be interested in a program of research and training in the use of computational concepts, methodologies, and technologies in all sciences (including physical, biological, geological, mathematical, social, behavioral, economic, computer, information, and data). They must identify a host research organization (college, university, privately-sponsored nonprofit institute, government agency, or laboratory) that has agreed to support the applicant's proposed research and educational activities and has identified a mentor to work with the applicant. Selection is based on the applicant's ability to contribute to computational research and educational efforts that integrate distinct theoretical models and computational methodologies to achieve overall goals and lead to a new generation of applications and technologies for solving important real-world problems using cyberinfrastructure (CI). The program encourages applications from all citizens, including women and men, underrepresented minorities, and persons with disabilities.

Financial Data Stipends are $60,000 for the first year, $65,000 for the second year, and $70,000 for the third year. Also provided are a research allowance supplement of $10,000 per year and an institutional allowance of $5,000 per year. Fellows who complete this program and move on to a tenure-track faculty position may apply for a research starter supplement of up to $50,000 to support the setup of their research environment.

Duration Up to 3 years.

Number awarded 6 to 8 each year. Approximately $2.0 million is available for this program annually.

Deadline January of each year.

[1010]
FIRST BOOK GRANT PROGRAM FOR MINORITY SCHOLARS

Louisville Institute
Attn: Executive Director
1044 Alta Vista Road
Louisville, KY 40205-1798
(502) 992-5432   Fax: (502) 894-2286
E-mail: info@louisville-institute.org
Web: www.louisville-institute.org/Grants/programs.aspx

Summary To provide funding to Hispanic Americans and other scholars of color who are interested in completing a major research and book project that focuses on an aspect of Christianity in North America.

Eligibility This program is open to members of racial/ethnic minority groups (African Americans, Hispanics, Native Americans, Asian Americans, Arab Americans, and Pacific Islanders) who have an earned doctoral degree (normally the Ph.D. or Th.D.). Applicants must be a pre-tenured faculty member in a full-time, tenure-track position at an accredited institution of higher education (college, university, or seminary) in North America. They must be able to negotiate a full academic year free from teaching and committee responsibilities in order to engage in a scholarly research project leading to the publication of their first (or second) book focusing on an aspect of Christianity in North America. Selection is based on the intellectual quality of the research and writing project, its potential to contribute to scholarship in religion, and the potential contribution of the research to the vitality of North American Christianity.

Financial Data The grant is $40,000. Awards are intended to make possible a full academic year of sabbatical research and writing by providing up to half of the grantee's salary and benefits for that year. Funds are paid directly to the grantee's institution, but no indirect costs are allowed.

Duration 1 academic year; nonrenewable.

Additional data The Louisville Institute is located at Louisville Presbyterian Theological Seminary and is supported by the Lilly Endowment. These grants were first awarded in 2003. Grantees may not accept other awards that provide a stipend during the tenure of this award, and they must be released from all teaching and committee responsibilities during the award year.

Number awarded Varies each year; recently, 2 of these grants were awarded.

Deadline January of each year.

[1011]
F.J. MCGUIGAN EARLY CAREER INVESTIGATOR RESEARCH PRIZE

American Psychological Foundation
750 First Street, N.E.
Washington, DC 20002-4242
(202) 336-5843   Fax: (202) 336-5812
E-mail: foundation@apa.org
Web: www.apa.org/apf/funding/mcguigan-prize.aspx

Summary To provide funding to young psychologists (particularly Hispanic Americans, other minorities, women, and individuals with disabilities) who are interested in conducting research related to the human mind.

Eligibility This program is open to investigators who have earned a doctoral degree in psychology or in a related field within the past 9 years. Nominees must have an affiliation with an accredited college, university, or other research institution. They must be engaged in research that seeks to explicate the concept of the human mind. The approach must be materialistic and should be primarily psychophysiological, but physiological and behavioral research may also qualify. Self-nominations are not accepted; candidates must be nominated by a senior colleague. The sponsor encourages nominations of individuals who represent diversity in race, ethnicity, gender, age, disability, and sexual orientation.

Financial Data The grant is $25,000.

Duration These grants are awarded biennially, in even-numbered years.

Additional data The first grant under this program was awarded in 2002.

Number awarded 1 every other year.

Deadline February of even-numbered years.

[1012]
FRAMELINE COMPLETION FUND

Frameline
Attn: Completion Fund
145 Ninth Street, Suite 300
San Francisco, CA 94103
(415) 703-8650   Fax: (415) 861-1404
E-mail: info@frameline.org
Web: www.frameline.org/filmmaker-support

Summary To provide funding to lesbian, gay, bisexual, and transgender (LGBT) film/video artists (particularly Hispanic Americans, other film/video artists of color, and women).

Eligibility This program is open to LGBT artists who are in the last stages of the production of documentary, educational, narrative, animated, or experimental projects about or of interest to LGBT people and their communities. Applicants may be independent artists, students, producers, or nonprofit corporations. They must be interested in completion work and must have 90% of the production completed; projects in development, script-development, pre-production, or production are not eligible. Student projects are eligible only if the student maintains artistic and financial control of the project. Women and people of color are especially encouraged to apply. Selection is based on financial need, the contribution the grant will make to completing the project, assurances that the project will be completed, and the statement the project makes about LGBT people and/or issues of concern to them and their communities.

Financial Data Grants range from $1,000 to $5,000.

Duration These are 1-time grants.

Additional data This program began in 1990.

Number awarded Varies each year; recently, 5 of these grants were awarded. Since this program was established, it has provided $389,200 in support to 118 films.

Deadline October of each year.

[1013]
FRONTIERS IN PHYSIOLOGY RESEARCH TEACHER FELLOWSHIPS

American Physiological Society
Attn: Education Office
9650 Rockville Pike, Room 3111
Bethesda, MD 20814-3991
(301) 634-7132   Fax: (301) 634-7098
E-mail: education@the-aps.org
Web: www.the-aps.org

Summary To provide an opportunity for middle/high school life science teachers (particularly Hispanic Americans and other underrepresented minorities) to participate in a summer research project in physiology.

Eligibility This program is open to science teachers at middle schools (grades 6-9) and high schools (grades 9-12) who do not have recent (within 10 years) laboratory experience in physiology or the life sciences, do not have an advanced degree in laboratory science, and are not a candidate for an advanced degree in a laboratory science. Applicants must be able to demonstrate a commitment to excellence in science teaching, a desire to learn new teaching methods, and a desire to learn about research first-hand. Teachers who are members of minority groups underrepresented in science (African Americans, Hispanics, Native Americans, and Pacific Islanders) or who teach in schools with a predominance of underrepresented minority students are especially encouraged to apply. Teachers must apply jointly with a member of the American Physiological Society (APS) at a research institution in the same geographic area as their home and school. Selection is based on the quality of the summer research experience and potential long-term impact on teaching and on students.

Financial Data For all activities, teachers receive a stipend of $5,700. They also receive $1,200 for reimbursement of travel costs to attend the Experimental Biology meeting.

Duration 1 year, including 7 to 8 weeks during the summer for participation in the research experience.

Additional data This program enables teachers to work on a summer research project in the laboratory of their APS sponsor, use the Internet to expand their repertory of teaching methods and their network of colleagues, and develop an inquiry-based classroom activity or laboratory, along with a corresponding web page. They also take a break from their summer research to attend a 1-week Science Teaching Forum in Washington D.C. where they work with APS staff, physiologists, and mentors to explore and practice effective teaching methods focused on how to integrate inquiry, equity, and the Internet into their classrooms. This program is supported by the National Center for Research Resources (NCRR) and the National Institute of Diabetes and Digestive and Kidney Diseases (NIDDK), both components of the National Institutes of Health (NIH).

Number awarded Varies each year; recently 17 of these fellowships were awarded.

Deadline January of each year.

[1014]
FUND FOR LATINO SCHOLARSHIP

American Political Science Association
Attn: Centennial Center Visiting Scholars Program
1527 New Hampshire Avenue, N.W.
Washington, DC 20036-1206
(202) 483-2512   Fax: (202) 483-2657
E-mail: center@apsanet.org
Web: www.apsanet.org/content_3471.cfm

Summary To provide funding for travel or research to members of the American Political Science Association (APSA) and other students and scholars who are involved with Latinos.

Eligibility Applications for this assistance should involve activities that 1) provide professional opportunities and financial assistance to Latino/a graduate students in political science programs; 2) support the teaching, research, and publishing activities of junior-level, tenure-track Latino/a political science faculty; or 3) support activities that advance our knowledge of Latino/a politics. Latino/a scholars (whatever their research field) and all scholars (including non-Latinos/as) who are studying Latino politics in the United States are eligible.

Financial Data Travel grants and most research grants are $500. Under exceptional circumstances, a grant of up to $1,000 may be awarded. Funding is intended for travel assistance to attend the APSA annual meeting, conduct field research, attend another scholarly conference, or participate in a program at the APSA Centennial Center for Political Science and Public Affairs.

Duration These are 1-time grants.

Additional data The APSA launched its Centennial Center for Political Science and Public Affairs in 2003 to commemorate the centennial year of the association.

Number awarded 1 or more each year.

Deadline May of each year.

[1015]
GAIUS CHARLES BOLIN DISSERTATION AND POST-MFA FELLOWSHIPS

Williams College
Attn: Dean of the Faculty
880 Main Street
Hopkins Hall, Third Floor
P.O. Box 141
Williamstown, MA 01267
(413) 597-4351   Fax: (413) 597-3553
E-mail: gburda@williams.edu
Web: dean-faculty.williams.edu

Summary To provide financial assistance to Hispanic Americans and members of other underrepresented groups who are interested in teaching courses at Williams College while working on their doctoral dissertation or building their post-M.F.A. professional portfolio.

Eligibility This program is open to members of underrepresented groups, including ethnic minorities, first-generation college students, women in predominantly male fields, and scholars with disabilities. Applicants must be 1) doctoral candidates in any field who have completed all work for a Ph.D. except for the dissertation; or 2) artists who completed an M.F.A. degree within the past 2 years and are building their professional portfolio. They must be willing to teach a course at Williams College. Along with their application, they must submit a full curriculum vitae, a graduate school transcript, 3 letters of recommendation, a copy of their dissertation prospectus or samples of their artistic work, and a description of their teaching interests within a department or program at Williams College. U.S. citizenship or permanent resident status is required.

Financial Data Fellows receive $36,000 for the academic year, plus housing assistance, office space, computer and library privileges, and a research allowance of up to $4,000.

Duration 2 years.

Additional data Bolin fellows are assigned a faculty adviser in the appropriate department. This program was established in 1985. Fellows are expected to teach a 1-semester course each year. They must be in residence at Williams College for the duration of the fellowship.

Number awarded 3 each year.

Deadline November of each year.

[1016]
GEOPHYSICAL FLUID DYNAMICS FELLOWSHIPS

Woods Hole Oceanographic Institution
Attn: Academic Programs Office
Clark Laboratory, MS 31
266 Woods Hole Road
Woods Hole, MA 02543-1541
(508) 289-2950　　　　　　Fax: (508) 457-2188
E-mail: gfd@whoi.edu
Web: www.whoi.edu/gfd

Summary To provide summer research and study opportunities at Woods Hole Oceanographic Institution (WHOI) to pre- and postdoctoral scholars (particularly Hispanic Americans, other underrepresented minorities, and women) who are interested in geophysical fluid dynamics.

Eligibility This program is open to pre- and postdoctorates who are interested in pursuing research or study opportunities in a field that involves non-linear dynamics of rotating, stratified fluids. Fields of specialization include classical fluid dynamics, physical oceanography, meteorology, geophysical fluid dynamics, astrophysics, planetary atmospheres, hydromagnetics, physics, and applied mathematics. Applications from women and members of underrepresented groups are particularly encouraged.

Financial Data Participants receive a stipend of $5,600 and an allowance for travel expenses within the United States.

Duration 10 weeks during the summer.

Additional data Each summer, the program at WHOI revolves around a central theme. A recent theme related to shear turbulence. The main components of the summer program are a series of principal lectures, a set of supplementary research seminars, and research projects conducted by the student fellows with the active support of the staff. Funding for this program, which began in 1959, is provided by the National Science Foundation and Office of Naval Research.

Number awarded Up to 10 graduate students are supported each year.

Deadline February of each year.

[1017]
GEORGE A. STRAIT MINORITY SCHOLARSHIP ENDOWMENT

American Association of Law Libraries
Attn: Chair, Scholarships Committee
105 West Adams Street, Suite 3300
Chicago, IL 60603
(312) 939-4764　　　　　　Fax: (312) 431-1097
E-mail: scholarships@aall.org
Web: www.aallnet.org

Summary To provide financial assistance to Hispanic American and other minority college seniors or college graduates who are interested in becoming law librarians.

Eligibility This program is open to college graduates with meaningful law library experience who are members of minority groups and intend to have a career in law librarianship. Applicants must be degree candidates at an ALA-accredited library school or an ABA-accredited law school. Along with their application, they must submit a personal statement that discusses their interest in law librarianship, reason for applying for this scholarship, career goals as a law librarian, and any other pertinent information.

Financial Data The stipend is $3,500.

Duration 1 year.

Additional data This program, established in 1990, is currently supported by Thomson Reuters.

Number awarded Varies each year; recently, 5 of these scholarships were awarded.

Deadline March of each year.

[1018]
GERALD OSHITA MEMORIAL FELLOWSHIP

Djerassi Resident Artists Program
Attn: Admissions
2325 Bear Gulch Road
Woodside, CA 94062-4405
(650) 747-1250　　　　　　Fax: (650) 747-0105
E-mail: drap@djerassi.org
Web: www.djerassi.org/artistresidencies.html

Summary To provide an opportunity for Hispanic Americans and other composers of color to participate in the Djerassi Resident Artists Program.

Eligibility This program is open to composers of Asian, African, Latino, or Native American ethnic background. Applicants must be interested in utilizing a residency to compose, study, rehearse, and otherwise advance their own creative projects.

Financial Data The fellow is offered housing, meals, studio space, and a stipend of $2,500.

Duration 1 month, from late March through mid-November.

Additional data This fellowship was established in 1994. The program is located in northern California, 45 miles south of San Francisco, on 600 acres of rangeland, redwood forests, and hiking trails. There is a $45 non-refundable application fee.

Number awarded 1 each year.

Deadline February of each year.

[1019]
GERTRUDE AND MAURICE GOLDHABER DISTINGUISHED FELLOWSHIPS

Brookhaven National Laboratory
Attn: Bill Bookless
Building 460
40 Brookhaven Avenue
Upton, NY 11973
(631) 344-5734   E-mail: wbookless@bnl.gov
Web: www.bnl.gov/hr/goldhaber.asp

Summary To provide funding to postdoctoral scientists (particularly Hispanic Americans, other minorities, and women) who are interested in conducting research at Brookhaven National Laboratory (BNL).

Eligibility This program is open to scholars who are no more than 3 years past receipt of the Ph.D. and are interested in working at BNL. Candidates must be interested in working in close collaboration with a member of the BNL scientific staff and qualifying for a scientific staff position at BNL upon completion of the appointment. The sponsoring scientist must have an opening and be able to support the candidate at the standard starting salary for postdoctoral research associates. The program especially encourages applications from minorities and women.

Financial Data The program provides additional funds to bring the salary to $75,000 per year.

Duration 3 years.

Additional data This program is funded by Battelle Memorial Institute and the State University of New York at Stony Brook.

Number awarded Up to 2 each year.

Deadline June of each year.

[1020]
GILBERT F. WHITE POSTDOCTORAL FELLOWSHIP PROGRAM

Resources for the Future
Attn: Coordinator for Academic Programs
1616 P Street, N.W., Suite 600
Washington, DC 20036-1400
(202) 328-5020   Fax: (202) 939-3460
E-mail: white-award@rff.org
Web: www.rff.org

Summary To provide funding to postdoctoral researchers (particularly Hispanic Americans, other minorities, and women) who wish to devote a year to scholarly work at Resources for the Future (RFF) in Washington, D.C.

Eligibility This program is open to individuals in any discipline who have completed their doctoral requirements and are interested in conducting scholarly research at RFF in social or policy science areas that relate to natural resources, energy, or the environment. Teaching and/or research experience at the postdoctoral level is preferred but not essential. Individuals holding positions in government as well as at academic institutions are eligible. Women and minority candidates are strongly encouraged to apply. Non-citizens are eligible if they have proper work and residency documentation.

Financial Data Fellows receive an annual stipend (based on their academic salary) plus research support, office facilities at RFF, and an allowance of up to $1,000 for moving or

living expenses. Fellowships do not provide medical insurance or other RFF fringe benefits.

Duration 11 months.

Additional data Fellows are assigned to an RFF research division: the Energy and Natural Resources division, the Quality of the Environment division, or the Center for Risk, Resource, and Environmental Management. Fellows are expected to be in residence at Resources for the Future for the duration of the program.

Number awarded 1 each year.

Deadline February of each year.

[1021]
GLORIA E. ANZALDUA BOOK PRIZE

National Women's Studies Association
Attn: Book Prizes
11 East Mount Royal Avenue, Suite 100
Baltimore, MD 21202
(410) 528-0355   Fax: (410) 528-0357
E-mail: awards@nwsa.org
Web: www.nwsa.org/content.asp?pl=16&contentid=16

Summary To recognize and reward members of the National Women's Studies Association (NWSA) who have written outstanding books on women of color and transnational issues.

Eligibility This award is available to NWSA members who submit a book that was published during the preceding year. Entries must present groundbreaking scholarship in women's studies and make a significant multicultural feminist contribution to women of color and/or transnational studies.

Financial Data The award provides an honorarium of $1,000 and lifetime membership in NWSA.

Duration The award is presented annually.

Additional data This award was first presented in 2008.

Number awarded 1 each year.

Deadline April of each year.

[1022]
GOALI FACULTY IN INDUSTRY AWARDS

National Science Foundation
Directorate for Engineering
Attn: Division of Industrial Innovation and Partnerships
4201 Wilson Boulevard, Room 550S
Arlington, VA 22230
(703) 292-7082   Fax: (703) 292-9056
TDD: (800) 281-8749   E-mail: dsenich@nsf.gov
Web: www.nsf.gov

Summary To provide funding to science, engineering, and mathematics faculty (particularly Hispanic Americans, other underrepresented minorities, women, and individuals with disabilities) who wish to conduct research in an industrial setting as part of the Grant Opportunities for Academic Liaison with Industry (GOALI) program of the National Science Foundation (NSF).

Eligibility This program is open to full-time faculty members at U.S. colleges and universities in science, engineering, and mathematics fields of interest to NSF. Applicants must be U.S. citizens, nationals, or permanent residents. They must present a plan for collaboration between their institution and industry, with a description of the facilities and resources that will be available at the industrial site to support the proposed research. In the selection process, consideration is given to the achievement of societally relevant outcomes, including full participation of women, persons with disabilities, and underrepresented minorities.

Financial Data Grants range from $30,000 to $75,000, including 50% of the faculty member's salary and fringe benefits during the industrial residency period. Up to 20% of the total requested amount may be used for travel and research expenses for the faculty and his/her students, including materials but excluding equipment. The industrial partner must commit to support the other 50% of the faculty salary and fringe benefits.

Duration 3 to 12 months.

Additional data This program is also offered by most other NSF directorates. Check the web site for a name and e-mail address of the contact person in each directorate.

Number awarded A total of 60 to 80 grants for all GOALI programs is awarded each year; total funding is approximately $5 million.

Deadline Applications may be submitted at any time.

[1023]
GOALI POSTDOCTORAL INDUSTRIAL FELLOWSHIPS

National Science Foundation
Directorate for Engineering
Attn: Division of Industrial Innovation and Partnerships
4201 Wilson Boulevard, Room 550S
Arlington, VA 22230
(703) 292-7082   Fax: (703) 292-9056
TDD: (800) 281-8749   E-mail: dsenich@nsf.gov
Web: www.nsf.gov

Summary To provide an opportunity for recent postdoctorates (particularly Hispanic Americans, other minorities, women, and individuals with disabilities) to work in industry as part of the Grant Opportunities for Academic Liaison with Industry (GOALI) program of the National Science Foundation (NSF).

Eligibility Applicants for these fellowships must have held a Ph.D. degree in a science, engineering, or mathematics field of interest to NSF for no more than 3 years. They must be U.S. citizens, nationals, or permanent residents. Along with their application, they must submit a plan for full-time work in industry under the guidance of an academic adviser and an industrial mentor. In the selection process, consideration is given to the achievement of societally relevant outcomes, including full participation of women, persons with disabilities, and underrepresented minorities.

Financial Data Grants range up to $75,000 per year. Funding, up to $4,000, may also be provided for transportation and moving expenses. Indirect costs are not allowed, but an institutional allowance of $5,000 is provided.

Duration 1 or 2 years.

Additional data This program is also offered by most other NSF directorates. Check the web site for a name and e-mail address of the contact person in each directorate.

Number awarded A total of 60 to 80 grants for all GOALI programs is awarded each year; total funding is approximately $5 million.

Deadline Applications may be submitted at any time.

[1024]
HARRY AND MIRIAM LEVINSON AWARD FOR EXCEPTIONAL CONTRIBUTIONS TO CONSULTING ORGANIZATIONAL PSYCHOLOGY

American Psychological Association
Attn: Office of Division Services
750 First Street, N.E.
Washington, DC 20002-4242
(202) 336-6022   E-mail: divisions@apa.org
Web: www.apa.org/about/awards/div-13-levinson.aspx

Summary To recognize and reward outstanding consulting psychologists, particularly Hispanic Americans and others who represent diversity in race, gender, age, etc.

Eligibility This award is presented to a member of the American Psychological Association (APA) who is a consulting psychologist. Nominees must have shown evidence of ability to convert psychological theory and concepts into applications through which managers and leaders can create effective, healthy, and humane organizations. The sponsor encourages nominations of individuals who represent diversity in race, ethnicity, gender, age, disability, and sexual orientation.

Financial Data The award is $5,000.

Duration The award is presented annually.

Additional data This award, first presented in 1992, is sponsored by Division 13 (Consulting Psychology) in conjunction with Division 12 (Society of Clinical Psychology), Division 14 (Industrial/Organizational Psychology), and Division 39 (Psychoanalysis) of the APA.

Number awarded 1 each year.

Deadline Nominations must be submitted by March of each year.

[1025]
HARVARD MEDICAL SCHOOL DEAN'S POSTDOCTORAL FELLOWSHIP

Harvard Medical School
Office for Diversity Inclusion and Community Partnership
Attn: Program Manager, Dean's Postdoctoral Fellowship
164 Longwood Avenue, Second Floor
Boston, MA 02115-5818
(617) 432-1083   Fax: (617) 432-3834
E-mail: brian_anderson@hms.harvard.edu
Web: www.hms.harvard.edu/dcp/deanspdfellowship

Summary To provide an opportunity for postdoctoral scholars (particularly Hispanic Americans or other minorities) with an advanced degree in the social and basic sciences who are interested in a postdoctoral fellowship to obtain research training at Harvard Medical School.

Eligibility This program is open to U.S. citizens and permanent residents who have completed an M.D., Ph.D., Sc.D., or equivalent degree in the basic or social sciences and have less than 5 years of relevant postdoctoral research experience. Applicants must be interested in a program of research training under the mentorship of a professor in 1 of the departments of Harvard Medical School: biological chemistry and molecular pharmacology, cell biology, genetics, global health and social medicine, health care policy, microbiology and immunobiology, neurobiology, stem cell and regenerative biology, or systems biology. Scientists from minority and disadvantaged backgrounds are especially encouraged to apply.

Selection is based on academic achievement, scholarly promise, potential to add to the diversity of the Harvard Medical School community, and the likelihood that the application will become an independent scientist and societal leader.

Financial Data Fellows receive a professional development allowance of $1,250 per year and a stipend that depends on the years of postdoctoral experience, ranging from $40,992 for zero to $47,820 for 4 years.

Duration 2 years.

Number awarded 2 each year.

Deadline Applications may be submitted at any time.

[1026]
HARVARD–NEWCOMEN POSTDOCTORAL FELLOWSHIP IN BUSINESS HISTORY

Harvard Business School
Attn: Fellowships
Rock Center 104
Boston, MA 02163
(617) 495-1003   Fax: (617) 495-0594
E-mail: wfriedman@hbs.edu
Web: www.hbs.edu/businesshistory/fellowships.html

Summary To provide residencies for study and research at Harvard Business School to scholars (particularly Hispanic Americans, other minorities, and women) in the fields of history, economics, or a related field.

Eligibility This program is open to scholars who, within the last 10 years, have received a Ph.D. degree in history, economics, or a related field. Applicants must be proposing to engage in research that would benefit from the resources at the Harvard Business School and the larger Boston scholarly community. In addition, they must be interested in participating in the school's business history courses, seminars, and case development activities. Along with their application, they must submit concise statements and descriptions of academic research undertaken in the past and a detailed description of the research they wish to undertake at Harvard. Women and minorities are especially encouraged to apply.

Financial Data The stipend is $46,000. In addition, a travel fund, a book fund, and administrative support are provided.

Duration 12 months, beginning in July.

Additional data This program began in 1949. Fellows spend approximately two-thirds of their time conducting research of their own choosing. The remainder of their time is devoted to participating in activities of the school, including attendance at the business history seminar and working with faculty teaching the business history courses offered in the M.B.A. program. Fellows are strongly encouraged to submit an article to *Business History Review* during their year at the school. Support for this fellowship is provided by the Newcomen Society of the United States.

Deadline October of each year.

[1027]
HEALTH AND AGING POLICY FELLOWSHIPS

Columbia University College of Physicians and Surgeons
Attn: Department of Psychiatry
Director, Health and Aging Policy Fellows
1051 Riverside Drive, Unit 9
New York, NY 10032
(212) 543-5401   Fax: (212) 543-6063
E-mail: pincush@nyspi.columbia.edu
Web: www.healthandagingpolicy.org

Summary To provide an opportunity for health professionals (particularly Hispanic Americans and members of other underrepresented groups) who have an interest in aging and policy issues to work as legislative assistants in Congress or at other sites.

Eligibility This program is open to physicians, nurses, and social workers who have a demonstrated commitment to health and aging issues and a desire to be involved in health policy at the federal, state, or local levels. Other professionals with clinical backgrounds (e.g., dentists, dieticians, economists, epidemiologists, health care administrators, psychologists) working in the field of health and aging are also eligible. Preference is given to professionals early or midway through their careers. Applicants must be interested serving as residential fellows by participating in the policymaking process on either the federal or state level as legislative assistants in Congress or as professional staff members in executive agencies or policy organizations. A non-residential track is also available to applicants who wish to work on a policy project throughout the year at relevant sites. Candidates from underrepresented groups are strongly encouraged to apply. Selection is based on commitment to health and aging issues and improving the health and well-being of older Americans, potential for leadership in health policy, professional qualifications and achievements, impact of the fellowship experience on the applicant's career, and interpersonal and communication skills. U.S. citizenship or permanent resident status is required.

Financial Data For residential fellows, the stipend depends on their current base salary, to a maximum of $120,000 per year; other benefits include a travel allowance for pre-fellowship arrangements and to fellowship-related meetings, a relocation grant of up to $3,500, and up to $400 per month for health insurance. For non-residential fellows, grants provide up to $30,000 to cover related fellowship and travel costs.

Duration 9 to 12 months; fellows may apply for a second year of participation.

Additional data This program, which began in 2009, operates in collaboration with the American Political Science Association Congressional Fellowship Program. Funding is provided by The Atlantic Philanthropies. The John Heinz/Health and Aging Policy Fellowship, an activity of the Teresa and H. John Heinz III Foundation, supports 1 fellow to work in the Senate. Support is also provided by the Centers for Disease Control and Prevention, the John A. Hartford Foundation, and the Gerontological Society of America.

Number awarded Varies each year; recently, 4 residential and 6 non-residential fellowships were awarded.

Deadline May of each year.

[1028]
HEALTH, EDUCATION, AND HUMAN SERVICES FELLOWSHIPS

American Association for the Advancement of Science
Attn: Science and Technology Policy Fellowships
1200 New York Avenue, N.W.
Washington, DC 20005-3920
(202) 326-6700   Fax: (202) 289-4950
E-mail: fellowships@aaas.org
Web: www.fellowships.aaas.org

Summary To provide postdoctoral scientists and engineers (particularly Hispanic Americans, other minorities, and individuals with disabilities) with an opportunity to work at designated federal agencies on issues of health, education, and human services.

Eligibility This program is open to doctoral-level scientists (Ph.D., M.D., D.V.M., D.Sc., and other terminal degrees) in any field of science (behavioral, biological, computational, earth, health, medical, physical, or social), engineering, or mathematics. Engineers with a master's degree and at least 3 years of professional experience are also eligible. Applicants should be able to support improved programs, policies, planning, risk analysis, regulation, monitoring, and evaluation for a broad range of initiatives in 1) preventive and community health, disease identification and response, and medical research; 2) individual, family, and community social services, systems, and support; 3) food processing and distribution safety; and 4) science education, research, and innovation. They must demonstrate solid scientific and technical credentials; a commitment to serve society; good communication skills; the ability to engage with non-scientific audiences; and an interest in working as special assistants for designated federal agencies (the Food Safety Inspection Service (FSIS) of the U.S. Department of Agriculture (USDA), National Science Foundation (NSF), National Institutes of Health (NIH), Department of Health and Human Services (DHHS), or Department of Veterans Affairs). U.S. citizenship is required; federal employees are not eligible. The sponsor seeks candidates from a broad array of backgrounds and a diversity of geographic, disciplinary, gender, and ethnic perspectives, as well as disability status.

Financial Data The stipend for fellows with 0 to 7 years of postdoctoral experience is $74,872 in the first year and $77,368 in the second year. For fellows with 7 to 15 years of experience, the stipend is $84,855 in the first year and $87,350 in the second year. Fellows who have 15 or more years of postdoctoral experience receive $97,333 in the first year and $99,420 in the second year. Also provided are a $4,000 relocation allowance for fellows from outside the Washington, D.C. area, reimbursement for health insurance, and a $4,000 travel allowance.

Duration 1 year, beginning in September.

Number awarded 30 to 40 each year.

Deadline October of each year.

[1029]
HEALTH SERVICES RESEARCH PROJECTS

Agency for Healthcare Research and Quality
Attn: Office of Extramural Research, Education, and
   Priority Populations
540 Gaither Road
Rockville, MD 20850
(301) 427-1556   Fax: (301) 427-1562
TDD: (301) 451-0088
E-mail: Kishena.Wadhwani@ahrq.hhs.gov
Web: grants.nih.gov/grants/guide/pa-files/PA-13-045.html

Summary To provide funding to scholars (particularly Hispanic Americans, other underrepresented minorities, and individuals with disabilities) who are interested in conducting research that is designed to improve the outcomes, quality, cost, and utilization of health care services.

Eligibility This program is open to investigators at domestic and foreign, nonprofit, public and private organizations, including universities, clinics, units of state and local governments, nonprofit firms, and nonprofit foundations. Applicants must be proposing projects in 1 of the research portfolio areas of the Agency for Healthcare Research and Quality (AHRQ): 1) the value portfolio, for research that can be used to reduce unnecessary health care costs (waste) while maintaining or improving health care quality; 2) the health information technology portfolio, for the use of information and communication technology in health care to support the delivery of patient or population care; 3) the comparative effectiveness portfolio, for research focusing on comparative effectiveness of different clinical treatments and services; 4) the prevention/care management portfolio, to improve the quality, safety, efficiency, and effectiveness of preventive services and chronic care management in ambulatory care settings; 5) the patient safety portfolio, for research projects to identify the risks and hazards encountered by patients as a result of health care; or 6) the innovations and emerging areas portfolio, for research on ideas that have the potential for high impact. Members of underrepresented ethnic and racial groups and individuals with disabilities are especially encouraged to apply as principal investigators.

Financial Data The maximum grant is $250,000 per year, including both direct costs and facilities and administrative costs.

Duration 1 year; may be renewed up to 4 additional years.

Number awarded Varies each year.

Deadline March, July, or November of each year.

[1030]
HENRY DAVID RESEARCH GRANT IN HUMAN REPRODUCTIVE BEHAVIOR AND POPULATION STUDIES

American Psychological Foundation
750 First Street, N.E.
Washington, DC 20002-4242
(202) 336-5843   Fax: (202) 336-5812
E-mail: foundation@apa.org
Web: www.apa.org/apf/funding/david.aspx

Summary To provide funding to young psychologists (particularly Hispanic Americans, other minorities, women, and individuals with disabilities) who are interested in conducting research on reproductive behavior.

Eligibility This program is open to doctoral students in psychology working on a dissertation and young psychologists who have no more than 7 years of postgraduate experience. Applicants must be interested in conducting research on human reproductive behavior or an area related to population concerns. Along with their application, they must submit a current curriculum vitae, 2 letters of recommendation, and an essay of 1 to 2 pages on their interest in human reproductive behavior or in population studies. The sponsor encourages applications from individuals who represent diversity in race, ethnicity, gender, age, disability, and sexual orientation.

Financial Data The grant is $1,500.

Duration The grant is presented annually.

Number awarded 1 each year.

Deadline February of each year.

[1031]
HIGH PRIORITY, SHORT-TERM BRIDGE AWARDS IN DIABETES RESEARCH

Juvenile Diabetes Research Foundation International
Attn: Grant Administrator
26 Broadway, 14th Floor
New York, NY 10004
(212) 479-7572   Toll Free: (800) 533-CURE
Fax: (212) 785-9595   E-mail: info@jdrf.org
Web: jdrf.org

Summary To provide funding to scientists (particularly Hispanic Americans, other underrepresented minorities, women, and individuals with disabilities) who are interested in conducting diabetes-related research but have not yet received any support.

Eligibility Applicants must have an M.D., D.M.D., D.V.M., Ph.D., or equivalent degree and have a full-time faculty position or equivalent at a college, university, medical school, or other research facility. They must have applied for grants previously and scored within 10% of the funding payline of a research funding agency but failed to receive support. Awards must be used to obtain new data to support the feasibility or validity of the research, address reviewers' concerns, or revise approaches to the research. There are no citizenship requirements. Applications are encouraged from women, members of minority groups underrepresented in the sciences, and people with disabilities. The proposed research may be conducted at foreign or domestic, for-profit or nonprofit, or public or private institutions, including universities, colleges, hospitals, laboratories, units of state or local government, or eligible agencies of the federal government.

Financial Data Awards are limited to $55,000 plus 10% indirect costs.

Duration 1 year; generally nonrenewable.

Number awarded Varies each year.

Deadline February, May, or October of each year.

[1032]
HIGH-RISK RESEARCH IN BIOLOGICAL ANTHROPOLOGY AND ARCHAEOLOGY GRANTS

National Science Foundation
Social, Behavioral, and Economic Sciences
Attn: Division of Behavioral and Cognitive Sciences
4201 Wilson Boulevard, Room 995 N
Arlington, VA 22230
(703) 292-8759   Fax: (703) 292-9068
TDD: (800) 281-8749   E-mail: jyellen@nsf.gov
Web: www.nsf.gov/funding/pgm_summ.jsp?pims_id=5319

Summary To provide funding to scholars (particularly Hispanic Americans, other underrepresented minorities, and individuals with disabilities) who are interested in conducting high-risk research in anthropology or archaeology.

Eligibility This program is open to scholars interested in conducting research projects in cultural anthropology, archaeology, or physical anthropology that might be considered too risky for normal review procedures. A project is considered risky if the data may not be obtainable in spite of all reasonable preparation on the researcher's part. Proposals for extremely urgent research where access to the data may not be available in the normal review schedule, even with all reasonable preparation by the researcher, are also appropriate for this program. Graduate students are not eligible. Applications are encouraged from all citizens, including women and men, underrepresented minorities, and persons with disabilities.

Financial Data Grants up to $35,000, including indirect costs, are available.

Duration 1 year.

Number awarded Generally, 5 of these grants are awarded each year.

Deadline Applications may be submitted at any time.

[1033]
HIVMA MINORITY CLINICAL FELLOWSHIPS

Infectious Diseases Society of America
Attn: HIV Medicine Association
1300 Wilson Boulevard, Suite 300
Arlington, VA 22209
(703) 299-1215   Toll Free: (888) 844-4372
Fax: (703) 299-8766   E-mail: info@hivma.org
Web: www.hivma.org/Minority_Clinical_Fellowship.aspx

Summary To provide an opportunity for Latino and African American physicians to participate in a clinical training program related to HIV.

Eligibility This program is open to physicians (M.D. or D.O.) who are of African American or Latino descent and have a demonstrated interest in HIV medicine. Applicants must be legal residents of the United States and have an intent to establish their practice in areas of the country with large minority populations. They must have completed their residencies (or be within the first 5 years of clinical practice) and be board eligible. Their proposed clinical training program must have a link to an academic institution where the majority of their time will be spent engaged in HIV clinical care and where they will have the opportunity to manage continuously at least 30 HIV patients in both inpatient and outpatient settings. Clinical settings with large minority patient populations are required. Applicants must identify a mentor to oversee their clinical experience; mentors must be members of the HIV Medicine Association (HIVMA).

Financial Data The stipend is $60,000. Fellows also receive fringe benefits equivalent to those enjoyed by staff of similar rank at the sponsoring institution, 1 year membership in HIVMA, and free registration and travel support for the annual meeting of the Infectious Diseases Society of America (IDSA). An additional $10,000 is paid to the institution to offset administrative costs.

Duration 1 year.

Additional data Fellows may elect to spend up to 2 months of their fellowship at another approved institution, clinic, or practice to supplement their clinical experience. Support for this program is provided by Pfizer, Gilead Sciences, Bristol-Myers Squibb, Janssen Therapeutics, and Genentech. Fellows currently in clinical practice are expected to spend at least 50% of their time on clinical care and clinical education associated with the fellowship.

Number awarded 2 each year: 1 African American and 1 Latino.

Deadline March of each year.

[1034]
HUBBLE FELLOWSHIPS

Space Telescope Science Institute
Attn: Hubble Fellowship Program Office
3700 San Martin Drive
Baltimore, MD 21218
(410) 338-5079   Fax: (410) 338-4211
E-mail: hfinquiry@stsci.edu
Web: www.stsci.edu/institute/smo/fellowships/hubble

Summary To provide funding to recent postdoctoral scientists (particularly Hispanic Americans, other minorities, and women) who are interested in conducting research related to the Hubble Space Telescope or related missions of the National Aeronautics and Space Administration (NASA).

Eligibility This program is open to postdoctoral scientists who completed their doctoral degree within the past 3 years in astronomy, physics, or related disciplines. Applicants must be interested in conducting research related to NASA Cosmic Origins missions: the Hubble Space Telescope, Herschel Space Observatory, James Webb Space Telescope, Stratospheric Observatory for Infrared Astronomy, or the Spitzer Space Telescope. They may U.S. citizens or English-speaking citizens of other countries with valid visas. Research may be theoretical, observational, or instrumental. Women and members of minority groups are strongly encouraged to apply.

Financial Data Stipends are approximately $66,500 per year. Other benefits may include health insurance, relocation costs, and support for travel, equipment, and other direct costs of research.

Duration 3 years: an initial 1-year appointment and 2 annual renewals, contingent on satisfactory performance and availability of funds.

Additional data This program, funded by NASA, began in 1990 and was limited to work with the Hubble Space Telescope. A parallel program, called the Spitzer Fellowship, began in 2002 and was limited to work with the Spitzer Space Telescope. In 2009, those programs were combined into this single program, which was also broadened to include the other NASA Cosmic Origins missions. Fellows are required to be in residence at their host institution engaged in full-time research for the duration of the grant.

Number awarded Varies each year; recently, 17 of these fellowships were awarded.

Deadline October of each year.

[1035]
INDEPENDENT SCIENTIST AWARD

Agency for Healthcare Research and Quality
Attn: Office of Extramural Research, Education, and
   Priority Populations
540 Gaither Road
Rockville, MD 20850
(301) 427-1555   Fax: (301) 427-1562
TDD: (301) 451-0088
E-mail: Kay.Anderson@ahrq.hhs.gov
Web: grants.nih.gov/grants/guide/pa-files/PA-09-086.html

Summary To provide funding to newly independent scientists (particularly Hispanic Americans, other underrepresented minorities, and individuals with disabilities) who are interested in conducting research to improve the outcomes, effectiveness, quality, cost, and utilization of health care services.

Eligibility This program is open to U.S. citizens or permanent residents who have a clinical (e.g., M.D., D.O., D.D.S., D.M.D., D.C., O.D., D.N.S., Pharm.D.) or research (e.g., Ph.D., Sc.D., Dr.P.H.) doctoral degree and are no more than 7 years beyond their latest research training experience. Applicants must be proposing projects in 1 of the research portfolio areas of the Agency for Healthcare Research and Quality (AHRQ): 1) the value portfolio, for research that can be used to reduce unnecessary health care costs (waste) while maintaining or improving health care quality; 2) the health information technology portfolio, for the use of information and communication technology in health care to support the delivery of patient or population care; 3) the comparative effectiveness portfolio, for research focusing on comparative effectiveness of different clinical treatments and services; 4) the prevention/care management portfolio, to improve the quality, safety, efficiency, and effectiveness of preventive services and chronic care management in ambulatory care settings; 5) the patient safety portfolio, for research projects to identify the risks and hazards encountered by patients as a result of health care; or 6) the innovations and emerging areas portfolio, for research on ideas that have the potential for high impact. Members of underrepresented ethnic and racial groups, individuals with disabilities, and individuals from disadvantaged backgrounds are especially encouraged to apply.

Financial Data Grants provide salary up to $90,000 annually, plus associated fringe benefits. Also available are up to $25,000 per year for research development support (tuition, fees, and books related to career development; research expenses such as supplies, equipment, and technical personnel; travel to research meetings or training; and statistical services, including personnel and computer time). Facilities and administrative costs are reimbursed at 8% of modified total direct costs.

Duration 3 to 5 years; nonrenewable.

Additional data At least 75% of the recipient's full-time professional effort must be devoted to the program and the remainder devoted to other research-related and/or teaching pursuits consistent with the objectives of the award.

Number awarded Varies each year.

Deadline February, June, or October of each year.

[1036]
INSTITUTIONAL RESEARCH AND ACADEMIC CAREER DEVELOPMENT AWARDS

National Institute of General Medical Sciences
Attn: MORE Special Initiatives Branch
45 Center Drive, Suite 2AS37
Bethesda, MD 20892-6200
(301) 594-3900   Fax: (301) 480-2753
TDD: (301) 451-0088   E-mail: singhs@nigms.nih.gov
Web: grants.nih.gov/grants/guide/pa-files/PAR-11-255

Summary To provide an opportunity for Hispanic American and other underrepresented postdoctoral biomedical scientists to gain experience at a research-intensive institution (RII) while they complete a teaching assignment at a Minority Serving Institution (MSI).

Eligibility This program is open to members of minority groups underrepresented in the biomedical and behavioral sciences, defined as individuals with disabilities and African Americans, Hispanic Americans, Native Americans (including Alaska Natives), and natives of the U.S. Pacific Islands. Candidates must have a Ph.D., M.D., or comparable doctoral degree, be committed to research, and have the potential to develop as independent investigators. They must be interested in a mentored research experience at an RII, typical of other competitive postdoctoral opportunities, combined with a mentored teaching experience at a partner MSI.

Financial Data Grants up to $500,000 per year are available. Funding includes salary support for the scholar at a rate consistent with the established salary structure at the sponsoring institution, research development support (e.g., tuition and fees related to career development, supplies and other modest research expenses, travel to a scientific meeting, statistical services such as personnel and computer time), academic development support, and program administration. Facilities and administrative costs are reimbursed at 8% of modified total direct costs.

Duration 2 to 4 years.

Additional data The National Institute of General Medical Sciences, a component of the National Institutes of Health (NIH), operates this program as part of its Minority Opportunities for Research (MORE) Division. Funds are issued through a principal investigator at an RII, which submits the application to NIH and which then partners with 1 or more MSI. Scientists interested in participating in the program apply through the MSI. Scholars are expected to devote approximately 25% of their time to their teaching experience at the partner MSI.

Number awarded 1 or 2 each year.

Deadline September of each year.

[1037]
INTERNATIONAL COLLABORATION IN CHEMISTRY BETWEEN U.S. INVESTIGATORS AND THEIR COUNTERPARTS ABROAD

National Science Foundation
Directorate for Mathematical and Physical Sciences
Attn: Division of Chemistry
4201 Wilson Boulevard, Room 1055 S
Arlington, VA 22230
(703) 292-7719   Fax: (703) 292-9037
TDD: (800) 281-8749   E-mail: zrosenzw@nsf.gov
Web: www.nsf.gov/funding/pgm_summ.jsp?pims_id=13627

Summary To provide funding to chemists in the United States (particularly Hispanic Americans, other underrepresented minorities, women, and individuals with disabilities) who are interested in conducting collaborative research with counterparts in designated foreign countries.

Eligibility This program is open to chemists at colleges and universities in the United States. Applicants must be interested in conducting a research project in collaboration with a scientist in Austria, Brazil, France, Israel, Japan, Luxembourg, Russia, or Taiwan. Preference is given to proposals where the efforts on the U.S. and foreign sides are balanced and complementary. Applications are encouraged from all citizens, including women and men, underrepresented minorities, and persons with disabilities.

Financial Data Awards average $140,000 per year.

Duration 3 years.

Additional data This program operates in conjunction with Austrian Science Fund, the State of São Paulo Research Foundation, the French National Research Agency, the United States-Israel Binational Science Foundation, the National Research Fund of Luxembourg, the Russian Foundation for Basic Research, and the National Science Council of Taiwan.

Number awarded 10 to 40 each year. A total of $10 million is available for this program annually.

Deadline Preliminary proposals must be submitted by July of each year; full proposals are due in October.

[1038]
INVESTIGATOR AWARDS IN HEALTH POLICY RESEARCH

Robert Wood Johnson Foundation
College Road East and U.S. Route 1
P.O. Box 2316
Princeton, NJ 08543-2316
(609) 932-8701   Toll Free: (877) 843-RWJF
E-mail: mail@rwjf.org
Web: www.rwjf.org

Summary To provide funding to Hispanic Americans and other investigators from diverse fields who are interested in conducting research on health policy.

Eligibility This program is open to investigators in the health, social, and behavioral sciences. Members of minority groups, researchers early in their careers, and individuals in non-academic settings, such as research firms and policy organizations, are especially encouraged to apply. The proposed research should help develop, interpret, or substantially advance ideas or knowledge that can improve health or health care policy in the United States. Selection is based on the relevance of the research to national policy and its potential to inform and improve policy-making; the contribution and potential significance of the project to the theoretical underpinnings and knowledge base of health care, health policy, or other disciplines; the extent to which the work represents an innovative perspective on health, health care, or health policy; the soundness of the project's conceptual framework and methodology; the feasibility of the work; the likelihood that the findings can be useful to policy-makers and other leaders; capability of the investigator to undertake and complete the project on schedule; and investigator's research record.

Financial Data Grants up to $335,000 are provided. Funds are to be used primarily for project salary support for the principal investigator(s) and for indirect costs at a rate of up to 12%.

Duration 24 to 36 months.

Number awarded Approximately 8 each year.

Deadline Letters of intent must be submitted by January of each year. Completed applications are due in June.

[1039]
INVESTIGATORS IN PATHOGENESIS OF INFECTIOUS DISEASE

Burroughs Wellcome Fund
21 T.W. Alexander Drive, Suite 100
P.O. Box 13901
Research Triangle Park, NC 27709-3901
(919) 991-5112   Fax: (919) 991-5160
E-mail: info@bwfund.org
Web: www.bwfund.org

Summary To provide funding to physician/scientists in the United States and Canada (particularly Hispanic Americans, other minorities, and women) who wish to conduct research on pathogenesis, with a focus on the intersection of human and pathogen biology.

Eligibility This program is open to established independent physician/scientists who are citizens or permanent residents of the United States or Canada and affiliated with accredited degree-granting U.S. or Canadian medical schools. Applicants must be interested in conducting research projects related to the fungal, metazoan, and protozoan pathogens. Candidates must have an M.D., D.V.M., or Ph.D. degree and be tenure-track investigators as an assistant professor or equivalent at a degree-granting institution. Each institution (including its medical school, graduate schools, and all affiliated hospitals and research institutes) may nominate up to 2 candidates. Institutions that nominate a researcher who has a D.V.M. are allowed 3 nominations. The sponsor also encourages institutions to nominate underrepresented minorities and women. Selection is based on qualifications of the candidate and potential to conduct innovative research; demonstration of an established record of independent research; and quality and originality of the proposed research and its potential to advance understanding of fundamental issues of how infectious agents and human hosts interact.

Financial Data The grant provides $100,000 per year. No more than $20,000 of the grant may be used for salary support, but institutions may supplement the award to a level consistent with its own scale.

Duration 5 years.

Additional data This program began in 2001 as a replacement for several former programs: New Investigator and Scholar Awards in Molecular Pathogenic Mycology, New Investigator and Scholar Awards in Molecular Parasitology, and New Initiatives in Malaria Awards. Awardees are required to devote at least 75% of their time to research-related activities.

Number awarded Varies each year; recently, 9 of these grants were awarded.

Deadline October of each year.

[1040]
J. ROBERT GLADDEN ORTHOPAEDIC SOCIETY BASIC RESEARCH GRANTS

J. Robert Gladden Orthopaedic Society
Attn: Scientific Committee
6300 North River Road, Suite 727
Rosemont, IL 60018-4226
(847) 698-1633   Fax: (847) 823-4921
E-mail: jrgos@aaos.org
Web: www.gladdensociety.org

Summary To provide funding to members of the J. Robert Gladden Orthopaedic Society (JRGOS) who are Hispanic American or from another underrepresented group and interested in conducting a basic research project.

Eligibility This program is open to members of underrepresented minority groups who are JRGOS members and interested in conducting a basic research project. Applicants must be affiliated with a research institution that provides laboratory space and basic facilities. They must be able to demonstrate the compatibility of their project's clinical relevance with the mission and goals of the society. Preference is given to applicants planning to work with a senior JRGOS member.

Financial Data The grant is $25,000.

Duration 1 year.

Additional data This program is sponsored by DePuy/Johnson & Johnson.

Number awarded 1 or more each year.

Deadline September of each year.

[1041]
JAMES A. RAWLEY PRIZE

Organization of American Historians
Attn: Award and Committee Coordinator
112 North Bryan Street
Bloomington, IN 47408-4141
(812) 855-7311   Fax: (812) 855-0696
E-mail: khamm@oah.org
Web: www.oah.org/awards/awards.rawley.index.html

Summary To recognize and reward authors of outstanding books dealing with race relations in the United States.

Eligibility This award is presented to the author of the outstanding book on the history of race relations in America. Entries must have been published during the current calendar year.

Financial Data The award is $1,000 and a certificate.

Duration The award is presented annually.

Additional data This award was established in 1990.

Number awarded 1 each year.

Deadline September of each year.

[1042]
JOEL ELKES RESEARCH AWARD

American College of Neuropsychopharmacology
Attn: Executive Office
5034-A Thoroughbred Lane
Brentwood, TN 37027
(615) 324-2360　　　　　　　　　Fax: (615) 523-1715
E-mail: acnp@acnp.org
Web: www.acnp.org/programs/awards.aspx

Summary To recognize and reward young scientists (particularly Hispanic Americans, other minorities, and women) who have contributed outstanding clinical or translational research to neuropsychopharmacology.

Eligibility This award is available to scientists who are younger than 50 years of age. Nominees must have made an outstanding clinical or translational contribution to neuropsychopharmacology. The contribution may be based on a single discovery or a cumulative body of work. Emphasis is placed on contributions that further understanding of self-regulatory processes as they affect mental function and behavior in disease and well-being. Membership in the American College of Neuropsychopharmacology (ACNP) is not required. Nomination of women and minorities is highly encouraged.

Financial Data The award consists of an expense-paid trip to the ACNP annual meeting, a monetary honorarium, and a plaque.

Duration The award is presented annually.

Additional data This award was first presented in 1986.

Number awarded 1 each year.

Deadline Nominations must be submitted by June of each year.

[1043]
JOHN AND POLLY SPARKS EARLY CAREER GRANT

American Psychological Foundation
750 First Street, N.E.
Washington, DC 20002-4242
(202) 336-5843　　　　　　　　　Fax: (202) 336-5812
E-mail: foundation@apa.org
Web: www.apa.org/apf/funding/sparks-early-career.aspx

Summary To provide funding to young psychologists (particularly Hispanic Americans, other minorities, women, and individuals with disabilities) who are interested in conducting research on serious emotional disturbance in children.

Eligibility This program is open to young psychologists who completed a doctoral degree (Ed.D., Psy.D., Ph.D.) within the past 7 years. Applicants must be interested in conducting research in the area of early intervention and treatment for serious emotional disturbance in children. The sponsor encourages applications from individuals who represent diversity in race, ethnicity, gender, age, disability, and sexual orientation.

Financial Data The grant is $10,000.

Duration 1 year.

Additional data This program began in 2013.

Number awarded 1 each year.

Deadline May of each year.

[1044]
JOHN MCLENDON MEMORIAL MINORITY POSTGRADUATE SCHOLARSHIP AWARD

National Association of Collegiate Directors of Athletics
Attn: NACDA Foundation
24651 Detroit Road
Westlake, OH 44145
(440) 788-7475　　　　　　　　　Fax: (440) 892-4007
E-mail: jbouyer@nacda.com
Web: www.nacda.com/mclendon/scholarship.html

Summary To provide financial assistance to Hispanic American and other minority college seniors who are interested in working on a graduate degree in athletics administration.

Eligibility This program is open to minority college students who are seniors, are attending school on a full-time basis, have a GPA of 3.2 or higher, intend to attend graduate school to earn a degree in athletics administration, and are involved in college or community activities. Also eligible are college graduates who have at least 2 years' experience in an athletics administration position. Candidates must be nominated by an official of a member institution of the National Association of Collegiate Directors of Athletics (NACDA) or (for college graduates) a supervisor.

Financial Data The stipend is $10,000.

Duration 1 year.

Additional data Recipients must maintain full-time status during the senior year to retain their eligibility. They must attend NACDA-member institutions.

Number awarded 5 each year.

Deadline Nominations must be submitted by April of each year.

[1045]
JOHN V. KRUTILLA RESEARCH STIPEND

Resources for the Future
Attn: Coordinator for Academic Programs
1616 P Street, N.W., Suite 600
Washington, DC 20036-1400
(202) 328-5020　　　　　　　　　Fax: (202) 939-3460
E-mail: krutilla-award@rff.org
Web: www.rff.org

Summary To provide funding for research related to environmental and resource economics to young scholars (particularly Hispanic Americans, other minorities, and women).

Eligibility This program is open to scholars who received their doctoral degree within the past 5 years. Applicants must be interested in conducting research related to environmental and resource economics. They must submit a short description of the proposed research, a curriculum vitae, and a letter of recommendation. Women and minority candidates are strongly encouraged to apply. Non-citizens are eligible if they have proper work and residency documentation.

Financial Data The grant is $5,500.

Duration 1 year.

Additional data This award was first presented in 2006.

Number awarded 1 each year.

Deadline February of each year.

[1046]
JONATHAN REICHERT AND BARBARA WOLFF-REICHERT AWARD FOR EXCELLENCE IN ADVANCED LABORATORY INSTRUCTION

American Physical Society
Attn: Honors Program
One Physics Ellipse
College Park, MD 20740-3844
(301) 209-3268   Fax: (301) 209-0865
E-mail: honors@aps.org
Web: www.aps.org/programs/honors/awards/lab.cfm

Summary To recognize and reward physicists (particularly Hispanic Americans, other underrepresented minorities, and women) who have developed and taught outstanding undergraduate laboratory courses.

Eligibility This award is available to individuals or teams of individuals who have taught, developed, and sustained advanced undergraduate physics laboratory courses for at least 4 years at an institution in the United States. Nominations should present evidence of the dissemination of the laboratory work to the broader physics community. Nominations of qualified women and members of underrepresented minority groups are especially encouraged.

Financial Data The award consists of $5,000 as an honorarium, a certificate citing the accomplishments of the recipient, and an allowance up to $2,000 for travel expenses to the meeting where the award is presented.

Duration The award is presented annually.

Additional data This award was established in 2012.

Number awarded 1 each year.

Deadline June of each year.

[1047]
JOSEPH B. GITTLER AWARD

American Psychological Foundation
750 First Street, N.E.
Washington, DC 20002-4242
(202) 336-5843   Fax: (202) 336-5812
E-mail: foundation@apa.org
Web: www.apa.org/apf/funding/gittler.aspx

Summary To recognize and reward scholars and graduate students in psychology (particularly Hispanic Americans, other minorities, women, and individuals with disabilities) whose work has transformed the philosophical foundations of the discipline.

Eligibility This award is available to scholars and graduate students whose body of work or whose individual work has transformed the philosophical foundations of psychological knowledge. Self-nominations are welcome. Selection is based on conformance with stated program goals and magnitude of contributions The sponsor encourages nominations of individuals who represent diversity in race, ethnicity, gender, age, disability, and sexual orientation.

Financial Data The award is $10,000.

Duration The award is presented annually.

Additional data This award was first presented in 2008.

Number awarded 1 each year.

Deadline Nominations must be submitted by May of each year.

[1048]
JRGOS CLINICAL RESEARCH GRANTS

J. Robert Gladden Orthopaedic Society
Attn: Scientific Committee
6300 North River Road, Suite 727
Rosemont, IL 60018-4226
(847) 698-1633   Fax: (847) 823-4921
E-mail: jrgos@aaos.org
Web: www.gladdensociety.org

Summary To provide funding to members of the J. Robert Gladden Orthopaedic Society (JRGOS) who are Hispanic American or from another underrepresented minority group and interested in conducting a clinical research project in areas where funding is difficult to obtain.

Eligibility This program is open to members of underrepresented minority groups who are new or experienced JRGOS members and interested in conducting a research project in clinical areas where funding is difficult to obtain. Applicants must be seeking seed money to initiate studies to obtain background data with the goal of obtaining future funding from other sources. They must be able to demonstrate the compatibility of their project's clinical problems with the mission and goals of the society. Preference is given to applicants planning to work with a senior JRGOS member.

Financial Data The grant is $30,000 per year.

Duration 1 year; may be renewed 1 additional year.

Additional data This program is sponsored by DePuy/Johnson & Johnson.

Number awarded 1 or more each year.

Deadline September of each year.

[1049]
JUDICIAL BRANCH FELLOWSHIPS

American Association for the Advancement of Science
Attn: Science and Technology Policy Fellowships
1200 New York Avenue, N.W.
Washington, DC 20005-3920
(202) 326-6700   Fax: (202) 289-4950
E-mail: fellowships@aaas.org
Web: www.fellowships.aaas.org

Summary To provide postdoctoral scientists and engineers (particularly Hispanic Americans, other minorities, women, and individuals with disabilities) with an opportunity to work with the federal judiciary.

Eligibility This program is open to doctoral-level scientists (Ph.D., M.D., D.V.M., D.Sc., and other terminal degrees) in any field of science (behavioral, biological, computational, earth, health, medical, physical, or social), engineering, or mathematics who have at least 3 years of professional postdoctoral experience. Preference is given to scientists and engineers who also have a J.D. degree or legal experience. Applicants should be able to contribute scientific and technical expertise to judicial administration, operations, education programs, protocol and discovery, or courtroom technology while learning first-hand about contemporary policy issues facing the judiciary. They must demonstrate solid scientific and technical credentials; a commitment to serve society; good communication skills; the ability to engage with non-scientific audiences; and an interest in working as special assistants for the Federal Judicial Center or the Federal Judicial Court of Washington, D.C. U.S. citizenship is required; federal employees are not eligible. The sponsor seeks candidates from a broad array of backgrounds and a diversity of geographic, disciplinary, gender, and ethnic perspectives, as well as disability status.

Financial Data The stipend for fellows with 0 to 7 years of postdoctoral experience is $74,872 in the first year and $77,368 in the second year. For fellows with 7 to 15 years of experience, the stipend is $84,855 in the first year and $87,350 in the second year. Fellows who have 15 or more years of postdoctoral experience receive $97,333 in the first year and $99,829 in the second year. Also provided are a $4,000 relocation allowance for fellows from outside the Washington, D.C. area, reimbursement for health insurance, and a $4,000 travel allowance.

Duration 1 year, beginning in September; may be renewed for 1 additional year.

Additional data This program began in 2014.

Number awarded 5 to 15 each year.

Deadline October of each year.

[1050]
JULIUS AXELROD MENTORSHIP AWARD

American College of Neuropsychopharmacology
Attn: Executive Office
5034-A Thoroughbred Lane
Brentwood, TN 37027
(615) 324-2360   Fax: (615) 523-1715
E-mail: acnp@acnp.org
Web: www.acnp.org/programs/awards.aspx

Summary To recognize and reward professionals and postdoctorates (particularly Hispanic Americans, other minorities, and women) who are members of the American College of Neuropsychopharmacology (ACNP) and have demonstrated outstanding mentoring of young scientists.

Eligibility This award is available to ACNP members who have made an outstanding contribution to neuropsychopharmacology by mentoring and developing young scientists into leaders in the field. Nominations must be accompanied by letters of support from up to 3 people who have been mentored by the candidate. Nomination of women and minorities is highly encouraged.

Financial Data The award consists of a monetary honorarium and a plaque.

Duration The award is presented annually.

Additional data This award was first presented in 2004.

Number awarded 1 each year.

Deadline Nominations must be submitted by June of each year.

[1051]
JUVENILE DIABETES RESEARCH FOUNDATION INNOVATIVE GRANTS

Juvenile Diabetes Research Foundation International
Attn: Grant Administrator
26 Broadway, 14th Floor
New York, NY 10004
(212) 479-7572   Toll Free: (800) 533-CURE
Fax: (212) 785-9595   E-mail: info@jdrf.org
Web: jdrf.org

Summary To provide funding to scientists (particularly Hispanic Americans, other underrepresented minorities, women,

and individuals with disabilities) who are interested in conducting innovative diabetes-related research.

Eligibility Applicants must have an M.D., D.M.D., D.V.M., Ph.D., or equivalent degree and have a full-time faculty position or equivalent at a college, university, medical school, or other research facility. They must be seeking "seed" money for investigative work based on a sound hypothesis for which preliminary data are insufficient for a regular research grant but that are likely to lead to important results for the treatment of diabetes and its complications. Applicants must specifically explain how the proposal is innovative. Selection is based on whether 1) the proposed research is innovative; 2) the underlying premise, goal, or hypothesis is plausible; 3) the proposed research can be completed in 1 year; and 4) the proposed research is relevant to the mission of the Juvenile Diabetes Research Foundation and its potential impact. There are no citizenship requirements. Applications are encouraged from women, members of minority groups underrepresented in the sciences, and people with disabilities. The proposed research may be conducted at foreign or domestic, for-profit or nonprofit, or public or private institutions, including universities, colleges, hospitals, laboratories, units of state or local government, or eligible agencies of the federal government.

Financial Data Awards are limited to $110,000 plus 10% indirect costs.

Duration 1 year; nonrenewable.

Number awarded Varies each year.

Deadline August of each year.

[1052]
LATINA LAWYERS BAR ASSOCIATION SCHOLARSHIPS

Latina Lawyers Bar Association
Attn: Scholarship Committee
P.O. Box 86488
Los Angeles, CA 90086
E-mail: office@llbalaw.org
Web: www.llbalaw.org/content/scholarship

Summary To provide financial assistance for tuition or bar review courses to students, especially Latinas, currently enrolled at law schools in California or preparing for the state bar examination.

Eligibility This program is open to students currently enrolled at California law schools and current candidates for the California State Bar examination. Preference is given to Latina law students. Applicants must be able to demonstrate community service, commitment to the Latina community, potential to succeed, and financial need. Along with their application, they must submit a 1,000-word statement that includes information regarding their background, reasons for pursuing further education, challenges they face outside of school, legal field of interest, career goals, special circumstances, and financial need.

Financial Data A stipend is awarded (amount not specified).

Duration Funds provide 1 year of support at a California law school or a 1-time grant for bar examination assistance.

Number awarded 1 or more each year.

Deadline April of each year.

[1053]
LATINO PUBLIC BROADCASTING PUBLIC MEDIA CONTENT FUND

Latino Public Broadcasting
2550 North Hollywood Way, Suite 301
Burbank, CA 91505
(818) 847-9656   Fax: (818) 847-9663
E-mail: info@lpbp.org
Web: www.lpbp.org/fundingguidelines.php

Summary To provide funding to film and video producers interested in developing projects for broadcast on public television that relate to the Latino experience in America.

Eligibility This program is open to independent producers and production entities that are creating programs on the Latino experience. The programs must be independent of the support of a film studio or commercial broadcast entity. The producer or production entity must retain the copyright and have artistic, budgetary, and editorial control over the proposed project. Applicants must be at least 18 years of age, be citizens or legal residents of the United States or its territories, and have previous film or television experience that can be documented by detailed personnel resumes and by sample tapes upon request. Projects that are ineligible include thesis projects and student films; producers or production entities that are foreign based, owned, or controlled; industrial or promotional projects; projects for which the exclusive domestic television rights are not available; projects with a primarily commercial interest; and proposals by current recipients of these grants who have not yet completed delivery. The project genres may include drama, documentary, narrative, performance, mixed genre, or new media. The project may be at any stage of production. Priority is given too programs that address Latino arts and culture.

Financial Data Grants range from $5,000 to $20,000 for research and development, $25,000 to $100,000 for production, $25,000 to $100,000 for post-production, or $5,000 to $20,000 for new media.

Additional data Funding for these grants is provided by the Corporation for Public Broadcasting. Producers must agree to complete the program according to the proposed schedule, project description, and budget, and to certain oversight rights and accountability obligations to the sponsor. The producer also agrees to royalty participation by the sponsor in a percentage of net revenues from ancillary distribution.

Number awarded Varies each year; recently, 8 of these grants were awarded, of which 2 were for new media.

Deadline May of each year.

[1054]
LAURENCE R. FOSTER MEMORIAL SCHOLARSHIPS

Oregon Student Access Commission
Attn: Grants and Scholarships Division
1500 Valley River Drive, Suite 100
Eugene, OR 97401-2146
(541) 687-7395   Toll Free: (800) 452-8807, ext. 7395
Fax: (541) 687-7414   TDD: (800) 735-2900
E-mail: awardinfo@osac.state.or.us
Web: www.oregonstudentaid.gov/scholarships.aspx

Summary To provide financial assistance to Hispanic Americans and other residents of Oregon who come from a diverse environment and are enrolled at a college or graduate school in any state to prepare for a public health career.

Eligibility This program is open to residents of Oregon who are enrolled at least half time at a 4-year college or university in any state to prepare for a career in public health (not private practice). Preference is given first to applicants from diverse environments; second to persons employed in, or graduate students working on a degree in, public health; and third to juniors and seniors majoring in a health program (e.g., nursing, medical technology, physician assistant). Applicants must be able to demonstrate financial need. Along with their application, they must submit essays of 250 to 350 words on 1) what public health means to them; 2) the public health aspect they intend to practice and the health and population issues impacted by that aspect; and 3) their experience living or working in diverse environments.

Financial Data Stipends for scholarships offered by the Oregon Student Access Commission (OSAC) range from $200 to $10,000 but recently averaged $2,300.

Duration 1 year.

Additional data This program is administered by the OSAC with funds provided by the Oregon Community Foundation.

Number awarded Varies each year; recently, 6 of these scholarships were awarded.

Deadline February of each year.

[1055]
LEO GOLDBERG FELLOWSHIPS

National Optical Astronomy Observatories
Attn: Human Resources Office
950 North Cherry Avenue
P.O. Box 26732
Tucson, AZ 85726-6732
(520) 318-8000   Fax: (520) 318-8494
E-mail: hrnoao@noao.edu
Web: ast.noao.edu/opportunities/post-doc-programs

Summary To provide an opportunity for postdoctorates in astronomy (particularly Hispanic Americans, other underrepresented minorities, and women) to conduct research at the facilities of the National Optical Astronomy Observatories (NOAO) in Arizona or Chile.

Eligibility This program is open to recent Ph.D. recipients in observational astronomy, astronomical instrumentation, or theoretical astrophysics. Applicants must be interested in conducting a research program of their own choosing or participating in a current NOAO initiative at Kitt Peak National Observatory (KPNO) near Tucson, Arizona or Cerro Tololo Inter-American Observatory (CTIO) in La Serena, Chile. Women and candidates from underrepresented minorities are particularly encouraged to apply. Preference is given to Native Americans living on or near the Tohono O'Odham Reservation in Arizona. Selection is based on the applicant's promise for an outstanding career in astronomy, their proposed use of KPNO or CTIO facilities, the relationship of their research to a proposed interaction with NOAO programs to develop community facilities, and the relationship of their research to programs conducted by NOAO staff.

Financial Data A competitive salary is paid. Additional support is provided to fellows and their families in Chile.

Duration 5 years. The first 4 years are spent either at Kitt Peak or in La Serena; the final year is spent at an U.S. university or astronomical institute willing to host the fellow.

Additional data NOAO is supported under a contract between the National Science Foundation and the Association of Universities for Research in Astronomy, Inc. This program, which began in 2002, was formerly known as the NOAO 5-Year Science Fellowship.

Number awarded 1 each year.

Deadline November of each year.

[1056]
LETRAS LATINAS/RED HEN POETRY PRIZE

Red Hen Press
Attn: Awards
P.O. Box 40820
Pasadena, CA 91114
(626) 356-4760   Fax: (626) 356-9974
E-mail: info@redhen.org
Web: redhen.org

Summary To recognize and reward outstanding second or third collections of poems by Latino or Latina poets.

Eligibility This competition is open to Latino and Latina poets who have had 1 or 2 full-length books of poetry professionally published. Manuscripts must be 50 to 100 pages in length, in English; there are no restrictions on the style of poetry or subject matter.

Financial Data The award is $1,000, publication by Red Hen Press, and support for travel costs associated with further promotion of the winning book through readings in Los Angeles, Chicago, New York, and Washington, D.C.

Duration The competition is held biennially, in odd-numbered years.

Additional data This competition began in 2012, with the first 2 winners selected in that year and published in 2013 and 2015. The program is sponsored by Red Hen Press in partnership with the Institute for Latino Studies at the University of Notre Dame. The Ragdale Foundation offers a 2-week residency to the winning poet.

Number awarded 1 each odd-numbered year.

Deadline January of each odd-numbered year.

[1057]
LIZETTE PETERSON-HOMER INJURY PREVENTION RESEARCH GRANT

American Psychological Foundation
750 First Street, N.E.
Washington, DC 20002-4242
(202) 336-5843   Fax: (202) 336-5812
E-mail: foundation@apa.org
Web: www.apa.org/apf/funding/peterson-homer.aspx

Summary To provide funding to graduate students and faculty (particularly Hispanic Americans, other minorities, women, and individuals with disabilities) who are interested in conducting research related to the prevention of injuries in children.

Eligibility This program is open to graduate students and faculty interested in conducting research that focuses on the prevention of physical injury in children and young adults through accidents, violence, abuse, or suicide. Applicants must submit a 100-word abstract, description of the project,

detailed budget, curriculum vitae, and letter from the supporting faculty supervisor (if the applicant is a student). Selection is based on conformance with stated program goals, magnitude of incremental contribution, quality of proposed work, and applicant's demonstrated scholarship and research competence. The sponsor encourages applications from individuals who represent diversity in race, ethnicity, gender, age, disability, and sexual orientation.

Financial Data Grants up to $5,000 are available.

Additional data This program began in 1999 as the Rebecca Routh Coon Injury Research Award. The current name was adopted in 2003. It is supported by Division 54 (Society of Pediatric Psychology) of the American Psychological Association and the American Psychological Foundation.

Number awarded 1 each year.

Deadline September of each year.

[1058]
LONG RANGE BROAD AGENCY ANNOUNCEMENT FOR NAVY AND MARINE CORPS SCIENCE AND TECHNOLOGY

Office of Naval Research
Attn: Acquisition Department, Code BD25
875 North Randolph Street
Arlington, VA 22203-1995
(703) 696-1474   E-mail: Ganesh.Krish@navy.mil
Web: www.onr.navy.mil

Summary To provide financial support to investigators (particularly Hispanic Americans and other minorities) who are interested in conducting long-range science and technology research on topics of interest to the U.S. Navy and Marine Corps.

Eligibility This program is open to researchers from academia (colleges and universities) and industry. Applicants must be interested in conducting long-range projects in fields of science and technology that offer potential for advancement and improvement of Navy and Marine Corps operations. The proposed research must relate to 1 of the following topic areas: 1) expeditionary maneuver warfare and combating terrorism; 2) command, control communications, computers, intelligence, surveillance, and reconnaissance; 3) ocean battlespace sensing; 4) sea warfare and weapons; 5) warfighter performance; and 6) naval air warfare and weapons. Researchers at Historically Black Colleges and Universities (HBCUs) and Minority Institutions (MIs) are encouraged to submit proposals and join others in submitting proposals, but no portion of funds is set aside for HBCU and MI participation.

Financial Data Grant amounts depend on the nature of the proposal.

Duration Applicants may specify the length of time they wish to devote to the project.

Number awarded Varies each year.

Deadline September of each year.

[1059]
LYMAN T. JOHNSON POSTDOCTORAL FELLOWSHIP

University of Kentucky
Attn: Vice President for Research
311 Main Building
Lexington, KY 40506-0032
(859) 257-5090   Fax: (859) 323-2800
E-mail: vprgrants@uky.edu
Web: www.research.uky.edu

Summary To provide an opportunity for recent postdoctorates, especially Hispanic Americans and other minorities, to conduct research at the University of Kentucky (U.K.).

Eligibility This program is open to U.S. citizens and permanent residents who have completed a doctoral degree within the past 2 years. Applicants must be interested in conducting an individualized research program under the mentorship of a U.K. professor. They should indicate, in their letter of application, how their participation in this program would contribute to the compelling interest of diversity at U.K. Race, ethnicity, and national origin are among the factors that contribute to diversity. Selection is based on evidence of scholarship with competitive potential for a tenure-track faculty appointment at a research university, compatibility of specific research interests with those in doctorate-granting units at U.K., quality of the research proposal, support from mentor and references, and effect of the appointment on the educational benefit of diversity within the research or professional area.

Financial Data The fellowship provides a stipend of $35,000 plus $5,000 for support of research activities.

Duration Up to 2 years.

Additional data In addition to conducting an individualized research program under the mentorship of a U.K. professor, fellows actively participate in research, teaching, and service to the university, their profession, and the community. This program began in 1992.

Number awarded 2 each year.

Deadline October of each year.

[1060]
MANY VOICES FELLOWSHIPS

Playwrights' Center
2301 Franklin Avenue East
Minneapolis, MN 55406-1099
(612) 332-7481   Fax: (612) 332-6037
E-mail: info@pwcenter.org
Web: www.pwcenter.org/fellows_voices.php

Summary To provide funding to Hispanic Americans and other playwrights of color so they can spend a year in residence at the Playwrights' Center in Minneapolis.

Eligibility This program is open to playwrights of color who are citizens or permanent residents of the United States; both residents of Minnesota and of any state are eligible. Applicants must be interested in playwriting and creating theater in a supportive artist community at the Playwrights' Center.

Financial Data Fellows receive a $10,000 stipend, $2,500 for living expenses, and $1,500 in play development funds.

Duration 9 months, beginning in October.

Additional data This program, which began in 1994, is funded by the Jerome Foundation. Fellows must be in residence at the Playwrights' Center for the duration of the program.

Number awarded 2 each year: 1 to a resident of Minnesota and 1 to a resident of any state.

Deadline February of each year.

[1061]
MARRIAGE AND FAMILY THERAPY MASTER'S STUDENT MINORITY SCHOLARSHIP

American Association for Marriage and Family Therapy
Attn: AAMFT Research and Education Foundation
112 South Alfred Street
Alexandria, VA 22314-3061
(703) 838-9808   Fax: (703) 838-9805
Web: www.aamft.org

Summary To provide financial assistance to Hispanic American and other minority students enrolled in master's and post-degree training programs in marriage and family therapy.

Eligibility This program is open to minority students (including African Americans, Hispanics, Native Americans, Asian Americans, and Pacific Islanders) enrolled in master's degree programs or post-degree institutes that provide training in marriage and family therapy. Applicants must be members of the American Association for Marriage and Family Therapy (AAMFT). They must be citizens or permanent residents of the United States or Canada and show promise in and commitment to a career in marital and family therapy education, research, or practice. Along with their application, they must submit a personal statement explaining how their racial or ethnic background has had an impact on them and their career decision; the statement should include their professional interests, goals, and commitment to the field of marriage and family therapy.

Financial Data The stipend is $2,000. Awardees also receive a plaque and funding up to $750 to attend the association's annual conference.

Duration 1 year.

Additional data This program began in 1986.

Number awarded Up to 3 each year.

Deadline January of each year.

[1062]
MATHEMATICAL SCIENCES POSTDOCTORAL RESEARCH FELLOWSHIPS

National Science Foundation
Directorate for Mathematical and Physical Sciences
Attn: Division of Mathematical Sciences
4201 Wilson Boulevard, Room 1025N
Arlington, VA 22230
(703) 292-4488   Fax: (703) 292-9032
TDD: (800) 281-8749   E-mail: jwang@nsf.gov
Web: www.nsf.gov/funding/pgm_summ.jsp?pims_id=5301

Summary To provide financial assistance to postdoctorates (particularly Hispanic Americans, other minorities, women, and individuals with disabilities) who are interested in pursuing research training in mathematics.

Eligibility Applicants for these fellowships must 1) be U.S. citizens, nationals, or permanent residents; 2) have earned a Ph.D. in a mathematical science or have had equivalent research training and experience; 3) have held the Ph.D. for no more than 2 years; and 4) have not previously held any other postdoctoral fellowship from the National Science Foundation (NSF) or been offered an award from this program. They must be proposing to conduct a program of postdoctoral research training at an appropriate nonprofit U.S. institution, including government laboratories, national laboratories, and privately sponsored nonprofit institutes, as well as institutions of higher education in any country. A senior scientist at the institution must indicate availability for consultation and agreement to work with the fellow. In the selection process, consideration is given to the achievement of societally relevant outcomes, including full participation of women, persons with disabilities, and underrepresented minorities.

Financial Data The total grant is $150,000, consisting of 3 components: 1) a monthly stipend of $5,000 for full-time support or $2,500 for half-time support, paid directly to the fellow; 2) a research allowance of $12,000, also paid directly to the fellow; and 3) an institutional allowance of $9,000, paid to the host institution for fringe benefits (including health insurance payments for the fellow) and expenses incurred in support of the fellow, such as space, equipment, and general purpose supplies. Fellows who wish to conduct their training at an international host institution may apply for an additional allowance of up to $20,000.

Duration Fellows may select either of 2 options: the research fellowship option provides full-time support for any 18 academic-year months in a 3-year period, in intervals not shorter than 3 consecutive months; the research instructorship option provides a combination of full-time and half-time support over a period of 3 academic years. Both options include 6 summer months.

Number awarded 30 to 33 each year. A total of $5.0 million is available for this program annually.

Deadline October of each year.

[1063]
MENTOR-BASED MINORITY POSTDOCTORAL FELLOWSHIPS IN DIABETES

American Diabetes Association
Attn: Research Programs
1701 North Beauregard Street
Alexandria, VA 22311
(703) 549-1500, ext. 2362   Toll Free: (800) DIABETES
Fax: (703) 549-1715
E-mail: grantquestions@diabetes.org
Web: professional.diabetes.org

Summary To provide financial assistance to Hispanic American and other minority postdoctoral fellows working with established diabetes investigators.

Eligibility Applications for these fellowships may be submitted by established and active investigators in diabetes research who wish to supervise the work of a postdoctoral fellow, whom they will select. They must currently hold a grant from the American Diabetes Association. The fellow selected by the investigator must be a member of an underrepresented minority group (African American; Spanish, Hispanic, or Latino; American Indian or Alaskan Native; Native Hawaiian or Pacific Islander); must have an M.D., Ph.D., D.O., D.P.M., or Pharm.D. degree; must not be serving an internship or residency during the fellowship period; and must not have more than 3 years of postdoctoral research experience in the field of diabetes/endocrinology. Applicant investigators

and fellows must be U.S. citizens or permanent residents. The applicant investigator must also hold an appointment at a U.S. research institution and have sufficient research support to provide an appropriate training environment for the fellow. The applicant investigator must be a member of the Professional Section of the American Diabetes Association; the fellow must also be, or agree to become, a member. Selection is based on the quality and activity of the applicant investigator's diabetes research program, the likelihood that the fellow trained by the mentor will actively pursue a career in diabetes research, the applicant investigator's past training record, and evidence of sufficient research support and adequate facilities to provide an appropriate training environment for a postdoctoral fellow.

Financial Data The grant is $45,000 per year. Within that total, the applicant investigator may determine the salary of the fellow; up to $3,000 per year of the total may be used for laboratory supply costs, up to $1,000 for travel by the fellow to attend diabetes-related scientific meetings, and up to $500 for book purchases.

Duration 2 to 3 years.

Number awarded Varies each year.

Deadline January of each year.

[1064]
MENTORED CAREER DEVELOPMENT AWARD TO PROMOTE FACULTY DIVERSITY/RE-ENTRY IN BIOMEDICAL RESEARCH

National Heart, Lung, and Blood Institute
Attn: Division of Cardiovascular Sciences
6701 Rockledge Drive
Bethesda, MD 20892-7940
(301) 435-0535   Fax: (301) 480-1455
E-mail: scottj2@nhlbi.nih.gov
Web: grants.nih.gov

Summary To provide funding to Hispanic Americans and members of other underrepresented groups who are interested in developing into independent biomedical investigators in research areas relevant to the mission of the National Heart, Lung, and Blood Institute (NHLBI).

Eligibility This program is open to U.S. citizens, nationals, and permanent residents who are full-time non-tenured faculty members at U.S. domestic institutions of higher education and eligible agencies of the federal government; applications are especially encouraged from faculty at Historically Black Colleges and Universities (HBCUs), Tribally Controlled Colleges and Universities (TCCUs), Hispanic Serving Institutions (HSIs), and Alaska Native and Native Hawaiian Serving Institutions. Candidates must have received, at least 2 years previously, a doctoral degree or equivalent in a basic or clinical area related to cardiovascular, pulmonary, or hematologic diseases. Applications are especially encouraged from members of a group that will promote greater diversity in scientific research, including 1) members of underrepresented racial and ethnic groups (African Americans, Hispanic Americans, Alaska Natives, American Indians, Native Hawaiians, non-Asian Pacific Islanders); 2) individuals with disabilities; and 3) individuals from disadvantaged backgrounds. Candidates who have experienced an interruption in their research careers for a period of at least 3 but no more than 8 years (e.g., starting and/or raising a family, an incapacitating illness or injury, caring for an ill immediate family member, performing military service) are also eligible. The proposed research development plan, under the guidance of an experienced mentor or supervisor, must enable the candidate to become an independent investigator in cardiovascular, pulmonary, hematologic, and sleep disorders research with either a clinical or basic science emphasis.

Financial Data The grant provides salary support of up to $75,000 per year plus fringe benefits. In addition, up to $30,000 per year may be provided for research project requirements and related support (e.g., technical personnel costs, supplies, equipment, candidate travel, telephone charges, publication costs, and tuition for necessary courses). Facilities and administrative costs may be reimbursed at the rate of 8% of total direct costs.

Duration 3 to 5 years.

Additional data At least 75% of the awardee's effort must be devoted to the research program. The remainder may be devoted to other clinical and teaching pursuits that are consistent with the program goals of developing the awardee into an independent biomedical scientist or the maintenance of the teaching and/or clinical skills needed for an academic research career.

Number awarded Varies each year; recently, 8 to 10 awards were available through this program; total funding was approximately $1,200,000.

Deadline Letters of intent must be submitted by January of each year; completed applications are due in February.

[1065]
MENTORED CLINICAL SCIENTIST RESEARCH CAREER DEVELOPMENT AWARD

Agency for Healthcare Research and Quality
Attn: Office of Extramural Research, Education, and
  Priority Populations
540 Gaither Road
Rockville, MD 20850
(301) 427-1555   Fax: (301) 427-1562
TDD: (301) 451-0088
E-mail: Kay.Anderson@ahrq.hhs.gov
Web: grants.nih.gov/grants/guide/pa-files/PA-13-039.html

Summary To provide funding to clinicians (particularly Hispanic Americans, other underrepresented minorities, and individuals with disabilities) who are interested in obtaining additional research training to enable them to become independent investigators in health services research.

Eligibility This program is open to U.S. citizens, nationals, or permanent residents who have received a clinical doctoral degree (e.g., M.D., D.O., D.C., O.D., N.D., D.D.S., D.M.D., Pharm.D.); scientists who have a Ph.D. or other doctoral degree in clinical disciplines such as clinical psychology, nursing, speech-language pathology, audiology, or rehabilitation are also eligible. Applicants must have identified a mentor with extensive research experience and be willing to spend at least 75% of full-time professional effort conducting research and developing a research career to promote improvements in clinical and health systems practices. They must be proposing projects related to the strategic goals of the Agency for Healthcare Research and Quality (AHRQ): safety and quality, effectiveness, and efficiency. Members of underrepresented ethnic and racial groups, individuals from disadvantaged backgrounds, and individuals with disabilities are especially encouraged to apply.

Financial Data Grants provide salary up to $90,000 annually, plus associated fringe benefits. Also available are up to $25,000 per year for research development support (tuition, fees, and books related to career development; research expenses, such as supplies, equipment, and technical personnel; travel to research meetings or training; and statistical services, including personnel and computer time). Facilities and administrative costs are reimbursed at 8% of modified total direct costs.

Duration 3 to 5 years.

Number awarded Varies each year.

Deadline February, June, or October of each year.

[1066]
MENTORED NEW INVESTIGATOR RESEARCH GRANTS TO PROMOTE DIVERSITY OF THE ALZHEIMER'S ASSOCIATION

Alzheimer's Association
Attn: Medical and Scientific Affairs
225 North Michigan Avenue, 17th Floor
Chicago, IL 60601-7633
(312) 335-5747   Toll Free: (800) 272-3900
Fax: (866) 699-1246   TDD: (312) 335-5886
E-mail: grantsapp@alz.org
Web: www.alz.org

Summary To provide funding for mentored research on Alzheimer's Disease to Hispanic Americans and other junior investigators who will contribute to diversity in the field.

Eligibility This program is open to investigators who have less than 10 years of research experience after receipt of their terminal degree. Applicants must be proposing to conduct research with focus areas that change annually but are related to Alzheimer's Disease. They must identify a mentor who is experienced in conducting Alzheimer's and related dementia research and in mentoring investigators. Eligibility is restricted to investigators who will contribute to diversity in the field of biomedical research, including members of underrepresented racial and ethnic minority groups (African Americans, Hispanic Americans, American Indians/Alaska Natives, Native Hawaiians, and Pacific Islanders) and individuals with disabilities.

Financial Data Grants up to $60,000 per year, including direct expenses and up to 10% for overhead costs, are available. The total award for the life of the grant may not exceed $170,000, including $150,000 for costs related to the proposed research, $10,000 to the fellow upon successful completion of the program, and $10,000 to the mentor upon successful completion of the program.

Duration Up to 3 years.

Number awarded 1 or 2 each year.

Deadline Letters of intent must be submitted by the end of January or September of each year. Final applications are due in March or October.

[1067]
MENTORED RESEARCH SCIENTIST RESEARCH CAREER DEVELOPMENT AWARD

Agency for Healthcare Research and Quality
Attn: Office of Extramural Research, Education, and
  Priority Populations
540 Gaither Road
Rockville, MD 20850
(301) 427-1555   Fax: (301) 427-1562
TDD: (301) 451-0088
E-mail: Kay.Anderson@ahrq.hhs.gov
Web: grants.nih.gov/grants/guide/pa-files/PA-09-087.html

Summary To provide funding to scientists (particularly Hispanic Americans, other underrepresented minorities, and individuals with disabilities) who are interested in obtaining additional research training to enable them to become independent investigators in health services research.

Eligibility This program is open to U.S. citizens, nationals, or permanent residents who have received a research doctoral degree (e.g., Ph.D., Sc.D., Dr.P.H.). Applicants must have identified a mentor with extensive research experience and be willing to spend at least 75% of full-time professional effort conducting research and developing a research career to promote improvements in clinical and health systems practices. They must be proposing projects in 1 of the research portfolio areas of the Agency for Healthcare Research and Quality (AHRQ): 1) the value portfolio, for research that can be used to reduce unnecessary health care costs (waste) while maintaining or improving health care quality; 2) the health information technology portfolio, for the use of information and communication technology in health care to support the delivery of patient or population care; 3) the comparative effectiveness portfolio, for research focusing on comparative effectiveness of different clinical treatments and services; 4) the prevention/care management portfolio, to improve the quality, safety, efficiency, and effectiveness of preventive services and chronic care management in ambulatory care settings; 5) the patient safety portfolio, for research projects to identify the risks and hazards encountered by patients as a result of health care; or 6) the innovations and emerging areas portfolio, for research on ideas that have the potential for high impact. Members of underrepresented ethnic and racial groups, individuals from disadvantaged backgrounds, and individuals with disabilities are especially encouraged to apply.

Financial Data Grants provide salary up to $90,000 annually, plus associated fringe benefits. Also available are up to $25,000 per year for research development support (tuition, fees, and books related to career development; research expenses, such as supplies, equipment, and technical personnel; travel to research meetings or training; and statistical services, including personnel and computer time). Facilities and administrative costs are reimbursed at 8% of modified total direct costs.

Duration 3 to 5 years.

Number awarded Varies each year.

Deadline February, June, or October of each year.

[1068]
MICROBIOLOGY OF THE BUILT ENVIRONMENT PROGRAM FELLOWSHIPS

Alfred P. Sloan Foundation
630 Fifth Avenue, Suite 2550
New York, NY 10111-0242
(212) 649-1649   Fax: (212) 757-5117
E-mail: olsiewski@sloan.org
Web: www.sloan.org

Summary To provide funding to recent doctorates (particularly Hispanic Americans and members of other underrepresented groups) who are interested in conducting research on the microbiology of the build environment.

Eligibility This program is open to early stage Ph.D. scientists and engineers in laboratories engaged in research on the microbiology of the build environment in the United States or Canada. Cross-disciplinary studies in microbial biology and engineering are encouraged. Applications may be submitted by graduate students if accompanied by a letter of commitment from a potential postdoctoral adviser. Members of underrepresented groups in science and engineering are especially encouraged to apply. Selection is based on an assessment of the proposed research, the arrangements for the interdisciplinary educational broadening of the fellow, and the previous research records of the potential fellow and adviser.

Financial Data The grant is $60,000 per year, including $48,000 as a stipend (may be supplemented by institutional or other sources), $2,000 for travel or research expenses, and $10,000 for fringe benefits.

Duration 2 years.

Additional data This program began in 2013.

Number awarded 8 each year.

Deadline September of each year.

[1069]
MIGRANT HEALTH SCHOLARSHIP

National Center for Farmworker Health, Inc.
Attn: Migrant Health Scholarship
1770 FM 967
Buda, TX 78610
(512) 312-2700   Toll Free: (800) 531-5120
Fax: (512) 312-2600   E-mail: info@ncfh.org
Web: www.ncfh.org/?pid=232

Summary To provide financial assistance to people working in the migrant health field, especially those with a farmworker background, who are interested in additional education.

Eligibility This program is open to staff in clinical, administrative, and support positions at community and migrant health centers who are interested in obtaining additional education at the undergraduate or graduate level. Applicants must submit a 1-page personal statement discussing such issues as why they are interested in migrant health, personal experiences and achievements, future career goals, and commitment to migrant health. Financial need is also considered in the selection process. Preference is given to applicants with a farmworker background.

Financial Data The stipend is $1,000.

Duration 1 year.

Additional data This program began in 1984.

Number awarded Varies each year; recently, 12 of these scholarships were awarded. Since the program was established, it has awarded 188 of these scholarships.

Deadline March of each year.

[1070]
MINORITIES AFFAIRS COMMITTEE VISITING PROFESSOR AWARDS

American Society for Cell Biology
Attn: Minority Affairs Committee
8120 Woodmont Avenue, Suite 750
Bethesda, MD 20814-2762
(301) 347-9323   Fax: (301) 347-9310
E-mail: dmccall@ascb.org
Web: www.ascb.org

Summary To provide funding for research during the summer to faculty members (particularly Hispanic Americans and other minorities) who are at primarily teaching institutions that serve minority students and scientists.

Eligibility Eligible to apply for this support are professors at primarily teaching institutions. They must be interested in working in the laboratories of members of the American Society for Cell Biology during the summer. Hosts and visitor scientists are asked to submit their applications together as a proposed team. Minority professors and professors at Minority Serving Institutions are especially encouraged to apply for this award. Minorities are defined as U.S. citizens of Black, Native American, Chicano/Hispanic, or Pacific Islands background.

Financial Data The stipend for the summer is $13,500 plus $700 for travel expenses and $4,000 to the host institution for supplies.

Duration From 8 to 10 weeks during the summer.

Additional data Funds for this program, established in 1997, are provided by the Minorities Access to Research Careers (MARC) program of the National Institutes of Health.

Number awarded Varies each year; recently, 3 of these grants were awarded.

Deadline March of each year.

[1071]
MINORITIES IN CANCER RESEARCH JANE COOK WRIGHT LECTURESHIP

American Association for Cancer Research
Attn: Scientific Awards
615 Chestnut Street, 17th Floor
Philadelphia, PA 19106-4404
(215) 440-9300   Toll Free: (866) 423-3965
Fax: (215) 440-9372   E-mail: awards@aacr.org
Web: www.aacr.org

Summary To recognize and reward investigators who, through leadership or by example, have furthered the advancement of minorities in cancer research.

Eligibility This award is available to investigators affiliated with institutions in any country involved in cancer research, cancer medicine, or cancer-related biomedical science. Nominees must have made meritorious contributions to the field of cancer research and, through leadership or by example, have furthered the advancement of minority investigators in cancer research. Selection is based on the nominee's contributions to cancer research and to the advancement of minorities; no

consideration is given to age, race, gender, nationality, geographic location, or religious or political views.

Financial Data The award consists of an honorarium (amount not specified), a commemorative item, and support for the winner and a guest to attend the sponsor's annual meeting where the winner delivers a major lecture.

Duration The award is presented annually.

Additional data This award was established in 2006.

Number awarded 1 each year.

Deadline October of each year.

[1072]
MINORITY FACULTY DEVELOPMENT SCHOLARSHIP AWARD IN PHYSICAL THERAPY

American Physical Therapy Association
Attn: Honors and Awards Program
1111 North Fairfax Street
Alexandria, VA 22314-1488
(703) 684-APTA   Toll Free: (800) 999-APTA
Fax: (703) 684-7343   TDD: (703) 683-6748
E-mail: honorsandawards@apta.org
Web: www.apta.org

Summary To provide financial assistance to Hispanic American and other minority faculty members in physical therapy who are interested in working on a post-professional doctoral degree.

Eligibility This program is open to U.S. citizens and permanent residents who are members of the following minority groups: African American or Black, Asian, Native Hawaiian or other Pacific Islander, American Indian or Alaska Native, or Hispanic/Latino. Applicants must be full-time faculty members, teaching in an accredited or developing professional physical therapist education program, who will have completed the equivalent of 2 full semesters of post-professional doctoral course work. They must possess a license to practice physical therapy in a U.S. jurisdiction and be enrolled as a student in an accredited post-professional doctoral program whose content has a demonstrated relationship to physical therapy. Along with their application, they must submit a personal essay on their professional goals, including their plans to contribute to the profession and minority services. Selection is based on 1) commitment to minority affairs and services; 2) commitment to further the physical therapy profession through teaching and research; and 3) scholastic achievement.

Financial Data A stipend is awarded (amount not specified).

Duration 1 year.

Additional data This program began in 1999.

Number awarded 1 or more each year.

Deadline November of each year.

[1073]
MLA PRIZE IN UNITED STATES LATINA AND LATINO AND CHICANA AND CHICANO LITERARY AND CULTURAL STUDIES

Modern Language Association of America
Attn: Committee on Honors and Awards
26 Broadway, Third Floor
New York, NY 10004-1789
(646) 576-5141   Fax: (646) 458-0030
E-mail: awards@mla.org
Web: www.mla.org

Summary To recognize and reward members of the Modern Language Association (MLA) who have written outstanding books on Latina, Latino, Chicana, or Chicano literature.

Eligibility This award is presented to authors of outstanding scholarly studies in any language of Latina and Latino and Chicana and Chicano literature or culture published the previous year. Books that are primarily translations are not eligible. Authors must be members MLA.

Financial Data The prize is $1,000 and a certificate.

Duration The prize is awarded biennially.

Additional data This prize was first awarded in 2002.

Number awarded 1 each odd-numbered year.

Deadline April of each odd-numbered year.

[1074]
MULTIDISCIPLINARY RESEARCH PROGRAM OF THE UNIVERSITY RESEARCH INITIATIVE

Office of Naval Research
One Liberty Center
875 North Randolph Street, Suite 1425
Arlington, VA 22203-1995
(703) 696-4111   E-mail: paula.barden.ctr@navy.mil
Web: www.onr.navy.mil

Summary To provide funding for research (particularly research conducted by Hispanic American and other minority researchers) on subjects of interest to the Department of Defense (DoD) that intersect several traditional science and engineering disciplines.

Eligibility This program is open to research teams at U.S. institutions of higher education with degree-granting programs in science and/or engineering or by consortia led by such institutions. Applications must be for research on topics that may change annually but are specified by the participating DoD agencies: the Office of Naval Research, the Army Research Office, and the Air Force Office of Scientific Research. Researchers at Historically Black Colleges and Universities (HBCUs) and other Minority Institutions (MIs) are encouraged to submit proposals and join others in submitting proposals, but no portion of funds is set aside for HBCU and MI participation.

Financial Data Grants normally range up to $1,500,000 per year, depending on the topic, technical goals, and availability of funds.

Duration Varies; recent grants have been for 3 years with 2 additional years possible as options.

Number awarded Varies each year; recently, 17 grants worth $25.5 million over 3 years were awarded.

Deadline White papers must be submitted by October of each year; full proposals are due by mid-December.

[1075]
NASA ASTROBIOLOGY PROGRAM MINORITY INSTITUTION RESEARCH SUPPORT

United Negro College Fund Special Programs
  Corporation
Attn: NASA Astrobiology Program
6402 Arlington Boulevard, Suite 600
Falls Church, VA 22042
(703) 205-6581   Toll Free: (800) 530-6232
Fax: (703) 205-7645   E-mail: malik.hopkins@uncfsp.org
Web: www.uncfsp.org

Summary To provide an opportunity for faculty at Minority Serving Institutions (MSIs) to work on a summer research project in partnership with an established astrobiology investigator.

Eligibility This program is open to full-time tenured or tenure-track faculty members at MSIs who have a Ph.D., Sc.D., or equivalent degree in a field of STEM (science, technology, engineering, or mathematics). Applicants must be interested in conducting a summer research project on a topic related to astrobiology. They must identify an established investigator of the National Aeronautics and Space Administration (NASA) Astrobiology Program who has agreed to serve as host researcher. Eligible fields of study include biology, microbiology, astronomy, planetary science, astrochemistry, astrophysics, geology, geochemistry, or geobiochemistry. U.S. citizenship or permanent resident status is required.

Financial Data Fellows receive a stipend of $10,000 and an additional grant of $5,000 to cover travel, lodging, and living expenses.

Duration 10 weeks during the summer.

Additional data This program is funded by the NASA Astrobiology Institute and administered by the United Negro College Fund Special Programs Corporation.

Number awarded Varies each year.

Deadline March of each year.

[1076]
NATIONAL CANCER INSTITUTE MENTORED CLINICAL SCIENTIST RESEARCH CAREER DEVELOPMENT AWARD TO PROMOTE DIVERSITY

National Cancer Institute
Attn: Center to Reduce Cancer Health Disparities
9609 Medical Center Drive
Sixth Floor, West Tower
Bethesda, MD 20892-9746
(240) 276-6186   TDD: (301) 451-0088
E-mail: ojeifojo@mail.nih.gov
Web: grants.nih.gov/grants/guide/pa-files/PAR-12-051.html

Summary To provide funding to Hispanic Americans and members of other underrepresented groups who are interested in a program of training in clinical cancer research under the supervision of an experienced mentor.

Eligibility This program is open to U.S. citizens, nationals, and permanent residents who have a clinical doctoral degree; individuals with a Ph.D. or other doctoral degree in clinical disciplines such as clinical psychology, nursing, clinical genetics, speech-language pathology, audiology, or rehabilitation are also eligible. Candidates must be nominated by an eligible institution on the basis of their intent to conduct a research project highly relevant to cancer biology, cancer health disparities, etiology, pathogenesis, prevention, diagnosis, and/or treatment that has the potential for establishing an independent research program. They must qualify as 1) members of an ethnic or racial group shown to be underrepresented in health-related sciences on a national basis; 2) individuals with a disability; or 3) individuals from a disadvantaged background, including those from a low-income family and those from a social, cultural, and/or educational environment that has inhibited them from preparation for a research career. The mentor must be a senior or mid-level faculty member with research competence and an appreciation of the cultural, socioeconomic, and research background of the individual candidate. Selection is based on the applicant's qualifications, interests, accomplishments, motivation, and potential for a career in laboratory or field-based cancer research.

Financial Data The award provides salary up to $100,000 per year plus related fringe benefits. In addition, up to $30,000 per year is provided for research development support. Facilities and administrative costs are reimbursed at 8% of modified total direct costs.

Duration Up to 5 years.

Additional data This program was originally established in 2002 as the successor of a program designated the Minorities in Clinical Oncology Program Grants. Recipients must devote at least 75% of their full-time professional effort to cancer-related research and training activities.

Number awarded Varies each year, depending on the availability of funds.

Deadline February, June, or October of each year.

[1077]
NATIONAL CANCER INSTITUTE TRANSITION CAREER DEVELOPMENT AWARD TO PROMOTE DIVERSITY

National Cancer Institute
Attn: Center to Reduce Cancer Health Disparities
9609 Medical Center Drive
Sixth Floor, West Tower
Bethesda, MD 20892-9746
(240) 276-6183   TDD: (301) 451-0088
E-mail: walia@mail.nih.gov
Web: grants.nih.gov/grants/guide/pa-files/PAR-12-062.html

Summary To provide funding to Hispanic Americans and other underrepresented scientists who are establishing an independent research and academic career in cancer research.

Eligibility This program is open to U.S. citizens, nationals, and permanent residents who have earned a terminal clinical or research doctorate and intend to conduct a research project highly relevant to cancer biology, cancer health disparities, etiology, pathogenesis, prevention, diagnosis, and treatment that has the potential for establishing an independent research program. Candidates must be sponsored by an eligible institution that can demonstrate a commitment to the promotion of diversity in their student and faculty populations. They must qualify as 1) members of an ethnic or racial group shown to be underrepresented in health-related sciences on a national basis; 2) individuals with a disability; or 3) individuals from a disadvantaged background, including those from a low-income family and those from a social, cultural, and/or

educational environment that has inhibited them from preparation for a research career.

Financial Data The award provides salary up to $100,000 per year plus related fringe benefits. In addition, up to $50,000 per year is provided for research support costs. Facilities and administrative costs are reimbursed at 8% of modified total direct costs.

Duration Up to 3 years.

Additional data Recipients must devote at least 75% of their full-time professional effort to cancer-related research and peer review activities. The remaining 25% can be divided among other activities only if they are consistent with the program goals, i.e., the candidate's development into an independent investigator.

Number awarded Approximately 10 each year.

Deadline February, June, or October of each year.

[1078]
NATIONAL CENTER FOR ATMOSPHERIC RESEARCH POSTDOCTORAL APPOINTMENTS

National Center for Atmospheric Research
Attn: Advanced Study Program
3090 Center Green Drive
P.O. Box 3000
Boulder, CO 80307-3000
(303) 497-1601   Fax: (303) 497-1646
E-mail: apply@asp.ucar.edu
Web: www.asp.ucar.edu/pdfp/pd_announcement.jsp

Summary To provide funding to recent Ph.D.s (particularly Hispanic Americans, other minorities, and women) who wish to conduct research at the National Center for Atmospheric Research (NCAR) in Boulder, Colorado.

Eligibility This program is open to recent Ph.D.s and Sc.D.s in applied mathematics, chemistry, engineering, and physics as well as specialists in atmospheric sciences from such disciplines as biology, economics, geography, geology, and science education. Applicants must be interested in conducting research at the center in atmospheric sciences and global change. Selection is based on the applicant's scientific capability and potential, originality and independence, and the match between their interests and the research opportunities at the center. Applications from women and minorities are encouraged.

Financial Data The stipend is $57,500 in the first year and $60,000 in the second year. Fellows also receive life and health insurance, a relocation allowance (up to $1,000 for travel within the United States or up to $2,500 for travel from abroad), an allowance of $750 for moving and storing personal belongings, and at least $3,500 per year for scientific travel and registration fees.

Duration 2 years.

Additional data NCAR is operated by the University Corporation for Atmospheric Research (a consortium of 70 universities and research institutes) and sponsored by the National Science Foundation.

Number awarded Varies; currently, up to 9 each year.

Deadline January of each year.

[1079]
NATIONAL ENDOWMENT FOR THE HUMANITIES FELLOWSHIPS

National Endowment for the Humanities
Attn: Division of Research Programs
1100 Pennsylvania Avenue, N.W., Room 318
Washington, DC 20506
(202) 606-8200   Toll Free: (800) NEH-1121
Fax: (202) 606-8204   TDD: (866) 372-2930
E-mail: fellowships@neh.gov
Web: www.neh.gov/grants/research/fellowships

Summary To provide funding to scholars and faculty members (particularly those at Hispanic Serving Institutions, Historically Black Colleges and Universities, and Tribal Colleges and Universities) who wish to conduct research in the humanities.

Eligibility This program is open to faculty and staff of colleges, universities, primary schools, and secondary schools, as well as independent scholars and writers. Applicants must be U.S. citizens or foreign nationals who have resided in the United States or its jurisdictions for at least 3 years. The proposed project should contribute to scholarly knowledge or to the public's understanding of the humanities, usually in the form of scholarly articles, monographs on specialized subjects, books on broad topics, archaeological site reports, translations, editions, or other scholarly tools. Applicants do not need to have advanced degrees, but students currently enrolled in a degree-granting program are ineligible. Grants are not provided for curriculum development; empirical social science research, unless part of a larger humanities project; specific policy studies; the development of pedagogical tools; educational or technical impact assessments; the creation or enhancement of databases, unless part of a larger interpretive project; inventories of collections; the writing of autobiographies or memoirs; the writing of guide books, how-to books, or self-help books; preparation or revision of textbooks; works in the creative or performing arts; projects that seek to promote a particular political, philosophical, religious, or ideological point of view; projects that advocate a particular program of social action; works in the creative or performing arts; or doctoral dissertations or theses. Selection is based on 1) the intellectual significance of the project to the humanities, including its value to scholars and general audiences in the humanities; 2) the quality or promise of quality of the applicant's work as an interpreter of the humanities; 3) the quality of the conception, definition, organization, and description of the project; 4) the feasibility of the proposed plan of work; and 5) the likelihood that the applicant will complete the project. The program encourages submission of applications from faculty at Historically Black Colleges and Universities, Hispanic Serving Institutions, and Tribal Colleges and Universities.

Financial Data The grant is $4,200 per month, to a maximum of $50,400 for 12 months.

Duration 6 to 12 months.

Additional data Fellows may hold other fellowships or grants in support of the same project during their tenure, including sabbaticals and grants from their own institutions.

Number awarded Approximately 90 each year.

Deadline April of each year.

[1080]
NATIONAL INSTITUTES OF HEALTH INDIVIDUAL RESEARCH PROJECT GRANTS

National Institutes of Health
Office of Extramural Research
Attn: Grants Information
6705 Rockledge Drive, Suite 4090
Bethesda, MD 20892-7983
(301) 435-0714   Fax: (301) 480-0525
TDD: (301) 451-5936   E-mail: grantsinfo@od.nih.gov
Web: grants.nih.gov/grants/guide/pa-files/PA-11-260.html

Summary To support professionals and postdoctorates (particularly Hispanic Americans, other minorities, and individuals with disabilities) who are conducting research in biomedical and behavioral areas that will improve human health in areas of interest to the National Institutes of Health (NIH).

Eligibility This program is open to investigators at 1) public and private institutions of higher education (especially Hispanic-serving institutions, Historically Black Colleges and Universities, Tribal Colleges and Universities, and Alaska Native and Native Hawaiian Serving Institutions); 2) nonprofit institutions; 3) for profit organizations; 4) units of state and local governments and eligible agencies of the federal government; 5) other organizations such as school districts, public housing authorities, Native American tribal organizations, and faith-based organizations; and 6) foreign institutions and foreign components of U.S. organizations. Applications are accepted for health-related research and development in all areas within the scope of the institutes' mission and by all component institutes and centers. Specific subjects of research are announced periodically either as Program Announcements (PAs) for ongoing research or as Requests for Applications (RFAs) for specific 1-time research projects. Usually, the research is to be conducted within the United States, but research projects conducted at foreign sites may be proposed if the project presents special opportunities for furthering research programs through the use of unusual talent, resources, populations, or environmental conditions that exist in other countries and either are not available in the United States or augment existing U.S. resources. For all projects, members of underrepresented racial or ethnic groups and individuals with disabilities are particularly encouraged to apply as principal investigators.

Financial Data The level of funding depends on the scope of the proposed research. Funds may be used for supplies, equipment, personnel, and travel. Foreign institutions do not receive support for administrative costs associated with the research.

Duration 1 year or longer.

Additional data These grants are offered by 23 of NIH's component institutes. The most meritorious first-time recipients of these awards who are new investigators (with no more than five years of research experience since completion of postdoctoral training) are also nominated to receive Presidential Early Career Awards for Scientists and Engineers.

Number awarded Varies each year; recently, 8,765 of these grants were awarded.

Deadline February, June, or October of each year.

[1081]
NATIONAL LATINO PLAYWRITING AWARD

Arizona Theatre Company
Attn: Literary Manager
343 South Scott Avenue
Tucson, AZ 85701
(520) 884-8210, ext. 8510   Fax: (520) 628-9129
E-mail: info@arizonatheatre.org
Web: www.arizonatheatre.org

Summary To recognize and reward outstanding unpublished, unproduced plays written by Latino/Latinas in the United States or Mexico.

Eligibility This program is open to all Latino playwrights currently residing in the United States, its territories, or Mexico. Applicants may submit scripts in English, Spanish and English, or solely in Spanish; scripts in Spanish must be accompanied by an English translation. Only unpublished, unproduced plays are eligible. Full-length and 1-act plays (at least 50 pages in length) are accepted.

Financial Data The prize is $1,000 and possible inclusion in Cafe Bohemia, the Arizona Theatre Company's play reading series.

Duration The competition is held annually.

Additional data Previously, this award was known as the National Hispanic Playwriting Contest.

Number awarded 1 each year.

Deadline December of each year.

[1082]
NATIONAL SCIENCE FOUNDATION ANTARCTIC RESEARCH PROGRAM

National Science Foundation
Office of Polar Programs
Attn: Division of Antarctic Sciences
4201 Wilson Boulevard, Room 755S
Arlington, VA 22230
(703) 292-7425   Fax: (703) 292-9079
TDD: (800) 281-8749   E-mail: vpapita@nsf.gov
Web: www.nsf.gov/funding/pgm_summ.jsp?pims_id=5519

Summary To provide funding to scientists (particularly Hispanic Americans, other underrepresented minorities, women, and individuals with disabilities) who are interested in conducting research related to Antarctica.

Eligibility This program is open to investigators at U.S. institutions, primarily universities and, to a lesser extent, federal agencies and other organizations. Applicants must be proposing to conduct Antarctic-related research in the following major areas: astrophysics and geospace sciences, earth sciences, glaciology, organisms and ecosystems, instrumentation and technology development, integrated system science, and ocean and atmospheric sciences. In the selection process, consideration is given to the achievement of societally relevant outcomes, including full participation of women, persons with disabilities, and underrepresented minorities.

Financial Data The amounts of the awards depend on the nature of the proposal and the availability of funds.

Additional data The NSF operates 3 year-round research stations in Antarctica, additional research facilities and camps, airplanes, helicopters, various types of surface vehicles, and ships.

Number awarded Varies each year; recently, the program planned to make 50 awards with a total budget of $55 million for standard and continuing awards, including $9 million for astrophysics and geospace science, $8 million for earth science, $6 million for glaciology, $12 million for instrumentation and technology development, $6 million for integrated system science, $6 million for ocean and atmospheric science, and $8 million for organisms and ecosystems.

Deadline April of each year.

[1083]
NATIONAL SCIENCE FOUNDATION ARCTIC RESEARCH OPPORTUNITIES

National Science Foundation
Office of Polar Programs
Attn: Division of Arctic Sciences
4201 Wilson Boulevard, Suite 755S
Arlington, VA 22230
(703) 292-4482   Fax: (703) 292-9082
TDD: (800) 281-8749   E-mail: rcrain@nsf.gov
Web: www.nsf.gov/funding/pgm_summ.jsp?pims_id=5521

Summary To provide funding to experienced researchers (particularly Hispanic Americans, other underrepresented minorities, women, and individuals with disabilities) who are interested in conducting research related to the Arctic.

Eligibility This program is open to investigators affiliated with U.S. universities, research institutions, or other organizations, including local or state governments. Applicants must be proposing to conduct research in the 5 program areas of Arctic science: 1) Arctic Natural Sciences, with areas of special interest in marine and terrestrial ecosystems, Arctic atmospheric and oceanic dynamics and climatology, Arctic geological and glaciological processes, and their connectivity to lower latitudes; 2) Arctic Social Sciences, including (but not limited to) anthropology, archaeology, economics, geography, linguistics, political science, psychology, science and technology studies, sociology, traditional knowledge, and related subjects; 3) Arctic System Science, for research focused on a system understanding of the Arctic, understanding the behavior of the Arctic system (past, present, and future), understanding the role of the Arctic as a component of the global system, and society as an integral part of the Arctic system; 4) Arctic Observing Networks, for work related to a pan-Arctic, science-driven, observing system; or 5) Polar Cyberinfrastructure, for projects using high-performance computing for direct and sustainable advances in current Arctic research. In the selection process, consideration is given to the achievement of societally relevant outcomes, including full participation of women, persons with disabilities, and underrepresented minorities.

Financial Data The amounts of the awards depend on the nature of the proposal and the availability of funds.

Number awarded Approximately 75 each year; recently, this program awarded approximately $25 million in grants.

Deadline October of each year.

[1084]
NATIONAL URBAN FELLOWS PROGRAM

National Urban Fellows, Inc.
Attn: Program Director
989 Avenue of the Americas, Suite 400
New York, NY 10018
(212) 730-1700   Fax: (212) 730-1823
E-mail: info@nuf.org
Web: www.nuf.org/fellows-overview

Summary To offer financial assistance to mid-career public sector professionals (especially Hispanic Americans, other minorities, and women) who are interested in working on a master's degree program coupled with a mentorship.

Eligibility This program is open to U.S. citizens who have a bachelor's degree, have at least 3 years of administrative or managerial experience, have demonstrated exceptional ability and leadership potential, meet academic admission requirements, have a high standard of integrity and work ethic, and are committed to the solution of urban problems. Applicants must a 1,000-word autobiographical statement and a 1,000-word statement on their career goals. They may be of any racial or ethnic background, but the program's goal is to increase the number of competent administrators from underrepresented ethnic and cultural groups at all levels of public and private urban management organizations. Semifinalists are interviewed.

Financial Data The stipend is $25,000. The program also provides full payment of tuition, a relocation allowance of $500, a book allowance of $500, and reimbursement for program-related travel.

Duration 14 months.

Additional data The program begins with a summer semester of study at Bernard M. Baruch College of the City University of New York. Following this, fellows spend 9 months in mentorship assignments with a senior administrator in a government agency, a major nonprofit, or a foundation. The final summer is spent in another semester of study at Baruch College. Fellows who successfully complete all requirements are granted a master's of public administration from that college. A $75 processing fee must accompany each application.

Number awarded Varies; approximately 40 each year.

Deadline February of each year.

[1085]
NCI MENTORED PATIENT-ORIENTED RESEARCH CAREER DEVELOPMENT AWARD TO PROMOTE DIVERSITY

National Cancer Institute
Attn: Comprehensive Minority Biomedical Branch
9609 Medical Center Drive
Sixth Floor, West Tower
Bethesda, MD 20892-9746
(240) 276-6186   TDD: (301) 451-0088
E-mail: ojeifojo@mail.nih.gov
Web: grants.nih.gov/grants/guide/pa-files/PAR-12-052.html

Summary To provide funding to Hispanic Americans and members of other underrepresented groups who are interested in a program of research training in patient-oriented oncology under the supervision of an experienced mentor.

Eligibility This program is open to U.S. citizens, nationals, and permanent residents who have a health professional doctoral degree or a doctoral degree in nursing research or practice; individuals with a Ph.D. degree in clinical disciplines such as clinical psychology, clinical genetics, speech-language pathology, audiology, or rehabilitation are also eligible. Candidates must be nominated by a domestic nonprofit or for-profit organization, public or private (such as a university, college, hospital, laboratory, unit of state or local government, or eligible agency of the federal government) that can demonstrate a commitment to diversification of their student and faculty populations. Institutions must certify that the candidate qualifies as 1) a member of an ethnic or racial group shown to be underrepresented in health-related sciences on a national basis; 2) an individual with a disability; or 3) an individual from a disadvantaged background, including those from a low-income family and those from a social, cultural, and/or educational environment that have inhibited them from preparation for a research career. At least 2 mentors are required: 1 who is recognized as an accomplished clinical investigator and at least 1 additional mentor or adviser who is recognized as an accomplished independent basic science investigator in the proposed research area.

Financial Data The award provides salary up to $100,000 per year plus related fringe benefits. In addition, up to $30,000 per year is provided for research development support. Facilities and administrative costs are reimbursed at 8% of modified total direct costs.

Duration 3 to 5 years.

Additional data Recipients must devote at least 75% of their full-time professional effort to cancer-related research and training activities.

Number awarded Varies each year.

Deadline February, June, or October of each year.

[1086]
NCI MENTORED RESEARCH SCIENTIST DEVELOPMENT AWARD TO PROMOTE DIVERSITY

National Cancer Institute
Attn: Center to Reduce Cancer Health Disparities
9609 Medical Center Drive
Sixth Floor, West Tower
Bethesda, MD 20892-9746
(240) 276-6186   TDD: (301) 451-0088
E-mail: ojeifojo@mail.nih.gov
Web: grants.nih.gov/grants/guide/pa-files/PAR-12-050.html

Summary To provide funding to Hispanic Americans and members of other underrepresented groups who need a period of "protected time" for intensive cancer research career development leading to research independence.

Eligibility This program is open to U.S. citizens, nationals, and permanent residents who have a research or health professional doctorate and have completed a mentored research training experience. Candidates must be proposing to conduct a research project to prepare for an independent research career related to cancer biology, cancer health disparities, etiology, pathogenesis, prevention, diagnosis, and/or treatment. They must be nominated by an eligible institution that can demonstrate a commitment to the promotion of diversity of their student and faculty populations. Institutions must certify that the candidate qualifies as 1) a member of an ethnic or racial group shown to be underrepresented in health-related sciences on a national basis; 2) an individual with a disability; or 3) an individual from a disadvantaged background, including those from a low-income family and those from a social, cultural, and/or educational environment that have inhibited them from preparation for a research career.

Financial Data The award provides salary up to $100,000 per year plus related fringe benefits. In addition, up to $30,000 per year is provided for research development support. Facilities and administrative costs are reimbursed at 8% of modified total direct costs.

Duration 3, 4, or 5 years.

Additional data Recipients must devote at least 75% of their full-time professional effort to cancer-related research and training activities.

Number awarded Varies each year.

Deadline February, June, or October of each year.

[1087]
NEH COLLABORATIVE RESEARCH GRANTS

National Endowment for the Humanities
Attn: Division of Research Programs
1100 Pennsylvania Avenue, N.W., Room 318
Washington, DC 20506
(202) 606-8200   Toll Free: (800) NEH-1121
Fax: (202) 606-8204   TDD: (866) 372-2930
E-mail: collaborative@neh.gov
Web: www.neh.gov

Summary To provide funding to teams of scholars (particularly those at Hispanic Serving Institutions, Historically Black Colleges and Universities, or Tribal Colleges and Universities) who wish to conduct research in the humanities.

Eligibility This program is open to 1) U.S. citizens and foreign nationals who have been living in the United States or its jurisdictions for at least 3 years; 2) state and local governmental agencies; and 3) nonprofit, tax-exempt institutions and organizations in the United States. It supports original research undertaken by a team of 2 or more scholars or research coordinated by an individual scholar that, because of its scope or complexity, requires additional staff or resources beyond the individual's salary. Eligible projects include research that significantly adds to knowledge and understanding in the humanities; archaeology projects that interpret and communicate the results of archaeological field work; research that uses the knowledge, methods, and perspectives of the humanities to enhance understanding of science, technology, medicine, and the social sciences; translations into English of works that provide insight into the history, literature, philosophy, and artistic achievements of other cultures; and conferences on topics of major importance in the humanities that will benefit ongoing research. Selection is based on 1) the intellectual significance of the project, including its potential contribution to scholarship in the humanities, the likelihood that it will stimulate new research, its relationship to larger themes in the humanities, and the significance of the material on which the project is based; 2) the pertinence of the research questions being posed, the appropriateness of research methods or conference design, the feasibility of the work plan, the quality of samples, and the appropriateness of the field work, the archival or source materials, and the research site; 3) the qualifications, expertise, and levels of commitment to the project of the project director and

key project staff or contributors, and the appropriateness of the staff to the goals of the project; 4) soundness of the dissemination and access plans; and 5) the potential for success, including the likelihood that the project will be successfully completed within the projected time frame. The program encourages submission of applications from faculty at Historically Black Colleges and Universities, Hispanic Serving Institutions, and Tribal Colleges and Universities.

Financial Data Grants range from $25,000 to $100,000 per year. The use of federal matching funds in encouraged. Normally, support does not exceed 80% of total costs.

Duration 1 to 3 years.

Additional data All grantees are expected to publish or in other ways to disseminate the results of their work.

Number awarded Approximately 17 each year.

Deadline December of each year.

[1088]
NEH SUMMER STIPENDS

National Endowment for the Humanities
Attn: Division of Research Programs
1100 Pennsylvania Avenue, N.W., Room 318
Washington, DC 20506
(202) 606-8200   Toll Free: (800) NEH-1121
Fax: (202) 606-8204   TDD: (866) 372-2930
E-mail: stipends@neh.gov
Web: www.neh.gov/grants/research/summer-stipends

Summary To provide funding to scholars and other professionals (particularly those at Hispanic Serving Institutions, Historically Black Colleges and Universities, and Tribal Colleges and Universities) who are interested in conducting research in the humanities during the summer.

Eligibility Faculty members teaching full time in U.S. colleges and universities may be nominated by their schools for these awards. Each school may nominate 2 candidates. Also eligible are independent scholars not affiliated with a college or university, non-faculty college and university staff members who will not be teaching during the academic year preceding the grant tenure, and adjunct and part-time faculty with academic appointments that terminate by the summer of the grant tenure; such applicants do not require nomination. All applicants must be U.S. citizens or foreign nationals who have lived in the United States or its territories for 3 years prior to the application deadline. They must be proposing to pursue research in the humanities that contributes to scholarly knowledge or to the public's understanding of the humanities, normally through scholarly articles, a monograph on a specialized subject, a book on a broad topic, an archaeological site report, a translation, an edition, a database, or other scholarly tools. Support is not provided for research for doctoral dissertations or theses by students enrolled in a degree program; specific policy studies or educational or technical impact assessments; preparation or publication of textbooks; studying teaching methods or theories, surveys of courses and programs, or curriculum development; works in the creative or performing arts; projects that seek to promote a particular political, philosophical, religious, or ideological point of view; projects that advocate a particular program of social action; or creating inventories of collections. Persons who have held a major fellowship or research grant or its equivalent during any of the preceding 3 academic years are ineligible. Selection is based on the intellectual significance of the proposed project, including its value to humanities scholars, general audiences, or both; the quality or promise of quality of the applicant's work as an interpreter of the humanities; the quality of the conception, definition, organization, and description of the proposed project; the feasibility of the proposed plan of work; and the likelihood that the applicant will complete the project. The program encourages submission of applications from faculty at Historically Black Colleges and Universities, Hispanic Serving Institutions, and Tribal Colleges and Universities.

Financial Data The stipend is $6,000.

Duration 2 months during the summer.

Additional data Previous recipients may reapply after 5 years. Recipients may hold other research grants during the tenure of their awards, and they must devote full time to their projects for the 2 months of their tenure.

Number awarded Approximately 74 each year.

Deadline September of each year.

[1089]
NEW INVESTIGATOR RESEARCH GRANTS TO PROMOTE DIVERSITY OF THE ALZHEIMER'S ASSOCIATION

Alzheimer's Association
Attn: Medical and Scientific Affairs
225 North Michigan Avenue, 17th Floor
Chicago, IL 60601-7633
(312) 335-5747   Toll Free: (800) 272-3900
Fax: (866) 699-1246   TDD: (312) 335-5886
E-mail: grantsapp@alz.org
Web: www.alz.org

Summary To provide funding for research on Alzheimer's Disease to junior investigators (particularly Hispanic Americans, other underrepresented minorities, and individuals with disabilities) who will contribute to diversity in the field.

Eligibility This program is open to investigators who have less than 10 years of research experience after receipt of their terminal degree. Applicants must be proposing to conduct research with focus areas that change annually but are related to Alzheimer's Disease. Eligibility is restricted to investigators who will contribute to diversity in the field of biomedical research, including members of underrepresented racial and ethnic minority groups (African Americans, Hispanic Americans, American Indians/Alaska Natives, Native Hawaiians, and Pacific Islanders) and individuals with disabilities.

Financial Data Grants up to $60,000 per year, including direct expenses and up to 10% for overhead costs, are available. The total award for the life of the grant may not exceed $100,000.

Duration Up to 2 years.

Number awarded 1 or 2 each year.

Deadline Letters of intent must be submitted by the end of January or September of each year. Final applications are due in March or October.

[1090]
NEW VISIONS AWARD

Lee & Low Books
95 Madison Avenue, Suite 1205
New York, NY 10016
(212) 779-4400   Fax: (212) 683-1894
E-mail: general@leeandlow.com
Web: www.leeandlow.com/p/new_visions_award.mhtml

Summary To recognize and reward outstanding unpublished fantasy or mystery books for young readers by Hispanic Americans and other writers of color.

Eligibility The contest is open to writers of color who are residents of the United States. Applicants must submit a manuscript of a fantasy, science fiction, or mystery book directed to readers at the middle grade or young adult level.

Financial Data The award is a $1,000 cash grant plus the standard publication contract, including the standard advance and royalties. The Honor Award winner receives a cash grant of $500.

Duration The competition is held annually.

Additional data This program began in 2012. Manuscripts may not be sent to any other publishers while under consideration for this award.

Number awarded 2 each year.

Deadline October of each year.

[1091]
NEW VOICES AWARD

Lee & Low Books
95 Madison Avenue, Suite 1205
New York, NY 10016
(212) 779-4400   Fax: (212) 683-1894
E-mail: general@leeandlow.com
Web: www.leeandlow.com/p/new_voices_award.mhtml

Summary To recognize and reward outstanding unpublished children's picture books by Hispanic Americans and other writers of color.

Eligibility The contest is open to writers of color who are residents of the United States and who have not previously published a children's picture book. Writers who have published in other venues, (e.g., children's magazines, young adult fiction and nonfiction) are eligible. Manuscripts previously submitted to the sponsor are not eligible. Submissions should be no more than 1,500 words and must address the needs of children of color by providing stories with which they can identify and relate and that promote a greater understanding of each other. Submissions may be fiction or nonfiction for children between the ages of 5 and 12. Folklore and animal stories are not considered. Up to 2 submissions may be submitted per entrant.

Financial Data The award is a $1,000 cash grant plus the standard publication contract, including the standard advance and royalties. The Honor Award winner receives a cash grant of $500.

Duration The competition is held annually.

Additional data This program began in 2000. Manuscripts may not be sent to any other publishers while under consideration for this award.

Number awarded 2 each year.

Deadline October of each year.

[1092]
NHLBI MENTORED CAREER AWARD FOR FACULTY AT INSTITUTIONS THAT PROMOTE DIVERSITY

National Heart, Lung, and Blood Institute
Attn: Division of Blood Diseases and Resources
6701 Rockledge Drive, Room 9176
Bethesda, MD 20892-7950
(301) 435-0067   Fax: (301) 480-1060
TDD: (301) 451-0088   E-mail: changh@nhlbi.nih.gov
Web: grants.nih.gov

Summary To provide funding to Hispanic Americans and members of other underrepresented groups who are interested in developing into independent biomedical investigators in research areas relevant to the mission of the National Heart, Lung, and Blood Institute (NHLBI).

Eligibility This program is open to full-time faculty members at colleges and universities that promote diversity, especially Hispanic Serving Institutions, Historically Black Colleges and Universities, Tribally Controlled Colleges and Universities, and Alaska Native and Native Hawaiian Serving Institutions. Candidates must have received a doctoral degree at least 2 years previously and be able to demonstrate a commitment to develop into an independent biomedical investigator in research areas related to cardiovascular, pulmonary, hematologic, and sleep disorders of interest to NHLBI. They must identify and complete arrangements with a mentor (at the same institution or at a collaborating research center) who is recognized as an accomplished investigator in the research area proposed and who will provide guidance for their development and research plans. They must also be U.S. citizens, nationals, or permanent residents.

Financial Data The awardee receives salary support of up to $75,000 per year plus fringe benefits. In addition, up to $36,000 per year may be provided for research project requirements and related support (e.g., technical personnel costs, supplies, equipment, candidate travel, telephone charges, publication costs, and tuition for necessary courses). Facilities and administrative costs may be reimbursed at the rate of 8% of total direct costs.

Duration 3 to 5 years.

Additional data Awardees must commit 75% of their effort to the proposed project.

Number awarded 2 to 3 each year; a total of approximately $300,000 is available for this program annually.

Deadline Letters of intent must be submitted by January of each year; final applications are due in February.

[1093]
NINR MENTORED RESEARCH SCIENTIST DEVELOPMENT AWARD FOR UNDERREPRESENTED OR DISADVANTAGED INVESTIGATORS

National Institute of Nursing Research
Attn: Office of Extramural Programs
6701 Democracy Boulevard, Suite 710
Bethesda, MD 20892-4870
(301) 496-9558   Fax: (301) 480-8260
TDD: (301) 451-0088   E-mail: banksd@mail.nih.gov
Web: grants.nih.gov/grants/guide/pa-files/PAR-09-074.html

Summary To provide funding for research career development to Hispanic American and other underrepresented or disadvantaged postdoctoral nursing investigators.

Eligibility This program is open to nurses who have a research or health-professional doctoral degree and are employed full time at an institution that conducts research. Applicants must qualify as an individual whose participation in scientific research will increase diversity, including 1) individuals from racial and ethnic groups that have been shown to be underrepresented in health-related science on a national basis; 2) individuals with disabilities; and 3) individuals from disadvantaged backgrounds, including those from a family with an annual income below established levels and those from a social, cultural, or educational environment that has demonstrably and recently directly inhibited the individual from obtaining the knowledge, skills, and abilities necessary to develop and participate in a research career. They must secured the commitment of an appropriate research mentor actively involved in research relevant to the mission of the National Institute of Nursing Research (NINR). Only U.S. citizens, nationals, and permanent residents are eligible.

Financial Data The grant provides up to $50,000 per year for salary and fringe benefits plus an additional $20,000 per year for research development support. Facilities and administrative costs are allowed at 8% of total direct costs.

Duration Up to 3 years.

Additional data These grants have been awarded annually since 1998. Grantees are expected to spend at least 75% of their professional effort time to the program and the other 25% to other research-related and/or teaching or clinical pursuits consistent with the objectives of the award.

Number awarded 3 to 4 new grants are awarded each year.

Deadline February, June, or October of each year.

[1094]
NLM EXPRESS RESEARCH GRANTS IN BIOMEDICAL INFORMATICS

National Library of Medicine
Attn: Extramural Programs
6705 Rockledge Drive, Suite 301
Bethesda, MD 20892-7968
(301) 496-4221   Fax: (301) 402-0421
TDD: (301) 451-0088   E-mail: moweryd@mail.nih.gov
Web: grants.nih.gov/grants/guide/pa-files/PAR-13-300.html

Summary To provide funding to scholars (particularly Hispanic Americans, other underrepresented minorities, and individuals with disabilities) who are interested in conducting research related to biomedical informatics.

Eligibility This program is open to investigators affiliated with institutions of higher education, nonprofit organizations, small businesses, for-profit organizations, state and local governments, and other organizations authorized to conduct research. Applicants must be interested in conducting a research project in the field of biomedical informatics. Relevant topics include, but are not limited to, health care; public health and health services; disaster information management; basic biological, social, and behavioral research; multi-level computational models of biological and clinical processes; translational research that supports uses of data in electronic health records to support biomedical research and translation of biomedical research outcomes through application to problems in clinical care; and information sciences, simulation, user customization, virtual environments, and innovative information techniques. Members of underrepresented racial and ethnic groups and individuals with disabilities are especially encouraged to apply. Applications are also welcome from engineers, computer scientists, information scientists, social and behavioral scientists, and others not traditionally involved in biomedical research.

Financial Data Grants may range up to $250,000 per year.

Duration Up to 4 years.

Number awarded Varies each year.

Deadline February, June, or October of each year.

[1095]
NOAA SMALL BUSINESS INNOVATION RESEARCH GRANTS

National Oceanic and Atmospheric Administration
Office of Research and Technology Applications
Attn: SBIR Program Manager
1335 East-West Highway, SSMC1, Room 106
Silver Spring, MD 20910-3284
(301) 713-3565   Fax: (301) 713-4100
E-mail: Kelly.Wright@noaa.gov
Web: www.oar.noaa.gov/orta

Summary To support small businesses (especially those owned by Hispanic Americans, other minorities, or women) that have the technological experience to contribute to the research and development mission of the National Oceanic and Atmospheric Administration (NOAA).

Eligibility For the purposes of this program, a "small business" is defined as a firm that is organized for profit with a location in the United States; is in the legal form of an individual proprietorship, partnership, limited liability company, corporation, joint venture, association, trust, or cooperative; is at least 51% owned and controlled by 1 or more individuals who are citizens or permanent residents of the United States; and has (including its affiliates) fewer than 500 employees. The primary employment of the principal investigator must be with the firm at the time of award and during the conduct of the proposed project. Applications are encouraged rom 1) women-owned small business concerns, defined as those that are at least 51% owned by a woman or women who also control and operate them; and 2) socially and economically disadvantaged small business concerns that are at least 51% owned by an Indian tribe, a Native Hawaiian organization, or 1 or more socially and economically disadvantaged individuals (African Americans, Hispanic Americans, Native Americans, Asian Pacific Americans, or subcontinent Asian Americans). Current priority areas of research include: 1) resilient coastal communities and economics; 2) healthy oceans; 3) climate adaptation and mitigation; or 4) weather-ready nation. Selection is based on the technical approach and anticipated agency and commercial benefits that may be derived from the research (25 points); the adequacy of the proposed effort and its relationship to the fulfillment of the requirements of the research topic (20 points); the soundness and technical merit of the proposed approach and its incremental progress towards topic solution (20 points); qualifications of the principal investigators, supporting staff, and consultants (15 points); and the proposal's commercial potential (20 points).

Financial Data Grants are offered in 2 phases. In phase 1, awards normally do not exceed $95,000 (for both direct and indirect costs); in phase 2, awards normally do not exceed $400,000 (including both direct and indirect costs).

Duration Phase 1 awards may extend up to 6 months; phase 2 awards may extend up to 2 years.

Number awarded Varies each year; recently, NOAA planned to award 15 Phase 1 contracts. Approximately half of Phase 1 awardees receive Phase 2 awards.

Deadline January of each year.

[1096]
NOTRE DAME INSTITUTE FOR ADVANCED STUDY RESIDENTIAL FELLOWSHIPS

University of Notre Dame
Institute for Advanced Study
Attn: Programs Administrator
1124 Flanner Hall
Notre Dame, IN 46556
(574) 631-6240   E-mail: csherman@nd.edu
Web: ndias.nd.edu/fellowships/residential

Summary To provide funding to scholars (particularly Hispanic Americans and members of other traditionally underrepresented groups) who are interested in conducting research on topics of interest to the Notre Dame Institute for Advanced Study (NDIAS) while in residence at the institute.

Eligibility This program is open to faculty, scholars, public intellectuals, fellows from other institutes, and professional researchers in all disciplines, including the arts, engineering, the humanities, law, and the natural, social, and physical sciences. Applicants must be interested in conducting research that aligns with the intellectual orientation of the NDIAS, which asks scholars "to include questions of values in their analyses, to integrate diverse disciplines, and to ask how their findings advance civilization." They must be able to demonstrate excellent records of scholarly, artistic, or research accomplishment in their field; ability to interact with other fellows and to engage in collegial discussions of research presentations; a willingness to contribute to a cooperative community of scholars; and projects that touch on normative, integrative, or ultimate questions, especially as the involve the Catholic intellectual tradition. Applications are especially encouraged from traditionally underrepresented groups. There are no citizenship requirements; non-U.S. nationals are welcome to apply.

Financial Data The grant is $60,000 for a full academic year or pro-rated amounts for shorter periods. Other benefits include subsidized visiting faculty housing, research support up to $1,000, a private office at the institute, a computer and printer, access to university libraries and other facilities, and weekly institute seminars and events.

Duration Up to 1 academic year.

Number awarded 1 or more each year.

Deadline October of each year.

[1097]
NSF SMALL BUSINESS INNOVATION RESEARCH GRANTS

National Science Foundation
Directorate for Engineering
Attn: Division of Industrial Innovation and Partnerships
4201 Wilson Boulevard, Room 590 N
Arlington, VA 22230
(703) 292-8050   Fax: (703) 292-9057
TDD: (800) 281-8749
Web: www.nsf.gov/eng/iip/spir

Summary To provide funding to small and creative engineering, science, education, and technology-related firms (particularly those owned by Hispanic Americans, other minorities, or women) to conduct innovative, high-risk research on scientific and technical problems.

Eligibility For the purposes of this program, a "small business" is defined as a firm that is organized for profit with a location in the United States; is in the legal form of an individual proprietorship, partnership, limited liability company, corporation, joint venture, association, trust, or cooperative; is at least 51% owned and controlled by 1 or more individuals who are citizens or permanent residents of the United States; and has (including its affiliates) fewer than 500 employees. The primary employment of the principal investigator must be with the firm at the time of award and during the conduct of the proposed project. Applications are encouraged from 1) women-owned small business concerns, defined as those that are at least 51% owned by a woman or women who also control and operate them; and 2) socially and economically disadvantaged small business concerns that are at least 51% owned by an Indian tribe, a Native Hawaiian organization, or 1 or more socially and economically disadvantaged individuals (African Americans, Hispanic Americans, Native Americans, Asian Pacific Americans, or subcontinent Asian Americans). Current priorities for critical technology areas of national importance include 1) biological and chemical technologies; 2) education applications; 3) electronics, information and communication technologies; and 4) nanotechnology, advanced materials, and manufacturing. Selection is based on the intellectual merit and the broader impacts of the proposed activity.

Financial Data Support is offered in 2 phases. In phase 1, awards normally may not exceed $150,000 (for both direct and indirect costs); in phase 2, awards normally may not exceed $500,000 (including both direct and indirect costs).

Duration Phase 1 awards may extend up to 6 months; phase 2 awards may extend up to 2 years.

Number awarded Depends on the availability of funds; the National Science Foundation (NSF) plans to award approximately 100 phase 1 grants each year; recently, $15 million was budgeted for this program.

Deadline June of each year.

[1098]
NSF SMALL BUSINESS TECHNOLOGY TRANSFER GRANTS

National Science Foundation
Directorate for Engineering
Attn: Division of Industrial Innovation and Partnerships
4201 Wilson Boulevard, Room 590 N
Arlington, VA 22230
(703) 292-8050   Fax: (703) 292-9057
TDD: (800) 281-8749
Web: www.nsf.gov/eng/iip/spir

Summary To provide financial support for cooperative research and development projects carried out between small business concerns and research institutions ((particularly those owned by Hispanic Americans, other minorities, or women) in areas of concern to the National Science Foundation (NSF).

Eligibility For the purposes of this program, a "small business" is defined as a firm that is organized for profit with a location in the United States; is in the legal form of an individual proprietorship, partnership, limited liability company, corporation, joint venture, association, trust, or cooperative; is at least 51% owned and controlled by 1 or more individuals who are citizens or permanent residents of the United States; and has (including its affiliates) fewer than 500 employees. Unlike the NSF Small Business Innovation Research Grants, the primary employment of the principal investigator does not need to be with the business concern. This program, however, requires that the small business apply in collaboration with a nonprofit research institution for conduct of a project that has potential for commercialization. Principal investigators from the nonprofit research institution must commit at least 10% of their effort to the project. At least 40% of the work must be performed by the small business and at least 30% of the work must be performed by the research institution. Applications are encouraged from 1) women-owned small business concerns, defined as those that are at least 51% owned by a woman or women who also control and operate them; and 2) socially and economically disadvantaged small business concerns that are at least 51% owned by an Indian tribe, a Native Hawaiian organization, or 1 or more socially and economically disadvantaged individuals (African Americans, Hispanic Americans, Native Americans, Asian Pacific Americans, or subcontinent Asian Americans). Recently, the program was accepting applications only for the topic area of enhancing access to the radio spectrum; previous topics have included 1) advanced materials, chemical technology and manufacturing; 2) biotechnology; 3) electronics; 4) information technology; and 5) emerging opportunities (projects with a focus on near-term commercialization). Selection is based on the intellectual merit and the broader impacts of the proposed activity.

Financial Data In the first phase, annual awards may not exceed $150,000 for direct costs, indirect costs, and negotiated fixed fees. In the second phase, awards up to $500,000 are available.

Duration Normally, 12 months for phase 1 and 2 years for phase 2.

Additional data Grants in the first phase are to determine the scientific, technical, and commercial merit and feasibility of the proposed cooperative effort and the quality of performance of the small business concern. In the second phase, the research and development efforts continue, depending on the results of the first phase.

Number awarded   35 phase 1 grants are awarded each year. Approximately one-third of phase 1 awardees receive phase 2 grants. Approximately $5,250,000 is budgeted for this program each year.

Deadline   December of each year.

[1099]
NSF STANDARD AND CONTINUING GRANTS

National Science Foundation
4201 Wilson Boulevard
Arlington, VA 22230
(703) 292-5111   TDD: (800) 281-8749
E-mail: info@nsf.gov
Web: www.nsf.gov

Summary   To provide financial support to engineers and educators (particularly Hispanic Americans, other underrepresented minorities, and women) for research in broad areas of science and engineering.

Eligibility   The National Science Foundation (NSF) supports research through its Directorates of Biological Sciences; Computer and Information Science and Engineering; Education and Human Resources; Engineering; Geosciences; Mathematical and Physical Sciences; and Social, Behavioral, and Economic Sciences. Within those general areas of science and engineering, NSF awards 2 types of grants: 1) standard grants, in which NSF agrees to provide a specific level of support for a specified period of time with no statement of NSF intent to provide additional future support without submission of another proposal; and 2) continuing grants, in which NSF agrees to provide a specific level of support for an initial specified period of time with a statement of intent to provide additional support of the project for additional periods, provided funds are available and the results achieved warrant further support. Although NSF often solicits proposals for support of targeted areas through issuance of specific program solicitations, it also accepts unsolicited proposals. Scientists, engineers, and educators usually act as the principal investigator and initiate proposals that are officially submitted by their employing organization. Most employing organizations are universities, colleges, and non-profit non-academic organizations (such as museums, observatories, research laboratories, and professional societies). Certain programs are open to for-profit organizations, state and local governments, or unaffiliated individuals. Principal investigators usually must be U.S. citizens, nationals, or permanent residents. In the selection process, consideration is given to the achievement of societally relevant outcomes, including full participation of women, persons with disabilities, and underrepresented minorities.

Financial Data   Funding levels vary, depending on the nature of the project and the availability of funds. Awards resulting from unsolicited research proposals are subject to statutory cost-sharing.

Duration   Standard grants specify the period of time, usually up to 1 year; continuing grants normally specify 1 year as the initial period of time, with support to continue for additional periods.

Additional data   Researchers interested in support from NSF should contact the address above to obtain further information on areas of support and programs operating within the respective directorates. They should consult with a program officer before submitting an application. Information on programs is available on the NSF home page. NSF does not normally support technical assistance, pilot plant efforts, research requiring security classification, the development of products for commercial marketing, or market research for a particular project or invention. Bioscience research with disease-related goals, including work on the etiology, diagnosis, or treatment of physical or mental disease, abnormality, or malfunction in human beings or animals, is normally not supported.

Number awarded   Approximately 11,000 new grants are awarded each year.

Deadline   Many programs accept proposals at any time. Other programs establish target dates or deadlines; those target dates and deadlines are published in the *NSF Bulletin* and in specific program announcements/solicitations.

[1100]
OAK RIDGE NATIONAL LABORATORY/OAK RIDGE ASSOCIATED UNIVERSITIES HBCU/MEI FACULTY SUMMER RESEARCH PROGRAM

Oak Ridge Institute for Science and Education
Attn: Science and Engineering Education
P.O. Box 117
Oak Ridge, TN 37831-0117
(865) 574-4550   Fax: (865) 241-5219
E-mail: Michael.Ickowitz@orau.gov
Web: see.orau.org

Summary   To provide funding to faculty at Minority-serving Educational Institutions (MEIs) who wish to engage in ongoing research at Oak Ridge National Laboratory (ORNL) in Tennessee.

Eligibility   This program is open to full-time faculty members at Hispanic Serving Institutions (HSIs), Historically Black Colleges and Universities (HBCUs), Tribal Colleges and Universities TCUs), Alaska Native Serving Institutions (ANSIs), and Native Hawaiian Serving Institutions (NHSIs). Applicants must be interested in collaborating on specific research projects at ORNL in computer science; earth, environmental, or marine sciences; engineering; life, health, or medical sciences; mathematics; or physical sciences. Research projects are currently available in quantum imaging by compressive sampling, quantum lightwave circuits, decadal-scale hydroclimatic predictions and impact assessments, novel neutron detector for scattering applications, timely discovery and situational understanding of cyber attacks, lignin as a precursor for high performance energy storage applications, intelligent advanced propulsion systems, incorporating molecular-scale mechanisms stabilizing soil organic carbon into terrestrial carbon cycle models, citizen engagement for energy efficient communities, ultrascale algorithms for verification of security properties, data-driven threat radar for local-to-regional energy grid stability, and unraveling the molecular and biochemical basis of crassulacean acid metabolism in agave for sustainable biofuel production. Selection is based on the strength of the applicant's capabilities and experience; the match between the applicant's qualifications and the research needs of the selected project; and the potential for establishing an ongoing research partnership.

Financial Data   The stipend is based on the recipient's regular university salary, at least $4,500 per month. Participants

also receive limited reimbursement for inbound and outbound transportation and a monthly dislocation allowance of $1,000.
Duration 10 weeks during the summer.
Additional data This program is funded by ORNL and Oak Ridge Associated Universities (ORAU) and administered by Oak Ridge Institute for Science and Education (ORISE).
Number awarded Varies each year.
Deadline January of each year.

[1101]
OCEAN SCIENCES POSTDOCTORAL RESEARCH FELLOWSHIPS

National Science Foundation
Directorate for Geosciences
Attn: Division of Ocean Sciences
4201 Wilson Boulevard, Room 725N
Arlington, VA 22230
(703) 292-7240   Fax: (703) 292-9085
TDD: (800) 281-8749   E-mail: lweber@nsf.gov
Web: www.nsf.gov

Summary To provide funding to Hispanic Americans and members of other underrepresented groups who are interested in conducting postdoctoral research training in the ocean sciences.
Eligibility This program is open to U.S. citizens, nationals, or permanent residents who are members of groups underrepresented in the ocean sciences (women, persons with disabilities, African Americans, Hispanics, Native Americans, Alaska Natives, and Pacific Islanders). Applicants must have earned within the past 24 months a doctoral degree in the ocean sciences, including biological oceanography, chemical oceanography, physical oceanography, marine geology and geophysics, ocean drilling, ocean science and technology, or ocean education. They must be interested in conducting research training at a U.S. or foreign host institution under the mentorship of a sponsoring scientist who will provide guidance for the research.
Financial Data Grants are $85,000 per year, including an annual stipend of $60,000 and an annual fellowship allowance of $25,000 that is intended to cover direct research expenses, facilities and other institutional resources, and fringe benefits.
Duration Up to 2 years.
Number awarded 10 each year.
Deadline January of each year.

[1102]
OCEAN SCIENCES RESEARCH INITIATION GRANTS

National Science Foundation
Directorate for Geosciences
Attn: Division of Ocean Sciences
4201 Wilson Boulevard, Room 725N
Arlington, VA 22230
(703) 292-7240   Fax: (703) 292-9085
TDD: (800) 281-8749   E-mail: lweber@nsf.gov
Web: www.nsf.gov

Summary To provide funding to Hispanic Americans and members of other underrepresented groups who are junior faculty members interested in conducting research in the ocean sciences.

Eligibility This program is open to U.S. citizens, nationals, or permanent residents who are members of groups underrepresented in the ocean sciences: women, persons with disabilities, African Americans, Hispanics, Native Americans, Alaska Natives, and Pacific Islanders. Applicants must have held a tenure-track assistant professor level faculty position or equivalent research appointment for no more than 3 years. They must be interested in conducting research in the ocean sciences, including biological oceanography, chemical oceanography, physical oceanography, marine geology and geophysics, ocean drilling, ocean science and technology, or ocean education.
Financial Data The maximum grant is $100,000 in direct and indirect costs for 12 to 24 months.
Duration Up to 2 years.
Number awarded 6 each year.
Deadline January of each year.

[1103]
OFFICE OF NAVAL RESEARCH SABBATICAL LEAVE PROGRAM

American Society for Engineering Education
Attn: ONR Summer Programs
1818 N Street, N.W., Suite 600
Washington, DC 20036-2479
(202) 331-3558   Fax: (202) 265-8504
E-mail: onrsummer@asee.org
Web: onr.asee.org/about_the_sabbatical_leave_program

Summary To provide support to faculty members in engineering and science (particularly those at Minority Serving Institutions) who wish to conduct research at selected Navy facilities while on sabbatical leave.
Eligibility This program is open to U.S. citizens with teaching or research appointments in engineering and science at U.S. universities or colleges. Applicants must intend to conduct research while in residence at selected facilities of the U.S. Navy. Faculty from Historically Black Colleges and Universities, Hispanic Serving Institutions, and Tribal Colleges and Universities are especially encouraged to apply.
Financial Data Fellows receive a stipend equivalent to the difference between their regular salary and the sabbatical leave pay from their home institution. Fellows who must relocate their residence receive a relocation allowance and all fellows receive a travel allowance.
Duration Appointments are for a minimum of 1 semester and a maximum of 1 year.
Additional data Participating facilities include the Naval Air Warfare Center, Aircraft Division (Patuxent River, Maryland); Naval Air Warfare Center, Naval Training Systems Division (Orlando, Florida); Naval Air Warfare Center, Weapons Division (China Lake, California); Space and Naval Warfare Systems Center (San Diego, California and Charleston, South Carolina); Naval Facilities Engineering Service Center (Port Hueneme, California); Naval Research Laboratories (Washington, D.C.; Stennis Space Center, Mississippi; and Monterey, California); Naval Surface Warfare Centers (Bethesda, Maryland; Indian Head, Maryland; Dahlgren, Virginia; and Panama City, Florida); Naval Undersea Warfare Center (Newport, Rhode Island; New London, Connecticut; and Keyport, Washington); Defense Equal Opportunity Management Institute (Cocoa Beach, Florida); Navy Personnel Research, Studies & Technology Department (Millington,

Tennessee); Naval Medical Research Unit (Dayton, Ohio); Naval Health Research Center (San Diego, California); Naval Medical Research Center (Silver Spring, Maryland); and Naval Submarine Medical Research Laboratory (Groton, Connecticut). This program is funded by the U.S. Navy's Office of Naval Research and administered by the American Society for Engineering Education.

Number awarded Varies each year.

Deadline Applications may be submitted at any time, but they must be received at least 6 months prior to the proposed sabbatical leave starting date.

[1104]
OFFICE OF NAVAL RESEARCH SUMMER FACULTY RESEARCH PROGRAM

American Society for Engineering Education
Attn: ONR Summer Programs
1818 N Street, N.W., Suite 600
Washington, DC 20036-2479
(202) 331-3558   Fax: (202) 265-8504
E-mail: onrsummer@asee.org
Web: onr.asee.org/about_the_summer_faculty_program

Summary To provide support to faculty members in engineering and science (particularly those at Minority Serving Institutions) who wish to conduct summer research at selected Navy facilities.

Eligibility This program is open to U.S. citizens and permanent residents who have teaching or research appointments in engineering and science at U.S. universities or colleges. In addition to appointments as Summer Faculty Fellows, positions as Senior Summer Faculty Fellows are available to applicants who have at least 6 years of research experience in their field of expertise since earning a Ph.D. or equivalent degree and a substantial, significant record of research accomplishments and publications. A limited number of appointments are also available as Distinguished Summer Faculty Fellows to faculty members who are preeminent in their field of research, have a senior appointment at a leading research university, and are internationally recognized for their research accomplishments. Faculty from Historically Black Colleges and Universities, Hispanic Serving Institutions, and Tribal Colleges and Universities are especially encouraged to apply.

Financial Data The weekly stipend is $1,400 at the Summer Faculty Fellow level, $1,650 at the Senior Summer Faculty Fellow level, and $1,900 at the Distinguished Summer Faculty Fellow level. Fellows who must relocate their residence receive a relocation allowance and all fellows receive a travel allowance.

Duration 10 weeks during the summer; fellows may reapply in subsequent years.

Additional data Participating facilities include the Naval Air Warfare Center, Aircraft Division (Patuxent River, Maryland); Naval Air Warfare Center, Naval Training Systems Division (Orlando, Florida); Naval Air Warfare Center, Weapons Division (China Lake, California); Space and Naval Warfare Systems Center (San Diego, California and Charleston, South Carolina); Naval Facilities Engineering Service Center (Port Hueneme, California); Naval Research Laboratories (Washington, D.C.; Stennis Space Center, Mississippi; and Monterey, California); Naval Surface Warfare Centers (Bethesda, Maryland; Indian Head, Maryland; Dahlgren, Vir-

ginia; and Panama City, Florida); Naval Undersea Warfare Center (Newport, Rhode Island; New London, Connecticut; and Keyport, Washington); Defense Equal Opportunity Management Institute (Cocoa Beach, Florida); Navy Personnel Research, Studies & Technology Department (Millington, Tennessee); Naval Medical Research Unit (Dayton, Ohio); Naval Health Research Center (San Diego, California); Naval Medical Research Center (Silver Spring, Maryland); and Naval Submarine Medical Research Laboratory (Groton, Connecticut). This program is funded by the U.S. Navy's Office of Naval Research and administered by the American Society for Engineering Education.

Number awarded Varies each year.

Deadline December of each year.

[1105]
OFFICE OF NAVAL RESEARCH YOUNG INVESTIGATOR PROGRAM

Office of Naval Research
One Liberty Center
875 North Randolph Street, Suite 1425
Arlington, VA 22203-1995
(703) 696-4111   E-mail: paula.barden.ctr@navy.mil
Web: www.onr.navy.mil

Summary To provide funding to academic scientists and engineers (particularly Hispanic Americans and other minorities) who are interested in conducting research on topics of interest to the U.S. Navy.

Eligibility This program is open to U.S. citizens, nationals, and permanent residents who received their first tenure-track faculty positions at a U.S. university within the preceding 5 years. Applicants must be proposing to conduct research relevant to 1 of the divisions within the Office of Naval Research: expeditionary maneuver warfare and combating terrorism; command, control communications, computers, intelligence, surveillance, and reconnaissance; ocean battlespace sensing; sea warfare and weapons; warfighter performance; and naval air warfare and weapons. Selection is based on 1) past performance, demonstrated by the significance and impact of previous research, publications, professional activities, awards, and other recognition; 2) a creative proposal, demonstrating the potential for making progress in a listed priority research area; and 3) a long-term commitment by the university to the applicant and the research. Researchers at Historically Black Colleges and Universities (HBCUs) and Minority Institutions (MIs) are encouraged to submit proposals and join others in submitting proposals, but no portion of funds is set aside for HBCU and MI participation.

Financial Data Awards up to $170,000 per year are available.

Duration 3 years.

Additional data Approximately 2 recipients of these awards are also nominated to receive Presidential Early Career Awards for Scientists and Engineers to provide an additional 2 years of funding.

Number awarded Approximately 16 each year.

Deadline December of each year.

[1106]
ONLINE BIBLIOGRAPHIC SERVICES/ TECHNICAL SERVICES JOINT RESEARCH GRANT

American Association of Law Libraries
Attn: Online Bibliographic Services Special Interest
  Section
105 West Adams Street, Suite 3300
Chicago, IL 60603
(312) 939-4764   Fax: (312) 431-1097
E-mail: aallhq@aall.org
Web: www.aallnet.org/sis/obssis/research/funding.htm

Summary To provide funding to members of the American Association of Law Libraries (AALL), particularly minorities and women, who are interested in conducting a research project related to technical services.

Eligibility This program is open to AALL members who are technical services law librarians. Preference is given to members of the Online Bibliographic Services and Technical Services Special Interest Sections, although members of other special interest sections are eligible if their work relates to technical services law librarianship. Applicants must be interested in conducting research that will enhance technical services law librarianship. Women and minorities are especially encouraged to apply. Preference is given to projects that can be completed in the United States or Canada, although foreign research projects are given consideration.

Financial Data Grants range up to $1,000.

Duration 1 year.

Number awarded 1 or more each year.

Deadline March or September of each year.

[1107]
OPEN BOOK AWARD

PEN American Center
Attn: Literary Awards Associate
588 Broadway, Suite 303
New York, NY 10012
(212) 334-1660, ext. 126   Fax: (212) 334-2181
E-mail: awards@pen.org
Web: www.pen.org/page.php/prmID/280

Summary To recognize and reward Hispanic Americans and other outstanding authors of color from any country.

Eligibility This award is presented to an author of color (African, Arab, Asian, Caribbean, Latino, and Native American) whose book-length writings were published in the United States during the current calendar year. Works of fiction, literary nonfiction, biography/memoir, poetry, and other works of literary character are strongly preferred. U.S. citizenship or residency is not required. Nominations must be submitted by publishers or agents.

Financial Data The prize is $5,000.

Duration The prizes are awarded annually.

Additional data This prize was formerly known as the Beyond Margins Award. The entry fee is $50.

Number awarded 5 each year.

Deadline January of each year.

[1108]
OUTSTANDING THESIS IN FOOD AND AGRICULTURAL SCIENCE COMPETITION

American Association of Hispanics in Higher Education
c/o JoAnn Canales, Thesis Competition Chair
Texas A&M University at Corpus Christi
Department of Teacher Education
Faculty Center 247
6300 Ocean Drive
Corpus Christi, TX 78412
(361) 825-3847   E-mail: joann.canales@tamucc.edu
Web: www.aahhe.org/OutstandingThesisCompetition.aspx

Summary To recognize and reward Hispanic authors of outstanding master's theses on topics related to priority areas of the United States Department of Agriculture (USDA).

Eligibility This competition is open to Hispanic U.S. citizens and permanent residents who have completed a thesis during the preceding period of approximately 30 months. The topic of the thesis must related to a food and agricultural science topic in a USDA priority area, including food safety, climate change, sustainable energy, childhood obesity, or global food security and hunger. Theses may use any research approach (e.g., historical, experimental, qualitative, survey). Applicants must submit an abstract, up to 25 pages in length, of their thesis. Judging is based on the appropriateness of the research design, approach, and data analysis; the conceptualization of inquiry and focus; the discussion of findings focused on comprehension and integration; the scholarly quality of the thesis; and significance of contribution to knowledge in the field. Based on the abstracts, 5 to 7 semifinalists are selected and asked to submit their complete thesis. From among those, 3 finalists are invited to present their theses at the national conference of the American Association of Hispanics in Higher Education (AAHHE), where winners are selected.

Financial Data Awards are $3,000 for first place, $2,000 for second, and $1,000 for third. All travel expenses of finalists to attend the AAHHE national conference are paid.

Duration The awards are presented annually.

Additional data This program is managed by the AAHHE in partnership with Texas A&M University at Corpus Christi. Funding is provided by the USDA National Institute of Food and Agriculture.

Number awarded 3 cash awards are presented each year.

Deadline August of each year.

[1109]
PAUL HOCH DISTINGUISHED SERVICE AWARD

American College of Neuropsychopharmacology
Attn: Executive Office
5034-A Thoroughbred Lane
Brentwood, TN 37027
(615) 324-2360   Fax: (615) 523-1715
E-mail: acnp@acnp.org
Web: www.acnp.org/programs/awards.aspx

Summary To recognize and reward members (particularly Hispanic Americans, other minorities, and women) who belong to the American College of Neuropsychopharmacology (ACNP) and have contributed outstanding service to the organization.

Eligibility This award is available to ACNP members who have made unusually significant contributions to the College. The emphasis of the award is on service to the organization, not on teaching, clinical, or research accomplishments. Any member or fellow of ACNP may nominate another member. Nomination of women and minorities is highly encouraged.

Financial Data The award consists of an expense-paid trip to the ACNP annual meeting, a monetary honorarium, and a plaque.

Duration The award is presented annually.

Additional data This award was first presented in 1965.

Number awarded 1 each year.

Deadline Nominations must be submitted by June of each year.

[1110]
PAUL TOBENKIN MEMORIAL AWARD

Columbia University
Attn: Graduate School of Journalism
Mail Code 3809
2950 Broadway
New York, NY 10027-7004
(212) 854-7696   Fax: (212) 854-3939
E-mail: lt2026@columbia.edu
Web: www.journalism.columbia.edu

Summary To recognize and reward outstanding newspaper writing that reflects the spirit of Paul Tobenkin, who fought all his life against racial and religious hatred, bigotry, bias, intolerance, and discrimination.

Eligibility Materials reflecting the spirit of Paul Tobenkin may be submitted by newspaper reporters in the United States, editors of their publications, or interested third parties. The items submitted must have been published during the previous calendar year in a weekly or daily newspaper.

Financial Data The award is $1,500 plus a plaque.

Duration The award is presented annually.

Additional data This award was first presented in 1961,.

Number awarded 1 or more each year.

Deadline March of each year.

[1111]
PAULA DE MERIEUX RHEUMATOLOGY FELLOWSHIP AWARD

American College of Rheumatology
Attn: Research and Education Foundation
2200 Lake Boulevard N.E.
Atlanta, GA 30319
(404) 633-3777   Fax: (404) 633-1870
E-mail: ref@rheumatology.org
Web: www.rheumatology.org/ref/awards/index.asp

Summary To provide funding to Hispanic Americans, other underrepresented minorities, and women who are interested in a program of training for a career providing clinical care to people affected by rheumatic diseases.

Eligibility This program is open to trainees at ACGME-accredited institutions. Applications must be submitted by the training program director at the institution who is responsible for selection and appointment of trainees. The program must train and prepare fellows to provide clinical care to those affected by rheumatic diseases. Trainees must be women or members of underrepresented minority groups, defined as Black Americans, Hispanics, and Native Americans (Native Hawaiians, Alaska Natives, and American Indians). They must be U.S. citizens, nationals, or permanent residents. Selection is based on the institution's pass rate of rheumatology fellows, publication history of staff and previous fellows, current positions of previous fellows, and status of clinical faculty.

Financial Data The grant is $25,000 per year, to be used as salary for the trainee. Other trainee costs (e.g., fees, health insurance, travel, attendance at scientific meetings) are to be incurred by the recipient's institutional program. Supplemental or additional support to offset the cost of living may be provided by the grantee institution.

Duration Up to 1 year.

Additional data This fellowship was first awarded in 2005.

Number awarded 1 each year.

Deadline July of each year.

[1112]
PEARSON EARLY CAREER GRANT

American Psychological Foundation
750 First Street, N.E.
Washington, DC 20002-4242
(202) 336-5843   Fax: (202) 336-5812
E-mail: foundation@apa.org
Web: www.apa.org/apf/funding/pearson.aspx

Summary To provide funding to early career psychologists (particularly Hispanic Americans, other minorities, and individuals with disabilities) who are interested in conducting a project in an area of critical society need.

Eligibility This program is open to psychologists who have an Ed.D., Psy.D., or Ph.D. from an accredited experience and no more than 7 years of postdoctoral experience. Applicants must be interested in conducting a project to improve areas of critical need in society, including (but not limited to) innovative scientifically-based clinical work with serious mental illness, serious emotional disturbance, incarcerated or homeless individuals, children with serious emotional disturbance (SED), or adults with serious mental illness (SMI). The sponsor encourages applications from individuals who represent diversity in race, ethnicity, gender, age, disability, and sexual orientation.

Financial Data The grant is $12,000.

Duration 1 year.

Additional data This grant was first awarded in 2010.

Number awarded 1 each year.

Deadline December of each year.

[1113]
PEMBROKE CENTER POSTDOCTORAL FELLOWSHIPS

Brown University
Attn: Pembroke Center for Teaching and Research on Women
172 Meeting Street
Box 1958
Providence, RI 02912
(401) 863-2643   Fax: (401) 863-1298
E-mail: Pembroke_Center@brown.edu
Web: www.brown.edu

Summary To provide funding to postdoctoral scholars (particularly Hispanic Americans and other underrepresented minorities) who are interested in conducting research at Brown University's Pembroke Center for Teaching and Research on Women on the cross-cultural study of gender.

Eligibility Fellowships are open to scholars in relevant fields who have completed their Ph.D. but do not have a tenured position at an American college or university. Applicants must be willing to spend a year in residence at the Pembroke Center for Teaching and Research on Women and participate in a research project related to gender and/or sexuality. The project focuses on a theme that changes annually (recently: "Aesthetics and the Question of Beauty"). The center encourages underrepresented minority and international scholars to apply.

Financial Data The stipend is $50,000. Health insurance is also provided.

Duration 1 academic year.

Additional data Postdoctoral fellows in residence participate in weekly seminars and present at least 2 public papers during the year, as well as conduct an individual research project. Supplementary funds are available for assistance with travel expenses from abroad. This program includes the following named fellowships: the Nancy L. Buc Postdoctoral Fellowship, the Artemis A.W. and Martha Joukowsky Postdoctoral Fellowship, and the Carol G. Lederer Postdoctoral Fellowship.

Number awarded 3 or 4 each year.

Deadline December of each year.

[1114]
POSTDOCTORAL FELLOWSHIP IN MENTAL HEALTH AND SUBSTANCE ABUSE SERVICES

American Psychological Association
Attn: Minority Fellowship Program
750 First Street, N.E.
Washington, DC 20002-4242
(202) 336-6127   Fax: (202) 336-6012
TDD: (202) 336-6123   E-mail: mfp@apa.org
Web: www.apa.org/pi/mfp/psychology/postdoc/index.aspx

Summary To provide financial assistance to postdoctoral scholars (particularly Hispanic Americans and members of other ethnic minority groups) who are interested in a program of research training related to providing mental health and substance abuse services to ethnic minority populations.

Eligibility This program is open to U.S. citizens, nationals, and permanent residents who received a doctoral degree in psychology in the last 5 years. Applicants must be interested in participating in a program of training under a qualified sponsor for research and have a strong commitment to a career in ethnic minority behavioral health services or policy. Members of ethnic minority groups (African Americans, Hispanics/Latinos, American Indians, Alaskan Natives, Asian Americans, Native Hawaiians, and other Pacific Islanders) are especially encouraged to apply. Selection is based on commitment to a career in ethnic minority mental health service delivery or public policy; qualifications of the sponsor; the fit between career goals and training environment selected; merit of the training proposal; potential as a future leader in ethnic minority psychology, demonstrated through accomplishments and goals; consistency between the applicant's

work and the goals of the program; and letters of recommendation.

Financial Data The stipend depends on the number of years of research experience and is equivalent to the standard postdoctoral stipend level of the National Institutes of Health (recently ranging from $39,264 for no years of experience to $54,180 for 7 or more years of experience).

Duration 1 academic or calendar year; may be renewed for 1 additional year.

Additional data Funding is provided by the U.S. Substance Abuse and Mental Health Services Administration.

Number awarded Varies each year.

Deadline January of each year.

[1115]
POSTDOCTORAL FELLOWSHIP IN THE HISTORY OF MODERN SCIENCE AND TECHNOLOGY IN EAST ASIA

Harvard University
Attn: Department of East Asian Languages and
  Civilizations
2 Divinity Avenue
Cambridge, MA 02138
(617) 495-2754   Fax: (617) 496-6040
E-mail: ealc@fas.harvard.edu
Web: harvardealc.org/postdoc.html

Summary To provide funding to postdoctoral scholars (particularly Hispanic Americans, other minorities, and women) who wish to conduct research at Harvard University on a topic related to the history of science and technology in east Asia.

Eligibility This program is open to junior scholars who completed a Ph.D. within the past 5 years. Applicants must be interested in conducting research in residence at Harvard University to revise their dissertation and prepare it for publication. Preference is given to research projects exploring the understudied histories of modern science and technology in Korea and Japan, but all proposals concerning the development of science and technology in post-19th century east Asia are eligible. Applicants from women and minority candidates are strongly encouraged.

Financial Data The stipend is $43,000.

Duration 1 academic year.

Additional data Fellows are provided with office space and access to the libraries and resources of Harvard University. They are invited to participate in the academic life of the Departments of East Asian Languages and Civilizations and the History of Science. Fellows are expected to reside in the Cambridge/Boston area during the term of the fellowship; work on revising their dissertation for publication; teach or collaborate on a course related to the history of modern science and/or technology in east Asia; and give at least 1 presentation of research to faculty and graduate students in East Asian Languages and Civilizations and the History of Science.

Number awarded 1 each year.

Deadline February of each year.

[1116]
POSTDOCTORAL FELLOWSHIPS AT FDA

National Science Foundation
Directorate for Engineering
Attn: Division of Chemical, Bioengineering,
    Environmental, and Transport Systems
4201 Wilson Boulevard, Room 565S
Arlington, VA 22230
(703) 292-7942   Fax: (703) 292-9098
TDD: (800) 281-8749   E-mail: lesterow@nsf.gov
Web: www.nsf.gov/funding/pgm_summ.jsp?pims_id=5605

Summary   To provide an opportunity for recent postdoctorates (particularly Hispanic Americans, underrepresented
minorities, women, and individuals with disabilities) to conduct research at an intramural laboratory of the U.S. Food
and Drug Administration (FDA).

Eligibility   Applicants for these fellowships must have held
a Ph.D. degree in a science, engineering, or mathematics
field of interest to NSF for no more than 3 years. They must
be U.S. citizens, nationals, or permanent residents. Along
with their application, they must submit a plan for full-time
work at an FDA laboratory under the guidance of an FDA
mentor. The program encourages applications from all citizens, including women and men, underrepresented minorities, and persons with disabilities.

Financial Data   Grants range up to $80,000 per year.
Funding includes 85% of the fellow's stipend and fringe benefits, transportation and moving expenses (up to $3,000), up
to 10% of the total as allowance to the faculty adviser for
research-related expenses, and an allowance of up to 15% of
the total direct costs as an administrative allowance for a
sponsoring academic institution. FDA provides office space,
research facilities, research costs in the form of expendable
and minor equipment purchases in the host laboratory, and
the time of its research staff.

Duration   1 to 2 years.

Additional data   This program is also offered by the NSF
Directorate for Computer and Information Science and Engineering.

Number awarded   A total of 3 to 10 grants for all FDA programs is awarded each year; total funding is approximately
$500,000.

Deadline   March of each year.

[1117]
POSTDOCTORAL FELLOWSHIPS IN DIABETES RESEARCH

Juvenile Diabetes Research Foundation International
Attn: Grant Administrator
26 Broadway, 14th Floor
New York, NY 10004
(212) 479-7572   Toll Free: (800) 533-CURE
Fax: (212) 785-9595   E-mail: info@jdrf.org
Web: jdrf.org

Summary   To provide research training to scientists (particularly Hispanic Americans, other underrepresented minorities, women, and individuals with disabilities) who are beginning their professional careers and are interested in participating in research training on the causes, treatment, prevention, or cure of diabetes or its complications.

Eligibility   This program is open to postdoctorates who are
interested in a career in Type 1 diabetes-relevant research.

Applicants must have received their first doctoral degree
(M.D., Ph.D., D.M.D., or D.V.M.) within the past 5 years and
may not have a faculty appointment. There are no citizenship
requirements. Applications are encouraged from women,
members of minority groups underrepresented in the sciences, and people with disabilities. The proposed research
training may be conducted at foreign or domestic, for-profit or
nonprofit, or public or private institutions, including universities, colleges, hospitals, laboratories, units of state or local
government, or eligible agencies of the federal government.
Applicants must be sponsored by an investigator who is affiliated full time with an accredited institution and who agrees to
supervise the applicant's training. Selection is based on the
applicant's previous experience and academic record; the
caliber of the proposed research; and the quality of the mentor, training program, and environment.

Financial Data   Stipends range from $44,764 to $59,680
per year (depending upon years of experience). In any case,
the award may not exceed the salary the recipient is currently
earning. Fellows also receive a research allowance of $5,500
per year.

Duration   3 years.

Additional data   Fellows must devote 100% of their effort
to the fellowship project.

Number awarded   Varies each year.

Deadline   August of each year.

[1118]
POSTDOCTORAL FELLOWSHIPS OF THE CONSORTIUM FOR FACULTY DIVERSITY

Consortium for Faculty Diversity at Liberal Arts Colleges
c/o Gettysburg College
Provost's Office
300 North Washington Street
Campus Box 410
Gettysburg, PA 17325
(717) 337-6796   E-mail: sgockows@gettysburg.edu
Web: www.gettysburg.edu/about/offices/provost/cfd

Summary   To make available the facilities of liberal arts colleges to scholars, particularly Hispanic Americans and others
who will enhance diversity at their college and who recently
received their doctoral/advanced degree.

Eligibility   This program is open to scholars in the liberal
arts and engineering who are U.S. citizens or permanent residents and received the Ph.D. or M.F.A. degree within the past
5 years. Applicants must be interested in a residency at a participating institution that is part of the Consortium for a Strong
Minority Presence at Liberal Arts Colleges. They must be
able to enhance diversity at the institution.

Financial Data   Fellows receive a stipend equivalent to the
average salary paid by the host college to beginning assistant
professors. Modest funds are made available to finance the
fellow's proposed research, subject to the usual institutional
procedures.

Duration   1 year.

Additional data   The following schools are participating in
the program: Allegheny College, Bard College, Bowdoin Col-
lege, Bryn Mawr College, Carleton College, Centenary Col-
lege of Louisiana, Centre College, College of Wooster, Colorado College, Denison University, DePauw University, Dickinson College, Gettysburg College, Goucher College, Grinnell

College, Gustavus Adolphus College, Hamilton College, Haverford College, Hobart and William Smith Colleges, Lafayette College, Lawrence University, Luther College, Macalester College, Mount Holyoke College, Muhlenberg College, New College of Florida, Oberlin College, Pitzer College, Pomona College, Reed College, Rhodes College, University of Richmond, Ripon College, Scripps College, St. Olaf College, Skidmore College, Smith College, Southwestern University, Swarthmore College, Transylvania University, Trinity College, Vassar College, and Wellesley College. Fellows are expected to teach at least 1 course in each academic term of residency, participate in departmental seminars, and interact with students.

Number awarded Varies each year.

Deadline October of each year.

[1119]
POSTDOCTORAL FELLOWSHIPS OF THE FORD FOUNDATION DIVERSITY FELLOWSHIP PROGRAM

National Research Council
Attn: Fellowships Office, Keck 576
500 Fifth Street, N.W.
Washington, DC 20001
(202) 334-2872   Fax: (202) 334-3419
E-mail: infofell@nas.edu
Web: sites.nationalacademies.org

Summary To provide funding for postdoctoral research to Hispanic American scholars and others whose success will increase the racial and ethnic diversity of U.S. colleges and universities.

Eligibility This program is open to U.S. citizens, permanent residents, and nationals who earned a Ph.D. or Sc.D. degree within the past 7 years and are committed to a career in teaching and research at the college or university level. The following are considered as positive factors in the selection process: evidence of superior academic achievement; promise of continuing achievement as scholars and teachers; membership in a group whose underrepresentation in the American professoriate has been severe and longstanding, including Black/African Americans, Puerto Ricans, Mexican Americans/Chicanos/Chicanas, Native American Indians, Alaska Natives (Eskimos, Aleuts, and other indigenous people of Alaska), and Native Pacific Islanders (Hawaiians, Micronesians, or Polynesians); capacity to respond in pedagogically productive ways to the learning needs of students from diverse backgrounds; sustained personal engagement with communities that are underrepresented in the academy and an ability to bring this asset to learning, teaching, and scholarship at the college and university level; and likelihood of using the diversity of human experience as an educational resource in teaching and scholarship. Eligible areas of study include most fields of the arts, sciences, humanities, or social sciences or many interdisciplinary ethnic or area studies, but not for most practice-oriented areas. Research may be conducted at an appropriate institution of higher education in the United States (normally) or abroad, including universities, museums, libraries, government or national laboratories, privately sponsored nonprofit institutes, government chartered nonprofit research organizations, or centers for advanced study. Applicants should designate a faculty member or other scholar to serve as host at the proposed fellowship institution.

They are encouraged to choose a host institution other than that where they are affiliated at the time of application.

Financial Data The stipend is $40,000. Funds may be supplemented by sabbatical leave pay or other sources of support that do not carry with them teaching or other responsibilities. The employing institution receives an allowance of $1,500, paid after fellowship tenure is completed; the employing institution is expected to match the grant and to use the allowance and the match to assist with the fellow's continuing research expenditures.

Duration 9 to 12 months.

Additional data Fellows may not accept another major fellowship while they are being supported by this program.

Number awarded Approximately 24 each year.

Deadline November of each year.

[1120]
POSTDOCTORAL RESEARCH FELLOWSHIPS IN BIOLOGY

National Science Foundation
Directorate for Biological Sciences
Attn: Division of Biological Infrastructure
4201 Wilson Boulevard, Room 615N
Arlington, VA 22230
(703) 292-8470   Fax: (703) 292-9063
TDD: (800) 281-8749   E-mail: bio-dbi-prfb@nsf.gov
Web: www.nsf.gov

Summary To provide funding for research and training in specified areas related to biology to junior doctoral-level scientists (particularly Hispanic Americans, other underrepresented minorities, and individuals with disabilities) at sites in the United States or abroad.

Eligibility This program is open to citizens, nationals, and permanent residents of the United States who are graduate students completing a Ph.D. or who have earned the degree no earlier than 12 months preceding the deadline date. Applicants must be interested in a program of research and training in any of 4 competitive areas: 1) Broadening Participation in Biology, designed to increase the diversity of scientists by providing support for research and training to biologists with disabilities and underrepresented minority (Native American, Native Pacific Islander, Alaskan Native, African American, and Hispanic) biologists; 2) Intersections of Biology and Mathematical and Physical Sciences, for junior researchers who have conducted doctoral research in biology or physical and mathematical sciences and who present a research and training plan at the intersection of biology with mathematical and physical sciences; 3) National Plant Genome Initiative Postdoctoral Research Fellowships, for postdoctoral training in plant improvement and associated sciences such as physiology and pathology, quantitative genetics, or computational biology; or 4) International Postdoctoral Research Fellowships in Biology, for junior biologists who wish to obtain training at a foreign institution. They must identify a sponsor at a host institution who will serve as a mentor for their training program.

Financial Data Grants are $69,000 per year, including $54,000 as a stipend for the fellow and $15,000 as a fellowship allowance that is intended to cover direct research expenses, facilities and other institutional resources, and fringe benefits.

Duration Fellowships in the area of Intersections of Biology and Mathematical and Physical Sciences are normally for 24 months; fellowships in other areas are normally for 36 months.

Number awarded Approximately 15 fellowships are awarded each year in each competitive area.

Deadline October of each year.

[1121]
POSTDOCTORAL RESEARCH TRAINING FELLOWSHIPS IN EPILEPSY

Epilepsy Foundation
Attn: Research Department
8301 Professional Place
Landover, MD 20785-2353
(301) 459-3700   Toll Free: (800) EFA-1000
Fax: (301) 577-2684   TDD: (800) 332-2070
E-mail: grants@efa.org
Web: www.epilepsyfoundation.org

Summary To provide funding for a program of postdoctoral training to academic physicians and scientists (particularly Hispanic Americans, other minorities, women, and individuals with disabilities) who are committed to epilepsy research.

Eligibility Applicants must have a doctoral degree (M.D., Sc.D., Ph.D., or equivalent) and be a clinical or postdoctoral fellow at a university, medical school, research institution, or medical center. They must be interested in participating in a training experience and research project that has potential significance for understanding the causes, treatment, or consequences of epilepsy. The program is geared toward applicants who will be trained in research in epilepsy rather than those who use epilepsy as a tool for research in other fields. Equal consideration is given to applicants interested in acquiring experience either in basic laboratory research or in the conduct of human clinical studies. Academic faculty holding the rank of instructor or higher are not eligible, nor are graduate or medical students, medical residents, permanent government employees, or employees of private industry. Applications from women, members of minority groups, and people with disabilities are especially encouraged. U.S. citizenship is not required, but the project must be conducted in the United States. Selection is based on scientific quality of the proposed research, a statement regarding its relevance to epilepsy, the applicant's qualifications, the preceptor's qualifications, and the adequacy of facility and related epilepsy programs at the institution.

Financial Data The grant is $45,000. No indirect costs are covered.

Duration 1 year.

Additional data Support for this program is provided by many individuals, families, and corporations, especially the American Epilepsy Society, Abbott Laboratories, Ortho-McNeil Pharmaceutical, and Pfizer Inc. The fellowship must be carried out at a facility in the United States where there is an ongoing epilepsy research program.

Number awarded Varies each year.

Deadline August of each year.

[1122]
PRESIDIO LA BAHIA AWARD

Sons of the Republic of Texas
Attn: Administrative Assistant
1717 Eighth Street
Bay City, TX 77414
(979) 245-6644   Fax: (979) 244-3819
E-mail: srttexas@srttexas.org
Web: www.srttexas.org/#!presidio-la-bahia/c6ns

Summary To recognize and reward the most outstanding works that demonstrate the impact and influence of the Spanish colonial heritage on the laws, customs, language, religion, architecture, and art of Texas.

Eligibility The competition is open to any person interested in Spanish colonial influence on Texas culture. Eligible to be considered are books, published papers, articles published in periodicals, and non-literary projects (such as art, architecture, and archaeological discovery).

Financial Data A total of $2,000 is available annually as awards. The prize for the best book is at least $1,200; the organization may award a second-place book prize. The amounts of prizes for best published paper, article published in a periodical, and non-literary project vary each year.

Duration The competition is held annually.

Additional data This award was established in 1968.

Number awarded From 1 to 5 each year.

Deadline September of each year.

[1123]
PRIZE FOR A FACULTY MEMBER FOR RESEARCH IN AN UNDERGRADUATE INSTITUTION

American Physical Society
Attn: Honors Program
One Physics Ellipse
College Park, MD 20740-3844
(301) 209-3268   Fax: (301) 209-0865
E-mail: honors@aps.org
Web: www.aps.org

Summary To recognize and reward physics faculty members (particularly Hispanic Americans, other underrepresented minorities, and women) who are at undergraduate institutions.

Eligibility Nominees for this prize must be members of the physics faculty at undergraduate institutions. They must have contributed substantially to physics research and provided inspirational guidance and encouragement to undergraduate students participating in that research. Nominations of qualified women and members of underrepresented minority groups are especially encouraged.

Financial Data The prize consists of a stipend of $5,000 to the recipient, a grant of $5,000 to the recipient's institution for research, a certificate citing the accomplishments of the recipient, and an allowance for travel expenses to the meeting of the American Physical Society (APS) at which the prize is presented.

Duration The prize is presented annually.

Additional data This prize was established in 1984 by a grant from the Research Corporation.

Number awarded 1 each year.

Deadline June of each year.

[1124]
PUBLIC HEALTH SERVICE SMALL BUSINESS INNOVATION RESEARCH PROGRAM

Public Health Service
c/o National Institutes of Health
Attn: SBIR/STTR Program Coordinator
6705 Rockledge Drive, Room 3534
Bethesda, MD 20892-7911
(301) 435-2688   Fax: (301) 480-0146
TDD: (301) 451-0088   E-mail: sbir@od.nih.gov
Web: grants.nih.gov/grants/funding/sbir.html

Summary To support small businesses (especially those owned by Hispanic Americans, other minorities, and persons with disabilities) that have the technological experience to contribute to the research and development mission of components of the U.S. Public Health Service.

Eligibility For the purposes of this program, a "small business" is defined as a firm that is that is independently owned and operated for profit, not dominant in the field in which it is operating, and meets the size standard of 500 employees or less. The primary employment of the principal investigator must be with the firm at the time of award and during the conduct of the proposed project. Individuals from underrepresented racial and ethnic groups as well as individuals with disabilities are encouraged to apply. Research is supported in all areas of biomedical and behavioral science that fall within the mission of the agency. Selection is based on scientific and technical merit of the proposed project, availability of funds, and relevance of the proposed project to program priorities.

Financial Data Support is offered in 2 phases. In phase 1, awards normally do not exceed $150,000 (for both direct and indirect costs); in phase 2, awards normally do not exceed $1,000,000 (including both direct and indirect costs).

Duration Phase 1 awards may extend up to 6 months; phase 2 awards may extend up to 2 years.

Additional data Grants are offered by 4 components of the Public Health Service (PHS): National Institutes of Health (NIH), Centers for Disease Control and Prevention (CDC), Food and Drug Administration (FDA), and Administration for Children and Families (ACF). For information on the research interests of each of those components and their various agencies, contact the sponsor. Actual solicitations are available only from that address.

Number awarded Varies each year.

Deadline April, August, or December of each year.

[1125]
PUBLIC HEALTH SERVICE SMALL BUSINESS TECHNOLOGY TRANSFER GRANTS

Public Health Service
c/o National Institutes of Health
Attn: SBIR/STTR Program Coordinator
6705 Rockledge Drive, Room 3534
Bethesda, MD 20892-7911
(301) 435-2688   Fax: (301) 480-0146
TDD: (301) 451-0088   E-mail: sbir@od.nih.gov
Web: grants.nih.gov/grants/funding/sbir.html

Summary To provide financial support to cooperative research and development projects carried out between small business concerns (especially those owned by Hispanic Americans, other minorities, and persons with disabili-

ties) and research institutions in areas of concern to the research and development mission of components of the U.S. Public Health Service.

Eligibility <EG>For the purposes of this program, a "small business" is defined as a firm that is organized for profit with a location in the United States; is in the legal form of an individual proprietorship, partnership, limited liability company, corporation, joint venture, association, trust, or cooperative; is at least 51% owned and controlled by 1 or more individuals who are citizens or permanent residents of the United States; and has (including its affiliates) fewer than 500 employees. Unlike the Public Health Service Small Business Innovation Research Grants, the primary employment of the principal investigator does not need to be with the business concern. This program, however, requires that the small business apply in collaboration with a nonprofit research institution for conduct of a project that has potential for commercialization. Principal investigators from the nonprofit research institution must commit at least 10% of their effort to the project. At least 40% of the work must be performed by the small business and at least 30% of the work must be performed by the research institution. Individuals from underrepresented racial and ethnic groups as well as individuals with disabilities are encouraged to apply. Research is supported in all areas of biomedical and behavioral science that fall within the mission of the agency. Selection is based on scientific and technical merit of the proposed project, availability of funds, and relevance of the proposed project to program priorities.

Financial Data Support is offered in 2 phases. In phase 1, awards normally do not exceed $150,000 (for both direct and indirect costs); in phase 2, awards normally do not exceed $1,000,000 (including both direct and indirect costs).

Duration Phase 1 awards may extend up to 6 months; phase 2 awards may extend up to 2 years.

Additional data Grants are offered by 4 components of the Public Health Service (PHS): National Institutes of Health (NIH), Centers for Disease Control and Prevention (CDC), Food and Drug Administration (FDA), and Administration for Children and Families (ACF). For information on the research interests of each of those components and their various agencies, contact the sponsor. Actual solicitations are available only from that address.

Number awarded Varies each year.

Deadline April, August, or December of each year.

[1126]
R. ROBERT & SALLY D. FUNDERBURG RESEARCH AWARD IN GASTRIC CANCER

American Gastroenterological Association
Attn: AGA Research Foundation
Research Awards Manager
4930 Del Ray Avenue
Bethesda, MD 20814-2512
(301) 222-4012   Fax: (301) 654-5920
E-mail: awards@gastro.org
Web: www.gastro.org/aga-foundation/grants

Summary To provide funding to established investigators (particularly Hispanic Americans, other minorities, and women) who are working on research that enhances fundamental understanding of gastric cancer pathobiology.

Eligibility This program is open to faculty at accredited North American institutions who have established themselves as independent investigators in the field of gastric biology, pursuing novel approaches to gastric mucosal cell biology, including the fields of gastric mucosal cell biology, regeneration and regulation of cell growth, inflammation as precancerous lesions, genetics of gastric carcinoma, oncogenes in gastric epithelial malignancies, epidemiology of gastric cancer, etiology of gastric epithelial malignancies, or clinical research in diagnosis or treatment of gastric carcinoma. Applicants must be individual members of the American Gastroenterological Association (AGA). Women and minority investigators are strongly encouraged to apply. Selection is based on the novelty, feasibility, and significance of the proposal. Preference is given to novel approaches.

Financial Data The grant is $50,000 per year. Funds are to be used for the salary of the investigator. Indirect costs are not allowed.

Duration 2 years.

Number awarded 1 each year.

Deadline August of each year.

[1127]
RALPH J. BUNCHE AWARD

American Political Science Association
1527 New Hampshire Avenue, N.W.
Washington, DC 20036-1206
(202) 483-2512   Fax: (202) 483-2657
E-mail: apsa@apsanet.org
Web: www.apsanet.org/content_4129.cfm?navID=756

Summary To recognize and reward outstanding scholarly books on ethnic/cultural pluralism.

Eligibility Eligible to be nominated (by publishers or individuals) are scholarly political science books issued the previous year that explore issues of ethnic and/or cultural pluralism.

Financial Data The award is $1,000.

Duration The award is presented annually.

Additional data This award was first presented in 1978.

Number awarded 1 each year.

Deadline January of each year for nominations from individuals; February of each year for nominations from publishers.

[1128]
REGINALD F. LEWIS FELLOWSHIP FOR LAW TEACHING

Harvard Law School
Attn: Lewis Committee
Griswold Two South
1525 Massachusetts Avenue
Cambridge, MA 02138
(617) 495-3109   E-mail: oaa@law.harvard.edu
Web: www.law.harvard.edu

Summary To provide funding to law school graduates, especially those of color, who are preparing for a career in law teaching and are interested in a program of research and training at Harvard Law School.

Eligibility This program is open to recent graduates of law school who have demonstrated an interest in law scholarship and teaching. Applicants must be interested in spending time in residence at Harvard Law School where they will audit courses, attend workshops, and follow a schedule of

research under the sponsorship of the committee. The program encourages the training of prospective law teachers who will enhance the diversity of the profession and especially encourages applications from candidates of color.

Financial Data The stipend is $50,000 per year.

Duration 2 years.

Number awarded 1 each year.

Deadline February of each year.

[1129]
RESEARCH AND EDUCATION PROGRAM FOR HISTORICALLY BLACK COLLEGES AND UNIVERSITIES AND MINORITY-SERVING INSTITUTIONS

Army Research Office
Attn: Army Contracting Command-Aberdeen Proving Ground
4300 South Miami Boulevard
P.O. Box 12211
Research Triangle Park, NC 27709-2211
(919) 549-4385   Fax: (919) 549-4388
E-mail: lanelle.t.shanks.civ@mail.mil
Web: www.arl.army.mil/www/default.cfm?Page=362

Summary To provide funding to researchers at Hispanic Serving Institutions (HSIs) and other Minority-Serving Institutions (MSIs) for the purchase of equipment.

Eligibility This program is open to researchers at HBCUs and MIs that have degree-granting programs in science, mathematics, and/or engineering. Applicants must be seeking funding for the acquisition of major equipment to augment current or to develop new research capabilities to support research in technical areas of interest to the Department of Defense. That includes basic equipment for use in research and education, as well as more sophisticated equipment and instrumentation (including software).

Financial Data Grants range from $50,000 to $500,000.

Duration Grants are typically 1 year in length.

Additional data This program is also offered by the Air Force Office of Scientific Research and the Office of Naval Research.

Number awarded Varies each year; recently, $25 million was available for this program.

Deadline August of each year.

[1130]
RESEARCH AND TRAINING FELLOWSHIPS IN EPILEPSY FOR CLINICIANS

Epilepsy Foundation
Attn: Research Department
8301 Professional Place
Landover, MD 20785-2353
(301) 459-3700   Toll Free: (800) EFA-1000
Fax: (301) 577-2684   TDD: (800) 332-2070
E-mail: grants@efa.org
Web: www.epilepsyfoundation.org

Summary To provide funding to clinically-trained professionals (particularly Hispanic Americans, other minorities, women, and individuals with disabilities) who are interested in gaining additional training in order to develop an epilepsy research program.

Eligibility Applicants must have an M.D., D.O., Ph.D., D.Sc., or equivalent degree and be a clinical or postdoctoral fellow at a university, medical school, or other appropriate research institution. Holders of other doctoral-level degrees (e.g., Pharm.D., D.S.N.) may also be eligible. Candidates must be interested in a program of research training that may include mechanisms of epilepsy, novel therapeutic approaches, clinical trials, development of new technologies, or behavioral and psychosocial impact of epilepsy. The training program may consist of both didactic training and a supervised research experience that is designed to develop the necessary knowledge and skills in the chosen area of research and foster the career goals of the candidate. Academic faculty holding the rank of instructor or higher are not eligible, nor are graduate or medical students, medical residents, permanent government employees, or employees of private industry. Applications from women, members of minority groups, and people with disabilities are especially encouraged. U.S. citizenship is not required, but the project must be conducted in the United States. Selection is based on the quality of the proposed research training program, the applicant's qualifications, the preceptor's qualifications, and the adequacy of clinical training, research facilities, and other epilepsy-related programs at the institution.

Financial Data The grant is $50,000 per year. No indirect costs are provided.

Duration Up to 2 years.

Additional data Support for this program is provided by many individuals, families, and corporations, especially the American Epilepsy Society, Abbott Laboratories, Ortho-McNeil Pharmaceutical, and Pfizer Inc. Grantees are expected to dedicate at least 50% of their time to research training and conducting research.

Number awarded Varies each year.

Deadline September of each year.

[1131]
RESIDENT RESEARCH GRANTS

J. Robert Gladden Orthopaedic Society
Attn: Scientific Committee
6300 North River Road, Suite 727
Rosemont, IL 60018-4226
(847) 698-1633   Fax: (847) 823-4921
E-mail: jrgos@aaos.org
Web: www.gladdensociety.org

Summary To provide funding to members of the J. Robert Gladden Orthopaedic Society (JRGOS) who medical residents, Hispanic Americans or from another underrepresented minority group, and interested in conducting a research project.

Eligibility This program is open to members of underrepresented minority groups who are medical residents and JRGOS members. Applicants must be seeking funding to conduct a research project with a measurable outcome that can be achieved at the end of the grant cycle. They must be able to demonstrate that their proposed project correlates with the mission and goals of the society. Preference is given to applicants planning to work with a senior JRGOS member.

Financial Data The grant is $10,000.

Duration 1 year.

Additional data This program is sponsored by DePuy/Johnson & Johnson.

Number awarded 1 or more each year.

Deadline September of each year.

[1132]
ROBERT L. FANTZ MEMORIAL AWARD

American Psychological Foundation
750 First Street, N.E.
Washington, DC 20002-4242
(202) 336-5843   Fax: (202) 336-5812
E-mail: foundation@apa.org
Web: www.apa.org/apf/funding/fantz.aspx

Summary To provide funding to promising young investigators in psychology (particularly Hispanic Americans and individuals from other diverse groups).

Eligibility This program is open to young investigators in psychology or related disciplines. Candidates must show 1) evidence of basic scientific research or scholarly writing in perceptual-cognitive development and the development of selection attention; and 2) research and writing on the development of individuality, creativity, and free-choice of behavior. The sponsor encourages applications from individuals who represent diversity in race, ethnicity, gender, age, disability, and sexual orientation.

Financial Data The award is $2,000. Funds are paid directly to the recipient's institution for equipment purchases, travel, computer resources, or other expenses related to the work recognized by the award.

Duration The award is presented annually.

Additional data This award was first presented in 1992.

Number awarded 1 each year.

Deadline Deadline not specified.

[1133]
ROBERT WOOD JOHNSON CLINICAL SCHOLARS PROGRAM

Robert Wood Johnson Foundation
c/o University of North Carolina at Chapel Hill
Department of Social Medicine
333 MacNider Hall
Chapel Hill, NC 27599-7105
(919) 843-1351   Fax: (919) 843-2666
E-mail: rwjcsp_admin@med.unc.edu
Web: rwjcsp.unc.edu

Summary To provide financial support to young physicians (particularly Hispanic Americans, other minorities, and women) who wish to conduct additional research and training in areas of importance to health care policy.

Eligibility This program is open to U.S. citizens and permanent residents who have completed residency requirements for an M.D. or D.O. degree. Applicants must be committed to a career in academic medicine, public health, health policy, or other career related to developing physician leaders and skilled researchers. They must be interested in participating in a research and training program at 1 of 4 designated universities. The program embraces racial, ethnic, and gender diversity and encourages applications from candidates with diverse backgrounds and clinical disciplines.

Financial Data The stipend is $67,000 for the first year and greater for the second year. Additional support is provided for research projects and professional travel.

Duration 2 years. Interested scholars may be considered for a third year.

Additional data Currently, the participating institutions are schools of medicine at the University of California at Los Angeles, the University of Michigan, the University of Pennsylvania, and Yale University. Each institution offers a program of study with generous protected time for research.

Number awarded Up to 20 each year, including 10 supported by the Robert Wood Johnson Foundation and 10 by the U.S. Department of Veterans Affairs through VA medical centers affiliated with the participating universities.

Deadline February of each year.

[1134]
ROBERT WOOD JOHNSON FOUNDATION HEALTH AND SOCIETY SCHOLARS PROGRAM

Robert Wood Johnson Foundation
c/o New York Academy of Medicine
1216 Fifth Avenue
New York, NY 10029-5202
(212) 419-3566   Fax: (212) 419-3569
E-mail: hss@nyam.org
Web: www.healthandsocietyscholars.org

Summary To provide support to scholars (particularly Hispanic Americans and other scholars from diverse backgrounds) who from a variety of disciplines and wish to become leaders in health policy.

Eligibility This program is open to scholars who have a doctoral degree in fields that include (but are not limited to) behavioral and social sciences, biological and natural sciences, health professions, public policy, public health, history, demography, environmental sciences, urban planning, or engineering. Applicants must be U.S. citizens or permanent residents who have significant research experience. They must be interested in participating in a program at 1 of 4 universities that includes intensive seminars, mentored research, and focused training in the skills necessary for effective leadership, program implementation, and policy change. The sponsor is committed to a program that embraces diversity and inclusion across multiple dimensions of race, ethnicity, gender, age, socioeconomic background, and academic discipline; it encourages applications from candidates who will help it include diverse perspectives and experiences.

Financial Data The stipend is $80,000 per year. Additional support is available for research-related expenses, training workshops, and travel to professional meetings.

Duration 2 years.

Additional data Fellows train at 1 of 4 nationally prominent universities: University of California at Berkeley (in collaboration with the University of California at San Francisco), Harvard University, Columbia University, or University of Wisconsin at Madison.

Number awarded Up to 12 each year.

Deadline September of each year.

[1135]
ROBERT WOOD JOHNSON HEALTH POLICY FELLOWSHIPS

Institute of Medicine
Attn: Health Policy Fellowships Program
500 Fifth Street, N.W.
Washington, DC 20001
(202) 334-1506   Fax: (202) 334-3862
E-mail: info@healthpolicyfellows.org
Web: www.healthpolicyfellows.org/fellowship.php

Summary To provide an opportunity for health professionals or behavioral and social scientists (particularly minorities and others with diverse backgrounds) who have an interest in health to participate in the formulation of national health policies while in residence at the Institute of Medicine (IOM) in Washington, D.C.

Eligibility This program is open to mid-career professionals from academic faculties and nonprofit health care organizations who are interested in experiencing health policy processes at the federal level. Applicants must have a background in allied health professions, biomedical sciences, dentistry, economics or other social sciences, health services organization and administration, medicine, nursing, public health, or social and behavioral health or health law. They must be sponsored by the chief executive officer of an eligible nonprofit health care organization or academic institution. Selection is based on potential for leadership in health policy, potential for future growth and career advancement, professional achievements, interpersonal and communication skills, and individual plans for incorporating the fellowship experience into specific career goals. U.S. citizenship or permanent resident status is required. Applications are especially encouraged from candidates with diverse backgrounds of race, ethnicity, gender, age, disadvantaged socioeconomic status, and discipline.

Financial Data Total support for the Washington stay and continuing activities may not exceed $165,000. Grant funds may cover salary support at a level of up to $94,000 plus fringe benefits. Fellows are reimbursed for relocation expenses to and from Washington, D.C. No indirect costs are paid.

Duration The program lasts 1 year and includes an orientation in September and October; meetings in November and December with members of Congress, journalists, policy analysts, and other experts on the national political and governmental process; and working assignments from January through August. Fellows then return to their home institutions, but they receive up to 2 years of continued support for further development of health policy leadership skills.

Additional data This program, initiated in 1973, is funded by the Robert Wood Johnson Foundation.

Number awarded Up to 6 each year.

Deadline November of each year.

[1136]
RUTH L. KIRSCHSTEIN NATIONAL RESEARCH SERVICE AWARDS FOR INDIVIDUAL POSTDOCTORAL FELLOWS

National Institutes of Health
Office of Extramural Research
Attn: Grants Information
6705 Rockledge Drive, Suite 4090
Bethesda, MD 20892-7983
(301) 435-0714   Fax: (301) 480-0525
TDD: (301) 451-5936   E-mail: grantsinfo@od.nih.gov
Web: grants.nih.gov/grants/guide/pa-files/PA-11-113.html

Summary To provide funding to postdoctoral scholars (particularly Hispanic Americans, other underrepresented minorities, and individuals with disabilities) who are interested in pursuing research training in the biomedical or behavioral sciences.

Eligibility Applicants must 1) be U.S. citizens, nationals, or permanent residents; 2) have received a Ph.D., M.D., D.O., D.D.S., D.V.M., or equivalent doctoral degree from an accredited domestic or foreign institution; 3) be interested in conducting biomedical or behavioral research; and 4) have arranged for appointment to an appropriate institution and acceptance by a sponsor who will supervise the training and research experience. The institution may be a 1) public or private institution of higher education (especially a Hispanic-serving institution, Historically Black College or University, Tribal College or University, or Alaska Native or Native Hawaiian Serving Institution); 2) nonprofit institution; 3) for profit organization; 4) eligible agency of the federal government; or 6) foreign organization. If a foreign institution is selected as the research training site, applicants must demonstrate that it presents special opportunities for furthering research programs through the use of unusual talent, resources, populations, or environmental conditions that exist in other countries and either are not available in the United States or augment existing U.S. resources. Members of underrepresented racial and ethnic groups and individuals with disabilities are especially encouraged to apply.

Financial Data The award provides an annual stipend based on the number of years of postdoctoral experience, ranging from $39,264 for less than 1 year to $54,180 for 7 or more years. For fellows sponsored by domestic nonfederal institutions, the stipend is paid through the sponsoring institution; for fellows sponsored by federal or foreign institutions, the monthly stipend is paid directly to the fellow. Institutions also receive an allowance to help defray such awardee expenses as self-only health insurance, research supplies, equipment, travel to scientific meetings, and related items; the allowance is $7,850 per 12-month period for fellows at nonfederal, nonprofit, and foreign institutions and $6,750 per 12-month period at federal laboratories and for-profit institutions. In addition, tuition and fees are reimbursed at a rate of 60%, up to $4,500; if the fellow's program supports postdoctoral individuals in formal degree-granting training, tuition is supported at the rate of 60%, up to $16,000 for an additional degree. Awards for training at a foreign site include economy or coach round-trip airfare for the fellow only; no allowance is provided for dependents.

Duration Up to 3 years.

Additional data This award is offered by all funding Institutes and Centers of the National Institutes of Health (NIH) as part of the National Research Service Award (NRSA) program, originally established in 1974.

Number awarded Varies each year; recently, 603 awards were made through this program.

Deadline April, August, or December of each year.

[1137]
RUTH L. KIRSCHSTEIN NATIONAL RESEARCH SERVICE AWARDS FOR INDIVIDUAL SENIOR FELLOWS

National Institutes of Health
Office of Extramural Research
Attn: Grants Information
6705 Rockledge Drive, Suite 4090
Bethesda, MD 20892-7983
(301) 435-0714   Fax: (301) 480-0525
TDD: (301) 451-5936   E-mail: grantsinfo@od.nih.gov
Web: grants.nih.gov/grants/guide/pa-files/PA-11-114.html

Summary To provide funding for mentored research training to experienced scientists (particularly Hispanic Americans, other underrepresented minorities, and individuals with disabilities) who wish to make major changes in the direction of their research careers.

Eligibility This program is open to U.S. citizens, nationals, and permanent residents who have a doctoral or equivalent degree from an accredited domestic or foreign institution and at least 7 subsequent years of relevant research or professional experience. Applications may be submitted on behalf of the candidates by a sponsoring institution, which may be a 1) public or private institution of higher education (especially a Hispanic-serving institution, Historically Black College or University, Tribal College or University, or Alaska Native or Native Hawaiian Serving Institutions); 2) nonprofit institution; 3) for profit organization; 4) eligible agency of the federal government; or 6) foreign organization. If a foreign institution is selected as the research training site, applicants must demonstrate that it presents special opportunities for furthering research programs through the use of unusual talent, resources, populations, or environmental conditions that exist in other countries and either are not available in the United States or augment existing U.S. resources. Members of diverse racial and ethnic groups, individuals with disabilities, and individuals from disadvantaged backgrounds are especially encouraged to apply.

Financial Data The award provides an annual stipend based on the number of years of postdoctoral experience, ranging from $39,264 for less than 1 year to $54,180 for 7 or more years. For fellows sponsored by domestic non-federal institutions, the stipend is paid through the sponsoring institution; for fellows sponsored by federal or foreign institutions, the monthly stipend is paid directly to the fellow. Institutions also receive an allowance to help defray such awardee expenses as self-only health insurance, research supplies, equipment, travel to scientific meetings, and related items; the allowance is $7,850 per 12-month period for fellows at non-federal, nonprofit, and foreign institutions and $6,750 per 12-month period at federal laboratories and for-profit institutions. In addition, tuition and fees are reimbursed at a rate of 60%, up to $4,500; if the fellow's program supports postdoctoral individuals in formal degree-granting training, tuition is supported at the rate of 60%, up to $16,000 for an additional degree. The initial 12 months of National Research Service

Award postdoctoral support carries a service payback requirement, which can be fulfilled by continued training under the award or by engaging in other health-related research training, health-related research, or health-related teaching. Fellows who fail to fulfill the payback requirement of 1 month of acceptable service for each month of the initial 12 months of support received must repay all funds received with interest.

Duration Up to 2 years.

Additional data This program is offered by 11 components of the National Institutes of Health: the National Institute on Aging, the National Institute on Alcohol Abuse and Alcoholism, the National Institute of Arthritis and Musculoskeletal and Skin Diseases, the National Cancer Institute, the National Institute of Dental and Craniofacial Research, the National Institute of Environmental Health Sciences, the National Heart, Lung, and Blood Institute, the National Institute of General Medical Sciences, the National Human Genome Research Institute, the National Institute of Neurological Disorders and Stroke, and the National Institute of Nursing Research.

Number awarded Varies each year.

Deadline April, August, or December of each year.

[1138]
SAN FRANCISCO INTERNATIONAL LGBT FILM FESTIVAL PRIZES

Frameline
Attn: Festival
145 Ninth Street, Suite 300
San Francisco, CA 94103
(415) 703-8650   Fax: (415) 861-1404
E-mail: info@frameline.org
Web: www.frameline.org

Summary To recognize and reward outstanding films of interest to the lesbian, gay, bisexual, and transgender (LGBT) audience, particularly those produced by people of color or women.

Eligibility This competition is open to directors of films by, about, and of interest to LGBT people. Applicants must submit previews of their work on DVD or VHS in the following categories: narrative feature films (40 minutes and longer), documentary feature films (40 minutes and longer), and shorts (all films less than 40 minutes in length). The program actively seeks out work by women and people of color. Recently, awards have been presented for best feature film, best documentary film, and best short film.

Financial Data Awards are $2,000 for best feature and best documentary and $1,000 for best short film.

Duration The awards are presented annually.

Additional data No fees are charged for the early deadline. Standard fees are $35 for the regular deadline, $50 for the late deadline, or $55 for the extended deadline. Student fees are $15 for regular, late, and extended deadlines. Fees are waived for youth up to 18 years of age.

Number awarded 3 each year.

Deadline December of each year for the early deadline; January of each year for the regular deadline; mid-February for the late deadline; and the end of February for the extended deadline.

[1139]
SARA WHALEY BOOK PRIZE

National Women's Studies Association
Attn: Book Prizes
11 East Mount Royal Avenue, Suite 100
Baltimore, MD 21202
(410) 528-0355   Fax: (410) 528-0357
E-mail: awards@nwsa.org
Web: www.nwsa.org/content.asp?pl=16&contentid=16

Summary To recognize and reward members of the National Women's Studies Association (NWSA), particularly Hispanic Americans and other women of color, who have written outstanding books on topics related to women and labor.

Eligibility This award is available to NWSA members who submit a book manuscript that relates to women and labor, including migration and women's paid jobs, illegal immigration and women's work, impact of AIDS on women's employment, trafficking of women and women's employment, women and domestic work, or impact of race on women's work. Both senior scholars (who have issued at least 2 books and published the entry within the past year) and junior scholars (who have a publication contract or a book in production) are eligible. Women of color of U.S. or international origin are encouraged to apply.

Financial Data The award is $2,000.

Duration The awards are presented annually.

Additional data This award was first presented in 2008.

Number awarded 2 each year: 1 to a senior scholar and 1 to a junior scholar.

Deadline April of each year.

[1140]
SBE POSTDOCTORAL RESEARCH FELLOWSHIPS

National Science Foundation
Directorate for Social, Behavioral, and Economic Sciences
Attn: Office of Multidisciplinary Activities
4201 Wilson Boulevard, Room 907.09
Arlington, VA 22230
(703) 292-4672   Fax: (703) 292-9083
TDD: (800) 281-8749   E-mail: fchowdhu@nsf.gov
Web: www.nsf.gov

Summary To provide financial assistance for postdoctoral research training to Hispanic American and other underrepresented minority scientists in fields of interest to the Directorate for Social, Behavioral, and Economic Sciences (SBE) of the National Science Foundation (NSF).

Eligibility This program is open to U.S. citizens, nationals, and permanent residents who completed a doctorate within the past 24 months but are not already in a full-time tenure-track faculty position. Applicants may be interested in either of 2 tracks offered by this program: 1) Broadening Participation, to increase involvement in social, behavioral, and economic research by members of ethnic groups that are currently underrepresented, including Native Americans (Alaska Natives and American Indians), African Americans, Hispanics, and Native Pacific Islanders; and/or 2) Interdisciplinary Research in which at least 1 of the disciplines is an SBE science. Proposals must involve research training to be conducted at any appropriate U.S. or foreign nonprofit institution (government laboratory, institution of higher education, national laboratory, or public or private research institute), but not at the same institution where the doctorate was obtained. For the first track, applications must include a statement on how the fellowship will help broaden the participation of scientists from currently underrepresented groups in the United States. For the second track, applications must include a statement on why the project requires interdisciplinary training beyond the core doctoral experiences.

Financial Data Grants include an annual stipend of $45,000, a research and travel allowance of $10,000 per year, an institutional allowance at the awardees current federal negotiated indirect cost rate, and additional travel expenses up to $10,000 if the project includes an international component.

Duration 2 years.

Number awarded Up to 15 each year.

Deadline October of each year.

[1141]
SCHOLARLY EDITIONS AND TRANSLATIONS GRANTS

National Endowment for the Humanities
Attn: Division of Research Programs
1100 Pennsylvania Avenue, N.W., Room 318
Washington, DC 20506
(202) 606-8200   Toll Free: (800) NEH-1121
Fax: (202) 606-8204   TDD: (866) 372-2930
E-mail: editions@neh.gov
Web: www.neh.gov

Summary To provide funding to scholars (particularly those at Minority Serving Institutions) and organizations interested in preparing texts and documents in the humanities.

Eligibility This program is open to 1) U.S. citizens and foreign nationals who have been living in the United States or its jurisdictions for at least 3 years; 2) state and local governmental agencies; and 3) nonprofit, tax-exempt institutions and organizations in the United States. It supports the preparation of editions and translations of pre-existing texts and documents of value to the humanities that are currently inaccessible or available in inadequate editions. Projects must be undertaken by a team of at least 1 editor or translator and 1 other staff member. Grants typically support editions and translations of significant literary, philosophical, and historical materials, but other types of work, such as the editing of musical notation, are also eligible. Selection is based on 1) the intellectual significance of the project, including its potential contribution to scholarship in the humanities, the likelihood that it will stimulate new research, its relationship to larger themes in the humanities, and the significance of the material on which the project is based; 2) the appropriateness of the research methods, critical apparatus, and editorial policies; the appropriateness of selection criteria; the thoroughness and feasibility of the work plan; and the quality of the samples; 3) the qualifications, expertise, and levels of commitment of the project director and key project staff or contributors, and the appropriateness of the staff to the goals of the project; 4) the promise of quality, usefulness, and impact on scholarship of any resulting publication or other product; and 5) the potential for success, including the likelihood that the project will be successfully completed within the projected time frame. The program encourages submission of applications from faculty at Historically Black Colleges and Universities, Hispanic Serving Institutions, and Tribal Colleges and Universities.

Financial Data Grants range from $50,000 to $100,000 per year. The use of federal matching funds in encouraged. Normally, support does not exceed 80% of total costs.

Duration 1 to 3 years.

Number awarded Approximately 26 each year.

Deadline December of each year.

[1142]
SCHOLARS IN HEALTH POLICY RESEARCH PROGRAM

Robert Wood Johnson Foundation
c/o Boston University Health Policy Institute
53 Bay State Road
Boston, MA 02215-2197
(617) 353-9220   Fax: (617) 353-9227
E-mail: rwjf@bu.edu
Web: www.healthpolicyscholars.org

Summary To provide support for postdoctoral training in health policy to scholars (particularly Hispanic Americans, other underrepresented minorities, and women) in economics, political science, and sociology.

Eligibility This program is open to scholars who have a doctoral degree in economics, political science, or sociology. Applicants must have earned their degree during the past 5 years and be U.S. citizens or permanent residents. Preference is given to applicants who have not worked previously in the areas of health or health policy research. Selection is based on the applicant's commitment to a health policy career, quality of the past research, capability to undertake this challenging program, recommendations, and potential to contribute creatively to future U.S. health policies. The program embraces racial, ethnic, and gender diversity and encourages applications from candidates from groups that historically have been underrepresented in the 3 disciplines of interest.

Financial Data The stipend is $89,000 per year.

Duration 2 years.

Additional data Fellows train at 1 of 3 nationally prominent academic institutions: University of California at Berkeley (in collaboration with the University of California at San Francisco), Harvard University, or the University of Michigan. There, they have the opportunity to work closely with faculty from the social sciences, as well as from medicine, public health, and public policy. Specific activities vary by institution but generally include seminars, workshops, tutorials, independent research projects, and policy placements in local or state government.

Number awarded Up to 9 each year.

Deadline October of each year.

[1143]
SHORT-TERM RESEARCH EDUCATION PROGRAM TO INCREASE DIVERSITY IN HEALTH-RELATED RESEARCH

National Heart, Lung, and Blood Institute
Attn: Division of Cardiovascular Diseases
6701 Rockledge Drive
Bethesda, MD 20892-7940
(301) 435-0535   Fax: (301) 480-1454
TDD: (301) 451-0088   E-mail: carlsonde@nhlbi.nih.gov
Web: grants.nih.gov

Summary To provide funding to Hispanic Americans and members of other underrepresented groups who are interested in conducting a research education program relevant to the mission of the National Heart, Lung, and Blood Institute (NHLBI).

Eligibility This program is open to principal investigators at U.S. domestic institutions (universities, colleges, hospitals, laboratories, units of state and local governments, and eligible agencies of the federal government) who are interested in conducting a research education program related to activities of NHLBI. Applications are especially encouraged from principal investigators who qualify as underrepresented: 1) a member of an ethnic or racial group shown to be underrepresented in health-related sciences on a national basis; 2) an individual with a disability; or 3) an individual from a disadvantaged background, including those from a low-income family and those from a social, cultural, and/or educational environment that has inhibited them from preparation for a research career. The proposed education program must encourage the participation of undergraduate and health professional students who are also currently underrepresented in the biomedical, clinical, and behavioral sciences. Students participating in the program are not required to be enrolled at the sponsoring institution.

Financial Data Grants depend on the nature of the project and the number of student participants. Maximum total direct costs should not exceed $319,000. Compensation to participating students must conform to the established salary and wage policies of the institution. Facilities and administrative costs may be reimbursed at the rate of 8% of total direct costs.

Duration Up to 5 years.

Number awarded 3 to 5 each year; a total of $900,000 is available for this program annually.

Deadline Letters of intent must be submitted by January of each year; final applications are due in February.

[1144]
SMALL GRANTS FOR NEW INVESTIGATORS TO PROMOTE DIVERSITY IN HEALTH-RELATED RESEARCH

National Institute of Diabetes and Digestive and Kidney
   Diseases
Attn: Office of Minority Health Research Coordination
6707 Democracy Boulevard, Room 906-B
Bethesda, MD 20892-5454
(301) 594-9652   Fax: (301) 594-9358
TDD: (301) 451-0088   E-mail: mcbrydekd@mailnih.gov
Web: grants.nih.gov/grants/guide/pa-files/PAR-13-074

Summary To provide funding to new investigators from underrepresented groups (e.g., Hispanic Americans) who are interested in conducting a research project in fields of interest to designated components of the National Institutes of Health (NIH).

Eligibility This program is open to U.S. citizens, nationals, and permanent residents who 1) have a health professional doctoral degree (e.g., M.D., D.D.S., D.O., D.V.M., O.D., Psy.D., Dr.P.H.); 2) have at least 2 to 4 years of postdoctoral research experience; 3) qualify as new investigators; and 4) belong to a population group nationally underrepresented in biomedical or behavioral research, including members of designated racial and ethnic groups (e.g., African Americans, Hispanics, Native Americans, Alaska Natives, Hawaiian Natives, and non-Asian Pacific Islanders), individual with disabilities, or individuals from a disadvantaged background (defined to include those who come from a low-income family and those who come from a social, cultural, and/or educational environment that has inhibited them from obtaining the knowledge, skills, and abilities necessary to develop and participate in a research career). Applicants must be interested in conducting a research project in areas of interest to the NIH National Institute of Diabetes and Digestive and Kidney Diseases (NIDDK), National Institute of Mental Health (NIMH), or Office of Dietary Supplements (ODS). Those include, for NIKKD, diabetes, endocrinology, metabolism, digestive diseases, hepatology, obesity, nutrition, kidney, urology, or hematology; for NIMH, mental disorders; or ODS, dietary supplements and/or their ingredients.

Financial Data Direct costs are limited to $125,000 per year. Facilities and administrative costs are reimbursed at 8% of modified total direct costs.

Duration 3 years; nonrenewable.

Number awarded Varies each year.

Deadline Letters of intent are due in May of each year; completed applications may be submitted in June.

[1145]
SOCIETY OF PEDIATRIC PSYCHOLOGY DIVERSITY RESEARCH GRANT

American Psychological Association
Attn: Division 54 (Society of Pediatric Psychology)
c/o Anna Maria Patino-Fernandez
University of Miami School of Medicine
Mailman Center for Child Development
Division of Clinical Psychology
1601 N.W. 12th Avenue, 4018B
Miami, FL 33136-1005
(305) 243-6837   Fax: (305) 243-8470
E-mail: Apatino-fernandez@med.miami.edu
Web: www.apadivisions.org

Summary To provide funding to graduate student and postdoctoral members of the Society of Pediatric Psychology (particularly Hispanic Americans and others who come from diverse backgrounds) who are interested in conducting research on diversity aspects of pediatric psychology.

Eligibility This program is open to current members of the society who are graduate students, fellows, or early-career (within 3 years of appointment) faculty. Applicants must be interested in conducting pediatric psychology research that features diversity-related variables, such as race or ethnicity, gender, culture, sexual orientation, language differences, socioeconomic status, and/or religiosity. Along with their application, they must submit a 2,000-word description of the project, including its purpose, methodology, predictions, and implications; a detailed budget; a current curriculum vitae, and (for students) a curriculum vitae of the faculty research mentor and a letter of support from that mentor. Selection is based on relevance to diversity in child health (5 points), significance of the study (5 points), study methods and procedures (10 points), and investigator qualifications (10 points).

Financial Data Grants up to $1,000 are available. Funds may not be used for convention or meeting travel, indirect costs, stipends of principal investigators, or costs associated with manuscript preparation.

Duration The grant is presented annually.

Additional data The Society of Pediatric Psychology is Division 54 of the American Psychological Association (APA). This grant was first presented in 2008.

Number awarded 1 each year.

Deadline September of each year.

[1146]
STANFORD HUMANITIES CENTER EXTERNAL FACULTY FELLOWSHIPS

Stanford Humanities Center
Attn: Fellowship Administrator
424 Santa Teresa Street
Stanford, CA 94305-4015
(650) 723-3054   Fax: (650) 723-1895
E-mail: rbarrick@stanford.edu
Web: shc.stanford.edu/fellowships/non-stanford-faculty

Summary To offer scholars In the humanities (particularly Hispanic Americans and other underrepresented minorities) an opportunity to conduct research and teach at Stanford University.

Eligibility External fellowships at Stanford University fall into 2 categories: 1) senior fellowships for scholars who are more than 10 years beyond receipt of the Ph.D.; and 2) junior fellowships for scholars who at the time of application are at least 3 but normally no more than 10 years beyond receipt of the Ph.D. The fields of study should be the humanities as defined in the act that established the National Foundation for the Arts and Humanities. There are no citizenship requirements; non-U.S. nationals are eligible. Scholars who are members of traditionally underrepresented groups are encouraged to apply. Applications are judged on 1) the promise of the specific research project being proposed; 2) the originality and intellectual distinction of the candidate's previous work; 3) the research project's potential interest to scholars in different fields of the humanities; and 4) the applicant's ability to engage in collegial interaction and to contribute to the discussion of presentations.

Financial Data The annual stipend is up to $70,000. In addition, a housing/travel subsidy of up to $30,000, depending on size of family, is offered.

Duration 1 academic year.

Additional data Fellows are expected to make an intellectual contribution not only within the center but to humanistic studies in general at Stanford. Normally, this requirement is fulfilled by teaching an undergraduate or graduate course or seminar or 1 quarter within a particular department or program. Fellows should live within 10 miles of Stanford University. Regular attendance at center events is expected and fellows are expected to be present during the fall, winter, and spring quarters and to attend weekday lunches on a regular basis.

Number awarded 6 to 8 each year.

Deadline October of each year.

[1147]
STUDIO MUSEUM IN HARLEM ARTIST-IN-RESIDENCE PROGRAM

Studio Museum in Harlem
Attn: Education and Public Programs Department
144 West 125th Street
New York, NY 10027
(212) 864-4500, ext. 230   Fax: (212) 864-4800
Web: www.studiomuseum.org/learn/artist-in-residence

Summary To support visual artists of Latino and African descent who are interested in a residency at the Studio Museum in Harlem.

Eligibility This program is open to artists of African and Latino descent locally, nationally, or internationally. Applicants may be working in sculpture, painting, photography, printmaking, film and video, digital art, or mixed media. They must be professional artists with at least 3 years of professional commitment and currently engaged in studio work; high school, college, and graduate students are not considered. Selection is based on quality of the work, a record of exhibition and critical review, demonstration of a serious and consistent dedication to the professional practice of fine arts, evidence that the applicant is at a critical juncture in development that will be advanced by a residency, and letters of recommendation.

Financial Data This fellowship provides non-living studio space, a stipend of $20,000, and a $1,000 material grant.

Duration 11 months.

Additional data Artists must spend at least 20 hours per week in their studios, exhibit their works in the museum, and conduct 2 public presentations/workshops.

Number awarded 3 each year.

Deadline March of each year.

[1148]
SYLVIA TAYLOR JOHNSON MINORITY FELLOWSHIP IN EDUCATIONAL MEASUREMENT

Educational Testing Service
Attn: Fellowships
660 Rosedale Road
MS 19-T
Princeton, NJ 08541-0001
(609) 734-5543   Fax: (609) 734-5410
E-mail: internfellowships@ets.org
Web: www.ets.org/research/fellowships

Summary To provide funding to Hispanic American and other minority scholars who are interested in conducting independent research under the mentorship of senior researchers at the Educational Testing Service (ETS).

Eligibility This program is open to scholars from diverse backgrounds (especially members of traditionally underrepresented groups such as African Americans, Hispanic/Latino Americans, and American Indians) who have earned a doctorate within the past 10 years and are U.S. citizens or permanent residents. Applicants must be prepared to conduct independent research at ETS under the mentorship of a senior researcher. They should have a commitment to education and an independent body of scholarship that signals the promise of continuing contributions to educational measurement. Projects should relate to issues involved in measurement theory, validity, natural language processing and computational linguistics, cognitive psychology, learning theory, linguistics, speech recognition and processing, teaching and classroom research, or statistics. Studies focused on issues concerning the education of minority students are especially encouraged. Selection is based on the scholar's record of accomplishment, proposed topic of research, commitment to education, and promise of continuing contributions to educational measurement.

Financial Data   The stipend is set in relation to compensation at the home institution. Scholars and their families also receive reimbursement for relocation expenses.

Duration   Up to 2 years.

Number awarded   1 each year.

Deadline   Preliminary application materials must be submitted by December of each year; final application materials are due by the end of February.

[1149]
TACHE DISTINGUISHED COMMUNITY COLLEGE FACULTY AWARD

Texas Association of Chicanos in Higher Education
Attn: Awards Committee
P.O. Box 396
Canyon, TX 79015
E-mail: maria.aguirre@tstc.edu
Web: www.tache.org/Awards.aspx

Summary   To recognize and reward outstanding community college faculty members in Texas who are members of the Texas Association of Chicanos in Higher Education (TACHE).

Eligibility   Eligible to be nominated for this award are active TACHE members who have taught for at least the last 5 years at a Texas community college. Nominees must have demonstrated a consistent pattern of teaching excellence, innovation in teaching, contributions to discipline-specific scholarship, a consistent pattern of service to the community, a consistent pattern of support of Chicano/Latino programs and students, support for and promotion of postsecondary education, and a consistent pattern of mentoring other faculty and/or students. Self-nominations are accepted.

Financial Data   The award is $1,000.

Duration   The award is presented annually.

Number awarded   1 each year.

Deadline   December of each year.

[1150]
TACHE DISTINGUISHED UNIVERSITY FACULTY AWARD

Texas Association of Chicanos in Higher Education
Attn: Awards Committee
P.O. Box 396
Canyon, TX 79015
E-mail: maria.aguirre@tstc.edu
Web: www.tache.org/Awards.aspx

Summary   To recognize and reward outstanding university faculty members in Texas who are members of the Texas Association of Chicanos in Higher Education (TACHE).

Eligibility   Eligible to be nominated for this award are active TACHE members who have taught for at least the last 5 years at a Texas university. Nominees must have demonstrated a consistent pattern of excellence in teaching, innovation in teaching, a record of scholarly publications or other contributions to the profession or academic discipline, a consistent pattern of service to the community, a consistent pattern of support of Chicano/Latino programs and students, support for and promotion of postsecondary and graduate education, and a consistent pattern of mentoring other faculty and/or students. Self-nominations are accepted.

Financial Data   The award is $1,000.

Duration   The award is presented annually.

Number awarded   1 each year.

Deadline   December of each year.

[1151]
THEODORE BLAU EARLY CAREER AWARD FOR OUTSTANDING CONTRIBUTION TO PROFESSIONAL CLINICAL PSYCHOLOGY

American Psychological Foundation
750 First Street, N.E.
Washington, DC 20002-4242
(202) 336-5843   Fax: (202) 336-5812
E-mail: foundation@apa.org
Web: www.apa.org/apf/funding/blau.aspx

Summary   To recognize and reward young clinical psychologists (particularly Hispanic Americans, other minorities, women, and individuals with disabilities) who have a record of outstanding professional accomplishments.

Eligibility   This award is available to clinical psychologists who are no more than 7 years past completion of their doctoral degree. Nominees must have a record of accomplishments that may include promoting the practice of clinical psychology through professional service; innovation in service delivery; novel application of applied research methodologies to professional practice; positive impact on health delivery systems; development of creative educational programs for practice; or other novel or creative activities advancing the service of the profession. Self-nominations are accepted. The sponsor encourages nominations of individuals who represent diversity in race, ethnicity, gender, age, disability, and sexual orientation.

Financial Data   The award is $4,000.

Duration   The award is presented annually.

Additional data   This award, first presented in 1998, is sponsored by Division 12 (Society of Clinical Psychology) of the American Psychological Association.

Number awarded   1 each year.

Deadline   Nominations must be submitted by October of each year.

[1152]
THEODORE MILLON AWARD IN PERSONALITY PSYCHOLOGY

American Psychological Foundation
750 First Street, N.E.
Washington, DC 20002-4242
(202) 336-5843   Fax: (202) 336-5812
E-mail: foundation@apa.org
Web: www.apa.org/apf/funding/millon.aspx

Summary To recognize and reward psychologists (particularly Hispanic Americans, other minorities, women, and individuals with disabilities) who have a record of outstanding contributions to the science of personality psychology.

Eligibility This award is available to psychologists engaged in advancing the science of personality psychology, including the areas of personology, personality theory, personality disorders, and personality measurement. Nominees should be between 8 and 20 years past completion of their doctoral degree. The sponsor encourages nominations of individuals who represent diversity in race, ethnicity, gender, age, disability, and sexual orientation.

Financial Data The award is $1,000.

Duration The award is presented annually.

Additional data This award, established in 2004, is sponsored by Division 12 (Society of Clinical Psychology) of the American Psychological Association.

Number awarded 1 each year.

Deadline Nominations must be submitted by October of each year.

[1153]
TIMOTHY JEFFREY MEMORIAL AWARD IN CLINICAL HEALTH PSYCHOLOGY

American Psychological Foundation
750 First Street, N.E.
Washington, DC 20002-4242
(202) 336-5843   Fax: (202) 336-5812
E-mail: foundation@apa.org
Web: www.apa.org/apf/funding/jeffrey.aspx

Summary To recognize and reward psychologists (particularly Hispanic Americans, other minorities, women, and individuals with disabilities) who have made outstanding contributions to clinical health psychology.

Eligibility This award is available to full-time providers of direct clinical services who demonstrate an outstanding commitment to clinical health psychology. Nominees must be members of Division 38 (Health Psychology) of the American Psychological Association. They must have a full and unrestricted license to practice psychology and typically spend 15 to 20 hours per week in direct patient care. Letters of nomination should be accompanied by a curriculum vitae, at least 1 letter of support from a non-psychologist professional colleague, and another letter of support from a psychologist colleague. The sponsor encourages nominations of individuals who represent diversity in race, ethnicity, gender, age, disability, and sexual orientation.

Financial Data The award is $3,000.

Duration The award is presented annually.

Additional data This award is sponsored by Division 38.

Number awarded 1 each year.

Deadline April of each year.

[1154]
TOMAS RIVERA MEXICAN AMERICAN CHILDREN'S BOOK AWARD

Texas State University at San Marcos
Attn: Department of Curriculum and Instruction
601 University Drive
San Marcos, TX 78666-4616
(512) 245-2157   Fax: (512) 245-3158
E-mail: riverabookaward@txstate.edu
Web: www.education.txstate.edu

Summary To recognize and reward outstanding children's books that reflect the culture of Mexican Americans in the United States.

Eligibility Eligible to be nominated for this award are books for children and young adults that authentically reflect the lives and experiences of Mexican Americans in the United States. Entries may be fiction or nonfiction. Works for younger children (grades preK-5) are eligible in even-numbered years; works for older children (grades 6-12) are eligible in odd-numbered years. Nominations may be submitted by authors, illustrators, published, and the public at large.

Financial Data The award is $3,000.

Duration The award is presented annually, during Hispanic Heritage month at Texas State University at San Marcos.

Additional data The award was first presented in 1995.

Number awarded 1 each year.

Deadline October of each year.

[1155]
TRAINEESHIPS IN AIDS PREVENTION STUDIES (TAPS)

University of California at San Francisco
Attn: Center for AIDS Prevention Studies
50 Beale Street, Suite 1300
San Francisco, CA 94105
(415) 597-9260   Fax: (415) 597-9213
E-mail: Rochelle.Blanco@ucsf.edu
Web: www.caps.ucsf.edu/training/taps

Summary To provide funding to scientists (particularly Hispanic American and other minority scientists) who are interested in conducting HIV prevention research at the Center for AIDS Prevention Studies (CAPS) of the University of California at San Francisco (UCSF).

Eligibility This program is open to U.S. citizens, nationals, and permanent residents who have a Ph.D., M.D., or equivalent degree. Applicants must be interested in a program of research training at CAPS in the following areas of special emphasis in AIDS research: epidemiological research, studies of AIDS risk behaviors, substance abuse and HIV, primary prevention interventions, research addressing minority populations, studies of HIV-positive individuals, policy and ethics, international research, and other public health and clinical aspects of AIDS. Recent postdoctorates who have just completed their training as well as those who are already faculty members in academic or clinical departments are eligible. Members of minority ethnic groups are strongly encouraged to apply.

Financial Data Stipends depend on years of relevant postdoctoral experience, based on the NIH stipend scale for Institutional Research Training Grants (currently ranging from $39,264 for fellows with no relevant postdoctoral experience to $54,180 for those with 7 or more years of experience). Other benefits include a computer, travel to at least 1 annual professional meeting, health insurance, and other required support. The costs of the M.P.H. degree, if required, are covered.

Duration   2 or 3 years.

Additional data   The TAPS program is designed to ensure that at the end of the training each fellow will have: 1) completed the M.P.H. degree or its equivalent; 2) taken advanced courses in research methods, statistics, and other topics relevant to a major field of interest; 3) participated in and led numerous seminars on research topics within CAPS, as well as in the formal teaching programs of the university; 4) designed several research protocols and completed at least 1 significant research project under the direction of a faculty mentor; and 5) made presentations at national or international meetings and submitted several papers for publication.

Number awarded   Varies each year.

Deadline   November of each year.

[1156]
TRAINING PROGRAM FOR SCIENTISTS CONDUCTING RESEARCH TO REDUCE HIV/STI HEALTH DISPARITIES

University of California at San Francisco
Attn: Center for AIDS Prevention Studies
50 Beale Street, Suite 1300
San Francisco, CA 94105
(415) 597-9139   Fax: (415) 597-9213
E-mail: dale.danley@ucsf.edu
Web: www.caps.ucsf.edu

Summary   To provide funding to scientists (particularly Hispanic Americans and other minorities) who are interested in obtaining additional training at the University of California at San Francisco (UCSF) Center for AIDS Prevention Studies (CAPS) for HIV prevention research in minority communities.

Eligibility   This program is open to scientists in tenure-track positions or investigators in research institutes who have not yet obtained research funding from the U.S. National Institutes of Health (NIH) or equivalent. Applicants must be interested in a program of activity at CAPS to improve their programs of HIV-prevention research targeting vulnerable ethnic minority populations. They must be eligible to serve as principal investigators at their home institutions. Selection is based on commitment to HIV social and behavioral research, prior HIV prevention research with communities and community-based organizations targeting communities with high levels of health disparities (e.g., communities with a high proportion of disadvantaged or disabled persons, racial and ethnic minority communities), creativity and innovativeness for a pilot research project to serve as a preliminary study for a subsequent larger R01 grant proposal to NIH or other suitable funding agency, past experience conducting research and writing papers, quality of letters of recommendation from colleagues and mentors, and support from the home institution (e.g., time off for research, seed money). A goal of the program is to increase the number of minority group members among principal investigators funded by NIH and other agencies. U.S. citizenship or permanent resident status is required.

Financial Data   Participants receive 1) a monthly stipend for living expenses and round-trip airfare to San Francisco for each summer; and 2) a grant of $25,000 to conduct prelimi-

nary research before the second summer to strengthen their R01 application.

Duration   6 weeks during each of 3 consecutive summers.

Additional data   This program is funded by the NIH National Institute of Child Health and Human Development (NICHHD) and National Institute on Drug Abuse (NIDA).

Number awarded   Approximately 4 each year.

Deadline   January of each year.

[1157]
UC BERKELEY'S CHANCELLOR'S POSTDOCTORAL FELLOWSHIPS FOR ACADEMIC DIVERSITY

University of California at Berkeley
Attn: Division of Equity and Inclusion
104 California Hall
Berkeley, CA 94720-1508
(510) 643-8235   E-mail: ppfpinfo@berkeley.edu
Web: diversity.berkeley.edu/ChancPostdocFellowship

Summary   To provide an opportunity for Hispanic Americans and other recent postdoctorates who will increase diversity at the University of California at Berkeley to conduct research on the campus.

Eligibility   This program is open to U.S. citizens and permanent residents who received a doctorate within 3 years of the start of the fellowship. The program particularly solicits applications from individuals who are members of groups that are underrepresented in American universities (e.g., women, ethnic minorities, religious minorities, differently-abled, lesbian/gay/bisexual/transgender). Special consideration is given to applicants committed to careers in university research and teaching and whose life experience, research, or employment background will contribute significantly to academic diversity and excellence at the Berkeley campus.

Financial Data   The stipend is $41,496 per year (11 months, plus 1 month vacation). The award also includes health insurance, vision and dental benefits, and up to $4,000 for research-related and program travel expenses.

Duration   1 year; may be renewed 1 additional year.

Additional data   This program operates in addition to the University of California President's Postdoctoral Fellowship Program for Academic Diversity. Interested candidates may apply to either program.

Number awarded   Varies each year; recently, 4 of these fellowships were awarded.

Deadline   October of each year.

[1158]
UC DAVIS CHANCELLOR'S POSTDOCTORAL FELLOWSHIP PROGRAM

University of California at Davis
Attn: Office of the Vice Provost for Academic Affairs
Mrak Hall, Fifth Floor
One Shields Avenue
Davis, CA 95616
(530) 752-0963   Fax: (530) 752-6359
E-mail: binsingh@berkeley.edu
Web: academicpersonnel.ucdavis.edu/cpf.html

Summary   To provide an opportunity for Hispanic Americans and other recent postdoctorates who will increase diversity at the University of California at Davis to conduct research at the university or its School of Medicine.

Eligibility This program is open to U.S. citizens and permanent residents who received a doctorate within 3 years of the start of the fellowship. Applicants must be interested in conducting research at UC Davis, either on the main campus or at the School of Medicine. The program particularly solicits applications from scholars whose research, teaching, and service will contribute to the diversity and equal opportunity at the university. Those contributions may include public service addressing the needs of our increasingly diverse society, efforts to improve equitable access to higher education, or research focusing on underserved populations or understanding inequities related to race, gender, disability, or LGBT status.

Financial Data The stipend ranges from $41,000 to $50,000 per year (11 months, plus 1 month vacation). The award also includes health insurance, vision and dental benefits, and up to $4,000 for research-related and program travel expenses.

Duration 1 year; may be renewed 1 additional year.

Additional data This program, which began in 2012, operates in addition to the University of California President's Postdoctoral Fellowship Program for Academic Diversity. Interested candidates may apply to either program.

Number awarded 2 each year: 1 supported by the Chancellor's office and 1 by the School of Medicine.

Deadline October of each year.

[1159]
UC SAN DIEGO CHANCELLOR'S POSTDOCTORAL FELLOWSHIP PROGRAM FOR ACADEMIC DIVERSITY

University of California at San Diego
Attn: Office of the Vice Chancellor for Equity, Diversity and Inclusion
302 University Center, Room 102
La Jolla, CA 92093-0029
(858) 822-3542   Fax: (858) 822-3013
E-mail: diversity@ucsd.edu
Web: www.diversity.ucsd.edu/fellowship

Summary To provide an opportunity for Hispanic Americans and other recent postdoctorates who will increase diversity at the University of California at San Diego to conduct research at the university.

Eligibility This program is open to U.S. citizens and permanent residents who received a doctorate within 3 years of the start of the fellowship. Applicants must be interested in conducting research at UCSD. The program particularly solicits applications from scholars whose research, teaching, and service will contribute to the diversity and equal opportunity at the university. Those contributions may include public service addressing the needs of our increasingly diverse society, efforts to improve equitable access to higher education for women and minorities, or research focusing on underserved populations or understanding issues of racial or gender inequalities.

Financial Data The stipend is $40,000 per year (11 months, plus 1 month vacation). The award also includes health insurance, vision and dental benefits, and up to $4,000 for research-related and program travel expenses.

Duration 1 year; may be renewed 1 additional year.

Additional data This program operates in addition to the University of California President's Postdoctoral Fellowship Program for Academic Diversity. Interested candidates may apply to either program.

Number awarded 2 each year: 1 supported by the Chancellor's office and 1 supported by a department expressing interest in hosting a fellow.

Deadline October of each year.

[1160]
UCLA CHANCELLOR'S POSTDOCTORAL FELLOWSHIP PROGRAM

University of California at Los Angeles
Attn: Office for Diversity and Faculty Development
3109 Murphy Hall
P.O. Box 951407
Los Angeles, CA 90095-1407
(310) 206-7411   Fax: (310) 206-8427
E-mail: facdiversity@conet.ucla.edu
Web: faculty.diversity.ucla.edu

Summary To provide an opportunity for Hispanic Americans and other recent postdoctorates who will increase diversity at the University of California at Los Angeles to conduct research at the university.

Eligibility This program is open to U.S. citizens and permanent residents who received a doctorate within 3 years of the start of the fellowship. Applicants must be interested in conducting research at UCLA. The program particularly solicits applications from scholars whose research, teaching, and service will contribute to the diversity and equal opportunity at the university. Those contributions may include public service addressing the needs of our increasingly diverse society, efforts to improve equitable access to higher education, or research focusing on underserved populations or understanding inequities related to race, gender, disability, or LGBT status.

Financial Data The stipend ranges from $41,000 to $50,000 per year (11 months, plus 1 month vacation). The award also includes health insurance, vision and dental benefits, and up to $4,000 for research-related and program travel expenses.

Duration 1 year; may be renewed 1 additional year.

Additional data This program operates in addition to the University of California President's Postdoctoral Fellowship Program for Academic Diversity. Interested candidates may apply to either program.

Number awarded 2 each year.

Deadline October of each year.

[1161]
UNDERSTANDING THE DEVELOPMENT AND DEVISING TREATMENTS FOR ALZHEIMER'S DISEASE IN INDIVIDUALS WITH DOWN SYNDROME

Alzheimer's Association
Attn: Medical and Scientific Affairs
225 North Michigan Avenue, 17th Floor
Chicago, IL 60601-7633
(312) 335-5747   Toll Free: (800) 272-3900
Fax: (866) 699-1246   TDD: (312) 335-5886
E-mail: grantsapp@alz.org
Web: www.alz.org

Summary To provide funding investigators (particularly Hispanic Americans and others from diverse groups) who are interested in conducting research on the development of Alzheimer's Disease in individuals with Down Syndrome.

Eligibility This program is open to investigators who have full-time staff or faculty appointments at research laboratories, medical centers, hospitals, or universities. Investigator-initiated grants are available to those at the level of assistant professor or higher; new investigator grants are available to those who have less than 10 years of research experience. Applicants must be interested in conducting research on understanding the mechanisms that lead to the initiation of Alzheimer's Disease in persons with Down Syndrome. Scientists from underrepresented groups are especially encouraged to apply.

Financial Data Investigator-initiated grants up to $125,000 per year and new investigator grants up to $60,000 per year are available; both types of grants cover direct expenses and up to 10% for overhead costs. The total award for the life of the grant may not exceed $300,000 for investigator-initiated grants or $150,000 for new investigator grants.

Duration 2 to 3 years.

Additional data This program began in 2013 with support from the Linda Crnic Institute for Down Syndrome and the Global Down Syndrome Foundation.

Number awarded Up to 2 investigator-initiated grants and up to 4 new investigator grants are awarded each year.

Deadline Letters of intent must be submitted by the end of January of each year. Final applications are due in March.

[1162]
UNIVERSITY OF CALIFORNIA PRESIDENT'S POSTDOCTORAL FELLOWSHIP PROGRAM FOR ACADEMIC DIVERSITY

University of California at Berkeley
Attn: Office of Equity and Inclusion
102 California Hall
Berkeley, CA 94720-1508
(510) 643-6566   E-mail: ppfpinfo@berkeley.edu
Web: ppfp.ucop.edu/info/uc_ppfp.html

Summary To provide an opportunity to conduct research at campuses of the University of California to recent postdoctorates (particularly Hispanic Americans and other groups historically underrepresented in higher education) who are committed to careers in university teaching and research and who will contribute to diversity.

Eligibility This program is open to U.S. citizens or permanent residents who have a Ph.D. from an accredited univer-

sity. Applicants must be proposing to conduct research at a branch of the university under the mentorship of a faculty or laboratory sponsor. Preference is given to applicants 1) with the potential to bring to their academic careers the critical perspective that comes from their nontraditional educational background or their understanding of the experiences of groups historically underrepresented in higher education; 2) who have the communications skill and cross-cultural abilities to maximize effective collaboration with a diverse cross-section of the academic community; 3) who have demonstrated significant academic achievement by overcoming barriers such as economic, social, or educational disadvantage; and 4) who have the potential to contribute to higher education through their understanding of the barriers facing women, domestic minorities, students with disabilities, and other members of groups underrepresented in higher education careers, as evidenced by life experiences and educational background.

Financial Data The stipend ranges from $41,000 to $50,000, depending on the field and level of experience. The program also offers health benefits and up to $4,000 for supplemental and research-related expenses.

Duration Appointments are for 1 academic year, with possible renewal for a second year.

Additional data Research may be conducted at any of the University of California's 10 campuses (Berkeley, Davis, Irvine, Los Angeles, Merced, Riverside, San Diego, San Francisco, Santa Barbara, or Santa Cruz). The program provides mentoring and guidance in preparing for an academic career. This program was established in 1984 to encourage applications from minority and women scholars in fields where they were severely underrepresented; it is now open to all qualified candidates whose research, teaching, and service will contribute to diversity and equal opportunity at the University of California. In addition to this program for UC campuses in general, the Universities of California at Berkeley, Davis, Los Angeles, and San Diego offer separate Chancellor's Postdoctoral Fellowship programs for their institutions. Interested candidates may apply to those programs and/or this system-wide program.

Number awarded Varies each year; recently, 30 of these fellows were selected.

Deadline October of each year.

[1163]
UNIVERSITY OF ILLINOIS AT CHICAGO ACADEMIC RESIDENT LIBRARIAN PROGRAM

University of Illinois at Chicago
Attn: Library Human Resources
801 South Morgan
MC 234
Chicago, IL 60607
(312) 996-7353
Web: library.uic.edu/about/employment

Summary To provide a residency at the University of Illinois at Chicago (UIC) to librarians (particularly Hispanic Americans, other underrepresented minorities, and individuals with disabilities) who are interested in preparing for a career in academic librarianship.

Eligibility This program is open to librarians who graduated within the past year with a master's degree from an ALA-accredited program. Applicants must be interested in preparing for a career as an academic librarian through a residency at (UIC). Preference is given to applicants who can demonstrate an interest in 1 or more of the following areas: 1) technical services, with an emphasis on development and assessment of library discovery tools; 2) outreach, with an emphasis on initiatives to rural and underserved users; 3) reference and instruction, with an emphasis on instructional technical design and the development of multimedia learning objects; 4) E-science, with an emphasis on data curation in support of university-wide data management and preservation initiatives; 5) digital preservation, with an emphasis on preservation architectures, standards, and workflows; or 7) digital image collections, with an emphasis on mapping using GIS technologies. A goal of the program is to increase diversity within the profession of academic librarianship; applications are especially welcome from women, underrepresented minority group members, persons with disabilities, members of sexual minority groups, and others whose background, education, experience, and academic interests would enrich the diversity of the profession.

Financial Data The stipend is at least $42,000.

Duration 1 year; may be renewed 1 additional year.

Number awarded 2 or more each year.

Deadline June of each year.

[1164]
UNIVERSITY OF NORTH CAROLINA POSTDOCTORAL PROGRAM FOR FACULTY DIVERSITY

University of North Carolina at Chapel Hill
Attn: Office of Postdoctoral Affairs
301 Bynum Hall, CB #4100
Chapel Hill, NC 27599-4100
(919) 843-4793   Fax: (919) 962-6769
E-mail: jhfraley@email.unc.edu
Web: www.research.unc.edu/carolina-postdocs/applicants

Summary To support Hispanic American and other minority scholars who are interested in teaching and conducting research at the University of North Carolina (UNC).

Eligibility This program is open to scholars from underrepresented groups (African Americans, Native Americans, and Hispanics) who have completed their doctoral degree within the past 4 years. Applicants must be interested in teaching and conducting research at UNC. Preference is given to U.S. citizens and permanent residents. Selection is based on the evidence of scholarship potential and ability to compete for tenure-track appointments at UNC and other research universities.

Financial Data Fellows receive $39,874 per year, plus an allowance for research and travel. Health benefits are also available.

Duration Up to 2 years.

Additional data Fellows must be in residence at the Chapel Hill campus for the duration of the program. They teach 1 course per year and spend the rest of the time in research. This program began in 1983.

Number awarded 5 or 6 each year.

Deadline November of each year.

[1165]
UNIVERSITY RESEARCH INSTRUMENTATION PROGRAM

Army Research Office
Attn: Army DURIP Program Manager
4300 South Miami Boulevard
P.O. Box 12211
Research Triangle Park, NC 27709-2211
(919) 549-4251   Fax: (919) 549-4248
E-mail: aro.durip@us.army.mil
Web: www.arl.army.mil/www/default.cfm?Page=8

Summary To provide funding to researchers at colleges and universities, especially those at Historically Black Colleges and Universities (HBCUs) and other Minority Institutions (MIs), for the purchase of equipment.

Eligibility This program is open to researchers at colleges and universities in the United States with degree-granting programs in science, mathematics, and/or engineering. Applicants must be seeking funding for the acquisition of major equipment to augment current or to develop new research capabilities to support research in technical areas of interest to the Department of Defense. Proposals are encouraged from researchers at HBCUs and MIs.

Financial Data Grants range from $50,000 to $1,100,000; recently, they averaged $305,000.

Duration Grants are typically 1 year in length.

Additional data This program is also offered by the Air Force Office of Scientific Research and the Office of Naval Research.

Number awarded Varies each year; recently, 169 of these grants, worth $51.4 million, were awarded.

Deadline October of each year.

[1166]
USDA SMALL BUSINESS INNOVATION RESEARCH PROGRAM

Department of Agriculture
National Institute of Food and Agriculture
Attn: Director, SBIR Program
1400 Independence Avenue, S.W.
Stop 2201
Washington, DC 20250-2201
(202) 401-4002   Fax: (202) 401-6070
E-mail: sbir@nifa.usda.gov
Web: www.csrees.usda.gov/funding/sbir/sbir.html

Summary To stimulate technological innovation related to agriculture in the private sector by small business firms, especially those owned by Hispanic Americans, members of other socially and economically disadvantaged groups, and women.

Eligibility For the purposes of this program, a "small business" is defined as a firm that is organized for profit with a location in the United States; is in the legal form of an individual proprietorship, partnership, limited liability company, corporation, joint venture, association, trust, or cooperative; is at least 51% owned and controlled by 1 or more individuals who are citizens or permanent residents of the United States; and has (including its affiliates) fewer than 500 employees. The primary employment of the principal investigator must be with the firm at the time of award and during the conduct of the proposed project. Applications are encouraged from 1) women-owned small business concerns, defined as those that are at least 51% owned by a woman or women who also control and operate them; and 2) socially and economically disadvantaged small business concerns that are at least 51% owned by an Indian tribe, a Native Hawaiian organization, or 1 or more socially and economically disadvantaged individuals (African Americans, Hispanic Americans, Native Americans, Asian Pacific Americans, or subcontinent Asian Americans). Proposals are accepted in 10 topic areas: forests and related resources; plant production and protection (biology); animal production and protection; air, water, and soils; food science and nutrition; rural development; aquaculture; biofuels and biobased products; small and mid-sized farms; and plant production and protection (engineering). Selection is based on scientific and technical feasibility of the project, importance of the problem, qualifications of the investigator and research facilities, appropriateness of the budget, and extent of duplication of the project with other ongoing or previous research.

Financial Data Support is offered in 2 phases. In phase 1, awards normally do not exceed $100,000 (for both direct and indirect costs); in phase 2, awards normally do not exceed $450,000 (including both direct and indirect costs).

Duration Phase 1 awards may extend up to 8 months; phase 2 awards may extend up to 2 years.

Additional data Phase 1 is to determine the scientific or technical feasibility of ideas submitted by the applicants on research topic areas. Phase 2 awards are made to firms with approaches that appear sufficiently promising as a result of phase 1 studies.

Number awarded Recently, the department granted 80 phase 1 awards and 32 phase 2 awards. Total program funding was approximately $19 million.

Deadline September of each year for phase 1 awards; February of each year for phase 2 awards.

[1167]
VISIONARY GRANTS

American Psychological Foundation
750 First Street, N.E.
Washington, DC 20002-4242
(202) 336-5843   Fax: (202) 336-5812
E-mail: foundation@apa.org
Web: www.apa.org/apf/funding/vision-weiss.aspx

Summary To provide funding to professionals (particularly Hispanic Americans and those from other diverse backgrounds) who are interested in conducting projects that use psychology to solve social problems related to the priorities of the American Psychological Foundation (APF).

Eligibility This program is open to professionals at nonprofit organizations engaged in research, education, and intervention projects and programs. Applicants must be interested in conducting an activity that uses psychology to solve social problems in the following priority areas: understanding and fostering the connection between mental and physical health; reducing stigma and prejudice; understanding and preventing all forms of violence; or addressing the long-term psychological needs of individuals and communities in the aftermath of disaster. Selection is based on the criticality of the proposed funding for the proposed work; conformance with stated program goals and requirements; innovative and potential impact qualities; quality, viability, and promise of pro-

posed work, and competence and capability of project leaders. The sponsor encourages applications from individuals who represent diversity in race, ethnicity, gender, age, disability, and sexual orientation.

Financial Data Grants range from $2,500 to $20,000.

Duration 1 year; nonrenewable.

Additional data This program began in 2003.

Number awarded 1 or more each year.

Deadline March of each year.

[1168]
WAYNE F. PLACEK GRANTS

American Psychological Foundation
750 First Street, N.E.
Washington, DC 20002-4242
(202) 336-5843   Fax: (202) 336-5812
E-mail: foundation@apa.org
Web: www.apa.org/apf/funding/placek.aspx

Summary To provide funding to pre- and postdoctoral scholars (particularly Hispanic Americans, other minorities, women, and individuals with disabilities) who are interested in conducting research that will increase the general public's understanding of homosexuality and alleviate the stress experienced by gay men and lesbians.

Eligibility This program is open to scholars who have a doctoral degree (e.g., Ph.D., Psy.D., M.D.) and to graduate students in all fields of the behavioral and social sciences. Applicants must be interested in conducting empirical studies that address the following topics: prejudice, discrimination, and violence based on sexual orientation, including heterosexuals' attitudes and behaviors toward lesbian, gay, bisexual, and transgender (LGBT) people; family and workplace issues relevant to LGBT people; and subgroups of the LGBT population that have been historically underrepresented in scientific research. Selection is based on conformance with stated program goals, magnitude of incremental contribution, quality of proposed work, and applicant's demonstrated scholarship and research competence. The sponsor encourages applications from individuals who represent diversity in race, ethnicity, gender, age, disability, and sexual orientation.

Financial Data The grant is $15,000.

Duration 1 year.

Additional data This program began in 1995.

Number awarded 1 or 2 each year.

Deadline February of each year.

[1169]
W.E.B. DUBOIS FELLOWSHIP PROGRAM

Department of Justice
National Institute of Justice
Attn: W.E.B. DuBois Fellowship Program
810 Seventh Street, N.W.
Washington, DC 20531
(202) 514-6205   E-mail: Marilyn.Moses@usdoj.gov
Web: www.nij.gov

Summary To provide funding to junior investigators (particularly Hispanic Americans and other minorities) who are interested in conducting research on "crime, violence and the administration of justice in diverse cultural contexts."

Eligibility This program is open to investigators who have a Ph.D. or other doctoral-level degree (including a legal degree of J.D. or higher). Applicants should be early in their careers and not have been awarded tenure. They must be interested in conducting research that relates to specific areas that change annually but relate to criminal justice policy and practice in the United States. The sponsor strongly encourages applications from diverse racial and ethnic backgrounds. Selection is based on quality and technical merit; impact of the proposed project; capabilities, demonstrated productivity, and experience of the applicant; budget; dissemination strategy; and relevance of the project for policy and practice.

Financial Data Grants range up to $100,000. Funds may be used for salary, fringe benefits, reasonable costs of relocation, travel essential to the project, and office expenses not provided by the sponsor. Indirect costs are limited to 20%.

Duration 6 to 12 months; fellows are required to be in residence at the National Institute of Justice (NIJ) for the first 2 months and may elect to spend all or part of the remainder of the fellowship period either in residence at NIJ or at their home institution.

Number awarded 1 each year.

Deadline January of each year.

[1170]
WILLIAM L. FISHER CONGRESSIONAL GEOSCIENCE FELLOWSHIP

American Geological Institute
Attn: Government Affairs Program
4220 King Street
Alexandria, VA 22302-1502
(703) 379-2480, ext. 212   Fax: (703) 379-7563
E-mail: govt@agiweb.org
Web: www.agiweb.org/gap/csf/index.html

Summary To provide members of an American Geological Institute (AGI) component society (particularly Hispanic Americans, other minorities, and women) with an opportunity to gain professional experience in the office of a member of Congress or a Congressional committee.

Eligibility This program is open to members of 1 of AGI's 49 member societies who have a master's degree and at least 3 years of post-degree work experience or a Ph.D. Applicants should have a broad geoscience background and excellent written and oral communications skills. They must be interested in working with Congress. Although prior experience in public policy is not required, a demonstrated interest in applying science to the solution of public problems is desirable. Applications from women and minorities are especially encouraged. U.S. citizenship or permanent resident status is required.

Financial Data Fellows receive a stipend of up to $65,000 plus allowances for health insurance, relocation, and travel.

Duration 12 months, beginning in September.

Additional data This program is 1 of more than 20 Congressional Science Fellowships operating in affiliation with the American Association for the Advancement of Science (AAAS), which provides a 2-week orientation on Congressional and executive branch operations.

Number awarded 1 each year.

Deadline January of each year.

[1171]
WILLIAM TOWNSEND PORTER FELLOWSHIP FOR MINORITY INVESTIGATORS

Marine Biological Laboratory
Attn: Chief Academic and Scientific Officer
7 MBL Street
Woods Hole, MA 02543-1015
(508) 289-7173   Fax: (508) 457-1924
E-mail: casoofice@mbl.edu
Web: hermes.mbl.edu

Summary To support Hispanic Americans and other underrepresented minorities who wish to conduct research during the summer at the Marine Biological Laboratory (MBL) in Woods Hole, Massachusetts.

Eligibility This program is open to young scientists (undergraduates, senior graduate students, and postdoctoral trainees) who are from an underrepresented minority group (African American, Hispanic American, or Native American), are U.S. citizens or permanent residents, and are interested in conducting research with senior investigators at MBL. Applicants must submit a statement of the potential impact of this award on their career development. Fields of study include, but are not limited to, cell biology, developmental biology, ecology, evolution, microbiology, neurobiology, physiology, regenerative biology, and tissue engineering.

Financial Data Grants range from $5,000 to $25,000, typically to cover laboratory rental and/or housing costs. Awardees are responsible for other costs, such as supplies, shared resource usage, affiliated staff who accompany them, or travel.

Duration 8 to 10 weeks during the summer.

Additional data This fellowship was first awarded in 1921. Funding is provided by the Harvard Apparatus Foundation.

Number awarded 1 or more each year.

Deadline December of each year.

[1172]
YERBY POSTDOCTORAL FELLOWSHIP PROGRAM

Harvard School of Public Health
Attn: Office of Faculty Affairs
90 Smith Street, First Floor
Boston, MA 02120
(617) 432-1047   Fax: (617) 432-4711
E-mail: cburkot@hsph.harvard.edu
Web: www.hsph.harvard.edu

Summary To provide Hispanic Americans and other postdoctorates who will contribute to diversity with an opportunity to pursue a program of research training at Harvard School of Public Health.

Eligibility This program is open to postdoctorates who are interested in preparing for a career in public health. The program emphasizes applicants who will contribute to academic diversity, meaning 1) members of minority groups underrepresented in public health (American Indians or Alaska Natives, Blacks or African Americans, Hispanics or Latinos, and Native Hawaiians or other Pacific Islanders); and 2) individuals with disabilities.

Financial Data Fellows receive a competitive salary.

Duration 1 year; may be renewed 1 additional year.

Number awarded   Up to 5 each year.

Deadline   October of each year.

[1173]
ZENITH FELLOWS AWARD PROGRAM

Alzheimer's Association
Attn: Medical and Scientific Affairs
225 North Michigan Avenue, 17th Floor
Chicago, IL 60601-7633
(312) 335-5747   Toll Free: (800) 272-3900
Fax: (866) 699-1246   TDD: (312) 335-5886
E-mail: grantsapp@alz.org
Web: www.alz.org

Summary   To provide funding to established investigators (particularly Hispanic Americans and members of other underrepresented groups) who are interested in conducting advanced research on Alzheimer's Disease.

Eligibility   Eligible are scientists who have already contributed significantly to the field of Alzheimer's Disease research and are likely to continue to make significant contributions for many years to come. The proposed research must be "on the cutting edge" of basic, biomedical research and may not fit current conventional scientific wisdom or may challenge the prevailing orthodoxy. It should address fundamental problems related to early detection, etiology, pathogenesis, treatment, and/or prevention of Alzheimer's Disease. Scientists from underrepresented groups are especially encouraged to apply.

Financial Data   Grants up to $250,000 per year, including direct expenses and up to 10% for overhead costs, are available. The total award for the life of the grant may not exceed $450,000.

Duration   2 or 3 years.

Additional data   This program began in 1991.

Number awarded   Up to 4 each year.

Deadline   Letters of intent must be submitted by the end of January of each year. Final applications are due in March.

Indexes

Program Title Index

If you know the name of a particular funding program open to Hispanic Americans and want to find out where it is covered in the directory, use the Program Title Index. Here, program titles are arranged alphabetically, word by word. To assist you in your search, every program is listed by all its known names or abbreviations. In addition, we've used an alphabetical code (within parentheses) to help you determine if the program is aimed at you: U = Undergraduates; G = Graduate Students; P = Professionals/Postdoctorates. Here's how the code works: if a program is followed by (U) 241, the program is described in the Undergraduates chapter, in entry 241. If the same program title is followed by another entry number—for example, (P) 901—the program is also described in the Professionals/Postdoctorates chapter, in entry 901. Remember: the numbers cited here refer to program entry numbers, not to page numbers in the book.

U–Undergraduates   G–Graduate Students   P–Professionals/Postdoctorates

393

U–Undergraduates   **G–Graduate Students**   **P–Professionals/Postdoctorates**

Arnstein New Student Minority Student Scholarship. *See* Sherry R. Arnstein New Student Minority Student Scholarship, entry (G) 871

Arnulfo D. Trejo Librarian of the Year Award, (P) 947

Arreola Returning Student Scholarships. *See* Philip Arreola Returning Student Scholarships, entry (U) 392

Arreola Scholarships. *See* Philip Arreola Scholarships, entry (U) 393

Artemis A.W. and Martha Joukowsky Postdoctoral Fellowship. *See* Pembroke Center Postdoctoral Fellowships, entry (P) 1113

Arthur H. Goodman Memorial Scholarships, (U) 41

Arts Award, (U) 42

ASCA Foundation Scholarships, (G) 546

ASCPA Educational Foundation Diversity Scholarships, (U) 43

ASH-AMFDP Awards, (P) 948

ASLA Council of Fellows Scholarships, (U) 44

ASME Graduate Teaching Fellowship, (G) 547

ASSE UPS Diversity Scholarships, (U) 45

Associated Food and Petroleum Dealers Minority Scholarships. *See* AFPD Minority Scholarships, entry (U) 10

Association for Compensatory Educators of Texas Student Scholarships, (U) 46

Association for Women Geoscientists Minority Scholarship, (U) 47

Association for Women in Science Seattle Scholarships. *See* Seattle Chapter AWIS Scholarships, entry (U) 435

Association of Cuban Engineers Scholarships, (U) 48, (G) 548

Association of Latino Administrators & Superintendents/ Houghton Mifflin Scholarship. *See* ALAS/Houghton Mifflin Harcourt Scholarship, entry (G) 522

Association of National Advertisers Multicultural Excellence Scholarship. *See* ANA Multicultural Excellence Scholarship, entry (U) 32

Astronomy and Astrophysics Postdoctoral Fellowships, (P) 949

Atherton Ministerial Scholarship. *See* Martha and Robert Atherton Ministerial Scholarship, entry (G) 756

Atkins North America Achievement Scholarship, (U) 49

Atkins Transportation YOU High School Scholarship, (U) 50

Atlanta Retailers Association and Coca-Cola Live Positively Scholarship Program, (U) 51

Atmospheric and Geospace Sciences Postdoctoral Research Fellowships, (P) 950

Augustyn Award in Digestive Cancer. *See* Caroline Craig Augustyn and Damian Augustyn Award in Digestive Cancer, entry (P) 962

Aurelio "Larry" Jazo Migrant Scholarship, (U) 52

Awards for Faculty at Hispanic-Serving Institutions, (P) 951

Axelrod Mentorship Award. *See* Julius Axelrod Mentorship Award, entry (P) 1050

B

Baccalaureate (Didactic or Coordinated Program) Scholarships, (U) 53

BACUS Scholarship. *See* SPIE Scholarship Program, entries (U) 445, (G) 879

Baker Corporation Scholarship Program for Diversity in Engineering. *See* Michael Baker Corporation Scholarship Program for Diversity in Engineering, entry (U) 311

Baker Donelson Diversity Scholarships, (G) 549

BakerHostetler Diversity Fellowship Program, (G) 550

Balfour Phi Delta Phi Minority Scholarship Program, (G) 551

Banks Memorial Undergraduate Scholarship. *See* Sharon D. Banks Memorial Undergraduate Scholarship, entry (U) 436

Banner Diversity Scholarship. *See* Donald W. Banner Diversity Scholarship, entry (G) 619

Banner Scholarship for Law Students. *See* Mark T. Banner Scholarship for Law Students, entry (G) 754

Barbara Jordan Memorial Scholarships, (U) 54, (G) 552

Barbara Wolff-Reichert Award for Excellence in Advanced Laboratory Instruction. *See* Jonathan Reichert and Barbara Wolff-Reichert Award for Excellence in Advanced Laboratory Instruction, entry (P) 1046

Barrow Minority Doctoral Student Scholarship. *See* Lionel C. Barrow Minority Doctoral Student Scholarship, entry (G) 742

Bechtel Undergraduate Fellowship Award, (U) 55

Beck Fellowship. *See* Stan Beck Fellowship, entries (U) 446, (G) 882

Behavioral Sciences Postdoctoral Fellowships in Epilepsy, (P) 952

Behavioral Sciences Student Fellowships in Epilepsy, (U) 56, (G) 553

Belfer Center for Science and International Affairs Fellowships, (G) 554, (P) 953

Bendix Minorities in Engineering Award. *See* DuPont Minorities in Engineering Award, entry (P) 988

Benjamin Webber Trust Scholarships. *See* Josephine and Benjamin Webber Trust Scholarships, entries (U) 246, (G) 714

Benton-Meier Neuropsychology Scholarships, (G) 555

Bernard Harris Math and Science Scholarships. *See* ExxonMobil Bernard Harris Math and Science Scholarships, entry (U) 157

Bernbach Diversity Scholarships. *See* Bill Bernbach Diversity Scholarships, entries (U) 58, (G) 557

Berrien Fragos Thorn Arts Scholarships for Migrant Farmworkers, (U) 57

Betancourt Award. *See* Association of Cuban Engineers Scholarships, entries (U) 48, (G) 548

Betty Lea Stone Research Fellowship, (G) 556

Beyond Margins Award. *See* Open Book Award, entry (P) 1107

Big Data and Analytics Fellowships of the American Association for the Advancement of Science, (P) 954

Bill Bernbach Diversity Scholarships, (U) 58, (G) 557

Bill Dickey Golf Scholarships, (U) 59

Biomedical Research Training Program for Underrepresented Groups, (P) 955

Birmingham Chapter AABE Scholarships, (U) 60

Bishop Thomas Hoyt, Jr. Fellowship, (G) 558

Blake Memorial Scholarship. *See* Connecticut Association of Latinos in Higher Education Scholarships, entry (U) 107

Blandy Experimental Farm Research Experiences for Undergraduates Program, (U) 61

Blaszcak Scholarship. *See* Fleming/Blaszcak Scholarship, entries (U) 161, (G) 645

Blau Early Career Award for Outstanding Contribution to Professional Clinical Psychology. *See* Theodore Blau Early Career Award for Outstanding Contribution to Professional Clinical Psychology, entry (P) 1151

Blechschmidt Award. *See* Geological Society of America Graduate Student Research Grants, entry (G) 661

Blitman, P.E. Scholarship to Promote Diversity in Engineering. *See* Maureen L. and Howard N. Blitman, P.E. Scholarship to Promote Diversity in Engineering, entry (U) 301

Bob Stanley Minority and International Scholarship. *See* Alan Compton and Bob Stanley Minority and International Scholarship, entry (U) 15

U–Undergraduates   **G–Graduate Students**   **P–Professionals/Postdoctorates**

U–Undergraduates   **G–Graduate Students**   **P–Professionals/Postdoctorates**

U–Undergraduates   **G–Graduate Students**   **P–Professionals/Postdoctorates**

U–Undergraduates   **G–Graduate Students**   **P–Professionals/Postdoctorates**

H

HACEMOS Scholarship Program of the Hispanic College Fund, (U) 194

HACER Scholarship Program. *See* Hispanic American Commitment to Educational Resources (HACER) Scholarship Program, entry (U) 207

Hailey AAJ Law Student Scholarships. *See* Richard D. Hailey AAJ Law Student Scholarships, entry (G) 851

Hall Memorial Scholarships. *See* James B. Morris Scholarships, entries (U) 236, (G) 700

HANA Scholarships, (U) 195, (G) 672

Harold T. Stearns Fellowship Award. *See* Geological Society of America Graduate Student Research Grants, entry (G) 661

Harriett G. Jenkins Predoctoral Fellowship Program, (G) 673

Harris Math and Science Scholarships. *See* ExxonMobil Bernard Harris Math and Science Scholarships, entry (U) 157

Harry and Miriam Levinson Award for Exceptional Contributions to Consulting Organizational Psychology, (P) 1024

Harry and Miriam Levinson Scholarship. *See* APF/COGDOP Graduate Research Scholarships, entry (G) 543

Harvard Medical School Dean's Postdoctoral Fellowship, (P) 1025

Harvard School of Public Health Summer Program in Biological Sciences in Public Health, (U) 196

Harvard–Newcomen Postdoctoral Fellowship in Business History, (P) 1026

Harvard-Smithsonian Center for Astrophysics Solar Summer Intern Program, (U) 197

Hattie J. Hilliard Scholarship, (U) 198

Haz La U Scholarship Program of the Hispanic Scholarship Fund, (U) 199

HBAPA Legal Education Fund Scholarships, (G) 674

Health and Aging Policy Fellowships, (P) 1027

Health, Education, and Human Services Fellowships, (P) 1028

Health Research and Educational Trust Scholarships, (U) 200, (G) 675

Health Sciences Student Fellowships in Epilepsy, (G) 676

Health Services Research Projects, (P) 1029

Hearst Endowment Scholarships. *See* William Randolph Hearst Endowment Scholarships, entry (U) 492

Heartland Latino Leadership Conference Academic Scholarships, (U) 201

H-E-B/Adelante Future Leaders Scholarship, (U) 202

Hécaen Scholarship. *See* Benton-Meier Neuropsychology Scholarships, entry (G) 555

Heckert Fellowship. *See* Richard Heckert Fellowship, entry (U) 415

Hector E. Lopez Scholarship. *See* The Rev. Dr. Hector E. Lopez Scholarship, entry (G) 895

HECUA Scholarships for Social Justice, (U) 203

Helen Brown COREM Scholarships. *See* Richard and Helen Brown COREM Scholarships, entry (G) 850

Helen R. Stulman Endowed Scholars Grants. *See* Leonard and Helen R. Stulman Endowed Scholars Grants, entry (G) 738

Helene M. Overly Memorial Graduate Scholarship, (G) 677

HENAAC High School Senior/College Freshman Awards, (U) 204

HENAAC Student Leadership Awards, (U) 205, (G) 678

Henry David Research Grant in Human Reproductive Behavior and Population Studies, (G) 679, (P) 1030

Henry Hécaen Scholarship. *See* Benton-Meier Neuropsychology Scholarships, entry (G) 555

Herbert W. Nickens Medical Student Scholarships, (G) 680

High Priority, Short-Term Bridge Awards in Diabetes Research, (P) 1031

High-Risk Research in Biological Anthropology and Archaeology Grants, (P) 1032

Hilda Sanchez-Henke Memorial Scholarship, (U) 206

Hill Scholarship. *See* Oliver W. Hill Scholarship, entry (G) 822

Hilliard Scholarship. *See* Hattie J. Hilliard Scholarship, entry (U) 198

Hillis Clark Martin & Peterson Diversity Fellowship, (G) 681

Hispanic American Commitment to Educational Resources (HACER) Scholarship Program, (U) 207

Hispanic American Police Command Officers Association Scholarship Award, (U) 208

Hispanic Annual Salute Scholarships, (U) 209

Hispanic, Asian, Native American Scholarships. *See* HANA Scholarships, entries (U) 195, (G) 672

Hispanic Bar Association of New Jersey Scholarship, (G) 682

Hispanic Bar Association of Pennsylvania Legal Education Fund Scholarships. *See* HBAPA Legal Education Fund Scholarships, entry (G) 674

Hispanic Business Council Scholarships, (U) 210

Hispanic Heritage Youth Awards, (U) 211

Hispanic Higher Education Scholarship Fund, (G) 683

Hispanic Leadership Development Fund, (U) 212, (G) 684

Hispanic Metropolitan Chamber Scholarships, (U) 213, (G) 685

Hispanic Professionals of Greater Milwaukee Advanced Degree Scholarships, (G) 686

Hispanic Public Relations Association Scholarship Program, (U) 214

Hispanic Public Relations Association-New York Scholarship Program. *See* HPRA-NY Scholarship Program, entry (U) 219

Hispanic Scholarship Fund/3S Scholarship, (U) 215

Hispanic Scholarship Fund General College Scholarships, (U) 216, (G) 687

Hispanic Scholarship Funds. *See* ABC Latino Ministries Scholarship, entries (U) 1, (G) 502

HIV Medicine Association Minority Clinical Fellowships. *See* HIVMA Minority Clinical Fellowships, entry (P) 1033

HIVMA Minority Clinical Fellowships, (P) 1033

Hoch Distinguished Service Award. *See* Paul Hoch Distinguished Service Award, entry (P) 1109

Holly A. Cornell Scholarship, (G) 688

Holy Family Memorial Scholarship Program, (U) 217

Honeywell International Scholarships, (U) 218

Horace and Susie Revels Cayton Scholarship. *See* Puget Sound Chapter/Horace and Susie Revels Cayton Scholarship, entry (U) 405

Howard Mayer Brown Fellowship, (G) 689

Howard N. Blitman, P.E. Scholarship to Promote Diversity in Engineering. *See* Maureen L. and Howard N. Blitman, P.E. Scholarship to Promote Diversity in Engineering, entry (U) 301

Howell Scholarship. *See* APF/COGDOP Graduate Research Scholarships, entry (G) 543

Hoyt, Jr. Fellowship. *See* Bishop Thomas Hoyt, Jr. Fellowship, entry (G) 558

HPRA-NY Scholarship Program, (U) 219

Hubble Fellowships, (P) 1034

Hugh J. Andersen Memorial Scholarships, (G) 690

Hughes Medical Institute Research Training Fellowships for Medical Students. *See* Year-Long Medical Research Fellows Program at an Academic or Nonprofit Research Institution, entry (G) 920

U–Undergraduates   **G–Graduate Students**   **P–Professionals/Postdoctorates**

Hyatt Hotels Fund for Minority Lodging Management. *See* AHLEF/Hyatt Hotels Fund for Minority Lodging Management Students, entry (U) 13

I

IBM Corporation SWE Scholarships, (U) 220

IBM PhD Fellowship Program, (G) 691

Idaho Latino Scholarship Fund, (U) 221

Idaho Migrant Council Latino Scholarship Fund. *See* Community Council of Idaho Hispanic Student Scholarship Program, entry (U) 104

Idaho State Broadcasters Association Scholarships. *See* ISBA Scholarships, entry (U) 232

Ike Crumbly Minorities in Energy Grant. *See* Isaac J. "Ike" Crumbly Minorities in Energy Grant, entry (G) 699

Illinois Dream Fund Scholarships, (U) 222

Illinois Legislative Latino Caucus Foundation Scholarships, (U) 223

Illinois Migrant Council Adult Education Scholarships, (U) 224

Illinois Nurses Foundation Centennial Scholarship, (U) 225, (G) 692

Ilumina Scholarship Program, (U) 226

Independent Scientist Award, (P) 1035

Indiana Chapter AABE Scholarships, (U) 227

Indiana Industry Liaison Group Scholarship, (U) 228

Indiana Minority Teacher/Special Education Services Scholarship, (U) 229

Industry Minority Scholarships. *See* American Meteorological Society Industry Minority Scholarships, entry (U) 28

Initiative to Recruit a Diverse Workforce, (G) 693

Institute for Supply Management Doctoral Dissertation Grant Program, (G) 694

Institutional Research and Academic Career Development Awards, (P) 1036

Intel Corporation Scholarships, (G) 695

Intellectual Property Law Section Women and Minority Scholarship, (G) 696

Interfaith Spirituality Scholarship, (G) 697

Intermountain Section AWWA Diversity Scholarship, (U) 230, (G) 698

International Collaboration in Chemistry between U.S. Investigators and their Counterparts Abroad, (P) 1037

International Society for Optical Engineering Scholarship Program. *See* SPIE Scholarship Program, entries (U) 445, (G) 879

Interpublic Group Scholarship and Internship, (U) 231

Investigator Awards in Health Policy Research, (P) 1038

Investigators in Pathogenesis of Infectious Disease, (P) 1039

Irma Rangel Memorial Scholarships. *See* State Representative Irma Rangel Memorial Scholarships, entries (U) 448, (G) 884

Isaac J. "Ike" Crumbly Minorities in Energy Grant, (G) 699

ISBA Scholarships, (U) 232

Itasker Thornton Memorial Scholarship. *See* Donald and Itasker Thornton Memorial Scholarship, entry (U) 135

ITW Scholarships, (U) 233

J

J. Paris Mosley Scholarship, (U) 234

J. Robert Gladden Orthopaedic Society Basic Research Grants, (P) 1040

J. Robert Gladden Orthopaedic Society Clinical Research Grants. *See* JRGOS Clinical Research Grants, entry (P) 1048

Jack D. Krasner Memorial Award. *See* Division 29 Early Career Award, entry (P) 982

Jackie Robinson Scholarships, (U) 235

Jackson Ministerial Scholars Fund. *See* Susan M. Jackson Ministerial Scholars Fund, entry (G) 889

James A. Rawley Prize, (P) 1041

James B. Morris Scholarships, (U) 236, (G) 700

James Carlson Memorial Scholarship, (U) 237, (G) 701

James J. Wychor Scholarships, (U) 238

James Legacy Scholarship. *See* APF/COGDOP Graduate Research Scholarships, entry (G) 543

James W. Stoudt Scholarships, (G) 702

Jane Cook Wright Lectureship. *See* Minorities in Cancer Research Jane Cook Wright Lectureship, entry (P) 1071

Jane Velez-Mitchell Scholarship. *See* National Association of Hispanic Journalists Broadcast Scholarships, entries (U) 349, (G) 793

Jazo Migrant Scholarship. *See* Aurelio "Larry" Jazo Migrant Scholarship, entry (U) 52

Jeanne Spurlock Research Fellowship in Substance Abuse and Addiction for Minority Medical Students, (G) 703

Jenkins Predoctoral Fellowship Program. *See* Harriett G. Jenkins Predoctoral Fellowship Program, entry (G) 673

Jim McKay Scholarship Program, (G) 704

Jimmy A. Young Memorial Education Recognition Award, (U) 239

Jo Ann Ota Fujioka Scholarship. *See* PDK/Dr. Jo Ann Ota Fujioka Scholarship, entry (U) 388

Joel Elkes Research Award, (P) 1042

Joel Garcia Memorial Scholarship. *See* CCNMA Scholarships, entry (U) 79

John A. Mayes Scholarship, (G) 705

John and Muriel Landis Scholarships, (U) 240, (G) 706

John and Polly Sparks Early Career Grant, (P) 1043

John Hope Franklin Dissertation Fellowship, (G) 707

John Kiel Scholarship. *See* SPIE Scholarship Program, entries (U) 445, (G) 879

John McLendon Memorial Minority Postgraduate Scholarship Award, (G) 708, (P) 1044

John Montagne Fund Award. *See* Geological Society of America Graduate Student Research Grants, entry (G) 661

John S. Martinez Leadership Scholarship, (U) 241

John Soto Scholarship. *See* Connecticut Association of Latinos in Higher Education Scholarships, entry (U) 107

John Stanford Memorial WLMA Scholarship, (G) 709

John T. Dillon Alaska Research Award. *See* Geological Society of America Graduate Student Research Grants, entry (G) 661

John T. Smith Scholarships, (U) 242

John V. Krutilla Research Stipend, (P) 1045

Johnson Clinical Scholars Program. *See* Robert Wood Johnson Clinical Scholars Program, entry (P) 1133

Johnson Foundation Health and Society Scholars Program. *See* Robert Wood Johnson Foundation Health and Society Scholars Program, entry (P) 1134

Johnson Health Policy Fellowships. *See* Robert Wood Johnson Health Policy Fellowships, entry (P) 1135

Johnson & Johnson-American Association of Colleges of Nursing Minority Nurse Faculty Scholars Program, (G) 710

Johnson, Jr. Scholarship Program. *See* Lloyd M. Johnson, Jr. Scholarship Program, entry (G) 745

Johnson Minority Fellowship in Educational Measurement. *See* Sylvia Taylor Johnson Minority Fellowship in Educational Measurement, entry (P) 1148

U–Undergraduates   G–Graduate Students   P–Professionals/Postdoctorates

U–Undergraduates   **G–Graduate Students**   **P–Professionals/Postdoctorates**

U–Undergraduates   G–Graduate Students   P–Professionals/Postdoctorates

U–Undergraduates   **G–Graduate Students**   **P–Professionals/Postdoctorates**

U–Undergraduates   **G–Graduate Students**   **P–Professionals/Postdoctorates**

U–Undergraduates **G–Graduate Students** **P–Professionals/Postdoctorates**

U–Undergraduates **G–Graduate Students** **P–Professionals/Postdoctorates**

U–Undergraduates   **G–Graduate Students**   **P–Professionals/Postdoctorates**

Sponsoring Organization Index

The Sponsoring Organization Index makes it easy to identify agencies that offer financial aid to Hispanic Americans. In this index, the sponsoring organizations are listed alphabetically, word by word. In addition, we've used an alphabetical code (within parentheses) to help you identify the intended recipients of the funding offered by the organizations: U = Undergraduates; G = Graduate Students; P = Professionals/Postdoctorates. For example, if the name of a sponsoring organization is followed by (U) 241, a program sponsored by that organization is described in the Undergraduate chapter, in entry 241. If that sponsoring organization's name is followed by another entry number—for example, (G) 915—the same or a different program sponsored by that organization is described in the Professionals/Postdoctorates chapter, in entry 915. Remember: the numbers cited here refer to program entry numbers, not to page numbers in the book.

U–Undergraduates   **G–Graduate Students**   **P–Professionals/Postdoctorates**

U–Undergraduates   **G–Graduate Students**   **P–Professionals/Postdoctorates**

U–Undergraduates   **G–Graduate Students**   **P–Professionals/Postdoctorates**

U–Undergraduates   **G–Graduate Students**   **P–Professionals/Postdoctorates**

U–Undergraduates   **G–Graduate Students**   **P–Professionals/Postdoctorates**

U–Undergraduates **G–Graduate Students** **P–Professionals/Postdoctorates**

U–Undergraduates   **G–Graduate Students**   **P–Professionals/Postdoctorates**

Residency Index

Some programs listed in this book are set aside for Hispanic Americans who are residents of a particular state or region. Others are open to applicants wherever they may live. The Residency Index will help you pinpoint programs available in your area as well as programs that have no residency restrictions at all (these are listed under the term "United States"). To use this index, look up the geographic areas that apply to you (always check the listings under "United States"), jot down the entry numbers listed for the recipient level that applies to you (Undergraduates, Graduate Students, or Professionals/Postdoctorates), and use those numbers to find the program descriptions in the directory. To help you in your search, we've provided some "see" and "see also" references in the index entries. Remember: the numbers cited here refer to program entry numbers, not to page numbers in the book.

A

Alabama: **Undergraduates,** 60, 94. *See also* United States

Alabama, southern: **Undergraduates,** 193. *See also* Alabama

Arizona: **Undergraduates,** 41, 90, 94, 136, 177, 194, 215, 246; **Graduate Students,** 576, 621, 657, 695, 714. *See also* United States

Arkansas: **Undergraduates,** 39-40, 94. *See also* United States

Atlanta, Georgia: **Undergraduates,** 177, 194, 211, 215; **Graduate Students,** 657. *See also* Georgia

Austin, Texas: **Undergraduates,** 42, 65, 105, 146, 177, 194, 450, 459; **Graduate Students,** 598, 657. *See also* Texas

B

Bell Gardens, California: **Undergraduates,** 42, 65, 105, 146, 450, 459; **Graduate Students,** 598. *See also* California

Belmont County, Ohio: **Undergraduates,** 458. *See also* Ohio

Boston, Massachusetts: **Undergraduates,** 177; **Graduate Students,** 657. *See also* Massachusetts

Burnett County, Wisconsin: **Undergraduates,** 150. *See also* Wisconsin

C

California: **Undergraduates,** 41, 67-69, 72-73, 77, 79, 88, 90, 94, 114, 117, 120-121, 131, 136, 181, 190, 214-215, 226, 264, 271, 306, 351, 353, 429, 473; **Graduate Students,** 565, 576, 578, 592, 596, 611, 617, 695, 731, 736, 764, 798, 800; **Professionals/Postdoctorates,** 971, 986, 1052. *See also* United States

California, southern: **Graduate Students,** 581, 842. *See also* California

Chicago, Illinois: **Undergraduates,** 177, 194, 211, 215, 490; **Graduate Students,** 657. *See also* Illinois

Cincinnati, Ohio: **Undergraduates,** 177; **Graduate Students,** 657. *See also* Ohio

Clark County, Washington: **Undergraduates,** 213; **Graduate Students,** 685. *See also* Washington

Colorado: **Undergraduates,** 80, 93-94, 103, 209, 266, 317, 374; **Graduate Students,** 695. *See also* United States

Columbiana County, Ohio: **Undergraduates,** 458. *See also* Ohio

Commerce, California: **Undergraduates,** 42, 65, 105, 146, 450, 459; **Graduate Students,** 598. *See also* California

Connecticut: **Undergraduates,** 17, 94, 107-108, 110, 155, 159, 191, 194, 231, 353, 451; **Graduate Students,** 631, 638, 741, 800. *See also* New England states; United States

Cook County, Illinois: **Undergraduates,** 42, 65, 105, 146, 450, 459; **Graduate Students,** 598. *See also* Illinois

D

Dallas, Texas: **Undergraduates,** 177, 194, 211; **Graduate Students,** 657. *See also* Texas

Delaware: **Undergraduates,** 94, 191, 263. *See also* United States

Denver, Colorado: **Undergraduates,** 177, 490; **Graduate Students,** 657. *See also* Colorado

Detroit, Michigan: **Undergraduates,** 177, 194; **Graduate Students,** 657. *See also* Michigan

District of Columbia. *See* Washington, D.C.

E

Edinburg, Texas: **Undergraduates,** 42, 65, 105, 146, 450, 459; **Graduate Students,** 598. *See also* Texas

Erie, Pennsylvania: **Undergraduates,** 177; **Graduate Students,** 657. *See also* Pennsylvania

F

Fairfield County, Connecticut: **Undergraduates,** 177; **Graduate Students,** 657. *See also* Connecticut

Florida: **Undergraduates,** 94, 115, 162, 164, 191, 193, 215, 245; **Graduate Students,** 646, 711. *See also* United States

Florida, central: **Undergraduates,** 194. *See also* Florida

Florida, southern: **Undergraduates,** 194. *See also* Florida

Fort Worth, Texas: **Undergraduates,** 194. *See also* Texas

Fresno, California: **Undergraduates,** 194. *See also* California

Tenability Index

Some programs listed in this book can be used only in specific cities, counties, states, or regions. Others may be used anywhere in the United States. The Tenability Index will help you locate funding that is restricted to a specific area as well as funding that has no tenability restrictions (these are listed under the term "United States"). To use this index, look up the geographic areas where you'd like to go (always check the listings under "United States"), jot down the entry numbers listed for the recipient group that represents you (Undergraduates, Graduate Students, Professionals/Postdoctorates), and use those numbers to find the program descriptions in the directory. To help you in your search, we've provided some "see" and "see also" references in the index entries. Remember: the numbers cited here refer to program entry numbers, not to page numbers in the book.

A

Alabama: **Undergraduates,** 43, 437; **Graduate Students,** 585, 877, 880. *See also* United States; names of specific cities and counties

Albuquerque, New Mexico: **Graduate Students,** 803. *See also* New Mexico

Allentown, Pennsylvania: **Graduate Students,** 608; **Professionals/Postdoctorates,** 1118. *See also* Pennsylvania

Amherst, Massachusetts: **Undergraduates,** 147; **Graduate Students,** 627, 643. *See also* Massachusetts

Anchorage, Alaska: **Graduate Students,** 885

Ann Arbor, Michigan: **Undergraduates,** 113, 345, 454; **Graduate Students,** 584, 589; **Professionals/Postdoctorates,** 1133, 1142. *See also* Michigan

Appleton, Wisconsin: **Graduate Students,** 608; **Professionals/Postdoctorates,** 1118. *See also* Wisconsin

Argonne, Illinois: **Graduate Students,** 541. *See also* Illinois

Arizona: **Undergraduates,** 38, 41, 71, 90, 123, 125, 177, 246, 272; **Graduate Students,** 576, 602, 621, 657, 714; **Professionals/Postdoctorates,** 1055. *See also* United States; names of specific cities and counties

Arkansas: **Undergraduates,** 39-40; **Graduate Students,** 877, 880. *See also* United States; names of specific cities and counties

Armonk, New York: **Undergraduates,** 66. *See also* New York

Athens, Georgia: **Graduate Students,** 916. *See also* Georgia

Atlanta, Georgia: **Undergraduates,** 58, 113, 177, 380, 472; **Graduate Students,** 557, 584, 589, 641, 657, 724, 824, 899, 916. *See also* Georgia

Austin, Texas: **Undergraduates,** 58, 113, 177, 202, 380; **Graduate Students,** 557, 584, 589, 657, 724, 799, 824, 903. *See also* Texas

B

Baltimore, Maryland: **Undergraduates,** 370; **Graduate Students,** 608, 916; **Professionals/Postdoctorates,** 1118. *See also* Maryland

Bangor, Maine: **Graduate Students,** 895. *See also* Maine

Baton Rouge, Louisiana: **Graduate Students,** 899. *See also* Louisiana

Beeville, Texas: **Undergraduates,** 202. *See also* Texas

Berkeley, California: **Undergraduates,** 468; **Graduate Students,** 584, 895; **Professionals/Postdoctorates,** 1134, 1142, 1157, 1162. *See also* California

Bethesda, Maryland: **Undergraduates,** 363; **Professionals/Postdoctorates,** 955, 1103-1104. *See also* Maryland

Big Rapids, Michigan: **Undergraduates,** 402. *See also* Michigan

Blacksburg, Virginia: **Undergraduates,** 370. *See also* Virginia

Bloomington, Indiana: **Graduate Students,** 584. *See also* Indiana

Boise, Idaho: **Graduate Students,** 885. *See also* Idaho

Boston, Massachusetts: **Undergraduates,** 126, 147, 177, 196, 453; **Graduate Students,** 588, 603, 627, 641, 657, 759, 906; **Professionals/Postdoctorates,** 977, 1025-1026, 1172. *See also* Massachusetts

Boulder, Colorado: **Undergraduates,** 411; **Graduate Students,** 637; **Professionals/Postdoctorates,** 1078. *See also* Colorado

Broomfield, Colorado: **Graduate Students,** 588. *See also* Colorado

Brownsville, Texas: **Undergraduates,** 202. *See also* Texas

Brunswick, Maine: **Graduate Students,** 608; **Professionals/Postdoctorates,** 1118. *See also* Maine

Bryn Mawr, Pennsylvania: **Graduate Students,** 608; **Professionals/Postdoctorates,** 1118. *See also* Pennsylvania

Buies Creek, North Carolina: **Undergraduates,** 402. *See also* North Carolina

Burlington County, New Jersey: **Graduate Students,** 674. *See also* New Jersey

Subject Index

There are hundreds of specific subject fields covered in this directory. Use the Subject Index to identify these topics, as well as the recipient level supported (Undergraduates, Graduate Students, or Professionals/Postdoctorates) by the available funding programs. To help you pinpoint your search, we've included many "see" and "see also" references. Since a large number of programs are not restricted by subject, be sure to check the references listed under the "General programs" heading in the subject index (in addition to the specific terms that directly relate to your interest areas); hundreds of funding opportunities are listed there that can be used to support activities in any subject area although the programs may be restricted in other ways. Remember: the numbers cited in this index refer to program entry numbers, not to page numbers in the book.

A

A.V. *See* Audiovisual materials and equipment

Academic librarianship. *See* Libraries and librarianship, academic

Accounting: **Undergraduates,** 18, 20, 43, 64, 145, 152, 162, 177, 277, 285, 291, 313, 320-321, 326, 338-340, 368, 431, 456, 464, 471, 478, 497; **Graduate Students,** 518, 657, 726, 739, 751, 767, 772, 776, 789-790, 815, 864, 917. *See also* Finance; General programs

Acoustical engineering. *See* Engineering, acoustical

Acoustics: **Graduate Students,** 505. *See also* General programs; Physics

Acquired Immunodeficiency Syndrome. *See* AIDS

Acting. *See* Performing arts

Actuarial sciences: **Undergraduates,** 5, 300, 341, 456. *See also* General programs; Statistics

Addiction. *See* Alcohol use and abuse; Drug use and abuse

Administration. *See* Business administration; Education, administration; Management; Personnel administration; Public administration

Adolescents: **Graduate Students,** 703. *See also* Child development; General programs

Advertising: **Undergraduates,** 32, 58, 155, 169, 214, 219, 231, 261, 380, 409; **Graduate Students,** 557, 631, 649, 729, 824, 847. *See also* Communications; General programs; Marketing; Public relations

Aeronautical engineering. *See* Engineering, aeronautical

Aeronautics: **Graduate Students,** 514, 673; **Professionals/Postdoctorates,** 927. *See also* Aviation; Engineering, aeronautical; General programs; Physical sciences

Aerospace engineering. *See* Engineering, aerospace

Aerospace sciences. *See* Space sciences

Affirmative action: **Undergraduates,** 228. *See also* Equal opportunity; General programs

Aged and aging: **Graduate Students,** 516, 617; **Professionals/Postdoctorates,** 968, 986, 1027. *See also* General programs; Social sciences

Agribusiness: **Undergraduates,** 159; **Graduate Students,** 638. *See also* Agriculture and agricultural sciences; Business administration; General programs

Agricultural engineering. *See* Engineering, agricultural

Agriculture and agricultural sciences: **Undergraduates,** 62, 126, 159, 365; **Graduate Students,** 603, 638, 760; **Professionals/Postdoctorates,** 977, 996, 1108, 1166. *See also* Biological sciences; General programs

Agrimarketing and sales. *See* Agribusiness

AIDS: **Undergraduates,** 196; **Professionals/Postdoctorates,** 1033, 1155-1156. *See also* Disabilities; General programs; Immunology; Medical sciences

Alcohol use and abuse: **Graduate Students,** 762; **Professionals/Postdoctorates,** 945. *See also* Drug use and abuse; General programs; Health and health care

Alzheimer's Disease: **Graduate Students,** 516; **Professionals/Postdoctorates,** 935-936, 999, 1066, 1089, 1161, 1173. *See also* Aged and aging; Disabilities; General programs; Medical sciences

American history. *See* History, American

American Indian language. *See* Language, Native American

American Indian studies. *See* Native American studies

American literature. *See* Literature, American

Animal science: **Undergraduates,** 440; **Graduate Students,** 505, 875; **Professionals/Postdoctorates,** 1166. *See also* General programs; Sciences; names of specific animal sciences

Animation: **Undergraduates,** 57. *See also* Cartoonists and cartoons; Filmmaking; General programs

Anthropology: **Undergraduates,** 56, 440; **Graduate Students,** 526, 553, 707, 797, 863, 875; **Professionals/Postdoctorates,** 952, 963, 1032, 1083. *See also* General programs; Social sciences

Antitrust and trade regulation: **Graduate Students,** 651. *See also* General programs; Law, general

Applied arts. *See* Arts and crafts

Aquaculture: **Professionals/Postdoctorates,** 1166. *See also* Agriculture and agricultural sciences; General programs

Calendar Index

Since most funding programs have specific deadline dates, some may have already closed by the time you begin to look for money. You can use the Calendar Index to identify which programs are still open. To do that, go to the recipient category (Undergraduates, Graduate Students, or Professionals/Postdoctorates) that interests you, think about when you'll be able to complete your application forms, go to the appropriate months, jot down the entry numbers listed there, and use those numbers to find the program descriptions in the directory. Keep in mind that the numbers cited here refer to program entry numbers, not to page numbers in the book.